Element	Symbol	Atomic number	Atomic weight	Element	Symbol	Atomic number	Atomic weight
Mercury	Hg	80	200.59	Samarium	Sm	62	150.4
Molybdenum	Mo	42	95.94	Scandium	Sc	21	44.9559
Neodymium	Nd	60	144.24	Selenium	Se	34	78.96
Neon	Ne	10	20.179	Silicon	Si	14	28.086
Neptunium	Np	93	237.0482	Silver	Ag	47	107.868
Nickel	Ni	28	58.71	Sodium	Na	11	22.9898
Niobium	Nb	41	92.9064	Strontium	Sr	38	87.62
Nitrogen	N	7	14.0067	Sulfur	S	16	32.06
Nobelium	No	102	(254)	Tantalum	Ta	73	180.9479
Osmium	Os	76	190.2	Technetium	Tc	43	98.9062
Oxygen	O	8	15.9994	Tellurium	Te	52	127.60
Palladium	Pd	46	106.4	Terbium	Tb	65	158.9254
Phosphorus	P	15	30.9738	Thallium	Tl	81	204.37
Platinum	Pt	78	195.09	Thorium	Th	90	232.0381
Plutonium	Pu	94	(242)	Thulium	Tm	69	168.9342
Polonium	Po	84	(210)	Tin	Sn	50	118.69
Potassium	K	19	39.102	Titanium	Ti	22	47.90
Praseodymium	Pr	59	140.9077	Tungsten	W	74	183.85
Promethium	Pm	61	(147)	Uranium	U	92	238.029
Protactinium	Pa	91	231.0359	Vanadium	V	23	50.9414
Radium	Ra	88	226.0254	Xenon	Xe	54	131.30
Radon	Rn	86	(222)	Ytterbium	Yb	70	173.04
Rhenium	Re	75	186.2	Yttrium	Y	39	88.9059
Rhodium	Rh	45	102.9055	Zinc	Zn	30	
Rubidium	Rb	37	85.4678	Zirconium	Zr		
Ruthenium	Ru	44	101.07				

INTRODUCTION TO CHEMISTRY

INTRODUCTION TO CHEMISTRY

Arthur L. Williams

Harland D. Embree

Harold J. DeBey

Department of Chemistry, San Jose State College, California

ADDISON-WESLEY PUBLISHING COMPANY

Reading, Massachusetts • Menlo Park, California • London • Don Mills, Ontario

This book is in the ADDISON-WESLEY SERIES IN CHEMISTRY

FRANCIS T. BONNER
Consulting Editor

Second printing, January 1971

PREFACE

Human beings are curious and have an intense urge to explore the secrets hidden in a grain of sand, a pulsating heart, or a fragrant petal. We often feel compelled to interpret creatively the discoveries we make. The creative scientist constructs visions of whirling electrons, charged ions, and double spirals of DNA. Out of the visions there emerges an awe-inspiring pattern of order and unity in the very essence of many seemingly unrelated substances in the universe. The concern with the fundamental structure and composition of all these substances is the part of human knowledge we call chemistry.

This book was written for any person who wants to experience this fascinating view of our universe, either for the pleasure of expanding his own understanding or for the additional goal of completing a specific course. We have emphasized those topics necessary if the reader is to understand chemistry and to interpret more intelligently the environment—both physical and, to a lesser extent, social—in which he finds himself. Not all statements in the book will have immediate, practical applications to daily life. Such a collection of facts would train a person only for today, rather than educate him. It would leave him with no historical perspective and little ability to understand the new discoveries and new interpretations which will surely develop from our current facts and theories.

We have attempted to describe the principles of chemistry in a logical manner and amplify them with meaningful examples. We have made a particular effort to show how scientific theories are developed from observations of natural events. A textbook or course which presents only a skeletal framework, beautifully articulated as it may be, is no more inspiring than the skeleton of a famous race horse or of a beautiful woman. Equally uninspiring is a shapeless mass of material without a supporting skeleton. The skeleton of principles is definitely present throughout this book, rounded out with facts which make chemistry live.

As often as possible, observations familiar to the reader, or well-known historical experiments, have been used as a foundation for developing concepts. We have presented logical and understandable methods for writing chemical equations and performing simple calculations.   Rarely have we suggested that a mathematical formula be memorized.   We have emphasized the use of the periodic table for predicting properties and valences, as opposed to memorizing such facts.

We have assumed that the reader already has some acquaintance with both the physical and biological sciences, but we have not assumed that he has had any previous course in chemistry.   We have limited mathematical calculations to those requiring only arithmetic and simple algebra.

This book differs from most introductory chemistry texts in that it treats not only inorganic chemistry, but includes extensive sections of organic chemistry and biochemistry. The growing knowledge and challenges in these fields make it essential to provide a balanced coverage of the topics for the many readers who use this book for their first study of chemistry. We have included the customary fundamentals of general chemistry. The important classes of organic compounds are surveyed, with the concept of structure providing the central theme. Systematic names for organic compounds are emphasized. Many common names are included for reference, but are used only when there seems to be a compelling reason for doing so. The chapter on polymers should be of special interest to many readers, since it describes the manner in which numerous well-known synthetic fibers and plastic materials are formed. The biochemistry section includes—in addition to the traditional discussion of carbohydrates, proteins, and lipids—chapters on the chemistry of heredity, on disease and therapy, and on plant biochemistry.

More and more colleges are offering a well-balanced, terminal course which provides a significant understanding of chemistry to students majoring in the liberal arts or in such fields as nursing, business, or home economics. We have had such a course at San Jose State College for many years. The need for a satisfactory text prompted us to write this book.

This book is suitable for a one-year course which includes one semester of general chemistry and one of organic and biochemistry. In colleges operating on the quarter system, one quarter could be devoted to each of the three fields. For courses taught in two quarters or one semester, several chapters and parts of chapters may be omitted without loss of continuity; we have been careful not to include in any of the optional sections those fundamental concepts which will be required later in the book. Courses for nurses or home economists may concentrate on the organic and biochemistry sections, especially if high school chemistry is prerequisite to such programs. Although this book is not intended as a text for chemistry majors, it can provide a useful introduction for any college science majors who have not had chemistry in high school. To provide greater understanding and enjoyment of the topics, we have included many paragraphs of explanatory or descriptive material, set off by flags (◄) and printed with different type. Even in the longer, more rigorous courses, students should rarely be held responsible for these details.

Now, a personal note to our readers: We believe you will discover that chemistry is a vital, fascinating subject which overflows the printed page. It will stimulate a new way of looking at the universe and should make life more meaningful by helping you understand and interpret the natural and technical world around you and the complex world of your own body chemistry. We hope you find chemistry as dynamic and intriguing as we do.

San Jose, California   A. L. W.
March, 1968   H. D. E.
                                                                                                      H. J. D.

TRADE NAMES

Reference is made within the text to the following trade names:

Trade Name	Registered Trademark of
ACHROMYCIN	Lederle, Inc., Division of American Cyanamid
ACRILAN	Chemstrand Corporation
AUREOMYCIN	Lederle, Inc., Division of American Cyanamid
BAKELITE	Union Carbide Corporation, Plastics Division
BENZEDRINE	Smith, Kline, and French Laboratories
CARBONA	Worthington Pump and Machinery Corporation
CHEER	Proctor and Gamble Company
CLOROX	Proctor and Gamble Company
COMPAZINE	Smith, Kline, and French Laboratories
CRISCO	Proctor and Gamble Company
DACRON	E. I. du Pont de Nemours and Company, Inc.
DEXEDRINE	Smith, Kline, and French Laboratories
DIABINESE	United States Vitamin Company
DRANO	The Dracket Company
DYNEL	Union Carbide Corporation
EQUANIL	Wyeth Laboratories
FAB	Colgate-Palmolive Company
FORMICA	Formica Corporation (subsidiary of American Cyanamid)
FREON	E. I. du Pont de Nemours and Company, Inc.
LUCITE	E. I. du Pont de Nemours and Company, Inc.
LUMINAL	Winthrop-Stearns, Inc.
MARPLAN	Hoffmann-La Roche, Inc.
MELMAC	American Cyanamid

Trade Name	Registered Trademark of
MICARTA	Westinghouse Electric Corporation
MILTOWN	Wallace Laboratories
MONEL	International Nickel Company, Inc.
MYLAR	E. I. du Pont de Nemours and Company, Inc.
NICHROME	Driver-Harris Company
ORINASE	Upjohn Company
ORLON	E. I. du Pont de Nemours and Company, Inc.
PLEXIGLAS	Rohm and Haas Company
PUREX	Purex Corporation, Ltd.
PYREX	Corning Glass Works
SARAN	Dow Chemical Company
SERPASIL	CIBA
SPRY	Lever Brothers Company
TEFLON	E. I. du Pont de Nemours and Company, Inc.
TERRAMYCIN	Pfizer Laboratories
THORAZINE	Smith, Kline, and French Laboratories
TIDE	Proctor and Gamble Company
TREND	Purex Corporation, Ltd.
VINYLITE	Union Carbide Corporation, Plastics Division
VINYON	Union Carbide Corporation, Plastics Division

CONTENTS

INORGANIC CHEMISTRY

Chapter 20   Radioactivity and Nuclear Chemistry

ORGANIC CHEMISTRY

Chapter 21   The Nature of Organic Compounds

Chapter 22   Saturated Hydrocarbons: The Alkanes

BIOCHEMISTRY

Chapter 1 THE SCIENCE OF CHEMISTRY

1–1 INTRODUCTION

The reader of an introductory chemistry book is seated at his desk, his unopened book before him, his mind filled with apprehension. He sees visions of men in white coats standing over bubbling glass contraptions which emit mysterious odors. These scientists in his vision speak a strange jargon, and the threat of explosion hangs in the air. The student thinks of chemists and chemistry as belonging to another world—a world far removed from his everyday life.

He is wrong, of course. While all the impressions listed have some basis in fact, they are only minor aspects of chemistry. The newcomer's major error is in thinking he knows nothing about chemistry. He knows, for instance, that the world is made up of many different kinds of materials—water, sand, copper, sugar, alcohol, and thousands of other materials. He probably knows that water is H_2O, although his idea of the composition of substances is hazy, and he may not be sure what H_2O really means. He knows that copper is a metal, as are silver, gold, tin, and many others. Thus he knows at least a bit about one of the major aspects of chemistry, the substances that make up our world—including our own bodies.

We are all aware that materials may change, sometimes drastically. Many such changes are so familiar from past experience that we can predict rather well when iron will rust, wood will burn, or a firecracker will explode. We may be less sure, however, of why or how the change occurs, exactly what the change has been, or why it sometimes fails to happen. Most of the sugar we use is in the form of tiny, white granules that taste sweet. If we put some sugar in water it disappears, but we're pretty sure that it's still there since the water now tastes sweet. What has happened to the sugar? If we spill some sugar on a hot stove, it softens for a moment and then turns to a black shapeless mass. If we taste the black material after it cools, it is no longer sweet. Is the black mass still sugar? What has happened to the sweetness? Many of us have been told that if we eat sugar, our bodies burn it for energy. How do we "burn" sugar? How does this process change the sugar? How does it produce energy?

By contrast, if we heat some lead metal, it softens and becomes liquid, but its color changes very little. If the molten lead is allowed to cool, it again looks very much like the original metal. Why did it not change as the sugar did when heated? We know that lead is poisonous, so obviously we derive not energy but death from lead. Why? We have all observed that a clean, shiny piece of iron metal changes if left very long in moist air. It becomes coated with a brownish-red crust. Is this crust still iron? Why does the color change? What does the water or the presence of oxygen in the air have to do with the rusting of iron? If we attempt to drive off the moisture by blowing on or heating rust, will it change back to iron? On the other hand, a piece of aluminum metal seems to be unchanged by exposure to moist air. Why doesn't aluminum rust? Most of our readers know the answers to many of these questions, but probably cannot explain exactly how or why these changes occur. Questions such as these are related to the second aspect of chemistry—the changes that substances undergo and the relation of various forms of energy to these changes. One of the major aspects of chemistry is the explanation of these changes.

Chemistry is concerned with all kinds of substances. Many people may think of lime, ammonia, sulfur, or turpentine as being "chemicals." Turpentine is produced by trees, but so are maple sugar, rubber, and olive oil. Are these chemicals, too? Is wool a chemical? Aluminum? Aspirin? Caffeine? Vitamin C? The chemist's answer is that they are all *chemicals*, and they are all *substances*. The two terms may be used interchangeably. Chemistry is concerned with the composition of materials; it matters not whether they are rare or common, edible or poisonous, explosive or inert. There is nothing necessarily mysterious or unusual about a "chemical." In a similar fashion, the term "chemical reaction" is often used to describe the change occurring when one substance is converted to another. The event could also be called a change in composition, whether it involves the digestion of food, the drying of paint, or the explosion of gunpowder.

If the bit of chemical knowledge possessed by the reader is coupled with the desire to know more about what things are made of and how they change, chemistry becomes fascinating. Unless it has been suppressed, we all have a great deal of curiosity—sometimes mixed with a degree of skepticism. We like to see things happen and greatly prefer watching them ourselves to hearing others tell about them. We may even want to watch a thing several times to be sure it always turns out the same way. Maybe it's because we want to confirm our underlying conviction that the universe and most things in it are orderly. If it is orderly, and we understand it, we can predict. The urge to know, often just for the sake of knowing and at other times so that one can understand, predict, and to some degree, control, is a powerful human motivation. It is the motivation responsible for most of science.

1–2 THE SCIENTIFIC APPROACH

A scientist, like a nonscientist, attempts to explain the world around him on the basis of observations and generalizations based on those observations. The scientist prefers to make observations that can be expressed in numbers. Although he must often be satisfied by saying, "This animal is sick," he would rather say, "This animal is breathing 25 times per minute and its body temperature is 102°F." The scientist makes and reports observations which he hopes can be measured in the same manner, with approximately the same results, by other persons. He is interested in observations that can be repeated many times and when all conditions are the same, he expects the results to be identical.

If we observe an event and its consequences many times, we can draw conclusions or make generalizations. If I observe that people who eat red berries from a certain tree on a hillside become violently ill and die, I may make a statement that red berries from the tree on the hillside are poisonous. I may extend my statement to a generalization involving all red berries, all berries, or all things that grow on trees on hillsides. To determine whether my generalizations are correct, I must either make many observations of persons eating things from trees or perhaps set up an experiment in which I feed persons (or perhaps other animals) berries and other products from trees both on hillsides and in valleys. On the basis of many observations, I should be able to make generalizations and on the basis of them, to predict what will happen when a person eats things from trees. If my generalizations are sufficiently sophisticated, they can even account (on a statistical basis) for the occasional person who eats poisonous berries and lives.

Man began making predictions based on observations long before recorded history. The periodic flooding of the Nile had important consequences for farmers in ancient Egypt. When the relation of the flooding to a certain pattern of stars in the sky at a certain time of the night was established, the coming of the floods could be predicted.* In such relationships it is always tempting to assume that correlation implies cause and effect, to assume here that the stars control the flooding. While common sense would probably argue against this interpretation, disproof of the theory that a pattern of stars caused the floods could be made only on the basis of the observation that flooding was caused by other means—by rains in far distant regions.

While the generalizations we make from our observations often have to wait on other observations for verification, a scientist usually tries to verify his generalization (which he may call a hypothesis or theory) by experimentation. He can intentionally arrange experiments which seem likely to yield information rather than wait for something to happen and hope that he will be present to observe the incident. One of the most difficult aspects of research work in chemistry and in other sciences is devising experiments or planning observations that will either support or refute a theory. Einstein's theories of relativity had to wait for years before a way was found to test them.

The value of experimentation began to be recognized relatively late in history (1500–1700 A.D.). The ancient Greek scientist-philosophers (600–400 B.C.) were reasonably accurate observers, excellent compilers of observations, and outstanding in proposing explanations. But they lacked one attitude which we now consider necessary for a curious, intelligent person who could be called a scientist; they did not experiment. The Greeks were satisfied if an explanation or theory was logical on the basis of the facts from which they argued. Aristotle, for instance, stated that a barrel full of ashes would hold as much water as would an empty barrel. Apparently no one was interested in testing this by a simple experiment.

We believe that the process of observation, generalization, and verification is the way that most of the important subject matter of chemistry, or of any science, has been established.

---

* It is interesting to note the political power that comes to the person who can predict, whether it be floods or the behavior of uranium and hydrogen in bombs.

Therefore, in this book, whenever possible we will first present observations, either those the reader can make or those that have been made historically. These will be followed by explanations and further applications. We hope that this arrangement will give the reader a sense of the excitement a scientist feels when he sees a new relation, and will provide him with a more meaningful picture of chemistry.

This method of presentation is not possible nor practical in many instances, however, because of the limitations of space and the difficulty of presenting the significant details in a manner understandable to readers inexperienced in the special techniques of chemistry. If we occasionally present facts as though they were dictated by authority or were divinely revealed, we do so for expedience. This is not the way scientific knowledge develops, of course. Today we have available a certain group of facts, and we accept theories which explain these facts consistently. But in the future there will surely be new facts, and new or modified theories. Science is a living, growing thing, not just a series of facts to be memorized. This is not to say that we can understand chemistry without learning some facts. But let us hope that learning the current facts and theories will not prevent us from seeing chemistry as a fascinating, changing way of examining and explaining our universe.

SUGGESTED READING

Asimov, I., *Asimov's Biographical Enclyclopedia of Science and Technology,* Doubleday, New York, 1964.

Asimov, I., *Life and Energy,* Doubleday, New York, 1962.

Asimov, I., *A Short History of Chemistry,* Anchor Books, Doubleday, New York, 1965.

Campbell, N., *What is Science?,* Dover, New York, 1952.

Conant, J. B., ed., *Harvard Case Histories in Experimental Science,* Vols. I and II, Harvard University Press, Cambridge, Mass., 1964.

Conant, J. B., *Science and Common Sense,* Yale University Press, New Haven, Conn., 1951. (Paperback.)

Day, F. H., *The Chemical Elements in Nature,* Reinhold, New York, 1963. Contains information concerning chemical properties of the elements and their occurrence and abundance in nature.

Deason, H. J., ed., *A Guide to Science Reading,* a Signet Science Library Book, New American Library, New York, 1963. A guide to books, principally paperbacks, in the sciences. The book includes general essays by H. Bentley Glass, Margaret Mead, and others.

Friend, J. N., *Man and the Chemical Elements,* Scribner's, New York, 1953. From stone-age hearth to the cyclotron.

Gamow, G., *Mr. Tompkins in Paperback,* Cambridge University Press, New York, 1965. A reprinting in paperback of Dr. Gamow's fanciful adventures of Mr. Tompkins. It contains *Mr. Tompkins in Wonderland* and *Mr. Tompkins Explores The Atom.* The books are a delightful way to explore some areas of chemistry with a master teacher-humorist.

Hall, A. R. and Marie Boas Hall, *A Brief History of Science,* a Signet Science Library Book (T2542), New American Library, New York, 1964.

Holton, G. and D. H. D. Roller, *Foundations of Modern Physical Science,* Addison-Wesley, Reading, Mass., 1958. An excellent, easily-read reference book for chemistry and physics.

Ihde, A. J., *The Development of Modern Chemistry,* Harper and Row, New York, 1964.

Leicester, H. M., *The Historical Background of Chemistry,* John Wiley and Sons, New York, 1965.

Lessing, L. P., *Understanding Chemistry,* Mentor Books, MD 276, New American Library of World Literature, New York, 1959.

McAnally, J. S., *Chemistry,* C. E. Merrill, Columbus, Ohio, 1966. A brief, easily-read introduction to chemistry.

Taylor, F. S., *The Alchemists,* Collier, New York, 1962.

Chapter 2 METHODS OF MEASUREMENT

2-1 INTRODUCTION

Having the skills and the instruments to make accurate, precise measurements is essential for scientific progress—both practical and theoretical. More accurate or precise measurements often lead to changes in basic theories. Newton's theory of the nature of gravity and of basic physics served to explain our observations of the universe for many years. However, when more precise measurements were made, Newton's theories were replaced by Einstein's theories of relativity.

The number of extremely fine measurements involved in the construction, launching, control, and accurate splashdown of a space capsule is almost fantastic. These quantities involve calculations that are so complex and that must be done so rapidly that computers must be used. More mundane measurements are perhaps more important to us in our daily lives. These may include calculations for setting the spark gap in the spark plugs of the cars we drive, measuring the amount of sodium in the blood of a victim of heart disease, or using a strobe light to set the speed of a phonograph turntable to get exactly the right pitch.

It is strange that in our space age, when time is measured in microseconds (millionths of a second) and distance in light years (6 trillion miles), we commonly use many awkward units of measurement. It is also unfortunate that most inhabitants of English-speaking countries are unfamiliar with units such as the gram, meter, and liter, which are common in the rest of the world and are used by all scientists.

Existing primitive societies still use primitive methods for measurement. We assume that ancient societies were similar and began by having words for one, two, few, and many. It is interesting to speculate as to which one came first, the ability to count, probably using the fingers, or the need for a number system in order to carry on trade and commerce. At any rate, the development of a system of counting made possible better measurements of time, distance, and—probably at a later date—of weight and volume. This chapter tells how some of our methods of measurement developed and explains both the units used and the significance of scientific measurements.

2–2 MEASUREMENT OF TIME

Nature divides time for us into days (or days and nights). Observations of the moon are used to show the passage of a month, and of the sun to indicate a year. Subdividing the day into 12 hours, 24 hours, or 8 watches is less natural. Why were the numbers 12 and 24 instead of 10, 50, or 100 chosen for division of the time from sunrise to sunrise—or sunset to sunset, for the late sleepers? These divisions, like most of our units of measurement, are arbitrary, and the fact that we use 24 hours per day, 60 minutes per hour, and 60 seconds per minute probably reflects an earlier numerical system based on 60—a most convenient number since it is divisible by 1, 2, 3, 4, 5, and 6, which eliminates many of the difficulties of calculations with fractions. However, in making precise measurements of time we now use the milli-second or microsecond which are, respectively, 1/1000 and 1/1,000,000 of a second, rather than continuing to subdivide by multiples of 60.

Precise measurements of time, or any other quantity, involve the development of an instrument to measure the units. While the Egyptians had water clocks, and we still use sand in glass vessels as egg timers, clocks and watches were not invented until after the Renaissance. In developing his laws of the pendulum, Galileo had to time the oscillations of the swinging lamp in the cathedral of Pisa by measuring his pulse.

2–3 MEASUREMENT OF DISTANCE

Early measurements of distance involved a certain number of paces or steps, longer distances being measured in the number of days or moons it took to walk the distance. Measures of shorter distances depended upon indicating a distance between two hands—as when we indicate the size of the fish that got away. These methods were not standard and tended to vary both with fishermen and others. Civilization and trade demanded that more precise, easily established standards be instituted.

Since there was no natural, world-wide unit of measurement of length as there was for time, most of the measures which developed as civilizations developed, depended on some human dimension.

The *cubit* is one of the oldest units of length which has persisted through the ages. In the book of Genesis it is recorded that Noah's Ark was 300 cubits long, 50 cubits wide and 30 cubits high. The cubit was established as the distance from the tip of the elbow to the end of the middle finger. If we check this with modern man we will find that it equals 18 to 19 inches. The cubit is presently a part of the British system and is defined as 18 inches. With this information it can be estimated that the Ark was about 450 feet long, 75 feet wide, and 45 feet high, a sizable craft for the time. It is of interest to note the cubit was the unit of measure used in building the Egyptian pyramids.

The *digit* was the breadth of a middle finger; the *inch,* the breadth of the thumb; the *foot,* the length of a man's foot; and the *fathom,* the distance from finger tip to finger tip of the outstretched arm. If we select several people at random and check these units for consistency, it can be seen that considerable variation exists. Sometimes these units were defined in terms of the dimensions of the king but that meant, of course, that a new king brought new measures.

2-4 BRITISH SYSTEM

By the eighteenth century the English speaking countries had developed a system of measurement involving inches, feet, yards, and miles, with other, less familiar, measurements such as the rod and furlong. These units were standardized and are relatively consistent with one another; there are, for example, exactly 12 inches in a foot and 3 feet in a yard. However, there is no consistent factor for converting one unit to another. From feet to inches the factor is 12, from feet to yards it is 3, from yards to miles it is 1760. As most of us know, the conversion of one unit to another, especially when fractions are involved, is extremely time-consuming. If we add the bushel, peck, gallon, quart, pint, cup, tablespoon, and teaspoon which are used to measure volume, and the ton, pound, ounce (both troy and avoirdupois), grain, and carat which are used to measure weight, we realize that the British system is extremely complex and unwieldy.

   As the nations of Europe started trading with one another, it became obvious that not only was the British system complex, but it did not correspond with the systems used in France, Germany, and elsewhere. Even within countries, different provinces or communities often used different measurements. You can imagine the haggling that went on. It was impossible for an international science to develop on a quantitative basis until standards of measurement were set.

2-5 METRIC SYSTEM

In 1790 the French National Assembly authorized the establishment of a committee to develop a new system of weights and measures. As a result, in 1799 a logical new system called the **metric system** was completed and adopted by the French government as its official system. This system is used not only for commerce in many countries, but has become the standard for all scientists. Only the United States and a few other countries still retain the outmoded, unwieldy British system. Great Britain itself is now in the process of converting to the metric system.

Measurement of Length—the Meter

The French, who established the metric unit of length, based this fundamental measurement on something more universal than a man's dimensions. They calculated the length of one-fourth of the circumference of the earth, the quadrant from the equator to the North Pole. They took one ten-millionth of this distance and called it a meter. Actually their measurements were in error, but what is important is that they established one basic unit of length and based every other measurement of length on that. The official meter was set as the distance between two fine scratches on a platinum-iridium bar maintained in the Bureau of Standards in Paris. Since metals expand and contract at different temperatures, this metal bar was kept at the standard temperature of 0° centigrade. The meter is about equal to a yard; it is 39.37 inches. In 1960 the meter was officially redefined as 1,650,763.73 wave lengths of the orange-colored light emitted by gaseous Krypton 86. This does not change the length of the meter but merely makes it more convenient to compare a measuring device with a known standard. Since the orange light emitted by Krypton can be generated by scientists in any part of the world, the meter is now based on a natural, universally-measurable quantity.

The real usefulness of the metric system is that the subdivisions or multiples of its basic units employ only factors of ten. A prefix is used to indicate the size of the unit compared to the basic unit. These prefixes are given below:

deca-	ten (10)	deci-	one-tenth (1/10)
centa-	one hundred (100)	centi-	one-hundredth (1/100)
kilo-	one thousand (1000)	milli-	one-thousandth (1/1000)
mega-	one million (1,000,000)	micro-	one-millionth (1/1,000,000)

The prefixes *kilo-, centi-, milli-,* and *micro-* are the most commonly used. The common measurements of length are the kilometer, centimeter, and millimeter. Relationships of these units are given below:

kilometer	(km):	1 kilometer = 1000 meters
centimeter	(cm):	1 centimeter = 0.01 meter
		100 centimeters = 1 meter
millimeter	(mm):	1 millimeter = 0.001 meter
		1000 millimeters = 1 meter
micrometer	(μ):	1 micron = 0.000001 meter
(micron)		1,000,000 microns = 1 meter

The micrometer is often called a micron. For very minute measurements such as the wavelengths of light, we subdivide microns into millimicrons which are one-billionth of a meter. To give some general idea of the size of these units, a kilometer is 0.6 mile, a centimeter is about half an inch, and the pages of this book are about 0.1 millimeter or 100 microns thick.

Conversion from one unit to another in the metric system, or in any decimal system, merely involves division or multiplication by 10 or multiples of 10, and is accomplished by moving a decimal point. We are accustomed to doing this in dealing with money. For example:

$$\$1.25 = 125 \text{ cents}$$
$$1.25 \text{ meters} = 125 \text{ centimeters}$$
$$\$0.17 = 17 \text{ cents}$$
$$0.17 \text{ meter} = 17 \text{ centimeters}$$
$$237 \text{ cents} = \$2.37$$
$$237 \text{ centimeters} = 2.37 \text{ meters}$$

In dealing with units of length we must remember that

10 mm = 1 cm,   100 cm = 1 m,   and 1000 m = 1 km.

Some other conversions are given below:

4328 meters = 4.328 kilometers
2.567 kilometers = 2567 meters
1.72 meters = 172 centimeters
243 centimeters = 2.43 meters
2.54 centimeters = 25.4 millimeters
760 millimeters = 76 centimeters = 0.76 meter
25,463 millimeters = 25.463 meters = 0.025463 kilometer

Measurement of Volume—the Liter

The unit of volume in the metric system is the *liter*. It was established as the volume of a cube 10 centimeters on a side, or 1000 cubic centimeters. It is slightly larger than a quart (1 liter = 1.06 quarts). For the measurement of smaller volumes the *milliliter* (ml) is used. The cubic centimeter (cc) can also be used; however, a slight discrepancy in calculations has resulted in a small difference in the volumes of these two units. This difference is so small that for ordinary work one can assume that 1 ml equals 1 cc. Since both terms are used, it is necessary that the reader be familiar with both cc and ml. However, in this text the term milliliter will be used exclusively.

Measurement of Weight—the Gram

The unit of weight in the metric system is the *kilogram,* which was originally set as the weight of 1 liter of pure water at 4° centigrade (the temperature at which water has the greatest density). One kilogram is about 2.2 pounds. The gram is the unit commonly used in the laboratory. The milligram is used when weighing very small amounts of material. It is the unit commonly used to indicate the content of drugs in a capsule or pill. For still smaller amounts, the microgram, 1/1000 of a milligram or 1/1,000,000 of a gram is used. It is helpful to remember that for practical purposes

1 liter of water weighs 1 kilogram, and
1 milliliter of water weighs 1 gram.

2–6 CONVERSIONS FROM METRIC TO BRITISH SYSTEM

Measurements and calculations involving only the metric system are simple, as indicated above. Persons living in the United States and some other countries, however, are faced with the necessity of converting measurements from one system to another. Since the metric and British systems are based on incompatible units, conversions involve many different numbers. Which conversion factor is used depends upon the accuracy and precision necessary and desirable. The following table gives figures of sufficient accuracy for under-

TABLE 2–1. Approximate British-Metric Conversion Factors

1 mile	1.60 kilometers
1 meter	40 inches
1 centimeter	0.40 inch
1 inch	2.5 centimeters
1 kilogram	2.2 pounds
1 liter	1.06 quarts
1 pound	454 grams
1 gram	15 grains
1 ounce (avoirdupois)	28 grams
1 ounce (liquid)	30 milliliters
1 micron	0.00004 inch
1 millimicron	0.00000004 inch

standing the numerical processes involved. Precise, scientific calculations, however, would demand more accurate conversion factors.

◄ The following are examples of conversions commonly used.

Along the highways in Mexico and many other foreign countries speed limitations and distances are stated in kilometers. It is therefore necessary for most of us to make conversions between kilometers and miles. Let us suppose a sign reads 40 km/hr. What is the equivalent in miles/hour? Since 1 mi equals 1.6 km, the mile is the larger unit: its numerical value will always be smaller than for the kilometer equivalent. We have, therefore,

$$\frac{40}{1.6} = 25 \text{ (mi/hr)}.$$

If we wish to convert 60 mph to the equivalent speed in kilometers/hour, we must multiply 1.6 × 60 since each mile equals 1.6 km:

$$60 \times 1.6 = 96 \text{ (km/hr)}.$$

Many hospitals and clinics in the United States now record the weights of their patients in kilograms rather than in pounds. This is of advantage since the dosage of many medicines is calculated in terms of milligrams of medicine/kilogram of body weight. Remembering that 1 kg is equal to 2.2 lb, how do you find the weight in pounds of a person who weighs 65 kg?

$$65 \times 2.2 = 143 \text{ (lb)}.$$

What is the weight in kilograms of an 800-lb horse?

$$\frac{800}{2.2} = 363 \text{ (kg)}.$$

Finally, at the supermarket the weights or volumes of many items are stated in both metric or British units. From Table 2–1 we find 1 fl oz is equal to about 30 ml. How many fluid ounces are there in a can containing 960 ml of fruit juice?

$$\frac{960}{30} = 32 \text{ (fl oz)}.$$

The following are examples of appropriate uses for common units of the metric system:

kilometer	distance between cities
meter	length of races at track meets
centimeter	dimensions of books
millimeter	diameter of pencils or glass tubing
microns	size of microorganisms (bacteria)
millimicron	dimensions of colloidal particles, wavelength of light
kilogram	weights of people, horses, or bags of potatoes
grams	weights of rats, chemicals, or canned goods
milligrams	weight of aspirin in a tablet or daily requirements of vitamins
liter	measure of milk, wine, or gasoline
milliliter	(in place of fluid ounces) on bottles or cans of soft drinks, etc. ▶

Since all scientists use the metric system almost exclusively, they usually are not concerned with making conversions from British to metric units. Laboratory practice soon makes it easy to think in terms of milliliters and grams instead of quarts, teaspoons, and ounces. Many scientists hope that the United States, Great Britain, and other countries that still use the British system will soon convert to the metric system. There would be difficulties at the time of change, but the advantages would much outweigh the disadvantages.

2–7 MASS AND WEIGHT

It is important to distinguish between these two terms. **Mass** *refers to the quantity of matter in a body*. A particular stone contains the same amount of matter whether it is on the earth or on the moon, but its weight is vastly different in the two places. Weight is a force, although it is commonly used to measure the quantity of mass present in objects. **Weight** *is the force caused by gravitational attraction* between an object, such as a stone, and the planet it is on or near. A stone which weighs 6 kg on the earth would weigh only about 1 kg on the moon, because the moon exerts much less gravitational pull. When an astronaut ventures far out into space where the gravitational pull from all planets is very weak, he becomes almost weightless. His mass does not change, however. (The physiological effects of near-weightlessness on animals are being carefully studied at present.)

2–8 DENSITY

Two items commonly found in the tackle boxes of fishermen are lead sinkers and cork floats. In describing the properties of these materials it is commonly said that lead is heavier, and cork is lighter than water. Let us examine the implications of this statement. If 1-oz quantities of lead, water, and cork are compared, Fig. 2–1, it will be observed that 1 oz of lead appears relatively small; 1 oz of water will occupy a volume approximately 11 times that of the lead and 1/5 that of the cork. While their volumes differ greatly they all weigh the same, and it cannot be said one is heavier than the other. What we really mean is that their relative weights are different or the weight (mass) of equal volumes of the three would be different.

Williams, Arthur L., Embree, DeBey
Introduction to Chemistry

Reading, MA   Addison-Wesley   c. 1968

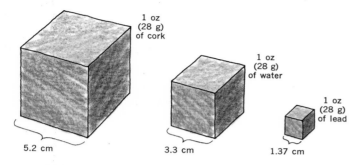

FIG. 2–1. Relative volumes of equal weights of cork, water, and lead.

Lead has a greater mass/milliliter than does cork or water, and therefore is said to have a greater *density*. **Density** is defined as *mass per unit volume*.

$$\text{Density} = \frac{\text{mass (weight)}}{\text{volume}} \qquad \text{or} \qquad D = \frac{M}{V}.$$

Different units may be used to express density, such as pounds/cubic foot or tons/cubic yard. With the metric system, grams/milliliter is used, and we represent this as

$$\text{Density} = \frac{\text{grams}}{\text{milliliter}}.$$

Since water was used as the standard in establishing the unit of mass in the metric system, 1 ml having a mass of 1 g, the density of water must be 1. Substituting in the above formula we have

$$D = \frac{M}{V} = \frac{\text{grams of water}}{\text{milliliters of water}} = 1.00.$$

Example 1. What is the density of chloroform, given that 40 ml of it weighs 60 g?

$$\text{Density} = \frac{60 \text{ g}}{40 \text{ ml}} = 1.5 \text{ g/ml}.$$

Example 2. Determine the density of alcohol, given that 90 ml weighs 71 g.

$$\text{Density} = \frac{71 \text{ g}}{90 \text{ ml}} = 0.79 \text{ g/ml}.$$

Example 3. What is the density of a piece of iron which has a volume of 120 ml and weighs 930 g?

$$\text{Density} = \frac{930 \text{ g}}{120 \text{ ml}} = 7.75 \text{ g/ml}.$$

2–9 SPECIFIC GRAVITY

Since water is conveniently available in most areas of the world, it has long been used to establish the *relative* densities or specific gravities of other materials. The weight of a given volume of a substance divided by the weight of an equal volume of water is called the **specific gravity** of the material. To illustrate, three identical jugs, (a), (b), and (c), are filled with three liquids—water, glycerol, and gasoline—and the weights are as shown in Fig. 2–2. Since water is the standard, with a density of 1, the densities of the others are compared to that of water in the following way.

glycerol: $\dfrac{10 \text{ lb}}{8 \text{ lb}} = 1.25 =$ specific gravity,

gasoline: $\dfrac{6 \text{ lb}}{8 \text{ lb}} = 0.75 =$ specific gravity.

Since specific gravity is a ratio it does not matter what units we use to express weight so long as they are the same for water and the other liquid.

(a)   (b)   (c)

FIG. 2–2. The relative weights of equal volumes of liquids.

Specific gravity is used in many ways in many occupations and may be determined by various methods. The attendant at the filling station uses an instrument called a hydrometer, Fig. 2–3(a), to determine the density of the liquid in your automobile battery (the density of this liquid is a measure of the charge of the battery). Those who live in climates where the winters are cold have observed the filling station attendant using a similar hydrometer to check the strength of the antifreeze in the automobile radiator. The greater the density of the liquid, the higher the hydrometer tube will float; conversely, it will sink deeper in liquids of lesser densities. Hydrometers are used in hospitals and clinical laboratories to determine the specific gravity of urine samples, Fig. 2–3(b). This information is helpful in the diagnosis of certain diseases.

Summarizing: Densities may be expressed in various ways, such as in grams/milliliter, pounds/gallon, pounds/cubic foot, or tons/cubic yard. Unless otherwise stated, in this book density will be expressed in metric terms, grams/milliliter. *Specific gravity* expresses the

(a)   (b)

FIG. 2–3. Hydrometers for determining specific gravity.

relative weight of one liquid compared to that of another. Since water with a density of 1 g/ml is the standard for the metric system, the density of a liquid is numerically equal to its specific gravity.

2–10 TEMPERATURE

The ancient Greek philosopher-scientist Aristotle was much concerned with heat and cold. Were they two different things, or merely extremes of one thing? At one point, his writings indicate, he came close to the idea of an instrument that would measure amounts of heat. However, like the other Greek philosophers of his day, he was interested in thinking in terms of qualities rather than of quantities. The thermometer was not invented until much later.

Once the idea of temperature was developed, the problem became one of constructing a device to measure it. Although others had previously worked on this problem, we owe our present thermometers to Fahrenheit and Celsius, who developed special types of thermometers in 1724 and 1742, respectively. We can reconstruct their measurements by the following procedure.

First, we partially fill two glass tubes with a liquid that will expand when heated and contract when cooled, and then we seal the tubes. We place these tubes in boiling water, and indicate the height of the liquid (mercury is most commonly used) when the tube is at the temperature of the boiling water. Then after allowing the tubes to cool, we immerse them in a mixture of ice and water and make another mark on each tube to indicate the position of the liquid at this temperature, the freezing point of water or the melting point of ice depending upon which way we choose to regard it. Now the problem becomes one of deciding what values to give to these points. Celsius set the freezing point of water equal to 0°

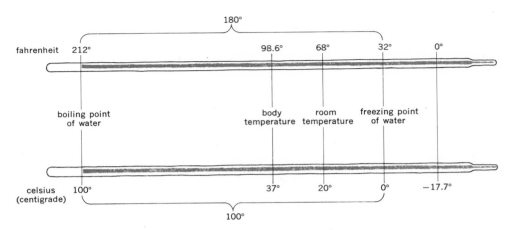

FIG. 2–4. Comparison of fahrenheit and centigrade temperature scales.

and the boiling point equal to 100° on the scale which officially bears his name but is more commonly known as the centigrade scale. Fahrenheit, apparently in an attempt to avoid negative numbers for reporting temperatures on cold days, selected the lowest temperature he could produce with an ice-salt mixture as his zero temperature. He then set body temperature 96 units above the minimum temperature, at 96°. Later he adjusted the scale slightly so that the freezing point of water was 32° and the boiling point of water 212°, exactly 180° above the freezing point. On this scale, body temperature was 98.6°.

It is interesting to note that both scales are based on values that are relatively easy to produce anywhere on earth. We now know, however, that the boiling point of water is affected by elevation and that the values of 100°C or 212°F are correct only at sea level. We also know that dissolving substances in water changes both the boiling and freezing points, so certain precautions must be taken if we are to make accurate thermometers.

In general, the English-speaking countries, those who use the British system of measure, use the fahrenheit scale. The rest of the world and scientists use the centigrade system. Consequently scientists need to know how to convert from one system to the other. It can be seen from the accompanying diagram, Fig. 2–4, that 100°C = 180°F. The reference point is the freezing point of water, 0°C and 32°F. The following examples will illustrate the method of conversion:

Example 1. Body temperature is 98.6°F; what is the equivalent on the celsius scale?

Since 0°F is 32° below the freezing point, body temperature is 98.6° minus 32° or 66.6° above the freezing point on the fahrenheit scale. Then 66.6/1.8 (1°C = 1.8°F) or 37°C is the body temperature on the celsius scale.

Example 2. Room temperature is often considered to be 20°C; what is the corresponding temperature on the fahrenheit scale?

Since 1°C = 1.8°F, 20°C will equal 20 × 1.8 = 36° above the freezing point on the fahrenheit scale. Therefore, 36° + 32° (the freezing point) = 68° above zero on the fahrenheit scale.

2–11 SIGNIFICANT FIGURES

When a person tells you that he is 18 years old you assume that he has passed his eighteenth but not his nineteenth birthday. A month before his nineteenth birthday he will still say that he is 18, although 18 and 11/12 would be more accurate. When we are told that it is 50 miles from one city to another we usually accept this as a fact. However, further reflection may make us ask from what point in each city was the distance measured, and is it really 50 miles, or perhaps 49.5, or 49, or does 50 only mean an approximate distance? It may not really matter how far it is from one city to another, but it becomes a vital matter of somewhat frightening importance if the distance is being measured to guide the flight of a missile or being used to pay for highway construction at $1,000,000/mile.

Scientists must measure precisely and must be honest when they tell how accurately they have measured a quantity. To accomplish this, a system expressing the significance of measurements is used. When a scientist says that a substance weighs 4 g we can assume only that its weight is nearer 4 g than it is to 3 or 5, that is, its weight is between 3.5 and 4.5 g. If we wish to indicate that a weight is exactly 4 g we may write 4.0 g. Actually we never know that a substance weighs exactly 4 g, but only that a scale or balance with a given accuracy has established this weight for the material. We might say that a substance weighs 4.000 g, which means that it weighs between 3.9995 and 4.0005 g. The rule followed is that the last figure is only approximate. The weight of 4 is said to have only one significant figure, and 4.000 has four significant figures. The degree of accuracy with which a scientific measurement was made should always be indicated by the number of significant figures used.

Zeros pose a problem in determining the number of significant figures in a measured quantity. It is generally accepted that zeros used only to locate a decimal place or to give the general size of a number are not significant. Thus the number 2.000 has four significant figures and 0.0002 has only one; that is, we assume that the zeros following the figure 2 in 2.000 were really measured and *are* zero, and not 1, 2, or another figure. Numbers containing several zeros such as 2000 are difficult to assess in terms of significant figures. We don't really know whether the number is between 1995 and 2005 or perhaps between 1500 and 2500. The best resolution of this problem is to use notation involving powers of 10. We can say that 2000 is 2×1000 or 2×10^3. If two of the zeros are really measured, then the value is between 1995 and 2005 and the number is expressed as 2.00×10^3. If only one zero is significant, the number is written 2.0×10^3. Thus the distance from the earth to the sun may be written as 93,000,000 miles or as 9.3×10^7 miles, to indicate an accuracy of two figures. The value 9.300×10^7 indicates that the figure is known to an accuracy of four figures.

In general, unless the power of 10 notation is used, we must assume that zeros at the end of a number are used only to give the relative magnitude of the number (locate the decimal place) and are not significant; that is, they have not really been measured. Thus, 2500 represents only two significant figures. If we want to indicate that figures are significant without using the power of 10 notation, we can use a period following the number. Using this convention, 2500. has four significant figures and 150. has three.

When we start multiplying and dividing measured values, we must be certain that we do not become dishonest in expressing the accuracy of our measurement. If we measure a room and find it to be 9.86 m by 14.35 m and then express the area of the room as 141.4910 sq m, we are reporting that the area is accurate to seven figures although we have taken measurements accurate to only three and four significant figures. We should report the area as 141 sq m. A simpler example illustrates the point more precisely. If a room is said to measure 10 m by 14 m this would mean only that it is between 9.5 m and 10.5 m wide and 13.5 m and 14.5 m long. Thus the area would be between 9.5 × 13.5 or 128.25 sq m and 10.5 × 14.5 or 152.25 sq m, and the value of 10 × 14 or 140 represents the average (280.50/2) and probably the best, most honest value to report.

The general rule when computing with measured quantities is that calculations lead to a result containing *no more significant figures than the least accurate measurement*. This is analogous to the fact that the strength of a chain is no greater than that of its weakest link. The value of 140 calculated above contains only two significant figures and does not violate the rule.

2–12 SUMMARY

In this chapter we have discussed how systems of measurement developed from being arbitrary and variable to the precise definitions of the metric system. In addition to its simple set of basic standards, the metric system is consistent with our numerical system, in being based on 10. This usage greatly simplifies conversions from one measurement to another.

Science without accurate measurements is limited to a discussion of theories, not unlike the proverbial bull sessions. With precise measurements we can now develop replaceable parts for motors of automobiles and perform other similar feats of technology. With more accurate measurements we can develop better theories, describe phenomena more accurately, and predict with greater confidence. Prediction of the time and area to be darkened in eclipses of the moon and sun are now routine. We are beginning to hear of computers that can be programmed with the results of a series of clinical tests (each involving several accurate measurements) to report the many possible diagnoses of a patient's illness. Yet measurements are not an end in themselves: they require interpretation. Without them science could not have developed. Moreover, we can safely predict that more accurate measurements and the measurement of things yet unmeasured will lead to further progress.

IMPORTANT TERMS

Centi-	*Kilo-*	*Mass*	*Micron*	*Specific gravity*
Density	*Liter*	*Meter*	*Milli-*	*Weight*

WORK EXERCISES

1. Make the following conversions:

   a) 25.5 meters to centimeters

   b) 150 centimeters to meters

   c) 50 centimeters to millimeters

   d) 6 meters to millimeters

   e) 2500 meters to kilometers

   f) 274 meters to kilometers

   g) 16 kilometers to meters

   h) 750 millimeters to meters

   i) 750 millimeters to centimeters

2. What is your weight in kilograms?

3. A horse weighs 400 kg. What is its weight in pounds?

4. A stone weighs 400 lb. What is its weight in kilograms?

5. How many kilograms are there in 1 ton?

6. As you approach a city in Mexico, you observe a sign reading 40 km/hr. What is the corresponding speed in miles/hour?

7. Suppose you are driving a European car with a speedometer registering kilometers/hour. What speed will be indicated if you are traveling 50 mph?

8. Make the following temperature conversions:

    a) 100°F to centigrade   b) 50°C to fahrenheit
    c) −10°C to fahrenheit   d) 200°C to fahrenheit
    e) 0°F to centigrade

9. Fifty milliliters (50.0) of mercury weighs 677.3 g. What is the density of mercury in g/ml?

10. An aluminum rod with a volume of 40 ml weighs 108 g. What is the density of aluminum in g/ml?

11. A gold nugget weighing 273 g was found to have a volume of 14.14 ml. What is the density of the nugget in g/ml?

12. A cube of magnesium metal 5 cm on a side weighs 217.5 g. What is the density of magnesium in g/ml? [*Note:* It should be remembered that 1 cc is considered to be equal to 1 ml.]

13. A bottle which holds 200 g of water can hold only 142.7 g of ether. What is the specific gravity of ether? What is the density of ether in g/ml?

14. Wood alcohol has a density of 0.796 g/ml. What will 25 ml weigh?

15. The weight of water and ice is 62.5 and 57.2 lb/cu ft, respectively. What is the specific gravity of ice?

16. A piece of jade which has a specific gravity of 3.5 weighs 640 g. What is its volume in milliliters?

17. The acid in an automobile battery has a specific gravity of 1.2. What will 200 ml of the acid weigh?

Chapter 3   FUNDAMENTAL CONCEPTS OF CHEMISTRY

3-1 INTRODUCTION

Once a scientist has said that he is concerned with the material of the universe and how it changes, he is faced with trying to determine what things are made of and how they are put together. There are many ways of answering the question, "What is everything really made of?" The ancient Greek philosophers tried to simplify the problem. Thales (600 B.C.) advanced the idea that everything was really water: gold, iron, rust, bread, and man himself were merely different arrangements of water. It is interesting to note in passing that Thales lived on a small island and was no doubt aware of the extreme importance of water. Shortly after Thales, two other philosophers, Anaximenes and Heraclitus, proposed that air and fire, respectively, were the elements of which all things were made. Since each of the theories that proposed only one basic substance were probably too simple to account for what could be observed, they were developed into a theory generally attributed to Empedocles, which said that there were four elements—water, air, fire, and earth.

This classification was generally accepted for almost two thousand years. If we substitute the term liquid for water, gas for air, and solid for earth, and realize that fire was somehow related to the tendency of things to burn or react, the theory makes relatively good sense even to a twentieth century person. According to the four-element theory, the different metals just contained different amounts of the various elements, and people reasoned that by altering the proportions it should be possible to change one metal (preferably a cheap one) into another (gold).

In addition to discussions about the kinds of things that made up the universe, there was also the question of the units into which this "stuff" of the universe was organized. About 400 B.C. Democritus developed a theory that the elements were made of atoms. Thus you could have an atom of earth, a different kind of atom in water, and so forth. Plato proposed that these atoms were actually different simple solid shapes, those of the earth being cubes;

fire, tetrahedrons; air, octahedrons; and water, twenty-sided solids, eicosahedrons. The primary idea about the atom, however, was that it could not be subdivided. The word atom comes from the Greek *tomos,* meaning to cut and the prefix *a* indicating a negative property, so that atom meant uncuttable.

Before we begin to discuss modern ideas about the composition and structure of matter, we must give some basic definitions and discuss them. All organized knowledge begins this way. Let us first establish certain terms without discussing them in too much detail, and then discuss the precise details and meanings of the terms.

3-2   DEFINITION OF CHEMISTRY

Chemistry is the science concerned with the composition of the substances of the universe, the properties of these substances, the changes they undergo, and the energy relationships involved in these changes.

Any such definition, of course, can indicate only the main subjects of interest to chemists. Perhaps the definition serves to set limits on the areas which a chemist ordinarily investigates. In our modern, complex world some limitation of interests is necessary if a subject is to be approached in depth.

3-3   MATTER, ELEMENTS, COMPOUNDS, MIXTURES

We say that the universe is composed of **matter** which we define as anything that has mass and occupies space. The simplest particle of matter that exists for any appreciable length of time is the **atom.** The simplest kind of matter is an **element.** Gold, oxygen, sulfur, and helium are all elements. *We define an element as a kind of matter that contains only one kind of atom.* Two or more elements can combine to give a substance called a *compound.* Table salt, sugar, and water are compounds. Table salt is composed of sodium and chlorine, sugar of carbon, oxygen, and hydrogen, and water of hydrogen and oxygen. *The smallest particle of a compound is a* **molecule.** Salt contains 1 atom of sodium and 1 of chlorine per molecule. Simple sugars contain 6 atoms of carbon, 12 of hydrogen, and 6 of oxygen per molecule. Their formula is $C_6H_{12}O_6$. Two atoms of the same element can also combine to give a molecule; the oxygen present in the air is ordinarily present as a diatomic molecule we represent as O_2.

Both elements and compounds are called pure substances, or often just **substances.** Most of the things we know about and work with in our daily life are **mixtures** of pure substances. While we are quite aware that cakes, concrete, cabbages, and kings are mixtures, it is not so obvious that air is also a mixture. Historically, air was thought of as being one of the basic elements, and it was not until the eighteenth century that scientists began to realize that it was a mixture. We now know that it contains the elements oxygen and nitrogen, the compounds water and carbon dioxide, and many other substances. Like all mixtures, the composition of air varies, particularly with respect to the amount of water, carbon dioxide, and pollutants it contains.

In contrast to mixtures, compounds have a constant composition; table salt, for example, is always 39% sodium and 61% chlorine.

◄ It seems obvious that elements also do not vary in composition since they contain only one kind of atom. However, in Section 4–8 we will find that some atoms of chlorine, for example, have slightly different weights than do other chlorine atoms. Natural samples of chlorine atoms nearly always contain the different types of chlorine atoms in the same proportions, however, so that the average weight of chlorine atoms in one sample is the same as that in another sample. Different atoms of the same element which have different weights are called **isotopes.** Since the discovery of isotopes, we realize that two samples of a compound or element may differ with respect to the kinds of sodium or chlorine atoms they contain. The statements given above are still essentially true, however. For a further discussion of isotopes, see Section 4–8. ►

3–4 STATES OF MATTER

Matter, whether in the form of elements or compounds, can exist as a solid, a liquid, or a gas. While these terms are in general use, and most persons have some idea of their meaning, the proverbial man in the street might have some difficulty in giving a precise definition of any one of these. As a matter of fact, scientists have found defining these words to be difficult. Simple but satisfactory definitions now generally used are as follows: A **solid** has definite shape and volume. A **liquid** has definite volume but no definite shape; it will take the shape of the container which holds it. A **gas** has neither definite shape nor definite volume. Gases can be compressed from larger to smaller volumes and will spontaneously fill any container in which they are placed. In a solid the atoms or molecules are close together; in a liquid, a bit farther apart and in gases, there are few particles and a great deal of empty space. This is shown by the observation that a given volume of a gas weighs less than the same volume of a liquid, and the liquid, in general, weighs less than the same volume of a solid.

◄ There are, of course, exceptions to the latter statement: ice, for example, is less dense than liquid water. This exception to the rule is most important since it means that ice floats when it forms on a lake or stream and eventually forms an insulating layer which protects the water at the bottom of the lake or stream from freezing. This is of great importance in allowing fish to live through the winter in colder climates. ►

With certain exceptions, matter may exist in any of the three states, and may be changed from one state to another under the influence of changes in temperature and pressure. We know, for instance, that water exists in the three forms, as solid ice, as liquid water, and as a gas or water vapor. Below 0°C water exists as ice and above 100°C it is steam. Steam may be condensed to water either by cooling or by increasing the pressure.*

The elements can exist in any of the three states, although the light gases hydrogen and helium must be cooled to very near absolute zero before they solidify, and very high temperatures are required to vaporize some of the heavier elements. While compounds such as water can exist in all three states, others decompose when heated.

---

* The atmosphere, regardless of its temperature, always contains some water vapor, and the amount present is influenced primarily by the temperature. Even in air cooled below 0°C, where we would expect water to change to ice, some water is present in the gaseous form.

3–5 PHYSICAL AND CHEMICAL PROPERTIES

In any study of the elements and compounds that make up the universe we must talk about the characteristics of the substances. Chemists use the term *properties* to describe the characteristics. Some of these properties of a substance can be determined by simple physical observations. The physical state (solid, liquid, gas), the color, and odor are obvious *physical properties*. Chemists also include in their list of physical properties other properties that can be measured without changing the composition of the substance. The melting and boiling points, the solubility, and the density are physical properties that help us to recognize or identify a substance.

We know that gasoline is flammable and that iron rusts. These are important properties of these substances. However, when gasoline burns or iron rusts, these substances are converted to new ones. There has been a change in composition, and we say a chemical reaction has occurred. A property that depends upon the composition of a substance or a change in its composition is a *chemical property*. The general degree of reactivity is also an important feature of chemical properties. We know that gold is inactive—it does not decompose and reacts with very few other substances. These properties are the basis of the high value placed on this metal. White phosphorus, on the other hand, is a very active substance. When exposed to the air it bursts into flame. We must be aware that the degree of reactivity is also influenced by temperature. Copper does not react with oxygen at room temperature, but does when it is heated.

If you were given three liquids—water, ethyl alcohol, and benzene—in three separate bottles you would probably be able to identify which of the liquids was in which bottle. You would do this by observing certain properties, primarily the odor. There are many other properties that can be used to distinguish between these three substances. Some of them are given in Table 3–1.

The properties listed in Table 3–1 are sufficient to indicate which of three liquids is in which bottle if you know that only three possible compounds are present. It would be much

TABLE 3–1. Some properties of water, alcohol, and benzene

Observation or Test	Water	Alcohol	Benzene
color	colorless	colorless	colorless
taste	tasteless	characteristic burning taste	acrid
odor	odorless	sweet	definite odor
state at room temperature	liquid	liquid	liquid
freezing point	0°C	−117°C	5.5°C
boiling point	100°C	78°C	80.1°C
solubility	soluble in alcohol	soluble in water	insoluble in water; soluble in alcohol
density	1.0 g/ml	0.78 g/ml	0.80 g/ml
flammability	nonflammable	flammable	flammable

more difficult, however, to prove beyond any doubt that of all the substances on earth, a certain bottle contained ethyl alcohol. There are many liquids that have the same freezing points and boiling points. Therefore properties other than those listed here would be necessary for the identification of a compound, especially an organic compound. Analysis of the components of a natural product such as strawberries, wood, or the human liver requires an extensive examination of the properties of each component.

3-6 PHYSICAL AND CHEMICAL CHANGES

Chemistry is concerned not only with the composition of the universe but in the changes that occur in all substances. While changes in physical properties might seem to belong in the realm of physics, chemistry is also very much concerned with such changes. A **physical change** is defined as a change which does not alter the chemical composition of a material. Changing ice to water, crushing salt into a fine powder, and condensing ethyl alcohol in a distillation process all involve physical changes. The rusting of iron and the burning of gasoline are examples of **chemical changes.** When iron rusts, it combines with oxygen to form an iron oxide. When gasoline burns, it combines with oxygen to produce carbon dioxide and water. Both of these chemical changes are accompanied by physical changes. Rust has a different color and is different from iron in hardness and other physical properties. Liquid gasoline is converted to two new gaseous substances when it burns. In general, it is true that a chemical change is accompanied by a physical change, whereas physical changes, as we have noted, do not involve a change in composition of matter. Both physical and chemical changes involve the absorption or release of energy.

3-7 ENERGETICS

When a piece of wood burns, heat and light are given off. Compounds from the wood have united with oxygen from the air and energy has been released. Where did this energy come from? Obviously from the wood, or perhaps from the oxygen. How can we describe the energy present in the wood? We use the term *potential* or *chemical energy* to describe this stored energy. Where did the wood get the energy? The simplest answer is that it came from the sun and was trapped by the green leaves which then converted it to the energy in wood. Chemical energy is a form of potential energy. Sunlight and heat are forms of *kinetic energy*.

An automobile traveling at 60 mph possesses energy which it does not have when it is standing still. This energy of motion is called **kinetic energy.** If the automobile is at rest on the side of a hill with its brakes set, it possesses **potential energy;** this is the energy of position which it would not have at the bottom of the hill. If the brake is released, its potential energy is converted into kinetic energy. If the hill is high enough to impart considerable kinetic energy to the car, the car may roll a considerable distance up the next hill, thus converting its kinetic energy to potential energy.

The powder in a rifle cartridge contains a great deal of chemical (potential) energy. If the rifle is pointed upward and fired, the stored chemical energy imparts kinetic energy (motion) to the bullet. As the bullet travels upward, its kinetic energy decreases, but it is gaining potential energy. At the top of its trajectory it has only potential energy. This is converted to kinetic energy as it falls back to earth.

In order to discuss transformations of energy it is necessary to talk about some of the forms of energy. **Energy** may be defined as the ability to do work, and work is done whenever a body is moved by a force. Heat, light, and electricity are well-known types of energy. Less widely recognized are the energy present in sound, nuclear energy, and chemical energy.

3–8 HEAT

A given quantity of matter contains more energy when it is hot than when it is cold, because when the temperature of a substance increases, its molecules move more rapidly; this usually also causes the substance to expand. Heat and temperature are closely related, but there is a distinction between them which should be clearly understood. **Heat** is a form of energy. **Temperature** is an indication, or measure, of the intensity of heat energy.

A very small amount of energy can produce enough heat to raise the temperature of the filament in a flashlight bulb to a very high point (nearly 1500°C). The same amount of heat would produce only a very slight change, however, in the temperature of a pound of iron. Similarly, a given amount of heat would raise the temperature of one liter of water more than it would that of two liters of water. The unit most commonly used to measure heat is the **calorie** (abbreviated cal) which is *the amount of heat required to raise the temperature of one gram of water on degree centigrade.* More accurately, a calorie is the amount of heat required to raise the temperature of 1.00 g of water from 14.5° to 15.5°C. The temperature range is specified because the heat capacity of water is slightly different at different temperatures.

Since the calorie is a small unit, the **kilocalorie** (1000 cal) is more commonly used to denote the energy lost or gained in chemical reactions. The kilocalorie (abbreviated kcal or Cal) is also the unit used to specify the calories in food.

3–9 RADIANT ENERGY

We are all aware, when we sit around a campfire or an electric heater, of the heat which is radiated, heat which is, in fact, energy. The outstanding illustration of a source of radiant energy is the sun. When the temperature of a heated object is relatively low, its radiation is in the form of invisible heat rays which we refer to as *infrared radiation*. When the temperature of the heated object is greater than about 500°C, the radiation becomes visible and we call it light. At high temperatures all matter, regardless of its state, radiates light. The incandescent flame, such as the flame of a match or a campfire, is produced by a gas that is so hot that it is radiating light. The glowing coals of the campfire are solids that are radiating light. Molten metals, such as one sees in furnaces in steel mills, are hot enough to emit light. All of these also radiate heat.

3–10 ELECTRICAL ENERGY

Although discussion of electrical energy belongs primarily to the physicists, certain aspects of the production and use of electrical energy are important to chemists. The production of electricity from the potential energy stored in batteries is basically a chemical process. The energy to initiate or continue many chemical reactions can be provided by electrical energy.

Biochemists are interested in the electrical nature of nerve impulses and especially those in that specialized animal, the electric eel, which converts chemical energy to electrical energy potent enough to deliver a respectable shock to his enemies.

3–11 SONIC ENERGY

A great many people were unaware of the energy possessed by sound until the advent of supersonic jets and the accompanying window-rattling sonic booms. Large explosions, lightning, and other violent forces also set the air in motion in such a way as to leave no doubt that energy is involved in the propagation, transmission, and reception of sound. Ultrasonic vibrations (sound pitched too high for the human ear to detect) are used to disrupt the bacterial cell walls in some types of biochemical experiments.

3–12 NUCLEAR ENERGY

A form of energy which is growing in importance both for the military and for industry is **nuclear energy.** It is, in fact, so important that it will be discussed at length in Chapter 20.

3–13 CHEMICAL ENERGY

We all know that many chemical reactions release energy. These range from explosions that release a great deal of sound along with a blast of direct kinetic energy, to the slower burning of wood and candles, to the reactions occurring whenever we move our muscles. The energy released in these reactions comes from the reacting substances. If energy has been released, we would expect that the products of the reaction must contain less energy than the substances that reacted. Experiments show that this is indeed true. Reactions of the opposite type—those in which energy is absorbed—are also known. They are less dramatic than the energy-releasing reactions, but are of extreme importance, particularly those involved in building the tissues of the human body.

Reactions that release energy are said to be **exergonic.** If the energy released is in the form of heat, they are said to be **exothermic.** Reactions that absorb energy or specifically heat are known as **endergonic** or **endothermic** reactions. The decomposition of water into hydrogen and oxygen gases by the passage of a current of electricity through the water is called *electrolysis.* This is an endergonic reaction, and whenever the source of electricity is shut off, the reaction stops. When hydrogen and oxygen are mixed and a small amount of energy is provided in the form of an electrical spark or a flame, a violent explosion results. Although it takes special instruments to measure it, the amount of energy given off in the explosion of hydrogen and oxygen to form 1 g of water is exactly the amount required to electrolyze 1 g of water into hydrogen and oxygen gas.

3–14 IMPORTANT ENERGY TRANSFORMATIONS

The primary source of some of the most important energy transformations is the energy of the sun. Light energy radiating from the sun travels approximately 93 million miles to the earth, where a substantial portion of it is converted to heat energy. Another portion of the sun's radiant energy is absorbed by green plants. Through the process of photosynthesis the light energy is transformed to stored chemical (potential) energy. We are indebted to this process, directly or indirectly, for all the natural fuels we have and all the energy in the foods we eat. For example, coal, petroleum, and natural gas which meet most of the energy needs of industry were, at one time, green plants. Furthermore, the warming of the earth by the sun causes water to evaporate into the atmosphere; variations in temperature cause this water to return to earth, forming streams which may be impounded behind dams. This potential energy due to the position of the water can be transformed into electrical energy, which in turn produces light, heat, chemical energy, mechanical power, and all the other things for which electricity is used.

3–15 CONSERVATION OF ENERGY AND MATTER

When discussing conversion of energy and matter from one state to another we might well ask about the efficiency of this conversion. Do we lose some energy in the process? What happens to the matter in a candle when it burns?

Careful experiments in which water is changed from ice to water to steam, and then back to water and ice show that not only does the mass of water *not* change, but also that the amount of heat required to melt ice is released—in fact, it must be removed—when water freezes.

When we burn a candle it seems as if the matter of the candle has actually been destroyed, but this is not true. In fact, if we trap the gases given off by the candle we will find that they weigh more than the original candle did. The increase in weight is due to the oxygen from the air which reacted with the carbon and hydrogen atoms in the wax of the candle. When a candle burns, stored chemical energy is released as light and heat, and the carbon and hydrogen atoms are converted to the gases carbon dioxide and water. While compounds are created and destroyed in the reaction, the same number of atoms are present before and after the reaction. The amount of energy also has not been changed; it has merely been converted into different forms.

On the basis of many such experiments, we can formulate the **laws of conservation of matter and energy.** These laws state that *matter is neither created nor destroyed*, and that *energy is neither created nor destroyed.* Until recently there were no known exceptions to these laws. The advent of the atomic bomb, however, proved dramatically that matter can be converted into energy. Therefore, a more general law of conservation states that the **sum of the mass and energy is not changed during reaction.**

We now believe that even when a match burns, an extremely small amount of matter is converted into energy. Although the exact amount of matter so converted cannot be measured with even our most precise balances, it can be calculated. In a nuclear reaction such as that in an atomic bomb or in a nuclear-reactor power generator, an appreciable amount of matter is converted into energy. In this case, atoms are transformed into new kinds of atoms, but the new atoms always weigh slightly less than the old ones. Speaking strictly then, we must change the laws of conservation of matter and of energy into the new statement that indicates that matter may be converted into energy. Theoretically, the opposite process, the conversion of energy into matter should occur, but evidence for this has not yet been presented. It has been postulated that processes of this kind are occurring in some stars.

Since the amount of matter destroyed in ordinary *chemical* reactions is negligible, we shall treat all chemical calculations as if the old laws were true. However, the very nature of *nuclear* reactions is such that matter *is* converted to energy, and for some calculations we must recognize this fact.

3-16 SUMMARY

In this chapter we have defined and discussed some of the terms basic to chemistry. We have specified that matter exists as either elements, compounds, or mixtures, and that these are made of particles called atoms and molecules. We have discussed the meaning of physical and chemical changes and properties. We have also discussed the energy that is important in chemical reactions. The perceptive reader will realize that we have not really told him what an atom or molecule is, and while defining the terms element and compound, we have not talked about the reasons why one element is different from another, what causes two atoms of different elements to combine to form a molecule of a compound, or what forces hold them together once they have combined. The next several chapters will discuss these questions.

IMPORTANT TERMS

Calorie	*Compound*	*Exergonic*	*Mixture*
Chemical change	*Element*	*Exothermic reaction*	*Physical change*
Chemical energy	*Endergonic*	*Kinetic energy*	*Physical properties*
Chemical properties	*Endothermic reaction*	*Matter*	*Potential energy*
Chemistry	*Energy*		

WORK EXERCISES

1. Contrast or distinguish between the physical characteristics of the three states of matter.
2. Describe three methods whereby potential energy may be converted into electrical energy.
3. Why has it been necessary to alter the original laws which pertain to the conservation of matter and energy?
4. Distinguish between physical changes and chemical changes.
5. State four physical properties of aluminum metal.
6. State some of the properties of gasoline and indicate whether they are physical or chemical.
7. Why are the terms exothermic and endothermic not always appropriate in describing the energy relationships of chemical reactions?
8. Why is the statement "below the freezing point water is a solid" not completely correct?

9. Distinguish between heat and temperature.

10. Why must chemical change always be accompanied by a physical change, whereas physical changes are not necessarily accompanied by a chemical change?

11. Distinguish between a small calorie and a kilocalorie.

12. Give three illustrations of kinetic energy and three forms of potential energy.

13. How may one form of energy be transformed into another form?

SUGGESTED READING

Van Allen, J. A. *et al.,* "Heat," *Scientific American,* Sept. 1954. This issue contains nine articles covering as many different aspects of heat.

Chapter 4 THE STRUCTURE OF MATTER

4-1 INTRODUCTION

In previous chapters we not only defined terms, but we discussed some of them so that the reader might gain understanding instead of merely memorizing definitions. However, we have not yet really discussed what an atom is. This chapter provides an answer, neither final nor detailed, but nevertheless an answer to the question, "What is an atom?" Along the way, we will also discuss the nature of molecules.

If we ask the question, "How small can a piece of gold be made?" there are two possible answers. One is that there is no limit: theoretically, you could go on cutting a piece of gold, or any other element, indefinitely if you had the proper tools or instruments. (Since this is purely a theoretical argument, we will assume that the finer and finer necessary tools exist.) You would never arrive at a particle that could not be further divided. The other possible answer is that the process of division is not infinite, but that eventually you would come to a particle that could not be cut. This fundamental, indivisible particle is what Democritus called an atom (Section 3-1). Once the two answers are proposed we could argue indefinitely about whether we wish to think that matter is infinitely divisible or not. This is the situation that existed for nearly two thousand years after Democritus proposed his theory. Some evidence was brought up to support each side, but common sense seemed to favor infinite divisibility. What was needed to settle the argument was experimentation, a deliberate effort to uncover enough new facts to settle the argument one way or the other.

In 1803, John Dalton, an English school teacher, published a series of statements regarding the nature of atoms and molecules. These statements which we call *Dalton's atomic theory* were based on some of his own experiments and on those of others who had gone before him. **Dalton's theory** can be stated as follows:

1) Matter is composed of tiny, indivisible particles called atoms.

2) Atoms of the same element are all alike.

3) Atoms of different elements are different.

4) In chemical reactions atoms combine, separate, or regroup. They are the units which enter chemical reactions, forming "compound atoms" (molecules).

5) In chemical reactions whole atoms are always involved. They may combine in a one-to-one ratio, a one-to-two ratio, or a one-to-three ratio, etc.

6) The weight of an atom never changes as a result of a chemical change.

These statements are simple and definite. They established chemistry as a science based on firm principles which were based on experimental evidence. Furthermore, there were many experiments that could be done to test the truth of Dalton's statements. They removed the discussion of divisibility of matter, and in fact, of the basic structure of matter, from the level of theoretical bull sessions to a theory based on and supported by experiments. In general, we still believe the principles of Dalton's theory. In common with almost all theories, it has been modified slightly to conform with the results of subsequent chemical observations and experiments. In this book we cannot give all the background that led to Dalton's proposals, but the following discussion of the laws of Definite and Multiple Proportions serve to illustrate two of the important laws supporting Dalton's atomic theory.

4–2 LAW OF DEFINITE PROPORTIONS

Careful studies of the manner in which elements combine and of the composition of the resulting compounds, produced evidence that in a pure substance or compound the percentage of each element is always the same. For instance, the percentages by weight of the elements in methane are always 75% carbon and 25% hydrogen. In water they are 88.8% oxygen and 11.2% hydrogen. This information led to the formulation of the **Law of Definite Proportions** which states that *in a specific chemical compound the elements are always present in a definite proportion by weight.*

From the percentages of the elements in methane one might be led to the (erroneous) conclusion that methane contains three carbon atoms and one hydrogen atom, since 75% is three times 25%. This conclusion is based on the false assumption that all atoms are of equal weight. Atoms do, in fact, vary greatly in weight. When the number of grams of carbon, 75 g contained in 100 g of methane (75% carbon), are divided by 12, the atomic weight* of carbon, the result is 6.25:

$$\frac{\text{grams of carbon (per 100 g of methane)}}{\text{atomic weight of carbon}} = \frac{75}{12} = 6.25.$$

When the number of grams of hydrogen, 25 g contained in 100 g of methane, are divided by 1, the atomic weight of hydrogen, the result is 25:

$$\frac{\text{grams of hydrogen (per 100 g of methane)}}{\text{atomic weight of hydrogen}} = \frac{25}{1} = 25.$$

---

* The establishment of atomic weights was a long and involved process. It is discussed in Section 4–4.

The above calculations indicate that 100 g of methane contain 6.25 atomic weights of carbon and 25 atomic weights of hydrogen, a ratio of 4 hydrogen atoms for each carbon atom, since

$$\frac{25}{6.25} = 4.$$

The empirical formula (which is the simplest ratio of atoms in a molecule) is therefore CH_4. Similarly for water, 11.2 divided by 1 is 11.2, and 88.8 divided by 16 is 5.6, so that the actual ratio (11.2/5.6) is expressed as the familiar formula H_2O.

4-3 LAW OF MULTIPLE PROPORTIONS

It must have been considerations such as those given above which led Dalton to conclude that the atoms always combine in the ratio of small whole numbers, such as one-to-one, one-to-two, or two-to-three. This realization meant that chemistry was really a science of studying compounds that were constant. Salt from England yielded the same results as salt from India, and when you combined pure hydrogen and pure oxygen you always got H_2O. This generalization, as has happened to countless other generalizations, was found to be only partly true. Carbon, for example, combines with two atoms of oxygen to give carbon dioxide, but under conditions where the supply of oxygen is limited, one atom of carbon reacts with only one atom of oxygen to form the poisonous gas carbon monoxide. Dalton studied the gases we call methane (CH_4) and ethene (C_2H_4) during the time he was pondering this problem. We now know also of hydrogen peroxide, H_2O_2, which seems to violate the simple statement of the Law of Definite Proportions, since in one instance the compound of hydrogen and oxygen is 11% hydrogen (H_2O) and in the other it is only 6% hydrogen (H_2O_2).

The usefulness of Dalton's original law is saved, however, if we introduce another law, the **Law of Multiple Proportions.** This law says that *two kinds of atoms may unite in a number of combinations forming different kinds of molecules with different percentages of composition, but that their combining ratios will always be in the ratios of small whole numbers.* This law was formulated by Dalton in the early years of the nineteenth century. Thus the original statement of the Law of Definite Proportions was found to be too simple a description of what was found in nature and the law had to be modified. Not until Dalton's proposal of the Law of Multiple Proportions and other results of his studies could the atomic theory really begin to be accepted. Much more work by many other scientists was necessary before the theory gained unquestioned acceptance.

4-4 ATOMIC WEIGHTS

In discussing the Law of Definite Proportions and giving a method for finding a formula for a compound, we introduced the fact that the atomic weight of carbon is 12. Actually the determination of atomic weights took many years. It has been said that the development of formulas required atomic weights and that atomic weights could only be determined when the formulas for compounds were known. Historically, both weights and formulas were being determined at the same time with results from one field requiring readjustment of the concepts in the other.

When Boyle, Dalton, and others were experimenting with gases such as hydrogen, oxygen, carbon dioxide, and the mixture air, they were able to weigh given volumes of the gases. It was soon established that hydrogen gas was the lightest and that a given volume of oxygen weighed about sixteen times as much as the same volume of hydrogen. It was proposed by the Italian scientist Avogadro that equal volumes of gases contained an equal number of particles (atoms or molecules). Thus the *relative* weight of hydrogen and oxygen atoms could be determined. This would not give us a definite weight for either hydrogen or oxygen, but if we assumed oxygen to be 100 (which some persons preferred) then hydrogen would have a weight of 6.25. If we assumed hydrogen to be 1, oxygen would have a weight of 16. After much discussion, the latter alternative was adopted. This gave a series of atomic weights, most of which were whole numbers, or at least were whole numbers as closely as might be expected with the analytical techniques then available. There were minor deviations from whole numbers, and in a few cases, notably with the element chlorine which had a weight of about 35.5, the differences were major. These discrepancies, however, did not really become critical until after the next development, the discovery of the subatomic particles.

4–5 SUBATOMIC PARTICLES

In the later years of the nineteenth century, evidence began to accumulate that the atoms which Dalton had thought were indivisible stable particles could not only be broken down under extreme conditions, but in some cases, would spontaneously fall apart. The evidence came from a variety of sources.

It had been known for a long time that electrical discharges would travel between electrodes more readily in an evacuated (vacuum) tube. An English physicist, William Crookes, found that the rays in such a tube, Fig. 4–1, could be deflected by a magnet. The direction of deflection indicated that these rays were negative in character. In 1897 another English physicist, J. J. Thompson, found that these rays, which were named **electrons,** were tiny particles bearing the elementary negative unit of electricity. Later it was found that their mass equaled 1/1837 that of a hydrogen atom. These discoveries proved definitely that the atom is not the smallest unit of matter, as had been postulated by Dalton.

Since matter is normally neutral in character, it was reasonable to speculate that if matter consists in part of negatively charged particles, there must also be positive particles. The

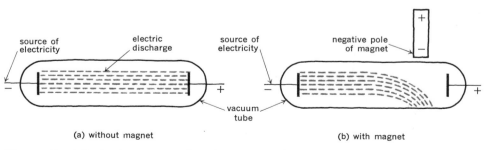

FIG. 4–1. The deflection by a magnet of rays in a vacuum tube.

search for such a particle was culminated in 1919 by Rutherford. He identified a particle, the **proton,** which carried a unit positive charge equal in magnitude to that of the electron but opposite in character. Its mass was found to be 1836 times that of the electron and almost identical to that of the hydrogen atom. By 1920 it had been suggested that an elementary uncharged particle was also present in atoms. The existence of this particle, named the **neu-tron,** was confirmed by Chadwick in 1932. The neutron has a mass essentially that of the proton or the hydrogen atom.

Discoveries during this period of active research aided and stimulated the many workers in this field. Henry Becquerel discovered radioactivity in 1895, and subsequently Madame Curie discovered the radioactive element radium in 1898. It was found that radium atoms slowly decompose, giving off three types of radiation: negative, *beta* (β) which are electrons; positive, *alpha* (α) which are positively charged helium atoms; and neutral, *gamma* (γ) which are considered to have no detectable mass. Gamma rays are comparable to X-rays. (A more detailed discussion of radium and radioactivity is given in Chapter 20 on nuclear chemistry.)

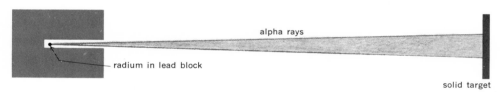

FIG. 4–2. Alpha particles striking a solid target.

4–6 STRUCTURE OF ATOMS

In 1911 Rutherford performed a unique experiment. It had been found that when alpha particles (charged helium atoms) struck a certain type of sensitized surface, flashes of light were visible. A piece of radium (an alpha-particle emitter) was placed in a lead tube closed at one end so that the only alpha particles escaping could be aimed toward a target. Under these conditions all the strikes were concentrated in one area. When a very thin section of gold foil, 1000 to 2000 atoms thick, was placed in the path of the alpha particles, about 1 particle in 100,000 was deflected while the rest passed through and hit the target as if nothing were in the way. (See Figs. 4–2 and 4–3.) The results of this experiment led to the belief that very little of the space in an atom was occupied by matter. In fact, it was commonly said that an atom was as porous as a solar system, and that if we considered the likelihood of a hit by a missile shot at random through our solar system, we would have an idea of the structure of matter.

As the result of Rutherford's experiment, we now believe that most of the matter within the atom is located in a very small space called the **nucleus.** It has been calculated that the diameter of the nucleus is somewhere between 1/10,000 and 1/100,000 that of the diameter of the atom. By way of illustration: if an atom could be enlarged until the nucleus were the size of a BB shot, the atom would approximate the dimensions of the Rose Bowl.

In Rutherford's experiment described above, most alpha particles went straight through the foil; however, some were deflected at right angles, indicating a hit, while others were deflected only slightly, indicating that they were repelled by an electromagnetic force. Since the alpha particles are positively charged, one would expect them to be repelled by other positively charged bodies. It was reasoned, therefore, that the nuclei of the atoms must also be positively charged.

While much has been learned about the structure of atoms in the last few decades, much still remains unknown. Atom-smashing, using highly accelerated electrons or protons, has released many subatomic particles. The significance of these particles and their relation to chemical processes is still a matter for research. However, *a great deal of fundamental chemistry is understandable on the basis of only three particles: the electron, the proton, and the neutron.*

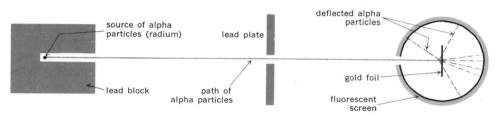

FIG. 4–3. Rutherford's experiment, showing paths of alpha particles after striking gold foil.

Rutherford and the brilliant Danish physicist Niels Bohr were largely responsible for the concept of the planetary atom. They envisioned a very dense compact nucleus surrounded by electrons traveling at exceedingly high speeds far from the nucleus, somewhat like planets traveling about the sun.

Thus our present conception of the atoms differs significantly from Dalton's. Instead of small, hard, indivisible particles, we think of the atom as being largely empty space containing a nucleus surrounded by orbiting electrons. The nucleus is composed of protons and neutrons. The simplest atom, hydrogen, contains only one proton and one electron. Other atoms contain both protons and neutrons in their nuclei. In the smaller atoms the numbers of each are approximately equal. In the larger atoms there are more neutrons than protons. In a complete atom of any element there are always as many electrons surrounding the nucleus as there are protons in the nucleus, and the atom is electrically neutral.

At the date of this writing, there are 103 known elements. The most characteristic property of each element is the number of protons in its nucleus. From the smallest atom, hydrogen, which has one proton in its nucleus, to the largest atom, Lawrencium, with 103 protons, each element has its definite *number of protons.* This number is called the **atomic number** of the element. Since complete atoms have the same numbers of electrons and protons, the atomic number will also represent the *number of electrons* in the complete atom of each element. (Compare the first and last columns of Table 4–1.)

TABLE 4–1. The structures of a few common atoms

	Number of Protons (Atomic Number)	Number of Neutrons	Atomic Weight	Composition of Nuclei	Number of Electrons
hydrogen	1	0	1.008	p*	1
helium	2	2	4.003	2p 2n†	2
carbon	6	6	12.011	6p 6n	6
oxygen	8	8	15.999	8p 8n	8
fluorine	9	10	18.998	9p 10n	9
sodium	11	12	22.990	11p 12n	11
chlorine	17	18	35.453	17p 18n	17

* p represents a proton.   † n represents a neutron.

4–7 ISOTOPES

The concept of an atom as being made of protons and neutrons having similar weights of 1 unit, and of electrons of negligible weight, gives us a reasonably good explanation of atomic weights. There are, however, discrepancies, as we have already noted. From Table 4–1 we can see that the weights of the elements in the table are near whole numbers except for chlorine. There are other exceptions not included in the table, where the weights do not approximate whole numbers as we would expect if the atoms were made only of simple building blocks, each with a weight of 1 unit. An explanation for this dilemma was provided by the experiments described below.

One of the outstanding scientific accomplishments of the early twentieth century was the development of the mass spectrograph by the British physicists J. J. Thompson and F. W. Aston (see Fig. 4–4). When electrically charged atoms (ions*) are directed through the powerful magnetic field of this instrument, they are separated according to their masses in a fashion not unlike the separation of leaves from walnuts by the wind, Fig. 4–5. The ions with greater masses are deflected less than are the lighter ions.

When neon gas was examined by the mass spectrograph it was found to be separated into two groups of ions with distinctly different masses, indicating that there were two varieties

---

* As will be discussed more fully in the next chapter, certain atoms have a tendency to lose one or more electrons, and when they do they become positively charged. In an opposite manner, other atoms gain one or more electrons and become negatively charged. Such charged atoms, whether positive or negative, are called *ions*.

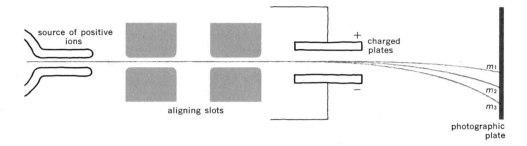

FIG. 4–4. A schematic drawing of a mass spectrograph, showing the variation in the paths of isotopes of different masses (m^1, m^2, and m^3) as recorded on a photographic plate.

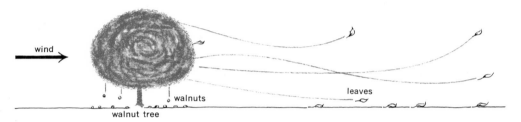

FIG. 4–5. The effect of an equal force on objects of different masses.

of neon ions. To the surprise of the investigators, they found many elements in addition to neon that gave indications of having atoms of different masses. It has since been determined that hydrogen also exhibits this property. Three kinds of hydrogen atoms exist (Section 9–4). The simplest and most common contains 1 proton and is sometimes called *protium* to distinguish it from the other forms. The second, *deuterium*, has a nucleus containing one proton and one neutron, while the third, *tritium*, has one proton and two neutrons. It must be remembered that each of the three forms of hydrogen has only one proton and each has one electron. They all have the fundamental characteristics of hydrogen. *Atoms of the same element (same atomic number) having varying numbers of neutrons in their nuclei are called* **isotopes.** Elements tend to occur as isotopes; in fact, most elements consist of mixtures of isotopes. Table 4–2 lists some common isotopes.

4–8 MASS NUMBERS AND ATOMIC WEIGHTS

The sum of the protons and neutrons in any atom is designated its **mass number.** It will be remembered that electrons account for very little of the actual mass of the atom, so the mass is due principally to the protons and neutrons present. Isotopes of the same element all have the same atomic number, but they may have different mass numbers. (The three isotopes of hydrogen have mass numbers of 1, 2, and 3.) In distinguishing between the different isotopes

TABLE 4–2. Some common isotopes

Isotope	Atomic Number	Protons	Neutrons	Mass Units	Atomic Weight	Percentage of Isotopes Found Naturally
hydrogen-1	1	1	0	1 ⎫		99.984
hydrogen-2	1	1	1	2 ⎬ 1.008	0.016
hydrogen-3	1	1	2	3 ⎭		trace
carbon-12	6	6	6	12 ⎫		98.892
carbon-13	6	6	7	13 ⎬ 12.011	1.108
carbon-14	6	6	8	14 ⎭		trace
fluorine-19	9	9	10	19	18.998	100.00
chlorine-35	17	17	18	35 ⎫		75.53
chlorine-37	17	17	20	37 ⎭ 35.453	24.47

of an element, we place the mass number of the isotope being considered at the upper left of the symbol, e.g., for chlorine, ^{35}Cl or ^{37}Cl. For hydrogen the three isotopes are identified as follows: ^{1}H, ^{2}H, and ^{3}H.

As a result of the interpretation of the experiments with neon and the knowledge accumulated by others, from Dalton to the present, chemists have developed an explanation for the observation that most atomic weights are not quite whole numbers (Table 4–2). All the atoms of a particular element have the same number of protons, but some atoms have more neutrons than others. All chlorine atoms have 17 protons. However, there are two kinds of chlorine atoms; some have 18 neutrons and some have 20. The ones with 18 neutrons have mass numbers of 35. Those with 20 neutrons have mass numbers of 37 (17 protons + 20 neutrons = 37 mass units). The atomic weight is simply the average of the weights of a great number of atoms of chlorine. If there were equal numbers of each of the isotopes, the atomic weight would be 36: (35 + 37)/2 = 36. If there were three of the lighter atoms for each one of the heavy atoms, the atomic weight would be 35.5: (3 × 35 + 37)/4 = 35.5. The actual atomic weight of 35.45 for natural chlorine indicates the number of light atoms is slightly more than ¾ of the total number of chlorine atoms in any sample. Checking with Table 4–2, we find that 75.4% of all chlorine atoms have a mass of 35.

On first examination it might be assumed that since hydrogen has isotopes with mass of 1, 2, and 3, its atomic weight should be higher than 1.008. However, if we again consult Table 4–2, we will note that 99.984% of all hydrogen atoms have a mass number of 1, while only 0.016% have mass of 2. (The occurrence of tritium is so rare that it need not be considered.) This ratio of hydrogen to deuterium is a ratio of 1 in slightly over 6000. In a simpler illustration, if we have 6000 chickens weighing 1 lb each and one chicken weighing 2 lb, the average weight of all the chickens will be very slightly more than 1 lb each.

The **atomic weight** *of an element represents the average weights of all the atoms in a representative sample of the element.* With elements such as fluorine having only one kind of atom, the atomic weight will correspond very closely to the mass number.

◄ In recent years it has become apparent that oxygen, with an atomic weight of 16, is somewhat undesirable as a standard. This is because oxygen has three isotopes, and the atomic weight of 16 is not the weight of a specific atom. In 1961 the isotope carbon-12 was chosen as a standard, and the mass unit was defined as being equal to 1/12 the mass of a carbon-12 atom. ►

We have said that atomic weights are only relative. They show, for example, that the ratio of the weight of oxygen atoms to hydrogen atoms is 16 to 1. Nevertheless, this fact is sufficient to allow us to understand and calculate what quantity of one element will react with a certain quantity of another element. We can, for instance, use *grams* as the units to weigh the relative amounts. *The atomic weight, when expressed in grams, is referred to as the* **gram atomic weight.** Thus the gram atomic weight of hydrogen is 1, that of oxygen is 16, and that of chlorine is 35.45. The gram atom is an extremely important unit for making various types of chemical calculations.

4–9 WEIGHT OF AN ATOM

At this point the student should be asking, "What does the atomic weight really mean? How much does one atom weigh?" It has been stated that the atomic weight indicates the *relative* weight of atoms of one element compared to those of other elements. However, this statement says nothing about the weight or mass of a single atom. We now have experimental evidence to prove the statement, made so long ago by Avogadro, that equal volumes of gases contain an equal number of particles, and we can easily determine the weight of a given volume of a gas. The problem, then, is to find the number of particles in a given volume of a gas. This has been done by various workers using various methods, and the number is known as Avogadro's number, although he did not determine it. We express **Avogadro's number** *as the number of atoms in one gram atomic weight of the element.* It has been established that it requires

$$602{,}300{,}000{,}000{,}000{,}000{,}000{,}000{,} \quad \text{or} \quad 6.023 \times 10^{23},$$

atoms of an element to give 1 atomic weight in grams, regardless of whether the element is hydrogen, carbon, oxygen, or chlorine.

Since 6.023×10^{23} hydrogen atoms weigh approximately 1 g, one hydrogen atom would weigh $1/(6.023 \times 10^{23})$ g, and one carbon-12 atom would weigh $12/(6.023 \times 10^{23})$ g. We know that weight varies with location whereas mass remains constant in all places. Therefore the terminology, *Atomic Mass Units*, abbreviated *amu*, is finding common use in place of atomic weight units.

4–10 SUMMARY

This chapter has been concerned with atoms. On the basis of his own experiments and those of many other scientists, Dalton was able to set down a series of statements about atoms and molecules. These were based on the atomic theory originally attributed to Democritus. Less than a hundred years after Dalton proposed his theory, it was found that atoms were not the ultimate particles but were made up of simpler particles called electrons, protons, and neutrons. Further research has indicated that there are many other subatomic particles. Subatomic particles, however, do not exist as such for any appreciable time as atoms do. In fact, we might say that the only way electrons, protons, neutrons, and other subatomic particles gain real stability is by joining a group called an atom. We can also say that each substance is composed of the same discrete particles or building units. An atom is the smallest possible particle of an element, and a molecule is the smallest particle of a compound which still retains the typical properties of that substance. Thus we can answer the question "Can an atom be divided?" only by saying, "Yes it can, but if it is divided it isn't really an atom." Can we split protons, neutrons, and electrons? The answer is that we can, and again we are left with the basic question about the divisibility of matter, except that we are talking about particles smaller than the atom. These smaller subatomic particles no longer have the properties of the substance, such as gold, which we originally started dividing.

In this chapter we have been concerned primarily with the units that make up an atom, but we have not specified exactly how these units are arranged and just what it is that really makes the properties of one atom different from those of another. The differences and the similarities of atoms, both in general terms and with respect to specific atomic structure, will be the subject of Chapter 5.

IMPORTANT TERMS

Alpha particle	*Atomic weight*	*Gram-atomic weight*	*Neutron*
Atom	*Beta rays*	*Ions*	*Proton*
Atomic mass units (amu)	*Electron*	*Isotopes*	
Atomic number	*Gamma rays*	*Mass number*	

WORK EXERCISES

1. In what way did Dalton's atomic theory differ from that proposed by Democritus?

2. Distinguish between the Law of Definite Proportions and the Law of Multiple Proportions.

3. Applying the method shown in Section 4–4, determine the correct formula for a compound containing 36% calcium and 64% chlorine.

4. Using the same method as above, determine the formula of a compound containing 38.7% potassium, 13.8% nitrogen, and 47.5% oxygen.

5. In what ways has it been necessary to modify Dalton's atomic theory?

6. What discoveries established the fact that atoms are not the smallest particles of matter?

7. Explain how Rutherford's experiment with the gold foil proved the porosity of matter.

8. What is the relationship between the size of an atom and the size of its nucleus?

9. Distinguish between the atomic number and the atomic weight of an element.

10. Why does the number of mass units in an atom not necessarily equal the atomic weight of the element?

11. Show diagrams representing the two isotopes of chlorine, atomic number 17, having mass numbers of 35 and 37.

12. Which of the chlorine isotopes (Exercise 11) is more abundant?

SUGGESTED READING

DA Costa Andrade, E. N., "The Birth of the Nuclear Atom," *Scientific American*, Nov. 1956, p. 93. A review of Rutherford's contributions to the knowledge of the structure of the atom.

Nier, A. O. C., "The Mass Spectrograph," *Scientific American,* Mar. 1953, p. 68. A description of the instrument that is used to separate the isotopes of an element.

Chapter 5 THE ELEMENTS AND THE PERIODIC TABLE

5–1 INTRODUCTION

Although scientists have made some modifications in the details of Dalton's atomic theory, it provided and continues to provide a firm basis for chemistry. There are at least 103 known atoms (and various isotopes of these 103), so there must be 103 kinds of matter that we would classify as elements. Many of the isotopes, and in some cases all the isotopes of an element, are so unstable that they decompose, some in fractions of a second. So the number 103 represents those that have been observed at one time or another.

In order to understand our universe from the viewpoint of chemistry, we must know something about the elements and compounds that compose it. Just as the study of words begins with a knowledge of the alphabet, the study of chemistry must start with a discussion of the elements. This is not the way the science developed, of course, and we could learn a great deal about the compound known as table salt without learning that it is made of sodium and chlorine. However, an understanding of why sodium chloride possesses various properties and why it reacts as it does depends upon understanding its components.

At first glance, the task of even knowing about all the many different elements, to say nothing of the more than a million known compounds, seems almost impossible. If you then realize that the amount of scientific knowledge is presently doubling every ten years, you are apt to throw up your hands at the prospect of ever understanding chemistry. Before you do, let us consider the matter further.

The proper approach in trying to understand a great deal of information is to take advantage of the way material can be classified. While we know, for example, that a person cannot be completely described by assigned categories, we can describe him as tall or short, energetic or lazy, sympathetic or not, or with any of thousands of other descriptive terms. Elements also have characteristics. Even before it was established that silver, gold, and copper were elements, it was realized that they were similar in some ways, slightly different in others.

We will begin this chapter by describing some of the elements and proceed to classifying them and making models of the structure of their atoms. This picture or model of an atom will provide yet another answer to the question that has been of concern for several chapters, "What is an atom?"

5-2 DISTRIBUTION OF COMMON ELEMENTS

In deciding where to begin, we might ask, "Which of the 103 elements should we choose to study first?" One answer would be to consider the elements that are most common. To the question, "Which elements are the most common?" you might be able to make a reasonable start in answering. You would probably think of water, which is found in great quantities. You might mention air, something called rock, or perhaps you would say sand. Here most nonchemists would have to stop. What elements compose water? What is rock? What is sand? Let us start then with a few simple facts about common elements.

Information obtained from study of the light given off by the stars and nebulae leads us to believe that hydrogen is the most abundant element in the universe. Approximately 90% of the matter in the universe is hydrogen. Helium makes up most of the remainder, and it is generally estimated that all other elements make up only slightly more than 1% of the universe.

Another way of talking about which elements are important is to think of those found in an area we know more about—the surface of the earth. For this purpose let us consider the surface as consisting of the atmosphere, the oceans, and the solid portion of the outer few miles, perhaps ten, of the land areas. When we analyze the compounds and elements found in these regions we find that twelve elements make up more than 99% of the material present. These elements are listed in Table 5-1. It should be remembered that this list includes the elements found in compounds as well as those found as the free element.

TABLE 5-1. Estimated composition of the surface of the earth*

Element	Percent by Weight	Element	Percent by Weight
Oxygen	49	Potassium	2.4
Silicon	26	Magnesium	1.9
Aluminum	7.5	Hydrogen	0.88
Iron	4.7	Titanium	0.58
Calcium	3.4	Chlorine	0.19
Sodium	2.6	Carbon	0.09
		All other elements	0.56

* Including oceans and atmosphere.

A third way of deciding which elements are of greatest importance is to think of the composition of the human body. The most abundant elements in the human body are listed in Table 5-2. At least twenty-five others are also found. Here, especially, most of the elements are found in compounds. It is interesting to note that ten of the twelve elements listed in

TABLE 5–2. Composition of the human body

Element	Percent by Weight	Element	Percent by Weight
Oxygen	65	Sodium	0.15
Carbon	18	Chlorine	0.15
Hydrogen	10	Magnesium	0.05
Nitrogen	3.0	Iron	0.004
Calcium	2.0	Iodine	trace
Phosphorus	1.0	Fluorine	trace
Potassium	0.35	Silicon	trace
Sulfur	0.25		

Table 5–1 also appear in Table 5–2. It has been facetiously estimated that all the chemical elements in a 150-pound man could be purchased from a chemical firm for $1.98. The significance of the elements found in the human body, in other animals, and in plants is discussed in Section 41–6. In the paragraphs which follow we shall discuss briefly the elements found in greatest abundance at the surface of the earth.

Oxygen. Oxygen, which is the most abundant element on the surface of the earth, is present in its elemental form as a gas in the atmosphere, where it makes up 20.95% of the total weight of dry air. Most of the remainder of the atmosphere is nitrogen, which, however, is not among the top ten in overall abundance. Oxygen is also present in the most abundant compound found at the earth's surface, water. Here it makes up 88.8% of the weight of water. It is also found in other compounds. Oxygen is so important that a whole chapter (Chapter 8) is devoted to this element. The element nitrogen is further discussed in the chapter on the atmosphere (Chapter 15).

Silicon. Silicon is the second most common element on the surface of the earth, but it occurs only in combination with other elements. Its most prevalent compound is silicon dioxide. Silicon dioxide is commonly found as sand. Large quantities of sand are used in the manufacturing of glass. Pure quartz is also silicon dioxide, and when it contains traces of impurities, it occurs as amethyst, agate, flint, and jasper. Combined with oxygen and certain metals silicon forms silicates, the primary constituents of granite, asbestos, mica, feldspar, and clay. The prevalence of the above materials makes it easy to see why silicon is so abundant. Although silicon does not occur free in nature, it can be prepared in a laboratory or factory. Pure silicon forms a glassy-appearing substance with a grayish metallic luster. In recent years silicon has been used extensively in the production of transistors, solar cells, and many other electronic devices used in space-age industries.

Aluminum. Many of the properties of the metal aluminum are well known. We use it for building purposes, for cooking utensils, and as aluminum foil. With this widespread usefulness of the metal, it is hard to realize that only a hundred years ago aluminum metal was an oddity and was worth approximately ninety dollars a pound. Although the element was abundant, it existed only in compounds. Aluminum reacts strongly with other elements and is difficult to separate from them. Clay is essentially a compound of aluminum, silicon, and oxygen; it results from the weathering of certain rocks. It is used in the manufacture of brick, tile, and chinaware. Aluminum occurs naturally with oxygen in the form of gems, rubies and sapphires.

An easy method of processing or extracting the metal from its ores was not known until 1886 when Charles Martin Hall, a student at Oberlin College, developed the electrolytic process, essentially the same as used today. Hall became a millionaire. He had been inspired by his chemistry professor who suggested the need for an inexpensive method of preparing this unusual metal.

Iron. The metal iron has been known since the dawn of history, and some believe that the methods of separating iron from its ores were discovered shortly before the rise of Greek civilization. Before this time weapons had been made of bronze; the change to the harder iron which could be sharpened gave a new impetus to warfare. Homer's *Iliad* speaks of iron as a precious metal. The only occurrence of iron as a free element is in meteorites.

Iron occurs widely in nature, however. Its principal ore is the oxide, hematite, which occurs in concentrated deposits in various parts of the world. The reddish color of many rocks and the red soils of the world are due to traces of iron compounds present. The color of the hemoglobin of the blood is also caused by iron compounds. Although iron ranks only fourth in amount among the elements on the surface of the earth, the amount of this metal produced each year surpasses by about fifteen times the combined amounts of all other metals. The number of tons of ore consumed each year is not a reliable index of the amount of iron used, since many millions of tons of scrap iron are utilized in the manufacturing of new products. The car that you drive may contain iron atoms from several generations of automobiles as well as from old tractors or old battleships.

Calcium. Calcium is found in limestone, marble, and gypsum, and is an important component of the bones of animals. Limestone, which covers great portions of the land surfaces to depths of several thousands of feet, is 40% calcium. It is obvious, then, why calcium makes up more than 3% of the surface of the earth. It is never found as the free element, and from this we can conclude that calcium readily enters into combination with other substances, in other words, that it is a very active substance.

Sodium and Potassium. Sodium and potassium are not found as free elements either, and again we can assume that they are quite active. In fact, if we place a sample of either of these elements in a container of water they float because of their low densities, and they react so violently with the water that they often cause an explosion. Sodium and potassium are similar in almost all their properties. They occur in combined forms throughout the surface of the earth in mineral deposits, in the soil, and dissolved in the ocean waters. Ordinary salt is a compound of 39% sodium and 61% chlorine by weight, and constitutes approximately 3% of the ocean. If we consider that the oceans hold enough water to cover the whole earth to a depth of nearly 10,000 feet, we may be able to imagine the vast amount of salt present. Great deposits of salt, in some cases hundreds of feet in depth, are found in many parts of the world. They are the result of the drying up of ancient seas. Potassium has been retained to a greater degree in the rocks and soils of the earth, and therefore only small amounts of it are found in the oceans.

Magnesium. Magnesium is an interesting metal that is also too active to be found free in nature. Its compounds occur in considerable quantities in the oceans, from which it is now commercially recovered. It is also found as a component of some limestone deposits. The metal burns with extreme brilliance and is used in some types of flares, fireworks, and incendiary bombs. It has a very low density, and when alloyed with aluminum its strength is increased and its density is decreased. Large amounts of this alloy are used in the airplane industry.

Hydrogen. Hydrogen is the lightest of the gases and as mentioned previously, its atoms are the simplest of the elements of the universe. Because of its low density, it was formerly used in filling balloons and lighter-than-air craft. Since hydrogen is a flammable gas, considerable danger was involved and accidents frequently occurred. Helium, the second lightest gas, which is nonflammable, has now taken the place of hydrogen for use in balloons. Elementary or free uncombined hydrogen occurs in minute amounts on the earth and in the atmosphere. A major portion of the earth's supply is combined with oxygen in water, which is more than 11% hydrogen by weight. The majority of the hydrogen in the universe is free, uncombined hydrogen. The discussion of hydrogen is continued in Chapter 9.

Titanium. Titanium is the tenth most abundant element on the surface of the earth. It occurs in all igneous rocks, is found in meteorites, and is also present on the sun. Pure titanium is a lustrous white metal, highly resistant to corrosion. Until recent years the metal was largely a novelty. In spite of its current price of six dollars a pound, considerable quantities are produced, and its alloys are used in the aircraft and missile industries. The oxides of titanium are used extensively as a white pigment by paint manufacturers.

Chlorine. Chlorine is another substance too active to exist in nature as a free element; it is found on earth primarily associated with sodium and other metals. As an element, it is a greenish-yellow gas that is extremely irritating and poisonous. It was used in World War I as the first war gas of modern times. Chlorine will be discussed further in Chapter 17.

5-3 SYMBOLS OF THE ELEMENTS

Referring to chemical elements by their full names is so laborious, we often use symbols. Historically, some of the metals had symbols almost as soon as they had names. Gold became associated with the sun and was given the astronomical symbol for the sun which was a circle, sometimes with a dot inside it. Silver was given the symbol associated with the moon, a crescent. Other ancient metals were given symbols, arising from some characteristic or myth. Iron, Mars, and war were associated, as were copper, Venus, and love. The modern symbols for the elements are much more prosaic but also somewhat more logical. The first letter of the name of the element is used as the symbol for many elements; we use C, H, O, N, S, and P for the elements carbon, hydrogen, oxygen, nitrogen, sulfur, and phosphorus. Since there are 103 elements and only 26 letters in our alphabet, most elements have symbols consisting of two letters, only the first of which is capitalized. Generally the letters are the first two letters of the name of the element. Because Ca was taken as the symbol for calcium, cadmium became Cd, and there are other similar examples. Some elements are given symbols derived from their Latin names. The symbol Na for sodium comes from the Latin *natrium,* and Cu for copper comes from the Latin word *cuprum*. With minor ex-

TABLE 5-3. Common elements and their symbols

Metals			Nonmetals	
Aluminum	Al		Carbon	C
Calcium	Ca		Chlorine	Cl
Copper	Cu	(*cuprum*)	Fluorine	F
Iron	Fe	(*ferrum*)	Helium	He
Magnesium	Mg		Hydrogen	H
Manganese	Mn		Iodine	I
Potassium	K	(*kalium*)	Nitrogen	N
Silver	Ag	(*argentum*)	Oxygen	O
Sodium	Na	(*natrium*)	Phosphorus	P
Zinc	Zn		Sulfur	S

ceptions, and these are fast disappearing, the chemical symbols are international. Scientists throughout the world know what is meant by NaCl even though they may use quite different common names for the substance we call salt or table salt.

The most common symbols appear in Table 5–3, and should be learned. Other names and symbols will be introduced from time to time. Usage will add these to your knowledge of familiar symbols.

5-4 CLASSIFICATION OF THE ELEMENTS

In the discussion of the most abundant elements several similarities were noted. Most of you knew, before starting this book, that aluminum (*Br.,* aluminium), iron, and magnesium were metals. You may also have known that calcium, sodium, potassium and titanium were metals. There is even a clue in the names given these elements since, except for iron, they all end in the suffix -*ium*. If we substitute the Latin name of iron, *ferrum,* the relationship becomes more obvious. We can say that whoever named these substances was aware of some similarity. We see similar relationships between oxygen and hydrogen, between carbon and silicon. We say that these latter elements are nonmetals.

What is a metal? Again, the general definition is not a simple one (although we will give a simple one later). We recognize metals by their properties. **Metals** have a characteristic luster; they can be hammered or rolled into sheets or drawn into wire; they can be melted and cast into desired shapes; and they are usually good conductors of electricity and heat. While we usually think of metals as being solids, one exception is mercury which is normally a liquid. When cooled, however, it becomes a solid, and you may have seen a hammer made of mercury that was poured into a mold and cooled with liquid air. All metals are opaque.

The **nonmetals** are not uniform in their properties. Half of them are gases; one, bromine, is a liquid; and the remainder are solids. We must recognize, of course, that the physical state depends upon temperature and pressure; customarily we assume room temperature at 20°C, and a standard atmospheric pressure. Few of the nonmetals have any of the characteristic properties of metals. In general, they are poor conductors of heat and electricity, cannot be hammered or rolled into sheets or drawn into wire, and do not have characteristic luster.

5–5 PERIODICITY OF ELEMENTS

While a classification into metals and nonmetals was helpful, many scientists looked for, and found, other properties common to certain groups of elements. These efforts culminated in the work of Dmitri Mendeleev, a Russian chemist, who is generally credited with developing the first workable periodic chart. We can recreate his work. Let us start by writing the names (or symbols) of the elements in the order of increasing weight, and then writing the properties—physical, and more importantly, the chemical properties—for each of the elements. We begin to see a certain pattern.

If we start with lithium we get the list shown in Table 5–4. We see that lithium is an active metal, beryllium is somewhat less active but still a metal, boron and carbon are non-metallic solids, the next three (nitrogen, oxygen, and fluorine) are gases and their activity increases with increasing weight. Sodium is a very active metal similar to lithium; magnesium is similar to beryllium; aluminum is somewhat different from boron; but silicon is similar to carbon. While phosphorus and sulfur are not gases, they are distinctly nonmetallic and their chemical properties are similar to those of nitrogen and oxygen; finally, chlorine is very similar to fluorine. If we continue with potassium and calcium, their similarity to sodium and magnesium and thus to lithium and beryllium is enough to make the relationship appear to be real.

TABLE 5–4. Characteristic properties of low atomic weight elements

Element	Properties
Lithium	active metal
Beryllium	metal
Boron	nonmetallic solid
Carbon	nonmetallic solid
Nitrogen	inactive gas
Oxygen	moderately active gas
Fluorine	very active gas
Sodium	very active metal
Magnesium	active metal
Aluminum	metal
Silicon	nonmetallic solid
Phosphorus	nonmetallic solid; chemical properties similar to nitrogen
Sulfur	nonmetallic solid; chemical properties similar to oxygen
Chlorine	gas; chemical and physical properties similar to fluorine
Potassium	very active metal similar to sodium and lithium
Calcium	active metal similar to magnesium

On the basis of these considerations, Mendeleev developed the arrangement shown in Table 5–5. Although this table is only a portion of Mendeleev's *Periodic Table of the Elements* which was published in 1869, it is sufficient to show the significance of his development. On the basis of his periodic table, Mendeleev was able to formulate his **Periodic Law** which states that *when elements are arranged in the order of their increasing atomic weights, they exhibit a periodic recurrence of properties.*

TABLE 5–5. Mendeleev's table of elements (in part)

Lithium	Beryllium	Boron	Carbon	Nitrogen	Oxygen	Fluorine
Sodium	Magnesium	Aluminum	Silicon	Phosphorus	Sulfur	Chlorine
Potassium	. . .	. . .	. . .	. . .	. . .	. . .

Mendeleev's original table contained 63 elements with numerous blank spaces that represented elements not yet discovered at that time. By carefully studying the properties of the elements around a blank space, Mendeleev and others who came after him were able to predict the properties of the missing element. In many instances, this information aided researchers in finding the missing element. There are no blanks in modern periodic tables, the last ones having been filled in the 1940's. New elements have been added at the end of the table, and it is possible that elements beyond 103 may be added in the future.

One group of elements that was unknown at the time Mendeleev did his work was what we now know as the *noble gases*. These gases—helium, neon, argon, krypton, xenon, and radon, formerly called the "inert gases"—are placed in the extreme right-hand column of modern periodic tables. The concept of atomic numbers was not developed until almost fifty years after Mendeleev's work, and thus the absence of these elements was not realized.

Mendeleev worked entirely with atomic weights, and in at least one case he had to depart from his order of increasing weights in order to make the table consistent. Tellurium is heavier than iodine, but because of its properties should come before iodine in the chart. Mendeleev believed that this inconsistency was due to inaccurate atomic weight determinations; we now know it is due to the fact that there was a higher percentage of heavy isotopes in tellurium than in iodine (Section 4–8). A similar discrepancy exists with argon and potassium. A modern version of the periodic table is given in Table 5–6, and there is another just inside the cover of this book. Many different forms of periodic tables have been devised. None is perfect. Some of the irregularities in the table are discussed in the next section.

5–6 PERIODIC TABLE

The periodic table is probably the most important single document for the chemist. It lists all the known elements and shows their relationships. In addition, almost all such tables give the atomic number and the atomic weight, and many give other details such as the physical state of the element, its melting and boiling point, and perhaps other data. Periodic tables are available in all introductory chemistry texts and hang in almost all laboratories and chemistry classrooms. In the paragraphs to follow, we will discuss the table and some of its uses. Other uses will be introduced in appropriate sections of the book.

The Metals and Nonmetals. The nonmetals are located on the right-hand side of the table, and the metals on the left. Since not only one property but several are used to distinguish metals from nonmetals, it is not strange that the elements form a continuum where some are distinctly metals, others good examples of nonmetals, and some elements—the metalloids —have a few characteristics of both groups. A zig-zag line can be drawn to separate the metals from the nonmetals. The elements bordering on this line are called *metalloids*.

TABLE 5–6. Periodic table of the elements
Simplified atomic weights for practice in chemical calculations
(*Not sufficiently accurate for quantitative work.*)
Values in parentheses indicate mass numbers of the most stable or best known isotope.

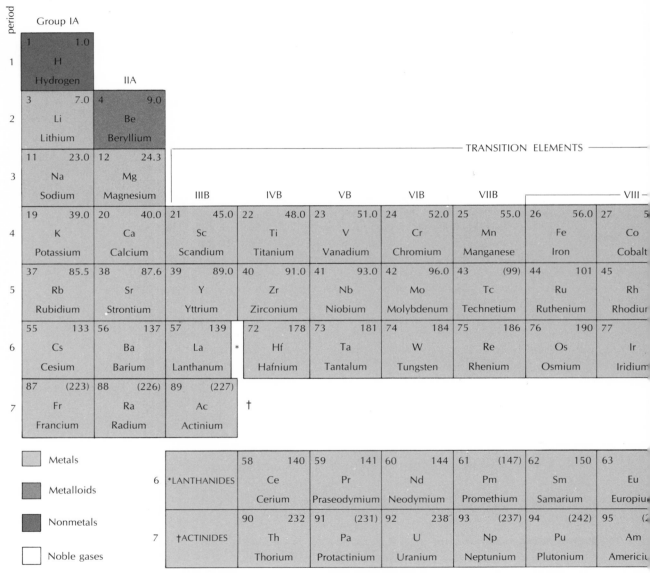

NOBLE
GASES

		IIIA	IVA	VA	VIA	VIIA	2 4.0 He Helium
IB	IIB	5 10.8 B Boron	6 12.0 C Carbon	7 14.0 N Nitrogen	8 16.0 O Oxygen	9 19.0 F Fluorine	10 20.0 Ne Neon
		13 27.0 Al Aluminum	14 28.0 Si Silicon	15 31.0 P Phosphorus	16 32.0 S Sulfur	17 35.5 Cl Chlorine	18 40.0 Ar Argon

58.7 Ni Nickel	29 63.5 Cu Copper	30 65.4 Zn Zinc	31 69.7 Ga Gallium	32 72.6 Ge Germanium	33 75.0 As Arsenic	34 79.0 Se Selenium	35 80.0 Br Bromine	36 84.0 Kr Krypton
106 Pd Palladium	47 108 Ag Silver	48 112 Cd Cadmium	49 115 In Indium	50 119 Sn Tin	51 122 Sb Antimony	52 128 Te Tellurium	53 127 I Iodine	54 131 Xe Xenon
195 Pt Platinum	79 197 Au Gold	80 201 Hg Mercury	81 204 Tl Thallium	82 207 Pb Lead	83 209 Bi Bismuth	84 (210) Po Polonium	85 (210) At Astatine	86 (222) Rn Radon

157 Gd Gadolinium	65 159 Tb Terbium	66 162 Dy Dysprosium	67 165 Ho Holmium	68 167 Er Erbium	69 169 Tm Thulium	70 173 Yb Ytterbium	71 175 Lu Lutetium
(247) Cm Curium	97 (249) Bk Berkelium	98 (251) Cf Californium	99 (254) Es Einsteinium	100 (253) Fm Fermium	101 (256) Md Mendelevium	102 (253) No Nobelium	103 (257) Lw Lr Lawrencium

The most active metals are found at the bottom and to the left of the table. Francium and cesium are more active than barium and radium. The metals sodium and potassium are also extremely active and are more active than magnesium and calcium. We can say that the activity of the metals decreases as we go to the right or towards the top of the table. The most active nonmetal, fluorine, is found at the upper right of the table. We find activity of nonmetals increases as we approach the top of the table and decreases as we go toward the left. An adequate explanation of activity cannot be presented until other concepts have been introduced, so it is deferred until later in this chapter.

Noble Gases. The noble gases are placed in the column at the right-hand side of the table. Until recently they were called the *inert* gases, since it was believed that they would not react to form chemical compounds. It is true they do not react readily; however, since 1962 several compounds containing these elements have been prepared. Such compounds are formed, however, only under drastic conditions.

Periods of the Table. The horizontal rows of elements, in order of their increasing atomic numbers, are called series or *periods*. The first period contains only two elements, the second and third periods contain eight, the fourth and fifth periods contain eighteen elements, and the sixth and seventh periods can contain thirty-two. The lanthanides and actinides, which are located at the bottom of the table, really belong in periods six and seven, but are included at the bottom only for convenience, so the table will be more compact.

Groups of the Table. There are eighteen vertical *columns* or *groups,* each consisting of a family of elements with similar properties. Some exceptions are involved. Hydrogen, to be discussed further in Chapter 9, is placed at the top of the group of active metals (IA) even though many of its properties are unlike those of the metals sodium and potassium. If we consider the groups having suffix A, in other words, IA through VIIA, we see that there is a progression from metallic to nonmetallic properties as we move from left to right.

The Transition Elements. Those elements in groups having the suffix B and in group VIII are known as the transition elements. They are all metals. While there is no clear progression of properties, as one views these elements from left to right, some relationship to elements in similar A groups are known. For instance, there is a relationship between the active metals in group IA (sodium, potassium, etc.) and the copper, silver, and gold in group IB.

Irregularities in the Table. The Periodic Table is not perfect. In common with almost all attempts to classify observations from nature, some data do not fit in neatly. In some cases the progression of atomic numbers departs from that of atomic weights as it does between the elements argon, 18, and potassium, 19, and between tellurium, 52, and iodine, 53. This apparent discrepancy is due to the fact that heavy isotopes of potassium and tellurium are prevalent. Hydrogen really does not "fit" anywhere in the table. In some versions it is included both in groups IA and VIIA. Locating the transition metals is somewhat awkward, particularly for the elements in group VIII. These groups of three metals have been moved from one place to another in the process of development of the periodic table. Even with its lack of perfection, however, the periodic or atomic table is an extremely valuable aid to chemists.

5–7 ATOMIC STRUCTURE AND THE PERIODIC TABLE

So far we have been presenting many statements about the periodic table without much explanation. You may be asking, "Why do the elements fall into periods of 8 or 18?" or "Why are the most active metals at the lower left?" Such questions were asked by scientists for many years. When the ideas of atomic composition developed by Rutherford and others were combined with a study of Mendeleev's table, a concept of atomic structure began to develop. If the difference in elements is due primarily to the difference in the number of protons (and electrons) present in the atoms, their similarities must also be due to some similarity in the arrangement of these electrons or protons. Speculations such as these culminated in the idea of atomic structure developed by Niels Bohr, Section 4–6, which we now call the *Bohr atom*. While this picture or model of atomic structure has to be modified in many cases, it still represents a valid and extremely useful device for understanding chemistry—particularly the chemistry of reactions.

The Bohr atom is based on the idea that there is a small, heavy nucleus containing the protons and neutrons of the atom. The electrons are found outside, circling about the nucleus much as the planets revolve around the sun. It is important to realize, however, that an electron does not travel only in a simple circular or elliptical path. Experimentally, it has not been possible to determine exactly where an electron is located at a given moment as it orbits about the nucleus. However, we can be reasonably certain that it is located somewhere within a certain space often called an electron cloud. Since the electron moves at a fantastically high speed (approximately the speed of light) it can be thought of as blurred or smeared through a certain volume which is designated as the electron cloud. We will use the terms electron shell and electron cloud more or less interchangeably. We think of the nucleus of an atom, then, as a tiny sphere and the electron orbits as the outside of a hollow sphere.

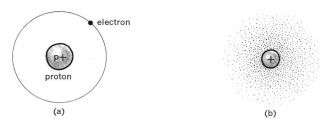

FIG. 5–1. (a) A sketch commonly used to represent a hydrogen atom. (b) The more recently used diagram of a hydrogen atom, depicting the electron cloud about a proton.

Using the Bohr atom as our model, we can represent a hydrogen atom as shown in Fig. 5–1(a). Figure 5–1(b) may be a more realistic representation. However, for simplicity we will use (a) in the following presentations. In this diagram the proton is represented by a p, and the electron by a dot. The isotopes of hydrogen, deuterium and tritium, which have weights of two and three respectively, can be pictured as having one and two neutrons in their nucleus in addition to the proton. They would still, however, have only one electron orbiting the nucleus. (We must keep in mind that atoms are three-dimensional structures. In drawing these diagrams we present them in only two dimensions.)

We can draw the structure of the helium atom as shown below.

The helium atom

The problem of representing the structure of atoms seems then to be one of where to place the correct number of electrons outside a nucleus. The genius of Bohr's conception of the atom was that he related periodicity of properties to the electrons. Let us suppose that the reason atoms have similar properties is that they have a similar number of electrons in an outer orbit or shell. Then sodium is similar to lithium because, despite the fact each has a different total number of electrons, both have one electron in the outer shell. This would mean that there are only two elements in the first period of the table because only two electrons can fit into the first shell; there are eight elements in the second period because the second shell can hold only eight electrons. This idea became the basis of Bohr's theory which said that there was space for only two electrons in the first shell, eight in the next, and as many as eighteen or thirty-two in the larger shells. This conclusion comes directly from the number of elements/period in the periodic table. Although this theory has had to be modified in details, it can be regarded as essentially true. The theory is logical since the larger shells are farther from the center. Just as in a prize fighting arena, the number of seats in each row (or circle) becomes greater as the distance from the ring increases.

Using Bohr's theory, we can draw the structures for some of the simpler atoms, as shown below. Lithium has an atomic number of 3; therefore, it has 3 protons and 3 electrons. Its weight is 7, so we say that its most common isotope has four neutrons, and we get the following structure.

2   1   Lithium

The structure of the fluorine atom, atomic number 9 and atomic weight 19, can be represented as

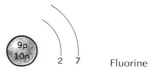

2   7   Fluorine

The structure of argon can be summarized as follows:

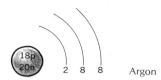

2   8   8   Argon

We can see that argon has a completed outer shell of electrons, and if we draw the structures of helium and neon we see that the same is true for them.

The information for drawing the structures of the simpler atoms is available in the periodic table. The reader should practice until he can produce them easily for any of the common, simple elements. However, for more complex elements such as transition and lanthanide elements, it is easier to use a chart such as that given in Table 5–7. From this table, you can see that the outer shell of an atom, no matter which one it is, never contains more than eight electrons and that in many instances filling of an outer shell stops while an inner shell is being completed. The way in which shells are filled, as atoms increase in complexity, gives a good explanation for the similar properties of the transition elements, the lanthanides, and the actinides.

From Table 5–7 we see that potassium, number 19, has an electron arrangement of 2, 8, 8, 1 and that calcium which follows it has 2, 8, 8, 2. Scandium, number 21, however, does not have the structure 2, 8, 8, 3 that we would anticipate, but has 2, 8, 9, 2. Following scandium each element contains an additional electron in its third shell until the number 18 is reached with copper. Then succeeding elements fill the outer shell until we reach krypton which has the following configuration:

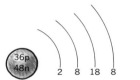

2   8   18   8   Krypton

You will note that while the process of filling an inner shell continues, there are inconsistencies as with chromium (number 24) where the most likely configuration has only 1 electron in the outer shell instead of 2 as in its nearest neighbors.

The lanthanide series and actinide series represent groups of elements in which inner shells are filling while the outer shells remain nearly constant. Since we have indicated that the properties of a substance depend primarily on the number of electrons in the outer shells, it is not surprising that the elements within these two groups have similar properties. Because of this they are difficult to separate from one another. It is also interesting to note that most of the members of the actinide series are radioactive. This property we attribute more to the overall size of the atom, which makes it unstable, than to any special placement in the periodic table.

TABLE 5–7. Electronic arrangements of the atoms (sublevels not shown)

Element	Symbol	Atomic Number	Orbital Electrons (Shells)						
			1	2	3	4	5	6	7
Hydrogen	H	1	1						
Helium	He	2	2						
Lithium	Li	3	2	1					
Beryllium	Be	4	2	2					
Boron	B	5	2	3					
Carbon	C	6	2	4					
Nitrogen	N	7	2	5					
Oxygen	O	8	2	6					
Fluorine	F	9	2	7					
Neon	Ne	10	2	8					
Sodium	Na	11	2	8	1				
Magnesium	Mg	12	2	8	2				
Aluminum	Al	13	2	8	3				
Silicon	Si	14	2	8	4				
Phosphorus	P	15	2	8	5				
Sulfur	S	16	2	8	6				
Chlorine	Cl	17	2	8	7				
Argon	Ar	18	2	8	8				
Potassium	K	19	2	8	8	1			
Calcium	Ca	20	2	8	8	2			
Scandium	Sc	21	2	8	9	2			
Titanium	Ti	22	2	8	10	2			
Vanadium	V	23	2	8	11	2			
Chromium	Cr	24	2	8	13	1			
Manganese	Mn	25	2	8	13	2			
Iron	Fe	26	2	8	14	2			
Cobalt	Co	27	2	8	15	2			
Nickel	Ni	28	2	8	16	2			
Copper	Cu	29	2	8	18	1			
Zinc	Zn	30	2	8	18	2			
Gallium	Ga	31	2	8	18	3			
Germanium	Ge	32	2	8	18	4			
Arsenic	As	33	2	8	18	5			
Selenium	Se	34	2	8	18	6			
Bromine	Br	35	2	8	18	7			
Krypton	Kr	36	2	8	18	8			
Rubidium	Rb	37	2	8	18	8	1		
Strontium	Sr	38	2	8	18	8	2		
Yttrium	Y	39	2	8	18	9	2		
Zirconium	Zr	40	2	8	18	10	2		
Niobium	Nb	41	2	8	18	12	1		
Molybdenum	Mo	42	2	8	18	13	1		
Technetium	Tc	43	2	8	18	14	1		
Ruthenium	Ru	44	2	8	18	15	1		
Rhodium	Rh	45	2	8	18	16	1		
Palladium	Pd	46	2	8	18	18	0		
Silver	Ag	47	2	8	18	18	1		
Cadmium	Cd	48	2	8	18	18	2		
Indium	In	49	2	8	18	18	3		
Tin	Sn	50	2	8	18	18	4		
Antimony	Sb	51	2	8	18	18	5		

TABLE 5–7 (cont'd)   57

Element	Symbol	Atomic Number	Orbital Electrons (Shells)						
			1	2	3	4	5	6	7
Tellurium	Te	52	2	8	18	18	6		
Iodine	I	53	2	8	18	18	7		
Xenon	Xe	54	2	8	18	18	8		
Cesium	Cs	55	2	8	18	18	8	1	
Barium	Ba	56	2	8	18	18	8	2	
Lanthanum	La	57	2	8	18	18	9	2	
Cerium	Ce	58	2	8	18	20	8	2	
Praseodymium	Pr	59	2	8	18	21	8	2	
Neodymium	Nd	60	2	8	18	22	8	2	
Promethium	Pm	61	2	8	18	23	8	2	
Samarium	Sm	62	2	8	18	24	8	2	
Europium	Eu	63	2	8	18	25	8	2	
Gadolinium	Gd	64	2	8	18	25	9	2	
Terbium	Tb	65	2	8	18	27	8	2	
Dysprosium	Dy	66	2	8	18	28	8	2	
Holmium	Ho	67	2	8	18	29	8	2	
Erbium	Er	68	2	8	18	30	8	2	
Thulium	Tm	69	2	8	18	31	8	2	
Ytterbium	Yb	70	2	8	18	32	8	2	
Lutetium	Lu	71	2	8	18	32	9	2	
Hafnium	Hf	72	2	8	18	32	10	2	
Tantalum	Ta	73	2	8	18	32	11	2	
Tungsten	W	74	2	8	18	32	12	2	
Rhenium	Re	75	2	8	18	32	13	2	
Osmium	Os	76	2	8	18	32	14	2	
Iridium	Ir	77	2	8	18	32	15	2	
Platinum	Pt	78	2	8	18	32	17	1	
Gold	Au	79	2	8	18	32	18	1	
Mercury	Hg	80	2	8	18	32	18	2	
Thallium	Tl	81	2	8	18	32	18	3	
Lead	Pb	82	2	8	18	32	18	4	
Bismuth	Bi	83	2	8	18	32	18	5	
Polonium	Po	84	2	8	18	32	18	6	
Astatine	At	85	2	8	18	32	18	7	
Radon	Rn	86	2	8	18	32	18	8	
Francium	Fr	87	2	8	18	32	18	8	1
Radium	Ra	88	2	8	18	32	18	8	2
Actinium	Ac	89	2	8	18	32	18	9	2
Thorium	Th	90	2	8	18	32	18	10	2
Protactinium	Pa	91	2	8	18	32	20	9	2
Uranium	U	92	2	8	18	32	21	9	2
Neptunium	Np	93	2	8	18	32	22	9	2
Plutonium	Pu	94	2	8	18	32	23	9	2
Americium	Am	95	2	8	18	32	24	9	2
Curium	Cm	96	2	8	18	32	25	9	2
Berkelium	Bk	97	2	8	18	32	26	9	2
Californium	Cf	98	2	8	18	32	27	9	2
Einsteinium	Es	99	2	8	18	32	28	9	2
Fermium	Fm	100	2	8	18	32	29	9	2
Mendelevium	Md	101	2	8	18	32	30	9	2
Nobelium	No	102	2	8	18	32	31	9	2
Lawrencium	Lw	103	2	8	18	32	32	9	2

5–8 ACTIVITY OF THE ELEMENTS

In the preceding section we have developed the idea that the similarity of properties of the elements which allows them to be placed in a periodic table is due to the number of electrons in their outer shells. It now remains to explain the differences in activity of substances with similar numbers of outer shell electrons. Why is potassium more active than sodium? Why are gold and silver, which also contain one electron in an outer shell, almost totally inactive? Why is calcium less active than potassium? Why do we find the most active nonmetals near the top of the table while the most active metals are near the bottom? Why are the noble gases quite inactive?

If we take our clue from the noble gases, we can postulate that there is something about having a completed outer shell that confers stability. When substances react they go from higher energy substances to lower energy substances, or become more stable. For elements in group 1 to complete an outer shell they most readily lose one electron; elements in group 2 can lose 2, and so on. Elements in group 7 could theoretically lose 7 electrons, but it would be a much simpler procedure to gain 1 electron. Thus the elements toward the left of the table tend to lose electrons and those to the right, to gain electrons. The definition of a **metal** then becomes *a substance that loses electrons,* and a **nonmetal** *is an element that gains electrons.* The gain and loss of electrons is the basis of all chemical reactions.

If we consider the outer electron attached to a lithium atom and the one attached to a potassium atom, we can see that the outer electron in potassium is much further from the nucleus. Since the forces holding the electron to its atom are due to the positive charge of the nucleus, the further the distance between the charges, the less is the attraction. The lesser attraction means that it is easier to lose an electron from potassium than from lithium, and thus we say potassium is more active than lithium. The same reasoning follows for all metals within a group of the periodic table—the greater the atomic weight, the greater the tendency to lose electrons. Just the opposite is found with nonmetals where the tendency is to gain electrons. For a given group of related nonmetallic elements, for example those in Group VIIA, the smaller the atom, the greater the tendency to gain electrons; thus, fluorine is much more active than iodine.

It is less likely that atoms will lose or gain two or more electrons than that they will gain or lose only one electron; therefore, we find the most active elements at the right- and left-hand sides of the periodic table.

In looking for an explanation for the difference between potassium and copper, we note that copper has 18 electrons in the next to outer shell while potassium has eight. Similar differences are shown between rubidium and silver, and cesium and gold. The difference in properties of these very active and most inactive elements is not due to the outer electrons, since both groups have only one electron in their outer shells. This is one example of the influence of inner electrons on reactivity.

When an atom gains or loses electrons to complete an outer shell, it becomes charged, since it no longer contains an equal number of protons and electrons. Such charged atoms are called **ions.** Metals form positive ions since they lose the negatively charged electrons, and nonmetals form negative ions. The structures for lithium and fluoride ions are shown below. These should be compared with the structures of the corresponding atoms, shown in Section 5–7.

The achievement of a complete outer shell of electrons helps an atom find some kind of stability, but the resultant loss of electrical neutrality has an important bearing on chemical behavior which will be explored in the next chapter.

5-9 SUMMARY

In this chapter, we started with a discussion of the occurrence and properties of some of the elements. We then indicated how similarities and differences in the properties of the elements led to the development of the law of periodicity and the periodic table. The periodic table which is now readily available is important, since it helps to summarize much information and also aids in predicting properties of elements which have not been studied. We can predict that all elements to the left of the table will be metals. If we know the properties of one element in the group (as with sodium for group IA) we can predict the properties of others in the group. Knowing that metals near the bottom of the chart are more active than those near the top, we know what kinds of properties to expect from an element even before experimenting with it. Our generalizations and predictions must, of course, be verified by experimentation.

From the periodic table and the knowledge of atomic structure provided by many experimenters, Bohr proposed a model for the structure of atoms which both summarized many previously known facts and led to greater understanding. It gave scientists a better basis on which to predict the properties of unknown elements. As with most important scientific ideas, interpretation of known facts was interspersed with predictions at all stages in the development of theories of atomic structure.

In discussing the tendency of elements to lose and gain electrons we have begun to approach the second major concern of chemistry, that of reactions.

IMPORTANT TERMS

Actinides	*Group (of the periodic table)*	*Noble gases*	*Periodic table*
Electron shell (or cloud)	*Lanthanides*	*Periodic law*	*Periods*

WORK EXERCISES

1. a) Make a list of the metals with which you have been familiar since childhood.
    b) Now list the nonmetals you have known since childhood and compare the size of the two lists.
2. State some of the properties of metals which are not common to nonmetals.

3. In some calculations the oceans and atmosphere are not included as part of the surface of the earth. Will the percentage of oxygen in these calculations be higher or lower than in Table 5–1? Justify your answer.

4. Why is the periodic table so called?

5. In what ways has the periodic table been of help to chemists?

6. List some of the inconsistencies of the periodic table.

7. Construct a rectangle proportional in dimensions to a periodic table. Locate the most positive and the most negative elements in their relative positions, and using arrows, indicate the changes occurring in the properties of elements as they recede from the original two elements located in the rectangle.

8. Indicate the positions of the groups and periods of the periodic table.

9. Starting with lithium, contrast the changes that take place in the characteristic properties of the elements as we proceed to the right across the table or toward the bottom of the table.

10. Write the structure for ten different atoms, showing the location of all particles involved.

11. What are some characteristics of the lanthanides and actinides which set them apart from other elements?

12. What is the explanation for the unusual properties of the noble gases?

SUGGESTED READING

Asimov, Isaac, *The Search for the Elements*, Basic Books, New York, 1962.

Day, F. H., *The Chemical Elements in Nature*, Reinhold, New York, 1963.

Weeks, Mary E., *Discovery of the Elements*, 6th ed., Chapter 24, "The Periodic System of the Elements," Journal of Chemical Education Publishing Co., Easton, Pa., 1956.

Chapter 6 COMPOUNDS AND CHEMICAL BONDS

6-1 INTRODUCTION

Much of the material of the universe is found either as elements or compounds.* In previous chapters we discussed the nature of the elements and the atoms of which they are made. Most of the materials on earth, however, are composed of atoms in combination with other kinds of atoms, in the form of compounds. Typical chemical compounds with which we are familiar are water, salt, and sugar. Water is formed by the union of atoms of hydrogen and oxygen. From the chemical name for table salt, sodium chloride, we can see that it is composed of sodium and chlorine atoms. It is striking to realize that the salt formed is totally different from the highly reactive metal sodium and the poisonous gas chlorine. To the chemist there are many kinds of sugars. All of them contain carbon, hydrogen, and oxygen. Molecules of compounds vary greatly in their complexity, from the simplest with only two atoms to the complex protein and nucleic acid molecules made up of thousands of the atoms of several different elements.

The combining of elements to form chemical compounds is due to the tendency of atoms to establish complete outer shells of electrons. In Section 5-8 we stated that atoms could complete outer shells either by gaining or losing electrons. In some instances electrons are completely transferred from one atom to another, causing the formation of an *electrovalent bond*. In other instances, the atom completes its outer electron shell by sharing electrons with another atom. This combination produces a *covalent bond*. Each of these two fundamental bond types as well as a variation, the *polar covalent bond*, will be discussed in the following sections.

---

* Under extreme conditions, such as the high temperature of the sun, some of the matter is broken down into smaller particles such as protons and electrons.

6–2 ELECTROVALENT OR IONIC BONDS

The atoms on the left-hand side of the periodic table, the metals, have in their outermost shell only one, two, or three electrons which are readily lost so that a new, but full, outside shell remains.   For example, sodium, atomic number 11, is neutral but readily loses an electron to become a positively charged sodium ion, Fig. 6–1. Fluorine, atomic number 9, has a great tendency to gain electrons, thereby becoming a negatively charged fluoride ion, Fig. 6–2.

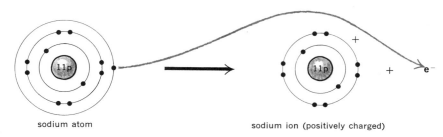

sodium atom   sodium ion (positively charged)

FIG. 6–1. Formation of a sodium ion.

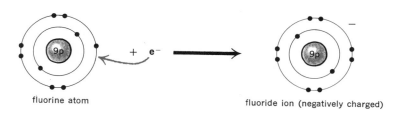

fluorine atom   fluoride ion (negatively charged)

FIG. 6–2. Formation of a fluoride ion.

If atoms of these highly reactive elements are brought together, an electron can be transferred from the sodium atom to the fluorine atom. The stable ions which result form a compound called sodium fluoride, Fig. 6–3. The process of combination is the simplest kind of chemical reaction. This reaction illustrates several important chemical principles. We have seen that when elements from the opposite sides of the periodic table combine, they may form compounds which are in reality made up of electrically charged particles called ions. The sodium ions are said to be *electropositive* since each has lost an electron, and the fluoride ions *electronegative*, since each has gained an electron. In the compound sodium fluoride, the attraction of the sodium ions (Na^+) for the fluoride ions (F^-) creates one of the types of chemical bonds. This type is an **electrovalent*** bond, also called an **ionic** bond.

It is entirely possible for more than one electron to be transferred between atoms. If an element from group IIA, such as calcium, reacts with chlorine, group VIIA, 2 atoms of chlorine are required to react with each calcium atom since a calcium atom has 2 electrons in its outer shell. The 2 electrons are readily given up, leaving a calcium ion bearing a positive charge of 2. Each chlorine atom requires only 1 electron to complete its outside shell; therefore, 2 atoms of chlorine are required to accept the 2 electrons released by calcium, Fig. 6–4.†

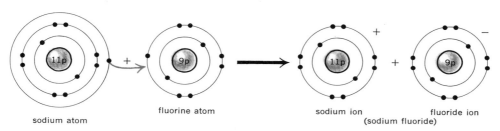

sodium atom   fluorine atom   sodium ion   fluoride ion
                                                        (sodium fluoride)

FIG. 6–3. Formation of a compound, sodium fluoride.

calcium atom   chlorine atoms   calcium ion   chloride ions
                                                    (calcium chloride, **CaCl₂**)

FIG. 6–4. Formation of calcium chloride.

In a like manner, when a sodium atom from group IA, with 1 electron in its outermost shell, combines with oxygen (group VIA) with 6 electrons in its outer shell (requiring two electrons to complete the shell), 2 sodium atoms are needed to supply the electrons re-

---

* The term *electrovalence* is based on the word *valence* which denotes the combining ability of an element, (Section 6–7).

† When working with the larger, more complex atoms, it is time-consuming to show all electrons graphically. We shall in the future usually use the type of structures shown in Fig. 6–4 to indicate the electron configurations of atoms and ions.

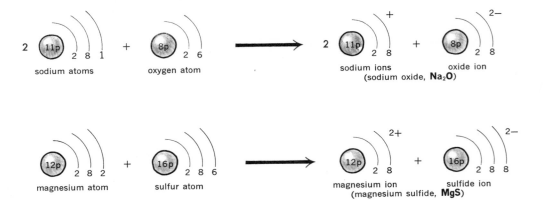

FIG. 6–5. Formation of sodium oxide and magnesium sulfide.

FIG. 6–6. Formation of aluminum chloride.

quired by oxygen. We find also that 1 atom of magnesium releases the 2 electrons from its outside shell to complete the outside shell of a sulfur atom which requires just 2 electrons, Fig. 6–5. However, when aluminum (atomic number 13) and chlorine (atomic number 17) react, 3 chlorine atoms, each taking 1 electron, are needed to remove the 3 electrons from the outside shell of the aluminum atom (see Fig. 6–6).

Combinations of atoms involve only the electrons in the outer shells, and many representations of atomic structure indicate only these electrons. These outer electrons are called *valence electrons*.

6–3 WRITING FORMULAS FOR COMPOUNDS

While we can repeat the procedure given in the previous section each time we want to know a formula for a compound, the process is much too time-consuming. In order to simplify the process, we use the concept of **valence** or combining power of atoms. From a knowledge of the events occurring when atoms combine with other atoms, we know that sodium loses 1 electron, calcium loses 2, and aluminum 3. We can say that sodium has a valence of 1+, calcium 2+, and aluminum 3+. Similarly, oxygen has a valence of 2− (two minus), and chlorine 1−. The relationship between valence and position on the periodic chart is obvious.

Elements in groups IA, IIA, and IIIA have valences of $1+$, $2+$, and $3+$, those in groups VA, VIA and VIIA have valences of $1-$, $2-$, and $3-$. Those in group IVA could possibly have either a $4+$ or $4-$. While there are some exceptions to this generalization, the results are sufficiently reliable to make this one of the most important uses of the periodic table, especially for beginning chemists.

From a knowledge of valences we can say that the formula for water is H_2O, calcium chloride is $CaCl_2$, and aluminum bromide is $AlBr_3$. Writing formulas for compounds such as aluminum oxide poses a slightly more complex problem. Aluminum loses 3 electrons, but oxygen gains only 2 when forming compounds. Thus the smallest number of electrons that can be exchanged to exactly satisfy each element when aluminum reacts with oxygen is 6. The number 6 is the least common multiple of the valence of aluminum (3) and oxygen (2). The formula for aluminum oxide is Al_2O_3.

While we can write formulas just by thinking carefully about the atoms which combine, it is sometimes better to have a procedure to follow. One good method of writing formulas is the following:

1) First write the symbols of the atoms in the compound.

2) Then write the valence of each atom above and to the right of the symbol.

3) Determine the least common multiple of the valences.

4) Write as subscripts the number of atoms required to give or receive the number of electrons indicated by the least common multiple.

◄ Following the steps outlined above, we can write the formulas for sodium sulfide and magnesium nitride as follows:

Sodium (Na) is in group IA of the periodic chart so it has a valence of $1+$ (generally written just as $+$), and sulfur (S) from group VIA has a valence of $2-$, so we write Na^+ S^{2-}. The least common multiple of 1 and 2 is 2, so the formula is Na_2S. For simple formulas such as this, we use the least common multiple largely unconsciously, and we say we are merely using common sense.

Magnesium has a valence of $2+$ and nitrogen could be either $5+$ or $3-$. Since we are studying the reaction of nitrogen with a metal which always gives up electrons, we realize that the nitrogen must receive electrons, so we use the valence of $3-$. We write Mg^{2+} N^{3-}. The least common multiple is 6, and the formula becomes Mg_3N_2. ►

In writing formulas we must remember that the number of atoms in a molecule is represented by a small number written just below and to the right of the symbol for the atom. Valences may be written at the upper right of the symbol during the process of deciding on the correct formula, but usually are not included in the final written formula. A number written in front of the formula indicates the number of molecules involved in a process: $3H_2O$ signifies three molecules of water. That is, there are 3 discrete particles, each one composed of H_2O. Altogether, these 3 molecules of water contain 6 hydrogen atoms and 3 oxygen atoms.

These procedures are sufficient for writing the formulas of electrovalent compounds, but problems arise when we try to understand the formula for a substance such as glucose. Analysis shows that the formula for glucose is $C_6H_{12}O_6$. All 24 atoms in this molecule are bound together. Why do such compounds form, and how does one know how to write the formulas for them? Part of the answer is given in our concept of covalent bonds.

6–4 COVALENT BONDS

When atoms of elements with less contrasting properties combine, there is less tendency for the atoms to capture or lose electrons. Such atoms may complete their outer shells by a process of sharing electrons. *A pair of shared electrons constitutes a* **covalent bond.** The simplest example of covalence is found in molecules of the elementary gases. Hydrogen atoms, it will be remembered, have 1 electron each. Since such a particle is unstable, if no other element is available for hydrogen atoms to react with, 2 hydrogen atoms combine with each other to form a diatomic molecule (a molecule with two atoms), Fig. 6–7. Here 2 hydrogen atoms share 2 electrons equally. The representation in Fig. 6–7, however, does not imply that the electrons are fixed in one spot. They are circling at a high speed about the two protons or hydrogen nuclei. A more realistic diagram would be that shown in Fig. 6–8 in which the shaded areas indicate the electron cloud, the most likely location of the electrons.

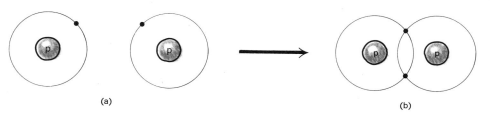

(a)   (b)

FIG. 6–7. (a) Two hydrogen atoms combine to form (b) a covalent molecule.

FIG. 6–8. Diagram of the distribution of electrons within a hydrogen molecule.

The elementary gases, with the exception of the noble gases whose outside shells of electrons are complete, occur as diatomic gases. Thus, we have H_2, N_2, O_2, F_2, and Cl_2. In addition, bromine (a liquid) and iodine (a solid) form diatomic molecules and at slightly elevated temperatures become gases. Illustrations of the atomic structure and the manner of bonding in some of these molecules may be helpful. In the following formulas the electrons are shown as dots, and only the electrons in the outer shell are shown, since they are the ones causing bonding.

atomic structure   H·   ·N :   : Cl ·

molecular structure   H : H   : N : : : N :   : Cl : Cl :

We can see that each hydrogen atom shares one electron with the other, so that each nucleus is surrounded by a complete shell of 2 electrons. The nitrogen atoms must share 6 electrons (three pairs) to reach stability. Chlorine atoms, which have 7 electrons each, become stable by sharing only one pair.

Compounds of carbon and hydrogen, of which there are many thousands, are held together by covalent bonds. The two simplest of these, methane and ethane, will serve as illustrations.

```
        H                H  H
        ..               ..  ..
    H : C : H        H : C : C : H
        ..               ..  ..
        H                H  H
methane (CH4)        ethane (C2H6)
```

In ethane the covalent bond between carbon atoms is typical of the connecting links between carbon atoms in the great molecules of complex carbon compounds. It should be remembered that only the electrons in the outside (valence) shells are shown since those in the inside shells are not involved in forming covalent bonds.

In writing formulas for covalent compounds, we usually use a dash to indicate a pair of electrons. Accordingly, we can write the formulas for methane and ethane as follows:

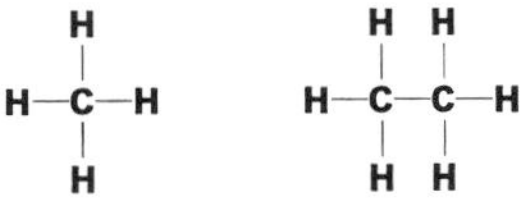

```
        H                H  H
        |                |  |
    H—C—H            H—C—C—H
        |                |  |
        H                H  H
```

We can say, then, that carbon always has 4 bonds, hydrogen has 1, and oxygen has 2. It so happens that there may sometimes be more than one bond between two given atoms, and it turns out that the structure for one of the sugars ($C_6H_{12}O_6$) is as follows:

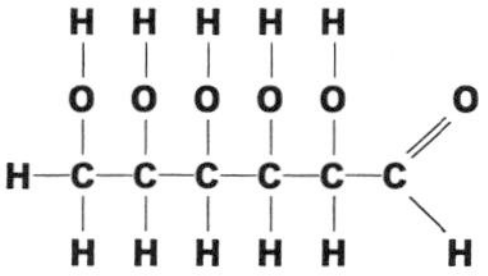

```
    H  H  H  H  H
    |  |  |  |  |
    O  O  O  O        O
    |  |  |  |        ||
 H—C—C—C—C—C
    |  |  |  |        \
    H  H  H  H        H
```

Formulas for the compounds containing carbon are discussed at length in the sections of the book devoted to organic chemistry and biochemistry. For a real understanding of how to write these complex formulas we must wait until we reach those sections.

6–5 POLAR COVALENT BONDS

Two types of chemical bonds have been discussed. The first is the ionic bond which exists between atoms which are strongly electrovalent. The second is the covalent bond consisting of a pair or pairs of electrons which are shared between identical atoms or atoms with relatively small electronegative-electropositive differences. Such categories are, of course, man-made; not all compounds fit into one or the other. Typical of such compounds is hydrogen chloride. Chlorine is an extremely negative element which has been shown to form ionic bonds with active metals; however, hydrogen is only moderately positive in character. The hydrogen and chlorine atoms are therefore bound together by a so-called **polar covalent bond** in which the pair of shared electrons is shifted toward the electronegative chlorine atom and away from the hydrogen.

$$\overset{\cdot\cdot}{\underset{\cdot\cdot}{H \; : Cl} :}$$

Such a shift in the electrons causes one end of the molecule to be negatively charged and the other, positively charged.

$$\underset{\delta^+ \;\; \delta^-}{H{-}Cl}$$

The Greek letter delta (δ) is used to designate the unequal distribution of electrons in such a bond, with a δ^- near the atom to which the electron is attracted and the δ^+ near the more electropositive atom. The chemical bonds in water molecules are polar covalent bonds.

$$\overset{\delta^+ \;\; \delta^-}{H{-}O\delta^-} \\ \underset{H}{\overset{}{\;\;\;\;\backslash\delta^+}}$$

Some molecules contain both polar covalent and nonpolar covalent bonds. Chloromethane is one such molecule, since chlorine is a very electronegative element whereas carbon and hydrogen are relatively neutral.

$$\begin{array}{c} H \\ | \\ \text{nonpolar covalent} \quad H{-}C \quad Cl \quad \text{polar covalent} \\ | \\ H \end{array}$$

At this point we should be able to visualize the gradual, continuous trend that takes place in chemical bonding between two extremes. On the one hand, the purely covalent bond that exists in molecules of similar atoms, such as H_2 or Cl_2, where the electrons are shared equally by the atoms, and on the other hand, the ionic bond in which an electron is transferred completely from one atom to another forming completely dissociated compounds such as sodium chloride. The polar covalent bond in varying degrees of polarity represents intermediate steps between the extremes. Examples of these three types of bonds are

$$H : H \qquad\qquad \overset{\cdot\cdot}{\underset{\cdot\cdot}{H : Cl}} : \qquad\qquad Na^+ \;\; \overset{\cdot\cdot}{\underset{\cdot\cdot}{: Cl}} : {}^-$$

covalent   polar covalent   ionic

6-6 ELECTRONEGATIVITY

In order to predict more readily the types of bonds that exist between atoms of any compound, we must know something of the relative degree of positiveness or negativeness of the elements involved.   The internationally known chemist, Dr. Linus Pauling,* has suggested a set of values which are quite workable.   Using theoretical and experimental data, he assigned an electronegativity value for each element.

Electronegativity is defined as *the attraction of an atom for the electrons in its outer shell.* To the most negative element, fluorine, Pauling assigned a value of 4; the most positive element, cesium, has a value of 0.7.   In Table 6–1 we can see that as we read from left to right through the periodic table and from bottom to top, the electronegativity values increase.

TABLE 6–1. Electronegativity values for some of the common elements

Increasing negativity ⟶

H							
2.1							
Li	Be	B	C	N	O	F	
1.0	1.5	2.0	2.5	3.0	3.5	4.0	
Na	Mg	Al	Si	P	S	Cl	Increasing
0.9	1.2	1.5	1.8	2.1	2.5	3.0	negativity
K	Ca				Se	Br	
0.8	1.0				2.4	2.8	
Rb	Sr					I	
0.8	1.0					2.5	
Cs	Ba						
0.7	0.9						

TABLE 6–2. Types of bonds present in some typical compounds

Compound	Electronegativity Values				Difference	Bond Type
NaF	sodium	0.9	fluorine	4.0	3.1	ionic
NaCl	sodium	0.9	chlorine	3.0	2.1	ionic
H_2O	hydrogen	2.1	oxygen	3.5	1.4	polar covalent
CO_2	carbon	2.5	oxygen	3.5	1.0	polar covalent
HCl	hydrogen	2.1	chlorine	3.0	0.9	polar covalent
CH_4	carbon	2.5	hydrogen	2.1	0.4	covalent
H_2	hydrogen	2.1	hydrogen	2.1	0.0	covalent

* Dr. Pauling, professor of chemistry, emeritus, of the California Institute of Technology, has the rare distinction of having received two Nobel prizes, one in chemistry in 1954 and the Peace Prize in 1963. Madame Curie is the only other person to have won two Nobel prizes; hers were, however, both in scientific areas.

We can now predict in a general way the type of bond that exists between the atoms in a compound. If the difference in electronegativity values between two elements is large, 2 or more, the bonds in the compound are largely ionic in nature. Where the difference is small, covalent bonds exist. Compounds with intermediate values will primarily contain polar covalent bonds. Table 6-2 contains a list of typical compounds and shows the electro-negativity differences and types of bonds predominating.

6-7 VALENCES AND OXIDATION NUMBERS

Earlier in this chapter it was stated that **valence** *is a term used to indicate the combining ability of elements*, and when combined with the prefixes electro- or co- describes the types of bonds existing between atoms. Oxygen, since it is not only the most prevalent element on the surface of the earth but also reacts in some manner with most of the known elements, has become the standard for determining valence. The term oxidation is used to describe not only the reaction of a substance with oxygen, but other related processes.

When magnesium combines with oxygen we say that magnesium has been oxidized:

magnesium + oxygen → magnesium oxide

Except for fluorine, oxygen has a greater electron affinity (electronegativity) than any other element, so that when another element combines with oxygen it loses electrons. In fact, **oxidation** *is defined as a loss of electrons* even in reactions in which no oxygen is involved. In the reaction of sodium with fluorine, Fig. 6-3, the sodium is oxidized, since it loses an electron. The valence or oxidation number of sodium becomes 1+. (The term *oxidation number* is often used rather than valence). Since the valence number of an unreacted element is zero, the valence of sodium increased by one unit in going from 0 to 1+. Oxidation is equivalent to a *gain in valence*.

By reacting with sodium, fluorine gains an electron and its valence changes from 0 to 1−. We say the fluorine has been *reduced*. **Reduction** *is defined as a decrease in valence number, and is due to a gain of electrons.*

In considering the valence numbers for elements in covalent compounds we are most often interested merely in how many bonds each element can form with its electrons. In ammonia, for example, we usually say that the valence of nitrogen is 3 and that of hydro-gen is 1.

```
        H                  H
        ..                 |
  H : N :      or     H——N :
        ..                 |
        H                  H
```

Since these are all covalent bonds we don't bother to say whether the valence of nitrogen is 3+ or 3−. However, if desirable, an element in a covalent compound can be assigned a positive or negative valence (oxidation number) depending on the number of electrons it would gain or lose if the compound were electrovalent. The element with the greater electro-negativity would be assigned a negative value and the other would be necessarily positive.

The relative negativity of the elements in question can be determined from their positions in a periodic table. In the periods of elements, negativity increases from left to right, and within the groups it increases from bottom to top. For example, we see that nitrogen is more negative than hydrogen, and therefore in ammonia, NH_3, nitrogen will have valence 3− and hydrogen will have valence 1+.

Some rules for establishing valence or oxidation number are helpful.

1) The valence of hydrogen is 1+ in all compounds except in the hydrides of metals, in which it is 1−.

2) The valence of oxygen is 2− in all compounds except in the peroxides such as H_2O_2, in which it is 1−.

3) The valence of uncombined elements is always zero.

4) The maximum valence of metals and nonmetals corresponds to the number of electrons in their outside shells, i.e., sodium, 1+; magnesium, 2+; carbon, 4+; and chlorine, 7+.

5) The negative valence exhibited by the nonmetals equals the number of electrons required to complete their outside electron shell, i.e., carbon, 4−; nitrogen, 3−; oxygen, 2−; and chlorine, 1−.

6) Since chemical compounds are neutral, it stands to reason that the algebraic sum of their valence numbers must equal zero.

6-8 MULTIPLE VALENCES

As we continue the study of chemistry we will find that many elements have more than one valence. In the laboratory when we burn sulfur in oxygen or in air, we get sulfur dioxide, SO_2. The valence of the sulfur in this compound is 4+ since oxygen is 2−. However, under certain conditions sulfur trioxide, SO_3, is formed, and the sulfur valence is 6+, as would be expected from the position of sulfur on the periodic table. An explanation for the variation of valence requires the introduction of a more complex theory of electron configuration, upon which we will touch very briefly. It is known that the electrons in a given shell can exist at different energy levels, so that some electrons are more available for action. Sulfur readily shares 4 of the 6 electrons in its outside shell (the valence shell) with oxygen to form sulfur dioxide. In order for oxygen to engage the remaining two electrons, special conditions must exist. In other atoms, under special excited conditions, one or more electrons may shift from an inner shell to the outside valence shell, thereby increasing the valence. Such is the case with copper, group IB, which has valences of 1+ and 2+, forming Cu_2O and CuO respectively. Iron, one of the transition metals in group VIII, has valences of 2+ and 3+ depending upon the conditions of the reaction and the nature of the element with which it is reacting. While many elements have more than one valence, the metals in groups IA and IIA have only the states of 1+ and 2+, respectively. Multiple valences might be compared to the amount of money a man gives or shares with his wife under normal conditions and under conditions of various kinds of stress. Table 6-3 lists the common valences of some of the elements.

TABLE 6–3. Common valences or oxidation numbers of some of the more familiar elements

Element	Valence Number	Element	Valence Number
aluminum	3+	iron	2+, 3+
barium	2+	lead	2+, 4+
bromine	1−	magnesium	2+
cadmium	2+	nitrogen	5+, 3+, 3−
calcium	2+	oxygen	2−
copper	1+, 2+	potassium	1+
carbon	4+, 4−	silver	1+
chlorine	1−	sulfur	6+, 4+, 2−
hydrogen	1+	zinc	2+

6–9 IONIC GROUPS

In many chemical compounds both ionic and covalent bonds exist simultaneously. Sodium hydroxide (NaOH) is a good example of such a compound. The bond between the sodium and the oxygen is strictly an electrovalent bond, and the one between the hydrogen and the oxygen is covalent. Sodium hydroxide is, therefore, composed of Na^+ and the OH^- (hydroxide) ions.

$$Na^+ \quad : \overset{..}{\underset{..}{O}} : H^-$$

Ions consisting of two or more atoms bound together by covalent bonds are called **ionic groups.** The majority of such groups are negatively charged, but some carry positive charges. Table 6–4 lists some of the common ionic groups with illustrative compounds.

For convenience, the charges carried by ions are often indicated as follows:

$$Na^+OH^- \qquad K^+NO_3^- \qquad Ca^{2+}SO_4^{2-} \qquad Na_2^+CO_3^{2-}$$

While the positive charges of the metals may be determined by their location on the periodic table, *the numerical charge on the ionic groups should be memorized.*

TABLE 6–4. Common ionic groups with illustrative compounds

Formula of Group	Name of Group	Illustrative Compound	Name of Compound
OH^-	hydroxide	$NaOH$	sodium hydroxide
NO_3^-	nitrate	KNO_3	potassium nitrate
SO_4^{2-}	sulfate	$CaSO_4$	calcium sulfate
CO_3^{2-}	carbonate	Na_2CO_3	sodium carbonate
PO_4^{3-}	phosphate	Na_3PO_4	sodium phosphate
SO_3^{2-}	sulfite	$CaSO_3$	calcium sulfite
NO_2^-	nitrite	KNO_2	potassium nitrite
NH_4^+	ammonium	NH_4Cl	ammonium chloride

6-10 SUMMARY

Although it is not proper to ascribe human emotions to elements and ions, the following analogies may be helpful. Atoms have a certain kind of stability; they are electrically neutral. Except for those in the noble gases, however, they feel somehow unsatisfied since they do not have completed outer shells of electrons. In an attempt to achieve happiness and stability they complete an outer shell by losing or gaining electrons. In gaining this stability they lose their electrical balance; they are now no longer electrically stable, but are charged. The existence of a lone charged ion is highly improbable; it always finds an oppositely charged ion, or perhaps two or three. Some ions and atoms form quite stable marriages of this sort, and these stable compounds are not easily disrupted. Those elements that combine and share electrons to form covalent bonds form the most stable compounds, but even these are subject to disruption. Only minor stimuli are needed to disrupt nitroglycerin, mercuric oxide, and hydrogen peroxide. These compounds tend to dissociate into elements (mercuric oxide when heated gives oxygen and mercury) or into a mixture of a stable compound and an element (as when hydrogen peroxide dissociates into water and oxygen). Only atoms in the noble gases are in nirvana where they have both electrical balance and complete outer shells. Even these are not totally immune to outside forces; under conditions of high pressure they may be made to react.

This constant changing from one form to another, always in search of stability, often under the influence of some outside agent, is the basis of all chemical reactions. The analogy to human society is obvious. In a universe of stable compounds with no outside forces to activate them, atoms would finally have achieved stability. This universe would be stable and unchanging; by analogy, it would be dead.

IMPORTANT TERMS

Covalent bond	*Electrovalent bond (ionic bond)*	*Oxidation*	*Reduction*
Electronegativity	*Ionic group*	*Polar covalent bond*	*Valence*

WORK EXERCISES

1. Distinguish between an atom and an ion.

2. a) What is your explanation for the great activity of the metals in Group IA and the nonmetals in Group VIIA?

   b) Why do the metals form positive ions and the nonmetals form negative ions?

3. Define the following terms: electrovalence, electropositive, electronegative, valence.

4. Distinguish between ionic and covalent bonds, and write formulas for five compounds in each category.

5. Write the formulas for several compounds in which polar covalent bonds are present.

6. What is the value of an electronegativity series such as the one developed by Dr. Linus Pauling?

7. Write formulas for five compounds that should be polar covalent according to the electronegativity scale.

8. Review the rules for establishing valence, then name five elements that may have either positive or negative valences.

9. For each of the five elements you have just listed, write formulas for two series of compounds, one involving the positive valence and one the negative.

10. Write formulas for the compounds formed when each of the negative groups in Table 6–4 combines with (a) lithium ions and (b) magnesium ions, and name the compounds formed.

SUGGESTED READING

Compton, C., *An Introduction to Chemistry,* Chapter 6.   Van Nostrand, Princeton, N.J., 1958.   The molecular, electronic, and structural formulas are shown for many inorganic and organic compounds.

Chapter 7 CHEMICAL EQUATIONS

7-1 CHEMICAL CHANGES

The universe around us is continually changing. While most of us are unaware of changes in the stars which are so distant, we are aware of changes in our immediate environment. Changes of temperature, the melting of ice, the burning of wood, the growing of plants, the decay of dead materials—these are all common changes. We recognize that some of these changes are physical, and others are chemical. The chemical changes, as the reader is now aware, are referred to as *chemical reactions*. In the previous chapter we discussed reactions of two elements and the resultant compound; actually, these reactions represent only the simplest of changes. Despite their simplicity, however, the results may be dramatic, such as we find when poisonous chlorine gas combines with intensively active sodium metal to make common table salt.

Chemists are interested in chemical changes, both those they observe taking place naturally and those they initiate. During chemical changes, bonds between atoms are broken, and new bonds are formed. The result of a chemical reaction is that the substances which react (reactants) are either converted into simpler substances (products) or are synthesized into products that are more complex than the starting materials. Energy is always involved in chemical reactions. In some reactions it is liberated, and in others it is absorbed.

7-2 CHEMICAL EQUATIONS

There are many ways of describing chemical changes. On the basis of observation we can say that natural gas, which is primarily methane, burns in the presence of the oxygen in the air to form carbon dioxide and water vapor. During this process some of the potential energy of the methane is released as heat. We can simplify our description of the process by writing what is called a word equation. The arrow in the middle of the equation indicates the direction in which the reaction is proceeding.

methane + oxygen → carbon dioxide + water vapor + energy   (7-1)

We can simplify this expression by substituting the chemical formulas for the various substances involved:

$CH_4 + O_2 → CO_2 + H_2O + energy$ (7-2)

This tells chemists much more about the process than either the sentence description or the word equation. However, as it is written, it says: 1 molecule of methane (CH_4) reacts with 1 diatomic molecule of oxygen to give 1 molecule of carbon dioxide and 1 molecule of water, with the release of energy. There are 4 hydrogen atoms on the left-hand side of our expression and only 2 on the right; also, there are unequal numbers of oxygen atoms on the two sides of the arrow. This gives the impression that hydrogen and oxygen atoms are being created or destroyed when methane burns. This conclusion is, of course, absurd. We must then proceed to make our expression truly an equation; that is, something that expresses an equality. First, we place a 2 in front of the symbol H_2O, so that the expression reads:

$CH_4 + O_2 → CO_2 + 2H_2O + energy$ (7-3)

The number of hydrogen atoms is now equal on both sides of our expression, but we see that there are 4 oxygen atoms on the right-hand side, 2 in the carbon dioxide and 1 each in 2 molecules of water. Therefore, we must indicate that there are 2 molecules of O_2 on the left-hand side of our expression in order to make it a true equation.

$CH_4 + 2O_2 → CO_2 + 2H_2O + 212$ kcal   (7-4)

If we compare Eqs. (7-1) and (7-4), we find that Eq. (7-4) gives us more information than (7-1). It shows that 1 molecule of methane requires 2 molecules of oxygen to produce 1 molecule of carbon dioxide and 2 molecules of water plus energy. We can say that the *qualitative* expression has now become *quantitative*. It became truly quantitative when we replaced the word "energy" by the number of kilocalories of heat released. Experimentally, the heat evolved when 1 mole of methane burns has been found to be 212 kcal. We must never lose sight of the fact, however, that a chemical equation is merely a convention for expressing what happens in a chemical reaction. The reaction is real, the equation only one way of representing that reality.

If finely divided magnesium and sulfur are mixed in the correct proportions and ignited, a chemical compound is produced which is called magnesium sulfide.

$$Mg + S \xrightarrow{\Delta} MgS$$ (7-5)

magnesium   sulfur   magnesium
                       sulfide

We use the symbol Δ to indicate that heat is required. Once we have written the expression given in Eq. (7-5), we must ask whether it is true in terms of quantities. We must first examine the formula for magnesium sulfide. Is this the correct formula or is it MgS_2 or perhaps Mg_2S? By consulting a periodic table or Table 6–3, we see that the valence of magnesium is 2+ and sulfur is 2−, consequently, the formula is correct as written in Eq. (7–5). Actually we might first go through a slightly more complex process and write

$$Mg^0 + S^0 \rightarrow Mg^{2+}S^{2-} \tag{7-6}$$

This expression indicates that the elements in an uncombined state are assigned a valence number of zero. Writing the valences above the atoms in magnesium sulfide helps us determine the correct formula.

An equation that involves another step is the one expressing the reaction of sodium and sulfur to form sodium sulfide. The first step is

$$\underset{\text{sodium}}{Na} + \underset{\text{sulfur}}{S} \rightarrow \underset{\substack{\text{sodium} \\ \text{sulfide}}}{NaS} \tag{7-7a}$$

Writing in the valence numbers, we get

$$Na^0 + S^0 \rightarrow Na^+S^{2-}$$

The formula NaS, then, is not the correct formula for sodium sulfide; we must indicate that the compound contains 2 atoms of sodium and 1 of sulfur. The completed, but still unbalanced expression is:

$$Na + S \rightarrow Na_2S \tag{7-7b}$$

In order to balance the equation we must place a 2 before the symbol for sodium on the left-hand side, and we get

$$2Na + S \rightarrow Na_2S \tag{7-7c}$$

We can summarize the process of writing balanced equations as follows:

1) Write the correct formulas for the reactants (substances) on the left-hand side of the arrow.
2) Write the correct formula(s) for the product(s) on the right.
3) Balance the number of atoms on either side of the equation.

It should be stressed that in step (3) we must not alter the formulas of either the products or reactants. We can indicate only that more molecules are present until we reach a situation where the equation is balanced.

7-3 GRAM ATOMIC, MOLECULAR, AND FORMULA WEIGHTS

Equations are good theoretical descriptions of chemical reactions. The equation

$$2H_2 + O_2 \rightarrow 2H_2O + \text{energy} \tag{7-8}$$

tells us that 2 diatomic hydrogen molecules react with 1 diatomic oxygen molecule to give 2 molecules of the compound water. We learned in Section 4–9 that the weight of an atom, or even of a molecule was extremely small. While an equation serves as an excellent theoretical description, any practical use of equations demands that there be some way of actually weighing or measuring the amounts of substances involved in the chemical reaction being described. We can do this by using the concept of the *Gram-Atomic Weight*. As defined in Section 4–9, a gram-atomic weight is a number of grams equal to the atomic weight of a substance. In dealing with molecules we may use the term *molecular weight* or *formula weight*. The **formula weight** *is the sum of the atomic weights of all the atoms in the formula.* The formula weight of oxygen (O_2) is 32, since the formula indicates 2 atoms of oxygen each having an atomic weight of 16. The formula weight for a hydrogen molecule is 2, and the formula weight for water is the sum of 2 and 16, or 18. Thus the equation telling about the reaction of hydrogen with oxygen to form water can also be interpreted as saying 4 g (2×2) of hydrogen react with 32 g (2×16) of oxygen to give 36 g (2×18) of water.

Example. The formula weight of sulfuric acid, H_2SO_4, is calculated as follows:

$$2\,H = 2 \times 1\ \ = \ \ 2$$
$$1\,S\ = 1 \times 32 = 32$$
$$\underline{4\,O = 4 \times 16 = 64}$$
$$98 = \text{the gram-formula weight of } H_2SO_4.$$

The formula weight may be called a **molecular weight** in referring to *covalent* substances such as O_2, H_2O, or CO_2, because these occur as discrete molecules. However, for an *ionic* substance such as calcium chloride the term formula weight is preferred since there are no individual particles consisting of 2 chloride atoms bound to 1 specific calcium atom. Thus there are really no molecules of calcium chloride. Instead we find, in either solid calcium chloride or a solution of calcium chloride, a collection of calcium *ions* and chloride *ions*. Since they occur in the ratio 1 to 2, we say the *formula* is $CaCl_2$, and the *formula weight* is 110.

To summarize, *for covalent molecules we may use either the term formula weight or molecular weight. But for ionic compounds we should use only formula weight.*

7–4 THE MOLE CONCEPT

The expression **mole** has been adopted by chemists as a substitute for a gram-molecular weight, a gram-formula weight, or a gram-ion weight. The word "mole" is derived from the Latin *moles* meaning heap or pile.

For the chemist, *the mole is Avogadro's number of particles,* whether they are ions, atoms, or molecules. One mole of sodium chloride, for example, is 1 gram-formula weight (58.5 g) and contains 6.023×10^{23} sodium ions and 6.023×10^{23} chloride ions. One mole of water is 1 gram-molecular weight (18 g) and contains 6.023×10^{23} water molecules composed of $2 \times 6.023 \times 10^{23}$ hydrogen atoms and $1 \times 6.023 \times 10^{23}$ oxygen atoms. The mole is a very useful term since with one small word we can express the numbers of units as well as the masses involved in chemical reactions.

7–5 WEIGHT RELATIONSHIPS

We have seen that a chemical equation can give us a description of a chemical reaction in terms of atoms. By adding the concept of formula weights we can extend the usefulness of a chemical equation so that we can calculate the amount of one reactant required to combine with another and determine the weight of the product. Rewriting Eq. (7–5), we get

$$\underset{\substack{\text{1 mole of} \\ \text{magnesium atoms} \\ 24.3}}{\text{Mg}} + \underset{\substack{\text{1 mole of} \\ \text{sulfur atoms} \\ 32}}{\text{S}} \xrightarrow{\Delta} \underset{\substack{\text{1 mole of} \\ \text{magnesium sulfide} \\ 56.3}}{\text{MgS.}} \qquad (7\text{–}9)$$

Placing the atomic weights under each element as indicated, we find that 24.3 units (grams, pounds, or tons) of magnesium will combine with 32 units (grams, pounds, or tons) of sulfur to produce 24.3 + 32 = 56.3 units (grams, pounds, or tons) of magnesium sulfide.

It must be remembered the unit used is not important so long as the same unit is used throughout any one calculation. In the laboratory, grams or moles are normally used in such calculations, but in industry where large amounts of chemicals are used, the most practical unit may be the ton. In fact, industry is not the only area where the ton is the most convenient unit. Coal, which is largely carbon, is used in industry but is still used in many countries to heat homes. The chemical reaction that takes place on burning of carbon is

$$\underset{12}{\text{C}} + \underset{(2 \times 16 = 32)}{\text{O}_2} \xrightarrow{\Delta} \underset{44}{\text{CO}_2.} \qquad (7\text{–}10)$$

If we assume that coal is carbon (actually the percentage of carbon in coal varies from 60 to 85%), it will be seen that 12 units of carbon require 32 units of oxygen to produce 44 units of carbon dioxide. Remember the units may be grams, pounds, or tons; however, in this case we are using the ton as a unit since we are concerned with large amounts of coal. If the average-sized home requires 12 tons of coal/winter, which is a reasonable amount, 32 tons of oxygen will be required for complete burning, and 44 tons of carbon dioxide will leave the furnace via the chimney. How fortunate for the homeowner that carbon dioxide is a gas which escapes rather than a solid which would have to be removed from the furnace and carried from the home.

It would be unreasonable to assume that all homeowners in coal-burning regions require 12 tons of coal/winter. The amount required is primarily dependent upon the size of the house. If a smaller house requires only 6 tons of coal/winter, how may we determine the amount of oxygen required and the amount of carbon dioxide that will be produced? From Eq. (7–10) we see that 32 tons of oxygen are required for 12 tons of carbon; therefore, for 6 tons of carbon,

$$\frac{6}{12} \times 32 = 16 \text{ tons of oxygen will be required, and}$$

$$\frac{6}{12} \times 44 = 22 \text{ tons of carbon dioxide will be produced.}$$

If a large home required 15 tons of coal, we would solve our problem in the same manner. It should be evident that more oxygen would be required and more carbon dioxide would be formed than for the smaller home. The solution is

$$\frac{15}{12} \times 32 = 40 \text{ tons of oxygen,} \quad \text{and} \quad \frac{15}{12} \times 44 = 55 \text{ tons of carbon dioxide.}$$

In all problems we should check our calculations to see whether the results are reasonable. In this instance, if fewer than 12 tons are used, the amounts of the other materials involved must be proportionately less than in the original equation, and if more than 12 tons are consumed, the other values must be higher.

◄ How many grams of carbon dioxide will be produced by the complete oxidation (burning) of 20 g of methane, CH_4? Remember that in solving such problems we first write the equation for the reaction and then supply the relative weights of the reactants and products. From Eq. (7–4), we have

$CH_4 + 2O_2 \rightarrow CO_2 + 2H_2O$
  16   64   44   36

to which we affix the relative molecular weights. This equation tells us that 16 units (grams) of methane react with oxygen to form 44 units (grams) of carbon dioxide; therefore, the oxidation of 20 g of methane will produce 55 g of carbon dioxide.

$$\frac{20}{16} \times 44 = 55.$$

From the same equation we can easily calculate the amount of water formed in the reaction. If 16 g of methane, on oxidation, produce 36 g of water, then

$$\frac{20}{16} \times 36 = 45 \text{ g of water.}$$

When aluminum unites with oxygen to form aluminum oxide, the balancing of the equation for the resulting reaction is accomplished in a similar fashion. Again, we first write the reacting elements and the incomplete formula of the product formed, using valences from the periodic chart.

$Al^0 + O_2^0 \rightarrow Al^{3+}O^{2-}$ (7–11)

We now know that each aluminum atom gives up 3 electrons and that each oxygen accepts 2. The least common multiple of 2 and 3 is 6, so that 6 is the smallest number of electrons that can be transferred in such a combination. The correct formula for aluminum oxide is therefore $Al_2^{3+}O_3^{2-}$, and we now have the completed but unbalanced equation,

$Al^0 + O_2^0 \rightarrow Al_2^{3+}O_3^{2-}$ (7–12)

In checking the correctness of the formula $Al_2^{3+}O_3^{2-}$, the product of the subscript times the ionic charge on the aluminum must equal the product of the subscript times the ionic charge on the oxygen. Once having arrived at the correct formula for the reactants and the product, we are not permitted to alter them in any way. We can only place numbers (coefficients) as needed before any atom or molecule. In balancing such an equation it is preferable to start with the element which requires a coefficient on each side of the equation. Oxygen occurs in groups of 2 on the left-hand side, and in groups of 3 on the right, so the common multiple can again be used:

$$Al + 3O_2 \rightarrow 2Al_2{}^{3+}O_3{}^{2-} \tag{7-13}$$

The number of aluminum atoms can now be equalized by placing a 4 before the Al:

$$4Al + 3O_2 \rightarrow 2Al_2{}^{3+}O_3{}^{2-} \tag{7-14}$$

and the equation is balanced.

A simplified method of balancing can be accomplished by starting with Eq. (7–12),

$$Al^0 + O_2{}^0 \rightarrow Al_2{}^{3+}O_3{}^{2-}$$

It will be seen that there are 3 atoms of oxygen on the right-hand side of the equation. Since $1\frac{1}{2} \times O_2$ will equal 3 oxygen atoms, we may write

$$Al^0 + 1\tfrac{1}{2}O_2 \rightarrow Al_2{}^{3+}O_3{}^{2-} \tag{7-15}$$

and all that remains is to place a 2 before the aluminum.

$$2Al + 1\tfrac{1}{2}O_2 \rightarrow Al_2O_3 \tag{7-16}$$
$$54 \qquad 48 \qquad\ \ 102$$

For the purposes of chemical calculations the above equation is as satisfactorily balanced as the one below:

$$4Al + 3O_2 \rightarrow Al_2O_3 \tag{7-17}$$
$$108 \qquad 96 \qquad 204$$

When we supply the weights for each, we see that Eq. (7–16) involves exactly half the weights of Eq. (7–17).

To emphasize that either equation may be used as a basis for chemical calculation, we may take the following problem: How much aluminum, when completely oxidized, is required to produce 60 g of Al_2O_3? Using the data in Eq. (7–16), we note that 54 g of aluminum, when oxidized, produced 102 g of Al_2O_3; therefore

$$\frac{60}{102} \times 54 = 31.76 \text{ g}.$$

Using Eq. (7–17), we see that 108 g of aluminum, when oxidized, produced 204 g of Al_2O_3. Consequently,

$$\frac{60}{204} \times 108 = 31.76 \text{ g}.$$

It can be seen that both equations provide the correct answer. If we want an equation that describes what happens to individual atoms or molecules, Eqs. (7–14) or (7–17) are preferable, since half-molecules of O_2 are not normally present. ▶

7-6 TYPES OF CHEMICAL REACTIONS

The chemist trying a new chemical reaction and the person studying chemistry are faced with the same problem: "What will be the products of the reaction?" Predicting the products of a reaction is no simple task; it becomes easier if we can use past experience to make generalizations. Chemists know, for example, that there are five common types of chemical reactions:

1) Direct combination or synthesis,

2) Decomposition,

3) Single displacement,

4) Double decomposition (double displacement),

5) Redox (reduction-oxidation).

We shall discuss each of these types, using familiar illustrations.

1. Direct Combination or Synthesis

In the simplest type of this reaction we have two elements combining directly to form a compound. For example, calcium reacts with sulfur to give calcium sulfide.

$$Ca + S \rightarrow CaS \tag{7-18}$$

If we wish to choose a simple analogy for this type of equation we might say that it is a "boy marries girl" situation. Two formerly single elements are united and held together by bonds. We have already encountered several chemical reactions of this type, and others will be found in Chapter 8, "Oxygen." In addition to the combination of one *element* with another, there are reactions in which two or more *molecules* combine directly to form a larger molecule. Oxides of active metals combine with carbon dioxide to form carbonates. We find, for example, that

$$CaO + CO_2 \rightarrow CaCO_3 \tag{7-19}$$

Calcium oxide and water react to produce calcium hydroxide,

$$CaO + H_2O \rightarrow Ca(OH)_2 \tag{7-20}$$

and sulfur dioxide and water combine to form sulfurous acid,

$$SO_2 + H_2O \rightarrow H_2SO_3 \tag{7-21}$$

Reactions involving direct combination or synthesis are easily identified when only two elements are involved, and the product is easily predicted. However, when a reaction involves two compounds as reactants it is often difficult to predict whether they will combine to form a more complex compound or whether a double displacement (type 4) will occur. In studying such reactions, we would have to identify the products by some experimental procedures before we could tell which type of reaction had occurred. On the basis of several experiments, generalizations could be developed about the reaction of oxides with water or with carbon dioxide, as illustrated above. Some of these generalizations will be made in succeeding chapters.

2. Decomposition

Some chemical compounds are unstable under certain conditions and decompose into simpler substances. Mercuric oxide, on heating, decomposes into metallic mercury and oxygen.

$$HgO \xrightarrow{\Delta} Hg + \tfrac{1}{2}O_2 \uparrow \tag{7-22}$$

or

$$2HgO \xrightarrow{\Delta} 2Hg + O_2 \uparrow \tag{7-23}$$

To extend our analogy, this is the opposite of the first type of reaction and is a "boy loses girl" reaction. Of course, there is always a reason for disruption of bonds, usually an outside factor, and in this reaction it is temperature. Decompositions may yield simpler compounds as well as elements. Carbonic acid readily decomposes at room temperature, forming carbon dioxide gas and water.

$$H_2CO_3 \xrightarrow{\Delta} H_2O + CO_2 \uparrow \tag{7-24}$$

Many metallic carbonates decompose on heating, forming the corresponding metallic oxide and carbon dioxide.

$$CaCO_3 \xrightarrow{\Delta} CaO + CO_2 \tag{7-25}$$

This reaction is the reverse of that described by Eq. (7–19).

Water can be decomposed into hydrogen and oxygen gases by passing a direct electric current through water to which sulfuric acid has been added.

$$2H_2O \xrightarrow[\substack{\text{direct} \\ \text{current}}]{H_2SO_4} 2H_2 \uparrow + O_2 \uparrow \tag{7-26a}$$

or

$$H_2O \xrightarrow[\substack{\text{direct} \\ \text{current}}]{H_2SO_4} H_2 \uparrow + \tfrac{1}{2}O_2 \uparrow \tag{7-26b}$$

Here, electrical energy is the force which literally pulls the two apart. Decomposition reactions can be identified by the fact that only one compound is involved and that a source of energy is required.

3. Single displacements

If we study the effects of placing copper wire in a solution of silver nitrate, we find that the solution becomes blue. We recognize that the blueness is due to the presence of copper ions, and we see a beautiful deposit of crystals forming on the surface of the copper wire. These crystals when analyzed prove to be silver. We can write the reaction as follows:

$$2AgNO_3 + Cu \rightarrow Cu(NO_3)_2 + 2Ag \downarrow \qquad (7\text{–}27)$$

We say that copper has replaced the silver in the compound.

Similarly, if we place iron in a solution of copper sulfate we find the copper being deposited and the iron going into solution. We can write this equation as

$$Fe + CuSO_4 \rightarrow Cu \downarrow + FeSO_4 \qquad (7\text{–}28)$$

If we reverse the situation and place some copper metal in a solution of iron sulfate, we find no evidence of reaction and we write the following:

$$Cu + FeSO_4 \rightarrow \text{no reaction} \qquad (7\text{–}29)$$

If we carry our analogy to life situations, we can say that this represents a person's "cutting in" at a dance or perhaps the replacement of one fraternity pin by another; the attempt succeeds only if the girl is receptive to the proposed change.

In single displacement there must be some way of predicting whether a reaction will proceed or not. Of course, we could try each reaction and check the evidence. Actually, such experiments have been done by many scientists, and as a result we can make some generalizations. We can say that in order for an element to replace another in a compound it must be more active than the element in the compound. Thus on the basis of the equations given above, we can say that copper is more active than silver but less active than iron. On the basis of many experiments we can develop an activity series or displacement table (see Table 9–1). Evidence from such reactions forms the basis for statements about the activity of metals on the periodic table.

We know from experiments that very active metals react with water, displacing hydrogen gas and forming hydroxides.

$$Na + HOH \rightarrow NaOH + \tfrac{1}{2}H_2 \uparrow \qquad (7\text{–}30)$$
$$Ca + 2HOH \rightarrow Ca(OH)_2 + H_2 \uparrow \qquad (7\text{–}31)$$

Single displacement reactions are not limited to metals; for instance, when we pass chlorine gas through a solution of potassium iodide we find that iodine is displaced.

$$KI + \tfrac{1}{2}Cl_2 \rightarrow KCl + \tfrac{1}{2}I_2 \qquad (7\text{–}32)$$

A single displacement reaction may be identified by having one element and one compound as reactants. Either the periodic table or a displacement series (Table 9–1) is required to predict whether or not a single displacement will take place.

4. Double Decomposition

Two compounds may react to form new compounds. Such reactions are called double displacement or double decomposition reactions. At first glance it may seem difficult to predict what will happen when silver nitrate reacts with sodium chloride:

$AgNO_3 + NaCl \rightarrow$

Placing the valence charges on the reacting groups,

$Ag^+NO_3^- + Na^+Cl^- \rightarrow$ (7–33)

makes the reaction to be expected much clearer. We can use the analogy of two couples who go dancing and decide to change partners. Our equation becomes:

a) $Ag^+NO_3^- + Na^+Cl^- \rightarrow Ag^+Cl^- \downarrow + Na^+NO_3^-$ (7–34)

Other examples of double decomposition reactions are:

b) $Na^+OH^- + H^+Cl^- \rightarrow Na^+Cl^- + HOH$ (7–35)

c) $H_2^+SO_4^{2-} + Zn^{2+}S^{2-} \rightarrow H_2S \uparrow + Zn^{2+}SO_4^{2-}$ (7–36)

It should be observed that compounds are formed when positively charged groups or ions combine with negatively charged groups or ions.

Some double decomposition reactions can be reversible: either the substances written on the right or those on the left may be considered as the reactants. Thus, some generalizations as to factors that influence the direction of reactions are necessary if we are to predict their outcome. The conditions listed below cause a reaction to go primarily in one direction.

When an Insoluble Precipitate Forms. In Eq. (7–34) silver chloride which is insoluble (as indicated by a downward arrow AgCl $\downarrow$) is formed. Since AgCl is insoluble, it cannot react with $NaNO_3$ and the reaction is not reversible.

When a Gas Forms and Escapes from the Reaction. In Eq. (7–36) the gas H_2S (indicated by an upward arrow $\uparrow$) escapes, and only $ZnSO_4$ remains.

When a Nonionized Compound Forms. In Eq. (7–35) the reaction does not reverse because water, which is a poorly ionized compound, is one of the products of the reaction.

If we place in water the two compounds, sodium chloride and potassium nitrate, we get

$Na^+Cl^- + K^+NO_3^- \rightarrow K^+Cl^- + Na^+NO_3^-$ (7–37)

and find that all possible combinations of ions form water soluble compounds which remain in solution. The above equation can logically be written as a complete ionic equation since all substances are completely ionized.

$Na^+ + Cl^- + K^+ + NO_3^- \rightleftharpoons Na^+ + NO_3^- + K^+ + Cl^-$ (7–38)

We can see that the same ions are present on both sides of the arrows so we say that no re-action has occurred or that the reaction is reversible. If the solution is evaporated to dryness, crystals of all four compounds, $NaCl$, KNO_3, $NaNO_3$, and KCl, will be present.

Double displacement reactions are characterized by having two compounds as re-actants. In predicting the products of double displacement reactions, it is necessary to know the solubility and degree of ionization of all compounds involved. The solubilities of salts are discussed in Section 12–6.

5. Redox (Reduction-Oxidation)

The fifth general type of chemical reaction involves oxidation of one substance and re-duction of another. In the definition of oxidation (Section 6–7) it was indicated that any loss of electrons or gain in positive valence is considered to be an oxidation. During a chemical change in which one element loses electrons, other elements or compounds must gain electrons and be reduced. While there are many complex reactions of this type, some of the simpler reactions may also be considered true redox reactions.

$$Ca^0 + \tfrac{1}{2}O_2^0 \rightarrow Ca^{2+}O^{2-} \tag{7–39}$$

or

$$Ca^0 + Cl_2^0 \rightarrow Ca^{2+}Cl_2^- \tag{7–40}$$

In each of the above, calcium lost electrons and its oxidation number increased from 0 to 2+; in each case, it was oxidized. Oxygen and chlorine were reduced. Each gained electrons and decreased in oxidation number.

Much more complex redox equations are known. They can be identified by the fact that there is a change in valence of at least two kinds of atoms—one being oxidized and the other reduced.

The reader may have noticed that oxidation and reduction occur in some direct com-binations and single displacements, which therefore could also be properly termed redox reactions. Examples are Eqs. (7–18) and (7–28). Once again we see that natural phenomena do not always fit perfectly into the categories we devise.

7–7 SUMMARY

In this chapter we have discussed several types of chemical reactions and have shown how we can describe these reactions by writing equations. It has been emphasized that the re-action is the reality and that an equation is merely a way of representing what happens. Actually, the reactions were first observed in nature or performed in the laboratory and the products identified by chemical means. Using the results of many experiments or ob-servations, we can make generalizations about the products to be expected in chemical reactions.

Although originally presented as a theoretical description of what happens when atoms and molecules react, equations may also have practical uses. When we add the idea of formula weights to that of the balanced equation, we can calculate the amount of products formed or amounts of reactants necessary. This knowledge would be very important, for example, if we were reacting corrosive substances such as hydrochloric acid and sodium hydroxide to give sodium chloride and water. We could calculate the exact amount of each reactant that should be used to prevent an excess of either corrosive reactant in the final mixture. Soap-making involves the use of either sodium or potassium hydroxide; an excess of these substances would cause serious skin irritations. There are many examples of the practical use of calculations involving equations.

We hope that this chapter has helped you understand those mysterious symbols that chemists use. Chemistry would be possible without them, but it would take much longer to describe reactions. Accordingly you must be able to use these symbols in the study of chemistry, but once you have mastered them you have added an international language to your vocabulary.

IMPORTANT TERMS

Formula weight   *Mole*
Gram atomic weight   *Molecular weight*

WORK EXERCISES

1. Direct combination reactions. Complete and balance:
   a) $C + O_2 \rightarrow$ b) $Mg + Cl_2 \rightarrow$
   c) $K + S \rightarrow$ d) $Al + S \rightarrow$
   e) $CaO + CO_2 \rightarrow$ f) $Na_2O + H_2O \rightarrow$
   g) $H_2O + SO_2 \rightarrow$ h) $H_2O + SO_3 \rightarrow$

2. Decomposition reactions. Complete and balance [If hydrogen is present, water will be a product.]:
   a) $HgO \xrightarrow{\Delta}$ b) $KClO_3 \xrightarrow{\Delta}$
   c) $NH_4OH \rightarrow$ d) $CaCO_3 \xrightarrow{\Delta}$
   e) $Na_2CO_3 \xrightarrow{\Delta}$ f) $H_2CO_3 \rightarrow$
   g) $H_2SO_3 \rightarrow$ h) $H_2O \xrightarrow{electricity}$
   i) $Ca(OH)_2 \xrightarrow{\Delta}$

3. Double decomposition reactions. Complete and balance:
   a) $KCl + AgNO_3 \rightarrow$ b) $Na_2SO_4 + BaCl_2 \rightarrow$
   c) $NaOH + FeCl_3 \rightarrow$ d) $NaOH + HNO_3 \rightarrow$
   e) $NH_4Cl + Ca(OH)_2 \rightarrow$ f) $CaO + HNO_3 \rightarrow$
   g) $CuO + HCl \rightarrow$ h) $BaCl_2 + H_2SO_4 \rightarrow$
   i) $KOH + H_2SO_4 \rightarrow$

4. Complete, balance, and identify the type of equation.

    a) $Zn + S \rightarrow$ b) $MgO + HCl \rightarrow$
    c) $Zn + CuSO_4 \rightarrow$ d) $NH_4OH \rightarrow$
    e) $Ca(OH)_2 + H_3PO_4 \rightarrow$ f) $Al_2O_3 + H_2SO_4 \rightarrow$
    g) $K + Cl_2 \rightarrow$ h) $Na_2O + CO_2 \rightarrow$
    i) $CuCO_3 \xrightarrow{\triangle}$ j) $C + Cl_2 \rightarrow$

5. According to the equation,

    $KClO_3 \xrightarrow{\triangle} KCl + 1\tfrac{1}{2} O_2,$

    a) How many grams of $KClO_3$ are required to produce 10 g of O_2?
    b) How much O_2 will be produced by the decomposition of 5 g of $KClO_3$?
    c) How many moles of O_2 will be produced from the decomposition of 2 moles of $KClO_3$?
    d) How many molecules are there in $1\tfrac{1}{2}$ moles of O_2?

6. According to the equation,

    $CaCO_3 \xrightarrow{\triangle} CaO + CO_2,$

    a) How many grams of CO_2 can be produced by heating 50 g of $CaCO_3$?
    b) How many grams of CaO will be found when 10 g of $CaCO_3$ are heated?
    c) How many moles of $CaCO_3$ will be required to liberate 88 g of CO_2?

7. How many grams of oxygen are required to completely burn 30 g of carbon?

8. How many grams of carbon dioxide will be produced by the complete oxidation of 3 g of carbon?

9. How many grams of carbon, completely oxidized, will be required to produce 33 g of CO_2?

SUGGESTED READING

Eblin, L. P., *The Elements of Chemistry,* Harcourt, Brace and World, New York, 1965. Chapter 5 contains a good discussion of the mole concept.

Kieffer, W. F., *The Mole Concept in Chemistry,* Reinhold, New York, 1962. A discussion of the mole and how it is employed in chemical calculations.

Chapter 8   OXYGEN

8-1 INTRODUCTION

Oxygen in one form or another is the most prevalent of the elements which make up the portion of the earth with which we are familiar. It is, in fact, estimated that approximately 50% by weight of the so-called crust* of the earth is composed of oxygen. About 21% of the atmosphere, nearly 90% of water, and more than 50% of sand is oxygen. In the atmosphere oxygen exists in the free uncombined state, while in sand and water it is in a combined form. From the standpoint of life, many elements are essential, but oxygen is the one which is the most continuously required. Under most conditions man can go for weeks without food, for days without water, but only minutes without oxygen. It may seem strange that so common an element was unidentified until less than 200 years ago.

8-2 THE DISCOVERY OF OXYGEN

Joseph Priestley, an English clergyman, teacher, and experimenter recognized a relationship between combustion and respiration. He demonstrated experimentally that a candle would soon stop burning when confined in a closed container of air. Afterward, if plants were grown in this atmosphere, a regeneration took place and the candle would burn again. In his experiments he also observed the effects of oxygen on animals, usually mice. Priestley .is generally credited with the distinction of being the first to prepare oxygen in a pure state, and certainly he was the one who announced to the world many of its interesting properties.

---

* Recall that we are using the term *crust* to include the atmosphere, oceans, and outer layer of dry land (see Section 5-2).

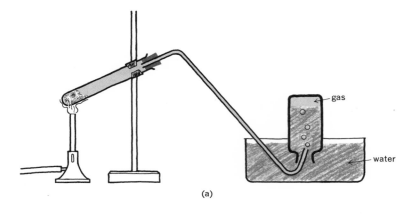

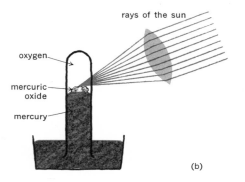

FIG. 8-1. Apparatus for collecting gases:
(a) equipment presently used in the laboratory,
(b) equipment used by Priestley.

Carl Scheele, a Swedish druggist, prepared oxygen a few years earlier but apparently did not realize the importance of the discovery and made no mention of it until after Priestley's work in 1774. Priestley prepared the "new air," as he referred to it, by heating mercuric oxide, a method you may easily observe yourself.

$2HgO \rightarrow 2Hg + O_2$ (8-1)

However, he used a magnifying glass to intensify the heat of the sun rather than a gas burner, and collected the gas over mercury instead of water. A comparison of Priestley's apparatus and that used today is shown in Fig. 8-1. He subjected the "new air" to the same kind of tests he used on the other gases he had prepared. The oxygen prepared over mercury was transferred to an apparatus in which water was substituted for the mercury, making experiments with animals more feasible.

◄ Priestley's results can best be appreciated by the following paragraphs from his writings.
"For the purpose of these experiments it is most convenient to catch the mice in small wire traps, out of which it is easy to take them, and holding them by the back of the neck, to pass them through the water into the vessel which contains the air. If I expect that the mouse will

live a considerable time, I take care to put into the vessel something on which it might conveniently sit, out of reach of the water. If the air be good, the mouse will soon be perfectly at its ease, having suffered nothing by its passing through the water. If the air be supposed to be noxious, it will be proper (if the operator be desirous of preserving the mice for further use) to keep hold of their tails, that they may be withdrawn as soon as they begin to show signs of uneasiness; but if the air be thoroughly noxious, and the mouse happens to get a full inspiration, it will be impossible to do this before it will be absolutely irrecoverable . . .

"From the greater strength and vivacity of the flame of a candle, in this pure air, it may be conjectured that it might be peculiarly salutary to the lungs in certain morbid cases, when the common air would not be sufficient to carry off the phlogistic putrid effluvium fast enough. But, perhaps, we may also infer from these experiments, that though pure dephlogisticated air might be very useful as a *medicine*, it might not be so proper for us in the usual healthy state of the body: for as a candle burns out much faster in dephlogisticated than in common air, so we might, as may be said, *live out too fast*, and the animal powers be too soon exhausted in this pure kind of air. A moralist, at least, may say that the air which nature has provided for us is as good as we deserve.

"My reader will not wonder that, after having ascertained the superior goodness of dephlogisticated air by mice living in it, and the other tests above mentioned, I should have the curiosity to taste it myself. I have gratified that curiosity by breathing it, drawing it through a glass siphon, and, by this means, I reduced a large jar full of it to the standard of common air. The feeling of it to my lungs was not sensibly different from that of common air; but I fancied that my breath felt peculiarly light and easy for some time afterward. Who can tell but that, in time, this pure air may become a fashionable article of luxury? Hitherto only two mice and myself have had the privilege of breathing it."*

The terms phlogistic and dephlogisticated used in the foregoing quotation refer to the Phlogiston Theory of combustion which was commonly accepted during the eighteenth century. According to this theory, any material capable of burning contained an element or substance called phlogiston. Phlogiston was supposed to be driven off during a combustion; the remaining ash was therefore "dephlogisticated." In the above, the dephlogisticated air had not yet been burned. ▶

Antoine Lavoisier, a French scientist and statesman, duplicated Priestley's experiments, then continued with others. He established the fact that Priestley's "new air" constituted approximately one-fifth of the atmosphere. He conceived the idea that combustion is usually a combination of a fuel with this portion of the air, and is credited with naming the gas oxygen, from the Greek meaning "acid former." Lavoisier erroneously believed that all acids contained oxygen.

8–3 PREPARATION OF OXYGEN

In the laboratory, oxygen may be made in a variety of ways. A common method for very small amounts is the one used by Priestley, the heating of mercuric oxide. In a modern laboratory we heat with a gas burner rather than a sun glass (a magnifying glass), but the results are the same. See Fig. 8–1.

---

* F. J. Moore, *A History of Chemistry.* McGraw-Hill Book Company, Inc. 1918.

For the preparation of larger quantities of oxygen, the most common laboratory method involves the heating of potassium chlorate, $KClO_3$, which gives up all its oxygen according to the equation:

$$KClO_3 \xrightarrow{\Delta} KCl + \tfrac{3}{2}O_2 \quad \text{or} \quad 2KClO_3 \xrightarrow{\Delta} 2KCl + 3O_2 \tag{8-2}$$

This reaction requires a relatively high temperature, but in the presence of manganese dioxide, MnO_2, the rate of reaction is greatly increased, even at much lower temperatures. The MnO_2 may be recovered unchanged when the reaction is complete. Substances which act in this manner are called **catalysts.** A satisfactory definition of a catalyst would be *a substance which alters the rate of a chemical reaction without being consumed in that reaction.* The presence of a catalyst during a chemical reaction is indicated by placing it over the arrow of the equation rather than on either side.

$$KClO_3 \xrightarrow[\text{catalyst}]{MnO_2} KCl + \tfrac{3}{2}O_2 \tag{8-3}$$

Not only are catalysts commonly used in industry, they are responsible for many of the chemical reactions taking place in living plants and animals. The laboratory instructor might be called a catalyst since his presence usually results in more work, and it is hoped that he will not be much changed at the end of the period. Substances which decrease the rate of chemical reactions are called *inhibitors.*

For demonstrations, oxygen is often prepared by the *electrolysis of water*, using an apparatus, Fig. 8–2, filled with water containing a little sulfuric acid. A direct current of electricity, such as that produced by a battery, is passed through the solution. Oxygen is liberated at the positive electrode, the **anode** (where electrons leave the solution), and hydrogen at the negative electrode, the **cathode** (where electrons enter the solution). The sulfuric acid is added to increase the electrical conductivity of the water.

$$2H_2O \xrightarrow[\text{current}]{\text{direct}} 2H_2 + O_2 \tag{8-4}$$

or

$$H_2O \xrightarrow[\text{current}]{\text{direct}} H_2 + \tfrac{1}{2}O_2$$

This method produces very pure oxygen, but is too expensive to be practical on a commercial scale.

Industrially, nearly all oxygen is obtained from the atmosphere. Air is liquified and cooled to about −200°C, using principles essentially the same, but in a higher degree of sophistication, as those used in a household refrigerator. When the liquid air is warmed to −196°C, the point at which nitrogen boils at atmospheric pressure, the temperature will remain almost constant until nearly all the nitrogen has been removed. Further warming, to −183°C, will ensure that the remaining liquid is almost pure oxygen (see Fig. 8–3). For permanent storage, the oxygen may be vaporized and pumped under pressure into steel cylinders. Alternatively, the liquid oxygen may be transferred to great Dewar flasks (essentially, large Thermos bottles) for brief storage or transportation to industrial users.

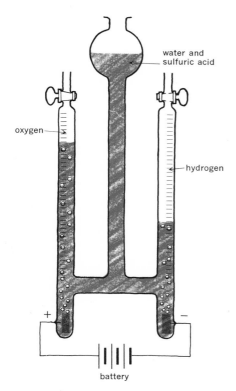

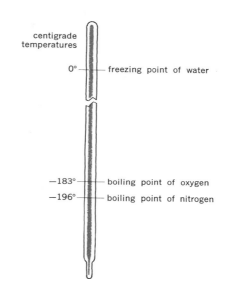

FIG. 8-2. Apparatus for the electrolysis of water.

FIG. 8-3. Separation of liquid nitrogen from liquid oxygen by difference in boiling points.

8-4 PROPERTIES OF OXYGEN

Physical Properties. Oxygen is a colorless, odorless, and tasteless gas which boils at $-183°C$ and freezes at $-216°C$. It occurs in the atmosphere in the diatomic form O_2. At room temperature and atmospheric pressure, oxygen dissolves in water to the extent of 3 ml/100 ml of water. As the temperature increases, the solubility of the oxygen decreases until, at temperatures near the boiling point of water, the solubility approaches zero. Conversely, if the water becomes colder, oxygen becomes more soluble. This greater solubility accounts in part for the greater activity of fish in cold water, and the decreasing solubility in warmer water causes sluggishness or even death of fish.

Chemical Properties. Only fluorine has greater combining ability than oxygen. In fact, oxygen forms compounds with nearly all the elements. The combination of oxygen with other elements or compounds is a form of oxidation. From its position on the periodic table we expect oxygen to be electronegative and to gain two electrons in most reactions. Compounds formed by the union of oxygen with other elements are called oxides. Typical reactions of nonmetals with oxygen are:

$$C + O_2 \rightarrow CO_2 \tag{8-5}$$

$$S + O_2 \rightarrow SO_2 \tag{8-6}$$

$$4P + 5O_2 \rightarrow 2P_2O_5* \tag{8-7}$$

$$2H_2 + O_2 \rightarrow 2H_2O \tag{8-8}$$

If we add water to the oxides of carbon, sulfur, or phosphorus and then test the solution with litmus paper, we find that blue litmus paper turns pink. Substances which turn blue litmus paper pink are called *acids* (Section 12–4). Since the addition of water to the oxide of a nonmetal forms an acid, we call these nonmetallic oxides **acid anhydrides** (*anhydro* means "without water"). Equations for the reactions of such oxides with water are:

$$H_2O + CO_2 \rightarrow \quad H_2CO_3 \tag{8-9}$$
carbonic acid

$$H_2O + SO_2 \rightarrow \quad H_2SO_3 \tag{8-10}$$
sulfurous acid

$$3H_2O + P_2O_5 \rightarrow \quad 2H_3PO_4 \tag{8-11}$$
phosphoric acid

Water, the most prevalent oxide on earth, will be studied in a separate chapter.

Oxygen also reacts with many metals to form oxides:

$$2Ca + O_2 \rightarrow 2CaO \tag{8-12}$$

$$2Mg + O_2 \rightarrow 2MgO \tag{8-13}$$

$$4Li + O_2 \rightarrow 2Li_2O \quad \text{or} \quad 2Li + \tfrac{1}{2}O_2 \rightarrow Li_2O \tag{8-14}$$

These oxides, when dissolved in water, turn litmus paper blue. Substances which turn litmus paper blue are called *bases*, and oxides of metals are therefore called basic oxides or **basic anhydrides.** Illustrations of such are

$$Li_2O + H_2O \rightarrow \quad 2LiOH \tag{8-15}$$
lithium hydroxide

$$CaO + H_2O \rightarrow \quad Ca(OH)_2 \tag{8-16}$$
calcium hydroxide

Many oxides of metals such as those of iron, aluminum, and zinc are quite insoluble in water and have little tendency to form bases with water. They do, however, have basic properties to the extent that they react with acids, Section 12–5. In general, oxides of non-metals are acidic oxides whereas those of metals are basic oxides.

The second most prevalent oxide, silicon dioxide, SiO_2, is the major constituent of sand and an important part of all granite-type rocks. This nonmetallic oxide is very insoluble,

---

* Phosphorus in reality occurs as P_4, but it seems unnecessary for our purpose to insist on such usage.

and under ordinary conditions will not react with water to form appreciable amounts of acid. A sand pile does not become acidic after a rainstorm!

8–5 COMBUSTION

A reaction in which energy is released so rapidly that flames and light are produced is called **combustion,** and a material which will burn is said to be *combustible*. Many reactions of substances with oxygen are combustions. In the presence of a spark or a flame, oxygen of the air reacts with methane, the main constituent of natural gas,

$$CH_4 + 2O_2 \rightarrow CO_2 + 2H_2O \tag{8-17}$$

or with octane, a typical constituent of gasoline,

$$C_8H_{18} + 12\tfrac{1}{2}O_2 \rightarrow 8CO_2 + 9H_2O* \tag{8-18}$$

The gasoline engine is often referred to as an internal combustion engine.

The combination of oxygen with most other substances liberates energy, usually in the form of heat. Heat brings about an increase in the rates of chemical reactions. If the heat produced by a chemical reaction is not dissipated the temperature may become so high a combustion occurs. This phenomenon is termed **spontaneous combustion,** and the temperature at which the substance bursts into flame is called its **kindling temperature.** In the laboratory white phosphorus is the material which most readily exhibits spontaneous combustion for it combines with the oxygen of the air and has a very low kindling temperature. Consequently, white phosphorus is stored under water; if exposed to the air at room temperature it bursts into flame.

8–6 EXPLOSIONS

Explosions and fires attributed to spontaneous combustion do much damage and cause considerable loss of life annually. When combustible substances such as coal, flour, starch, and wood dust are finely divided into dustlike particles, their surface areas are enormously increased. Oxidation can take place only on the surface of solids; therefore, the rate of oxidation increases with a decrease in particle size. Many coal mine explosions and fires in grain elevators, flour mills, and woodworking factories are caused by the explosion of small particles of coal, flour, or wood dust. Any substance which can be burned will form an explosive mixture when finely divided and suspended in oxygen or air. Many of these explosions are set off by electric sparks; others may be due to spontaneous combustion.

Many fires are touched off by explosions which result from the very rapid oxidation of flammable gases or dustlike combustible particles. A faulty gas jet or a cracked pipe may permit sufficient gas to escape into a room to form an explosive mixture which can be ignited by a lighted match or the spark of the ordinary light switch.

---

* In the automobile engine there is insufficient oxygen to convert all the carbon to CO_2; consequently some of the extremely dangerous carbon monoxide, CO, results.

◄ The following examples of actual catastrophies serve to illustrate the dangers of gaseous explosions. A mechanical ditch digger working along a street in San Jose, California, struck a gas line connecting a house to the main line. The connection at the house was damaged and a leak resulted. That evening when the occupants of the home turned on the lights, the spark produced by the electric switch set off an explosion that shattered the house, killing the occupants. Some years ago in New London, Texas, a gas leak under a school building caused an explosion that killed 413 children and 14 teachers. ►

In a laboratory, explosions may result from heating substances which are unstable at higher temperatures, or by heating or grinding combustible substances which are mixed with oxidizing agents such as $KClO_3$. This type of explosion is particularly violent since solids are converted into gases at high temperatures, causing a sudden and tremendous increase in volume.

8-7 FIRE EXTINGUISHERS

Each year extensive damage and loss of life result from fires in homes, automobiles, aircraft, and forests. The methods of controlling these fires are as varied as the conditions under which they exist. Since the fighting of major fires is usually handled by professional fire fighters, the discussion here will be limited to the prevention and control of minor fires.

In Section 8-5 we found that combustible substances must reach their kindling temperatures before they will burn; therefore, if the temperature of a burning substance is lowered below this temperature, the burning stops. The primary purpose of throwing water on a fire is to lower the temperature of the burning material below its kindling temperature.

Since oxygen is necessary for the continuance of all ordinary fires, another method of fire control is to exclude air and thus smother the fire. This may be done in various ways. For small fires, a coat, blanket, or small rug thrown over or around the fire tends to exclude air and subdue the flames. The most commonly used modern fire extinguishers contain liquid carbon dioxide which is under a pressure of many hundreds of pounds/square inch (psi). Releasing it produces a blast of cold CO_2 which cools the burning substance and at the same time excludes the air. This type of extinguisher is particularly safe for use in extinguishing electrical fires since there is less danger of the operator's being electrocuted than if H_2O is used; carbon dioxide will not conduct electricity as will water or the solutions found in some types of extinguishers. While carbon dioxide in concentrations up to several percent is not harmful, higher concentrations cause suffocation; persons should leave rooms after extensive use of extinguishers and should not return until the room has been adequately ventilated. Carbon dioxide extinguishers have another advantage in that no damage to materials is caused by its presence. Often considerable damage to homes and businesses results from the water and chemicals used in extinguishing fires.

Finally, if clothing catches fire, lying down offers the best chance of survival. In an upright position, flames from the clothing will envelop the head, a vulnerable portion of the body, whereas in the prone position the flames are away from the head. If no material is available to throw over the victim, continuous rolling will smother the flames and cause a cooling which may eventually extinguish the fire.

8–8 OXYGEN AND LIFE

At the beginning of this chapter the continuous need of the body for oxygen was mentioned. The average active adult inhales at least 10,000 liters of air/day (more than half the volume of a large gasoline transport truck). From this amount of air some 500 liters of oxygen will be removed and more than 400 liters of carbon dioxide, produced by various body reactions, will be exhaled. While this may appear to be quite a task, we unconsciously accomplish it day after day throughout our lives. In serious illnesses such as pneumonia, when the lungs are incapacitated, the process of breathing may become laborious. Under these circumstances a patient may be placed in an oxygen tent where the percentage of oxygen will be increased from the normal 21% to 40–60%, considerably reducing the energy required in his breathing. Higher concentrations of oxygen, when inhaled over a period of time, produce undesirable effects. Smoking or any type of open flame is not permitted in a room where an oxygen tent is in operation because of the greatly increased rate at which fires burn in oxygen-enriched atmospheres.

When breathing becomes extremely difficult, helium rather than nitrogen can be used to dilute the oxygen. Helium, which is much lighter than nitrogen, diffuses through small openings of the lungs at almost twice the rate that nitrogen does, Section 16–6. This easy passage in and out of the lungs further decreases the effort of breathing.

The atmosphere diminishes in density with increases in altitude at such a rate that at approximately 17,500 ft its density is only one-half that at sea level. Above this altitude the oxygen concentration is so low that breathing becomes difficult and supplementary oxygen must be used unless a person has become acclimated to the higher elevation. Mountain climbers use base camps at high elevations for this purpose. A lack of oxygen is called **anoxia** and is present in many forms of asphyxiation. Unfortunately, the body has no satisfactory warning system to alert us to an impending state of anoxia. The gasping for breath after strenuous exercise is brought about by an oversupply of carbon dioxide produced by the increased demand for energy and not by any deficiency of oxygen in the bloodstream. In fact, pressure chamber experiments show that a person loses consciousness from lack of oxygen without experiencing any discomfort. In the early days, passengers and crewmen of aircraft wore oxygen masks on high altitude flights. While the pressurized cabins of modern aircraft have eliminated this necessity, the law requires that oxygen equipment, including masks, must be available in the event of an emergency.

Deep Sea Diving

The combination of oxygen and helium as a breathing mixture is used to advantage in deep sea diving. As the diver descends, the water pressure increases approximately 15 psi for every 34 ft. At slightly more than 200 ft the pressure of the water is 100 psi. Breathing at this pressure causes no inconvenience, and the diver is comfortable as long as he remains under pressure. The solubility of gases in liquids is increased by pressure; therefore, more oxygen and nitrogen will be dissolved in the bloodstream when the pressure is great. If the diver surfaces quickly, the nitrogen becomes less soluble, forming bubbles in the bloodstream in much the same manner that carbon dioxide bubbles form when the cap is removed from a bottle of carbonated beverage. Within the bloodstream small bubbles of nitrogen collect to form larger bubbles that may block the flow of blood to a portion of the body. This malady, known as the "bends," is very painful and sometimes fatal. If the diver is brought up very slowly, he is decompressed slowly and suffers no ill effects. This is a monotonous procedure since an ascent from 200 or more feet would require many hours. In an emergency situation requiring rapid ascent, there are two alternatives. One is to bring the diver up quickly and put him into a decompression chamber immediately. The second choice is to start forcing a mixture of oxygen and helium through the air lines a few minutes before the ascent. Helium is practically insoluble in the blood plasma, and in the absence of atmospheric nitrogen, the nitrogen in the blood is rapidly eliminated. The diver may then be brought quickly to the surface with no ill effects.

◄ In the fall of 1965 the astronaut Scott Carpenter and his associates spent thirty days in the Sealab more than 200 ft below the surface of the ocean off the coast of La Jolla, California. The atmospheric pressure in the Sealab was roughly seven times that at the surface. The artificial atmosphere in the Sealab consisted primarily of oxygen and helium. This was a precaution taken in the event that an emergency surfacing became necessary. An unusual effect of the presence of helium was the odd sound of the voices of persons in the Sealab, caused by the decreased density of the atmosphere inside the Sealab. ►

8–9 INDUSTRIAL USES OF OXYGEN

In addition to the ever-increasing demand for oxygen in hospitals and in the aircraft industry, there are many other important uses. Large quantities are used in oxyacetylene torches for cutting and welding steel. Almost every garage and machine shop in the country uses oxygen for such purposes. In machine shops where large quantities of oxygen are used it has been found that liquid oxygen is the more economical. For such purposes the liquid oxygen is stored in specially designed Thermos bottle type containers.

Relatively pure oxygen (95–99.5%) is being used in ever increasing amounts in the manufacturing of iron and steel. With the use of nearly pure oxygen, comparable equipment can produce iron and steel several times faster than conventional processes which use air (Section 19–6).

During the past decade another field has opened for the use of oxygen. The rocket program uses such large amounts of liquid oxygen that many great industrial plants for producing it are located on or near the rocket bases. Thus we have an ever ready source with minimum delivery costs. The only material other than electricity needed for such a plant is air which is, of course, available at all locations.

8–10 OZONE

It has been previously stated that certain of the nonmetals exist in the elementary state as diatomic molecules. Oxygen may also exist as the triatomic molecule O_3, called **ozone.** Ozone occurs naturally in traces in the atmosphere, being produced at high altitudes by the ultraviolet rays of the sun. It can be prepared by passing ordinary oxygen gas through an electrical discharge, as follows:

3O₂ + energy → 2O₃   (8–19)

The reaction is reversible, i.e., certain conditions cause the reaction to proceed from left to right. Since energy is required to convert oxygen into ozone, reactions involving ozone liberate more energy than comparable reactions with oxygen. The reaction,

3C + 2O₃ → 3CO₂   (8–20)

liberates almost 25% more energy than

3C + 3O₂ → 3CO₂   (8–21)

even though in each reaction the same amount of carbon is oxidized to carbon dioxide. Industrially, ozone is sometimes used to advantage in place of oxygen in the preparation of chemicals.

Oxygen and ozone are termed **allotropic** forms of the element. This phenomenon is not limited to the element oxygen; allotropes of carbon and phosphorus will be discussed in Chapter 18.

IMPORTANT TERMS

Acid anhydrides	*Basic anhydrides*	*Kindling temperature*
Allotropic form	*Catalyst*	*Ozone*
Anode	*Cathode*	*Spontaneous combustion*
Anoxia	*Combustion*	

WORK EXERCISES

1. Write the equation involved in the electrolysis of water.
2. Write chemical equations for the reaction between (a) oxygen and three different non-metals, and (b) oxygen and four metals from Groups IA or IIA.
3. Write chemical equations for the reactions between each of the above oxides and water.
4. What two types of compounds are produced by the reactions in Question 3?
5. Define: combustion, combustible, spontaneous combustion, and kindling temperature.
6. Why do finely divided combustible materials burn more rapidly than larger particles of the same material?
7. Name three methods of controlling fires.
8. Distinguish between oxygen and ozone.
9. Is ozone an isotope of oxygen?
10. What term is employed to distinguish ozone from oxygen?

11. Why are carbon-dioxide filled fire extinguishers preferred to water and water solutions for some types of fire?

12. Would there be advantages or disadvantages in an atmosphere containing 50% or more oxygen?

13. Why is the danger less that deep-sea divers will have the "bends" if they breathe a helium-oxygen mixture instead of ordinary air which contains primarily oxygen and nitrogen?

14. Would you predict that Indians living at high elevations (17,000 ft) in the Andes mountains would have relatively smaller or larger lungs than people who live near sea level? Why?

15. List several uses for oxygen.

16. Make a drawing of an apparatus which could be used for the electrolysis of water, and label where necessary.

SUGGESTED READING

Asimov, I., *Asimov's Biographical Encyclopedia of Science and Technology*, Doubleday, New York, 1964. A good source of information on the discovery of many of the elements.

Day, F. H., *The Chemical Elements in Nature*, "Oxygen," pp. 114–124, Reinhold, New York, 1963.

Partington, J. R., "The Discovery of Oxygen," *Journal of Chemical Education* **39,** 123 (1962). This article relates the work of Priestley and Scheele.

Sittig, M., "Oxygen, Chemical Raw Material," *Chemical Engineering News*, Nov. 27, 1961, p. 92. A chronology of oxygen and its uses, an interesting and comprehensive review of the industries that prepare and use it.

Weeks, Mary E., *Discovery of the Elements*, 6th ed., Chapter 7, "Three Important Gases," Journal of Chemical Education Publishing Co., Easton, Pa., 1956.

Chapter 9 HYDROGEN

9-1 THE DISCOVERY OF HYDROGEN

The gas we know as hydrogen was given its name by the great French chemist Lavoisier. He derived the name from Greek terms meaning water-former, because his experiments showed that water was formed when hydrogen burned in air. Hydrogen had been known as "inflammable air" for at least 200 years before Lavoisier gave it its current name. In 1670 Robert Boyle knew that the gas could be produced by adding iron to acids. Much later, the English scientist Henry Cavendish collected the gas and studied it systematically. In 1766 he read a paper before the Royal Society reporting on his experiments. Cavendish is generally credited with the discovery of hydrogen, which he called "inflammable air." As with so many scientific discoveries, the man finally credited with the discovery based his work on that of many, many other investigators.

9-2 OCCURRENCE

In many ways hydrogen is unique among the elements. Throughout the universe it is by far the most abundant element. Scientists believe that approximately 90% of the mass of the universe is hydrogen. The great mass of the sun is chiefly hydrogen which is undergoing a nuclear reaction (Section 20-6) to become helium. Tremendous amounts of energy are released in this conversion. Only a small percentage of this energy reaches the earth, but even this is sufficient to provide the heat and light necessary for life on earth.

The most prevalent material of the universe is also the simplest in atomic structure. The hydrogen molecule is composed of two hydrogen atoms, each of which contains one proton and one electron. Hydrogen combines with most of the elements to form compounds, and it is believed by some to exist in more chemical compounds than any other element. Hydrogen is the lightest known substance, being only 1/16 as dense as oxygen, and 1/14 as dense as air. It is interesting that element No. 1 should be first in so many different respects.

Hydrogen is widely distributed on earth, almost entirely in the form of compounds. The greater portion of hydrogen on the surface of the earth occurs in water, since it constitutes about 11% by weight of this substance. In petroleum compounds it is combined with carbon: e.g., methane CH_4, butane C_4H_{10}, and octane C_8H_{18}. Hydrogen is also present in compounds in all plant and animal tissues. The rocks of the earth's surface contain small amounts of combined hydrogen, present as water in the form of hydrated minerals such as gypsum, $CaSO_4 \cdot 2H_2O$. Large amounts of free hydrogen are found in volcanic gases, and small amounts are found in natural gas. Two factors account for the almost complete absence of free hydrogen in the atmosphere. One, it reacts with the oxygen in the air forming water, and two, the gravitational attraction of the earth is insufficient to hold the small, fast-traveling hydrogen molecules. Hydrogen molecules that reach "escape velocities" are continually being lost to outer space.

9–3 PHYSICAL PROPERTIES

As previously stated, hydrogen is an extremely light substance. At standard conditions,* 1 liter weighs 0.0897 g. If we wish to transfer hydrogen gas from one container to another, we use the method of upward displacement, letting it rise into a container, rather than the usual method of pouring (see Fig. 9–1). Because of its low density, for many years hydrogen was used to fill airships and observation balloons as well as the small rubber balloons sold at carnivals. But hydrogen is flammable, and disasters accompanied its use for such purposes.

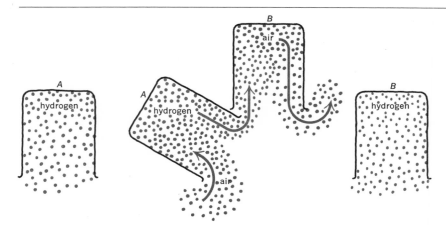

FIG. 9–1. Pouring hydrogen upward.

* See Section 16–5 for a definition of standard conditions.

◄ Beginning in the 1920's, the large scale production of helium in the United States made possible its substitution for hydrogen in our lighter-than-air craft. The American Navy built several enormous dirigibles for experimental purposes, and Germany built such craft for the purpose of transporting passengers across oceans. The German airship Hindenburg was the largest to be built and was completed in 1936. It was 803 ft long, weighed 220 tons, and carried 100 persons at an airspeed of 78 mph. It was powered by 4 diesel engines and provided the fastest and most luxurious manner of transocean travel. Unfortunately, Germany had no source of helium so the airship was necessarily inflated with hydrogen. On May 3, 1937, after 10 successful round trip crossings from Germany, it caught fire as it approached the mooring mast at Lakehurst, New Jersey. Of the 97 persons aboard, 36 died and many more were severely burned.

In the meantime the United States had also been experiencing difficulty with airships, due to a lack of maneuverability and stability. Several had crashed with extensive loss of life. The Hindenburg disaster brought to a close the era of large airships. ►

Hydrogen is colorless, odorless, and is only slightly soluble in water. At room temperature and sea level pressure, the solubility is about 2 ml/100 ml of water. The boiling point of liquid hydrogen at standard atmospheric pressure is −252.7°C, or 20.3°K.

9–4 ISOTOPES OF HYDROGEN

The isotopes of an element are usually described by naming the element and giving the weight of each isotope, for example, ^{35}Cl, Section 4–8. They do not normally have individual names with corresponding individual symbols. However, the isotopes of the other elements have masses which are in the same order of magnitude (for example, ^{35}Cl and ^{37}Cl), whereas the mass numbers for the isotopes of hydrogen are in the order of 1, 2, and 3, respectively. These differences are sufficient to appreciably alter the properties of the isotopes. Therefore, the three isotopes of hydrogen have been given separate names and symbols: hydrogen (occasionally called **protium**), H; **deuterium,** D; and **tritium,** T. The numerical ratio of occurrence of protium to deuterium is in the order of 6400 to 1. It is believed that tritium is produced in small amounts at high altitudes, but decomposes so rapidly that it occurs on the earth only in extremely small amounts. Tritium is produced in thermonuclear reactions, Section 20–9.

A variety of kinds of water molecules are possible. Using symbols of the isotopes, we have H_2O, HDO, D_2O, HTO, T_2O, and DTO. Considering that there are also three isotopes of oxygen, 18 different water molecules are possible. *Heavy water*, containing D_2O and HDO molecules, is obtained by separating the lighter H_2O molecules from the heavier particles by electrolytic processes. When natural water is decomposed by electrolysis, molecules containing ordinary hydrogen react more readily than those containing deuterium. As electrolysis of a quantity of water approaches completion, the remaining water contains most of the deuterium which was originally present, so that the percentage of deuterium is much higher than in ordinary water. In this manner nearly pure deuterium oxide can be obtained. The density, boiling point, and freezing point are slightly higher than the corresponding values for H_2O. Heavy water in high concentration is toxic; in low concentration, however, no ill effects have been observed. The use of compounds containing heavy hydrogen (deuterium or tritium) has made it possible to trace the path of these labelled molecules in both chemical and biochemical reactions. This technique has been especially useful in studying the fate of foods in the animal body.

9–5 CHEMICAL PROPERTIES

We discovered in Chapter 5 that the structure of an atom determines its properties and that sensible patterns occur in the periodic table. Hydrogen is usually placed at the top of Group IA of the periodic table, and also commonly placed at the top of Group VIIA. If we consider the characteristics of hydrogen, we find that it is like sodium, potassium, and other Group IA elements, each of which may lose 1 electron and become a positively charged ion with a valence of 1+. It readily combines with the electronegative elements on the right-hand side of the periodic table as do other Group IA elements. However, as a gas, its physical characteristics have little resemblance to IA elements and a greater resemblance to VIIA elements. Furthermore, hydrogen commonly combines with active metals such as sodium and calcium, forming metallic **hydrides:**

	NaH	CaH$_2$
	sodium hydride	calcium hydride

In such compounds the hydrogen gains an electron to complete its orbit and becomes negatively charged as do other Group VIIA elements. The resultant ion, H$^-$, is called a hydride ion.

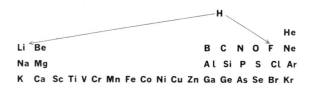

FIG. 9–2. Proposed location of hydrogen in a periodic table.

Thus, hydrogen can react either by losing an electron or by gaining one. Since the valence shell of hydrogen is half filled, it might be almost as logical to assign hydrogen a new position in the periodic table above carbon, or between and above boron and carbon. Lines connecting hydrogen to Groups IA and VIIA would indicate that it has properties relating it to both of these groups, Fig. 9–2. This position approximately halfway across the table would also be consistent with the electronegativity of hydrogen; from Table 6–2, it will be seen that hydrogen with a value of 2.1 is between boron with 2.0 and carbon with 2.5. Thus, it is logical that hydrogen forms both ionic and covalent bonds. The bonds are ionic in the hydrides of active metals (as H$^-$) and in some acids (as H$^+$). Other compounds of hydrogen exhibit covalence, typically:

```
    H              H                            H
    ··             ··             ··            
  : N : H        H : C : H      H : Br :      H : O :
    ··             ··             ··            ··
    H              H
```

Hydrogen and oxygen react very slowly at room temperature, but with an increase in temperature or in the presence of a proper catalyst they combine explosively:

$$H_2 + \tfrac{1}{2}O_2 \xrightarrow[\text{catalyst}]{\text{heat}} H_2O + \text{energy} \tag{9-1}$$

In the laboratory great care must be exercised in preventing the ignition of hydrogen-air mixtures. The oxyhydrogen torch takes advantage of the great amount of heat liberated in the above reaction. Hydrogen reacts with oxides of many metals, removing the oxygen but leaving the pure metal. In Section 6–7 we stated that the removing of oxygen from a substance (decreasing positive valence) is called reduction. If hydrogen is passed over heated copper oxide it removes the oxygen, producing pure copper and water.

$$CuO + H_2 \xrightarrow{\Delta} Cu + H_2O \tag{9-2}$$

Hydrogen is commonly used as a reducing agent in the recovery of metals such as tungsten, for which other reducing agents are not so adaptable.

9–6 PREPARATION OF HYDROGEN

The most common method of preparing hydrogen in the laboratory is by the reaction of an acid on one of the moderately active metals such as zinc or iron:

$$H_2SO_4 + Fe \rightarrow FeSO_4 + H_2 \tag{9-3}$$
$$2HCl + Zn \rightarrow ZnCl_2 + H_2 \tag{9-4}$$

Commercial preparation depends upon two processes:

a)   The "water gas" method utilizes steam which is passed over white-hot carbon,

$$H_2O + C \xrightarrow{\Delta} H_2 + CO \tag{9-5}$$

Carbon monoxide and hydrogen both burn readily in air, so this method has been used extensively for the manufacture of a gaseous fuel. If carbon monoxide and water are heated to 500°C in the presence of a catalyst, hydrogen and carbon dioxide result:

$$H_2O + CO \xrightarrow[\Delta]{\text{catalyst}} H_2 + CO_2 \tag{9-6}$$

If we combine reactions (9–5) and (9–6) the complete reaction would be:

$$2H_2O + C \rightarrow CO_2 + 2H_2 \tag{9-7}$$

The carbon dioxide can easily be removed, leaving pure hydrogen.

b)   The greatest amount of hydrogen produced in the United States is obtained by heating (cracking) hydrocarbons (Section 23–2).

$$CH_4 \xrightarrow[\Delta]{\text{catalyst}} C + 2H_2 \tag{9-8}$$

and

$$CH_4 + 2H_2O \xrightarrow[\Delta]{\text{catalyst}} CO_2 + 4H_2 \tag{9-9}$$

Smaller amounts are produced by the electrolysis of water and as a by-product from electrolytic industries. Production of hydrogen in the United States was approximately 120 billion cu ft in 1965. Such a volume would fill a container 1 mi square and 4000 ft high.

9–7 USES OF HYDROGEN

Of the enormous quantity of hydrogen produced in the United States annually, by far the greater portion is used in producing ammonia synthetically. Ammonia, in turn, is used primarily as an agricultural fertilizer:

$$N_2 + 3H_2 \xrightarrow[\substack{\text{heat and} \\ \text{pressure}}]{\text{catalyst}} 2NH_3 \tag{9-10}$$

Another important use of hydrogen is in the food industries. Large quantities of vegetable oils—cottonseed, soybean, etc.,—are hydrogenated and thereby changed from liquids to solids (Section 27–4). The hydrogenated products have superior keeping qualities. Hydrogen is also used in the manufacture of hydrogen chloride.

$$H_2 + Cl_2 \rightarrow 2HCl \tag{9-11}$$

9–8 THE ACTIVITY SERIES OF THE METALS

We noted in Section 7–6(3) that active metals like potassium, sodium, and calcium react readily with water at room temperature, forming hydrogen gas and the corresponding hydroxides. We also know that some metals such as gold and platinum not only do not react with water but are very inactive with many other substances. In the form of nuggets in which they may be found or in jewelry, they remain untarnished even after years of exposure. All metals can be arranged in an order of decreasing activity, called an activity or displacement series. Table 9–1 is a portion of such a list and includes several common metals. This table is sufficient for understanding the principles involved. Potassium, the most active metal, is at the top; gold, the least active metal, is at the bottom. The activity of the metals reflects their tendency to lose electrons, thereby becoming positively charged. Potassium metal readily loses electrons whereas gold holds electrons tenaciously. *Any metal is able to displace from solution the ions of any metal below it in the series.* Since zinc is above copper, we know that if zinc metal is placed in a solution of copper ions, the copper will be displaced as metal.

$$Zn + Cu^{2+} + SO_4^{2-} \rightarrow Zn^{2+} + SO_4^{2-} + Cu \downarrow \tag{9-12}$$

If copper metal is placed in a solution of silver nitrate, the silver ions will be displaced.

$$Cu + 2Ag^+ + 2NO_3^- \rightarrow Cu^{2+} + 2NO_3^- + 2Ag \downarrow \tag{9-13}$$

In the above equations the sulfate and nitrate ions are sometimes called **spectator** ions, since they are not changed in the course of the reaction. The equation is just as meaningful

TABLE 9–1. Activity series of metals

K
Ca   } react readily with cold water
Na   } $Na + HOH \rightarrow NaOH + \frac{1}{2}H_2 \uparrow$

Mg
Al
Zn
Cr   heated metals react with steam   react with acids
Fe $Mg + H_2O \rightarrow MgO + H_2 \uparrow$ $Zn + H_2SO_4 \rightarrow ZnSO_4 + H_2 \uparrow$
Cd
Co
Ni

Sn   react very slowly with acids
Pb   — — — — — — — — — — — —
H

Cu
Hg
Ag   } will not liberate hydrogens from acids
Pt
Au

if we omit them, as follows:

$$Zn + Cu^{2+} \rightarrow Zn^{2+} + Cu \downarrow \tag{9-14}$$

and

$$Cu + 2Ag^+ \rightarrow Cu^{2+} + 2Ag \downarrow \tag{9-15}$$

In the recovery of the more valuable metals from solutions, we take advantage of this principle by adding a less expensive metal such as iron which displaces the more valuable metal. For example, silver from the salts which are present in the solutions in which photographic films are processed can be removed by placing metallic iron in the solution.

$$Fe + 2Ag^+ \rightarrow Fe^{2+} + 2Ag \downarrow \tag{9-16}$$

The metals above hydrogen in the series can be used to displace hydrogen from an acid. Again this process results from a transfer of electrons. The metal gives off electrons to become an ion, while the H^+ accepts an electron to become a neutral H atom; as usual, 2 H atoms pair to become an H_2 molecule.

$$2HCl + Zn \rightarrow ZnCl_2 + H_2 \uparrow \tag{9-17}$$

$$H_2SO_4 + Fe \rightarrow FeSO_4 + H_2 \uparrow \tag{9-18}$$

Interpretation of Table 9–1 yields some important generalizations. The most active metals readily liberate hydrogen from cold water. The less active metals, magnesium through iron, when heated will react with steam forming oxides and liberating hydrogen. The reaction of magnesium with steam is violent.

$$H_2O \text{ (steam)} + Mg \xrightarrow{\Delta} MgO + H_2 \uparrow \tag{9-19}$$

For this reason water cannot be successfully used in controlling aircraft fires where magnesium alloys are present. The oxides of the less active metals, those below chromium, can be reduced by hydrogen.

An understanding of basic chemistry should not require memorization of the exact order of metals in the activity series, but the table should be studied carefully so that the relative activity of the more familiar metals can be recalled.

IMPORTANT TERMS

Deuterium	*Protium*	*Tritium*
Hydride	*Spectator ions*	

WORK EXERCISES

1. How do you account for the fact that there are such minute amounts of hydrogen in the atmosphere?

2. A liter of helium weighs almost twice as much as a liter of hydrogen. Does this fact indicate that hydrogen has twice the lifting power of helium?

3. State four uses of hydrogen.

4. Why should heavy water have a higher boiling point than ordinary water?

5. How would you defend each of the three suggested locations of hydrogen in the periodic table?

6. Determine the molecular weights of all the possible kinds of water in which ^{16}O is involved.

7. State four methods of preparing hydrogen.

8. If you did not have an activity series available, how would you go about locating an unknown metal in the series?

9. What is a spectator ion?

10. How many grams of zinc are needed to prepare 5 g of hydrogen according to Eq. (9-4)?

11. How many grams of H_2SO_4 are required to release 6 g of hydrogen according to Eq. (9-3)?

12. Why have the isotopes of hydrogen been assigned special names whereas isotopes of other elements have not?

13. Write all the possible formulas for water, using the isotopes of hydrogen combining with oxygen 16.

14. Complete and balance the following equations. If no reaction takes place, write *no reaction*.

    a) $Zn + HCl \rightarrow$

    b) $Ca + H_2SO_4 \rightarrow$

    c) $Ca + H_2O \rightarrow$

    d) $Zn + CuSO_4 \rightarrow$

    e) $Cu + FeCl_2 \rightarrow$

    f) $Cu + AgNO_3 \rightarrow$

    g) $Zn + Pb(NO_3)_2 \rightarrow$

    h) $CuSO_4 + Fe \rightarrow$

    i) $H_2O + C \xrightarrow{\triangle}$

    j) $Fe + AgNO_3 \rightarrow$

SUGGESTED READING

Day, F. H., *The Chemical Elements in Nature*, "Hydrogen," pp. 23, 95–106, Reinhold, New York, 1963.

Weeks, Mary E., *The Discovery of the Elements*, "Hydrogen," pp. 197–205, Journal of Chemical Education Publishing Co., Easton, Pa., 1956.

Chapter 10 WATER

10-1 OCCURRENCE

Water is such a common, well-known substance that it might seem unnecessary to discuss it in an introductory chemistry book. It is true we have all been aware of this interesting substance since earliest recollections—we have known its quenching of thirst, the irresistible urge to wade in puddles on the way home from school, the pleasures and dangers of water sports, and the devastation of floods and ocean storms. It is difficult to conceive of the great prevalence of water on the earth unless you have crossed a major ocean. If you have not had this experience, imagine yourself on any beach of the Pacific ocean and try to visualize that the water, to a depth of several miles, is almost uninterrupted for about twice the distance from New York to San Francisco.

Water also comprises a major portion of many of the things with which we are familiar. For example, consider the percentage of water in the following items found in a supermarket: potatoes, 78%; apples, 84%; cucumbers, 96%; watermelons, 92%; milk, 87%; round steak, 74%; fresh bread, 35%; and cheese, 40%. Even so-called dried foods often contain consider-able amounts of water. Two-thirds of our body weight is made up of water. Surprisingly enough, many of the rocks and minerals with which we are familiar also contain water com-bined chemically with other substances.

10-2 NATURAL WATER

Water is such a good solvent that in a natural state it is never pure. The term "pure" has various meanings; in the previous statement it should not be construed that natural waters always contain substances detrimental from the standpoint of ordinary uses. While rainwater is commonly considered to be pure, the gaseous constituents of the atmosphere are always present along with some solids, such as dust particles from the air. River and lake waters always contain some minerals which have been leached from the earth. The oceans and inland lakes without outlets, therefore, contain considerable amounts of these materials which have accumulated throughout the ages. Water which is satisfactory for human consumption may require chemical treatment for many commercial uses, and the reverse is also true.

◄ The concentrations of minerals in large bodies of water vary greatly. The Great Salt Lake in Utah contains in excess of 22% minerals, primarily sodium chloride. The oceans contain approximately 3.5% dissolved solids, again primarily sodium chloride. The large salt deposits which occur throughout the world resulted when inland lakes or seas evaporated during past geological ages. Some of these salt deposits are thousands of feet thick. The salt bed in Death Valley is more than 5000 ft deep. The chemical compositions of these deposits vary somewhat, depending upon the composition of the earth over which the waters, which deposited them, flowed. ►

10–3 PHYSICAL PROPERTIES

Since water is so prevalent, it has been used as a standard in establishing certain units of measurements. The unit of mass in the metric system—the kilogram—is the weight of 1 liter of water at 4°C. On the centigrade temperature scale, the freezing point and boiling point of water were conveniently placed at 0° and 100°, respectively. The unit of heat—the calorie—is approximately the amount of heat required to change 1 g of water 1° on the centigrade scale.

10–4 SPECIFIC HEAT

The **specific heat** or the heat capacity of any substance is the amount of heat in calories required to change the temperature of 1 g of a substance 1°C. The specific heat of water is 1.0, since it is used as the standard. Table 10–1 lists the approximate specific heat values of several common materials at or near 0°C.

TABLE 10–1. The specific heats of common materials

lead	0.0297	aluminum	0.208
mercury	0.033	ammonia	0.502
iron	0.107	ethyl alcohol	0.535
glass (flint)	0.117	water	1.000
granite	0.192		

◄ The high specific heat of water accounts for the moderate climates of many areas of the world. Perhaps the best known example of this is observed in the Hawaiian Islands where temperatures always approximate the little-changing temperature of the ocean about them. Temperatures of the coastal areas of the world are more moderate than those of the same land masses farther inland, due to the temperature of the bordering ocean. ►

10-5 HEAT OF VAPORIZATION

When a small beaker of water is placed over a lighted burner, the water soon reaches the boiling point. If heating is continued, considerable time is required to change the water to steam. This fact would imply that a larger amount of heat energy is required to convert water at the boiling point into steam. It has been found that 540 cal are required to convert 1 g of water at its boiling point of 100°C to steam at 100°C. *The amount of energy required to convert a quantity of liquid to a vapor at its boiling point is its* **heat of vaporization.** The heat of vaporization for water, then, is 540 cal/g. Water has the highest heat of vaporization of any known substance (see Table 10–2). It should be emphasized that the heat of vaporization is utilized to bring about a change in physical state, liquid to vapor, *without a change in temperature.*

TABLE 10–2. Heats of vaporization of some common substances (at their boiling points, cal/g)

chloroform	59	ethyl alcohol	204
mercury	71	ammonia	327
benzene	94	water	540

10-6 HEAT OF FUSION

When an ice cube melts in a glass of water, the temperature of the water is lowered more than it would be if ice water equal in weight to the cube were added to the glass of water. This fact indicates that energy is absorbed when ice melts. *The energy required to convert a solid to a liquid* (that is, to melt the solid) *is its* **heat of fusion.** As with the heat of vaporization, *no temperature change* is involved in the fusion process. The energy is that which is required to bring about a change of physical state. For water, this value is high compared to that of most other substances. As we can see from Table 10–3, the heat of fusion of water is 80 cal/g.

TABLE 10–3. Heats of fusion for various solids (cal/g)

lead	5.5	glycerol	47.5
ethyl alcohol	24.9	copper	49
benzene	30	water	80
paraffin	35	aluminum	94

If the same amount of heat that is required to melt an ice cube were absorbed instead by the same amount of water at 0°C, the temperature of the water would be raised to 80°C, which is close to the boiling point of water.

10-7 HYDROGEN BONDING IN WATER

The unusually high heats of vaporization and fusion for water, as compared to the other substances, Tables 10-2 and 10-3, require some explanation. In a water molecule, covalent bonds hold the two hydrogens to the oxygen. The angle between the two bonds is approximately 105°.

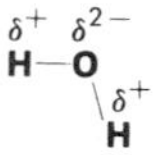

$$\overset{\delta^+}{H}-\overset{\delta^{2-}}{O}$$
$$\qquad\underset{H}{\diagdown}_{\delta^+}$$

Most important, each of the oxygen-hydrogen bonds is highly polar, as symbolized by the δ^+ and δ^- in the formula. Because oxygen is strongly electronegative, the electrons in the bonds are distorted toward it. As a result, the polar molecules attract each other; the negative end of one water molecule is attracted like a magnet to a positive end of another molecule:

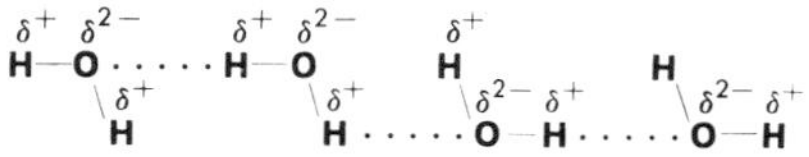

FIG. 10-1. Hydrogen bonding between water molecules.

This unusual linkage is called a hydrogen bond. It is customary to use dotted lines to represent hydrogen bonds, as shown in Fig. 10-1, so they will not be mistaken for covalent bonds.

This may be considered as a case of particularly strong attraction between polar molecules. In the covalent bonds between hydrogen and oxygen, the polarities are so intense that the effects on physical and chemical properties are great. Consequently, we often think of hydrogen bonds as a special kind of attraction.

For hydrogen bonding to occur, the hydrogen must be held between two highly electronegative atoms. It is linked by a polar covalent bond to one of them, and is attracted by the polarity of the other negative atom. (The second attraction is, of course, not a covalent bond because a hydrogen atom cannot hold four electrons in its outer shell.) Besides oxygen, other atoms with which hydrogen bonds can form are fluorine and nitrogen. As can be predicted from the electronegative series of the atoms, Table 6-1, the hydrogen bonds to fluorine are relatively strong, and those to nitrogen are quite weak.

Because of hydrogen bonding, water molecules in the solid or liquid form occur as clusters rather than as individual molecules. It is estimated that at room temperature 5 or 6 molecules make up the average cluster. To represent 4 molecules, as in Fig. 10-1, we might write a formula of $(H_2O)_4$. Since the number of molecules in the cluster is not definite, the formula for water is correctly written $(H_2O)_x$; in common usage, however, we tend to ignore this technicality and write H_2O. As the temperature of water increases, the molecules move more rapidly and the average size of the clusters decreases; it is therefore reasonable to suspect that the high specific heat of water is due to the energy required to break the hydrogen bonds holding water molecules together. Finally, for water in the form of steam, the value for x in most cases becomes 1, as there is little hydrogen bonding in the gaseous state. A large number of calories is required (the heat of vaporization) to change 1 g of water to steam, since it is necessary to break down the hydrogen bonds between the water molecules during this change of physical state.

10-8 EFFECT OF TEMPERATURE ON THE DENSITY OF WATER

Another peculiarity of water is the way its density changes with respect to temperature. Because of the decrease in speed or motion of molecules, the volumes of gases, liquids, or solids normally decrease with a decrease in temperature, thereby causing an increase in their densities. Furthermore, the change in state from liquid to solid also usually causes a shrinking of volume with a related increase in density.

Water conforms with the above generalization, decreasing in volume and increasing in density until it reaches 4°C. At this point, however, it begins to expand, causing a slight *decrease* in density. This abnormality is responsible for the fact that water at the bottom of an ice-covered lake is warmer than the water next to the ice (since water of 0°C is less dense than water at 4°C).

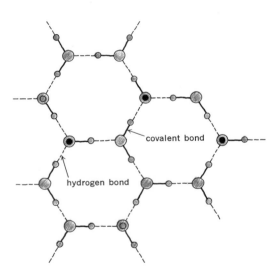

FIG. 10-2. Vertical view of arrangement of water molecules in an ice crystal: ⊙ represents a hydrogen atom above an oxygen atom; ◎ represents a hydrogen atom below an oxygen atom.

The change of water to ice at 0°C again reverses the usual trend by an almost spectacular increase in volume with a corresponding decrease in density. This change accounts for the floating of ice on water, and the bursting of water pipes and automobile radiators. The increased volume when water changes into ice results because the molecules of water arrange themselves in a pattern which is less compact in the ice crystal than their random arrangement in the liquid state. See Fig. 10-2.

An important consequence of the lower density of ice is that it forms on top of a pond or lake and provides an insulation from cold air temperatures; thus, the water under the ice usually does not freeze. If lakes froze solid every winter, it would greatly diminish the number of living things that presently survive a cold winter under the protective insulation of a blanket of ice.

10–9 CHEMICAL PROPERTIES

Compared with other substances commonly found in nature, water cannot be considered very active at room temperatures. At this temperature, it will react readily only with very active elements or compounds.

Water reacts with active metals to form hydroxides (bases) and hydrogen, as shown in Table 9–1,

$$2Na + 2HOH \rightarrow 2NaOH + H_2 \tag{10-1}$$

Water reacts with soluble oxides of metals to form hydroxides and with oxides of nonmetals to form acids (Section 8–4).

$$Na_2O + HOH \rightarrow 2NaOH \tag{10-2}$$

$$SO_2 + HOH \rightarrow H_2SO_3 \tag{10-3}$$

Water combines chemically in definite proportions with some salts to form substances called **hydrates.** Hydrates are commonly formed when certain salts are allowed to crystallize from water solutions. If copper sulfate ($CuSO_4$) is dissolved in water, and the water is allowed to evaporate, crystals of "blue vitriol" ($CuSO_4 \cdot 5H_2O$) will form. These crystals constitute a chemical compound containing approximately 36% water. The dot in the formula indicates a special sort of chemical bond which can be easily broken. When hydrated copper sulfate is heated, the hydrate decomposes:

$$CuSO_4 \cdot 5H_2O \xrightarrow{\Delta} CuSO_4 + 5H_2O \tag{10-4}$$

When hydrates lose their water of crystallization, they are said to become **anhydrous** (literally, without water). Hydrates are common in the home, the laboratory, and in nature. Typical examples are washing soda, $Na_2CO_3 \cdot 10H_2O$; epsom salts, $MgSO_4 \cdot 7H_2O$; and plaster of Paris, $(CaSO_4)_2 \cdot H_2O$.

Gypsum, $CaSO_4 \cdot 2H_2O$, occurs as a transparent crystalline hydrate, Fig. 10–3(a), which loses part of its water of crystallization on heating:

$$2CaSO_4 \cdot 2H_2O \xrightarrow{\Delta} (CaSO_4)_2 \cdot H_2O + 3H_2O \tag{10-5}$$

to form plaster of Paris, a white powder, Fig. 10–3(b). When water is added to the powder, the above process is reversed:

$$(CaSO_4)_2 \cdot H_2O + 3H_2O \rightarrow 2CaSO_4 \cdot 2H_2O \tag{10-6}$$

plaster of Paris   gypsum

(a)   (b)   (c)

FIG. 10–3. Hydrated forms of calcium sulfate: (a) is a naturally occurring transparent hydrated mineral, $CaSO_4 \cdot 2H_2O$ (gypsum). The gypsum when heated is changed to a white powder (b) with the formula, $(CaSO_4)_2 \cdot H_2O$. The powdered form is commonly called plaster of Paris. Plaster casts (c) are formed by adding the proper amount of water and molding into the desired form or shape.

and the product quickly sets to form a strong solid. Plaster of Paris is used in making casts such as the one shown on the victim of a skiing accident, Fig. 10–3(c).

In the laboratory, a survey of the labels of reagent bottles will reveal many hydrates, and frequently their corresponding anhydrous counterparts. A few of the hydrates which occur in nature are

gypsum	$CaSO_4 \cdot 2H_2O$	borax	$Na_2B_4O_7 \cdot 10H_2O$
opal	$SiO_2 \cdot xH_2O$	talc or soapstone	$3MgO \cdot 4SiO_2 \cdot H_2O$
clay	$Al_2O_3 \cdot 2SiO_2 \cdot 2H_2O$		

10–10 EFFLORESCENCE

Some hydrates readily lose their water of crystallization when exposed to dry air. The icy-appearing crystals of sodium carbonate, $Na_2CO_3 \cdot 10H_2O$, decompose at room temperature to an anhydrous white powder:

$$Na_2CO_3 \cdot 10H_2O \rightarrow Na_2CO_3 + 10H_2O \qquad (10\text{–}7)$$

Loss of water to the atmosphere is called **efflorescence** and the crystalline carbonate is said to be an *efflorescent* salt. It should be evident that efflorescence will take place more rapidly on a hot day in a desert where the air is very dry than it would on a humid or rainy day.

10–11 DELIQUESCENCE

If crystals of calcium chloride, $CaCl_2$, or sodium iodide, NaI, are exposed to the air on an average day, in a short time moisture collects on them, and in due time the crystals disappear, having been completely dissolved by water absorbed from the atmosphere. On a warm, moist day, when the humidity is high, this phenomenon is hastened. The above salts are said to be **deliquescent** and are only two of many such compounds.

Deliquescent substances are often used to help control moisture. Anhydrous calcium chloride is used as a drying agent (desiccant) in laboratores, and is included in airtight containers to prevent rusting of sensitive instruments in storage. It is used in large quantities on dusty roads since its tendency to absorb moisture is so great the roads become moist, and the dust nuisance is controlled for a period of time.

10–12 HYGROSCOPIC COMPOUNDS

A wide variety of substances—wood, hair, sugar, and many fabrics—have a tendency to absorb moisture but not in such copious quantities as the deliquescent substances. Such substances are said to be **hygroscopic.** Since the moisture content of the air controls the amount of moisture in the hair, and since the moisture content of the hair affects its tendency to stretch or shrink, human hair is used in the manufacture of instruments to measure the humidity of the atmosphere. We should be thankful that hair is only hygroscopic, not deliquescent.

10–13 DEHYDRATION

Water is removed during the processing of many foods, usually to improve their keeping qualities. This practice is not a twentieth century innovation. From antiquity, man has dried certain foods such as figs, prunes, apricots, and even fish and beef. The twentieth century, however, has seen improvement in some of these processes, and the list of dried foods has been extended. There is a trend toward using mechanical dehydrators instead of the age-old sun drying. Perhaps the greatest recent advance in food dehydration is in the processing of milk. Much chemical research was required to produce a satisfactory powdered milk which can be easily mixed with water.

The increasing availability of dried foods is a boon to the thousands of vacationers who are interested in lighter loads when they carry packs into the mountain country. A vast array of special dehydrated foods has been prepared for such uses.

10–14 PURIFICATION OF WATER

Most water-borne diseases of man are those which have been spread by man; therefore, as our population increases, the pollution of our natural waters also increases. The day is past when it is safe to drink untreated stream water except in wilderness areas unfrequented by people.

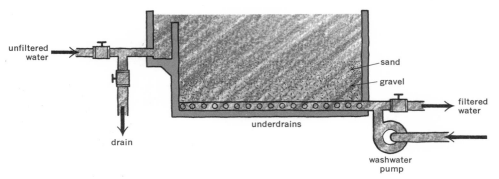

FIG. 10-4. Cross section of a large filter bed.

Many cities are dependent for their water supplies upon streams that contain the sewage of upstream cities. Present day purification of the water for most of our major cities requires elaborate equipment and technical procedures. To prepare natural waters for public use, we must treat them to remove bacteria, suspended clay-like particles, and objectionable odors. Usually dissolved minerals are not present in such quantities that they need be removed.

To remove suspended solids, the water is thoroughly mixed with slaked lime, $Ca(OH)_2$, and aluminum sulfate, $Al_2(SO_4)_3$. These chemicals react to produce a flocculating agent, aluminum hydroxide:

$$3Ca(OH)_2 + Al_2(SO_4)_3 \rightarrow 2Al(OH)_3 \downarrow + 3CaSO_4 \tag{10-8}$$

The flocculating agent is a gelatinous solid that tends to sweep all suspended particles with it as it settles to the bottom of the sedimentation tanks. The water is then passed through great filters, Fig. 10-4, constructed by covering coarse gravel with successive layers of fine gravel, coarse sand, and fine sand. Such a filter removes the remaining $Al(OH)_3$, suspended particles, and most of the bacteria.*

If undesirable odors are present, they may be removed by aeration, that is, by spraying the water, fountain-like, into the air or causing it to cascade over simulated waterfalls. This operation not only frees the water of the unpleasant odors, but dissolves oxygen from the air, helping to destroy bacteria. As a final precaution, most cities treat their water with small amounts of chlorine.

In emergencies, when water within a system is contaminated, drinking water should be boiled for fifteen minutes before it is used. The same precaution should be observed on camping trips when the purity of drinking water is questionable. It should be emphasized, however, that boiling water destroys only bacteria. It does not remove poisonous chemicals, radioactive substances, or other nonvolatile objectionable materials.

---

* The filters are rejuvenated periodically, as needed, by reversing the flow of water. The layer of fine silt-like particles which have accumulated are flushed from the filter in a short time and the filtering is resumed.

10–15 WATER SOFTENING

As previously mentioned, ordinary minerals are not removed by most city water-purification systems. If the minerals present react with soap to prevent it from sudsing properly, and form undesirable insoluble scum (responsible for bathtub rings and also for sticky hair), the water is said to be *hard*. Sodium and potassium compounds in moderate amounts are not objectionable since they do not prevent sudsing of soaps. Water containing only small amounts of these metallic ions is said to be *soft*. Calcium and magnesium compounds are the most common causes of hardness in water. They combine chemically with soap as follows:

$$2C_{15}H_{31}COONa + CaCl_2 \rightarrow (C_{15}H_{31}COO)_2Ca + 2NaCl \tag{10-9}$$

(a soluble soap)   (an insoluble soap)

Magnesium salts react in a similar fashion.

The minerals present in natural waters correspond to the minerals in the soil or the rocks over which the water has run. Areas of Kansas and Oklahoma contain great deposits of gypsum, $CaSO_4 \cdot 2H_2O$. Since gypsum is soluble to the extent of 2 g/liter, much of the natural water of these areas is unfit to drink and objectionable for household use. By contrast, the waters of the High Sierra of California come in contact only with granite or its decomposed constituents which are extremely insoluble. This water is almost free of all dissolved minerals.

Variations in the mineral content of water range from 1000 parts per million (ppm) in some areas of the southwest United States, to 13 ppm in some mountain waters. Water containing less than 50 ppm of dissolved solids is considered to be soft water.

Much of the water of the United States comes in contact with limestone which is composed primarily of calcium carbonate, $CaCO_3$, with small amounts of magnesium carbonate, $MgCO_3$. Since all natural water dissolves carbon dioxide from the air, these waters will necessarily contain carbonic acid, H_2CO_3:

$$H_2O + CO_2 \rightarrow H_2CO_3 \tag{10-10}$$

The carbonic acid in water reacts with limestone forming soluble bicarbonates,

$$CaCO_3 + H_2CO_3 \rightarrow \quad Ca(HCO_3)_2 \tag{10-11}$$
calcium bicarbonate

and

$$MgCO_3 + H_2CO_3 \rightarrow \quad Mg(HCO_3)_2 \tag{10-12}$$
magnesium bicarbonate

The solubility of limestone in water containing carbonic acid accounts in part for limestone caverns and the great gorges formed by water flowing over limestone formations. The process is slow, requiring many thousands of years, but nature often works at a leisurely gait. When water and carbon dioxide are lost from solutions of bicarbonates, reaction (10–11) is reversed, and calcium carbonate is deposited. In this manner, stalactites and stalagmites form in limestone caverns when solutions of $Ca(HCO_3)_2$ and $Mg(HCO_3)_2$ seep in and evaporate.

The salts commonly contributing to the hardness in water are

Ca(HCO₃)₂   Mg(HCO₃)₂   CaCl₂   CaSO₄   MgCl₂   MgSO₄   CaCl₂   CaSO₄

While they actually occur as ions, it is convenient to consider them as compounds. These substances may be removed or rendered inactive to soaps as follows: The bicarbonates can be converted to carbonates by boiling the water:

$$Ca(HCO_3)_2 \xrightarrow{\Delta} CaCO_3 \downarrow + H_2CO_3 \ (H_2O + CO_2 \uparrow) \tag{10-13}$$

Since calcium carbonate is insoluble and settles out, it cannot react with soap. Chemicals must be added to remove other salts of magnesium and calcium. Some of the water softening chemicals which combine with calcium and magnesium ions to produce insoluble precipitates are sodium carbonate, Na_2CO_3, sodium phosphate, Na_3PO_4 or even NaOH:

$$CaCl_2 + Na_2CO_3 \rightarrow CaCO_3 \downarrow + 2NaCl \tag{10-14}$$

$$3MgSO_4 + 2Na_3PO_4 \rightarrow Mg_3(PO_4)_2 \downarrow + 3Na_2SO_4 \tag{10-15}$$

$$3Ca(HCO_3)_2 + 2Na_3PO_4 \rightarrow Ca_3(PO_4)_2 \downarrow + 6NaHCO_3 \tag{10-16}$$

After the hardness-producing materials have been removed, only a small amount of soap is required to produce the suds desired for cleansing. The synthetic detergents which have largely replaced soaps in the home will be discussed in Chapter 27.

In recent years, the use of mechanical or so-called automatic water softeners for the home has become commonplace. These softeners, regardless of name or system, employ similar types of chemical mechanisms and are called *zeolite* softeners. Zeolite is a naturally occurring substance, sodium aluminum silicate, which we will designate as zeolite · 2Na⁺. When water containing calcium ions, $(Ca^{2+} + 2\,Cl^-)$, is passed through the softener, the following reaction takes place:

$$Ca^{2+} + 2Cl^- + zeolite \cdot 2Na^+ \rightarrow zeolite \cdot Ca^{2+} + 2Na^+ + 2Cl^- \tag{10-17}$$

The calcium ions are removed from the water, and sodium ions are released from the zeolite. This process continues until the sodium zeolite has all reacted, and the water shows indications of hardness, at which time a strong solution of sodium chloride is forced into the softener causing a reversal of the above reaction:

$$2Na^+ + 2Cl^- + zeolite \cdot Ca^{2+} \rightarrow zeolite \cdot 2Na^+ + Ca^{2+} + 2Cl^- \tag{10-18}$$

After standing for a time, a valve is opened permitting the brine with its retrieved calcium ions to be flushed away and the softener is ready for another period of usefulness. Persons on salt-free diets should avoid water softened in such a manner because, if the water is quite hard, considerable sodium chloride will be added during the softening process. Large-sized, specially built zeolite softeners are used in industrial plants where soft water is required.

A more ingenious method of purification employs two resins, one of which removes all metallic (positive) ions from the water, replacing them with H⁺ ions. The other resin replaces nonmetallic (negative) ions with OH⁻. The H⁺ and OH⁻ ions immediately unite to form water, leaving essentially no ions in the water. Such ion-exchange softeners are used in laboratories or industries where extremely pure water is essential. On a smaller scale they are also being used in households to purify water for use in steam irons.

10–16 HEAVY WATER

It was stated in Chapter 9 that hydrogen has three isotopes with masses of 1, 2, and 3, respectively. As a result, water molecules will have variable masses. Most of the atoms of deuterium (^2_1D) will occur in water molecules as HOD, with 19 mass units. Water can also be synthesized by combining pure deuterium with oxygen, forming deuterium oxide to yield a water molecule of 20 mass units:

$$2D_2 + O_2 \rightarrow 2D_2O \tag{10-19}$$

Water with a mass of 20 is commonly called heavy water. Heavy water has a greater density and a slightly higher boiling point than ordinary water. Large quantities are employed in certain types of nuclear reactors. Physiologically, pure D_2O is somewhat toxic to animals.

10–17 IMPORTANCE OF WATER TO LIFE

Life as we know it cannot exist without water. While it is interesting to speculate that perhaps life on other planets could use H_2S or NH_3 for some of the purposes for which life on earth uses water, neither of these related compounds has the properties which make water so vital to the life of our plants and animals.

We know that animals or plants die when deprived of water. While some plants and animals can survive on little water, no living organism can exist in the total absence of water. The question naturally arises, "Why is water vital?" The answer lies in the amazing properties of water.

Plants and animals depend upon chemical reactions for their life and growth. In chemical reactions, the reacting particles must be able to collide. While collisions are routine for gas molecules and present no real difficulty in molecules of a liquid, molecules of solids must generally be in solution in order to react. In some cases, the molecules must also dissociate or ionize* before they can react. Water is the best solvent known, and because of its polar nature, it promotes ionization. The extremely large protein molecules, which are so necessary for life, are kept in solution by being surrounded by hundreds of water molecules. The elimination of waste products as water solutions (especially in the urine but also in perspiration) represents another important use of water as a solvent.

In addition to the function of water as a neutral, nontoxic solvent, it is estimated that water participates as a reactant or product in 50% of the reactions of living organisms. Digestion of food is primarily a series of hydrolysis reactions. The process of photosynthesis involves water as a reactant:

$$6H_2O + 6CO_2 \rightleftarrows C_6H_{12}O_6 + 6O_2 \tag{10-20}$$
$$\text{(a sugar)}$$

---

* In other words, the ionic compound must be broken down into individual ions; for example, $CaCl_2 \rightarrow Ca^{2+} + 2Cl^-$. This process is discussed in Section 12–2.

The reverse of this reaction is the oxidation of sugar which requires oxygen and yields water.

One of the major problems of the higher animals is temperature regulation. If the normal temperature of the body varies only a few degrees, serious consequences result. If body temperature is sufficiently elevated, brain damage and eventually death may occur. Since many of the reactions taking place in animals release heat, it is necessary that cooling processes be employed. Water is well suited to act as a coolant. It has a high specific heat. Consequently small volumes of it can absorb relatively large quantities of heat without a large increase in temperature. Water also has a high heat of vaporization. This property means that evaporation from the skin or lungs consumes large amounts of heat. Furthermore, water is a reasonably good heat transfer agent, and, as such, serves to help transfer the heat from the places where it is produced to places where it can be dissipated.

◄ When we consider the importance of water, we wonder how some animals manage to survive with almost no water intake. The desert rat (kangaroo rat) apparently never drinks water. While other animals get appreciable amounts of water from their foods (as is obvious from the water content of foods listed in Section 10-1), the desert rat's main food is dry seeds which contain only small quantities of water. The desert rat derives a great deal of its water from the oxidation of hydrogen-containing substances in its food. Water that is produced as the result of reactions within an animal is called **metabolic water** (metabolism is a general term used to describe all the reactions of an animal or plant). Seeds contain relatively large amounts of fats which are rich in hydrogen, and thus are a good source of metabolic water.

The desert rat conserves his meagre supply of water in many ways. Although he lives on the hot, dry desert, where it would be expected that he would have to use large amounts of water for cooling purposes, he remains in burrows where it is relatively cool (60–75°F) and relatively humid (15–40% relative humidity) during the day, and he confines his activities to the night hours when the desert is cool. Whereas humans cannot excrete urine which contains more than 1.75% NaCl,* the desert rat can excrete urine that is 7% NaCl. He excretes other waste products as concentrated solutions, also. By these various adaptations, he is able to survive under conditions which provide little water. He maintains a nearly constant body temperature, and water always makes up 66% of his body weight.

Many reptiles use some of the processes available to the desert rat, but they have an advantage (at least as far as desert life is concerned) in that they do not need to maintain a constant body temperature; it fluctuates with the surroundings. While it is tempting to assume that these animals learned how to get along with little water, it is much more likely that their inherited behavior patterns and inherited biochemical patterns have enabled them to live in areas where the competition for survival is less rigorous.

The camel survives desert conditions by various adaptations, some of which are different from those of the desert rat. The camel certainly produces metabolic water to supplement what he drinks. His hump is largely fat, a good source of metabolic water. Camels also excrete a concentrated urine. The unusual adaptations of camels are that their body temperature can vary from 93° to 105°F without serious consequences, and they can lose up to 40% of their body water without dying. (Humans, on the contrary, become delirious when 10% of their body water is lost, and cannot survive a 20% loss of body water.) In addition, the camel can replenish his

---

* This explains why people excrete additional water and dehydrate themselves when they drink sea water containing 3.5% NaCl.

water supply in a short time. He can drink an amount of water equivalent to one third of his body weight in 10 minutes!

Sea birds face a problem not of the lack of water, but of the lack of fresh, unsalty water. They solve their problem by drinking salt water and then excreting a solution containing 5% NaCl through special salt glands in their beaks.

The animals discussed above represent exceptions to general rules about requirements for fresh water. The majority of animals need large amounts of the amazing substance we call water for the maintenance of life. ▶

IMPORTANT TERMS

Anhydrous	*Hard water*	*Hydrates*	*Metabolic water*
Deliquescence	*Heat of fusion*	*Hydrogen bond*	*Specific heat*
Efflorescence	*Heat of vaporization*	*Hygroscopic*	*Zeolite*

WORK EXERCISES

1. Describe three different meanings for the word "pure" as applied to water.

2. Why do inland bodies of water, typically the Great Salt Lake and the Great Lakes, differ so much in mineral content?

3. What is the explanation for the comparatively high heats of fusion and vaporization of water? Might the same explanation apply to the specific heat of water?

4. How many calories are required to convert 10 g of ice at 0°C to steam at 100°C?

5. Illustrate the structure of a typical unit of water as it occurs in the liquid state.

6. Most liquids decrease in volume when changing to a solid. How do you account for the fact that ice does not follow this pattern?

7. Complete and balance the following:

   a) $Na + H_2O \rightarrow$

   b) $Ca + H_2O \rightarrow$

   c) $H_2O + CO_2 \rightarrow$

   d) $H_2O + SO_3 \rightarrow$

   e) $H_2O + K_2O \rightarrow$

   f) $H_2O + CaO \rightarrow$

   g) $CuSO_4 \cdot 5H_2O \xrightarrow{\Delta}$

8. Contrast the meaning of the terms (a) efflorescence, and (b) deliquescence.

9. List five possible ways of purifying water.

10. Complete and balance:

    a) $Ca(HCO_3)_2 \xrightarrow{\Delta}$

    b) $CaCl_2 + Na_2CO_3 \rightarrow$

    c) $MgSO_4 + Na_3PO_4 \rightarrow$

    d) $Ca(HCO_3)_2 + Na_3PO_4 \rightarrow$

    e) $Ca^{2+} + zeolite \cdot 2Na^+ \rightarrow$

    f) $Ca(OH)_2 + Al_2(SO_4)_3 \rightarrow$

11. How do the small animals that live in desert areas survive on so little water?

12. How is metabolic water produced in the animal body?

SUGGESTED READING

Ambroggi, R. P., "Water Under the Sahara," *Scientific American*, May 1966, p. 21. Large reservoirs of water beneath the Sahara desert are being tapped and used for irrigation.

Buswell, A. M., and W. H. Rodebush, "Water," *Scientific American*, Apr. 1956, p. 76. While water is a very common substance, its properties are most unusual. An interesting report on some of these unusual properties.

Garner, H. F., "Rivers in the Making," *Scientific American*, Apr. 1967, p. 84. Unusual stream-bed patterns produced by rivers.

Greulach, V. A., "The Rise of Water in Plants," *Scientific American*, Oct. 1952, p. 78. A report on the theories that have been suggested and the experiments that have been performed in trying to explain this phenonomenon.

Runnels, L. K., "Ice," *Scientific American*, Dec. 1966, p. 118. The arrangement of molecules in ice crystals and the astonishing movement of some of the molecules in the crystals.

Chapter 11   SOLUTIONS

11-1 TYPES OF SOLUTIONS

Life exists only in the presence of water. It is believed that life originated in the ocean, and although some forms were able to escape the necessity of being continuously bathed in water, they were never able to adapt to a total absence of water. Pure water does not occur naturally because gases of the atmosphere, minerals from the soil, and many other substances may become mixed with it. These mixtures of water and the chemicals found in it are called **solutions.** Solutions may be defined as homogeneous mixtures composed of two or more kinds of atoms, molecules, or ions.

Several distinct types of solutions are covered by our definition. The atmosphere is composed largely of nitrogen and oxygen molecules, with lesser quantities of molecules of other elementary gases. There are also molecules of carbon dioxide and water vapor. The air is a homogeneous mixture of gas molecules and can be called a solution. Many alloys of metals are true solutions: they consist of homogeneous mixtures of molecules (or atoms) of metals. Solutions may therefore exist in the solid and gaseous states, as well as in the more familiar liquid form. Some examples of the various types of solutions are listed in Table 11-1.

TABLE 11-1. Types of solutions

Type	Example
solids in liquids	syrup; sugar in water
liquids in liquids	alcoholic beverages; alcohol in water
gases in liquids	soda water; carbon dioxide in water
gases in gases	the atmosphere—a mixture of nitrogen, oxygen, argon, water vapor, etc.
solids in solids	metallic alloys; silver coins, silver and copper

11-2 SOLVENTS AND SOLUTES

If sugar crystals are stirred with water a solution is formed. The sugar is *dissolved* by the water. We call the water the **solvent,** and the sugar the **solute.** The distinction between solvent and solute is not always so clear. If, for example, both components of a solution are liquids, e.g., water and alcohol, the one present in the greater amount is called the solvent. However, if we have a solution containing equal parts of alcohol and water, this distinction cannot be made. If a solid and a liquid are the components of a solution, we usually consider the liquid to be the solvent. In general, rules for distinguishing between solvent and solute are somewhat arbitrary and should be considered as guidelines rather than as absolute criteria.

11-3 FACTORS AFFECTING SOLUBILITY

Many factors influence the amount of solute that can be dissolved in a given amount of solvent. Common experience is a good guide in making generalizations about solubilities. It is not, however, completely reliable.

Solids in Liquids. From the observation that more sugar can be dissolved in hot water than in an equal volume of cold water, we could conclude that *the solubility of solids in liquids increases as the temperature of the solvent is increased.* This generalization is not infallible, however, for in a few cases the reverse is true, and with sodium chloride the solubility is only slightly changed with temperature change. Pressure does not materially affect the solubility of solids in liquids.

Gases in Liquids. The memory of times we have opened warm bottles of carbonated beverages compared to our usual experience with chilled bottles would lead us to believe that the gas (CO_2) is less soluble—and more likely to spurt out violently—when the temperature is high. Thus we would conclude that *the solubility of gases in liquids decreases with an increase in temperature.* Observation of a variety of gases in a variety of liquids would show that this generalization is almost always true. Similar observations and experiments about the effect of pressure on solubility of gases in liquids would lead to the discovery that pressure is just as important as temperature in its effect on the solubility of gases but that it operates in the opposite manner. *An increase of pressure tends to increase the solubility of gases in liquids.* In the example given above, we should note that the carbon dioxide was in solution in the carbonated beverage until the cap was removed, releasing the pressure. The bottle was originally filled under pressure; in other words, a quantity of carbon dioxide gas was literally pushed into the solution.

Nature of Solvent and Solute. Many liquids can be considered solvents, and many solids behave as solutes. An excellent solvent for one substance may not be satisfactory for another. To dissolve a spot of grease we use organic solvents such as alcohol or carbon tetrachloride; water would be ineffective. To dissolve a spot of syrup containing sugar, we find water is the best solvent; the organic solvents would not work. In general, water (a polar solvent) is the best solvent for ionic substances and those which are able to form hydrogen bonds. Oils and greases which have little polarity are more soluble in organic solvents like alcohol or carbon tetrachloride.

11-4 FACTORS AFFECTING RATES OF SOLUTION

Particle Size. Particle size is important in determining the rate at which solids dissolve in liquids. Solution takes place, of course, only at the surface. Consequently, small particles dissolve more rapidly than large particles, because the small particles have a greater surface area per unit of weight. Powdered sugar, for example, dissolves more rapidly than granulated sugar.

Agitation. Since the solute is usually more dense than the solvent it settles to the bottom of the container and is soon surrounded and covered with a layer of solution *which contains dissolved solute.* Agitation or stirring brings the undissolved solute into contact with fresh solvent. This action explains why stirring coffee helps dissolve added sugar.

11-5 MISCIBLE AND IMMISCIBLE LIQUIDS

If two liquids form a homogeneous mixture or solution, they are said to be **miscible.** If they do not dissolve in each other, they are **immiscible.** Water and alcohol are miscible; water and gasoline are immiscible. There are many cases in which two liquids are only partially soluble in each other. One such combination is ether and water. Liquids in this category are said to be partially miscible.

11-6 PROPERTIES OF SOLUTIONS

Solutions have many characteristic properties, some of which will be discussed. Since all particles in a solution are of molecular size or smaller (ions), there is no tendency for the solute and solvent to separate or settle. Once the sugar in your cup of coffee is dissolved, it will not settle to the bottom. Sweetened coffee can be filtered without removing the sugar. All solutions may be filtered without removing the solute. While many solutions may be colored, they are clear and transparent. A beam of light will pass through a solution without showing the path of light. When the light path can be seen, it is evidence that larger particles are suspended in the liquid.

11-7 VAPOR PRESSURE

We have all observed that water evaporates. Wet clothes on the clothesline become dry, and perspiration disappears. We have also probably observed that evaporation takes place more rapidly when it is warm: wet clothes dry more rapidly in summer than in winter. With many observations we can predict that the higher the temperature the more rapid the rate of evaporation.

For an explanation we must recall that while molecules are always in motion, they are not all traveling at the same speed. They resemble somewhat the automobiles on a busy highway, with the important distinction that there are no traffic rules for molecules—only physical laws. To say that there is an average speed does not mean they are all traveling at the same speed. There are some slow ones which may be bumped from behind, and a few which are going much faster than the average. While it is incorrect to say that two automobiles evaporate when they collide at high speed, they at least set themselves apart from the rest. When two high-speed molecules collide near the surface of water, one or both may escape the attractive forces of the other molecules and pass into the atmosphere above. These energetic molecules are said to evaporate since they are no longer visible as a part of a larger group of molecules which can be seen as a liquid. When molecules are heated, they gain kinetic energy and are more likely to have sufficient energy to escape from the liquid.

At a given temperature the rate of evaporation from a liquid remains the same, for it depends upon how many molecules have sufficient energy to escape. The rate at which molecules return to the liquid depends, however, on the number of molecules of that kind already in the space above the liquid. If we place a liquid in an evacuated flask, evaporation at first takes place rapidly. There is practically no interference with escaping molecules, for initially there are no molecules in the gas phase which can return to the liquid (Fig. 11–1a). Soon, however, molecules are returning from the gas to the liquid as rapidly as other molecules are escaping from the liquid. When this condition prevails, we say that equilibrium has been established (Fig. 11–1b). Although an exchange of molecules continues indefinitely, the net change is zero; vaporization no longer decreases the amount of liquid present.*

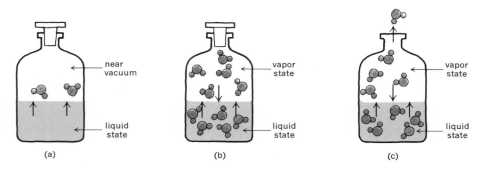

FIG. 11–1. Evaporation of a liquid under different conditions.

We have just described a closed flask in which equilibrium has been established. If we remove the stopper (Fig. 11–1c) molecules in the gas phase will begin to escape into the atmosphere and the equilibrium will be upset. If we maintain the same temperature, molecules will continue to pass from liquid to gas at the same rate. But with the stopper removed, very few gas molecules return to the liquid. Consequently, equilibrium cannot be reestablished, and eventually all the liquid evaporates, escaping into the atmosphere.

A satisfactory method for determining the vapor pressure of a liquid at a given temperature is to place a sample of the liquid in an evacuated flask (Fig. 11–1a). Molecules imme-

---

* Principles of equilibrium are discussed more extensively in Chapter 13.

diately begin to evaporate to form a gas above the liquid. The resultant gas pressure can be measured; as soon as it becomes constant we know that the gas and liquid are in equilibrium (Fig. 11–1b). When this condition is reached, the pressure observed is the vapor pressure of the pure liquid, since no other molecules were present in the evacuated flask originally.

As the temperature increases, the vapor pressure of all volatile liquids also increases. Finally, the liquid boils. Further heating may increase the rate of evaporation but will not increase the temperature of the boiling liquid. The **boiling point** of any liquid or solution is defined as *the temperature at which the vapor pressure equals the atmospheric pressure above the liquid.* A change in atmospheric pressure therefore changes the boiling point. At higher elevations where the atmospheric pressure is relatively low, the boiling point is lower than at sea level. Since cooking of foods is dependent upon temperature rather than on the observable fact of boiling, it takes longer at high elevations to cook foods by boiling.

In the above discussion of vapor pressures and boiling points we have been concerned primarily with pure liquids. Let us turn now to consider what happens when substances are dissolved in a solvent.

11–8 BOILING POINTS OF SOLUTIONS

When nonvolatile solutes such as sugar are placed in water, the concentration of the solvent is somewhat diluted. The nonvolatile particles tend to keep some of the volatile molecules from leaving the solution, thereby slightly reducing the vapor pressure at any given temperature. The temperature of the solution must therefore be raised before the vapor pressure exceeds the atmospheric pressure. When 1 mole of a nonvolatile solute is added to 1000 g of water, the boiling point is raised 0.51°C. For example, when 342 g of sucrose (1 mole) is placed in 1000 g of water, the boiling point of the solution at standard atmospheric pressure will be 100.51°C. If 2 moles of sugar are dissolved in 1000 g of water, the boiling point will be elevated 2 × 0.51°C; thus the boiling point for such a solution will be 101.02°C.

When 1 formula weight of sodium chloride is dissolved in 1000 g of water, the boiling point is about 101°C instead of 100.5°C, as we might expect from the experiment with sugar. Although 1 mole of sugar weighs 342 g and 1 mole of sodium chloride only 58.5 g, the salt elevates the boiling point twice as much as the sugar. Repeated experiments to study the effect of both covalently bonded and electrovalently bonded compounds show that the latter elevate the boiling point more than the former. From these experiments we can generalize that the change in boiling point depends primarily on the number of particles rather than on the size of the particles in solution. Furthermore, such experiments support the idea that electrovalent compounds dissociate into smaller particles called ions, as will be discussed in Section 12–1.

11–9 FREEZING POINTS OF SOLUTIONS

The freezing points of water solutions are lower than are those of pure water. Advantage is taken of this phenomenon when alcohol or other antifreeze materials are added to automobile radiators. When 1 mole of a covalent solute is dissolved in 1 liter of water, the freezing point of the water is depressed 1.86°C. Here again, electrovalent substances cause a greater change: 1 mole of sodium chloride lowers the freezing point of water twice times 1.86°C. It might seem, therefore, that electrovalent substances such as calcium chloride, $CaCl_2$, would be more effective than alcohol or glycol for automobile radiators, but they are too corrosive for use in automobiles. Such salts, however, are used in commercial refrigeration plants.

11–10 OSMOSIS

Since all plant and animal life is dependent upon solutions, there must be some way for these solutions to pass through living tissues. These tissues are largely made up of cells surrounded by membranes which are semipermeable in character, that is, they permit the passage of certain components of a solution more readily than others. This selective passage of liquids through a semipermeable membrane in a direction which tends to make concentrations of all substances on one side of the membrane equal to those on the other side of the membrane is called **osmosis.** Blood is a solution containing many components. The solution inside the blood cells contains approximately 1% salt. If blood cells are placed in pure water (see Fig. 11–2a) molecules of water pass through the membrane into the cells more rapidly than molecules move in the opposite direction, thus causing the cells to swell and burst. Solutions which contain a *lower* salt concentration than that which exists in the blood cells are said to be **hypotonic.** If, on the other hand, blood cells are placed in a concentrated salt solution there is again the tendency to reach equilibrium. Under these circumstances, it can be attained only if water passes through the membranes to the outside, causing the cells to shrink in size (Fig. 11–2b). Solutions which contain a higher concentration of salt than that found in the blood are called **hypertonic.** If blood cells are placed in a solution such that the salt concentration is equal to that of the blood cells, no change occurs and the solution is **isotonic** (Fig. 11–2c).

Medicines and solutions containing nutritious substances are often administered to sick persons by injecting large volumes (often a liter) of the solution into the veins. This process is described as intravenous or IV administration. It can be seen that in intravenous feeding it is essential that the salt concentration of the solution be carefully adjusted in order to prevent rupture or shrinking of the red blood cells.

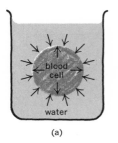
(a)

(b)

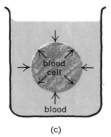
(c)

FIG. 11–2. Factors controlling the direction of osmosis in blood cells.

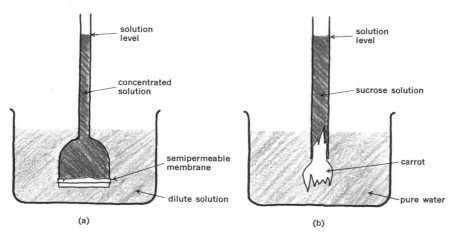

FIG. 11–3. Osmosis. Water passing through (a) a semipermeable membrane and (b) a carrot, diluting the concentrated sugar solutions above.

Osmosis can easily be demonstrated by placing a strong sugar solution in a tube which is covered at the lower end by a synthetic membrane or even plugged with a piece of carrot. When lowered into water, the water molecules readily pass through the membrane or carrot, diluting the sugar solution above, Fig. 11–3. The level of the solution rises rapidly in the tube.

It is helpful to remember that water travels in a direction which will dilute the more concentrated solution. There is nothing mysterious about this; it is merely diffusion to establish an equilibrium in which concentrations of all substances on both sides of a membrane are equal.

11–11 CONCENTRATION OF SOLUTIONS

Several kinds of terminology are used to describe the concentration of the solutes in solutions. The terms dilute and concentrated are very common. A **dilute** solution has a relatively low concentration of solute in the solvent, and a **concentrated** solution has a relatively high percentage of solute. Because of the great variability in the solubility of different substances we do not attempt to set limits as to when solutions cease being dilute and become concentrated.

Concentration is sometimes expressed in percent, but this can be confusing since it could be percent by volume or by weight. A convenient and often-used terminology is grams of solute/100 ml of solution, the weight/volume method. This type of solution is easily prepared. If 5 parts/100 ml is desired, 5 g of solute are dissolved in enough solvent to produce 100 ml of solution. Each milliliter will then contain 0.05 g of solute. The concentration of solutions is also expressed in terms of their **molarity,** which indicates the moles or fraction of moles of solute/liter of solution (Section 11–14).

11-12 SATURATED SOLUTIONS

If a solid substance is added to a solvent until no more will dissolve under existing conditions, the solution is said to be **saturated** or it may be said that *the undissolved solid and the solute are in equilibrium.* Most solids become more soluble in liquids with an increase of temperature. Consequently, if the temperature is increased, more solute is required to maintain a saturated solution. A lowering of temperature has the opposite effect. If the temperature is reduced the solute crystallizes from the solution to maintain equilibrium, and the solution remains saturated.

11-13 SUPERSATURATED SOLUTIONS

Now, if more of the undissolved solute is added to a solution which is saturated at 20°C and the solution is warmed until all solute is dissolved, the resulting solution is certainly holding more solute than it did at the original temperature. However, if it is carefully cooled to 20°C, all the solute may remain in solution. It is evident that this solution is holding more solute than it could have dissolved at 20°C. Such a solution is said to be **supersaturated.** A supersaturated solution is one that is *holding more solute than it can dissolve at existing conditions,* and therefore an equilibrium does *not* exist between the dissolved solute and the undissolved material. If, however, a crystal of the solute is placed in a supersaturated solution, the crystal grows rapidly, and soon all excess solute crystallizes out of the solution, and once again an equilibrium exists.

  Clouds are often supersaturated with moisture. Spraying of tiny particles of silver iodide into a cloud may induce precipitation of the water.

11-14 MOLAR SOLUTIONS AND MOLARITY

Chemists must be concerned with the quantitative aspects of reactions. How much acid is required to neutralize the base (alkali) left after the manufacture of a batch of soap?—or perhaps—How much base must be used in the reaction so that no acid will be needed at the end of the process? While we can weigh out the various numbers of grams of substances required, it is often more convenient to add the necessary reagent in a dissolved form. The latter procedure has two advantages. In the first place, it is easier to measure the volume of solutions than it is to weigh the required number of grams of the reagent. This is especially true when a large volume of solution is made up in advance, and only small amounts are added each time it is necessary. For instance, canneries which must sweeten each batch of canned fruits usually add a measured volume of sugar solution (sugar syrup) instead of a given weight of sugar. The second advantage of adding reagents in their dissolved form is that it saves time; we do not have to wait for particles to dissolve. If a chemist is measuring the rate of a chemical reaction, he must know that his reactants are dissolved and ready to react when he adds them together; he cannot worry about the time required for his reactants to dissolve.

  Once we have decided to use solutions, the question becomes, "How do we express their concentrations?" At first glance, indicating the percentage of solute would seem best. This is true of substances which do not participate in a chemical reaction, such as the sugar solutions used to sweeten fruits. However, if we add a 5% solution of HCl to an equal amount of a 5% solution of KOH, the resulting mixture will contain an excess of acid, since 36.5 g of HCl react with 56.1 g of KOH (see Section 12–7). For most chemical purposes it is easier to specify solutions in terms of **molar** concentration. *A molar solution contains 1 mole of solute per liter of solution (not per liter of solvent).* If we place 342 g (1 mole) of sucrose in a flask and add water until the total volume is 1 liter, we will have a one-molar (1 *M*) solution of sucrose. If we have $2 \times 342 = 684$ g of sucrose/liter of solution, we have a 2 *M* solution; and if we have 34.2 g of sucrose/liter of solution, we obtain a 0.1 *M* solution.

The following examples may provide an understanding of molar solutions:

Calculations of amounts required for a certain molarity.

1) To prepare 1 liter of 2.0 *M* methyl alcohol, CH_3OH, molecular weight 32.0, requires $2 \times 32 = 64$ g and enough solvent to make 1 liter of solution.

2) To prepare 5 liters of 3.0 *M* methyl alcohol requires

$$5 \text{ (number of liters)} \times 3 \text{ (molarity)} \times 32 \text{ (molecular weight)} = 5 \times 3 \times 32 = 480 \text{ g}$$

of methyl alcohol in enough solvent to make 5 liters of solution.

3) To prepare 3 liters of 0.1 *M* methyl alcohol requires

$$3 \text{ (number of liters)} \times 0.1 \text{ (molarity)} \times 32 \text{ (molecular weight)} = 3 \times 0.1 \times 32 = 9.6 \text{ g}$$

of methyl alcohol in enough solvent to make 3 liters of solution.

4) To prepare 1 liter of 1 *M* calcium chloride we will use 1 mole (1 gram-formula weight) and enough solvent to make 1 liter of solution.

Determination of molarity when grams of solute in a given volume of solution are known

1) A solution contains 186 g of glycol, $C_2H_4(OH)_2$ (molecular weight 62), per liter. What is its molar strength (molarity)?

$$\frac{186 \text{ (grams of glycol)}}{62 \text{ (molecular weight of glycol)}} = 3 \text{ (moles of glycol)},$$

and

$$\frac{3 \text{ moles of glycol}}{1 \text{ liter}} = 3 \text{ } M.$$

2) Two liters of a solution contain a total of 93 g of ethylene glycol, molecular weight 62. What is its molarity?

$$\frac{93 \text{ (grams of glycol)}}{62 \text{ (molecular weight of glycol)}} = 1.5 \text{ moles of glycol},$$

$$\frac{1.5 \text{ moles}}{2 \text{ liters}} = 0.75 \text{ } M.$$

11-15 FORMAL SOLUTIONS AND FORMALITY

It has been a common practice to use the terminology *molecular weights* and *molar solutions* for both electrovalent and covalent solutes. Since electrovalent materials do not form molecules but are always in an ionic state, the use of "molecular weight" in referring to them is perhaps not completely correct. The terms "formula weight" and "formal solutions" (which refer to identical quantities) are sometimes used. However, since we interpret a molar solution as one which contains 1 *mole* of solute/liter of solution, we may properly speak of molar solutions. Review the definition of mole in Section 7-4. To determine the number of moles, we use molecular weights for nonionic substances and formula weights for ionic substances, e.g., acids, bases, and salts.

11-16 SUMMARY

In this chapter some of the characteristics of solutions have been discussed and several definitions provided. The effect of dissolved substances on the boiling and freezing points of solutions has been discussed. Several methods for expressing the concentration of solutions were considered, and the use of formal and molar solutions was introduced. These differences in expressing concentrations are based upon differences in types of compounds, electrovalent or covalent, or more specifically, on the differences in the bonds that hold the compounds together. In the following chapter we will see a modification of the concept of molar and formal solutions to that of normal solutions.

IMPORTANT TERMS

Boiling point	Hypertonic solution	Molar solution	Solution
Concentrated solution	Hypotonic solution	Molarity	Solvent
Dilute solution	Immiscible	Osmosis	Supersaturated solution
Formal solution	Isotonic solution	Saturated solution	Vapor pressure
Freezing point	Miscible	Solute	

WORK EXERCISES

1. Define the term "solution."
2. Name and give illustrations of three common kinds of solutions.
3. Make at least three distinctions between "solvent" and "solute."
4. State the effects of temperature and pressure on the solubility of gases in liquids.
5. Does pressure materially affect the solubility of solids in liquids?
6. Calculate the number of grams of solute required to make up the following solutions:

    a) 200 ml of 10% NaCl   b) 2 liters of 0.95% NaCl
    c) 50 ml of 5% NaOH   d) 25 ml of 10% NaOH
    e) 10 liters of 5% sugar

7. Calculate the number of grams of solute required to prepare the following molar solutions:

    a) 2 liters of 2 M NaOH
    c) 10 liters of 0.5 M NaCl
    e) 100 ml of 0.5 M HCl

    b) 3 liters of 0.1 M H_2SO_4
    d) 500 ml of 1.0 M H_2SO_4

8. Calculate the molar strength of solutions containing the following:

    a) 60.0 g of NaOH/liter
    c) 4.0 g of NaOH/liter
    e) 49.0 g of H_2SO_4 in 10 liters

    b) 200.0 g of NaOH in 2 liters
    d) 98.0 g of H_2SO_4 in 4 liters

Chapter 12 ACIDS, BASES, SALTS, AND IONIZATION

12-1 ELECTROLYTES AND NONELECTROLYTES

Since the days of the first experiments with electricity it has been known that solutions of some substances in water would conduct an electric current, whereas solutions of other substances in water would not. The former were called **electrolytes** and the latter **nonelectrolytes.** It was later observed that electrolytes invariably belonged to one of three classes of compounds called acids, bases, or salts.

There were other distinguishing differences between electrolytes and nonelectrolytes. When substances are dissolved in water, the freezing point of the solution is lower than that of pure water, and the depression of the freezing point is in proportion to the number of particles present in a given volume of water, Section 11-9. It was known that solutions of nonelectrolytes such as sugar, alcohol, and glycerol in equal molar concentrations have the same freezing point; however, acids, bases, and salts of corresponding concentrations invariably had lower freezing points than the nonelectrolytes. The abnormal depression of the freezing points indicated that more particles were produced from a molecular weight (1 mole) of an electrolyte in solution than from a mole of a nonelectrolyte. The boiling points of water solutions were elevated in a comparable manner when nonvolatile substances were in solution. For many decades these phenomena baffled chemists and physicists, and while various theories to explain them were advanced, none stood up under close scrutiny.

12-2 ARRHENIUS' THEORY OF IONIZATION

In 1884 the Swedish chemist Arrhenius proposed a theory which, with certain exceptions, has weathered the years and is in many ways still considered to be essentially correct. Arrhenius stated that when an electrolyte is placed in water the molecules separate into particles with positive charges and particles with negative charges. Such particles are called **ions** (from the Greek word for wanderer). These ions account for the ability of solutions of electrolytes to conduct electricity. Furthermore, since dissociation in solution yields two or more particles from each molecule, the freezing point would be "abnormally" lowered.

◄ At first Arrhenius received little support for his theory: even his professors were skeptical of its merits. He used it as a portion of his Doctor of Philosophy dissertation and was given the lowest possible passing grade for it. Twenty years later, for the same work, he was awarded the Nobel Prize in Chemistry. Outstanding scientists, like great artists, musicians, and poets, often have to wait many years before their works are fully understood and appreciated. ►

Arrhenius proposed that sodium chloride in water would form two ions:

$$NaCl \leftrightharpoons Na^+ + Cl^-$$

(12-1)

and calcium chloride would produce three ions:

$$CaCl_2 \rightleftarrows Ca^{++} + 2Cl^-$$

(12-2)

We now know that electrovalent compounds exist as ions even in crystals. While such compounds will not conduct electricity when in the solid or dry state, when dissolved in water or melted, they have freedom of movement within the liquid and can conduct electricity.

When an electric current is passed through a water solution, the negative ions migrate toward the positive electrode where they give up electrons and become free atoms or molecules:

$$2Cl^- \rightarrow Cl_2 + 2e^- \text{ (electrons)}$$

(12-3)

The positive ions migrate toward the negative electrode. If they are ions of relatively inactive metals such as copper, they combine with electrons from the electrode and become atoms of the metal:

$$Cu^{++} + 2e^- \rightarrow Cu$$

(12-4)

If the positive ions in solution are those of active metals such as sodium, potassium, or calcium the electrons entering the solution combine with water molecules, producing hydrogen and hydroxide ions:

$$2HOH + 2e^- \rightarrow 2OH^- + H_2$$

(12-4a)

The ions in the solution act as a bridge between the electrodes, Fig. 12–1.

Some electrolytes do conform with Arrhenius' original theory, in that they do not ionize until forming a solution. For example, a molecule of hydrogen chloride is covalent. Although the bond is highly polar, hydrogen chloride is not ionized in a sample of pure hydrogen chloride, which is a gas at ordinary temperatures.

$$\overset{\delta^+}{H} \overset{\delta^-}{\text{—}Cl}$$

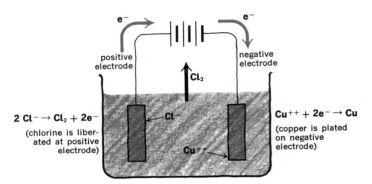

$2 \text{ Cl}^- \rightarrow \text{Cl}_2 + 2\text{e}^-$

(chlorine is liberated at positive electrode)

$\text{Cu}^{++} + 2\text{e}^- \rightarrow \text{Cu}$

(copper is plated on negative electrode)

FIG. 12-1. Conductivity of copper chloride ions in solution.

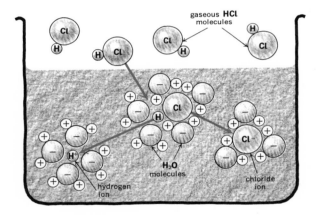

FIG. 12-2. When the gaseous hydrogen chloride molecules enter the water, they are literally pulled apart by the polar water molecules. They form hydrogen (hydronium) ions and chloride ions, which are surrounded by water molecules and oriented as shown.

Hydrogen chloride gas, when dissolved in a nonpolar solvent such as benzene, remains nonionized; the solution does not conduct an electric current. In water, hydrogen chloride is very soluble, and the resulting solution is an excellent conductor of electricity. The very polar water molecules induce the hydrogen chloride molecules to split into hydrogen ions and chloride ions. Each ion is surrounded by water molecules and is thereby "insulated" from other ions. Recall that in a polar water molecule the oxygen is the negative end and the hydrogens the positive, Sections 6-5 and 10-7. We see that water molecules can cluster around the ions, as shown in Fig. 12-2. Although we understand that it is this action of the water which causes **ionization** of hydrogen chloride, for many occasions we find it more convenient to represent ionization by using an equation that does not show the water molecules:

$$HCl \rightarrow H^+ + Cl^-$$ (12–5)

◄ Figure 12–2 shows that molecules of water surround the hydrogen and chloride ions. Exactly how many molecules of water surround each ion undoubtedly depends on the concentration of the ions in the solution. In high concentrations of ions fewer water molecules would be present than in dilute solutions. We are, however, quite sure that hydrogen ions as such do not exist in water solutions; they are always associated with water molecules and are called *hydrated ions*. It has been common practice to show one molecule of water with one hydrogen ion:

$$H^+ + H_2O \rightarrow H_3O^+ \qquad H^+ + \; :\!\overset{..}{\underset{..}{O}}\!:\!H \rightarrow H\!:\!\overset{+}{\overset{..}{\underset{..}{O}}}\!:\!H$$ (12–6)
$$\qquad\qquad\qquad\qquad\qquad\quad H \qquad\quad H$$

The H_3O^+ ion is called a *hydronium* ion. When chemists speak of hydrogen ions they really mean hydrated hydrogen ions or hydronium ions. The addition of water to nitric acid is indicated:

$$H_2O + HNO_3 \rightarrow H_3O^+ + NO_3^-$$ (12–7)

For a simplification in writing equations many chemists prefer to leave out the water in such formulas and simply write

$$HNO_3 \rightarrow H^+ + NO_3^-$$ (12–8)

In this book we will usually indicate hydrogen ions as we have done in Eq. (12–8). ►

12–3 ACIDS, BASES, AND SALTS

The terms *acid*, *base* (or alkali), and *salt* have long been used to describe certain kinds of compounds. The original classifications were based primarily on physical properties, and the names acid and salt still suggest the taste of some of the compounds. The medieval alchemist, Paracelsus (see Section 32–1) reported the isolation of "salt" from the urine of a diabetic person. This "salt" surely contained some sugar. A really good way of differentiating between acids, bases, and salts had to wait for the concepts of ionization.

We mentioned in Chapter 8 some of the properties of acids and bases. When acids react with bases, salts and water are produced:

$$\begin{matrix} HCl & + & NaOH & \rightarrow & NaCl & + & H_2O \\ \text{hydrochloric} & & \text{sodium} & & \text{sodium} & & \text{water} \\ \text{acid} & & \text{hydroxide} & & \text{chloride} & & \end{matrix}$$ (12–9)

More correctly, using ionic formulas we would write

$$H^+ + Cl^- + Na^+ + OH^- \rightarrow Na^+ + Cl^- + HOH$$ (12–10)

The only nonionic substance in the reaction is the water produced by the combination of the H^+ and OH^- ions. Arrhenius defined acids as substances which liberate hydrogen ions (H^+) in solutions. Bases are substances which liberate hydroxide (OH^-) ions in solution. Acids and bases react to form salts and water.

Since there are many acids and many bases, there are literally thousands of salts. Later in this chapter we will discuss other methods for the preparation of salts. Let us turn now to a more detailed discussion of acids, bases, and salts.

12-4 ACIDS

The term **acid** is from a Latin word *acidus*, meaning sour. All water-soluble acids taste sour unless they are very weak. Furthermore, only acids taste sour. If we examine the formulas of a few common acids,

hydrochloric	**HCl**		carbonic	**H_2CO_3**
nitric	**HNO_3**		boric	**H_3BO_3**
sulfuric	**H_2SO_4**		acetic*	**$HC_2H_3O_2$**
phosphoric	**H_3PO_4**		hydrocyanic	**HCN**

we note that the only element common to all is hydrogen. However, not all compounds containing hydrogen are acids; for instance, water H_2O, ammonia NH_3, methane CH_4, and sucrose (common sugar) $C_{12}H_{22}O_{11}$ are not acids. When hydrogen is bonded to another element in such a manner that hydrogen ions can form in solution, we say that the compound is an acid. Acids are commonly referred to as *proton donors*.

Litmus, a vegetable substance obtained from lichens, occurs in two colors. In basic solutions it is blue; in acid solutions it is pink. Because acids turn blue litmus pink, we use litmus as a convenient way of establishing whether a solution is acidic or basic.

Chemical Properties of Acids

Acids react with active metals (Section 9–6), producing hydrogen and metallic salts:

$$H_2SO_4 + Zn \rightarrow ZnSO_4 + H_2 \uparrow \tag{12-11}$$

$$2HCl + Fe \rightarrow FeCl_2 + H_2 \uparrow \tag{12-12}$$

Acids react with oxides of metals forming salts and water:

$$2HNO_3 + CaO \rightarrow Ca(NO_3)_2 + H_2O \tag{12-13}$$

$$2HCl + Na_2O \rightarrow 2NaCl + H_2O \tag{12-14}$$

$$2H_3PO_4 + 3K_2O \rightarrow 2K_3PO_4 + 3H_2O \tag{12-15}$$

---

* The formula for the acetate ion, $C_2H_3O_2^-$, is sometimes written more briefly Ac^-. When this symbol is used, sodium acetate is NaAc, and acetic acid is HAc.

Acids react with carbonates forming salts, water, and carbon dioxide. The reaction may be written in two steps:

$$2HCl + Na_2CO_3 \rightarrow 2NaCl + H_2CO_3 \tag{12-16}$$

Carbonic acid is unstable and decomposes into water and carbon dioxide:

$$H_2CO_3 \rightarrow H_2O + CO_2 \uparrow \tag{12-17}$$

The complete equation, obtained by combining Eqs. (12–16) and (12–17), is

$$2HCl + Na_2CO_3 \rightarrow 2NaCl + H_2O + CO_2 \tag{12-18}$$

While carbon dioxide is quite soluble in cold water, its solubility decreases rapidly with an increase in the temperature of the water. The excess carbon dioxide bubbles from the solution. Cold water will dissolve CO_2, and some of it will react with water forming carbonic acid:

$$H_2O + CO_2 \rightarrow H_2CO_3 \tag{12-19}$$

Equations (12–17) and (12–19) show that, depending upon the conditions, the reaction may go in either direction. We say that it is reversible; it may be written

$$H_2O + CO_2 \leftrightarrows H_2CO_3 \tag{12-20}$$

Occurrence and Preparation of Acids

Acids occur throughout nature in both living and nonliving substances. Some common acids and their sources are listed below:

Acid	Source	Acid	Source
citric	citrus fruits	carbonic	all natural waters
tartaric	grapes	hydrochloric ⎫	
oxalic	rhubarb	hydrofluoric ⎬	volcanic gases
acetic	vinegar	sulfuric ⎭	
hydrochloric	stomachs of animals		

Acids can be obtained from many salts by chemical treatment. One common method of preparing acids is by the action of a nonvolatile acid like sulfuric on salts of volatile acids:

$$H_2SO_4 + 2NaCl \rightarrow Na_2SO_4 + 2HCl \uparrow \tag{12-21}$$

$$H_2SO_4 + FeS \rightarrow Fe_2SO_4 + H_2S \uparrow \tag{12-22}$$

$$H_2SO_4 + NaNO_3 \xrightarrow{\Delta} NaHSO_4 + HNO_3 \uparrow \tag{12-23}$$

Many other acids are prepared by comparable reactions. Hydrogen chloride is also produced by a direct union of hydrogen and chlorine gases:

$$H_2 + Cl_2 \rightarrow 2HCl \tag{12-24}$$

The reaction is exothermic; in the presence of light, hydrogen and chlorine react explosively.

In section 8–4 we stated that soluble oxides of the nonmetals react with water forming acids:

$$H_2O + SO_2 \rightarrow \quad H_2SO_3 \tag{12-25}$$
$$\text{sulfurous acid}$$

$$H_2O + SO_3 \rightarrow \quad H_2SO_4 \tag{12-26}$$
$$\text{sulfuric acid}$$

$$H_2O + 3NO_2 \rightarrow 2HNO_3 + NO \tag{12-27}$$
$$\text{nitric acid}$$

The reactions above are utilized in the commercial preparation of acids.

Strong and Weak Acids

While all soluble acids liberate hydrogen ions in water solutions, they differ greatly in their ability to do so. There are only a few **strong acids,** which are those able to produce high concentrations of hydrogen ions. The most common are sulfuric acid, hydrochloric acid, and nitric acid. These are assumed to be almost completely ionized in solution. There are a great many acids in which the hydrogen atoms are combined with other elements, often oxygen, by covalent bonds which are not readily broken by the polar attractions of water molecules. Only a small percentage of their hydrogens are able to escape to form hydrogen ions at a given time, so that they never produce high concentrations of hydrogen ions. These are called **weak acids.** One example is hydrocyanic acid (hydrogen cyanide):

$$HCN \quad + H_2O \overset{*}{\longleftrightarrow} \quad H_3O^+ \quad + \quad CN^- \tag{12-28}$$

hydrocyanic		hydronium	cyanide
acid		ion	ion
99.999%		0.001%	0.001%

or

$$HCN \longleftrightarrow H^+ + CN^- \tag{12-29}$$

Other examples of weak acids are

acetic acid	$HC_2H_3O_2$	sulfurous	H_2SO_3
carbonic acid	H_2CO_3	hydrosulfuric	H_2S
boric acid	H_3BO_3		

---

* The long arrow indicates the higher concentration of reactants.

Nearly all organic acids are weak acids. Strong acids will have a greater degree of sourness than weak acids of equal concentrations.

Polyprotic Acids

All acids do not have the same number of potential hydrogen ions (protons). If we think of acids as proton donors, some can give one, some two, and some three protons per molecule. Therefore, the terms *monoprotic, diprotic,* and *triprotic* are conveniently used in referring to them. Examples are

HNO_3 monoprotic
H_2SO_4 diprotic
H_3PO_4 triprotic

Polyprotic acids ionize in two or three steps depending upon the acid:

$$H_2SO_4 \leftrightarrows H^+ + HSO_4^- \tag{12-30}$$
$$HSO_4^- \leftrightarrows H^+ + SO_4^{2-} \tag{12-31}$$

and

$$H_3PO_4 \leftrightarrows H^+ + H_2PO_4^- \tag{12-32}$$
$$H_2PO_4^- \leftrightarrows H^+ + HPO_4^{2-} \tag{12-33}$$
$$HPO_4^{2-} \leftrightarrows H^+ + PO_4^{3-} \tag{12-34}$$

Nomenclature of Acids

Most acids are made up of either two or three elements. Those with only two elements are called **binary acids.** Most of the elements in Groups VIA and VIIA of the periodic table form such acids; for example, HCl and H_2S. Acids containing three elements are called **ternary acids;** oxygen is usually the third element present. Sulfuric acid, H_2SO_4, is a good example of a ternary acid. In writing formulas for acids, we always place the hydrogen first and the oxygen, if present, last.

The names of binary acids are prefixed by *hydro-* and always end in *-ic:*

hydrochloric   **HCl**   hydrobromic   **HBr**   hydrosulfuric   **H₂S**

There are many ternary acids, since elements with several valences (oxidation states) may form several acids. Usually when the valence of the key element in the acid coincides with the positive valence indicated by the periodic table, the name of the element followed by the suffix *-ic* will be the name of the acid:

sulfuric acid   **H₂SO₄**   carbonic acid   **H₂CO₃**

In other cases the last syllable or part of the name may be dropped when the *-ic* is added:

phosphoric acid   **H₃PO₄**   nitric acid   **HNO₃**

TABLE 12-1. Some of the common acids with -ic and with -ous endings

sulfuric acid	H_2SO_4	sulfurous acid	H_2SO_3
nitric acid	HNO_3	nitrous acid	HNO_2
chloric acid	$HClO_3$	chlorous acid	$HClO_2$
phosphoric acid	H_3PO_4	phosphorous acid	H_3PO_3

The halogen acid names are exceptions. The chart indicates halogen valences of 7+; however, the formula for chloric acid is $HClO_3$ in which chlorine has a valence of 5+. Bromic and iodic acids have comparable formulas.

Another series of ternary acids exists for many elements, in which the valence of the key element is lower than that of the -ic acid. For these acids the -ic ending is changed to -ous. As can be seen in Table 12-1, the number of oxygen atoms is one less in an -ous acid than in an -ic acid.

Additional information on the nomenclature of acids will be found in Section 17-9.

12-5 BASES

Substances which liberate hydroxide ions (OH^-) in solution have long been called **bases** or **alkalis.** A common function of bases is that of neutralizing acids. A typical reaction is

$$NaOH + HCl \rightarrow NaCl + HOH \tag{12-35}$$

or

$$Na^+ + OH^- + H^+ + Cl^- \rightarrow Na^+ + Cl^- + HOH \tag{12-36}$$

Equation (12-36) is representative of reactions of many bases since a hydroxide ion, OH^-, combines with a hydrogen ion, H^+ (a proton), to form water. The remaining ions form a salt. This process is called **neutralization.**

Fundamentally, a hydroxide ion is a base because it has a pair of electrons available which it readily shares with a proton:

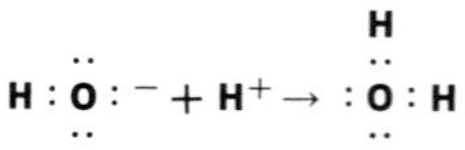

$$H:\overset{..}{\underset{..}{O}}:^- + H^+ \rightarrow \;\overset{\overset{\textstyle H}{|}}{\underset{..}{:\overset{..}{O}:H}}$$

Strictly speaking, it is not necessary for the base to have a negative charge; having an electron pair is the important feature. Therefore, some other group, having an electron pair which it shares fairly well with a proton, would be a base. By a broader definition, a **base** is a proton acceptor. Ammonia, NH_3, is an excellent example:

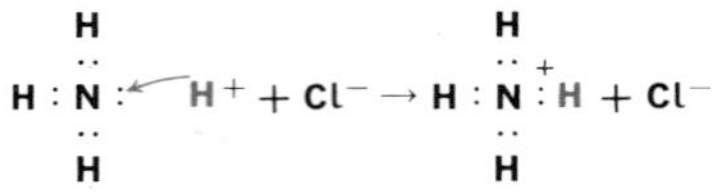

$$H:\overset{\overset{\textstyle H}{..}}{\underset{\underset{\textstyle H}{..}}{N}}:\!\!\overset{\frown}{}H^+ + Cl^- \rightarrow H:\overset{\overset{\textstyle H}{..}}{\underset{\underset{\textstyle H}{..}}{N}}:\!H^+ + Cl^- \tag{12-37}$$

Thus, if ammonia gas were passed into a solution of hydrochloric acid, the reaction represented in Eq. (12–37) would occur and the acidity of the solution would be reduced.

◄ The basic properties of ammonia are apparent even in a water solution. The solution turns litmus blue, has a slippery feeling, and tastes bitter. Careful analysis reveals that the solution contains about one hydroxide ion for every hundred ammonia molecules. Apparently the ammonia molecules can occasionally take a proton from a water molecule:

$$\begin{array}{ccccc}
\text{H} & & \text{H} & & \\
\ddot{\text{H}\!:\!\text{N}\!:} & + \text{ H}\!:\!\ddot{\text{O}}\!:\!\text{H} \rightleftharpoons & \text{H}\!:\!\overset{+}{\ddot{\text{N}}}\!:\!\text{H} & + \quad {}^{-}\!:\!\ddot{\text{O}}\!:\!\text{H} & \qquad\qquad (12\text{--}38) \\
\text{H} & & \text{H} & &
\end{array}$$

99%   1%   1%

or

$$NH_3 \quad + \quad HOH \rightleftharpoons \quad NH_4{}^+ \quad + \quad OH^-$$

ammonia   ammonium   hydroxide
                                                ions   ions

Equation (12–38) represents the basic strength or degree to which ammonia forms ions. The reaction does not occur to a great extent, and few hydroxide ions are present at any one time. Ammonia is a weak base, compared to OH^-, because it does not share its electrons so readily.

A solution of ammonia in water is often called "ammonium hydroxide," because of the ions formed, Eq. (12–38). However, in terms of the *amount* of ammonia present, compared to the ions, we see it is much more accurate to call it an *ammonia* solution. Even more important, there is no covalent compound having formula NH_4OH. ►

The reaction of a base like ammonia is of extreme importance in organic and biochemical reactions; however, for the present our discussion of bases will be largely limited to the hydroxides of metals.

Properties of Bases

It is the hydroxide ions that determine the properties of the hydroxide bases. They are bitter;
have a slippery, soapy feel;
turn pink litmus blue;
neutralize acids, forming salts and water.
Bases range from extremely strong caustic substances (NaOH, KOH) capable of destroying flesh and many fabrics, to mild materials (NH_3) which may be used in the laundry and household cleaning. Magnesium hydroxide, $Mg(OH)_2$, may be taken internally. The strength of bases, like that of acids, depends upon the degree of ionization, since this determines the hydroxide ion concentration in a solution. The more active metals form the stronger bases; therefore, sodium and potassium hydroxides are the strongest common bases. They are electrovalent and are completely ionized in a solid state as well as in solution.

Preparation of Bases

In Chapter 8, "Oxygen," it was stated that oxides of active metals combine with water to form bases.

$$Na_2O + H_2O \rightarrow 2NaOH \tag{12-39}$$

$$CaO + H_2O \rightarrow Ca(OH)_2 \tag{12-40}$$

$$MgO + H_2O \rightarrow Mg(OH)_2 \tag{12-41}$$

As the metals become less active, their hydroxides become less soluble, with a corresponding decrease in the tendency to form hydroxide ions. Sodium and calcium hydroxide, the most important commercial bases, are used in enormous quantities in industry. Calcium hydroxide is made according to the reaction in Eq. (12–40). Sodium hydroxide, one of the products of the electrolysis of sodium chloride, will be discussed in Chapter 17.

Reactions of Bases

As previously stated, a common reaction of a base is that of neutralizing acids:

$$NaOH + HNO_3 \rightarrow NaNO_3 + HOH \tag{12-42}$$

$$2KOH + H_2SO_4 \rightarrow K_2SO_4 + 2HOH \tag{12-43}$$

$$NH_3 + HCl \rightarrow NH_4Cl \tag{12-44}$$

$$2NH_3 + H_2SO_4 \rightarrow (NH_4)_2SO_4 \tag{12-45}$$

$$3NaOH + H_3PO_4 \rightarrow Na_3PO_4 + 3HOH \tag{12-46}$$

$$Ca(OH)_2 + 2HNO_3 \rightarrow Ca(NO_3)_2 + 2HOH \tag{12-47}$$

Bases also react with acidic oxides to form salts and water:

$$Ca(OH)_2 + CO_2 \rightarrow CaCO_3 + H_2O \tag{12-48}$$

$$2NaOH + CO_2 \rightarrow Na_2CO_3 + H_2O \tag{12-49}$$

$$2KOH + SO_2 \rightarrow K_2SO_3 + H_2O \tag{12-50}$$

$$Ca(OH)_2 + SO_3 \rightarrow CaSO_4 + H_2O \tag{12-51}$$

The strongest base found in the home is sodium hydroxide (lye), which is used as a cleaner to cut grease and as a water softener. Drano and similar products contain sodium hydroxide mixed with small particles of aluminum metal. These react in water liberating a great amount of heat. When such products are flushed down a sewer pipe, the heat produced melts the grease, loosens scale, and kills any tree roots that may be clogging the sewer. The chemical reaction is

$$NaOH + Al + H_2O \rightarrow \underset{\substack{\text{sodium} \\ \text{aluminate}}}{NaAlO_2} + \tfrac{3}{2}H_2 \tag{12-52}$$

The ability of certain metals to react with strong bases is discussed in the next section.

Amphoterism

It has been stated that oxides of nonmetals have acidic characteristics and that oxides of active metals in solution form basic hydroxides. It is reasonable, then, that oxides of some of the in-between metals exhibit both characteristics. Zinc, tin, and aluminum are typical examples. The hydroxides of these metals, which are largely covalent, react with either strong acids or strong bases to form salts. They must, therefore, be considered as both weak acids and weak bases. Such substances are said to be **amphoteric** (from the Greek word *amphoteros*, meaning both. This word is closely related to amphibian.) Some reactions of tin hydroxide are

$$Sn(OH)_2 + 2HCl \quad \rightarrow SnCl_2 + 2H_2O \tag{12-53}$$

$$Sn(OH)_2 + 2NaOH \rightarrow SnO_2^{2-} + 2Na^+ + 2H_2O \tag{12-54}$$

Any substance which can react either as an acid or a base is an amphoteric substance.

12–6 SALTS

Salts may be defined as electrolytes which dissociate to produce positive ions other than hydrogen ions, and negative ions other than hydroxide ions. They may be more readily visualized if we think of them as a product of the reaction between an acid and a base. Thousands of salts have been prepared, and nearly all of them that are soluble are completely ionized. The degree of ionization of electrolytes is easily demonstrated by the conductivity device shown in Fig. 12–3. Solutions of strong electrolytes are good conductors of electricity, and those of weak electrolytes are poor conductors. The brightness of the filament of the light bulb indicates the degree of ionization of the solutions being tested. With nonelectrolytes the filament shows no light.

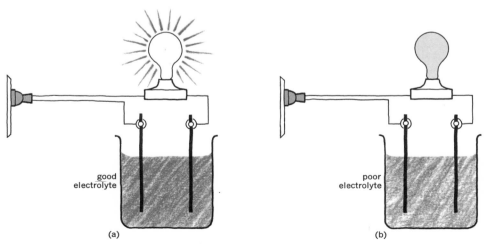

FIG. 12–3. A device to determine the relative conductance of solutions.

Preparation of Salts

Salts may be prepared by several methods.
Reaction between an acid and a base:

$$H_2SO_4 + Mg(OH)_2 \rightarrow MgSO_4 + 2H_2O \qquad (12\text{-}55)$$

sulfuric   magnesium   magnesium
acid   hydroxide   sulfate

Reaction between an acid and an active metal:

$$2HCl + Fe \rightarrow FeCl_2 + H_2\uparrow \qquad (12\text{-}56)$$

hydrochloric   iron   iron (II)
acid   chloride

Reaction between an acid and a metallic oxide:

$$2HNO_3 + CaO \rightarrow Ca(NO_3)_2 + H_2O \qquad (12\text{-}57)$$

nitric   calcium   calcium
acid   oxide   nitrate

Reaction between a base and an acidic oxide:

$$2NaOH + CO_2 \rightarrow Na_2CO_3 + H_2O \qquad (12\text{-}58)$$

sodium   carbon   sodium
oxide   dioxide   carbonate

Direct union of elements:

$$Na + \tfrac{1}{2}Cl_2 \rightarrow NaCl \qquad (12\text{-}59)$$

sodium   chlorine   sodium chloride

Formation of an insoluble salt from two soluble salts:

$$AgNO_3 + NaCl \rightarrow AgCl\downarrow + NaNO_3 \qquad (12\text{-}60)$$

silver   sodium   silver   sodium
nitrate   chloride   chloride   nitrate

While the above list of reactions is not complete, it gives some idea of the various methods of preparation.

Nomenclature of Salts

The names of all compounds containing only two kinds of elements (binary compounds) end in *-ide*. The full name of the more positive element, usually a metal, is written first and the last portion of the name of the second element is replaced by *-ide:*

KCl	potassium chloride	$CaBr_2$	calcium bromide
MgS	magnesium sulfide	NaF	sodium fluoride
$CuCl_2$	copper chloride		

Name endings for salts of ternary acids indicate the series of acids from which they are derived. Acids ending in *-ic* form salts ending in *-ate:*

$$H_2SO_4 + 2NaOH \rightarrow Na_2SO_4 + 2H_2O \qquad\qquad (12\text{–}61)$$

sulfur*ic*   sodium
  acid   sulf*ate*

Acids ending in *-ous* form salts ending in *-ite:*

$$H_2SO_3 + 2KOH \rightarrow K_2SO_3 + 2H_2O \qquad\qquad (12\text{–}62)$$

sulfur*ous*   potassium
  acid   sulf*ite*

Additional examples:

Formula	Name of Acid	Name of Corresponding Salt
HNO_3	nitric	nitrate
HNO_2	nitrous	nitrite
H_3PO_4	phosphoric	phosphate
H_3PO_3	phosphorous	phosphite
$HClO_3$	chloric	chlorate
$HClO_2$	chlorous	chlorite

Salts of Metals with Variable Valences

When metallic ions have more than one valence it is proper to indicate with roman numerals which valence is involved in a salt. For example, iron has valences of 2+ and 3+, forming the chlorides $FeCl_2$ and $FeCl_3$. Their proper names are iron(II) chloride and iron(III) chloride. Another example is Cu_2O, copper(I) oxide and CuO, copper(II) oxide.

This simplified system, unfortunately, is so new that an older system is still often used. It is necessary that you be familiar with both. In the older system, the *-ous, -ic* endings are used in the same manner as in naming acids, and therefore $FeCl_2$ and $FeCl_3$ are called ferrous chloride and ferric chloride, respectively. The major disadvantage of the older system is that the name does not indicate a definite valence, it shows merely whether the element in consideration has the lower or higher valence.

Acidic and Basic Salts

If 2 formula weights of sodium hydroxide are added to 1 formula weight of sulfuric acid, the acid is neutralized, and a salt is formed:

$$2NaOH + H_2SO_4 \rightarrow Na_2SO_4 + 2H_2O \qquad\qquad (12\text{–}63)$$

If only 1 formula weight of sodium hydroxide is added to 1 formula weight of sulfuric acid, only one-half of the hydrogen atoms in the acid are replaced or neutralized,

$$NaOH + H_2SO_4 \rightarrow NaHSO_4 + H_2O \qquad\qquad (12\text{–}64)$$

and the product is part salt and part acid. Such substances are called *acid salts*. Bicarbonate of soda, more correctly called sodium hydrogen carbonate, is an acid salt which can be formed by partially neutralizing carbonic acid with sodium hydroxide:

$$H_2CO_3 + NaOH \rightarrow NaHCO_3 + H_2O \tag{12-65}$$

For phosphoric acid, which is triprotic, three steps are necessary to bring about complete neutralization:

$$NaOH + H_3PO_4 \rightarrow \quad NaH_2PO_4 \quad + H_2O \tag{12-66}$$
sodium
dihydrogen
phosphate

$$2NaOH + H_3PO_4 \rightarrow \quad Na_2HPO_4 \quad + 2H_2O \tag{12-67}$$
sodium
monohydrogen
phosphate

$$3NaOH + H_3PO_4 \rightarrow \quad Na_3PO_4 \quad + 3H_2O \tag{12-68}$$
sodium
phosphate

In a similar manner basic salts are prepared. If 1 formula weight of hydrochloric acid is added to 1 formula weight of calcium hydroxide,

$$HCl + Ca(OH)_2 \rightarrow Ca(OH)Cl + H_2O \tag{12-69}$$
calcium
hydroxide
chloride

the product is a basic salt, since the base has been only partially neutralized.

Solubility of Salts

When writing equations in which salts are formed, we frequently find it desirable to know the solubility of these salts, (see Section 7–6). While such information is available in handbooks of chemistry, the knowledge and understanding of a few simple rules concerning the solubilities of the more common salts will be a help.

In formulating such generalizations, we place the salts in categories or groups made up of

1) those which are soluble and
2) those which are
   a) insoluble, but the majority of the same kind of salts are soluble,
   b) soluble, although the majority of the same type of salts are insoluble.

The following table summarizes the rules for common salts:

Soluble Salts	Insoluble Salts
1. all nitrates	4. all sulfates
2. all sodium ⎫	_except_ strontium
potassium ⎬ salts	barium
ammonium ⎭	lead
3. all chlorides	5. all carbonates and phosphates
except silver	_except_ those of the alkali metals*
lead	and ammonium
mercury (I) chloride	

* The metals of Group IA are known as the alkali metals.

We can use Eq. (12–70) to illustrate the applications of the above rules:

$$AgNO_3 + NaCl \rightarrow AgCl + NaNO_3 \qquad (12\text{–}70)$$

rule (1) applies to $AgNO_3$,
rule (2) applies to NaCl,
rule (3) applies to AgCl,
rules (1) and (2) both apply to $NaNO_3$.

We have, therefore, determined that AgCl is the only insoluble salt in this reaction.

12–7 EQUIVALENT WEIGHTS

In the previous chapter (Section 11–15) we introduced the concepts of molar and formal solutions. These methods of expressing concentration are very useful, but in certain types of chemical calculations they are somewhat inconvenient. A few chemical equations will serve to prove this point. When molecular weights of hydrochloric acid and sodium hydroxide react,

$$H^+Cl^- + Na^+OH^- \rightarrow HOH + Na^+Cl^- \qquad (12\text{–}71)$$

1 mole	1 mole	1 mole	1 mole
36.5 g	40 g	18 g	58.5 g

it can be seen that they are chemically equivalent or equal, 36.5 g of the acid reacting with exactly 40 g of NaOH. Thus, 10 ml of a 1 M solution of acid would require 10 ml of a 1 M solution of the base. Similarly, 98 g, 1 mole, of sulfuric acid would react with and be chemically equal to 74 g, 1 mole, of calcium hydroxide:

$$H_2SO_4 + Ca(OH)_2 \rightarrow 2HOH + CaSO_4 \qquad (12\text{–}72)$$

1 mole	1 mole	2 moles	1 mole
98 g	74 g	36 g	136 g

However, when sodium hydroxide reacts with sulfuric acid,

$$2NaOH + H_2SO_4 \rightarrow Na_2SO_4 + 2HOH$$

2 moles	1 mole	1 mole	2 moles
$2 \times 40 =$ 80 g	98 g	142 g	$2 \times 18 =$ 36 g

2 moles of sodium hydroxide are required to react with 1 mole of sulfuric acid, or 1 mole of sodium hydroxide reacts with exactly 1/2 mole of sulfuric acid. Similarly, when hydrochloric acid reacts with calcium hydroxide,

$$2HCl + Ca(OH)_2 \rightarrow CaCl_2 + 2HOH \tag{12-73}$$

2 moles	1 mole	1 mole	2 moles
$2 \times 36.5 =$ 73 g	74 g	111 g	$2 \times 18 =$ 36 g

2 moles of the hydrochloric acid are needed to react with 1 of calcium hydroxide. It is evident, therefore, that moles are not always equivalent to one another. If molar solutions are used, additional factors must be introduced to make calculations of equivalent amounts meaningful. In the reactions between sodium hydroxide and phosphoric acid, we find

$$NaOH + H_3PO_4 \rightarrow NaH_2PO_4 + H_2O \tag{12-74}$$

$$2NaOH + H_3PO_4 \rightarrow Na_2HPO_4 + 2H_2O \tag{12-75}$$

$$3NaOH + H_3PO_4 \rightarrow Na_3PO_4 + 3H_2O \tag{12-76}$$

Here we see that 1 mole of phosphoric acid can react with 3 moles of sodium hydroxide.

If we return to a consideration of the mole, we recall that by definition it contains Avogadro's number, 6.02×10^{23} units, of the substance under consideration. One mole of hydrochloric acid can furnish 6.02×10^{23} H^+, and 1 mole of sodium hydroxide the same number of OH^-, so they are therefore chemically equivalent. However, 1 mole of sulfuric acid, H_2SO_4, can yield $2 \times 6.02 \times 10^{23}$ H^+, and 1 mole of phosphoric acid, H_3PO_4, $3 \times 6.02 \times 10^{23}$ H^+. It should be obvious that 1 mole of calcium hydroxide, $Ca(OH)_2$, is able to produce twice as many OH^- as 1 mole of sodium hydroxide. To simplify this situation, we can use the idea of an **equivalent,** *which is one mole of the reacting unit.* The reacting units may be OH^- ions, H^+ ions, or in redox reactions, electrons. An equivalent always contains 6.02×10^{23} reacting units. Thus we say that each mole of H_3PO_4 provides 3 equivalents. Similarly, HCl provides 1 eq/mole and $Ca(OH)_2$ provides 2 eq/mole.

An **equivalent weight** of any acid or base is that amount of substance that can furnish 1 mole of hydrogen ions or hydroxide ions. In terms of weight it is approximately 1 g of H^+ and 17 g of OH^-. The formula weight divided by the number of equivalents in the formula equals the equivalent weight.

$$\frac{\text{formula weight}}{\text{number of equivalents}} = \text{equivalent weight.}$$

Table 12-2 lists formula weights, the number of equivalents per formula weight, and the equivalent weights of some common acids and bases.

TABLE 12–2. **Calculation of equivalent weight**

Compound	Formula Weight	No. of Equivalents	Formula Weight/No. of Equivalents	Equivalent Weight
HCl	36.5	1	36.5/1	36.5
H$_2$SO$_4$	98	2	98/2	49
H$_3$PO$_4$	98	3	98/3	32.666
NaOH	40	1	40/1	40
Ca(OH)$_2$	74	2	74/2	37
HNO$_3$	63	1	63/1	63

12–8 NORMAL SOLUTIONS

A **normal solution** of an acid or base contains an equivalent weight of the solute per liter of solution. *Normality* refers to the number of equivalent weights per liter regardless of whether it is 1/10 normal (0.1 N) or 36 normal (36 N). Stated another way:

$$\text{normality} = \frac{\text{g/liter}}{\text{eq wt}}$$

Normal values are convenient since equal volumes of solutions of equal normality all contain an equal number of reacting units. Thus 1 liter of a 1 N solution of acid equals (can neutralize) 1 liter of 1 N base solution.

In many laboratory operations we wish to handle several milliliters, not several liters, so it is more convenient to use the unit milliequivalent, abbreviated meq.

1 equivalent = 1000 milliequivalents, and
   1 eq wt = 1000 meq wts.

We can also say that a

1 N solution = 1 eq/liter or 1 meq/ml, and

$$\text{normality} = \frac{\text{g/ml}}{\text{meq wt}} \; .$$

If we wish to know the number of *milliequivalents* of a substance in a given volume of solution, we multiply the normality by the volume (in ml) of the solution. Thus,

milliliters × normality = number of milliequivalents.

If the *normality* of a solution is known, the weight of solute in any volume can be calculated.

Example 1. How many grams of NaOH are there in 11 ml of a 1 N solution?
   The solution contains 1 meq of NaOH/ml, so 11 ml contains 11 meq. Now the eq wt of NaOH is 40 g and:

$$\text{meq wt} = \frac{40 \text{ g}}{1000} = 0.040 \text{ g}$$

Therefore, 11 meqs × 0.040g/meq = 0.44 g of NaOH.

Example 2. How many grams of NaOH are present in 25 ml of 0.5 N solution?

Since a normal solution contains 1 meq/ml, a 0.5 N solution contains 0.5 meq/ml, and 25 ml of 0.5 N will contain $25 \times 0.5 = 12.5$ meq. The meq of NaOH is

$$\frac{40}{1000} = 0.04 \text{ g.}$$

The amount of NaOH in 25 ml of a 0.5 N solution, then, is $12.5 \times 0.04 = 0.5$ g.

◄ If the above problem appears difficult, try to work this one—the operations are identical: How many grams do 25 half dollars weigh if 1 silver dollar weighs 28 g? (It must be assumed that silver dollars weigh twice as much as half dollars.)

25×0.5 (dollar) = 12.5 (dollars).

$\quad 12.5 \times \quad 28 \quad = 350$ g.

(dollars) (grams) ►

12-9 TITRATIONS OF ACIDS AND BASES

In a chemical reaction one molecule of a substance reacts with one or more molecules of another substance. Using the concepts of equivalents, we can modify this to say that in a chemical reaction one equivalent of one substance always reacts with one equivalent of the other reactant. We can, of course, go one step further and state that 1 meq of an acid neutralizes 1 meq of a base. These statements lead to an important method for establishing the concentration of an unknown acid or base. If we measure 10.0 ml of a 2.00 N base into a flask and then find that 4.00 ml of an unknown acid just neutralizes the base, we can find the concentration of the acid. Since 10.0 ml of 2.00 N base contain 20.0 meq of base, at the point of neutrality we must have added just 20.0 meq of acid. This 20.0 meq was contained in 4.00 ml of acid, so there were 5.00 meq/ml or 5 equivalents/liter in the acid, and the concentration is 5.00 N.

The process described for determining the concentration of an unknown substance by reacting it with a substance of known nature and concentration, is called *titration*. The apparatus commonly consists of burettes (Fig. 12-4) which enable us to measure accurately the volumes of acid and base. We customarily add an indicator substance to tell us when one reactant neutralizes the other. We could use litmus, but the change from blue to red involves intermediate shades of purple and makes it difficult to determine the exact point of equivalence (the endpoint). If we add the compound called phenolphthalein to a solution of base, the solution turns a brilliant red-purple. When sufficient hydrogen ions have been added to react with all the hydroxide ions of the base, the phenolphthalein solution becomes colorless. If we started with phenolphthalein and an acid of known concentration, we could add the base of unknown concentration until the red-purple color formed. There are many substances such as phenolphthalein which serve as indicators (Table 13-4).

The usefulness of titrations employing normal solutions lies in the fact that only one base of known concentration is needed to establish the concentration of many different acids. In the same way, an acid of known concentration can be used to determine the concentration of many bases. At the neutralization point we know that an equal number of

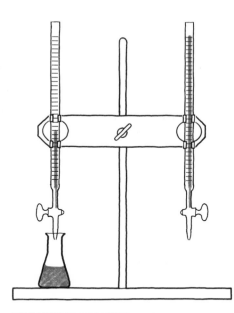

FIG. 12–4. Burettes may be used in determining the relative strengths of solutions of acids and bases.

milliequivalents of acid and base have reacted, and we can say that

meq of acid = meq of base.

Since the number of milli-equivalents of either acid or base is found by multiplying the number of milliliters by the normality we can say that

milliliters of acid × normality of acid = milliliters of base × normality of base.

If we know any three of these four values, we can find the unknown quantity.

Example. If 30 ml of NaOH requires 20 ml of HCl to neutralize it, and we have prepared the solution of NaOH to contain 0.20 equivalents/liter, what is the concentration of the HCl?

We started with 30 × 0.20 or 6.0 meq of NaOH, so we must have used 6.0 meq of HCl. This 6.0 meq was contained in 20 ml of solution, so 1 ml of HCl contained 6/20 = 0.30 meq, and its normality is 0.30 N. We could solve the problem by substituting in the formula given above and get

$$30 \text{ ml} \times 0.20 \ N \text{ (base)} = 20 \text{ ml} \times ? \ N \text{ (acid)} \quad N \text{ acid} = \frac{30 \times 0.20}{20} = 0.30.$$

Although a titration can never tell us *which* acid is present, it can tell us the concentration of any acid. Titrations are widely used in chemical processes. We use them, for example, to determine how much base to add to a batch of soap, to determine how much ascorbic acid (Vitamin C) is produced in a synthetic reaction, and to assay the amount of silver in an ore. The concentration of acid in the stomach of a person may be determined by titrating a sample of his gastric juice with standardized sodium hydroxide. This kind of titration helps to decide whether or not the person has a gastric ulcer.

12–10 FIRST AID FOR ACCIDENTS INVOLVING ACIDS AND BASES

Since acids and bases are used extensively in the laboratory, in industry, and even in the home, accidents involving them occur from time to time. An understanding of how persons should be treated, internally and externally, may change what would be a major accident into a minor incident. Most strong acids are not poisonous if diluted sufficiently; therefore, the washing or dilution with water should be the first and immediate treatment. This treatment is recommended for all strong chemicals including bases. The second step is neutralization. The so-called weak acids and bases should be used to avoid the danger of "overcorrecting" which might cause additional damage. Table 12–3 lists suitable antidotes for acids and bases.

TABLE 12–3. Antidotes

Poison	Treatment	
	Internal	External
acids	milk of magnesia [$Mg(OH)_2$] sodium bicarbonate* (in solution) milk†	ammonia solution sodium bicarbonate
bases	dilute acetic acid or diluted vinegar citrus juices fruit juices	dilute acetic acid (vinegar)

* The reaction between sodium bicarbonate and an acid liberates carbon dioxide. This may cause some uncomfortable "inflation."
† Milk, which is usually available in the home, is not only soothing to the irritated membranes, but the proteins present are proton acceptors and therefore act as a weak base in neutralizing the acid.

For any chemical in the eyes, flush with large amounts of water immediately; then, for acids use a very dilute solution of bicarbonate of soda. For bases, use a solution of boric acid. If there is irritation, see a doctor immediately.

Some controversy exists regarding induced vomiting to remove poisons from a victim's stomach. This was a common procedure years ago when hospitals and doctors were sometimes hours away. As most of you know, the physical act of vomiting is not always gentle, and when the esophagus or stomach walls have been badly damaged by a corrosive chemical, vomiting may cause additional damage or a rupture. Consequently, the odds favor rushing an accident victim to the hospital and a stomach pump. However, many drugs, such as aspirin which may be fatal when taken in excess, do not cause immediate deterioration to the tissues. It seems logical that if a child swallows a noncorrosive drug, that a glass of water or milk followed by induced vomiting would not be harmful. A glance at the lips, mouth, or throat will tell whether corrosive materials have been swallowed.

12-11 SUMMARY

In this chapter we have seen how Arrhenius' ideas of ionization helped to establish a firm basis for the then incomplete classification of compounds as acids, bases, or salts. Organic chemistry and biochemistry add other classifications of compounds, but in inorganic chemistry, we use principally the three classifications of acid, base, and salt to describe compounds. Just as we found we could simplify the discussion of elements when we had the classifications of metal and nonmetal, and of the degree of activity, we find we can simplify the chemistry of compounds by using categories of strong and weak acids and bases, and soluble and insoluble salts.

These classifications also provide us with a basis for naming compounds. While the name acid generally identifies a member of that group and hydroxide is used in the names of most common bases, the names of salts are less easily identified until we understand the basic conventions and rules. We can deduce a great deal both about the nature of the compound and the products of reactions in which it is involved if we know the name and solubility of the salt.

When we extend our ideas of the quantitative nature of chemical reactions with the concepts of normality and equivalent weights, we develop one of the most useful techniques of chemistry. Titration is widely used to determine the concentration of many substances of vital importance to chemists.

IMPORTANT TERMS

Acid	Electrolyte	Normal solution	Ternary acid
Amphoteric	Equivalent	Polyprotic acid	Titration
Base	Ion	Salt	Weak acid
Binary acid	Ionization	Strong acid	

WORK EXERCISES

1. What observations were made which set the stage for Arrhenius' development of the theory of ionization?

2. Illustrate the role of water molecules in the ionization of hydrogen chloride, HCl.

3. Distinguish between a hydrogen ion and a hydronium ion.

4. Write equations for the action of sodium hydroxide, NaOH, with each of the acids listed in Table 12-1 and name the products.

5. List all the possible ions that might be found in the water solutions of the acids listed in Table 12-1.

6. What chemical reaction takes place when water containing carbonic acid, H_2CO_3, is warmed?

7. What is the principal distinction between strong and weak acids?

8. Name and write the formulas for four polyprotic acids.

9. Name each of the salts formed in Eqs. 12–42 to 12–51.

10. Contrast the properties of acids and bases.

11. Name three substances which are found in the home that could be used in the treatment of a child who has swallowed some strong lye (NaOH) solution.

12. Under what circumstances is it inadvisable to induce vomiting when a poisonous substance has been swallowed?

13. Write the chemical equations for the reactions involved in five methods of preparing salts.

14. Review the rules for the solubility of salts, and write the names and formulas for two salts in each category.

15. Calculate the number of grams of solute required to prepare the following solutions:

   a) 2 liters of 0.5 N NaOH

   b) 5 liters of 2 N NaOH

   c) 2 liters of 0.5 N H_2SO_4

   d) 6 liters of 1 N H_3PO_4

   e) 4 liters of 0.1 N $Ca(OH)_2$

   f) 200 ml of 0.1 N NaOH

16. What is the normality of solutions containing the following amounts of solute?

   a) 10 g of NaOH/liter

   b) 49 g of H_2SO_4/liter

   c) 0.04 g of NaOH/ml

   d) 0.5 g of NaOH/10 ml

   e) 0.0365 g of HCl/2 ml

17. Twenty-five milliliters of 0.6 N NaOH is exactly neutralized by 30 ml of a solution of HCl. What is the normality of the HCl?

18. Fifteen milliliters of 0.6 N HCl is neutralized by 10 ml of NaOH. What is the normality of the base?

19. Solve for the normality of the following solutions:

   a) 24 ml of 0.8 N H_2SO_4 = 48 ml of NaOH

   b) 16 ml of 3 N NaOH = 48 ml of HCl

   c) 18 ml of 0.1 N $Ca(OH)_2$ = 30 ml of H_3PO_4

   d) 18 ml of 0.1 N $Ca(OH)_2$ = 12 ml of H_2SO_4

20. How many grams of solute are present in

   a) 1 liter of 0.30 N NaOH?

   b) 1 liter of 2.0 N H_2SO_4?

   c) 500 ml of 0.60 N NaOH?

   d) 250 ml of 2.0 N HCl?

   e) 10 ml of 0.50 N H_3PO_4?

SUGGESTED READING

Holum, J. R., *Elements of General and Biological Chemistry*, Chapter 6, "Ionic Reactions," John Wiley, New York, 1962. A nicely illustrated treatment of ionic reactions.

Chapter 13 EQUILIBRIUM

13-1 SOME TYPES OF EQUILIBRIUM

If we add a small amount of ordinary table salt, NaCl, to water, it soon dissolves. As we continue to add salt to our solution, we find that the speed with which it dissolves decreases and, finally, the salt begins to settle on the bottom and further additions only increase the amount of the undissolved salt. Stirring or some other form of agitation may hasten the rate at which the salt dissolves, but it does not increase the amount of salt that can be dissolved.

When we reach the state at which no more salt appears to dissolve, we might reasonably assume that nothing is happening in our saturated solution. However, there is evidence, described below, that ions of the salt are still leaving the crystals and entering the solution, and that ions in the solution are returning to the solid crystals. When the rate at which the ions leave the crystals equals the rate at which they leave the solution and return to the crystals, we say that a state of **equilibrium** exists (Fig. 13-1).

If we remove a small corner from a single salt crystal and place it in a saturated salt solution for some time, we find that the broken crystal has been transformed into a perfect cubic crystal. If we weighed the broken crystal and now weigh the perfect crystal we find that they weigh the same amount. We conclude that sodium and chloride ions from the solution attach themselves to the broken crystal in such a way as to form a slightly smaller but perfect crystal. The fact that the crystal neither gains nor loses weight is good evidence for believing that there existed an equilibrium involving continuous exchange.

Another way to show that such an equilibrium occurs is by adding radioactive sodium chloride crystals to a saturated salt solution. After a period of time, we find that there is radioactivity in the solution and that the amount of radioactivity in the solid salt has decreased. After a longer time we find that an equilibrium between radioactive ions going into and out of solution becomes established, and the proportion of radioactivity in the solution and in the crystals does not change.

An equilibrium is a state of balance. However, a chemical equilibrium is not like a seesaw where the balance is static. A chemical equilibrium is dynamic; although the system as a whole is balanced, individual particles are continually being exchanged. If anything happens to alter the action of the particles, the equilibrium shifts. A somewhat complex example of equilibrium and a simple way of altering it is illustrated in the following paragraph.

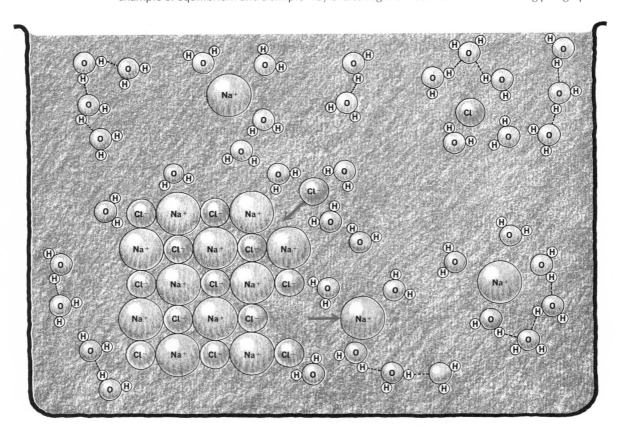

FIG. 13–1. An equilibrium existing between undissolved and dissolved sodium chloride.

We can take a large bottle about half full of water, add some sulfur dioxide gas, close the bottle with a stopper, and then allow it to stand for a period of time (Fig. 13–2). We may even shake the stoppered bottle to hasten any processes that might be occurring. If we then remove the stopper, we can detect the odor of sulfur dioxide, and we might conclude that it had not dissolved in the water. However, if we remove some of the water and heat it, we find that sulfur dioxide is released. A test of the water with litmus paper would show that it is slightly acid. We can conclude, therefore, that sulfur dioxide is soluble in water,

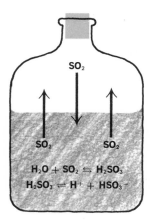

FIG. 13–2. Equilibria in a closed bottle containing water and sulfur dioxide.

but that sulfur dioxide molecules also tend to escape from a water solution. We would assume that when a bottle containing sulfur dioxide and water is allowed to stand for a period of time, an equilibrium is established and sulfur dioxide molecules are entering the solution at the same rate at which others are escaping.

The presence of hydrogen ions in our solution of sulfur dioxide in water is explained by the fact that sulfur dioxide not only dissolves in the water, but also reacts with it to form sulfurous acid:

$$HOH + SO_2 \rightarrow H_2SO_3 \tag{13–1}$$

The sulfurous acid then dissociates to produce hydrogen and hydrogen sulfite ions:

$$H_2SO_3 \rightarrow H^+ + HSO_3^- \tag{13–2}$$

If we remove the stopper from our bottle of sulfur dioxide and water that has reached equilibrium, and allow molecules of sulfur dioxide gas to escape from the bottle, and especially if we apply heat or reduce the pressure above the liquid by use of a vacuum pump, we find that the water no longer turns blue litmus red. From this we can conclude that there were three equilibria involved in our bottle of sulfur dioxide and water. The sulfur dioxide molecules in the space above the solution are in equilibrium with the dissolved sulfur dioxide molecules. There is another equilibrium in which dissolved sulfur dioxide molecules and water molecules combine to form molecules of sulfurous acid which can in turn decompose to give back sulfur dioxide and water, Eq. (13–1). There is a further equilibrium between molecules of sulfurous acid and hydrogen and hydrogen sulfite ions, Eq. (13–2). The situation is illustrated in Fig. 13–2.

When we remove the stopper from the bottle, the equilibrium between dissolved and gaseous molecules of SO_2 shifts. The sulfur dioxide molecules tend to leave the solution, which in turn causes the decomposition of some of the sulfurous acid molecules. Consequently, fewer hydrogen and hydrogen sulfite ions remain in the solution. Continuation of these processes results in the formation of pure water and the escape of all the SO_2 as gas. Equations (13–1) and (13–2) should properly be written to show that they are reversible and really represent equilibrium situations.

$$HOH + SO_2 \rightleftharpoons H_2SO_3 \tag{13-3}$$

$$H_2SO_3 \rightleftharpoons H^+ + HSO_3^- \tag{13-4}$$

As a result of studies of reactions such as those of sulfur dioxide and water, it is now believed that all chemical reactions are really equilibrium processes. In many cases, the equilibrium concentrations of the reacting molecules are so small that for all practical purposes we can say that the reaction has gone totally in one direction. If we give a general example of substance A reacting with B to give C and D, Eq. (13–5a), we could say that when the amounts of A and B are very small and the amounts of C and D are very large, the reaction is thought of as going "completely" to the right. If the opposite is true, so that the amounts of A and B are relatively large and the amounts of C and D relatively small, we often say that "no reaction" has occurred.

$$A + B \rightleftharpoons C + D \tag{13-5a}$$

Modern chemistry theory, however, states that there are always small amounts of A, B, C, and D present, and our classification of a reaction as being reversible or "complete" depends upon the relative amounts of each substance involved. Arrows of different lengths are often used to indicate which reaction is dominant. For example, Eq. (13–5b) means that the two opposing reactions arrive at an equilibrium which strongly favors C and D rather than A and B:

$$A + B \overrightarrow{\rightleftharpoons} C + D \tag{13-5b}$$

For a chemical reaction to occur, we must have a collision of two (or perhaps more) molecules that are in a reactive state. The probability that any reaction will occur (that A will react with B, or C with D) depends upon the concentration of reactive particles in the space in which the reaction may take place. When we combine these ideas with those of equilibrium, we arrive at a better explanation of the effects of temperature and pressure on shifting an equilibrium in one direction or another, particularly in reactions of gases.

If the temperature of a sulfurous acid solution is increased, the energy, and therefore the speed of the molecules, also increases. Since high-speed molecules are generallly in the gaseous state, the increased molecular action increases the rate at which the sulfur dioxide molecules escape from the solution, decreases the concentration of SO_2 molecules that are available to react with water, and the equilibrium in Eq. (13–3) shifts to the left. Conversely, a decrease in temperature causes sulfur dioxide molecules to slow down, and when they reenter the water very few of them still have sufficient velocity to escape from solution. Since there are now more molecules of SO_2 in the water, the possibility that they will react with a water molecule is increased, and the equilibrium in Eq. (13–3) is shifted to the right, Fig. 13–3. Temperature has a similar effect on the solubilities of most gases in liquids, although not all gases react with their solvents as does SO_2 with water.

Since gases are compressible, an increase in pressure causes an increase in the concentration of the molecules of a gas above a solution. Because there are more molecules in a given volume, the chance of their being captured by the liquid solvent is increased. Con-

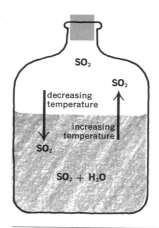

FIG. 13–3. The effect of temperature on the solubility of sulfur dioxide in water.

sequently, an increase in the pressure of a gas above a liquid increases the solubility of the gas in a liquid, and a decrease in pressure decreases the solubility.

Reactions that result in the formation of insoluble or non-ionized substances are usually said to go in one direction only. Actually, they represent equilibrium situations in which the reverse reaction is difficult to detect by many ordinary chemical procedures. Some examples of reactions which go primarily in one direction are given below:

$$AgNO_3 + NaCl \rightarrow AgCl \downarrow + NaNO_3 \quad \text{(AgCl is insoluble)} \tag{13-6}$$

$$HNO_3 + KOH \rightarrow HOH + KNO_3 \quad \text{(water is only slightly ionized)} \tag{13-7}$$

$$Zn + 2HCl \rightarrow ZnCl_2 + H_2 \uparrow \quad \text{(H}_2 \text{ is an insoluble gas)} \tag{13-8}$$

13–2 IONIZATION OF WATER AND pH

While we usually think of water as a covalent, non-ionizing substance, in reality we find that an extremely small percentage of water molecules exists in the ionic state:

$$HOH \xrightleftharpoons{} H^+ + OH^-$$

In this equilibrium there are 550,000,000 molecules of water for each hydrogen ion and hydroxide ion. Although the water molecules are continually ionizing, this process is balanced because hydrogen and hydroxide ions are combining to produce water molecules. Since these two ions are present in equal concentrations in water, the solution is neutral.

Hydrogen and hydroxide ions are present in many solutions in only very small concentrations. Nevertheless even a weak concentration may be important for a chemical reaction, or a matter of life or death to a living organism. We use the term "pH" to indicate the concentration of hydrogen ions in a solution. The pH scale ranges from 0 to 14. A pH value of 7 indicates the solution is neutral; 14, strongly basic; and values below 7, acidic. It is very important to realize that on this scale when the pH changes by 1 unit the hydrogen ion concentration changes by 10; thus, a solution of pH 2 is 10 times as acidic as one of pH 3. Tables 13–1 and 13–2 show the pH of some common substances.

TABLE 13-1. The pH scale with values for some common substances

very acid	0	hydrochloric acid
	1	
		gastric juice
	2	lemons
	3	apples
		oranges
	4	
	5	boric acid
	6	bland vegetables
	7	pure water
		blood
	8	
		baking soda
	9	
	10	
		milk of magnesia, $Mg(OH)_2$
	11	ammonia, NH_3
	12	washing soda, Na_2CO_3
	13	
		sodium hydroxide, NaOH
very basic	14	

TABLE 13-2. The pH of some common foods

apples	2.9–3.3	milk	6.3–6.6
asparagus	5.4–5.8	oranges	3.0–4.0
cabbage	5.2–5.4	peas	5.8–6.4
corn	6.0–6.5	potatoes	5.6–6.0
eggs	7.6–8.0	raspberries	3.0–3.5
(fresh egg white)		tomatoes	4.0–4.4
grapes	3.5–4.5	vinegar	2.4–3.4
lemons	2.2–2.4		

◄ In order to understand the significance of the pH scale, some understanding of logarithms is necessary. Logarithms are conveniently used in dealing with very large or very small numbers. The logarithms of a few numbers are shown in the following table:

Number	Logarithm	Number	Logarithm
1	0	1	0
10	1	1/10 or 0.1	−1
100	2	1/100 or 0.01	−2
1000	3	1/1000 or 0.001	−3
10,000	4	1/10,000 or 0.0001	−4

It should be observed that in multiplying a number by 10, we increase the logarithm by one. To find the logarithm of numbers between the powers of 10, you would need a table of logarithms. For our purposes, however, the table will not be necessary. ►

TABLE 13-3. The pH of varying H⁺ ion concentrations

Number of Liters Required to Contain 1 Mole of H⁺ Ions	pH (logarithm of liters at left)	
1	0	very acid
10	1	
100	2	
1000	3	
10,000	4	
100,000	5	
1,000,000	6	
10,000,000	7	neutral
100,000,000	8	
1,000,000,000	9	
10,000,000,000	10	
100,000,000,000	11	
1,000,000,000,000	12	
10,000,000,000,000	13	
100,000,000,000,000	14	very basic

A change of 1 in pH represents a tenfold change in H⁺ concentration.

Although **pH** is really defined as the negative logarithm of the concentration of hydrogen ions in a solution, it may also be expressed as the logarithm of the number of liters of solution required to contain 1 mole of hydrogen ion. We will use the latter concept in our discussion:

The numerical value of the pH of a solution equals the logarithm of the number of liters of solution required to contain 1 mole of hydrogen ions.

Now, let us see how this works. If a solution contains 1 mole of hydrogen ions/liter (this is a very strong acid), the pH is 0 since the logarithm of 1 is 0. If a second solution is only 1/100 as strong as the first, 100 liters of solution would be required to contain 1 mole of hydrogen ions, and the pH would be 2, the logarithm of 100. As the H⁺ ion concentration decreases, the pH increases. Table 13-3 gives the pH for varying concentrations of H⁺ ions.

Pure water has a pH of 7, which tells us that it will take 10,000,000 liters of water to contain 1 mole of H⁺ ions. Since the only source of H⁺ ions is from water molecules which have ionized,

$$HOH \rightleftharpoons H^+ + OH^-$$
(13-9)

there must be an equal concentration of OH⁻ ions. Therefore there is 1 mole of OH⁻ ions in 10,000,000 liters of pure water. Now suppose we add a base to pure water. The excess of OH⁻ ions from the base will combine with H⁺ ions to form water and reduce the H⁺ ion concentration. The number of liters required to contain 1 mole would be increased, and the pH would also increase to some value above 7. The more OH⁻ ions added, the higher the pH. When an acid is added to pure water, the hydrogen ion concentration increases (and the hydroxide ion concentration decreases), so the pH becomes lower.

In a solution, the product of the concentrations of the H$^+$ and OH$^-$ ions is constant:

concentration H$^+$ $\times$ concentration OH$^-$ = K   (13-10)

Expressing the concentration of OH$^-$ ions as pOH, in a manner similar to the way we use pH, we may say

pH + pOH = 14*   (13-11)

Therefore,

pH = 14 − pOH   (13-12)

and

pOH = 14 − pH

13-3 MEASUREMENT OF pH

In Chapter 12, we noted that litmus is used to indicate whether solutions are acidic or basic. It is called an *indicator*. Actually the change in color from red in an acid solution to blue in a basic solution takes place over a pH *range*.

Suppose we start by placing litmus paper or a litmus solution in a solution with a pH of 1, which is quite acidic. Then we slowly add sodium hydroxide. As the H$^+$ ions are neutralized, the pH gradually increases. The litmus will remain red until the pH reaches about 5. Between a pH of 5 and about 8, the color changes from red to violet to blue and remains blue at any pH above 8.

In addition to litmus, more than 75 compounds which may be used as acid-base indicators are listed in chemistry handbooks. Each has a color change that takes place at a definite pH. By selecting the proper indicator we can determine the pH of almost any clear colorless solution. Table 13–4 lists a few of these indicators.

TABLE 13–4. Common acid-base indicators

Indicator	pH Range	Color Change on Proceeding from Low to Higher pH
thymol blue	1.2–2.8	red–yellow
methyl orange	3.1–4.4	red–yellow
methyl red	4.2–6.3	pink–yellow
bromocresol purple	5.2–6.8	yellow–red
litmus	4.7–8.2	red–blue
phenolphthalein	8.3–10.0	colorless–pink
thymolphthalein	9.3–10.5	colorless–blue
thymol blue	8.0–9.6	yellow–blue
alizarin yellow	10.1–12.1	yellow–red

---

* If the pH of pure water is 7, the pOH of pure water must also be 7. A solution with a pH of 6 will have a pOH of 8, and a solution with a pH of 13 will have a pOH of 1.

The *colorimetric method* for determining the pH of solutions was the first method developed and is still quite useful. However, a more accurate measurement of pH can be made by using an electric pH meter. With the *electrometric method* cloudy or colored solutions do not present the difficulties that they do with the colorimetric method. For example, in order to test the pH of blood colorimetrically, the red blood cells must be removed. Electrometrically, the electrodes of the pH meter are dipped into whole blood and the pH may be read directly from the dial.

13-4 WHO USES pH?

An understanding of pH is required in many occupations. The term is used in industrial laboratories, food processing industries, and by medical technicians. During medical examinations, the pH of many body fluids may be determined. The pH of saliva is normally between 6.5 and 7.5, of the stomach somewhere between 1 and 3, and of urine 4.8 to 8.4. The pH of the blood remains constant at about 7.35; a change of only a few tenths of a pH unit is serious enough to cause death.

Agriculturists are concerned with the pH of the soil. Ranchers and farmers test their soils to determine whether acidic or basic type fertilizers are needed for each crop. Soils containing large amounts of humus, such as are found in much of Iowa and neighboring states, are often so acid that they must be neutralized before certain crops will grow satisfactorily. Crushed or powdered limestone is used in large amounts to compensate for the acidity. In large sections of California and other western states, the soils are so alkaline that acid (phosphate) fertilizers are required for certain crops. The modern nurseryman can tell his customers the optimum pH of soil for each of the plants he sells.

13-5 HYDROLYSIS OF SALTS

If we dissolve a salt in water, we expect the solution to be neither acidic nor basic, but neutral. While the solutions of many salts are, in fact, neutral, others are either slightly acidic or basic. We might be led to postulate that such salts were really acid salts or basic salts, i.e., formed by incomplete neutralization of an acid or base. Such salts are known, salts such as $NaHCO_3$ or $BiOHCl_2$. Others, such as ammonium chloride and sodium acetate which are formed by addition of exact equivalent amounts of acids and bases, also give solutions that are not neutral. We can get a clue that helps in explaining these observations by comparing the formulas for salts that produce acidic, neutral, and basic solutions.

acid solutions	NH_4Cl, $AlCl_3$, $Pb(NO_3)_2$, $(NH_4)_2SO_4$
neutral solutions	KCl, $NaCl$, NH_4Ac, KNO_3, Na_2SO_4
basic solutions	$NaAc$, KAc, K_3PO_4, Na_3PO_4, $NaCN$

We see that the salts producing acid solutions are formed from the combination of a strong acid and a weak base, those producing alkaline solutions from the combination of a weak acid and a strong base, and the neutral salts either from the combination of a strong base and strong acid or of a weak base and a weak acid. Experiments in dissolving other salts would support our conclusions.

Once we have made this generalization, we must look for an explanation of the presence of excesses of H$^+$ or OH$^-$ ions in solutions of salts. The concept of equilibrium and our definitions of weak acids and bases helps us reach an explanation. We assume that most salts dissociate to give ions in water solutions. So a solution of NaCN would give Na$^+$ and CN$^-$ ions:

$$\text{NaCN} \rightleftharpoons \text{Na}^+ + \text{CN}^- \tag{13-13}$$

Now CN$^-$ ions have a tendency to form covalent, nondissociated bonds with hydrogen ions. (This is why we classify HCN as a weak acid.) Since water always contains small amounts of OH$^-$ and H$^+$ ions, some of the H$^+$ ions are bound to the CN$^-$ group giving undissociated HCN:

$$\text{H}^+ + \text{CN}^- \rightarrow \text{HCN} \tag{13-14}$$

While OH$^-$ ions may be attracted to the Na$^+$ ions formed by the dissociation of NaCN, there is almost no tendency for Na$^+$ and OH$^-$ ions in water solutions to form a compound, so we are left with both Na$^+$ and OH$^-$ in the ionic form. We can write the reaction:

$$\text{Na}^+ + \text{CN}^- + \text{H}^+ + \text{OH}^- \rightleftharpoons \text{HCN} + \text{Na}^+ + \text{OH}^- \tag{13-15}*$$

On the right-hand side of the equation we have an excess of OH$^-$ ions, and since the solution is basic when tested with an indicator, we assume that the equilibrium is displaced somewhat to the right. This reaction of salts with water to produce solutions that are not neutral is called **hydrolysis.** The term hydrolysis is also applied to other reactions, but all involve the lysis (splitting) of the compounds by water. Another way of looking at the same phenomenon is as the splitting of the H$^+$ and OH$^-$ of water, whereby the water is "lysed."

On examination, we see that Eq. (13-15) is just the reverse of the expression for the neutralization of HCN with NaOH. In general, we would think of Eq. (13-15) as going strongly to the left (as written here). In fact, if water is removed, it will go to completion. In the presence of water, however, an equilibrium situation exists in which a small amount of the salt is hydrolyzed to give a slight reversal of the neutralization reaction.

---

* Actually most of the water is present as undissociated molecules (HOH). It is also true that HCN has some tendency to dissociate. It is more nearly correct, although much more complex to write Eq. (13-15) as follows:

$$\text{Na}^+ + \text{CN}^- + \text{H}^+ + \text{OH}^- \rightleftharpoons \text{HCN} + \text{Na}^+ + \text{OH}^-$$

We should not forget, however, that solutions of sodium cyanide are quite basic, and do contain an excess of the hydroxide ion.

A solution of aluminum chloride in water is found to be slightly acidic. The equations for the hydrolysis of aluminum chloride can be written:

$$AlCl_3 \rightleftharpoons Al^{3+} + 3Cl^- \tag{13-16}$$

$$Al^{3+} + 3Cl^- + 3H^+ + 3OH^- \longrightarrow Al(OH)_3 + 3H^+ + 3Cl^- \tag{13-17}$$

Since HCl is a strong acid, we know it is almost totally dissociated. But aluminum hydroxide is a weak base, so the Al^{3+} and OH^- ions tend to associate, leaving a slight excess of H^+ ions and therefore an acidic solution.

The salts of strong acids and bases tend to be completely dissociated and therefore do not react with H^+ or OH^- of water to give non-ionized compounds:

$$K^+ + Cl^- + H^+ + OH^- \rightleftharpoons K^+ + Cl^- + H^+ + OH^- \quad \text{(no reaction)} \tag{13-18}$$

If a salt such as aluminum acetate has been formed from a weak acid and a weak base, both of which have about equal tendencies to dissociate, the salt will produce a neutral solution in water. Its ions will associate with approximately equal quantities of H^+ and OH^- ions:

$$Al^{3+} + 3Ac^- + 3H^+ + 3OH^- \rightleftharpoons Al(OH)_3 + 3HAc \tag{13-19}$$

We can formulate the rules governing the hydrolysis of salts as follows:

Salts formed by the reaction of	Produce
a) a strong acid and a weak base	acid solutions
b) a strong base and a weak acid	basic solutions
c) a strong acid and a strong base	neutral solutions
d) a weak acid and a weak base	either acidic or basic solutions, depending upon the relative strength (degree of association) of the acid and the base.

13-6 BUFFERED SOLUTIONS

The terms *buffer* or *buff* are used in several ways but always imply similar meanings—to smooth or to lessen shock. In the beauty shop, the nails are buffered or buffed to remove the rough spots. The bumpers of automobiles are buffered after they are chromeplated so they will shine. The bumper also serves at times as a buffer to lessen the shock of minor collisions. In chemistry, the term is used to describe a solution in which the pH remains relatively stable despite additions of acids or bases. One cannot listen to radio or television long without hearing commercials praising the properties of buffered aspirin or of some product which relieves acid indigestion because of its buffering action. The body fluids and many of the foods we eat act as buffers within the body.

A **buffer solution** can be prepared by dissolving in water approximately equal amounts of a weak acid and its salt. For example, 1 liter of water containing 0.1 mole of acetic acid and 0.1 mole of sodium acetate makes a good buffer. It has a pH of 4.6, that is, it is a weakly acidic buffer. Either acid or base can be added to the solution without changing its pH appreciably. While this phenomenon may seem to be illogical or mysterious, it can be explained logically.

We know that acetic acid molecules are largely non-ionized, and conversely, that if hydrogen ions and acetate ions encounter each other, they combine to form undissociated acetic acid molecules. Now, suppose we add some hydrochloric acid (which is completely ionized) to the acetic acid-sodium acetate buffer described above. The excess acetate ions will combine with the H^+ ions, removing them from solution and forming some new acetic acid molecules. Thus, although we have added a strong acid, there is little change in the pH of the solution:

$$H^+ + Ac^- \rightarrow HAc \tag{13-20}$$

If, on the other hand, we add sodium hydroxide to the solution of acetic acid and sodium acetate, the OH^- ions of the base will react with the H^+ ions present in the solution to form water. Almost as fast as the H^+ ions are removed by the OH^- ions, additional molecules of acetic acid will ionize, replacing the H^+ ions which have been removed:

$$HAc \rightarrow H^+ + Ac^- \tag{13-21}$$

Again, there is little change in the pH of the solution.

Solutions containing a polyprotic acid and its salts also have buffering action. It will be recalled that phosphoric acid has three steps or phases of ionization:

$$H_3PO_4 \rightleftarrows H^+ + H_2PO_4^- \tag{13-22}$$

$$H_2PO_4^- \rightleftarrows H^+ + HPO_4^{2-} \tag{13-23}$$

$$HPO_4^{2-} \rightleftarrows H^+ + PO_4^{3-} \tag{13-24}$$

When phosphoric acid reacts with a base such as NaOH, the neutralization takes place in three corresponding steps:

Reaction	pH at completion of each step	
$NaOH + H_3PO_4 \rightarrow Na^+ + H_2PO_4^- + HOH$	4.0	(13-25)
$NaOH + H_2PO_4^- \rightarrow Na^+ + HPO_4^{2-} + HOH$	8.5	(13-26)
$NaOH + HPO_4^{2-} \rightarrow Na^+ + PO_4^{3-} + HOH$	12.0	(13-27)

The HPO_4^{2-} ion readily accepts hydrogen ions,

$$H^+ + HPO_4^{2-} \rightarrow H_2PO_4^- \tag{13-28}$$

to give $H_2PO_4^-$, and thus the HPO_4^{2-} may be thought of as a type of base. Since $H_2PO_4^-$ ions also give up protons, these ions are acidic. A dilute solution containing equivalent amounts of these two acid salts, NaH_2PO_4 and Na_2HPO_4, is an excellent buffer. Such a solution has a pH of 6.8. The addition of small amounts of OH^- ions or H^+ ions has very little effect upon the pH of such a solution. An incomplete equation showing only reacting ions is shown below:

$$H_2PO_4^- \xrightleftharpoons[+\ H^+]{+\ OH^-} HPO_4^{2-}$$ (13-29)

Another important buffer consists of $NaHCO_3$ and H_2CO_3 which are present in the blood. They react as follows:

$$NaHCO_3 + H^+ \rightarrow Na^+ + H_2CO_3$$ (13-30)

$$H_2CO_3 + OH^- \rightarrow HOH + HCO_3^-$$ (13-31)

Proteins, which constitute the major portion of the body tissues, contain $-NH_2$ groups which are proton acceptors and $-COOH$ groups which are proton donors. Phosphates, carbonates, and proteins are the principal buffers that are able to stabilize the pH of the body.

The importance of buffers is not limited to biological processes. Industrial and research chemists find use for them in controlling the pH of many chemical reactions.

13–7 SUMMARY

Very few processes ever reach completion. In some cases external factors interfere with the process, and in others we find that as soon as many units are put together, decomposition starts. A similar situation exists with chemical reactions. We can represent a process in which A and B react to give C and D as follows:

$$A + B \rightleftharpoons C + D$$ (13-32)

In general, it is true that C and D also react to give some A and B. We think of reactions as going primarily one way (to the right as written above) when either C or D is removed as an insoluble solid or gas, or as a non-ionized compound. Indeed, we find that when we remove one of the products such as D, there is a tendency for the reaction to produce more of both D and of C, and the reaction goes toward the right. However, since no solid or gas is absolutely insoluble and especially because no compound is completely non-ionized, there is always a slight reversal—a maintenance of a dynamic equilibrium—in chemical reactions. Such slight reversals are responsible for the phenomenon known as hydrolysis and for the presence of hydrogen and hydroxide ions in water solutions. Such reversals are found in so many chemical reactions that we assume they are present in all reactions, even when the amounts of A and B are so small that we cannot measure them. The tendency of a reaction to go to an equilibrium position and to act in a way to reestablish the equilibrium when we remove a product is almost mysterious. This phenomenon has led to much speculation.

The presence of definite concentrations of hydrogen ions is absolutely essential for many chemical reactions, and especially those occurring in living plants and animals. The slight dissociation of water and the substances in buffers make possible the control of pH and the continuation of life.

IMPORTANT TERMS

Buffered solution   Equilibrium   Hydrolysis

WORK EXERCISES

1. Describe three different situations or conditions in which some type of equilibrium is involved.

2. Write three equations using arrows to indicate that in each equation an equilibrium is involved.

3. State three factors which bring about changes in equilibrium.

4. Write an equation using appropriate arrows to indicate that the reaction goes almost entirely to completion.

5. State four factors which cause reactions to go toward completion.

6. What evidence do we have that water is only slightly ionized?

7. According to the information shown in Table 13-2, approximately how much greater is the hydrogen ion concentration in lemons than in cabbage?

8. Explain why solutions having a relatively high concentration of hydrogen ions always have low OH^- ion concentrations.

9. Name three indicators of pH commonly used in the laboratory, and state the pH ranges of each.

10. List five different professions in which some knowledge of pH is essential.

11. Why do some salts, when dissolved in water, form solutions that are not neutral?

12. Referring to the discussion of strong and weak acids in Section 12-4, indicate whether solutions of the following salts would be acidic, basic, or neutral:

    a) $NaCl$ _____   b) Na_2CO_3 _____
    c) KAc _____   d) $(NH_4)_2SO_4$ _____
    e) KNO_3 _____   f) Na_2SO_3 _____
    g) Na_2S _____

13. Consult your collegiate dictionary for the meaning of the word "hydrolysis."

14. It is essential for life that the pH of the blood be held very constant. How does the body maintain this constant pH?

Chapter 14 COLLOIDS

14-1 INTRODUCTION

A common sight in urban communities is the beam of light from a giant searchlight piercing the evening sky, informing the community of some attraction located near the source of the beam. Since a beam of light is invisible when passed through a true solution or a colorless gas, larger particles, suspended in the atmosphere, must reflect the light, thereby making its path visible. Particles which can remain suspended in the atmosphere or in solutions for long periods of time belong to an interesting class of materials called **colloids.** Colloid chemistry has been described as "the chemistry of grains, drops, bubbles, filaments, and films." Small solid particles are grains; drops are composed of liquids; bubbles are small gas particles surrounded by a solid or a liquid; and **filaments,** like a thread, have minute dimensions except for length. The **film** of a soap bubble is extremely thin.

14-2 THE SIZE OF COLLOIDAL PARTICLES

The unit used in measuring the size of colloids is the *millimicron,* $m\mu$; 1 $m\mu$ = 1/1,000,000 mm. Colloid particles range in size from 1 to 100 $m\mu$ in diameter (a page of this text approximates 100,000 $m\mu$ in thickness). Particles smaller than 1 $m\mu$ in diameter are molecular in size and usually form true solutions; those of slightly more than 100 $m\mu$ in diameter remain in suspension for only a short time.

When speaking of colloids, we consider the particles which are suspended to be in a *dispersed phase,* whereas the material in which they are suspended is the *dispersing phase.* These are sometimes referred to as the *discontinuous* and the *continuous phases,* respectively. There must, in all cases, be two phases.

14-3 TYPES OF COLLOIDAL SYSTEMS

The visibility of light beams from searchlights is due to two types of particles which are held in the atmosphere. Solids such as **smoke** and dust particles are prevalent over most cities. They are so small they do not readily settle to earth, yet they are large enough to reflect and scatter light rays. These represent *solids (grains) dispersed in a gas.* Moisture tends to condense on dust particles, and as the air nears saturation with moisture, tiny droplets of water are formed, which we call **fog.** A slight amount of fog is also very effective in scattering light, causing the searchlight beams to appear as solid columns above the city. Fog is an example of a *liquid (droplets) dispersed in a gas.* The name aerosol is used to describe any airborne colloidal particle.

A common type of colloidal suspension is that of *solids in liquids.* Examples are muddy water, in which clay particles are suspended, and starch suspensions such as are found in puddings.

Fruit jellies belong to a type of colloids called **gels.** They have, in general, an invisible lattice or "brush pile" structure which literally traps a liquid in a solid. While absorbent cotton is composed of large filaments and is not a colloid, the manner in which it holds water is not unlike that of the solid portion of a gel. Fruits usually contain a substance called pectin; this solid compound helps keep the fruit firm and causes jellies to "set." Gels and jellies are examples of *liquids dispersed in solids.*

When two liquids, which are insoluble in each other, are intimately mixed, they form a suspension which is called an **emulsion.** Many salad dressings, including mayonnaise, are examples of emulsions. Cream, which is primarily a suspension of fat droplets in water, is an emulsion. If the droplets are reduced to very small sizes, as in homogenized milk, they become permanent emulsions. Often, upon standing, emulsions separate into two layers. To make such emulsions more stable, an emulsifying agent can be added. Soap is an excellent emulsifying agent in that it causes fat and oil particles to remain suspended in water. Emulsions are colloidal suspensions of *liquids in liquids.*

Whipped cream, meringue, and foams are suspensions of *air (a gas) in liquids.* In some cases the air bubbles may not be of colloidal dimensions, but the film of liquids separating the bubbles is.

14-4 WHY DO COLLOIDS REMAIN IN SUSPENSION?

Many colloidal particles have much greater densities than the medium in which they are dispersed, and we would expect them to settle out. However, it has been observed that dust from great volcanic disturbances has remained in the atmosphere for several years. Finely divided gold will remain suspended in water almost indefinitely. Three factors are credited with effecting this stabilization of colloids: (1) Brownian movement, (2) electrical charges, and (3) protective films.

Brownian Movement

It is known that molecules of gases and liquids are in continuous motion. Because of the extremely small size of molecules, it is impossible to observe this motion. However, it is possible to observe the effects of high speed impacts of these molecules on larger colloidal particles suspended in liquids or gases. Although ordinary molecules are so small that they do not reflect light rays, we have seen that the larger colloidal particles do, Section 14–1.

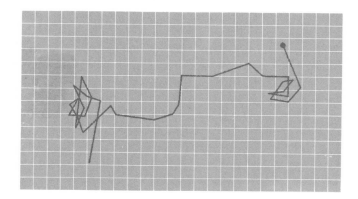

FIG. 14–1. Brownian movement: the observed path of a particle suspended in water for a few seconds.

Robert Brown, in 1827, discovered that if a strong beam of light was directed through a colloidal suspension at right angles to the field of vision of an ordinary microscope, erratic flashes of light were visible. Many years later scientists learned that these flashes of light resulted from the jostling of the larger colloidal particles by the impact of smaller molecules in the solution or gas. This observable motion of colloidal particles, Fig. 14–1, is called Brownian movement in honor of the discoverer. The motion is believed to be one of the factors keeping colloidal particles in suspension. Smoke particles in air or starch in suspension are satisfactory materials for demonstrating this phenomenon. Brownian movement, as seen through a microscope, is nothing more than a magnification of what we see on a large scale in the searchlight beams mentioned earlier.

Electrical Charges

Colloidal particles of similar composition have similar electrical charges. Some carry a positive charge and other types a negative one. In a given colloid, each particle repells every other particle of similar charge. Milk is a good example: the protein particles in milk are all negatively charged, causing the protein to stay in suspension. When milk sours and lactic acid is produced, or when an acidic substance is added, the hydrogen ions which are released neutralize the charges on the proteins. This neutralization of the charges on protein molecules allows them to coagulate or curdle, and they lose the colloidal characteristics. Since droplets of fog or particles of smoke take on electrical charges, repelling forces keep them dispersed.

Protective Films

Substances like gelatin or certain gummy materials form films around colloidal particles which tend to prevent them from clumping into larger particles which would settle from the dispersing medium. Soap is a good illustration of a protective colloid. Soap surrounds minute droplets of oil and prevents them from coalescing into a large drop which would separate from the water (see Section 27–6).

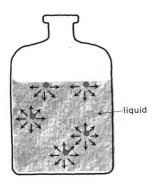

FIG. 14–2. The variable forces acting on the molecules within a liquid.

14–5 PROPERTIES OF COLLOIDS

Surface Phenomena: Adsorption

One of the interesting as well as important properties of colloids is a result of the great amount of surface area they possess. For a given mass of material, the surface area increases rapidly as the size of the particles decreases. A cube which is 10 cm on a side has 600 cm² of surface (10 × 10 or 100 cm² for each of 6 sides). If we divide this cube into cubes 1 cm on a side, we will have 1000 (10 × 10 × 10) cubes. Each side of each of the small cubes will have an area of 1 cm² and each cube a surface area of 6 cm², so that we will have 1000 × 6 or a total surface area of 6000 cm². By reducing the size of the cubes by 1/10 we have increased the surface area by 10 times, from 600 cm² to 6000 cm². Since colloidal particles are very small, their surface areas are enormous when compared with the areas of similar weights of large particles. The atoms or molecules which make up a surface have different forces acting on them than those in the interior of a substance. Particles within a solid or a liquid exert attractive forces in all directions on other particles, whereas the particles on the surface are attracted from one side only (Fig. 14–2). This allows the formation of a "surface film" on liquids or drops. Such surfaces attract other kinds of molecules or ions, often bringing about chemical reactions which would not otherwise occur. For example, mixtures of hydrogen and oxygen, which remain uncombined for long periods of time, ignite with explosive force on contact with finely divided platinum metal.

    Charcoal which has been prepared from coconuts, peach pits, or certain types of hard wood is very porous. This porosity gives the substance a large surface area. Thus charcoal is used in gas masks because it can adsorb a large amount of toxic gases from the atmosphere. The attraction of molecules to such surfaces is called **adsorption.**

In the purification of sugar and other organic substances, large quantities of charcoal and other similar-acting materials are used to remove undesirable color and foreign substances. For example, when brown sugar is dissolved in water and charcoal is added, the brown coloration is removed so that on filtration and evaporation, pure white sugar is obtained.

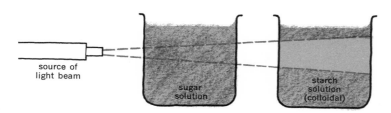

FIG. 14–3. The Tyndall Effect. The beaker on the left contains a sugar solution; the one on the right contains a colloidal dispersion of starch. When the light beam passes through the true solution of sugar it leaves no perceptible path; however, when it passes through the starch solution, the starch particles are large enough to reflect light, and the beam produces a visible path.

Tyndall Effect

Approximately 100 years ago the Irish physicist John Tyndall observed that a beam of light passing through pure water and certain types of solutions, such as those prepared from sugar or common salts, did not produce a visible path. However, if a small amount of milk, starch, soap, or any of numerous noncrystalline materials was suspended in water, the light beam did produce a definite path (Fig. 14–3). Tyndall suggested that the phenomenon resulted from the light-scattering ability of the larger particles which were suspended in the liquid. This light-scattering is known as the **Tyndall effect.**

14–6 PRECIPITATION OF COLLOIDS

Colloids are useful in many instances. Food processors add many ingredients to produce and stabilize the colloids in foods such as mayonnaise and ice cream. In other instances it may be desirable to remove particles from a colloidal suspension. If we approach logically the problem of breaking down a colloid, we must think of the forces that hold the particles in suspension—Brownian motion, electrical charges, and protective films. There is probably little we can do to stop Brownian motion, although we know that cooling a substance slows the activity of the molecules. It may be possible to remove protective films—or probably it would be better to stop their forming—but the most common way of "breaking" a colloidal suspension involves neutralizing the electrical charges on the particles.

We see this process occurring naturally in areas where freshwater streams enter the ocean. The fine particles of silt and clay which are carried by freshwater streams are negatively charged. When freshwater mixes with seawater, these charges are neutralized and the solids precipitate. Such processes which have been occurring over the centuries and continue today are responsible for the formation of large land areas called deltas at the mouths of rivers. The deltas of the Nile and Mississippi rivers which extend for many miles are outstanding examples of precipitation of colloids.

Air pollution is a serious problem in many cities. It would be much more severe, however, were it not for a device called the Cottrell Precipitator. This device is installed in the smoke stacks of many industrial firms to remove the solids that would otherwise be scattered over the surrounding areas. While there are many modifications of the device, it consists essentially of plates bearing opposite electrical charges, which are installed between the furnaces and the stacks. Positively charged particles are attracted to one of the plates, and negatively charged particles to the other. They collect and fall into receptacles for removal. The system is so effective that many industrial plants, such as smelters, install them to prevent the loss of valuable metals and other materials which would otherwise be blown into the atmosphere. Many of the problems of air pollution depend on developing and applying methods for control of the colloids in the air.

14-7 COLLOIDS AND LIFE

Living matter is primarily colloidal in character. Muscle tissue is essentially colloid-like fibers in which water is dispersed. Blood plasma is colloidal in that it is a suspension of macromolecules in a liquid, mostly water. Within the cells of both plants and animals, jelly-like substances result from fibrous macromolecules holding water so securely that it is only slightly mobile. We cannot understand the physical complexity of life without understanding the colloids.

IMPORTANT TERMS

Adsorption	Colloids	Filament (colloidal)	Fog	Smoke
Brownian movement	Emulsion	Film	Gel	Tyndall effect

WORK EXERCISES

1. Why would the great searchlights used in night advertising be less effective in the clear air of some desert communities?

2. Compare the size of colloidal particles to the size of particles we can see with the unaided eye.

3. What factors tend to keep colloidal particles suspended in air or in liquids?

4. Give some examples of substances which may be of colloidal size in one dimension but not in another.

5. Illustrate the different attractive forces between the molecules within a glass of water and between those which make up the surface film.

SUGGESTED READING

Debye, P., "How Giant Molecules are Measured," *Scientific American*, Sept. 1957, p. 90. The light-scattering ability of colloidal particles as an indication of their size.

Chapter 15 THE ATMOSPHERE: Nitrogen and the Noble Gases

15-1 INTRODUCTION

"The earth's atmosphere is a vast, churning mixture of gases and trace quantities of liquids and solids. Held to the earth by the pull of gravity, it is the transparent envelope without which life on earth would cease to exist.

"The atmosphere is the source of oxygen essential to man and of carbon dioxide essential to plants. It is the source of rain. It is the shield that absorbs the sun's ultraviolet radiation that would otherwise destroy all life on earth. It is the barrier that dissipates most of the bombarding cosmic rays from outer space. It is the protective layer that burns up the meteors that would otherwise leave the earth as crater-pocked as the moon.

"The earth's atmosphere maintains the temperature and climate that make man's survival possible. Without the atmosphere, the temperature at the equator would reach as high as 180°F in the day and as low as −220°F at night.

"The atmosphere makes flight possible. It makes sound propagation possible. The free electrons in the upper atmosphere make conventional long-distance radio communications possible.

"Tenuous, impalpable, ceaselessly in flux, the atmosphere is as vital to man as the sun, the oceans, and the solid earth itself."*

15-2 DENSITY OF THE ATMOSPHERE

When people who live near sea level travel to higher elevations in the mountains, they find that for a few days exercise causes them to breathe more rapidly than they were accustomed to do at lower elevations. Balloons which rise rapidly in the lower atmosphere eventually come to rest at higher altitudes. These observations indicate the atmosphere becomes thinner as height above sea level increases. In 1643, the Italian physicist Torricelli

---

* Taken from "Chemistry and the Atmosphere," special report, *Chemical and Engineering News,* March 28, 1966.

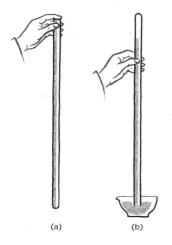

(a) (b)

FIG. 15–1. The first barometer. The production of a Torricellian vacuum: (a) a glass tube, more than thirty inches long, is filled with mercury and closed with the finger. (b) the tube is inverted, the open end placed in a bowl of mercury, and the finger removed. The mercury level in the tube drops until it is about thirty inches above the level of the mercury in the bowl. The top part of the tube is then empty (a vacuum).

performed an experiment in which he sealed the end of a glass tube, filled it with mercury, then inverted it in an open container of mercury, Fig. 15–1. He found the top of the column of mercury fell to approximately 30 in. above the level of the mercury in the container. When the instrument was carried to the top of the mountain, the height of the mercury column decreased. Torricelli and other scientists decided the height of the column was proportional to the weight of the atmosphere pushing down on the mercury in the container. Such instruments, which measure the atmospheric pressure, are called *barometers*.

The average atmospheric pressure at sea level is 14.7 *pounds per square inch* (psi). Since there are 144 sq in./sq ft, more than 1 ton of atmosphere rests on each square foot of the surface of the earth (each inhabitant of the earth presently has for his share in excess of 1.5 millions of tons).

In scientific work, the pressure of the atmosphere is usually measured in terms corresponding to the height of a column of mercury it will support. The average sea-level pressure is somewhat arbitrarily given as 760 mm or 29.92 in. of mercury.

◄ There is considerable fluctuation in atmospheric pressure at sea level or at other elevations. Some of the factors that influence changes in pressure are latitude on the earth, temperature, and circulation of atmosphere locally, particularly in storms or seasonal changes. In severe tropical storms, barometers often drop more than 2 in.; in the center of hurricanes, perhaps more. The "falling" of the barometer, which is often taken as an indication of rain, may be due in part to the high moisture content of the air. Since water molecules are lighter than molecules of nitrogen or oxygen, moist air is lighter than dry air. ►

The usefulness of a mercury barometer is limited in that accurate data can be obtained only when it is used in fixed locations such as in laboratories. Mechanical barometers have therefore been developed. With a change in atmospheric pressure, they cause a hollow, flat, wafer-like mechanism to increase or decrease in thickness. The change in thickness of the mechanism actuates a pointer which indicates the atmospheric pressure.

As we have mentioned, gravitational attraction causes a concentration of atmosphere at the surface of earth; the concentration diminishes as the altitude increases. Barometric pressure decreases by approximately 1 in. for each 1000 ft of altitude as we begin to move upward from the surface of the earth. Approximately one-half of all the atmosphere is within 17,500 ft of the earth. Interestingly, this ratio of pressure to altitude continues: for each 17,500 ft, the pressure of the atmosphere is reduced by one-half until very high altitudes are reached. The aircraft altimeter is essentially a mechanical barometer which is calibrated in terms of altitude rather than pressure.

15-3 COMPOSITION OF THE ATMOSPHERE

Although the atmosphere is composed of ions, atoms, compounds, and colloidal particles, three elements—nitrogen, oxygen and argon—account for more than 99.9% of its so-called fixed components, Table 15-1. In this section we will discuss first a highly variable component of the atmosphere, water vapor, and then carbon dioxide and nitrogen. In Section 15-6, the noble gases will be described.

TABLE 15-1. Composition of clean, dry air near sea level

Component	Content, Percent by Volume
nitrogen	78.084
oxygen	20.9476
argon	0.934
carbon dioxide	0.0314
neon	0.001818
helium	0.000524
krypton	0.000114
xenon	0.0000087
hydrogen	0.00005

Water Vapor

Water vapor is the major variable constituent of the atmosphere. The capacity of the air to hold water vapor depends upon the temperature, increasing with an increase in temperature. In fact, air at 95°F is able to hold 8 times more water vapor than it can at the freezing point. Warm tropical air can hold 40 times as much water as air in extremely cold polar air masses. The air is said to be *saturated* when it contains all the water vapor it can hold at the existing temperature and pressure.

Humidity is a term which is used to indicate the amount of water vapor in the air. **Relative humidity** is the ratio of the amount of water vapor in the atmosphere to the amount necessary for saturation at the same temperature. Saturated air, therefore, has a relative humidity of 100. It can be seen that air which has a relative humidity of 100 in the cool of the morning becomes unsaturated as the day becomes warmer. Roughly speaking, an increase of 20°F doubles the moisture-holding ability of air, and therefore, air which is saturated at 60°F has a relative humidity of approximately 50 when the air temperature becomes 80°F. If warm air which is near saturation is cooled appreciably, it becomes saturated, and with continued cooling it will lose moisture in the form of condensation or precipitation.

Carbon Dioxide

Although carbon dioxide concentration in the atmosphere is extremely low, Table 15–1, it plays an unusual and most important role in the scheme of life on the earth. Although there is only 1 molecule of CO_2 for each 3000 molecules of air, carbon dioxide is essential for the growth of green plants. It must be remembered that animals depend directly or indirectly upon plants for all their food. The concentration of CO_2 in the atmosphere is kept near a constant level, since the processes which remove it from the air are counterbalanced by those which return it to the air.* All green plants remove CO_2 from the air, but when these plants are oxidized by decay or burning, carbon dioxide is returned to the atmosphere. Animals exhale, as carbon dioxide, the carbon occurring in the foods they eat. An average adult exhales about a pound of carbon dioxide per day.

The presence of CO_2 in the atmosphere helps to bring about other desirable effects. Carbon dioxide has the ability to absorb ultraviolet light from the sun, which is damaging to living cells. The CO_2 in the atmosphere helps also to regulate the temperature of the earth's surface, since it absorbs infrared rays. Light rays from the sun penetrate the atmosphere, strike the earth and are reflected as infrared rays which warm the air in which they are absorbed. This is referred to as a *greenhouse effect*. Our automobiles furnish us the best example of this phenomenon. We have all experienced the extreme heat which accumulates in a closed car on a sunny day. Like the atmosphere, windows of the car are transparent to the sun's visible light. This light radiates infrared rays which are trapped by the glass and metal and thus warm the interior of the car.

Because of its ability to absorb infrared radiation, an increase in the CO_2 concentration in the atmosphere would cause an increase in the temperature. Such a change is presently taking place. The enormous amounts of fossil fuels (coal and petroleum) which have been burned in the past half century, have produced a slight increase in the CO_2 of the atmosphere, and a corresponding increase in the average world temperature. This warming effect is evidenced by the diminishing sizes of the glaciers of the world. It is estimated that a doubling of the amount of CO_2 in the atmosphere would increase the temperature sufficiently to cause tropical climates throughout much of the world. Such a climate would melt the icecaps of the north and south polar regions, releasing sufficient water to raise the level of the oceans by an estimated 100 ft. Consider the effects of such a catastrophe on the major seaport cities of the world. Fortunately, the oceans dissolve CO_2 from the air and therefore help stabilize the atmospheric content. The knowledge we now have indicates that the waters of the oceans contain 50 times more CO_2 than does the atmosphere.

---

* Over long geological periods of time, it is believed there has been considerable fluctuation in the concentration of CO_2 in the air.

Nitrogen

The major portion of the nitrogen that occurs on the earth is in the atmosphere in an elementary or uncombined form. Many nitrogen compounds undergo chemical changes which release nitrogen in a free state, whereas free nitrogen does not readily engage in chemical reactions. The reactions between nitrogen and oxygen forming the oxides are in most instances endothermic, requiring a large amount of energy to bring about the reaction. Energy is therefore liberated when these nitrogen compounds decompose to form free nitrogen. The instability of nitrogen compounds accounts for their use in many explosives.

Nitrogen is a colorless gas with a density a little less than that of air. It is only slightly soluble in water at normal temperatures and pressures. Compounds of nitrogen are essential to life; every living cell contains them. Nitrogen makes up approximately 16% of all proteins.

15-4 NITROGEN FIXATION

Animals are unable to utilize elementary nitrogen, and only a few plants—the legumes, with the aid of certain microorganisms—can do so. Any process whereby elementary nitrogen is converted to compounds which can be used by plants or animals is called *nitrogen fixation*. Lightning is an important factor in natural fixation. In the presence of an electric discharge through the atmosphere, the following reaction occurs:

$$N_2 + O_2 \rightarrow 2NO \tag{15-1}$$

Nitrogen(II) oxide, NO (also called nitric oxide), is a colorless gas which combines readily with oxygen in the air, forming nitrogen(IV) oxide.

$$NO + \tfrac{1}{2}O_2 \rightarrow NO_2 \tag{15-2}$$

Nitrogen(IV) oxide, NO_2 (nitrogen dioxide), is a reddish-brown gas which dissolves in water to form nitric acid:

$$3NO_2 + H_2O \rightarrow 2HNO_3 + NO \tag{15-3}$$

The nitric oxide produced in reaction (15-3) can react with more O_2, and then more water, to form more nitric acid.

Nitrogen compounds formed naturally are collected in soil and in surface waters where they are used by plants. There are in the world a few salt deposits which are rich in nitrates. One of the most important of these is in the Andes Mountains of Chile. It furnished nitrates for much of the world from 1850 until World War I. Coal is another source of nitrogen compounds. When coal is heated in the absence of air, as in the production of coke, ammonia and other nitrogenous compounds are produced. This source also was important throughout the past century and until shortly after World War I.

Awareness of the importance of nitrogen to life and the scarcity of usable nitrogen compounds in nature caused considerable concern during the 19th century. There was no known method of producing nitrogen synthetically to augment nature's supply. It was predicted that the people of the world faced eventual starvation. This was long before the current population explosion.

Several methods of combining elementary nitrogen with other elements were developed and tried with some success. The Haber process, however, has replaced all others. This process, developed in Germany during World War I, involves combining nitrogen with hydrogen through the use of catalysts. In order to secure a profitable yield, high pressures, 200 atm or more, and temperatures of 550°C are necessary.

$$N_2 + 3H_2 \xrightleftharpoons{\text{catalyst}} 2NH_3 \tag{15-4}$$

The reaction is reversible; pressure tends to force it to the right. While elevated temperatures are required, they also tend to reverse the reaction. Cooling the mixture under pressure stabilizes the ammonia and reduces its decomposition.

15-5 UTILIZATION OF NITROGEN

Enormous quantities of *ammonia* are produced by the Haber process. It is estimated that 11 million tons were produced in 1966. The major portion is utilized by the fertilizer industries. Ammonia is a gas at normal temperatures and pressures; however, it can be liquefied under pressure. It is extremely soluble in water. Once dissolved, the ammonia reacts to a small extent with water, giving a weakly basic solution:

$$NH_3 + HOH \xrightleftharpoons{} NH_4^+ + OH^- \tag{15-5}$$

Ammonia reacts with either sulfuric or nitric acids to form the corresponding salts:

$$2NH_3 + H_2SO_4 \rightarrow \quad (NH_4)_2SO_4 \tag{15-6}$$
$$\text{ammonium sulfate}$$

and

$$NH_3 + HNO_3 \rightarrow \quad NH_4NO_3 \tag{15-7}$$
$$\text{ammonium nitrate}$$

These fertilizer salts can be mechanically spread on fields. Or, with the use of especially designed machines, ammonia gas under pressure can be released below the surface when the soil is moist; the moisture in the soil dissolves and retains the ammonia. Another method is to release liquid ammonia into the water in irrigation ditches, which carries it directly into the fields.

Ammonium nitrate is a powerful explosive when properly detonated. It is often combined with dynamite where heavy blasting is required.

Nitric acid is used in large amounts throughout the world. Production in the United States equaled about five million tons in 1966. It is used in the preparation of nitrates such as ammonium nitrate, in the production of nearly all explosives, and in the steel industry.

Nitric acid can be made by the oxidation of ammonia:

$$4NH_3 + 5O_2 \rightarrow \quad 4NO \quad + 6H_2O \tag{15-8}$$

$$\text{nitrogen (II)}$$
$$\text{oxide}$$

The nitrogen(II) oxide is further oxidized by O_2 from the atmosphere. The resulting nitrogen(IV) oxide is dissolved in water to give nitric acid, Eqs. (15-2) and (15-3).

15-6 THE NOBLE GASES

The atmosphere contains a family of gaseous elements—the noble gases—which were undiscovered on the earth until 1894. These gases are helium, neon, argon, krypton, xenon, and radon. The evidence for the existence of helium in the atmosphere of the sun was first observed, by spectroscopic methods, in 1868. The element was named *helium*, from the Greek name for the sun, *helios*. It was not discovered on the earth until 1895 when it was found in uranium-containing ores. Today it is obtained commercially from the natural petroleum gases occurring in some of the fields of Kansas, Oklahoma, and Texas.

A hundred years before the discovery of helium, it was suspected that the atmosphere contained gases other than oxygen and nitrogen, but it was not until 1894 that such a gas, which was named *argon*, was identified. The name argon was suggested since it is the Greek word for "inert." This was indeed a logical name since all the members of this family are so inactive they do not naturally react with other elements. For more than sixty years they were called the *inert gases*. Subsequently, other members were isolated and identified. Some of their physical properties are shown in Table 15-2.

TABLE 15-2. **Some of the properties of the noble gases**

	Atomic Weights	Boiling Point, °C.	Melting Point, °C
helium	4.003	−268.9	−272.0
neon	20.183	−245.9	−248.8
argon	39.948	−185.8	−189.2
krypton	83.80	−152.9	−156.6
xenon	131.3	−108.1	−111.9
radon	222.0	− 61.8	− 71.0

The discovery of the noble gases posed a problem in that there appeared to be no ideal place for them in the periodic table. They have been justifiably placed in either of two locations in the table. Since it appeared for many years that they were inert, they were considered to have a valence of zero and were therefore placed before Group I under a heading of "0" valence. However, it was established that the inertness of the noble gases was due to the fact that the outside shell of electrons for each was complete; therefore they were also placed at the extreme right-hand side of the chart and sometimes indicated as Group VIII.

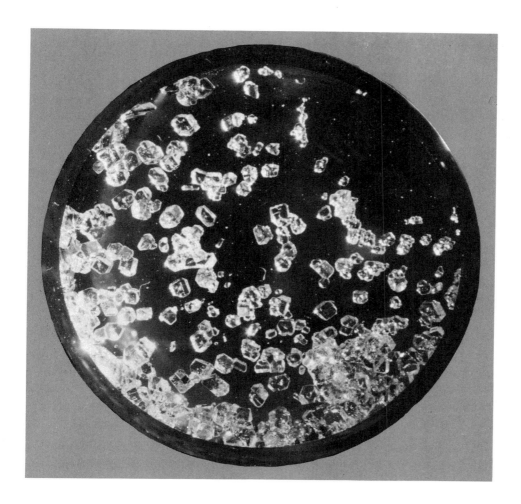

FIG. 15–2. Xenon tetrafluoride crystals, prepared at the Argonne National Laboratory in 1962 and first appearing as a cover photograph on *Science*, Vol. **138**, 12 October 1962. [Courtesy of the Argonne National Laboratory and *Science*.]

Uses

The noble gases have many uses, some of which derive from their inactive characteristics. Argon is used in electric light bulbs to replace air, which would destroy the hot filament by oxidation. Electricity, when passed through an evacuated glass tube containing neon gas at low pressure produces the characteristic "neon light."

Helium has many uses. The most important one for many years, after it was obtained in quantity, was in balloons and other lighter-than-air craft. Helium eliminated the fire hazard always present when hydrogen was used. As we noted in Section 8–8, helium has been used by deep sea divers to prevent the "bends" and in hospitals it is used to dilute the oxygen needed to treat respiratory diseases. Helium is also used by the welding industry when oxygen-free atmospheres are necessary. The National Aeronautics and Space Administration is presently one of the heavy users. Since helium has the lowest boiling point of any known substance, $-268.9°C$, it is used as the cooling agent when extremely low temperatures are necessary. Because of the rarity of the other noble gases, there are few practical applications of them.

In 1933, Professor Linus Pauling stated that it should be possible for a so-called inert gas to form compounds. Despite the fact that the outer electron shell of such an atom has a completed set of eight electrons, he predicted that under the proper circumstances these electrons could be used for bonding to other elements. However, it was not until 1962 that chemists succeeded in making any of the compounds. Since that time, several compounds have been prepared, consisting of the noble gases with fluorine or oxygen. Xenon tetrafluoride XeF_4 is a typical example (Fig. 15–2). In general, it is still proper to regard these gases as inert, for they do not participate in most of the common chemical reactions.

15-7 POLLUTION OF THE ATMOSPHERE

One of the major problems facing many cities of the world is the pollution of the atmosphere. This problem was experienced by relatively few communities until the middle 1900's. In the United States, Pittsburgh, Pennsylvania, was one of the first cities to be plagued by this unpleasantness. Troubles there stemmed primarily from the soot and gases of incompletely burned coal. The problem was largely eliminated by methods of controlling industrial waste gases. At the present time, the automobile is believed to be the major cause of the smog which envelops many cities. Because the engine in the typical automobile does not completely burn the fuel, considerable carbon monoxide (CO) is produced. It is estimated that 10% of the hydrocarbon fuels escape unburned into the atmosphere. The modern high compression engine also converts an appreciable amount of elementary nitrogen from the atmosphere into nitric oxide, NO, which is converted immediately into nitrogen dioxide, NO_2, Eqs. (15–1) and (15–2), the reddish-brown ingredient that is noticeable in smog. The reaction of the nitrogen oxides, the unburned hydrocarbons, and ozone, in the presence of ultraviolet light from the sun, produces the highly irritating materials in smog. These substances cause extreme irritation of the eyes, nose, and throat, and are implicated in such diseases as lung cancer, pneumonia, and bronchitis. They also cause great damage to crops in surrounding areas. Specially designed exhaust and antismog devices are required in California and no doubt will soon be required in other congested areas.

IMPORTANT TERMS

Absolute humidity	*Haber process*	*Nitrogen fixation*
Barometer	*Humidity*	*Relative humidity*

WORK EXERCISES

1. What evidence do we have which indicates that the atmosphere becomes thinner with an increase in altitude above the earth?

2. Why is moist air lighter than dry air?

3. It is estimated that the pressure of the atmosphere is halved for each 17,500 ft of altitude above the earth. Assuming this estimate is correct, find the atmospheric pressure in pounds per square inch and in millimeters of mercury at 70,000 ft.

4. If the air was saturated when the temperature was 40°F, what would be the relative humidity of the air at 80°F? Assume that there is no change in moisture content.

5. What changes would likely take place if the concentration of the CO_2 in the atmosphere were doubled?

6. Describe three methods of nitrogen fixation.

7. Why was finding a synthetic method for nitrogen fixation considered such an important achievement?

8. Can you make any correlation between the fact that it is difficult to form compounds of nitrogen and the fact that nitrogen compounds are used in most explosives?

9. What are the important uses of nitrogen compounds?

10. List the more objectionable materials commonly found in city smog.

SUGGESTED READING

Batten, L. J., *The Unclean Sky*, Anchor Books, Doubleday, New York, 1966. A meteorologist looks at air pollution.

Day, F. H., *The Chemical Elements in Nature*, "The Inert Gases," pp. 107–113. Reinhold, New York, 1963.

Hyman, H. H., "The Chemistry of the Noble Gases," *Journal of Chemical Education* **41,** 174 (1964). This article is based on a lecture presented at the 1963 summer conference of the California Association of Chemistry Teachers.

Kamen, M. D., "Discoveries in Nitrogen Fixation," *Scientific American*, Mar. 1953, p. 38. The discoveries of new microorganisms that are able to bring about nitrogen fixation.

Watt, G. W., L. F. Hatch, and J. J. Lagowski, *Chemistry*, Norton, New York, 1964. Chapter 6 contains a good presentation of the properties of gases.

Chapter 16 THE PROPERTIES OF GASES

16-1 INTRODUCTION

In Section 3–4 we described briefly the solid, the liquid, and the gas states. While all of us have long been accustomed to these three states of matter, and know that solids melt to give liquids and liquids boil to give gases, further thought may make us ask, "Why is this true? What is the real difference between a liquid and a gas? Why can we compress gases and not liquids or solids? Why does a gas tend to fill any container into which it is placed?"

Questions such as these have concerned scientists for hundreds of years. As a result of the questioning and the answers found in the experiments of Robert Boyle, J. A. C. Charles, Joseph Gay-Lussac, Amedeo Avogadro, Thomas Graham, and many, many others, a theory which we call the kinetic theory of gases has been developed. Interpretations of the nature of gases made by these pioneers of science also helped to establish the atomic theory which was discussed in Chapter 4. We will now tell the story of our present explanation of the properties of gases. We will include some of the kinds of calculation that were important in establishing the theory and that are still used in either setting up or interpreting experiments today.

16-2 ROBERT BOYLE AND THE RELATIONSHIP OF PRESSURE TO VOLUME

Most of you are aware that air can be compressed into a smaller volume. After it has been compressed, it can be used for many purposes. If we encase it in an automobile tire, it supports the weight of the automobile and its springiness makes the automobile ride more smoothly. Compressed air can also be used to drive jack hammers and sand blasting machines.

Robert Boyle, who lived from 1627 to 1691, was one of the first scientists to study the effect of pressure on a gas; the gas he used was air. His experiments were made possible by the prior invention of a good vacuum pump. For his experiments he used a container from which air could be pumped or in which pressures could be varied by adding or removing mercury. A somewhat simplified representation of his experiments is shown in Fig. 16-1. In this diagram three cylinders, each holding 4 liters of air are fitted with pistons which move up and down but will not allow air either to escape or to enter the cylinder. In cylinder (a) the pressure is the same inside and outside the container. We say it is at atmospheric pressure or has a pressure of 1 atm.* In cylinder (b) the pressure on the gas is double that in (a), and we say (b) is under 2 atm of pressure. In cylinder (c) the total pressure on the gas is 4 atm. We find that the volume of air in the three cylinders is 4 liters in (a), 2 liters in (b) and only 1 liter in (c).

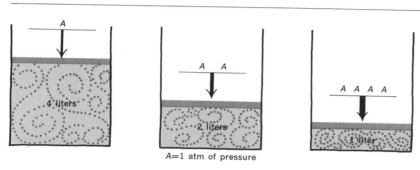

FIG. 16-1. Diagrams showing the effect of different pressures on the volume of air.

When we interpret these data shown in Fig. 16-1, we see that not only does increasing the pressure decrease the volume of air, but that doubling the pressure halves the volume, and that increasing the pressure by a factor of four reduces the original volume to one-fourth. The *qualitative* nature of the relation between pressure and gas volumes was probably known to many scientists who were contemporaries of Boyle, just as it is common knowledge today. The important contribution Boyle made was in stating the relationship in specific *quantities*. We can express this quantitative relationship in two ways. We can say that the product of the volume and pressure for a given gas is always the same number (or is constant). From Fig. 16-1, we can see that 1 atm × 4 liters = 2 atm × 2 liters = 4 atm × 1 liter. Another way of saying this is given in the statement we now usually refer to as **Boyle's law:**

The volume occupied by a given weight of gas is inversely proportional to the pressure if the temperature is held constant.

---

* In Chapter 15 we stated that the average atmospheric pressure at sea level was equal to the pressure exerted by a column of mercury 760 mm high. This pressure has been adopted as a unit called *one atmosphere*. In dealing with extremely high pressures, we generally express the total pressure in terms of multiples of atmospheres; a pressure of 1520 mm of mercury is called 2 atm. When dealing with lower pressures, we generally record them in millimeters of mercury. Engineers routinely use pounds per square inch (psi) when describing pressure. Atmospheric pressure is 14.7 psi.

Actually Boyle expressed his original statement in terms of the constant value obtained when pressure and volume were multiplied, and he does not seem to have been concerned with the effects of temperature. He was probably fortunate in that the gases he studied were at the same temperature throughout his experiments. The fact that temperature could effect the results was first made known by the Frenchman Edme Mariotte, and the French still designate the statement just quoted as Mariotte's law, rather than as Boyle's law.

There are many applications, both practical and theoretical, for Boyle's law. For illustration, let us take first a practical example. If we have a known volume of gas under a known pressure, we can calculate its volume at any other pressure, providing the temperature is the same in both cases. Thus, if we increase the pressure, the volume will be decreased, and vice versa. The original volume multiplied by a factor composed of the two pressures, the old and the new, will in one case decrease the volume; in the other it will increase the volume, depending on how the factor is derived. We must decide which way to apply the factor.

Example: If we fill a perfectly elastic balloon with 500 ml of air at sea level when the atmospheric pressure is 760 mm and transport it to the mountains where the atmospheric pressure is 600 mm, what will be its new volume?

The pressure is decreasing from 760 mm to 600 mm so the volume will increase. We therefore must set up our factor with the largest value on top:

$$500 \text{ ml} \times \frac{760 \text{ mm}}{600 \text{ mm}} = 633 \text{ ml (the new volume).}$$

Now, assuming the same atmospheric pressures, suppose we reverse the procedure and fill the balloon with 500 ml of air on the mountain and return to sea level. The sample will be subjected to an increased pressure as we approach sea level, and the volume will decrease. Our factor must now be arranged to produce a smaller volume and therefore the smaller value will be in the numerator:

$$500 \text{ ml} \times \frac{600 \text{ mm}}{760 \text{ mm}} = 394.7 \text{ ml (the new volume).}$$

Any units of volume and units of pressure may be used. For example, the steel cylinders ordinarily used to transport hydrogen, oxygen, or other gases, have a volume of about 2 cu ft, and they may be filled to a pressure of 2000 psi. If we fill such a cylinder with oxygen, what volume of oxygen would we obtain by opening the valve and allowing it to expand to a pressure of 1 atm? [Assume 1 atm = 15 psi].

Since the pressure will be less, the volume will increase:

$$2 \text{ cu ft} \times \frac{2000 \text{ psi}}{15 \text{ psi}} = 266.6 \text{ cu ft of oxygen.}$$

When we think further about the implications of the fact that doubling the pressure exactly halves the volume of a gas, we realize that the gas must really be mostly space.

The volume of the molecules is so small that we don't even need to consider it. The same is true of all gases studied, not only of air with which Boyle did his experiments. This realization lent a great deal of support to crucial parts of Dalton's atomic theory which was not developed and stated until more than a hundred years after Boyle's work.

◄ Under ordinary conditions, Boyle's law is entirely satisfactory. When a gas under high pressure is compressed to a very small volume, however, we find that we cannot properly neglect the volume of the atoms. To be precise, we must add correction factors to Boyle's law to make it truly fit the behavior of a gas under these conditions. The correction factors are necessary because when the total gas volume is extremely small the molecules themselves occupy a significant part of the volume. Also, when molecules are very close to one another, there are attractions and repulsions between them. ►

Even though molecules are minute and occupy only an extremely small part of the volume of a gas under normal pressures, they definitely affect the pressure. Boyle talked about the "spring of air" when describing the tendency of molecules to resist efforts to compress them. We see this springiness or resistance to compression in our automobile tires, in the various devices that use compressed air, and in what happens when we pop a paper bag filled with air.

16–3 THE RELATIONSHIP OF VOLUME TO TEMPERATURE—CHARLES'S LAW

We are all now familiar with the fact that heating a gas causes it to expand. Mariotte was one of the first to describe this fact. If the gas is contained in a vessel that does not expand, such as a steel cylinder or an automobile tire, the pressure of the gas increases when heated. During the latter part of the 18th century (also some 100 years after Boyle's work) precise measurements were made of the effect of temperature on the volume of gases. Such measurements were probably first made by the French scientist J. A. C. Charles, who did not publish his observations. They were made later, apparently independently, by another French scientist, Joseph Gay-Lussac, who did publish them. The qualitative observation from which both men started was that hot air was lighter than cold air, and that a bag which had been inverted over a fire until it was full of heated gases would float for some time.

◄ It is interesting to note that neither Charles nor Gay-Lussac were merely academic scientists. When Charles heard of the bags of hot air being carried into the air, he realized that hydrogen, a newly discovered gas, would have much greater buoyancy than hot air. Charles was the first to make hydrogen balloons, and he and a co-worker were the first men to go aloft. On one occasion he went more than a mile high. Gay-Lussac also went up in balloons, eventually reaching a height of four miles. He even took samples of air at that altitude and concluded that the composition of air did not vary with height. More precise measurements, however, have shown that his conclusion was incorrect. ►

One feature of Charles's observations was most significant. He established the fact that a sample of any gas at 0°C would expand by 1/273 of its volume for each degree he heated it, and would contract by 1/273 of its volume for each degree he cooled it. This was true for all gases. (See Fig. 16–2 for a graphic presentation of Charles's results.) This

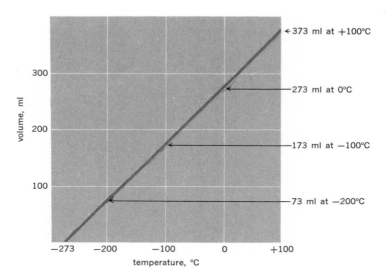

FIG. 16-2. The influence of temperature on the volume of a gas.

relationship can be expressed in a statement now generally known as **Charles's law** (alternately as Gay-Lussac's law):

The volume occupied by a gas (pressure remaining constant) is directly proportional to the absolute temperature.

At the time of his work, Charles did not have methods for producing extremely low temperatures. Also, there was no temperature scale that could be directly applied in calculations, for some temperatures were plus and some were minus. A satisfactory temperature scale was first suggested by William Thomson, better known as Lord Kelvin, a Scottish mathematician and physicist.

Kelvin reasoned that if gases lost 1/273 of their volume at 0°C for every degree they were cooled, there must be a temperature of −273°C that was the lowest possible temperature. Theoretically, this would be the place where gases had no volume at all; he realized,

Description	Computation	°C	°K
boiling point:	100°C + 273 = 373°K	100	373
freezing point:	0°C + 273 = 273°K	0	273
absolute zero:	−273°C + 273 = 0°K	−273	0

FIG. 16-3. Relationship between centigrade and kelvin temperatures.

of course, that gases would undoubtedly condense to the liquid state long before this temperature was reached. He took −273°C, which he called absolute zero, as the temperature at which the molecules of a gas would have lost all their energy. As a result of his reasoning, a temperature scale was developed in which zero corresponded to −273° centigrade (celsius). The new scale, now known as the *kelvin* or *absolute scale*, is related to the centigrade scale and uses the same size of degrees. The only difference is the zero point. Centigrade temperature is converted to kelvin temperature by adding the number 273 (Fig. 16–3). In recent years a temperature approaching absolute zero, 0.004°K, has been reached.

The tremendous advantage of the absolute temperature scale is that the volume of a gas is *directly* proportional to the numerical value of the temperature. That is, at 200°K a gas will have twice the volume it has at 100°K, and at 300°K it will have three times the volume. With the use of the absolute scale we can now calculate the change in volume of a sample of a gas for any change in temperature: *if the temperature is lowered, the volume will be less; if the temperature is raised, the volume will increase.*

Sample problem. Suppose we have collected 150 ml of oxygen at 30°C and wish to know what volume it will occupy at 0°C. [Assume no change in pressure]

We first change temperatures to the kelvin scale:

$$30°C + 273 = 303°K, \qquad 0°C + 273 = 273°K.$$

To find the new volume, we multiply the original volume (150 ml) by a factor composed of the two temperatures involved, 273 and 303. Since the temperature is decreasing, the volume will also decrease, so the factor must be less than one. Only two factors are possible:

(a) $\dfrac{303}{273}$ or   (b) $\dfrac{273}{303}$.

It should be obvious that (b) is the correct one since its value is less than one (the numerator is smaller than the denominator). Multiplying the volume by the correct factor, we get

$$150 \text{ ml} \times \frac{273°K}{303°K} = 135 \text{ ml}, \text{ the new volume of oxygen.}$$

This method may be used whenever it is necessary to calculate a change in the volume of a gas, brought about by a change in temperature.

16-4 THE RELATIONSHIP OF TEMPERATURE TO PRESSURE

We know that if the volume of a gas is held constant by a nonexpanding container, an increase in temperature will produce an increase in pressure. We can modify Charles's law and say that *the pressure of a gas is directly proportional to the absolute temperature if the volume is held constant.*

This application of Charles's law, which is also sometimes called the law of Gay-Lussac, is convenient to apply, for example, in calculating the pressure changes that will take place in automobile tires with ordinary changes in temperature.

Example. Let us assume that we check our tires early in the morning before starting out on a trip that will take us across a desert in midafternoon. The tires are checked with 30 psi when the temperature is 15°C (59°F). By midafternoon the high temperature of the desert air combined with hot pavement and tire friction will easily produce tire temperatures of 100°C (212°F). What will the pressure be in the tires at this temperature?

15°C + 273 = 288°K morning temperature
100°C + 273 = 373°K afternoon temperature

If at starting the psi is 30 and the temperature 288°K, what will the psi be at 373°K? The temperature increased; therefore, the pressure will increase:

$$30 \text{ psi} \times \frac{373°K}{288°K} = 39 \text{ psi.}$$

These figures have actually been observed by one of the authors of this book. Much higher tire temperatures have been reported.

16-5 COMBINED EFFECTS OF TEMPERATURE AND PRESSURE— STANDARD CONDITIONS

Using both Boyle's and Charles's relationships, we can study the effects on volume when we vary both pressure and temperature at the same time. Both volume and pressure increase with increasing temperature, so we say these quantities are directly proportional to temperature. Volume decreases with an increase in pressure and increases with a decrease in pressure, so we say that volume and pressure are in an inverse relationship.

Since the volume of a gas is affected so distinctly by both pressure and temperature, it means very little to report that we measured a gas volume and found it to be 1.5 liters. It is essential that the conditions of temperature and pressure during the measurement also be reported. If we are to make meaningful comparisons of one gas volume with another, all observations should be based on the same conditions. Scientists have agreed upon a standard for this purpose. *Standard temperature and pressure (STP) are defined as a temperature of 273°K (or 0°C) and a pressure of 760 mm of mercury (or 1 atm).* It is not necessary, of course, that we actually do the experiment under these conditions. If we know the volume of a gas at say, 25°C and 745 mm of pressure, we can calculate the volume at STP. Or conversely, from someone else's report of a gas volume at STP, we could calculate what the volume would be if we decided to use a different temperature and pressure. The important point is that we must clearly state the temperature and pressure, and preferably use standard conditions.

Examples. Let us consider the steel cylinder of oxygen mentioned previously, which had a volume of 2 cu ft. The stated pressure of 2000 psi was measured at 17°C. Now we can ask, "What volume would this oxygen occupy at standard temperature and pressure?"

We have already calculated the correction for change in pressure to 1 atm. Now we can calculate the correction for change in temperature from 17°C to standard temperature, 0°C:

$$266.6 \text{ cu ft} \times \frac{273 + 0}{273 + 17} = 266.6 \times \frac{273}{290} = 250 \text{ cu ft.}$$

For a more conventional laboratory-type problem: 800 ml of oxygen is collected in the laboratory where the temperature is 23°C and the barometric pressure 740 mm. What will be the volume of the oxygen at standard conditions (0°C and 760 mm)?

It makes no difference whether we adjust first for temperature or for pressure. We know that the temperature is being decreased, so the numerator of this fraction must be smaller than the denominator. We also know that the pressure is being increased from 740 to 760, so this part of the problem will also decrease the volume of oxygen. We have, then,

$$800 \times \frac{273 + 0}{273 + 23} \times \frac{740}{760} = 718 \text{ ml of oxygen}$$

(at conditions of standard temperature and pressure, STP).

16–6 DIFFUSION OF GASES—GRAHAM'S LAW

The migration of molecules among other molecules is called *diffusion*. We are familiar with the phenomenon of diffusion of gases, since we know that if a gas with a characteristic odor is released on one side of a room, it is soon detectable on the other side. If we invert a container of hydrogen gas over a container of oxygen gas, it can soon be demonstrated that the two gases have mixed. Why should this be so, since hydrogen is much lighter than oxygen? This and similar questions concerned the Scottish scientist Thomas Graham. We can perform a demonstration similar to the experiments he did when he was trying to answer questions about the diffusion of gases. Again we see that experiments suggested by a qualitative observation can transform data into a quantitative expression from which reliable, exact predictions can be made.

FIG. 16–4. The rates of diffusion of NH_3 and HCl gases.

For our demonstration of the diffusion of gases we will use a glass tube that is 3 cm or more in diameter and about 1 m long (Fig. 16–4). Small containers, one filled with concentrated HCl and the other with a concentrated solution of NH_3 in water, are placed at the opposite ends of the tube, and stoppers are inserted at each end of the tube. Some time later a faint white cloud of smoke, which eventually forms a white band around the inside of the tube, is observed somewhat nearer the end of the tube that contains the HCl. We know that such white solid particles are formed when HCl reacts with NH_3 according to the equation:

$$NH_3 + HCl \rightarrow NH_4Cl \qquad\qquad (16\text{-}1)$$

We interpret our experiment by saying that hydrogen chloride gas and ammonia diffuse through the tube, and where they meet, a reaction occurs. The zone of reaction is nearer the hydrochloric acid source. We know that the molecular weight of NH_3 is 17, and the molecular weight of HCl is 36.5, more than twice as great. Our conclusion must be that small molecules move faster than large molecules and therefore diffuse faster. If we place our containers of HCl and NH_3 exactly 1 m apart in the tube and measure the distance to the zone where NH_4Cl forms, we will find that it is about 60 cm from the NH_3 and 40 cm from the HCl.

After doing many experiments similar to the one outlined above, Thomas Graham could formulate the law which now bears his name:

The rates of diffusion of two gases are inversely proportional to the square roots of their densities.

The diffusion of oxygen and hydrogen gases provides examples which are easily calculated. Oxygen with a molecular weight of 32 is 16 times more dense than hydrogen with a molecular weight of 2. The ratio of their densities is 16 to 1. The square roots of their densities are

oxygen, $\sqrt{16} = 4$ and   hydrogen, $\sqrt{1} = 1$.

Since the rates of diffusion are inversely proportional to the square roots of their densities, hydrogen will diffuse four times as fast as oxygen. To illustrate: If two identical automobile tires are filled, one with oxygen and the other with hydrogen, and they are punctured with identical nails at the same time, the tire with hydrogen will go flat four times as fast as the tire filled with oxygen. This phenomenon would be fully appreciated if a person filled his lungs with helium* and then exhaled in the normal fashion. He would literally collapse, since the less dense molecules would escape from the lungs much more rapidly than those of normal breath.

Let us further consider the results indicated in Fig. 16–4. Using Graham's law, we can now predict where the white ring will form in the glass tube. The molecular weight of HCl is 36.5 and that of NH_3 is 17. Using approximations in our calculations, we find that the square roots for the two densities are

for HCl, $\sqrt{36.5} \simeq 6$ and   for NH_3, $\sqrt{17} \simeq 4$.

---

* For the sake of safety, hydrogen should *not* be used for such an experiment, however. Enough oxygen remains in the lungs to cause an explosive mixture that would be fatal if ignited.

The simplest interpretation of the results is to say that NH_3 travels 6 spaces while HCl travels 4. Therefore, NH_3 will travel 6/10 of the way, and the white ring should form 6/10 of the way from the NH_3 container toward the HCl container.

16–7 GAY-LUSSAC AND THE LAW OF COMBINING VOLUMES

Gay-Lussac, who shared with Charles the discovery of the effect of temperature on gases and an enthusiasm for ballooning, is credited with another important observation. Actually others had probably made similar observations, but he was able to state a simple generalization of the observations.

Gay-Lussac's experiments involved the volumes of gases that react with one another. He found that when chemical reactions involving gases take place, the reacting volumes are always in the ratios of small whole numbers. This is not so startling when we react one volume of hydrogen gas with one of chlorine to get two volumes of hydrogen chloride,

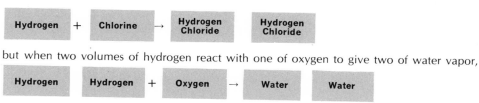

but when two volumes of hydrogen react with one of oxygen to give two of water vapor,

and when one volume of nitrogen gas reacts with three of hydrogen to give only two volumes of ammonia gas, some explanation is needed.

The basic observations were made by Gay-Lussac, but the explanation for them was provided by the Italian scientist, Amadeo Avogadro. It is interesting that his explanation was made only a few years after Gay-Lussac reported his generalizations, but Avogadro's explanation was neglected by the scientific community for fifty years. In fact, Dalton, who lived and worked at the same time as Gay-Lussac and Avogadro never accepted Gay-Lussac's data as having any real validity, since they seemed to contradict his atomic theory. For instance, if equal volumes of gases contained equal numbers of atoms, then one atom (liter) of oxygen reacted to form two particles (liters) of water. This would imply that the oxygen atom had actually been split. Such a thing was impossible according to Dalton's atomic theory. The explanation and the reconciliation of Dalton's atomic theory and Gay-Lussac's law of combining volumes came from Avogadro, and his fellow countryman Cannizzarro, who championed Avogadro's theory after his death.

16–8 AVOGADRO'S LAW

It had been believed by many that equal volumes of gases (under similar temperatures and pressures) contained the same number of atoms. Gay-Lussac's experiments seemed to contradict this. If we change the statement slightly, however, and say that equal volumes of gases at the same temperature and pressures contain an equal number of *molecules*, we have a statement of Avogadro's law. The substitution of the word molecule (we could just as well have used particle) for atom, and the idea that there might be more than one atom in a molecule, made all the evidence consistent with one theory. According to this theory we can write the equations for the formation of hydrochloric acid, water, and ammonia as follows:

$$H_2 \quad + \quad Cl_2 \quad \rightarrow \quad HCl \quad HCl$$

$$H_2 \quad + \quad Cl_2 \quad \rightarrow \quad 2HCl \tag{16-2}$$

$$H_2 \quad H_2 \quad + \quad O_2 \quad \rightarrow \quad H_2O \quad H_2O$$

vapor

$$2H_2 \quad + \quad O_2 \quad \rightarrow \quad 2H_2O \tag{16-3}$$

$$N_2 \quad + \quad H_2 \quad \quad H_2 \quad \quad H_2 \quad \rightarrow \quad NH_3 \quad NH_3$$

$$N_2 \quad + \quad 3H_2 \quad \rightarrow \quad 2NH_3 \tag{16-4}$$

Like all really great theories, Avogadro's not only explained the observations but also led to other predictions that were important and were found to be correct. If we weigh equal volumes of different gases (at the same temperature and pressure, of course) we can determine their relative weights. If we know the molecular weight of one gas, we can then determine the molecular weight of the other. For example, if a flask which holds exactly 1 g of O_2 will hold 1.375 g of an unknown gas, a molecule of the unknown must weigh 1.375 times as much as an oxygen molecule. Since an oxygen molecule weighs 32 on our relative scale, the molecular weight of the unknown gas is 44. This happens to be the molecular weight of CO_2. Such a determination does not, however, prove that the gas is CO_2; chemical tests are necessary for this.

16-9 THE MAGIC BOX—THE MOLE VOLUME OF GASES

The densities of the gases are usually measured in terms of grams/liter. Table 16–1 lists densities of some common gases.

In calculations involving moles (molecular weights in grams) of gases, it is convenient to know what size container is required to hold 1 mole of a gas at standard conditions. From Table 16–1 we find that 1 liter of oxygen weighs 1.4290 g. By dividing the molecular weight of oxygen, 32, by the weight of 1 liter of oxygen we get

$$\frac{32}{1.4290} = 22.4$$

Therefore 22.4 liters are required to hold 32 g of oxygen at STP.

TABLE 16-1. The densities of several gases in grams/liter (measured at standard conditions)

hydrogen	0.0899
helium	0.1785
ammonia	0.7710
nitrogen	1.2506
air	1.2930
oxygen	1.4290
hydrogen chloride	1.6392
carbon dioxide	1.9769
chlorine	3.214

Making the same calculations for hydrogen, we find that

$$\text{molecular weight of hydrogen} = \frac{2.016}{\text{weight/liter of hydrogen} = 0.0899} = 22.4.$$

We obtain the same figure. If we continue the same calculations for other gases, we invariably arrive with answers which are very near to 22.4, and so we conclude that *the volume occupied by 1 mole of any gas at standard conditions is 22.4 liters*. A mole contains Avogadro's number of molecules (6.023×10^{23}) of any gas at standard conditions. Therefore, 22.4 liters can be used in determining the molecular weight of a gas when the weight of 1 liter is known:

weight/liter $\times$ 22.4 = molecular weight.

Since we may not always have a liter of an unknown gas, we can start with another value.

Example. It was determined that 8 ml of an unknown gas weighs 0.016 g. What is its molecular weight?

First, we find the weight of 1 ml:

$\frac{0.016}{8} = 0.002$ g = weight of 1 ml, then

$0.002 \times 1000 = 2.0 =$ weight of 1 liter, and finally
$2 \times 22.4 = 44.8 =$ molecular weight of the gas.

Conversely, knowing the molecular weight, we can find the weight of 1 liter by dividing the molecular weight by 22.4:

$$\frac{\text{molecular weight (g/mole)}}{22.4 \text{ (liters/mole)}} = \textbf{weight (g/liter)}$$

The volume of a container needed to hold 22.4 liters is a cube of approximately 11 inches on a side, as is shown in Fig. 16–5.

16-10 THE KINETIC THEORY OF GASES

We have now introduced our readers to most of the information used in formulating our present day explanation of the behavior of gases, known as the *kinetic theory*. Boyle's

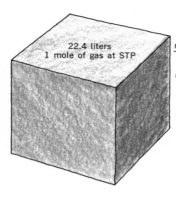

22.4 liters
1 mole of gas at STP

$$\frac{\text{molecular weight}}{22.4} = \text{grams/liter}$$

(grams/liter)×22.4=
molecular weight in
grams/mole

FIG. 16–5. The gram-molar volume (magic box).

experiments meant that gases contained an extremely small amount of particles and a lot of space. He did not really explain why there was the "spring" of air, or to rephrase the question, "Why does a gas exert pressure?" Charles and Gay-Lussac had shown that volume and pressure increased with temperature. Graham's work indicated that molecules are in motion, and that small molecules move faster than larger ones. There were many attempts to explain the "spring" of air and to explain why gases expand or their pressures increase when they are heated. Some of the ideas were fanciful: one involved an invisible layer of "caloric" that surrounded particles and increased in size when they were heated. This and most of the other explanations have not withstood the attacks of logic and the findings of subsequent experimental research. Most of them have been forgotten except by the historians of science.

The important new idea in our current theory is that molecules of a gas are in constant motion. This was suggested by Graham's observations and the Brownian movement (see Section 14–4) seemed to support it, even though no one had ever seen a moving molecule (we still haven't). The concept that molecules are in continuous motion contains some apparent inconsistencies. If molecules are in motion, then they must collide, and if they collide, why don't they stop? We know they don't stop because we can measure the pressure of a gas in an impermeable container and show that it does not change with time. The best explanation of this observation that is consistent with our theory is that the collisions are perfectly elastic—whatever energy is lost by one particle is gained by another.

When we combine the idea that molecules of a gas are in motion but that each collision is perfectly elastic, with the interpretations of the experiments of Boyle, Charles, Graham and others, we can state the **kinetic theory of gases** as follows:

1) All gases are composed of particles which are called molecules. Compared to their own dimensions, the molecules are extremely far apart; under normal pressures, molecules occupy a portion of the volume of gases so small as to be insignificant. If the pressure is increased, they are forced closer together; if the pressure is diminished, they move farther apart.

2) The molecules of a gas are in rapid motion, colliding with each other and with the walls of their container, in the order of millions of times/second. The pressures produced by gases are the results of these collisions. An increase in temperature causes the molecules to move faster, and to increase either the pressure or the volume of the gas.

3) Molecules of a gas are perfectly elastic. No energy is lost by their collisions; however, energy may be transferred from one molecule to another.

4) Under normal pressures, the attraction between molecules is so small that it may be considered negligible.

5) The kinetic energy of all gases at the same temperature is the same. According to Avogadro's law, equal volumes of different gases have the same number of molecules. Therefore, small molecules (hydrogen) must be traveling much faster than large molecules (oxygen) if they possess equal kinetic energy. (Figure 16–4 demonstrated that the smaller NH_3 molecules traveled farther than the larger HCl molecules.)

The kinetic theory of gases can be extended to liquids and also to solids. When we cool a gas and compress it we decrease the speed of its molecules and bring them closer together. At some stage the attractive forces between molecules become so great that the molecules condense to form a liquid. The molecules in a liquid still move and collide, and occasionally a few are hit so hard that they have sufficient energy to evaporate. Those left behind are cooler and have less energy. We know that rapid evaporation of a liquid from the surfaces of our bodies by a wind definitely produces a cooling effect.

Cooling a liquid slows down the activity of the molecules, and can result in the formation of a solid. Most liquids shrink slightly when they freeze, but this contraction is slight compared to the shrinkage involved when a gas changes to a liquid. We think of molecules in a solid as being close together, and moving only slightly. They are often arranged in regular patterns called crystals.

16–11 SUMMARY

In this chapter we have seen that the experiments of Boyle culminated nearly 300 years later in our modern kinetic theory. This theory helps us to explain, and thereby understand, the differences between solids, liquids, and gases. It gives us a great deal of information about molecules in the gaseous state and makes it possible to interpret reactions in which the products or reactants are gases. The use of quantitative calculations based on Boyle's and Charles's laws makes it relatively simple to find the molecular weight of any gas, or of any compound that can be converted to a gas.

The kinetic theory of gases, which also helps us understand liquids and solids, illustrates many of the important aspects of science. When generally known observations become the object of careful experimentation, exact numerical relationships can often be seen, such as those discovered by Boyle and Charles. The mathematical relationships not only make it possible for scientists to predict other events, but indicate an order and regularity in nature. One is then challenged to learn more about the order and explain why it is present. The discovery of facts about the universe is so intellectually exciting it provides one of the major incentives for study and research in the sciences.

IMPORTANT TERMS

Absolute zero	*Boyle's law*	*Gay-Lussac's law*	*Mole volume of gases*
Atmosphere	*Charles's law*	*Graham's law*	*Standard conditions (gases)*
Avogadro's law	*Diffusion*	*Kinetic theory of gases*	

WORK EXERCISES

1. The normal temperature of the human body is 98.6°F. What is this on the centigrade scale and on the kelvin scale?

2. What is absolute zero on the fahrenheit scale?

3. Convert −40°C to fahrenheit.

4. How can you account for such a phenomenon as "absolute zero"?

5. A sample of oxygen has a volume of 300 ml at a temperature of 30°C. What will be its volume at 0°C?

6. The pressure in an automobile tire is 40 psi when the tire temperature is 100°C. What will be the pressure in the tire when the tire cools to 25°C?

7. A steel cylinder with a capacity of 10 liters contains hydrogen gas at a pressure of 50 atm. What will be the volume of the hydrogen at 1 atm of pressure?

8. The heating of a sample of potassium chlorate liberated 250 ml of oxygen at a pressure of 730 mm. Assuming no change in temperature, find the volume of the sample at 760 mm.

9. The volume of a sample of nitrogen gas at 720 mm and 20°C is 160 ml. What will be its volume at STP?

10. A balloon holds 1000 ml of oxygen at a temperature of 0°C. Assuming no change in pressure, find its volume when the temperature is 30°C.

11. A large balloon is filled with helium which occupies 120,000 cu ft when the atmospheric pressure is 730 mm and the temperature 15°C. What will be the volume of the helium when the balloon climbs to an altitude such that the pressure is 640 mm and the temperature 8°C?

12. A liter of an unknown gas weighs 1.4 g/liter at STP. What is the molecular weight of the gas?

13. The molecular weight of butane is 58. What is the weight of 1 liter at STP?

14. At STP, 5 ml of a gas weighs 0.220 g. What is the molecular weight of the gas?

15. A liter of gas at a temperature of 25°C and a pressure of 730 mm weighs 1.5 grams. (a) What volume will the gas occupy at STP? (b) What is the molecular weight of the gas?

16. Two balloons are filled to the same size, one with helium and the other with a gas having a molecular weight of 36. If the contents of both balloons are allowed to escape through the same size openings, which gas will escape more rapidly? What will be the comparative rates of escape?

17. In the equation $N_2 + 3 H_2 \rightarrow 2 NH_3$ how many liters of hydrogen are required to react with 3 liters of nitrogen?

18. What is the volume at STP of 4.2 g of oxygen?

SUGGESTED READING

Davis, H. M., "Low Temperature Physics," *Scientific American*, June 1949, pp. 30–39. The usual ceaseless motion of molecules would cease at absolute zero.

Hall, M. B., "Robert Boyle," *Scientific American*, Aug. 1967. Boyle was one of those most responsible for the establishment of the experimental method. This article describes his activities and reproduces illustrations of some of his apparatus.

Chapter 17 THE HALOGENS

17–1 THE SALT FORMERS

The five elements in Group VIIA, fluorine, chlorine, bromine, iodine, and astatine are known as the **halogens.** This name, which is derived from Greek words for salt formers, was suggested in 1825 by the Swedish chemist Berzelius. While elemental chlorine and iodine were known at that time, fluorine was known only in its compounds. Bromine was not discovered until later, probably because of its rarity and its tendency to form compounds that were so similar to chlorides that separation was difficult. Astatine was unknown until 1940. Since all the known isotopes of astatine are radioactive and have only short half-lives, astatine must be made synthetically, for example, by bombardment of bismuth with alpha particles. Small amounts of astatine may be produced naturally during the decay of other radioactive compounds (see Chapter 20).

The most important compound of the halogen elements is sodium chloride, commonly known as salt or table salt. In our present civilization because of mining, extraction of minerals from seawater, and rapid transportation, possession of sodium chloride has lost most of its urgency. To primitive peoples, this compound was precious, and some archeologists have pointed to the development of civilizations in areas close to dried-up lakes and seas, as indicating the importance of salt to survival. Wars have been fought for the control of salt deposits.

The halogens are similar in most properties; however, they differ greatly in activity; fluorine is the most active, and astatine the least active. Although the properties of astatine have not been widely studied, it is reasonable to assume that they are similar to those of the other halogens. The evidence that is available concerning astatine confirms this assumption.

TABLE 17–1. Some physical properties of the halogens

	Fluorine	Chlorine	Bromine	Iodine
melting point, °C	−223	−102	−7.3	114
boiling point, °C	−187	− 34.6	58.8	183
atomic weight	19.0	35.5	80.0	126.9
color	pale yellow	greenish yellow	reddish brown	grayish black (vapors are violet)

17–2 PHYSICAL PROPERTIES

The halogens are the only family of elements with members existing in the three physical states at room temperature. Fluorine and chlorine are gases. Bromine is the only non-metallic element that is a liquid. And iodine is a solid. Table 17–1 lists some of the physical properties of the halogens. With gentle heating, iodine readily sublimes, forming beautiful violet vapors. When cooled, the vapors condense to form shiny, purple-black, metallic-appearing crystals.

17–3 CHEMICAL PROPERTIES

The halogens decrease in activity with an increase in atomic weight. Typical displacement reactions are

$$F_2 + CaCl_2 \rightarrow CaF_2 + Cl_2 \tag{17-1}$$

$$Cl_2 + 2KBr \rightarrow 2KCl + Br_2 \tag{17-2}$$

$$Br_2 + 2NaI \rightarrow 2NaBr + I_2 \tag{17-3}$$

Fluorine, with the lowest atomic weight, is the most electronegative and the most active of the elements.

The great reactivity of the halogens is due to the tendency of each atom to acquire one electron, thereby becoming a relatively stable ion. They react with the more active metals forming salts which are completely ionic. The halogens react even with relatively inactive metals, forming simple salts:

$$Cu + Cl_2 \rightarrow CuCl_2 \tag{17-4}$$

With less active metals there is an increasing tendency of halogens to form covalent bonds because of the decreasing differences in electronegativity between the reacting elements (Section 6–5). With nonmetals they form covalent bonds:

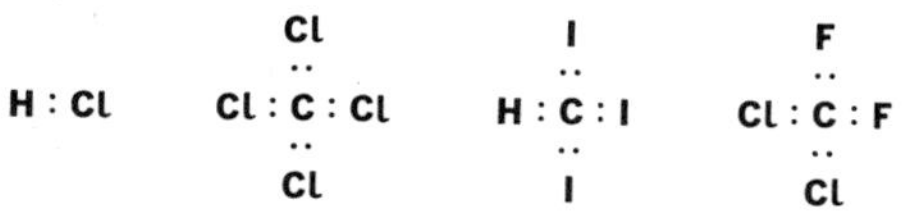

$$\text{H}:\text{Cl} \qquad \overset{\text{Cl}}{\underset{\text{Cl}}{\text{Cl}:\text{C}:\text{Cl}}} \qquad \overset{\text{I}}{\underset{\text{I}}{\text{H}:\text{C}:\text{I}}} \qquad \overset{\text{F}}{\underset{\text{Cl}}{\text{Cl}:\text{C}:\text{F}}}$$

The halogens react with hydrogen to form the corresponding halogen acids:

$H_2 + F_2 \rightarrow 2HF$ hydrofluoric acid   (17-5)

$H_2 + Cl_2 \rightarrow 2HCl$ hydrochloric acid   (17-6)

$H_2 + Br_2 \rightarrow 2HBr$ hydrobromic acid   (17-7)

$H_2 + I_2 \rightarrow 2HI$ hydroiodic acid   (17-8)

◄ It is convenient to use X as a general symbol to represent any halogen, particularly when the reaction involved is applicable to all halogens. In the equation below, the X could be Cl or Br, or some other halogen.

$H_2 + X_2 \rightarrow 2HX$ ►

The reactions of hydrogen with the halogens fluorine and chlorine are violent, liberating considerable heat. Bromine and iodine, however, do not react with hydrogen unless heated.

17-4 OCCURRENCE

Although the halogens are much too active to occur naturally in the elementary state, their compounds are widely distributed, with the exception of radioactive astatine. Fluorine and chlorine are the most prevalent. It is estimated that they occur in almost equal amounts on the earth, but chlorine is more easily separated from its compounds. Most of the chlorine exists in the form of chloride ions in the oceans and in the salt deposits resulting from the evaporation of inland oceans. Fluorine, which occurs in low concentration in the ocean, is found primarily as a constituent of minerals and rocks. Table 17-2 shows the halide ion content of seawater.

TABLE 17-2. Concentration of halide ions in sea water

Ion	Milligrams/Liter	Liters of Sea Water Required for 1 g of Halide Ions
chloride	19,000 (19 g)	0.052 (52 ml)
bromide	65	15.4
fluoride	1.3	769
iodide	0.05	20,000

17-5 FLUORINE

The element fluorine is so reactive that it resisted the efforts of chemists to isolate it for more than half a century, even though its compounds were plentiful. Not until platinum vessels were utilized could the liberated element be restrained from combining with the container. Its great toxicity caused the death or serious illness of several scientists. It is very important to note, however, that the vigorously reactive *element*, fluorine, is not the same as the fluor*ide* ion which is found in rocks and in many natural water supplies used for drinking water. Fluorine occurs in a number of mineral forms, the most common being fluorspar, CaF_2, cryolite, Na_3AlF_6, and fluorapatite, $Ca_5(PO_4)_3F$. Hydrofluoric acid is made by the reaction between calcium fluoride and sulfuric acid:

$$CaF_2 + H_2SO_4 \rightarrow CaSO_4 + 2HF* \tag{17-9}$$

Hydrogen fluoride is commercially important. Because it can dissolve glass, it is used in large quantities for etching designs on glass and in the "frosting" of light bulbs. Obviously, it cannot be kept in glass containers. For many years wax containers were used for laboratory storage; at the present time plastic bottles are being used.

Fluorine is used in the production of the well-known **Teflon,** a material made from fluorine and carbon, and for **Freon,** CCl_2F_2, which is used as a refrigerant in household refrigerators. The solvent propellents in some aerosol pushbutton dispensers are types of Freon.

Fluoride ions are highly toxic when taken in *excess*, but some form of the element is a physiological necessity. In the body it occurs primarily in the teeth and bones. Fluoride in drinking water, in the amount of one part per million (ppm) inhibits tooth decay. In areas where there are several ppm of fluoride naturally in the drinking water, a mottling or spotting of the tooth enamel occurs. Many communities in the United States now add fluoride to water supplies in amounts that prevent tooth decay but do not produce mottling. There is also considerable evidence to indicate that fluoride is important in the maintenance of good health and strong bones in elderly people.

17-6 CHLORINE

Chlorine is a greenish-yellow poisonous gas, first prepared by Scheele in 1774. It was used in World War I, the first poison gas to be part of modern warfare.

Chlorine is made commercially by the electrolysis of a solution of sodium chloride in specially constructed electrolytic cells. In these cells chloride ions migrate to the anode where they give up electrons and form chlorine gas:

$$2Cl^- \rightarrow Cl_2 \uparrow + 2e^- \tag{17-10}$$

At the cathode, hydrogen ions which are always present in small amounts in water and are less active than the sodium ions, receive electrons and are discharged as hydrogen gas:

$$2H^+ + 2e^- \rightarrow H_2 \uparrow \tag{17-11}$$

The remaining solution contains sodium hydroxide. The overall reaction is:

$$2NaCl + 2H_2O \xrightarrow{\text{electrolysis}} H_2 \uparrow + Cl_2 \uparrow + 2NaOH \tag{17-12}$$

---

* Because of the hydrogen bonding, the formula for hydrofluoric acid resembles that of water and is more correctly written as H_2F_2 or $(HF)_2$. It should be recalled that water exists as the monomer (H_2O) only in the vapor state, and that in the liquid state it exists as $(H_2O)_x$. For our purpose we will use the HF simplified notation.

In the process not only chlorine but two other highly useful substances, hydrogen and sodium hydroxide, are produced.*

The uses of chlorine are many. More than six million tons of chlorine were produced in the United States in 1966.

◄ You can appreciate how much 6,000,000 tons of chlorine is if you realize that it would require a train of tank cars 1200 miles long (reaching from San Francisco to Denver) to hold this quantity. ►

Large quantities of chlorine are used in the purification of water. The plastic industry uses it in the manufacture of many articles, such as shower curtains, phonograph records, and floor coverings. Chlorine is used in the manufacture of special types of solvents which are needed for water insoluble materials. Most paper is produced from wood pulp; without a bleach, paper would resemble wood in color. Chlorine is one of the important bleaches used for this purpose. If we inspect the labels in a chemistry laboratory or storeroom, we find that many bottles contain compounds of chlorine. Organic chemists often use chlorine-containing compounds to synthesize new compounds.

Sodium chloride is the most prevalent and most widely used halogen compound. Many millions of tons are annually obtained from underground salt deposits and by evaporation of water from the ocean or from inland seas. In some underground deposits, it is mined in much the same way as coal. In other areas, water is circulated through the salt deposits, and the salt is recovered by evaporation of water from the brine. Sodium chloride reacts with sulfuric acid to produce hydrogen chloride which dissolves in water, forming hydrochloric acid. This process is used in the laboratory and industrially:

$$NaCl + H_2SO_4 \rightarrow NaHSO_4 + HCl \tag{17-13}$$

Reaction (17–13) takes place at low temperature. If the temperature is raised, more sodium chloride reacts, giving another molecule of HCl:

$$NaCl + NaHSO_4 \rightarrow Na_2SO_4 + HCl \tag{17-14}$$

Sodium chloride is used extensively by the chemical industries in the production of hundreds of compounds which contain chlorine. It is also used in the recharging of water softeners and the melting of ice on roads. For centuries it has been used to preserve foods.

Chlorine is the most plentiful and therefore the cheapest of the halogens. Sodium compounds, in turn, are less expensive than those of potassium. Consequently, when metallic halogen compounds are needed, sodium chloride is most commonly used.

17–7 BROMINE

Bromine is a reddish-brown, volatile liquid with a density of 3.12 g/ml. It has a pungent odor from which its name was derived; the Greek word for stench is *bromos*. Contact of bromine with the skin causes severe burns.

---

* In a separate reaction, hydrogen can be combined with chlorine to produce hydrochloric acid: $H_2 + Cl_2 \rightarrow 2\ HCl$. This is one of the most important sources of hydrochloric acid.

Bromine is manufactured from bromide salts. These are obtained from the saturated brine from which common salt has been crystallized. The bromide salts, being more soluble, remain in solution after the sodium chloride has been removed. Bromine is a relatively rare element. All known sources contain only very low concentrations. Natural brines from wells of the eastern United States were the principal sources until a satisfactory method of recovery from the ocean was perfected. Seawater contains 65 ppm of bromine. While this may seem like a small amount, calculations show that 1 cu mi of ocean water contains more than 300,000 tons of bromine.

Since bromine is less active than chlorine, Section 17-3, it can be replaced in its compounds by the action of its sister element:

$$\text{MgBr}_2 + \text{Cl}_2 \rightarrow \text{MgCl}_2 + \text{Br}_2 \qquad\qquad (17-15)$$

In practice, ocean water is made slightly acid to decrease the solubility of the bromine which is then replaced by chlorine. The free bromine is removed by aeration and collected in an alkaline solution.

The greatest need for bromine grew from the practice of adding tetraethyl lead to gasoline as an antiknock compound. Since lead fouls the ignition points in an engine, it is necessary to add something which will form a volatile compound with lead. The addition of 2 or 3 ml of $\text{C}_2\text{H}_4\text{Br}_2$/gal of ethyl gasoline results in the formation of lead bromide, PbBr_2, which is volatile and is removed in the exhaust gases. The use of tetraethyl lead in gasoline, which began in 1924, accelerated the demand for bromine so much that the process of extraction of bromine from the sea was developed.

Bromine is used extensively in the field of photography. Silver bromide, AgBr, is the light-sensitive substance on photographic film. Bromine is also used in the manufacture of dyes, drugs, and many other organic chemicals.

17-8 IODINE

Elementary iodine is a dense solid, usually occurring as lustrous, almost-black crystals. It is only slightly soluble in water. While iodine occurs only in low concentration in ocean water, it is concentrated in seaweeds. Iodine was first obtained from the ashes of seaweeds.

Early in the 19th century, nitrate deposits containing an unusually high concentration of iodine were discovered in Chile. This was the world's major source for many years. Some years ago it was noted that the saltwater brines occurring in some California oil wells contained considerable amounts of iodine. This source is now a major one, and broke the monopoly which had controlled the price for many years. Iodine now sells for a small fraction of what it previously cost.

Iodine is a physiological necessity for animals, and in areas where its natural occurrence is low, a dietary deficiency may exist unless a supplement is provided. Nearly all the iodine in the body is located in the thyroid glands which are found encircling the windpipe (trachea) of most animals. A deficiency of iodine in the diet of animals lowers the ability of the thyroid glands to produce certain hormones and causes an enlargement of the thyroid glands, a condition known as goiter. The inclusion of a small amount of sodium iodide, NaI, in the salt used is adequate to prevent the condition. It is interesting to note that stockmen throughout iodine-depleted areas find that livestock are healthier if they, too, are fed iodized salt.

Thyroid selectivity is so effective that the iodine concentration of the thyroid glands is normally 2000 to 4000 times that of blood. Adult humans require only 0.1 mg of iodine/day. This is such a small amount that 1 g, properly administered, would be adequate for more than 24 years. In areas near oceans, the wind-blown sprays carry iodine and deposit it on soils from which plants absorb it. Seafood also is rich in iodine. In contrast, areas within some large continents are almost without iodine. The north central part of the United States is such an area.

Iodine and iodine compounds are used extensively in the laboratory and in the preparation of organic compounds. Silver iodide is used in the making of photographic films.

17-9 HALOGEN ACIDS AND THEIR SALTS

In addition to the hydrohalide acids, such as HCl, series of ternary, or oxy acids, can be formed with each of the halogens with the exception of fluorine. Since fluorine is more electronegative than oxygen, it does not react to form these compounds. Bromine and iodine form a series of acids and salts similar to those of chlorine listed in Table 17-3. By substituting the word stems brom- and iod- in place of chlor-, you get the names of the corresponding acids and salts. This system of naming acids and their salts is used wherever such series occur. Other metallic ions may be substituted for sodium.

TABLE 17-3. The nomenclature of the acids and salts of chlorine and the valence number of chlorine in each

Acid		Corresponding Salt		Valence Number of Chlorine
hydrochloric	HCl	sodium chloride	NaCl	$1-$
hypochlorous	HClO	sodium hypochlorite	NaClO	$1+$
chlorous	$HClO_2$	sodium chlorite	$NaClO_2$	$3+$
chloric	$HClO_3$	sodium chlorate	$NaClO_3$	$5+$
perchloric	$HClO_4$	sodium perchlorate	$NaClO_4$	$7+$

Sodium hypochlorite, NaClO, is the active ingredient in common household bleaches such as Clorox or Purex. Sodium hypochlorite can be made by passing an electric current through a dilute solution of NaCl in a specially designed cell.

The chlorates and perchlorates are powerful oxidizing agents, and under certain conditions are explosive. Great caution should be exercised to avoid mixing these substances with any easily oxidizable materials. Sodium chlorate, $NaClO_3$, is used in sprays to kill weeds.

17-10 SUMMARY

The halides are probably the most important anions, from a quantitative standpoint, in chemistry. Halogen compounds are widely used in organic reactions. Iodine is essential for animal life, and apparently fluorine is also required. No specific biological function has been found for chlorine, and it may be that it is present primarily as the anionic partner of the essential cations, sodium and potassium.

IMPORTANT TERMS

Freon   *Halogen*
Halide ion   *Teflon*

WORK EXERCISES

1. Why are the halogens not found free in nature?

2. Name two sources for each of the halogens.

3. Write equations for the actions of each of the halogens on two metals, one from Group IA and one from Group IIA.

4. Name the halogens in the order of their prevalence in seawater. How does this compare with the order of their prevalence on the earth?

5. Name two important uses for each of the halogens.

6. Make a table comparable to Table 17–3, using bromine for the halogen and potassium for the metal.

7. State uses for

    a) sodium hypochlorite   b) hydrofluoric acid
    c) sodium chlorate   d) sodium chloride
    e) sodium iodide

8. Are each of the halogens of physiological importance? State some of the more common physiological needs for halogens.

9. Complete and balance the equations for which a reaction will occur:

    a) $H_2 + Cl_2 \rightarrow$ b) $KI + Cl_2 \rightarrow$
    c) $KBr + I_2 \rightarrow$ d) $Cu + Cl_2 \rightarrow$
    e) $KCl + F_2 \rightarrow$ f) $H_2 + F_2 \rightarrow$
    g) $NaF + Cl_2 \rightarrow$

10. Considering Table 17–1, predict corresponding properties for astatine.

SUGGESTED READING

Day, F. H., *The Chemical Elements in Nature*, "The Halogens," pp. 302–319, Reinhold, New York, 1963.

Hyler, J. E., "The Production of Salt," *Journal of Chemical Education* **12,** 203 (1935). The history of the production of salt from biblical times to the present. Very interestingly written.

Weeks, Mary E., *The Discovery of the Elements*, Chapter 27, "The Halogens," Journal of Chemical Education Publishing Co., Easton, Pa., 1956.

Chapter 18   OTHER NONMETALS

18-1 INTRODUCTION

In Chapter 5 the concept of metals and nonmetals was introduced. In Chapter 8 one of the most important nonmetals, oxygen, was discussed. Nitrogen was the subject of Chapter 15, and the nonmetallic halogens, of Chapter 17. But this still leaves a number of the most important nonmetallic elements, namely boron, carbon, silicon, phosphorus, and sulfur which should be discussed. Let us consider them now.

The less important nonmetals, arsenic, selenium, and tellurium, will be mentioned only briefly at the end of this chapter. Except for the poisonous nature of arsenic compounds, these elements have been of little use in our civilization. The same could have been said of many elements which were mere curiosities only a few years ago but are highly important in today's technology. It is the continuing nightmare of authors of chemistry books that the element or compound they chose to omit will suddenly zoom to real importance.

On the basis of abundance and importance, however, there is no need to defend our discussion of boron, carbon, silicon, phosphorus, and sulfur. Carbon is the most abundant element in nearly all the compounds of living organisms, and silicon is found in almost all rocky material. Phosphorus and sulfur, particularly in the form of phosphates and sulfates, are widely distributed and are important in plants, in animals, and in the chemical industries. Although boron is not especially abundant (48th among the 103 elements), it is concentrated in a few places and is relatively easy to obtain. Recent investigations of certain compounds of boron, known as the boranes, have added to the importance of this element.

18-2 BORON

Compounds of boron have been known for thousands of years. It is reported that they were used as a preserving agent in the Egyptian mummies. They are still used as preservatives in some parts of the world. For centuries metalsmiths have used boron compounds as a flux for removing oxide films from metals. These compounds have also long been used in medicines.

Boron belongs to a small cluster of elements called **metalloids.** Since elements form a continuum from the most positive metals to the most negative nonmetals, it is reasonable to assume that some of the elements must fall on a borderline somewhere in between. On the periodic table a heavy line is sometimes used to indicate this borderline. The elements close to this line have properties that in part are those of metals and in part those of non-metals. These are the metalloids.

Boron resembles the metal aluminum in that both have valences of 3, and both form similar compounds. Boron is like carbon in that in a crystalline form it resembles a diamond (a form of carbon), both being transparent and extremely hard. Both aluminum and boron form hydrides.

Occurrence

Boron compounds, in low concentration, are widespread throughout the world. Ores of boron are believed to be of volcanic origin; all workable deposits are in areas of volcanic action—present or past. More than 85% of the world's supply comes from California; most of it from the Death Valley area mines, Searles Lake, and from an enormous open-pit mine in the Barstow area. Apparently these deposits are associated with the past volcanic activity of the Sierra Mountains and the collecting of these minerals in lakes that later became dry. Boric acid, H_3BO_3, is found in volcanic areas; so, too, are the more important mineral ores, borax, $Na_2B_4O_7 \cdot 10 \, H_2O$, of 20-mule-team fame, and kernite, $Na_2B_4O_7 \cdot 4 \, H_2O$.

Uses of Boron

Borax is used in the manufacturing of Pyrex and similar types of glass which have very low coefficients of thermal expansion. It is also used in enamels and glazes. Borax is the salt of a strong base and a weak acid, and therefore it produces a basic reaction in water. The borate ion hydrolyzes as follows:

$$B_4O_7^{2-} + 7H_2O \rightarrow 4H_3BO_3 + 2OH^-$$

$$(18\text{-}1)$$

Borates react with calcium or magnesium ions, forming insoluble calcium or magnesium borates:

$$Na_2B_4O_7 + Ca^{2+} \rightarrow CaB_4O_7 + 2Na^+$$

$$(18\text{-}2)$$

These properties make borax a very good water-softening agent.

18-3 CARBON AND ITS COMPOUNDS

Carbon is unique among the elements. It is the key element in organic compounds of which all living matter is primarily composed. More than one million such compounds are known. Carbon dioxide is present in the atmosphere, the oceans, and all natural water. (The importance of carbon dioxide in the atmosphere was emphasized in Section 15-3). Carbon and carbon compounds constitute a major portion of the fuels—coal, petroleum, and natural gas. Carbon is the element in our foods that, on oxidation, supplies much of our body energy. Furthermore, it is an important constituent of clothing, wood, paper, drugs, dyes, many explosives, auto finishes, and plastics. Diamonds and graphite are allotropic forms of elemental carbon. The second section of this text in which we discuss organic chemistry and biochemistry will also be concerned with the compounds of carbon. For now, we will emphasize the elemental forms and the *inorganic* compounds of carbon.

Limestone, which is primarily calcium carbonate, $CaCO_3$, has been formed by the combination of carbon dioxide or carbonic acid with calcium-containing substances. Marble is also calcium carbonate, but in most cases it has been formed by a metamorphosis brought about by the action of heat and pressure on limestone.

Diamonds

Diamond, a pure form of crystalline carbon, is the hardest substance known. Everyone is aware of the beauty and durability of the jewel. Most of the diamonds found are not of gem quality, however, and are known as commercial diamonds. These are in great demand by industry where they are used in cutting and polishing metals or stones. Diamonds are found in many parts of the world, often in alluvial formations. Most diamonds come from Africa where they are found in great pipes or necks which resemble the necks of old volcanoes. It is believed they are formed deep in the earth and forced to the surface by extreme pressure. Commercial grades of diamonds are now being made synthetically.

Graphite

Another form of crystalline carbon, **graphite,** occurs as soft, black, shiny, flat crystals. It occurs naturally in many parts of the world and is also produced synthetically. The minute, flat particles slide over each other like the cards in a deck, producing a slick feel when rubbed between the fingers. This property makes graphite an excellent lubricant for dry bearings such as are used in many electric motors, and in door locks. It is also used in motor oil additives. The "lead" in lead pencils is compressed graphite; when we write, a thin layer of the minute flat crystals is left on the paper. Graphite is also used as electrodes, since it is a good conductor of electricity but has little tendency to react chemically.

Coal, Coke, and Charcoal

During past geological periods, enormous deposits of **coal** were formed from the luxuriant vegetation of tropical climates. For many years coal was the most important source of carbon and carbon compounds. In recent years, however, petroleum has surpassed it for this purpose.

When coal is heated in the absence of air, a process called *destructive distillation*, large quantities of combustible gases and considerable amounts of organic liquids and nitrogenous substances are expelled. The remaining portion, approximately three-fourths by weight, is called **coke.** Coke, which is nearly pure carbon, is used extensively in the recovery of iron from its ores, Section 19–6. Approximately 500 million tons of coal are mined yearly in the United States and of this, about 100 million tons are used for making

(a)   (b)

FIG. 18–1. (a) This 530-carat diamond, approximately actual size, is the largest of the stones cut from the famous Cullinan diamond. [Courtesy of the Gemological Institute of America.] (b) Synthetic diamonds such as these produced by General Electric are superior to natural diamonds for many industrial uses. The crystals are actually about the size of granules of coarse sand. [Courtesy of the General Electric Company.]

coke. The major portion of the remainder is burned, and its energy converted to electrical power. **Charcoal** is made by the destructive distillation of wood. It is commonly known as a fuel for backyard barbecues, but it is used extensively in the laboratory and by industry as a decolorizing agent, Section 14–5.

Carbon Black

Nearly all organic compounds contain hydrogen as well as carbon. If such compounds are burned in an atmosphere which is deficient in oxygen, the hydrogen will unite with oxygen, and the carbon will be left in an unoxidized state. When the carburetor of a car is so adjusted that there is insufficient oxygen for proper burning of the fuel, we are warned of the situation by the black smoke which comes from the exhaust. The black smoke is **carbon black.**

Carbon black is manufactured in large amounts from natural gas which is primarily methane, CH_4. Just enough air is admitted in the furnace to burn the hydrogen, so that unburned carbon is left:

$$CH_4 + O_2 \rightarrow C + 2H_2O \tag{18-3}$$

The carbon is removed by filters.

The two main uses of carbon black are in automobile tires and as the pigment in printer's ink. The carbon which is compounded with the rubber to the extent of several pounds per tire adds materially to the durability of the rubber. If we consider the amount of printed material produced annually in the United States, we realize that a large amount of printer's ink is required.

Petroleum

This important commodity will be discussed in Chapter 22.

Chemical Reactions Involving Carbon and Carbon Compounds

At high temperatures carbon reacts with oxygen of the air, forming carbon dioxide:

$$C + O_2 \rightarrow CO_2 \tag{18-4}$$

If the amount of oxygen is limited, carbon monoxide is produced:

$$2C + O_2 \rightarrow 2CO \tag{18-5}$$

and at high temperatures when the concentration of oxygen is low, carbon reacts with carbon dioxide forming carbon monoxide:

$$CO_2 + C \rightarrow 2CO \tag{18-6}$$

Furthermore, carbon monoxide will react with oxygen to produce carbon dioxide:

$$2CO + O_2 \rightarrow 2CO_2 \tag{18-7}$$

All these reactions take place in the blast furnaces used to recover iron from its ores, Section 19-6.

Usually when oxygen reacts with hydrocarbons, carbon dioxide and water are produced:

$$CH_4 + 2O_2 \rightarrow CO_2 + 2H_2O \tag{18-8}$$

$$C_8H_{18} + 12.5O_2 \rightarrow 8CO_2 + 9H_2O \tag{18-9}$$

If insufficient oxygen is present, some carbon monoxide may be produced instead of carbon dioxide.

Carbon dioxide dissolves in water to the extent of about 1.5 g/liter at room temperature and normal atmospheric pressure (at sea-level pressure). About 1% of this amount reacts with water to form carbonic acid:

$$H_2O + CO_2 \rightleftharpoons H_2CO_3 \tag{18-10}$$

Carbonic acid is a weak acid, ionizing to form hydrogen ions and hydrogen carbonate ions:

$$H_2CO_3 \leftrightharpoons H^+ + HCO_3^-$$ (18-11)

Although small amounts of carbonic acid can be detected in water solution, and it forms salts, carbonic acid is so unstable that it cannot be isolated as free H_2CO_3. In solution, or exposed to soil, it readily forms salts such as sodium carbonate, Na_2CO_3, sodium hydrogen carbonate or baking soda, $NaHCO_3$, and calcium carbonate (limestone or marble), $CaCO_3$.

Properties and Uses of Carbon Dioxide

Carbon dioxide is a colorless, odorless gas with a density 1.5 times that of air. At atmospheric pressure it liquefies at $-78°C$, or we might say, the liquid boils at that temperature. At room temperature, $22°C$, it is converted to a liquid if the pressure is raised to 900 psi. This is the pressure that exists inside the ordinary carbon dioxide fire extinguisher (Section 8–7). If the pressure is suddenly released, the liquid evaporates very rapidly, and since evaporation requires heat, the temperature of the escaping gas is rapidly lowered. At atmospheric pressure, carbon dioxide sublimes, and a sudden lowering of temperature causes the gaseous carbon dioxide to turn to a solid called **dry ice** with a temperature of $-78°C$(or $-109°F$). This solid also sublimes, changing directly from the solid to the gaseous state, which accounts for the name "dry ice." Large amounts of dry ice are used as a refrigerant. The carbonated beverage industries provide a large market for carbon dioxide. It is dissolved in the beverage under pressure, which increases its solubility. When the pressure is released, bubbles of CO_2 are liberated. Some of the dissolved carbon dioxide combines with water. This reaction forms carbonic acid, which lowers the pH sufficiently to act as a preservative.

Carbon dioxide is nontoxic in low concentrations, and it makes up approximately 4% of our exhaled breath. It has an interesting physiological function in that the concentration of CO_2 in our blood controls the rate of our breathing. During heavy exercise the rate of carbon dioxide formation in the body is increased, and therefore we breathe more rapidly. Small amounts of carbon dioxide can be used during surgery and resuscitation to stimulate breathing. The inhalation of high concentrations of carbon dioxide over prolonged periods of time, however, causes asphyxiation.

Carbon Monoxide

As mentioned previously, carbon monoxide is produced when there is insufficient oxygen for complete oxidation of carbon or carbon compounds. A great amount of energy is produced when carbon monoxide is burned to form CO_2, Eq. (18–7), and it is therefore used as an industrial fuel.

◄ The oxidation of the hydrocarbons in automobile engines is never complete; about 7% remains as carbon monoxide. This poisonous gas can combine with the hemoglobin in the blood, rendering it incapable of carrying oxygen from the lungs to body tissues. Prolonged breathing of CO, even in very low concentration (0.05%,) can cause serious illness. Breathing air containing 1% of carbon monoxide will cause death within a few minutes.

Each year many people die of asphyxiation from carbon monoxide poisoning. An automobile engine running in a closed garage can cause death. Improperly installed gas heaters in small rooms are also extremely dangerous. The heater soon reduces the oxygen content of the air to a point where complete oxidation does not take place and carbon monoxide is formed. ▶

18-4 SILICON

It has been estimated that 95%* of the materials of the earth's surface, other than water, contain silicon. In Section 5-2 some of the more common silicon minerals were listed. The formulas for these compounds are given in Table 18-1. Silicon compounds, then, are a part of most of the more common rocks and of the finest gems. Carbon and silicon, members of the same family of elements—Group IVA—have many similar properties. Carbon is the key element in the plant and animal world. Silicon is the dominant element in the mineral world.

TABLE 18-1. Formulas of some compounds of silicon

Name	Uses	Formula
garnet	gems and abrasives	$3\ CaO \cdot Al_2O_3 \cdot 3\ SiO_2$
talc	talcum powder	$3\ MgO \cdot 4\ SiO_2 \cdot H_2O$
feldspar	ceramics	$K_2O \cdot Al_2O_3 \cdot 6\ SiO_2$
zircon	gems	$ZrO_2 \cdot SiO_2$
clay	ceramics	$Al_2O_3 \cdot 2\ SiO_2 \cdot 2\ H_2O$
asbestos	insulation	$3\ MgO \cdot 2\ SiO_2 \cdot 2\ H_2O$
sand or quartz	innumerable	SiO_2

Feldspar is a term applied to several of the minerals occurring in granite. The minerals are usually sodium or potassium aluminum silicates, for example, $K_2O \cdot Al_2O_3 \cdot 6\ SiO_2$, which on weathering, are transformed into clay or kaolin, $Al_2O_3 \cdot 2\ SiO_3$, sand, and soluble compounds. Clay is the principal material of which porcelain, china, and pottery are composed. Calcium and aluminum silicates are the main ingredients of Portland cement which is manufactured by heating clay, limestone, and a small amount of gypsum, $CaSO_4 \cdot 2\ H_2O$, and then grinding the mixture to a very fine powder. It is estimated that 80 million tons of Portland cement were produced in the United States in 1966.

When minerals in a molten state cool *slowly*, they form crystals. *Granite*, which is a mixture of several different compounds, is a rock that has cooled very slowly while still underground. It contains several kinds of crystals. *Obsidian*, or volcanic glass as it is commonly called, is similar to granite in composition. However, it was forced to the surface of the earth while still molten, and therefore cooled rapidly into a noncrystalline material we call glass. The *glass* with which we are familiar is a rapidly cooled silicate material.

---

* F. H. Day, *The Chemical Elements in Nature*, Reinhold, New York, 1963.

The common varieties, such as are used in windows and bottles, are made by heating mixtures of sodium-carbonate, Na_2CO_3; calcium carbonate, $CaCO_3$; and sand, SiO_2. The reactions are

$$Na_2CO_3 + SiO_2 \rightarrow Na_2SiO_3 + CO_2 \uparrow \qquad (18\text{-}12)$$

and

$$CaCO_3 + SiO_2 \rightarrow CaSiO_3 + CO_2 \uparrow \qquad (18\text{-}13)$$

The resulting material, a mixture of sodium silicate, Na_2SiO_3 ($Na_2O \cdot SiO_2$) and calcium silicate, $CaSiO_3$ ($CaO \cdot SiO_2$) is the basic ingredient of common glass. Glass for special purposes has somewhat different ingredients. In Pyrex glass, the type used for ovenware and laboratory glassware, the percentages of sodium and calcium are lower, but boron oxide, B_2O_3, is added. Such glass withstands sudden temperature changes because it has a low coefficient of expansion.

Color in glass results from the presence of traces of what might be called impurities. Iron (III) compounds produce the yellow to brown colors common in beer bottles. Cobalt produces an intense blue; manganese(IV), pink to violet; and colloidal selenium the red color such as was used in automobile tail lights before the days of plastics.

18-5 PHOSPHORUS

Phosphorus bears some similarity to nitrogen, the member of this family of elements we discussed in Chapter 15. Both have valences of 3−, as shown in ammonia, NH_3, and phosphine, PH_3. And both have valences of 5+, as in nitrogen(V) oxide, N_2O_5, and phosphorus(V) oxide P_2O_5. These oxides react with water, forming acids. Both nitrogen and phosphorous are essential to life and are present in every cell of our bodies.

Phosphorus and nitrogen also exhibit striking contrasts. They are different in that elementary nitrogen, N_2, is very inactive, occurring on the earth primarily in the atmosphere. Phosphorus, however, is a solid, much too active to be found in the free state. In fact, white phosphorus burns spontaneously in air. In combined forms it is widely distributed in nature, being present to a small extent in igneous rocks.

The mineral content of bones is primarily calcium phosphate, $Ca_3(PO_4)_2$. It appears that the rich deposits of phosphorus compounds such as those now being worked in Montana, Wyoming, Utah, Florida, and numerous other locations are the result of prehistoric bone piles (animal graveyards).

Phosphorus is found in proteins and plays an important role in the utilization of carbohydrates by the body. Grains, beans, and nuts are particularly good dietary sources of phosphorus.

Phosphorus was first prepared in the pure state about 300 years ago (1669) by Brand, one of the last of the alchemists. Heating urine, sand, and carbon produced a substance which glowed in the dark and was therefore given the name *phosphorus*, from the Greek, meaning a bearer of light. The reactions which took place in Brand's experiment are not unlike the reactions involved in the present-day preparation of phosphorus shown by Eqs. (18–14) and (18–15). Soluble phosphates in the urine reacted in the same manner as the $Ca_3(PO_4)_2$ in Eq. (18–14).

Phosphorus is obtained commercially by heating calcium phosphate with sand and carbon (reaction shown stepwise):

$$Ca_3(PO_4)_2 + 3SiO_2 \rightarrow 3CaSiO_3 + P_2O_5 \tag{18-14}$$

and

$$P_2O_5 + 5C \rightarrow 5CO + 2P \tag{18-15}$$

Elementary phosphorus exists in two allotropic forms. The more active form, white phosphorus, is a waxy substance which melts at 44°C. It must be stored under water (in which it is insoluble), since it combines with the oxygen of the air and is rapidly warmed to its kindling temperature, 35 to 40°C. On catching fire, it melts and every drop is covered with flames. It produces serious, slow-healing burns.

The other allotrope is red phosphorus. It is a stable, relatively nonpoisonous form which can be used for laboratory experiments if special precautions are taken.

White phosphorus can be converted into the red form by heating it to a temperature of 230 to 300°C in the absence of air. When either form burns in air, phosphorus(V) oxide is formed. It is a white solid, appearing as smoke. Except at very high temperatures, phosphorus occurs with 4 atoms to the molecule, P_4, and the oxide formed when it is burned in the air is P_4O_{10}:

$$P_4 + 5O_2 \rightarrow P_4O_{10} \tag{18-16}$$

Although Eq. (18–16) shows the correct formulas of the molecules as they actually exist, simpler formulas, Eqs. (18–17) and (18–18), will show the proper *ratios* and are sufficient for calculations:

$$2P + \tfrac{5}{2}O_2 \rightarrow \quad P_2O_5 \tag{18-17}$$

phosphorus(V)
oxide

or

$$4P + 5O_2 \rightarrow 2P_2O_5 \tag{18-18}$$

In this book we will use the simpler versions. The reaction of phosphorus(V) oxide with water forms phosphoric acid:

$$P_2O_5 + 3H_2O \rightarrow 2H_3PO_4 \tag{18-19}$$

The greatest use for phosphorus is in agricultural fertilizers. Several forms of phosphates are utilized. For quick action, readily soluble forms such as ammonium phosphate are best. Since calcium phosphate is quite insoluble, it becomes effective only as acids in the soil cause weathering, a slow process. A fertilizer called superphosphate is made by adding dilute sulfuric acid to finely powdered calcium phosphate. The result is the appreciably soluble calcium dihydrogen phosphate:

$$Ca_3(PO_4)_2 + 2H_2SO_4 \rightarrow Ca(H_2PO_4)_2 + 2CaSO_4 \qquad (18\text{-}20)$$

Extensive use of phosphoric acid is made by the chemical industries. Phosphates are also used in the treatment of hard water.

18–6 SULFUR

Sulfur is one of the few elements that has been known to man since the dawn of history. The Bible refers to sulfur as brimstone. If one has been in the vicinity of burning sulfur, the unpleasantness of the Biblical place of "fire and brimstone" can be imagined. Sulfur is reported to be the first material to be used in chemical warfare and as an incendiary. In medieval times sticks were wrapped in cloth dipped in molten sulfur, ignited, and thrown into enemy castles.

Sulfur is a water-insoluble yellow solid with a density of slightly more than twice that of water, and a melting point of 114°C. The molecular formulas for sulfur range from S_8 in the solid, to S_2 in the vapor state and at high temperatures. We will ignore the subscripts when writing equations.

Sulfur is found in a free state in areas of active volcanoes. In fact, such areas served as the source of sulfur until recent times. The Mediterranean area and Japan were principal producers of sulfur until a new process for its recovery, the Frasch Process, was developed in the United States just before the end of the last century.

The Frasch Process

Until the present century the demand for sulfur was relatively small; it was used in gunpowder, the vulcanizing of rubber, the chemical industries (which were small), and for medicinal purposes. There was scarcely enough sulfur produced from the age-old sources to meet these needs, and the demands were increasing. Approximately a hundred years ago enormous underground deposits of sulfur were located in eastern Texas and western Louisiana. The deposits were too deep to work by open-mining methods, and the earth around them was not sufficiently solid to make possible the use of shafts and tunnels such as were used in mining coal. Considering not only the fact that sulfur is more dense than water, but that it is insoluble in water, and has a melting point above the boiling point of water, the task was a challenge.

About 1890 Herman Frasch, a chemical engineer who had solved problems for the petroleum industry, conceived a plan for removing sulfur from the underground deposits. This method is now known as the **Frasch Process.** The first step is to drill a large hole into the sulfur deposit. Into this hole three concentric pipes are lowered, Fig. 18–2. Superheated water at about 180°C is forced down the outside pipe, melting the surrounding sulfur. Because of its density the sulfur does not float, but compressed air is forced down the inside pipe to produce a froth which is forced (literally blown) up through the intermediate pipe.

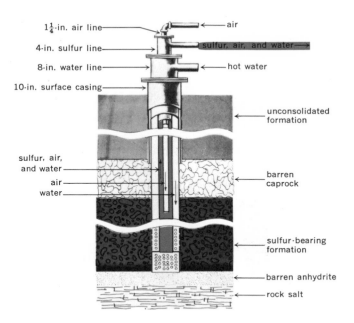

$1\frac{1}{4}$-in. air line ——
4-in. sulfur line ——
8-in. water line ——
10-in. surface casing ——

air

sulfur, air, and water ——→

hot water

unconsolidated formation

sulfur, air, and water ——
air ——
water ——

barren caprock

sulfur-bearing formation

barren anhydrite

rock salt

FIG. 18–2. Sketch with partial cutaway of the mechanism used in the Frasch process. [Courtesy of the Freeport Sulfur Company.]

The molten sulfur and the hot water are discharged into a storage bin where the sulfur solidifies and the water drains away. The sulfur obtained is remarkably pure, being 99.5 to 99.9% sulfur.

Some wells produce in excess of 500 tons of sulfur per day. The storage bins are of fantastic dimensions; some are 400 ft long by 200 ft wide, and are filled to a depth of as much as 100 ft, Fig. 18–3.

Before shipment, holes are drilled into the sulfur and it is blasted into chunks which can be loaded onto gondola cars. Millions of tons of sulfur are produced by this method each year. Total production in the United States is about ten million tons yearly. Presently the demands in this country for sulfur are greater than production, and the United States is importing it from Mexico where similar methods are in operation.

Chemical Properties of Sulfur

Sulfur is relatively inactive at ordinary temperatures, and can remain exposed to the elements for years with little change. The three most common valences of sulfur are 2−, 4+, and 6+. Sulfur burns readily in the atmosphere, producing sulfur dioxide, an irritating, strong-smelling gas.

$$S + O_2 \rightarrow SO_2$$

(18–21)

FIG. 18–3. Loading of sulfur from one of the large blocks formed by the Frasch process. [Courtesy of the Freeport Sulfur Company.]

Sulfur dioxide reacts with water forming sulfurous acid:

$$SO_2 + H_2O \leftrightharpoons H_2SO_3 \qquad (18-22)$$

On noting the odor of a solution of sulfurous acid, we come to realize that sulfurous acid is not a very stable substance, for the odor of sulfur dioxide is present. This indicates that the reaction (18–22) is reversible (see Section 13–3). Sulfur dioxide and sulfurous acid are used as bleaching agents.

If sulfur dioxide and oxygen are passed over a catalyst—finely divided platinum works well—sulfur trioxide, a choking and extremely irritating gas, is formed:

$$O_2 + 2SO_2 \xrightarrow{\text{catalyst}} 2SO_3 \qquad (18-23)$$

The sulfur trioxide can react with water, forming sulfuric acid:

$$SO_3 + H_2O \rightarrow H_2SO_4 \qquad (18-24)$$

The last two equations constitute what is known as the **contact process** for the manufacturing of sulfuric acid. It is the prevailing method of production. Sulfuric acid is a nonvolatile, oily substance having a density of 1.84 g/ml. The "concentrated" reagent is 96% sulfuric acid.

More sulfuric acid is used than is any other manufactured chemical. Twenty-six million tons were produced in the United States in 1966. You can better appreciate this amount, if you realize that it would require a train of railroad tank cars more than 5000 miles long to hold such an amount. The greatest demand for sulfur is from the manufacturers of agricultural fertilizers such as superphosphates and ammonium sulfate. It is also used in the manufacture of steel, petroleum products, rayon, and other chemicals.

Other Compounds of Sulfur

Compounds of sulfur are widespread in nature. Most of the metals combine with sulfur forming sulfides. Iron occurs in enormous amounts in the form of the pyrite, FeS_2. Copper appears as chalcocite, CuS, and chalcopyrite, $CuFeS_2$. The most important mercury ore is cinnabar, HgS. The sulfates of metals are also prevalent. Gypsum, $CaSO_4 \cdot 2\ H_2O$, occurs in large deposits throughout the midwest. It is used in the manufacture of plaster and plasterboard. Others are Epsom salts, $MgSO_4 \cdot 7\ H_2O$, and Glauber's salt, $Na_2SO_4 \cdot 10\ H_2O$. Hydrogen sulfide, or hydrosulfuric acid, may be prepared in the laboratory by the action of an acid on a metallic sulfide:

$$FeS + H_2SO_4 \rightarrow FeSO_4 + H_2S \qquad (18\text{-}25)$$

Hydrogen sulfide is found naturally in some mineral waters and is produced in sewage and other materials when sulfur compounds are attacked by reducing substances and microorganisms.

Sulfur also occurs widely in organic compounds, particularly in proteins, in which it plays several important roles.

18-7 THE ELEMENTS ARSENIC, SELENIUM, AND TELLURIUM

Arsenic and tellurium are metalloids since they are near the line separating the metals from nonmetals and share properties of both groups. Many of the uses of arsenic, particularly in alloys, rely on a metallic property. The salts of arsenic, particularly the arsenates, show the relationship of arsenic to phosphorus, which is just above it in the periodic table. However, arsenic compounds are extremely toxic. Because arsenates resemble the phosphates physically, it may be that they are absorbed by plants and animals, but that they block biochemical reactions with the result that the animal is poisoned.

Selenium is much like sulfur, its sister element. In fact, most compounds of sulfur are admixed with small amounts of selenium. In large amounts selenium is poisonous, although in certain instances selenium compounds serve as well as the corresponding sulfur compounds in biochemical reactions. Tellurium also has the properties of sulfur and selenium, forming similar compounds and participating in similar reactions. It is, however, more metallic than its two sister elements.

From the above discussion, we can see that knowledge of the properties of one element in a family on the periodic table along with certain generalizations about variation of properties with atomic weight and size, can give us some basic information about another element. Other properties, such as the poisonous nature of arsenic, can be found only by observation and experiment.

IMPORTANT TERMS

Carbon black *Contact process* *Frasch process* *Metalloid*
Coke *Dry ice* *Graphite*

WORK EXERCISES

1. In what respect does boron resemble metals? Nonmetals?

2. What are some important uses of boron or its compounds?

3. What are the differences between graphite and diamond?

4. What conditions are necessary for the production of carbon black, and what are its principal uses?

5. Contrast the properties of CO_2 and CO.

6. If coal is 80% carbon, how much CO_2 will be produced by the complete oxidation of 1 ton of coal?

7. Compare the properties of carbon and silicon. In what ways are they similar and in what ways different?

8. Consulting a handbook, compare the formulas of the hydrides (ammonia for nitrogen) and the oxides of the first four elements in Group VA.

9. Name some elements, other than phosphorus, that exhibit allotropic forms.

10. What nonmetals other than sulfur are found free in nature?

11. Write the reactions involved in the contact process for the preparation of sulfuric acid.

12. List five uses for sulfuric acid.

13. Complete and balance:

   a) $Na_2B_4O_7 + Mg^{2+} \rightarrow$

   b) $CO + O_2 \xrightarrow{\triangle}$

   c) $C_3H_8 + O_2 \rightarrow$

   d) $CaCO_3 + SiO_2 \xrightarrow{\triangle} CaSiO_3 +$

   e) $P_2O_5 + H_2O \rightarrow$

   f) $SO_2 + O_2 \xrightarrow{\text{catalyst}}$

14. Name five elements that occur in nature in combination with sulfur.

SUGGESTED READING

Hall, H. T., "The Synthesis of Diamonds," *Journal of Chemical Education* **38,** 484 (1961). An illustrated report on the synthesis of diamonds from graphite.

Killeffer, D. H., "Solid Carbon Dioxide Industry," *Journal of Chemical Education* **19,** 482 (1942). Dry ice was first prepared in 1835. Production did not become commercially important until 1926. Methods of preparation are described.

Plass, G. N., "Carbon Dioxide and Climate," *Scientific American*, July 1959, p. 41. We are presently releasing billions of tons of carbon dioxide into the atmosphere each year. What effect this may have on our climate is interestingly discussed in this article.

Chapter 19   THE METALS

19-1 THE ANCIENT METALS

The metals gold and silver were known and valued even in prehistoric times. Ancient tombs contain articles made of these metals, and the earliest writings mention silver and gold. Both metals were used for coins and ornaments in almost all civilizations. To a great extent the value placed on gold and silver is due to their lack of reactivity. In this world where all things perish and pass away, gold—and to a lesser extent, silver—remains. It is easy to see how gold was associated with the gods and immortality. The classical Greek civilization knew of seven metals, gold, silver, copper, iron, tin, lead, and mercury. Antimony was also known even before the Greek era but was not among the seven commonly mentioned by them. Gold and silver have been used for ornamental purposes, but never for tools.

The archeological classification of civilizations as the stone age, bronze age, and iron age depends primarily on the kind of tools used. Civilizations in the Americas, although they certainly used silver and gold, remained in the stone age until the time of Columbus. The bronze age occurred at different times in different cultures of the Mediterranean area. Bronze is an alloy of copper and tin that is much harder than pure copper and much easier to cast into molds. Once bronze became available, stone implements and tools were obsolete. The bronze age did not last long in most civilizations, since the people soon learned how to produce iron which was much harder than the bronze (at least in the degree of purification they could achieve) and could be sharpened to make better tools and swords.

Gold, silver, and copper occur as free metals, and free iron occurs in some meteorites, although this is not a significant source of the metal. The other metals known to ancient civilizations are easily extracted from their ores by heating. Metallurgy was probably established when observant men noted that certain stones around a campfire had been "changed" into a metal. If the stone was blue (as are most copper ores) and it gave copper, the relationship between the color and the product should have been obvious. We know that copper was plentiful in the Sinai area and that mines had been developed there as early as 2500 B.C. Impetus was added to the mining and use of copper when someone learned how to combine tin with copper to make bronze. When this happened, civilization changed. A similar major change came when methods for extracting iron from its ores were developed.

Iron was probably first produced by the Hittites about 1500 B.C. This metal cannot be separated from its ores by heating; extraction requires the presence of carbon. Perhaps the combination of coal, or more likely of charcoal, with iron ore, probably again in a campfire, led to the discovery of the process for purifying iron. This accidental purification of iron could have happened hundreds of times before some prehistoric "scientist" observed and interpreted his facts carefully. Thus began the iron age. The knowledge of iron was carried from one civilization to another largely by men with iron weapons who were conquering other peoples. This fusion of different peoples and knowledge resulted in new, more powerful societies, much as combining metals in alloys gives products with properties surpassing those of the individual components.

From the time of the Greeks until about 1700, no new metals were discovered and used. Since that time more than fifty metals that occur naturally have been recovered from their compounds, and in the past three decades several synthetic metals have been produced in atomic accelerators.

The transition from the stone age through the bronze age to the iron age took centuries. It is difficult to classify our present age; perhaps we are still living in an age of steel and aluminum, or perhaps we are in an age of plastics. We are much too close to the most recent developments to have historical perspective. Another way of classifying ages is based on sources of power rather than on materials used, and we are said to be entering the atomic age in this respect. How historians of the future eventually classify our civilization is not very important to us, but the metals themselves are of great significance. Chapters 3 and 5 provided an introduction to some of the metals. We will now discuss in detail the chemistry of some of the most important ones—iron, copper, aluminum, and magnesium—and will mention others that have interesting or outstanding properties.

19–2 METALS AND NONMETALS

Of the known elements, approximately three-fourths are classified as metals. While there is no distinct line of demarcation between metals and nonmetals, there are several differences which are usually characteristic. Some of these characteristics are so well known that most persons have little difficulty in distinguishing a metal from a nonmetal.

1) Metals have luster, particularly when freshly cut or when polished.

2) Metals are malleable; most of them can be hammered into desired shapes.

3) Metals are ductile; they may be drawn into wire.

4) In general, metals have greater densities than nonmetals. (There is much variation here—from lithium with a density in g/ml of 0.53, to osmium with a density of 22.57. Of the nonmetals, iodine has the greatest density, 4.93.)

5) Metals are generally good conductors of electricity, whereas nonmetals are not.

6) Metals form simple positive ions such as Fe^{2+}, Zn^{2+}, and Na^+, while nonmetals form simple negative ions, Cl^-, S^{2-}, and I^-.

It should be remembered that the metalloids (Section 18-2) have some properties typical of both metals and nonmetals.

19-3 THE REACTIONS OF METALS

There are other properties of metals that vary as greatly as do their densities. Chemical reactivity ranges from that of gold, which is not attacked by ordinary acid (it requires a combination of acids), to metals like sodium and potassium which react violently with water, Table 9-1. Some typical reactions of the more active metals involve

1) direct union with nonmetals:

$$Zn + S \rightarrow ZnS \tag{19-1}$$

$$Cu + Cl_2 \rightarrow CuCl_2 \tag{19-2}$$

$$2Ca + O_2 \rightarrow 2CaO \tag{19-3}$$

2) reaction with water:

$$2Na + 2HOH \rightarrow 2NaOH + H_2 \tag{19-4}$$

$$Mg + H_2O \xrightarrow{\text{high temperature}} MgO + H_2 \tag{19-5}$$

3) reaction with acids:

$$Zn + H_2SO_4 \rightarrow ZnSO_4 + H_2 \tag{19-6}$$

$$Cu + 4HNO_3 \rightarrow Cu(NO_3)_2 + 2NO_2 + 2H_2O \tag{19-7}$$

19-4 OXIDES OF METALS

Oxides of all the metals are known, but only those of the more active metals are formed according to Eq. (19-3). For those less active metals that do not unite directly with oxygen, the oxides are produced by the decomposition of other less stable compounds. Typically, silver oxide can be formed by adding a hydroxide to a solution containing silver ions:

$$Ag^+ + NaOH \rightarrow AgOH + Na^+ \tag{19-8}$$

The silver hydroxide is unstable and decomposes to the oxide and water:

$$2AgOH \rightarrow Ag_2O + H_2O \tag{19-9}$$

---

* Those metals, such as copper, located below hydrogen in the activity series of metals do not react to liberate hydrogen from acids. However, most of them will react with strong oxidizing acids such as nitric acid.

Oxides of the less active metals may be formed by decomposing their oxygen-containing salts with heat:

$$2Cu(NO_3)_2 \xrightarrow{\Delta} 2CuO + 4NO_2 + O_2 \tag{19-10}$$

$$PbCO_3 \xrightarrow{\Delta} PbO + CO_2 \tag{19-11}$$

19–5 METALLURGY

Metallurgy is the art or science of separating metals from their ores and preparing them for use by smelting, refining, or other processing. Much of what is known about metallurgy was discovered centuries ago by trial and error. Many of the early methods have been greatly improved and new methods have been discovered by scientific research.

Materials which can be commercially used as a source of metals are called *ores*. The most common ores are oxides, sulfides, halides, and carbonates. Silicates are sometimes used as sources of certain metals, but in general it is difficult to separate metals from silicate compounds. Three steps are usually involved in obtaining metals from ores.

1) In most instances it is necessary to *concentrate* the ore since impurities are usually present. This step is a physical or mechanical operation, consisting of removing dirt, other rocks, and similar materials.

2) The second step involves the chemical treatment of the ores and varies with their composition. If the ores are sulfides or carbonates, a preliminary treatment called *roasting* is used to convert the ores to their oxides. Roasting consists of heating the ore in the presence of air as illustrated in Eqs. (19–12) and (19–13):

$$2ZnS + 3O_2 \xrightarrow{\Delta} 2ZnO + 2SO_2 \tag{19-12}$$

$$PbCO_3 \xrightarrow{\Delta} PbO + CO_2 \tag{19-13}$$

The oxides produced in this manner, or the ores such as hematite which occur as oxides, can then be reduced to metals. Reduction is a loss of oxygen or a decrease in valence; metals are reduced from a positive valence in the ore to zero valence as a metal. Carbon and carbon monoxide are common reducing agents:

$$ZnO + C \rightarrow Zn + CO \tag{19-14}$$

$$Fe_2O_3 + 3CO \rightarrow 2Fe + 3CO_2 \tag{19-15}$$

3) The third step involves *purification* of the metals thus obtained, which is accomplished in various ways depending on the metal. Very pure copper, 99.955%, can be produced by electrolytic methods. Some metals such as zinc, cadmium, or mercury are purified by distillation.*

---

* Distillation is a process in which a substance is heated until it boils; the vapor escapes to a cool chamber where it condenses to become a liquid (or, in some cases, a solid). Substances having different boiling points can be separated by distillation, since the one of lowest boiling point will pass over first.

19-6 IRON AND STEEL

Of all the metals, iron is the cheapest in terms of price per pound, but the most valuable in terms of its importance to our civilization. It goes into the more than 120 million tons of steel which are produced annually in the United States. This figure appears incongruous with the statement that somewhat *less* than 100 million tons of iron ore are mined yearly. As we have pointed out, however, much of the steel is produced from scrap iron which has been reclaimed from old cars and worn out machinery, rather than from iron ore. Ore is needed to replace the iron that is lost by corrosion and by the discarding of small items such as tin cans which are primarily iron.

Very little iron is found in the free state. The small amounts which reach the earth in the form of meteorites, alloyed with nickel, are thought to be fragments of the interior of a disintegrated member of the solar system. Free iron of terrestrial origin has been found in rather rare instances, apparently forced up from the interior of the earth. Iron is too active chemically to remain in a pure state for long periods at the earth's surface unless it is protected from weathering. While there are many naturally occurring minerals or compounds of iron, only a few are used as ores. The most widely used are hematite, Fe_2O_3, limonite, a hydrated form of hematite, $2 Fe_2O_3 \cdot 3 H_2O$, and magnetite, Fe_3O_4.

◄ The name hematite is of Greek origin, from *haimatites*, blood-like. The ore is red in color and is sometimes used as the pigment in red paint. Magnetite has magnetic properties which are utilized in separating it from impurities in its ores. When the molecules in a specimen of magnetite are properly oriented (polarized) the mineral will attract a compass needle. Such rocks are called lodestones or natural magnets. ►

The most important iron deposits in the United States and perhaps in the world are in the Lake Superior region which produces 80% of the American ore processed. The second most important deposits are near Birmingham, Alabama.

The Blast Furnace

While the chemistry involved in separating iron from its ores is relatively simple, the equipment needed is elaborate. The modern **blast furnace,** Fig. 19-1, is approximately 100 ft high and has a maximum diameter of 25 ft. A mixture of iron ore, coke, and limestone, $CaCO_3$, is loaded at the top and preheated air* is forced in near the base. Temperature in the lower portion of the furnace approximates 2000°C, and diminishes toward the top. In the first reaction, which takes place within the furnace, coke combines with the heated oxygen to form carbon dioxide:

$$C + O_2 \rightarrow CO_2 \tag{19-16}$$

---

* In recent years the preheated air has been enriched with relatively pure oxygen, natural gas, and fuel oil. This speeds up the process and permits a higher proportion of iron ore to coke in the blast furnace.

FIG. 19-1. Photograph of a modern blast furnace. [Courtesy of the United States Steel Corporation.]

As the carbon dioxide rises it reacts with heated coke (the oxygen supply in this area has been exhausted) to form carbon monoxide:

$$C + CO_2 \rightarrow 2CO \tag{19-17}$$

Carbon monoxide is the active reducing agent which removes the oxygen from the hematite:

$$Fe_2O_3 + 3CO \rightarrow 2Fe + 3CO_2 \tag{19-18}$$

The intense heat decomposes the limestone, $CaCO_3$, to calcium oxide and carbon dioxide:

$$CaCO_3 \xrightarrow{\Delta} CaO + CO_2 \tag{19-19}$$

The ore still contains impurities, such as sand, which must be removed. The calcium oxide melts and reacts with sand and other impurities to form a low melting calcium silicate:

$$CaO + SiO_2 \rightarrow CaSiO_3 \tag{19-20}$$

which collects as liquid slag above the layer of molten iron at the bottom of the furnace.

The carbon dioxide released in the decomposition of calcium carbonate reacts with the carbon in coke according to Eq. (19-17), to form carbon monoxide, reducing more iron ore. The heated air, which is forced into the furnace is provided by a battery of enormous stoves (usually 4 to each furnace), Fig. 19-2. Every few hours the *iron notch* is opened and the white hot molten pig iron rushes from the furnace. It may be transported in a liquid state to nearby Bessemer converters, where impurities are burned from it, converting it into steel, or it may be cast into pigs, for storage and convenient handling. The molten slag, which cools to a glasslike material, is also removed periodically. It is used as building material and for making cheap glass, such as is used in nonreturnable beverage bottles.

To produce 1 ton of pig iron requires approximately 2 tons of ore, 1 ton of coke, 1/2 ton of limestone, and 4 tons of air. We can express the amount of materials needed for one day's operation of one blast furnace in the following way:

material	number of carloads
iron ore	50
coke	25
limestone	15

It will require about 30 railroad cars to transport the 1500 tons of iron that will be produced.

Pig Iron

The product of the blast furnace, **pig iron,** is extremely hard and brittle because of the large amount of impurities present. These must be partially removed before it can be used satisfactorily. The impurities consist of 3–5% of carbon, and lesser amounts of phosphorus, sulfur, and silicon. Pig iron is melted with high grade scrap iron to make *cast iron*, which has about half the impurities of pig iron. Cast iron is used in making castings, but is too hard to be forged, rolled, or welded. When pig iron is treated in a **Bessemer converter,** the air is forced through the molten metal for a few minutes to remove the carbon. Then the desired amounts of carbon, manganese, and other materials which are needed to impart the correct properties to the steel, are added. Construction steel and the rails of the early railroads were made by the Bessemer process. The term **steel** is applied to iron which has had its properties altered by the addition of small amounts of carbon and/or other metals.

The Open-Hearth Process

This process is now used in the manufacture of most of the steel. While it is not as rapid as the Bessemer process, it produces better quality steel, since sulfur and phosphorus, which

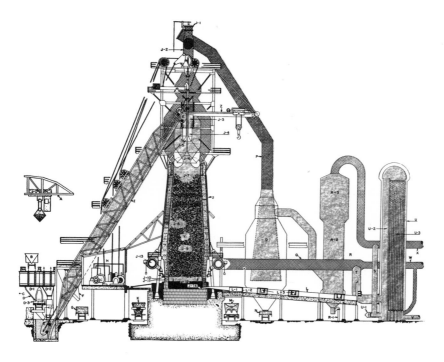

FIG. 19–2. Idealized cross section of a typical modern blast furnace plant (with legend). Skip cars, E, which carry ore to the top of the furnace may be seen at the extreme lower left and at the upper end of the slanted track. One of a battery of stoves is at the extreme right. [Courtesy of the United States Steel Corporation.]

A   Ore bridge
B   Ore transfer car
C   Ore storage yard
D   Stockhouse
   D-1 Ore and limestone bins
   D-2 Coke bin
   D-3 Scale car
E   Skip
F   Coke dust recovery chute
G   Freight car
H   Skip and bell hoist
I   Skip bridge
J   Blast furnace
   J-1 Bleeder valve
   J-2 Gas uptake
   J-3 Receiving hopper
   J-4 Distributor

J-5 Small bell
J-6 Large bell
J-7 Stock line
J-8 Inwall
J-9 Bosh
J-10 Tuyeres
J-11 Slag notch
J-12 Hearth
J-13 Bustle pipe
J-14 Iron notch
K   Slag ladle
L   Cast house
   L-1 Iron trough
   L-2 Slag skimmer
   L-3 Iron runner
M   Hot-metal ladle
N   Flue dust car
O   Dust catcher

P   Downcomer
Q   Hot blast line to furnace
R   Gas washer
   R-1 Sludge line to thickener
   R-2 Spray washer
   R-3 Electrical precipitator
S   Gas offtake to stove burner
T   Hot blast connection from stove
U   Stove
   U-1 Gas burner
   U-2 Combustion chamber
   U-3 Checker chamber
V   Exhaust gas line to stack
W   Cold blast line from blower
X   Surplus gas line
Y   Stock—Iron ore, coke, limestone
Z   Jib boom crane

occur as objectionable impurities in pig iron, can be removed. The eight hours required for a run provides time for the proper analysis and control that is necessary in the production of high quality steel. Another advantage of the **open-hearth** process is that scrap steel, which is in plentiful supply, is necessary for the proper reactions of the process.

19-7 THE ALLOYS OF IRON AND OTHER METALS

Pure iron is so soft that it would be useless for most of the tasks assigned to this metal. It is therefore necessary to add materials, which might be considered "desirable impurities," to alter its properties. The materials to be added may be either metals or nonmetals, and the products are called **alloys.*** The addition of small amounts of carbon to pure iron increases its hardness, and if more is added, as in pig iron, it becomes brittle. Numerous metals, when added in very small amounts, produce great differences in the properties of iron. Thousands of alloys are known.

Let us consider some of the many purposes for which iron alloys are used, and the variety of properties required. Within a modern automobile we find many examples. The engine is made of cast iron which must be soft enough to be machined and polished, yet hard enough to resist wear. The springs must be flexible and resilient to the extent that they maintain their original shape after millions of bumps. The axles must be rigid and tough enough to withstand the pressures exerted by today's high-powered engines. The body is composed of sheet metal which can be dented and rolled back to the original shape. The gears also require special alloys that are strong and resistant to wear.

We also use many alloys which contain no iron. Typical of these are bronze, brass, solder, and pewter. These and other alloys, their compositions, and typical uses are found in Table 19-1. More complete tables of alloys can be found in a chemistry handbook.

19-8 COPPER

Copper, it will be remembered, is one of the metals known since the dawn of history. While small amounts are found in the free state, most of it occurs as the sulfides—chalcocite, Cu_2S; chalcopyrites, $CuFeS_2$; and bornite, Cu_5FeS_4. The main producing areas in the United States are Montana, Arizona, Utah, and Nevada. The ores are first concentrated and roasted:

$$2Cu_2S + 3O_2 \xrightarrow{\Delta} 2Cu_2O + SO_2 \tag{19-21}$$

The oxide can then be reacted with more of the sulfide to give pure copper and sulfur dioxide:

$$Cu_2S + 2Cu_2O \rightarrow 6Cu + SO_2 \tag{19-22}$$

The impure copper which results is cast into large slabs and refined electrolytically to produce copper that is 99.9% pure.

Properties of Copper

Pure copper is a soft reddish-yellow metal which can easily be hammered into desired shapes and drawn into wire. Because of the ease with which it can be worked, it was used extensively by primitive craftsmen, and it is believed to be the first metal to be shaped into

---

* Alloys are materials with metallic characteristics. They consist of two or more metals or, in some cases, of a metal or metals with small proportions of nonmetals such as carbon and silicon.

TABLE 19-1. Common alloys

Name	Composition Percentage	Properties	Uses
steel, high speed	Fe 77.7, W 18, Cr 4, Mn 0.3	very hard, retains temper at very high temperatures	drill bits, cutting tools
steel	Fe 99, C 1.0	hard, durable	structures of steel, rails, etc.
steel, stainless*	Fe 74, Cr 18, Ni 8	corrosion resistant	chemical equipment, tanks for trucks, railroad cars
steel, molybdenum	Fe 97–99, Mo 1–3	hard, heat resistant	axles for autos
brass	Cu 85, Zn 15	easily machined, corrosion resistant	fittings, hardware, radiator cores
brass, cartridge	Cu 70, Zn 30	easily shaped	shell cases
brass, naval	Cu 60, Zn 39, Sn 1	resistant to seawater and corrosion, polishes well	ship fittings
bronze	Cu 70–95, Zn 1–25, Sn 1–18	harder than brass	fittings, statuary
nickel coinage	Cu 75, Ni 25		
silver, sterling	Ag 92.5, Cu 7.5	durable, beautiful	silverware and service, jewelry
silver, coinage	Ag 90, Cu 10		
gold, coins	Au 90, Cu 10		
gold, 12-carat	Au 50, Cu 35, Ag 15		jewelry
gold, 18-carat	Au 75, Ag 10–20, Cu 5–15		jewelry
Monel metal	Ni 60, Cu 33, Fe 7	strong, durable, bright	marine shafts, vats for foods and chemicals
pewter	Sn 85, Cu 6.8, Bi 6, Sb 1.7	soft, corrosion-free	decorative vases, pitchers, etc.
solder, plumbers'	Pb 67, Sn 33	low melting point	soldering
type metal	Pb 70, Sb 18, Sn 10, Cu 2	low melting point	printer's type
Wood's metal	Bi 50, Pb 25, Sn 12.5, Cd 12.5	very low melting point (70°C)	soft plugs in automatic sprinklers
Nichrome	Ni 80–85, Cr 15–20	high melting point, low electrical conductivity	heating elements

* Example of one of many stainless steels.

utensils. Addition of tin to copper produces the alloy bronze. This alloy is harder and better for making cast objects, since it has a lower melting point than copper and it contracts less when it cools. The discovery of bronze initiated the bronze age about 3000 B.C.

Copper is a relatively inactive metal which has valences of 1+ and 2+. The higher valence is more common.

Almost 1,500,000 tons of copper were produced in the United States in 1966. Major uses include wire and cables for the transmission of electricity, tubing for water lines in homes and industry, tanks, and vats. About 20% of the output is used in alloys such as brass, bronze, and coinage metals.

19-9 ALUMINUM

It is interesting to note that aluminum, now the second most common metal in terms of quantities produced, is so new that it is almost a 20th-century metal. It was first produced in 1828, but for many years it was primarily an expensive curiosity. It is reported that Emperor Napoleon III of France was so fascinated by this light and beautiful metal that he had a set of tableware made of it to be used in place of gold for his most important banquets. The unusual lightness, strength, and durability of aluminum indicated that it should have great utility, but the price remained so high, several dollars per pound, that its uses were limited. Aluminum compounds are plentiful since it is the third most prevalent element in the crust of the earth. Aluminum combines chemically with other elements so tenaciously, however, that isolation of the metal was difficult. Aluminum is now obtained by an electrolytic process.

◄ The story is told that one day in 1885 Charles Martin Hall, a student at Oberlin College, was listening to his chemistry professor who made the statement that fame and fortune awaited the man who could find an inexpensive method of making aluminum. Hall turned to his laboratory partner and said, "I'm going after that metal." He started his work in a backyard laboratory, and in February, 1886, he produced small amounts of aluminum by a unique method of electrolysis, a method still being used. He dissolved aluminum oxide in molten cryolite, Na_3AlF_6, and using carbon electrodes passed a strong current of electricity through the molten liquid. Hall did become famous and wealthy, but much effort was required to convince the world of the advantages of this unusual metal. ►

Aluminum is a silvery metal with a density of 2.7 g/ml, which is approximately one-third that of iron. It is a soft, malleable, and ductile metal that is an excellent conductor of heat and electricity. Industrial users take advantage of some or all of these properties. It is hammered or rolled into many useful objects. It is used, for example, in cooking utensils where a transfer of heat is essential, and it is drawn into wires for conducting electricity.

Aluminum has a valence of 3+. It is quite active chemically, and were it not for one peculiar characteristic, it would be useless, or used for much different purposes. It reacts with oxygen to form a very thin invisible film of Al_2O_3 which serves as a protective coating that renders the surface inactive. The fact that aluminum forms a wide variety of alloys with greatly different properties has added materially to its importance. It seems doubtful that one of our largest industries—aviation—could have reached any degree of importance without the light-weight aluminum and its alloys. The structure and the skin of large aircraft are made of aluminum and its alloys. Aluminum is also used in structural beams, window frames, doors, canoes, house trailers, siding for buildings, pots, pans, foil, and countless other items.

Approximately 3,000,000 tons of aluminum metal were produced in the United States in 1966. The price at that time was 25 cents a pound. The source of practically all the metal is bauxite, $Al_2O_3 \cdot XH_2O$.

Aluminum forms some interesting compounds. Corundum, Al_2O_3, is an important abrasive. Sapphires and rubies are also naturally occurring oxides of aluminum containing small amounts of impurities. In recent years synthetic sapphires and rubies of high quality have been made. They are used for jewels in watches and as gems.

19–10 MAGNESIUM

Magnesium, with a density of 1.74 g/ml, is the least dense of the metals which are used for structural purposes. The source of the metal is seawater, which contains 0.13% magnesium as Mg^{2+} ions. While this percentage seems small, 1 cu mi of seawater contains 6,000,000 tons of magnesium. It is estimated there are 300,000,000 cu mi of water in the oceans. The United States produces 80,000 tons of this metal annually.

The magnesium ions are extracted from seawater by adding calcium hydroxide, $Ca(OH)_2$, so that the insoluble magnesium hydroxide is precipitated from solution and can be removed by filtration:

$$Mg^{2+} + Ca(OH)_2 \rightarrow Ca^{2+} + Mg(OH)_2 \downarrow \tag{19-23}$$

Magnesium hydroxide is converted to magnesium chloride by the addition of hydrochloric acid:

$$Mg(OH)_2 + 2HCl \rightarrow MgCl_2 + 2H_2O \tag{19-24}$$

The metal is separated from magnesium chloride by electrolysis.

Magnesium is used extensively in aluminum alloys where light, strong metals are required. Most of it goes into the construction of aircraft. When ignited, magnesium metal burns vigorously in the air, producing a brilliant light. This property has made it useful in the making of flares, fireworks, and incendiary bombs. Heated magnesium reacts with steam forming the oxide and hydrogen:

$$Mg + H_2O \text{ (steam)} \xrightarrow{\Delta} MgO + H_2 \tag{19-25}$$

19–11 OTHER IMPORTANT METALS

Iron, copper, aluminum, and magnesium are probably the most important metals—at least from a quantitative standpoint—in our civilization. However, many other metals and their alloys also play significant roles. Table 19–2 lists some of these metals, their sources, and important uses. Many volumes have been written about the metals; it is beyond the scope of this book to discuss them at length. A brief description of each of the elements, both metallic and nonmetallic, which includes their history, occurrence, properties, and uses may be found in the *Handbook of Chemistry and Physics* published by the Chemical Rubber Company.

TABLE 19-2. Other common metals: their ores, sources, and important uses

Metal	Common Ore	Source	Uses
antimony	Sb_2S_3	China, Bolivia, Chile	primarily in alloys (see Table 19-1)
bismuth	Bi_2S_3, Bi_2O_3	(by-products of Pb, Cu, Sn, Ag ores)	type metal, low melting alloys
cadmium	CdS	(by-product of Zn, Cu, Pb ores)	batteries, electroplating
chromium	$FeO \cdot Cr_2O_3$	Southern Rhodesia, Cuba, Philippines	alloys, electroplating, pigments
cobalt	CoAsS, $CoAs_2$	Ontario (Canada)	magnets, alloys
lead	PbS	Oklahoma, Kansas, Missouri	paints, storage batteries, ammunition, solder
manganese	MnO_2, $MnCO_3$	ocean floor, Russia, United States	alloys
mercury	HgS	Spain, Italy, California	scientific instruments, vapor lamps
molybdenum	MoS_2	Colorado	electrical resistance wire, alloys for withstanding high temperatures
nickel	sulfides	Ontario, Cuba, Norway	alloys, structural steel, coin metal
silver	Ag, Ag_2S	Mexico, United States	coin metals, photographs, jewelry
tin	SnO_2	Bolivia, East Indies	alloys, coating for tin cans, solder
tungsten	$(Fe,Mn)WO_4$	Nevada, California, North Carolina	electric filaments, alloys for high speed cutting tools (highest melting point of all metals, 3410°C.)
zinc	ZnS, $ZnCO_3$	Oklahoma, Kansas, Missouri	ZnO (adhesive tape), alloys, galvanized coating

19-12 SUMMARY

The metals have found many different uses because of great variety in their properties, which range from the very light to the very dense, and from the extremely reactive to the un-reactive. In general, their properties include hardness, strength, and durability. The dis-covery of a new metal or a new mixture of metals—an alloy—can change a civilization. The number of possible alloys is almost limitless. Thousands have already been produced, and new ones are being developed to meet the needs of today's exploration of space. Although certain synthetic organic compounds, the plastics, are replacing metals for many purposes, our civilization needs both the metals and the plastics. To understand many of the events occurring in our world and the factors bringing about change, some knowledge and understanding of both the inorganic world of metals and nonmetals, and of the organic compounds is necessary. After a slight digression to take up the subject of nuclear chemistry in the next chapter, we will turn to the discussion of the fascinating compounds of carbon which are the subject matter of organic chemistry.

IMPORTANT TERMS

Alloys	*Brass*	*Malleable*	*Pig iron*
Bessemer converter	*Bronze*	*Metallurgy*	*Steel*
Blast furnace	*Ductile*	*Open-hearth furnace*	

WORK EXERCISES

1. Review the characteristic properties of the metals listed, Section 19–1, and try to recall how many of these you were aware of before reading this book.

2. How many metals do you think you could have identified before studying chemistry?

3. What is the term assigned to the elements along the border between the true metals and the nonmetals?

4. Name two important reactions typical of active metals which the less active metals do not undergo.

5. Name three steps involved in separating metals from their ores.

6. What purpose does limestone play in the separation of iron from its ore?

7. Why should a metal as prevalent in nature as iron be so rarely found in a free state?

8. Complete and balance the equations for which a reaction occurs, or state "no reaction."

   a) $Zn + HCl \rightarrow$ b) $Mg + H_2SO_4 \rightarrow$

   c) $Cu + HCl \rightarrow$ d) $K + HOH \rightarrow$

   e) $Zn + S \xrightarrow{\Delta}$ f) $PbCO_3 \xrightarrow{\Delta}$

   g) $ZnS + O_2 \xrightarrow{\Delta}$ h) $Fe_2O_3 + CO \xrightarrow{\Delta}$

   i) $CaCO_3 \xrightarrow{\Delta}$ j) $CaO + SiO_2 \xrightarrow{\Delta}$

9. Some metals do not combine directly with oxygen even at high temperatures. Can you suggest a method for preparing such oxides?

10. Name three types of compounds which are common to many metallic ores.

11. What are some of the advantages of alloys over pure metals?

12. Name some of the properties of copper which make it more desirable than iron for certain uses.

13. State some of the properties of aluminum which make it more desirable for some purposes than either copper or iron.

14. Which of the metals listed in Table 19–2 do you consider the most prevalent?

SUGGESTED READING

Dudley, T. E., Jr., "Early Metallurgy in the New World," *Scientific American*, Apr. 1966, p. 72. A most interesting resume of the history of metallurgy on the North American continent during the past 6000 years.

Fine, M. M., "The Beneficiation of Iron Ores," *Scientific American*, Jan. 1968. Lower-grade ores, formerly discarded, can now be used because of ingenious changes in mining and processing.

Parker, C. M., "Panorama of Steel," *Journal of Chemical Education* **28,** 236 (1951). A well-written review of the iron industry, from locations of ore deposits and recovery of the metal to the uses and properties of the finished products.

Chapter 20   RADIOACTIVITY AND NUCLEAR CHEMISTRY

20-1 THE HOPES OF THE ALCHEMISTS

When we contemplate the history of chemistry, it is interesting to see how a few theories once widely held were completely overthrown only to emerge again, usually much altered, centuries later. The possibility of the transmutation of one element into another is an example of a theory with this history.

Alchemy, which developed as a fusion of Greek science with some aspects of religion, had many facets. Among them was the idea that baser metals such as lead and mercury could be transformed into gold. Both charlatans and honest, though naive, experimenters claimed some success in this endeavor. All hopes of changing one kind of element to a different one were dimmed when Dalton's atomic theory gained acceptance early in the 19th century. According to this theory, atoms of elements could enter into compounds, but the elements themselves were immutable. By the end of the 19th century, evidence was accumulating that atoms were not the simple, indivisible, unalterable particles Dalton had proposed, but that they were made of yet simpler units which came to be known as electrons, protons, and neutrons. Even more amazing was the observation that some atoms spontaneously gave off radiation, which was later identified as electrons or even larger particles. If an atom is made of a precise number of protons and electrons and owes its distinctive nature to the precise number of each it contains, what happens when it loses an alpha particle containing 2 protons and 2 neutrons? If mercury, which contains 80 protons, loses a proton, it must become element 79, gold. So the theory has come full cycle, and transmutation is again believable. The tools for this transformation are no longer the alembic and philosopher's stone, but cyclotrons and atomic piles. Modern alchemists, moreover, are interested in reactions more exciting and even more profitable than ones which change mercury to gold. This chapter tells the story of these latter-day alchemists—of their discoveries, their theories, their promise, and the threat to society inherent in these discoveries.

20-2 THE DISCOVERY OF RADIUM AND RADIOACTIVITY

In 1896, Henry Becquerel, a French physicist, accidentally discovered that a uranium compound with which he was working darkened photographic films that were wrapped to protect them from light. It was evident to him that some type of radiation was coming from the uranium. On further investigation, it was found that all uranium compounds, regardless of source, produced similar radiations. Mme. Marie Curie named this phenomenon **radioactivity.**

Mme. Curie and her husband, Pierre, undertook a search for substances which showed radioactive properties, and to their surprise found that the ore from which uranium was recovered was more radioactive than the pure uranium compound. They acquired a large amount of uranium ore, and, after many chemical separations, produced an impure material which was 400 times more radioactive than uranium. From its chemical properties, they knew it to be a compound of a new element. This element they named *polonium* (atomic number 84) after Mme. Curie's native country, Poland. Continuing their search, they obtained an entirely different compound with chemical properties similar to barium, which, even in an impure state, was 900 times more radioactive than uranium. This element (atomic number 88) they called *radium* because of its great radioactivity. The immensity of their task is indicated by the fact that from 1 ton of ore they obtained only 0.10 g of radium chloride.

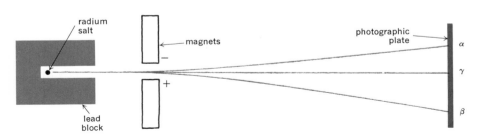

FIG. 20–1. The separation of alpha, beta, and gamma rays by a magnetic field.

Radium emits three types of radiation: alpha (α) particles which are positively charged helium ions, beta (β) particles which are electrons, and gamma (γ) rays which are shortwave X-rays (see Section 4–5). The presence of these radiations can best be demonstrated by placing a small quantity of radium in a hole within a block of lead, Fig. 20–1. A strong magnet is placed near the hole so that escaping radiations must pass through the magnetic field. Beside this is placed a photographic plate. The positive alpha particles are deflected toward the negative field whereas the beta rays are attracted by the positive field. The gamma rays are unaffected. When developed, the photographic plate shows the areas of radiation impact.

TABLE 20–1. Characteristic properties of alpha, beta and gamma radiations

Ray	Character	Charge[a]	Mass[b]	Velocity[c]	Penetration
α	He^{2+}	$2+$	4.0026	about 0.1 speed of light	stopped by paper or human skin
β	electron	$1-$	0.000548	up to 0.9 speed of light	several mm in human tissue
γ	short X-rays	0	0	speed of light	human body or several feet of concrete

[a] The unit of charge employed here is the amount of charge of the electron itself.
[b] The mass is expressed in atomic mass units (Section 4–8).
[c] The velocity of light in a vacuum is 3.00×10^{10} cm/sec.

Table 20–1 shows characteristic properties of alpha, beta, and gamma radiations.

It is now known that by losing alpha, beta, and gamma radiations, uranium disintegrates through an elaborate series of transmutations, terminating as the element lead. The decomposition of radium is only one step in this series.

The first step in the disintegration of uranium-238 is

$$^{238}_{92}\text{U} \quad \rightarrow \quad ^{234}_{90}\text{Th} \quad + \quad ^{4}_{2}\text{He}$$
uranium   thorium   helium

(20–1)

The alpha particle comes from the nucleus of the atom, and the reaction is called a nuclear reaction to distinguish it from a chemical reaction which involves valence electrons. *The balancing of nuclear equations requires the total number of mass units (superscript) and atomic numbers (subscript) be the same on each side of the equation.*

The thorium initially formed decomposes also:

$$^{234}_{90}\text{Th} \quad \rightarrow \quad ^{234}_{91}\text{Pa} \quad + \quad ^{0}_{-1}\text{e}$$
thorium   protactinium   electron

(20–2)

In Eq. (20–2), the mass of protactinium is equal to that of thorium—both are 234. However, a nuclear transformation occurs which can be represented as

$$^{1}_{0}\text{n} \quad \rightarrow \quad ^{1}_{1}\text{p} \quad + \quad ^{0}_{-1}\text{e}$$
neutron   proton   electron

(20–3)

Thus the nucleus increases its positive charge one unit, and a new element is formed even though the mass number does not alter.

Later in the series, radium breaks down:

$$^{226}_{88}\text{Ra} \rightarrow {}^{222}_{86}\text{Rn} + {}^{4}_{2}\text{He}$$

radium   radon   helium

(20-4)

Table 20-2 lists the entire series of steps in the transformation of uranium to lead.

In the process of nuclear disintegration some elements emit only alpha particles while others emit only beta particles. However, both alpha and beta emission is usually accompanied by gamma radiation. Some elements emit all three.

20-3 HALF-LIFE OF RADIOACTIVE ELEMENTS

The rates of nuclear reactions, unlike those of chemical reactions, are not altered by environmental changes. The disintegration of radium proceeds as rapidly at −100°C as at high temperatures. Apparently the rates of decay are determined entirely by the stability of the nuclei.

The term used to indicate the rate of decay is the **half-life** which is the interval of time required for one-half of a given quantity of a radioactive element to decompose. For example, if 1 kg of radium were observed for a period of 1620 years, it would be found that one-half of it would remain as radium. The other portion would contain all the elements below radium in the uranium disintegration series, Table 20-2. At the end of the next 1620 years, $\frac{1}{2} \times \frac{1}{2}$—or $\frac{1}{4}$ kg—of radium would remain. It can be seen that disintegration would eventually become minute. The situation is comparable to that in the old conundrum—if a frog is placed at one end of a yard stick and starts jumping toward the other end, each

TABLE 20-2. The steps in the disintegration of uranium-238

Element	Mass Number	Neutrons	Atomic Number	Particle Emitted	Half-Life
uranium	238	146	92	α	4.498×10^9 y
thorium	234	144	90	β	24.10 d
protactinium	234	143	91	β	69 s
uranium	234	142	92	α	2.48×10^5 y
thorium	230	140	90	α	8.3×10^4 y
radium	226	138	88	α	1620 y
radon	222	136	86	α	3.82 d
polonium	218	134	84	α	3.05 m
lead	214	132	82	β	26.8 m
bismuth	214	131	83	β	19.7 m
polonium	214	130	84	α	1.64×10^{-4} s
lead	210	128	82	β	22 y
bismuth	210	127	83	β	4.85 d
polonium	210	126	84	α	138 d
lead	206	124	82	stable	stable

time jumping exactly one-half the distance to the end, how many jumps will he take to reach the end?

Table 20–2 reveals that half-life periods vary from millions of years to less than a millisecond. We cannot predict when one individual nucleus will decay. However, in an ordinary sample, containing approximately Avogadro's number of atoms, we can predict statistically that a definite number of the nuclei present will decay within a certain time.

20–4 MAN-MADE TRANSMUTATIONS

The discovery of radioactivity offered new thresholds of research for chemists and physicists alike, and many of the world's most able scientists were attracted to this field. From a humanitarian standpoint, radium was of tremendous help in the treatment of cancer. From a strictly scientific standpoint, it proved to be an exciting source of miniature high-speed projectiles with which to bombard all sorts of matter.

The invention of the **cloud chamber** by Wilson, in 1912, made it possible to actually observe the effect of radiation with the unaided eye. In the cloud chamber a piece of radioactive material is surrounded by air which is supersaturated with moisture; each radiation particle leaves a minute vapor trail as it passes through the air. These vapor trails, or **fog-tracks** as they are commonly called, are produced when moisture condenses around the many ions caused when radiating particles collided with air molecules. These trails are similar to the condensation trails of high-flying jet aircraft. These fog-tracks can be photographed, and a trained scientist can identify the tracks of the different radiating particles, Fig. 20–2.

In 1919, the English physicist Ernest Rutherford tried bombarding various gases with alpha particles emitted by a radioactive substance. To his surprise, after nitrogen was bombarded, he discovered that very small quantities of hydrogen and an isotope of oxygen were present. The equation for such a reaction is

$$\,^4_2\text{He} + \,^{14}_7\text{N} \rightarrow \,^{17}_8\text{O} + \,^1_1\text{H} \tag{20–5}$$

Rutherford, by changing one element to another, had accomplished what the alchemists had dreamed of—a transmutation of elements.

This discovery so intensified research in radioactivity that within less than fifty years hundreds of transmutations have been carried out. The detection of many subatomic particles, including the neutron, resulted from such studies. A few such reactions are as follows:

$$\,^4_2\text{He} + \,^9_4\text{Be} \rightarrow \,^{12}_6\text{O} + \,^1_0\text{n} \tag{20–6}$$

$$\,^4_2\text{He} + \,^{27}_{13}\text{Al} \rightarrow \,^{30}_{15}\text{P} + \,^1_0\text{n} \tag{20–7}$$

$$\,^4_2\text{He} + \,^{24}_{12}\text{Mg} \rightarrow \,^{27}_{14}\text{Si} + \,^1_0\text{n} \tag{20–8}$$

$$\,^{12}_6\text{C} + \,^1_1\text{H} \rightarrow \,^{13}_7\text{N} \tag{20–9}$$

$$\,^{40}_{20}\text{Ca} + \,^1_0\text{n} \rightarrow \,^{40}_{19}\text{K} + \,^1_1\text{H} \tag{20–10}$$

FIG. 20–2. A cloud chamber photograph showing tracks produced by subnuclear particles. [Courtesy of the Brookhaven National Laboratory.]

20–5 CHARGED-PARTICLE ACCELERATORS

Until 1930, all bombarding of atomic nuclei was brought about by high-speed alpha particles from naturally occurring radioactive isotopes, such as those used by Rutherford. In 1930, E. O. Lawrence, of the University of California, devised a method which involved the artificial acceleration of charged particles, such as protons and deuterium ions. Such a device gives them greatly increased speeds and therefore greater energy. Transmutation reactions involving protons or alpha particles would otherwise be very unlikely, since these positively charged particles are repelled by a nucleus which is positive. The projectile particles are accelerated to energies much higher than are usually provided by most natural radioactive decay.

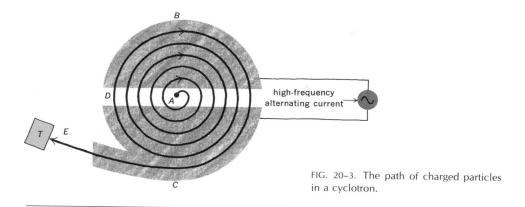

FIG. 20–3. The path of charged particles in a cyclotron.

Two types of devices are used, the cyclotron (which is circular in shape, Fig. 20–3), and the linear accelerator (Fig. 20–4). The earlier devices were relatively small, being measured in inches, but the ones built more recently are of enormous proportions.

◄ The function of a **cyclotron** may be described as follows. The two half-sections, B and C, are attached to a high-frequency alternating current which alternates the electric charge on each half of the device many times each second. A positively charged particle released at A moves outward and toward B, which at the moment is negative. It accelerates rapidly and, on reaching D, the fields are reversed so that the particle is literally pushed and pulled into the other section. This procedure happens millions of times per second until the particle is finally shot through E to a target, T. Because of the effect these particles produce, a device such as this is called an **atom smasher.**

The **linear accelerator** projects a charged particle in a straight line from its source to the target. In the diagram of a linear accelerator shown in Fig. 20–4, the odd-numbered sections will always have charges opposite to those of the even-numbered sections. Charges on sections will be alternating at a high frequency. Suppose a positively charged particle is released at S, when section 1 is negative. It will be attracted into the cylinder but, as it passes through, the electrical fields are changed so that section 1 is positive and section 2 is negative. The speed of the particle will be greatly increased since it is being pulled by section 2 and repelled or pushed by section 1. This process continues, with the particles increasing in speed with each step, until they reach the target, T. The phase of the oscillating field has to be adjusted over the length of the accelerator, of course, so that the field will keep in step with the particles. ►

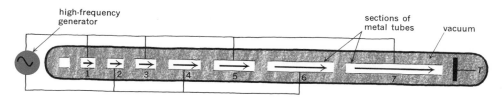

FIG. 20–4. Sketch of a linear accelerator. See also Fig. 20–5.

FIG. 20–5. An aerial view of the linear accelerator at Stanford University. This accelerator is two miles in length, the largest and the longest one in the world. [Courtesy of the Stanford Linear Accelerator Center.]

20–6 MASS-ENERGY RELATIONSHIP

In the early years of this century, Einstein formulated the famous equation $E = mc^2$, in which E represents energy, m equals mass, and c is the speed of light. Since the speed of light is almost inconceivable (3×10^{10} cm/sec), E must have a still more fantastic value. The equation implies that there is a relationship between matter and energy, and that each may be converted into the other.

At first, only a few people were able to grasp the significance of the equation. It appeared, however, to answer heretofore unanswered questions regarding the source of the sun's energy. It was known that the sun was largely composed of hydrogen, but also contained some helium. On the basis of the Einstein equation, it was reasoned that four hydrogen atoms might in some manner combine to form one helium atom, with a small amount of the matter being converted into energy. In fact, if we compare the masses of four hydrogen atoms, accurate to three or four decimal places, with the accurate mass of a helium atom, we discover a discrepancy in the masses, which could be the source of energy. Equation (20–11) shows the reaction and the masses of the particles (the masses of the electrons have a very small effect and are not being counted). In this reaction, four protons can combine to form a helium nucleus if two of the protons lose their charge to become neutrons; thus, we are left with 2 protons and 2 neutrons, which makes a helium nucleus.

$$4 \, {}^{1}_{1}\text{H} \quad \rightarrow \quad {}^{4}_{2}\text{He} + \textbf{energy} \tag{20–11}$$

$$\begin{array}{cc} 4.032 & 4.003 \\ (4 \times 1.008) & \end{array}$$

During reaction, Eq. (20–11), the mass changed from 4.032 to 4.003, a loss of 0.029 mass units. This decrease in weight has been called the **mass defect** of the helium atom. However, in a reaction of nuclear particles this lost mass is not expelled as particles or small fragments of matter, but instead is transformed to energy. Let us now see how much energy this would be, according to Einstein's equation.

In order to have a reasonable quantity of material in our calculation we will, as usual, consider *gram*-atomic weights. Thus, 4.032 g of hydrogen would yield 4.003 g of helium, with 0.029 g transformed to energy. Using this value in Einstein's equation gives:

$$\begin{aligned} E &= mc^2 \\ &= 0.029 \text{ g } (3 \times 10^{10} \text{ cm/sec})^2 \\ &= 2.6 \, (10^{19}) \text{ g cm}^2/\text{sec}^2 \\ &= 6.2 \, (10^8) \text{ kcal} \\ &= 620 \text{ million kcal.} \end{aligned}$$

Although 0.029 g is a very small amount of material, it can be transformed to a tremendous amount of energy. The 620 million kilocalories released is enough to heat an average home for about twenty years. If one whole gram of mass, still a small amount, were all transformed to energy, it would heat an average home for hundreds of years! To say it yet another way, one mole of material participating in a nuclear reaction releases approximately one to ten million times as much energy as it does in an ordinary chemical reaction in which valence bonds are formed.

It is now known that energy loss of this type occurs during the formation of nuclei of all elements. Whenever protons and neutrons are packed together to form a nucleus, energy is released. The more energy that is lost, per nuclear particle, the more stable is the resulting nucleus. Therefore, this is called the **binding energy.** The most stable nuclei, that is, those that have lost the most energy during binding, are those of medium size (mass about 40 to 100). Large nuclei are somewhat less stable, and we see them breaking down during radioactive decay. Apparently if too many protons and neutrons are packed together in a nucleus, it cannot be as stable as a medium-sized nucleus. Binding energy is definitely released during the formation of a large nucleus, but not so much per nuclear particle as is released in the building of nuclei of medium size.

20-7 TYPES OF NUCLEAR REACTIONS: FUSION AND FISSION

Since nuclei of medium size are the most stable, there are two ways that nuclei can release energy in the process of being converted to different nuclei. Small nuclei can engage in a **fusion reaction,** combining to form a medium-sized nucleus. Although considerable binding energy was lost when the small nuclei were formed from protons and neutrons, still more energy can be lost when the small nuclei unite to produce a more stable medium-sized nucleus. In the other process, a large nucleus can release additional binding energy (beyond that lost during the original formation of the nucleus) if it breaks down into two or more medium-sized nuclei. This is called a **fission reaction.**

Both of these nuclear reactions have been studied experimentally and theoretically, especially since World War II. Experimentally, the fission reaction was the one first examined here on earth.

◄ Possibly the energy changes associated with nuclear fission and fusion will be understood better in terms of more familiar objects. Suppose it was discovered that the most desirable fruits were those of medium size, say the size of a grapefruit. As a result, a regulation was passed that, whenever possible, people should convert their fruit to the best size.

If we had a watermelon, we could cut it into smaller fragments of the optimum size. Of course, in the process a little juice would be lost. The important difference in nuclear conversions is that the loss could not come out as matter, but would have to emerge as energy.

Or, if we had four oranges, they could be pressed together to make one larger mass of fruit, again with some loss. As before, if this were a nuclear combination, the loss would be emitted as energy. ►

20-8 THE NUCLEAR FISSION BOMB

By 1935, attempts were being undertaken to bombard uranium atoms with neutrons in the hope that the neutrons would be captured in the nucleus, so that new elements, heavier than uranium, might be synthesized. The Italian physicist Enrico Fermi, one of the leaders in this research, produced isotopes which were difficult to identify. In Germany, Meitner and Hahn were obtaining comparable results from similar experiments. Their detection of barium in these radiation products indicated that instead of making larger, heavier atoms, uranium atoms were being broken down into smaller atoms by impact of a neutron.

The scientific world was informed of this discovery in 1939, but its true significance was recognized at the time by only a few of the research workers who were studying nuclear structure.

The possibility of obtaining energy by splitting atoms was a new concept. When uranium atoms were split into two or more smaller atoms, not only was energy produced in great amounts, but there was also a production of excess neutrons. Since a neutron can cause an atom to fission or split, which in turn liberates two or more neutrons, it seemed logical that these freed neutrons could cause other atoms to split. If this continued, a so-called chain reaction would take place in which tremendous numbers of atoms would be split and tremendous amounts of energy released. Such energy, if controlled, would be a formidable weapon in the form of a bomb.

At the time of the publication of the findings of Meitner and Hahn in 1939, the United States was on the verge of entering World War II. Scientists in several countries soon realized the military possibilities of the energy from nuclear fission. There were, however, a great many difficulties in developing and handling such energy.

The American government established a highly secret project, staffed by top-rate scientists, to develop an atomic bomb. It was found that uranium-235 was the fissionable isotope of uranium. Since normally available uranium contained 140 uranium-238 atoms for every 1 of the uranium-235, a difficult task was involved in separating the two kinds of atoms that were identical chemically and very similar physically. Thousands of scientists collaborated to overcome this and many other technical problems involved in the production of the atomic bomb.

The mechanics of a fission bomb depend upon the fact that for each fissioning atom of uranium-235, more than one neutron is released, and that these in turn trigger more fissions. If we have a small amount of uranium-235, the size of a ping pong ball, many of the neutrons will escape without striking a nucleus. As the size of the mass of uranium increases, however, the chance that neutrons will escape becomes less. Finally, at some point, known as the **critical mass,** the number of effective (i.e., captured) neutrons per fission is more than one and a chain reaction takes place which liberates literally billions of neutrons almost instantly. While the actual size of a critical mass of uranium-235 is not commonly known, the minimum size is estimated to be approximately that of a baseball. The mechanism in the bomb provides that two or more pieces of uranium-235 be arranged in such a manner that they can be suddenly forced together. At this instant the explosion occurs. The energy released from each reacting atom in such a device is nearly ten million times the energy released for each atom in chemical explosions.

Following the end of World War II, the United States began an extensive program of testing atomic bombs. Many of these tests occurred on or near remote Pacific islands, and later on the Nevada desert north of Las Vegas. In the Pacific, bombs were exploded underwater in the midst of a naval fleet of obsolete warships, to determine their effects on ships and the extent of radioactivity produced. In Nevada, numerous atomic devices were detonated underground, at ground level, and in the air to determine the resultant radiation and concussion intensities at different distances from the detonation point. The U.S.S.R. carried out similar experiments. Throughout the world, monitoring stations measured considerable increase in atmospheric radioactivity after these explosions. It was feared by some that continued release of such materials would increase the concentration of radioactive species enough to endanger life on earth. Consequently, the explosions of nuclear devices have been greatly curtailed by the United States and Russia. At the present time, the majority of such explosions are detonated underground where the radioactive debris does not reach the atmosphere.

The diplomatic situation has been complicated recently by the nuclear achievements of China and France. These nations have shown little or no inclination to agree to controlling radioactive pollution of the atmosphere.

20-9 NUCLEAR FUSION

In Section 20–6, we noted that for some years prior to 1939 it was believed that the energy of the sun resulted from the fusion of hydrogen atoms into helium atoms. It was also be-lieved that such reactions could take place only at the extremely high temperatures existing on the sun. Since no known method of producing such temperatures on earth existed, it was felt that the control of such forces was not available to man. The development of the atomic bomb, however, created the means of providing temperatures comparable to those of the sun, and for the first time it seemed possible that fusion reactions could be produced on earth.

By including a quantity of deuterium or tritium,* or a mixture of the two, with the fis-sionable material in an atomic bomb, the first hydrogen or *thermonuclear* bomb was produced and exploded in 1952. The advantage of the thermonuclear bomb lies in the fact that the power of the bomb can be increased many times without an increase in the radioactive fallout. The greater power of the fusion bomb results from the higher percentage of material which is converted from matter to energy in the fusion reaction.

20-10 NUCLEAR POWER FOR PEACEFUL PURPOSES

Fissionable materials are increasingly being used in the production of electrical power. Uranium (or some other fissionable material) is utilized in reactors, Fig. 20–6. The fission takes place in uranium metal (or other fissionable substance) which is often present in the shape of rods. The neutrons from fissions which occur in one rod trigger other disintegrations both in that rod and in other rods of the reactor. Low-speed neutrons have proved to be more effective than high-speed neutrons in causing fission. Graphite is one of the substances that tends to decrease the speed of neutrons flowing through it. Consequently, graphite, or a similar neutron-slowing substance, is incorporated in nuclear reactors.

Several other devices are used to control the rate of nuclear fission in a reactor. One of the major dangers of a reactor is that it may become too efficient, or that an uncontrolled chain reaction may be initiated which will produce an explosion. To guard against this, cadmium metal, or some similar material which is a good absorber of neutrons, is also incorporated into a nuclear reactor. The cadmium is present in the form of rods that can

---

* Deuterium occurs in ordinary water, and can be readily isolated (Section 9–4). Tritium is made syn-thetically by bombarding lithium-6 with a neutron: ${}^6_3Li + {}^1_0n \rightarrow {}^3_1H + {}^4_2He$.

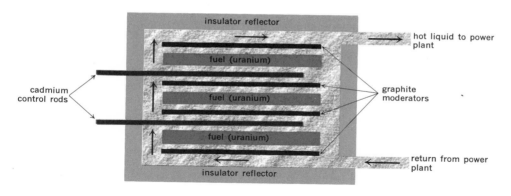

FIG. 20–6. Schematic diagram of the cross section of a nuclear reactor.

be inserted into or withdrawn from the reactor. When inserted, these rods absorb neutrons and thus decrease the rate of nuclear reactions, and when withdrawn they allow the reaction to proceed. The cadmium rods act as a control mechanism.

The energy from the nuclear reactor is converted into heat and absorbed by a fluid of some sort which flows through a heat exchanger and converts water into steam. The steam is then used to generate electricity; it could be used for other types of power. Since the amount of heat generated by a reactor is an indication of the rate of fission in the reactor, automatic control devices have been developed to insert the cadmium rods further into the reactor when the temperature of the reactor rises and withdraw them at lower temperatures. Devices such as this and various kinds of shielding make nuclear reactors safe sources of power.

The United States, having good supplies of inexpensive fossil fuels (coal and petroleum), has been slow in commercializing large-scale nuclear reactors. However, there has been much research, and many types of nuclear reactors have been developed in the United States and in many other countries. The countries, such as Great Britain, which do not have low-priced fossil fuels have moved faster than the United States. Numerous large nuclear plants are presently under construction in the United States, however, or are being planned by large power companies. Present forecasts indicate the production of electricity from nuclear power in this country will increase by a factor of eight in the ten-year period beginning in 1970. Dr. Glen Seaborg, head of the Atomic Energy Commission, predicts that nuclear power will produce 50% of the electrical power in the United States by the year 2000. It will also be used for many other purposes such as the desalting of sea water and powering large ships. Several ships—including the world's largest aircraft carrier, the Enterprise—are already nuclear-powered.

In spite of the fact that the ocean contains so much deuterium, which can serve as the fuel for *fusion* reactors, methods have not been developed for the utilization of nuclear fusion for power. Temperatures in the millions of degrees which are necessary for such processes are difficult to generate and control. One of the important advantages of fusion power is that the amounts of radioactive "ashes" produced are very small compared to the residue from fission reactors. Some of the best minds in our country are working on the fusion problem, and it is believed that a practical solution will be found.

While it seems likely that nuclear power will be used primarily for large installations rather than for automobiles and airplanes, miniature nuclear devices are currently being used in navigational satellites and weather stations. Enrico Fermi, who contributed so much to the development of nuclear physics, said, "I believe that the conquest of atomic energy may be readily used to produce not destruction, but an age of plenty for the human race."

20–11 RADIOACTIVE ISOTOPES

The presence of radioactive material can easily be detected by a Geiger counter, a device which may, according to the degree of sophistication, crackle, flash a light, or actually record the impulse of escaping rays. During the "big hunt" for uranium at the close of World War II, thousands of Geiger counters were bought by people to use on mountain vacations, as well as by professional prospectors hoping to strike it rich. Geiger counters have also become necessary in industrial and medical research laboratories. With the hundreds of radioactive isotopes now available, technicians and doctors have many ways of using the new techniques in the diagnosis and treatment of disease. Just as a car with its horn honking can readily be located and followed as it winds its way through city traffic, a radioactive isotope, which is continuously broadcasting its disintegration signals, can readily be located or followed in the body with the aid of a Geiger counter.

Sodium-24 is a radioactive isotope with a half-life of 14.8 h. If radioactive ions are included in an isotonic salt solution and injected into the bloodstream, they can be used to detect faulty circulation. For example, if a Geiger counter gives a higher count from one foot than from the other, we know there is poor circulation in the one with the low count.

Iodine-131, an isotope which has a half-life of eight days, is used in checking the efficiency of thyroid glands. When the gland is functioning properly, it quickly removes iodine from the bloodstream. When a malfunctioning thyroid is suspected, the patient is given a drink of water containing a known amount of iodine-131. Since the normal rate at which the thyroid absorbs iodine is known, a Geiger counter placed on the thyroid will indicate whether the thyroid is functioning properly. In cases of cancer of the thyroid glands, iodine-131 is added to the diet so that the patient will receive continuous radiation treatment. Pure iodine-131 goes almost exclusively to the thyroid gland and destroys the cancerous (along with some normal) tissue. The short half-life of the isotope makes it possible to control radiation dosages. Within a month, less than 10% of the original activity remains.

In recent years, cobalt-60 has been used extensively in the treatment of other forms of cancer. It is an inexpensive isotope, and only very small quantities are required for adequate radiation therapy.

Industrially, radioactive isotopes are used widely. Petroleum pipeline companies use plugs containing radioactive material to separate different grades of crude oil in their lines. As the plug moves through the line, Geiger counters monitor its progress. In the steel industry, the thickness of steel plates, which are being rolled, is controlled by a counter recording the rate at which the radiations pass through the plate; thin plates permit more radiation to pass than do thicker plates.

20–12 RADIOCARBON DATING

There are three isotopes of carbon: C-12, C-13, and C-14. Carbon-14 is a radioactive isotope produced in the higher atmosphere when neutrons from cosmic rays strike nitrogen-14:

$$^{14}_{7}N + {}^{1}_{0}n \rightarrow {}^{14}_{6}C + {}^{1}_{1}H$$

(20-12)

It has a half-life of approximately 5600 years, decaying to form nitrogen-14 and an electron:

$$^{14}_{6}C \rightarrow {}^{14}_{7}N + {}^{0}_{-1}e$$

(20-13)

Carbon dioxide molecules in the atmosphere exist in three isotopic forms in the ratio:

carbon-12: 99%,   carbon-13: 1%,   carbon-14: trace.

Carbon compounds in living tissues retain the same ratio of the three types of carbon atoms.

Dr. Willard Libby, formerly with the Atomic Energy Commission and now with the University of California, conceived the idea that the ages of carbon-containing substances, such as wood, could be determined by their degree of radioactivity. Carbon in recently grown plants undergoes approximately 16 disintegrations per gram per minute. One gram of carbon from wood grown 5600 years ago (one half-life of C-14) would be expected to show only half as many disintegrations. Thus a determination of the radioactivity of the carbon in any organic substance can help in establishing the date the substance was synthesized. Figure 20–7 shows the correlation between ages indicated by carbon dating and ages established by other methods. Redwood trees serve well as a check for our theory. Even though the tree is alive, there is no exchange of carbon from the atmosphere into the wood within the tree, so we may count the annual rings and check the result with the age

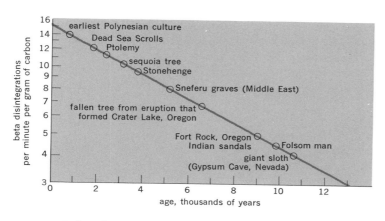

FIG. 20–7. Radiocarbon dating. The beta-disintegration rate, noted at the left, fixes the approximate age of the carbon-containing specimens examined. [Adapted from Mahan, Bruce H., *College Chemistry*, Addison Wesley, 1966.]

established by the carbon-dating method. The older the specimen, the less radioactivity is present, and dating becomes less accurate. Fairly accurate datings going back more than 10,000 years have been made on wood and charcoal.

20-13 MAN-MADE ELEMENTS

By the beginning of 1937, all but four of the first 92 elements had been discovered. On the periodic tables of that time, numbers 43, 61, 85 and 87 were blank spaces. Now all these appear in the table, plus eleven transuranium elements that have been prepared by synthesis in cyclotrons or linear accelerators. Some typical reactions for these preparations are:

$$\underset{42}{^{98}}Mo \quad + \quad \underset{1}{^{2}}H \quad \rightarrow \quad \underset{43}{^{99}}Tc \quad + \quad \underset{0}{^{1}}n \tag{20-14}$$

molybdenum + deuterium ion → technetium + a neutron

The name *technetium* is derived from the Greek word meaning artificial; it was the first artificially produced element. In 1940, neptunium and plutonium were prepared by neutron bombardment of the stable uranium-238 isotope, producing the unstable uranium-239 with a half-life of 23.5 minutes:

$$\underset{92}{^{238}}U + \underset{0}{^{1}}n \rightarrow \underset{92}{^{239}}U + \gamma \tag{20-15}$$

Uranium-239 forms neptunium-239, which decomposes to form plutonium-239:

$$\underset{92}{^{239}}U \quad \xrightarrow[\substack{\text{half-life} \\ \text{23.5 m}}]{\beta} \quad \underset{93}{^{239}}Np \quad \xrightarrow[\substack{\text{half-life} \\ \text{2.35 d}}]{\beta} \quad \underset{94}{^{239}}Pu \quad \substack{\text{half-life} \\ \text{26,360 y}}$$

uranium   neptunium   plutonium

It was soon determined that plutonium-239 has fissionable characteristics similar to those of uranium-235. Plutonium-239 was produced in such quantities that it was used in the second atomic bomb exploded over Japan in 1945. Since World War II, plutonium has been used extensively in the production of electrical power. It has been produced in larger amounts than have any of the other artificially produced elements. Dr. Seaborg believes there is a reasonable possibility that several more elements may be prepared artificially.

20-14 THE DANGERS OF RADIATION

Much has been said and written about the dangers of using radioactive isotopes and of fallout from nuclear testing. The problem is complex, and there are no simple answers to questions about these dangers. Unfortunately, much of what has been said has been influenced by emotion and by the attitude that either scare tactics or, on the other hand, false complacency is justified because the ends sought are good. The following discussion attempts to present the significant facts that must be considered in making an intelligent evaluation.

We are exposed to many kinds of radiation during our entire lifetime. The radiations of heat and visible light, for example, are usually not especially damaging. Ultraviolet radiation, however, can cause not only sunburn, but in some cases, skin cancer. When a person speaks of radiation damage he generally means damage from high-energy radiation. Alpha, beta, and gamma rays, along with X-rays, may have high energy and great penetrating power which would make them dangerous. X-rays and gamma radiation are particularly potent and likely to produce damage. Ordinarily, alpha and beta radiations have relatively low energies and are absorbed by the skin or clothing; however, the radiation may be dangerous if materials emitting such rays are eaten or inhaled, and thereby incorporated into the human body.

Any high-energy radiation can provide sufficient energy to break a chemical bond. Most of these breakages are harmful. While it may be possible to repair a watch by hitting it with a hammer, it is much more likely that its value as a watch will be permanently destroyed. If the chemical bond is broken in a vital molecule in a vital cell, the consequences may be serious. Cancer can be produced by high energy irradiation, although the usual effects of exposure to X-rays or gamma radiation is destruction of parts of the tissues followed by healing and regeneration of tissue.

We cannot avoid exposure to radiation. It reaches us continually from radioactive isotopes in the air we breathe (C-14), from the rocks of the earth's crust (K-40), or from the cosmic rays (ions such as H^+ and He^{++} traveling at high speeds) of outer space which penetrate the earth's atmosphere. We are also occasionally exposed to X-rays during medical examinations for tuberculosis, broken bones, or dental decay; in these cases, we decide that the benefits outweigh the probable disadvantages.

Although radioactive fallout to date has increased the exposure of the general population by less than 1%, there are instances of concentration of fallout where exposures have been much greater, and the consequences serious. The fact that one of the isotopes produced by nuclear fallout, strontium-90, is found in milk and becomes concentrated in the bones of growing children leads to concern.

The effects of high-energy radiation are random. We cannot predict what any given ray will do. It can produce changes that lead to cancer or abnormal sperm or egg cells, or it may pass completely through the body with no effect. The question is one of probability. Each time we drive a car we face a certain probability of being involved in a fatal accident. Most of us believe the odds are such that we will take a chance. It is probable that the normal background radiation plus that from occasional X-rays and from the fallout up to the present time is not likely to produce serious damage. More research and study is needed, however, to establish the various probabilities involved in exposure to radiation.

On the other hand, there is no reason for complacency regarding the dangers of radioisotopes and fallout. Any exposure involves a potential hazard. Research experiments by high school students are probably not worth the potential dangers if the work involves radioisotopes. Similar experiments by a trained researcher using proper shielding and other safeguards may be worth the risk. The advantages in treating tumors of the thyroid gland with radioactive iodine or in X-ray therapy for malignancies must be weighed against the possible dangers.

The values of atomic testing and dangers from fallout are much harder to assess. We cannot predict what the long-range genetic effects of radiation will be. There is one point, however, on which most scientists agree—a full-scale nuclear war would be disastrous, and would lead to the end of our civilization and perhaps of man himself.

IMPORTANT TERMS

Cloud chamber	Half-life	Mass-energy relationship	Nuclear reactor
Critical mass	Linear accelerator	Nuclear fission	Radioactive isotopes
Fog tracks	Mass defect	Nuclear fusion	Radioactivity

WORK EXERCISES

1. What discovery first caused doubt to be cast on Dalton's atomic theory?

2. Name the events which led up to Madame Curie's discovery of radium.

3. Describe the rays emitted by radium.

4. How does radioactive disintegration differ from ordinary chemical reactions?

5. What is meant by the term *half-life?*

6. Would the whole life of a radioactive element be twice the half-life? Why?

7. Distinguish between the terms *fission* and *fusion.*

8. What does one actually see when fog-tracks are formed in a cloud chamber?

9. Who was the first person to produce the long-dreamed-of transmutation of an element?

10. What is the chief difference between a cyclotron and a linear accelerator?

11. In your own words, what is *mass defect?*

12. What physical condition prevented until 1945 the possibility of a nuclear fusion on the earth?

13. How is the rate of nuclear reactions controlled in a nuclear reactor used for the production of electrical power?

14. Define the term *critical mass* as used in nuclear reactions.

15. What is the natural source of carbon-14, the isotope which makes carbon-dating possible?

16. If a sample of carbon from an ancient specimen produces 4 disintegrations/min/g, how old is the specimen? (See Section 20–12.)

17. Why are X-rays and gamma radiations more damaging than alpha and beta radiations?

18. Why is it impossible to find an environment free from radiation?

19. Why is strontium-90 a particularly dangerous isotope?

20. List a few radioactive isotopes, and explain how they may be used to advantage.

21. What is a major difficulty in harnessing a nuclear fusion reaction?

SUGGESTED READING

Badash, L., "How the 'Newer Alchemy' was Received," *Scientific American*, Aug. 1966, p. 89. An account of the announcement of the theory of radioactive decay.

Barker, P. A., *Atoms and the Cell*, Hawthorn Books, New York, 1966. A readable discussion of radioactivity from basic nuclear chemistry to the effects of radiation, radiation accidents, civil defense, and moral problems involved in the use of nuclear weapons.

Fowler, T. K., and R. F. Post, "Progress Toward Fusion Power," *Scientific American*, Dec. 1966, p. 84. Recent steps that have been taken toward solving the problems of containing a hot plasma.

Libby, W. F., "Radiocarbon Dating," University of Chicago Press, 2nd ed., Chicago, 1955. An interesting discussion of radiocarbon dating, with detailed descriptions, locations, and ages of hundreds of samples taken from throughout most of the world.

Panofsky, W., "The Linear Accelerator," *Scientific American*, Oct. 1954. A report on the smaller linear accelerators which were the forerunners of the present two-mile accelerator at Stanford University.

Seaborg, G. T., and A. R. Fritsch, "Synthetic Elements III," *Scientific American*, Apr. 1963, p. 68. This article brings the account of the preparation of synthetic elements up to date. References for the earlier articles are included.

Chapter 21 THE NATURE OF
ORGANIC COMPOUNDS

21–1 EARLY EXPERIMENTS

By 1800, chemistry had become firmly established as a science, so that during the next half-century there was keen interest in studying the composition of substances and the manner in which one might be changed to another. Because good methods of analysis had been developed, it was possible to determine the composition of a substance with considerable accuracy. The successful analyses stimulated two important results. First, they provided the facts which led to the concepts of atomic weights and of atoms as discrete units which combined with one another to form larger particles called molecules (Chapters 5 and 6). Second, chemists were encouraged to investigate the composition of almost any sort of material they discovered in nature.

As a result of these investigations, chemists began to distinguish two groups of substances. Those derived from plant or animal sources became known as **organic** compounds. All the others, which were obtained in one way or another from the mineral constituents of the earth, were called **inorganic** substances.

The concepts of atoms and molecules, mentioned above, were developed in terms of the inorganic compounds, which had relatively simple formulas. Formulas such as NaOH or $BaCl_2$, once assigned to particular compounds, seemed to represent their constitution very well. First of all, each inorganic compound had a unique formula; only one substance, for example, had formula $BaCl_2$. Second, the ratio of 1 barium to 2 chlorines in the compound was explained by the recently proposed concept of a valence or combining power for each atom. Finally, the Swedish chemist J. J. Berzelius proposed a logical explanation of why barium combined with a substance such as chlorine, rather than with sodium or magnesium. During this period of time, there was great interest in the newly-discovered electric currents and in their effect on compounds in water solutions. Chemists had discovered that metals collected at one electrode, and nonmetals at the other electrode. Therefore, Berzelius theorized, a barium atom, because it was positive, was attracted to the negative chlorine atoms to make up the substance $BaCl_2$.

The chemists of the early 1800's were acquainted with a very large number of organic compounds. Some had been known for centuries, some had only recently been isolated, but all were fascinating. Among them were dyes, soap, vinegar, sugar, perfumes, gums, and rubber, to mention but a few. For a variety of reasons chemists were led to believe that these were a distinctly different type of compound than the inorganic substances. Not only were they produced by plants or animals, but more impressive was the knowledge that there was a tremendous number of different organic compounds and that they were made up from very few elements. The elements found were carbon, hydrogen, oxygen, sometimes nitrogen, and occasionally phosphorus. How could one imagine that hundreds or perhaps thousands of different organic compounds could be assembled from only three or four elements? Among the inorganic compounds it was possible to find FeO and Fe_2O_3, Cu_2O and CuO. However, different combinations between oxygen and one particular metal were limited, and were explained by assuming that iron or copper had two different valences.

If one studied the formulas of even a small group of organic compounds, it seemed impossible to decide what the combining power of the atoms could be. For example, among compounds containing only carbon and hydrogen, the formulas C_2H_6, C_2H_4, C_3H_6, C_4H_{10}, and C_7H_8 were all discovered, and there were many more. Did this mean that the valence of carbon in the first is 3, in the next two is 2, and in the last two, 2 1/2 or 1 1/8? Furthermore, a compound such as C_2H_6 could be transformed to C_2Cl_6 by treatment with chlorine. If a negative chlorine could be substituted for a hydrogen, apparently Berzelius' theory of positive and negative atoms did not apply to organic compounds. Anyhow, almost none of the organic substances would conduct an electric current!

21–2 VITAL FORCE AND SYNTHETIC COMPOUNDS

Because of the profusion and complexity of organic compounds, many chemists despaired of ever understanding their nature. Furthermore, no organic compound had ever been made in a laboratory from simpler compounds or from the elements, although a number of inorganic compounds had been made synthetically. Consequently, many people believed that organic compounds were formed only under the influence of a "vital force" originating in living plants or animals.

In 1828, Friedrich Wöhler made a remarkable discovery at the University of Göttingen in Germany. He attempted to prepare ammonium cyanate by means of a double decomposition reaction in a solution of ammonium chloride and silver cyanate, both of which were regarded as inorganic substances. Instead of ammonium cyanate, Wöhler obtained crystals of urea!

$$NH_4Cl + AgCNO \underset{\searrow}{\overset{?\;\nearrow}{}} \begin{array}{l} NH_4CNO + AgCl \downarrow \\ \text{ammonium} \\ \text{cyanate} \\ \\ CH_4N_2O + AgCl \downarrow \\ \text{urea} \end{array} \qquad (21\text{–}1)$$

Previously, urea had been obtained only from the urine of animals. Now Wöhler had synthesized it without the presence of the "vital force." The synthesis was confirmed four years later when Wöhler and Justus Liebig succeeded in preparing ammonium cyanate by a different method. It proved to have properties entirely different from those of urea. However, when a solution of ammonium cyanate was boiled down to induce crystallization, the product isolated was always urea!

Within a few years, when acetic acid ($C_2H_4O_2$) and several other organic compounds were prepared by synthesis from inorganic materials, further doubt was cast on the need for a "vital force." As time passed, chemists also synthesized a number of *new* compounds; these were not merely copies of those produced by living plants or animals, but were compounds never before observed on earth. Because of their properties, however, the new compounds seemed clearly to belong in the same class as the organic compounds from natural sources. If it is not necessary for all organic compounds to be associated with living organisms or a "vital force," how then do we define "organic" compounds?

In the mid-1800's, it became apparent that the one factor common to all organic compounds was the element carbon. Therefore, we now say simply that **organic compounds** *are the compounds of carbon.* At the present time, more than one million organic compounds are known; that is, they have been isolated or synthesized, and their names, properties, and formulas have been described in some chemical journal.

21-3 ISOMERS

The formulas for urea and ammonium cyanate, shown in Eq. (21-1), reveal that both consist of the same amounts of identical elements, CH_4N_2O. Yet the properties of the two substances are different. So Wöhler's experiment had disspelled the need to believe in a "vital force," but had added a new complexity. Within a decade or two, many other groups of compounds related in this unusual way were discovered. It became clear that *compounds having different properties can have the same composition.* Such related compounds are called **isomers** (Gr. *iso*, equal plus *meros*, part). This possibility contributes to the great number of different organic compounds. To consider just a few examples, there are three different compounds having formula C_3H_8O, and three compounds having formula C_5H_{12}. Corresponding to the formula $C_4H_{10}O$ there are seven compounds, each differing distinctly from the others in many of its properties.

21-4 IMPORTANCE OF STRUCTURE

We shall not be able to describe the many efforts made between 1840 and 1860 to solve the puzzle concerning the constitution of organic compounds. Suffice it to say, however, that there was much experimentation by the most skilled chemists of the era, and that many theories were proposed which later had to be discarded when it was found that they were not in harmony with all the observed facts. It turned out that the key to the whole puzzle was the idea of *structure.* We shall describe the concept as we now understand it.

If covalent bonds exist between the atoms of a molecule, the atoms are held in some particular arrangement; that is, *the molecule has a structure.* In a water molecule, for example,

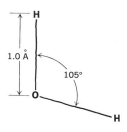

FIG. 21–1. Structure of the water molecule.

covalent bonds hold two hydrogen atoms in a specific way to an oxygen atom. Each hydrogen nucleus is 1.0 Ångstroms* from the oxygen nucleus, and the angle between the two bonds is 105°, as shown in Fig. 21–1. The water molecule has a definite structure.

◄ In contrast, an electrovalent compound such as barium chloride exists as ions in either a solution or a crystal. In a solution, we do not find two particular chloride ions held at definite distances and angles to one certain barium ion. All we know is that there are twice as many Cl⁻ ions as there are Ba²⁺ ions in the solution. It is true that a *crystal* of barium chloride has a structure in the sense that the ions are stacked together in a certain pattern, at regular distances from each other. But there is no *molecular* structure. In the crystal we cannot find distinct groups of atoms we could designate as $BaCl_2$ molecules. The two chloride ions are not definitely associated more with one certain barium ion than with another barium ion. ►

Carbon compounds (the organic compounds) *have structure because a carbon atom can form stable covalent bonds to other carbon atoms and to a number of different atoms.* For instance, a molecule having composition C_3H_8O can have the structure shown in Fig. 21–2(a). In that structure, the covalence of each carbon is 4, each oxygen is 2, and each hydrogen is 1.

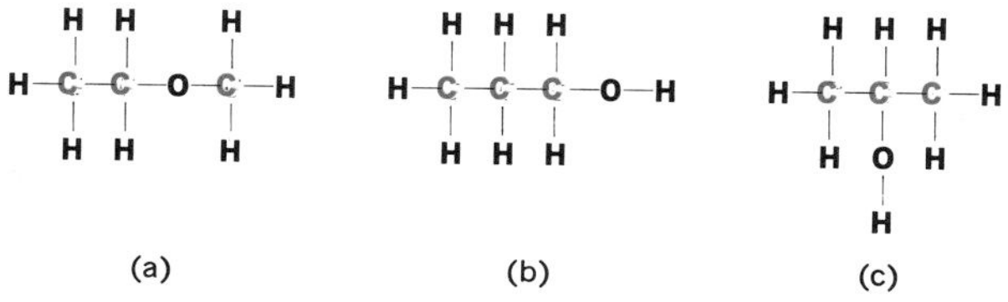

FIG. 21–2. Structures of the C_3H_8O isomers.

A formula such as C_3H_8O is a **molecular formula:** it states the number and kind of atoms in the molecule. A formula such as that in Fig. 21–2(a) is a **structural formula:** it shows which atom is bonded to which.

* One Ångstrom unit (Å) is 0.0000001 mm.

The fact that a carbon atom can form *covalent* bonds with other atoms leads us to an interesting discovery. It should be possible for three carbons, eight hydrogens, and one oxygen to be arranged into structures different from the one described in Fig. 21–2(a). The other two possibilities are shown in Figs. 21–2(b) and (c). These three different structures we have defined on paper explain the existence of three separate, real compounds having different properties.

The concept of structures based upon covalent bonds also explains why carbon can combine with other elements in so many different ratios, Section 21–1. In the molecular formulas C_2H_6 and C_4H_{10}, the ratios of the hydrogens to the carbons are different. However, when we examine possible structural formulas for these two substances, we see that all carbon atoms can have a valence of 4 in both compounds.

$$
\begin{array}{ccc}
\text{H} \quad \text{H} & & \text{H} \quad \text{H} \quad \text{H} \quad \text{H} \\
| \quad | & & | \quad | \quad | \quad | \\
\text{H}-\text{C}-\text{C}-\text{H} & & \text{H}-\text{C}-\text{C}-\text{C}-\text{C}-\text{H} \\
| \quad | & & | \quad | \quad | \quad | \\
\text{H} \quad \text{H} & & \text{H} \quad \text{H} \quad \text{H} \quad \text{H} \\
C_2H_6 & & C_4H_{10}
\end{array}
$$

Quite a few elements can form covalent bonds. However, *carbon is unique in its ability to form long chains built up of carbon atoms bonded to one another.* An example is shown in Fig. 21–3(a). The chains may be of varying lengths or they may be branched, as in Fig. 21–3(b). Furthermore, a chain of carbon atoms can twist in such a way that carbons at the ends of the chain come close to each other and can link to form a ring. Fig. 21–3(c) is an example of a ring structure. For simplicity, the atoms occupying the other valences of the carbons in Fig. 21–3 are not shown. The simplified diagrams therefore represent the skeletons of the molecules.

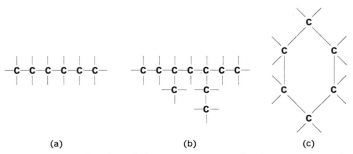

(a)   (b)   (c)

FIG. 21–3. Typical carbon skeletons in organic molecules: (a) a chain of carbon atoms; (b) a branched chain; (c) a ring.

Every organic molecule consists of some kind of carbon skeleton, to which are attached other atoms. Nearly always a large portion of the skeleton is filled out with hydrogen atoms. *The elements most often found in organic compounds, in addition to carbon and hydrogen, are nitrogen, oxygen, sulfur, and the halogens.*

21-5 ASSIGNMENT OF STRUCTURE

In the previous section, we discovered that structural formulas can correctly account for the number of different compounds that actually exist. But how do we decide which structure, of several possible, represents a real substance that we have in a bottle? We do it by observing enough different properties of the substance so that we can logically say that the facts fit one, and only one, structure. In this way we can relate, or *assign*, a structure to a real substance.

For illustration, let us use a simple case in which there are only two possible compounds having the same molecular formula. The first one we obtain from fermented fruit juice. It is a clear, colorless liquid which we will call alcohol. (We could just as well have called it something else. All that matters is that we all agree upon a name, so that each of us knows what the other is referring to. We can at least identify the substance to the extent of naming it, even though we don't know its structure.) By experimenting a little, we discover that alcohol vaporizes easily, has a distinctive odor, has a stinging taste, affects our nervous systems in a peculiar way, is very soluble in water, and burns with a hot, almost invisible flame. None of these facts tells us what the structure is, however. By observing the combustion of alcohol more carefully, we can discover that the products are carbon dioxide and water. Now suppose we burn a *weighed* amount of alcohol and then catch and weigh, separately, all the CO_2 and H_2O produced. By the appropriate calculations we can determine the amounts of carbon and hydrogen originally composing the alcohol. We find its molecular formula to be C_2H_6O.

The second compound is obtained by heating wood alcohol (a different sort of alcohol) with concentrated sulfuric acid. The reaction produces a colorless gas which we will call methyl ether. Besides being a gas rather than a liquid, this compound is decidedly different from alcohol in other ways. It is only slightly soluble in water, and its taste and odor are quite unlike those of alcohol. Methyl ether also burns readily. If we do a combustion quantitatively we find the molecular formula of methyl ether is C_2H_6O, the same as that of alcohol. In other words, the two compounds are isomers.

On paper we can write two, and only two, possible structures for formula C_2H_6O:

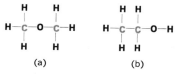

(a)   (b)

FIG. 21-4. Structures possible for C_2H_6O.

The possibility of two different structures agrees with the fact that we have isolated two real compounds, but does alcohol have structure (a) or structure (b)? Clearly, we need more information in order to make a decision. So we will treat both alcohol and methyl ether with a number of other substances; hopefully, any reactions which occur may give us some clues.

As far as we can tell, neither the liquid alcohol nor the gaseous methyl ether are changed by sodium hydroxide solution, so we try something else. Methyl ether is likewise unchanged (aside from dissolving to a certain extent) by being heated to about 90°C with concentrated hydrobromic acid solution. [The experiment is done in a sealed vessel so that the gaseous ether does not escape.] However, when alcohol is heated to 90°C with hydrobromic acid, the alcohol disappears completely, and we find a new product—an oily, colorless liquid with a sweetish, medicinal odor. Analysis shows that the new compound has formula C_2H_5Br. Now let us compare this formula with the original formula of the alcohol and attempt to write a partial equation for the reaction:

$$C_2H_6O + HBr \rightarrow C_2H_5Br \tag{21-2}$$
alcohol   oily product

From Eq. (21-2) it appears that one O and one H were lost from the alcohol formula and were replaced by a Br in the product. If we compare these changes with the possible structures shown in Fig. 21-4, we suspect that structure (b) may be the correct one for alcohol. The O and H which were lost *may* have been the whole OH group of structure (b), and the C_2H_5 which survived in the oily product may have been the residue of structure (b) made of the two carbons and their five hydrogens. In other words, the change *may* have involved something like this:

$$\tag{21-3}$$

Of course, we do not know, from this experiment, *how* or *why* the reaction occurred; Eq. (21-3) merely represents what we *think* is the total change. At any rate, if we *assume* structure (b) for alcohol, then Eqs. (21-2) and (21-3) seem to be a more logical interpretation of the actual experiment than anything we could write if we assumed structure (a).

However, this interpretation might be wrong. If we are to have faith in it, we must find some other supporting evidence. Sodium metal provides some revealing facts. Once again we find that methyl ether does not react, but alcohol does. When we drop a piece of sodium into liquid alcohol, there is a vigorous evolution of colorless gas. The gas is highly flammable, and thorough investigation proves that it is hydrogen. We can also isolate from the reaction mixture a white solid which is strongly basic. It has molecular formula C_2H_5ONa. Furthermore, even if we use an *excess* of sodium, the only products which result are hydrogen gas and the C_2H_5ONa compound. This must mean that *one* of the six hydrogens of alcohol is different from the other five. This makes it even more certain that the correct structure for alcohol must be Fig. 21-4(b) rather than (a).

In fact, this conclusion is especially appealing in view of the whole behavior of alcohol with sodium. It is surprisingly similar to the reaction of water with sodium. Both compounds evolve hydrogen gas and are converted to a basic product. In a water molecule, a hydrogen atom covalently bonded to the oxygen atom can be displaced by sodium, as shown in Eq. (21-4):

$$2HOH + 2Na \rightarrow NaOH + H_2 \tag{21-4}$$
(a base)

The fact that structure (b) [but not (a)] also has a hydrogen covalently bonded to an oxygen apparently explains why alcohol can react with sodium in an analogous way (see Eq. 21–5).

$$2\,HOC_2H_5 + 2Na \rightarrow 2NaOC_2H_5 + H_2 \qquad\qquad (21\text{–}5)$$

alcohol   (a base)
structure (b)

In view of all the facts observed for alcohol and methyl ether, the argument for assigning structure (b) to alcohol, and hence (a) to methyl ether, is quite convincing. We are therefore justified in using these structures to represent the compounds and to aid us in predicting their probable behavior in other situations. Of course, if the outcome of some future experiment can *not* be explained in terms of the assumed structures, the situation will have to be reevaluated. Either there must be faulty observation in the new experiment or the structures as we have been describing them are wrong.

In another case involving a more complex molecule, a greater number of experiments would have to be observed in order to accumulate sufficient facts to assign a structure. Nevertheless, the process of logically comparing the properties of the real compound with a likely structure would be the same as that described above for alcohol and methyl ether. In one way or another, every structural formula you see written in this book, or elsewhere, has been deduced from experimental investigation.

21–6 CARBON BOND ANGLES

Structural formulas of the type in Fig. 21–2 are adequate to show which atoms are bonded to each carbon atom, but do not necessarily represent exact details, such as bond angles, shown in Fig. 21–1 for the water molecule. It is important that we understand just how much our structural formulas can accurately represent, and how much we may imagine or read into these symbols when we see them.

Let us consider a compound having a composition CH_2Cl_2. Assuming a covalence of 1 for hydrogen and 1 for chlorine, the only possible arrangement is for these four atoms to be bonded to the carbon atom. Accordingly, we can write two conceivable structures, (a) and (b) of Fig. 21–5:

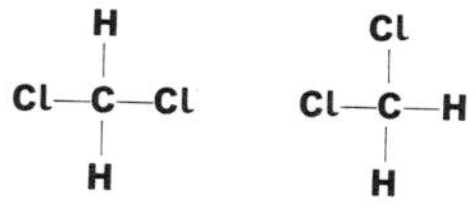

```
      H                   Cl
      |                   |
Cl—C—Cl            Cl—C—H
      |                   |
      H                   H
     (a)                 (b)
```

FIG. 21–5. Possible structural formulas for CH_2Cl_2.

A model is often useful to facilitate our thinking about a structure. One simple kind of model to represent the written structure of Fig. 21–5 consists of balls and pegs, as pictured in Fig. 21–6. The pegs represent the valence bonds (really electron pairs) holding the atoms together. The balls represent the nuclei of the atoms. (The balls, however, are much too large in proportion to the bond distance between them, and therefore too large in proportion

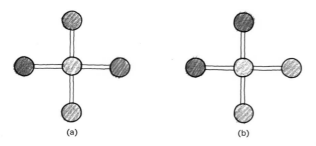

(a)   (b)

FIG. 21–6. Models of possible structures for CH_2Cl_2.

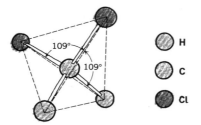

109°

109°

H

C

Cl

FIG. 21–7. Ball-and-peg model of CH_2Cl_2 showing the correct bond angles and therefore the correct arrangement in space of the bonded atoms.

to the size of the nuclei.) According to the models in Fig. 21–6, the angles between carbon bonds are 90°, and the CH_2Cl_2 molecules are flat; that is, the carbon atom and the four atoms attached to it are all in the same plane.

If the models are correct, there are two different structures, (a) and (b) of Fig. 21–6, having composition CH_2Cl_2. In (a) the chlorines (more accurately the chlorine nuclei) are farther apart than they are in (b). These models, however, do *not* agree with the experimental facts concerning CH_2Cl_2. No chemist, no matter how good his equipment or how carefully and skillfully he works, has ever been able to isolate more than one kind of material having composition CH_2Cl_2. Furthermore, although the structure of a molecule cannot be seen in a microscope, the same kind of information can be obtained by other modern experimental techniques, particularly X-ray diffraction studies. From such methods we find abundant evidence that the distance between the chlorine atoms is the same in all molecules of CH_2Cl_2, and that the bond angles are approximately 109° (rather than 90°). Clearly, we need to revise the models of CH_2Cl_2 proposed in Fig. 21–6.

In Fig. 21–7 is a model of CH_2Cl_2 having the correct bond angles. One striking feature of this model is the fact that the bonded atoms are spread out in space; the molecule is three-dimensional rather than planar. Another interesting aspect of this model is that regardless of which two valence bonds hold the chlorine atoms, the chlorines are always the same distance apart. The fundamental reason for all this is that the four atoms bonded to carbon spread out in space as far from each other as possible. Mathematically, it turns out that the angles between objects arranged in space in this fashion are 109° (more accurately, 109°28').

A carbon atom is often said to have **tetrahedral** bonding. This is merely a term from mathematics which describes a proper three-dimensional model of a carbon compound such as Fig. 21–7. If we imagine lines drawn between the four atoms bonded to the carbon atom, the resultant geometric figure is a tetrahedron (Gr. *tetrahedros*, four-sided).

◄ The use of the term tetrahedron, or tetrahedral, does not mean that we believe a carbon atom is a sharp chunk of material with triangular sides. The dotted lines forming the tetrahedron simply represent a mapping device, like the imaginary line around the earth called the equator.

We should also point out that in the molecule CH_4, in which the four atoms attached to carbon are identical, all the H—C—H bond angles will be exactly equivalent and will be 109°28'. In the molecule CH_2Cl_2 the chlorine atoms are surrounded by larger electron clouds and occupy more space than do the hydrogen atoms. Therefore, the two chlorines repel each other somewhat more than do the two hydrogens, causing the Cl—C—Cl bond angle to be slightly larger than 109°28' and the H—C—H bond angle to be slightly smaller. However, all the angles are *near* 109°, and the important three-dimensional arrangement of the CH_2Cl_2 molecule is correctly represented in Fig. 21–7. ►

Figure 21–8 shows the diagrams of a CH_2Cl_2 molecule which would result if the three-dimensional model were projected onto two-dimensional surfaces. These two diagrams are precisely the same as the structural formulas written in Fig. 21–5!

Both the professional chemist and the beginning student find it helpful to assemble models of organic compounds, so that their shapes can be visualized better. However, it is inconvenient (and for some of us perhaps nearly impossible!) to be artistic enough to draw a three-dimensional sketch of CH_2Cl_2, such as Fig. 21–7, each time we wish to represent this molecule in a chemical equation. Since we must write on a flat surface, we use for a structural formula either Fig. 21–5(a) or (b). When we write the structural formula in

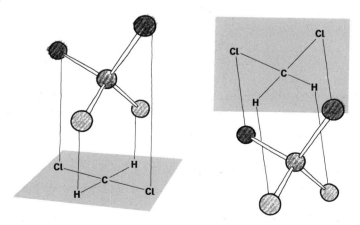

FIG. 21–8. Projections of a CH_2Cl_2 model onto flat surfaces.

this way we must imagine that the actual molecule is really three-dimensional and that the formula we have written is really a projection, Fig. 21-8. We are as justified in using formula 21-5(a) as 21-5(b). We must remind ourselves that, despite the appearance of these formulas, the carbon bond angles are *not* 90° and the molecules are *not* flat. That is, the formulas do *not* represent the models of Fig. 21-6.

21-7 MOLECULES: STRUCTURES, PROPERTIES, AND MODELS

We first introduced the concept of structure solely for the purpose of explaining the great number of existing organic compounds, Section 21-4. Then we assigned structures to individual compounds on the basis of their properties, Section 21-5. The relation between structure and properties will be our main concern throughout the remaining chapters on organic compounds. The reason is that *structure determines properties.*

For analogy, let us consider that we are going to rent or purchase a home. The structure of a house or an apartment determines whether it is most suitable for a retired colonel, a young, single girl, or a family with four teenagers. We inspect it, if possible to see whether the structure has the properties which will satisfy our needs. If the house cannot be seen, because it has not yet been built or is presently occupied, a model would help us visualize its properties. However, we would have to use a certain amount of imagination to understand how the real house would function. If a model were not available either, we could inspect a floor plan drawn by someone who had measured the house and observed its various properties. To look at the floor plan and visualize the properties of the real object would require an even better imagination than to look at a model.

So it is with an organic molecule, although we are limited by the fact that *no one* has ever seen the molecule itself. We can, however, observe its properties and measure it in several ways. From these observations, we can draw a structural formula (a floor plan), which symbolizes its structure and therefore suggests what its properties are. However, with the structural formula, it may not be easy to imagine certain properties, especially those depending on three-dimensional relations. Therefore, it is helpful to build a model of the molecule.

Most of us do not try to make all the observations necessary to deduce the structural formula of an organic molecule. Instead, we use the formula developed from the observations of many other chemists. In fact, even a chemist who is particularly interested in the challenging game of "structure proof" would be able to assign structures to no more than several molecules within his lifetime. For the structures of the thousands of other molecules he must use and think about, he relies on the work of others. It is highly important that we keep in mind the fact that all the models or structural formulas we use depend basically on experimental observations.

A structure that has been assigned may not correspond to the real molecule for several reasons. One of the measurements may have been in error. We may not have measured some important feature at all, because we were not aware of it. (We didn't notice the window at the rear of the house!) Or, in constructing the structural formula and model from all the data, we may have interpreted some observation incorrectly. We accept the fact that formulas and models may have limitations and could be based on downright errors, but we use them because they are so essential. We trust that sooner or later any errors will become apparent, so that we can rebuild the model in a more satisfactory way.

Now that we have a better understanding of the purpose and limitations of models, we can examine two useful types. The ball-and-peg variety was first mentioned in Section 21–6; another useful type is a space-filling model. Figure 21–9 shows a water molecule represented by the two types. The ball-and-peg model (Fig. 21–9a) is not much more than a skeleton. The locations of the nuclei are indicated by the balls, and the bonds holding them together are represented only by pegs.

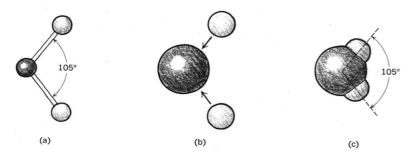

(a)   (b)   (c)

FIG. 21–9. Structure of the water molecule. (a) A ball-and-peg model. (b) Spheres representing the space occupied by electron clouds of oxygen and of hydrogen atoms. Sharing of the electron clouds results in the structure represented by (c), a space-filling model.

The space-filling model more accurately shows the *relative size* of the atoms in a molecule. Recall that the electrons swirl about the nucleus of an atom in a very large space compared to the tiny nucleus. Also, two atoms are held together by a covalent bond when they share electrons. This can be thought of as a merging or overlapping of the electron clouds of the two atoms. In Fig. 21–9(b), a sphere of proper size portrays the space occupied by the electron cloud around an oxygen nucleus. A smaller sphere shows the volume in which the hydrogen electron may be found. If we imagine these electron clouds merging into each other, in the process of bond-formation, the result would be shown by the model of Fig. 21–9(c). To make such a model, we can slice off sections of plastic spheres and cement the remaining portions together.

Figure 21–10 shows an alcohol molecule portrayed by models of both types. Although we can picture the shape of the molecule better from the space-filling model, the ball-and-peg model reveals the bond angles more clearly. Observe that all the carbon bond angles are 109° and, as far as we can judge without careful measurement, the oxygen bond angle is about the same. Actually, the oxygen bond angle is near 105°, as it is in water.

We can make a projection of the ball-and-peg model, a three-dimensional object, onto a flat surface. This is what an architect or engineer does when he draws a plan of an object. In Fig. 21–10 we make a projection of the alcohol molecules by imagining that we are stand-

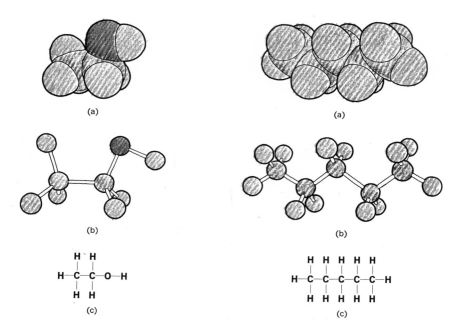

FIG. 21-10. The alcohol molecule, C_2H_6O: (a) space-filling model; (b) ball-and-peg model; (c) projection, a structural formula.

FIG. 21-11. The n-pentane molecule, C_5H_{12}: (a) space-filling model; (b) ball-and-peg model; (c) projection, a structural formula.

ing above (b). By looking straight down upon (b), we would see it flattened out as in diagram (c). The resultant projection gives us a structural formula we can write on paper, that is, in two dimensions. Note that this projection of the alcohol molecule, Fig. 21-10(c), is essentially the structural formula we had previously decided was satisfactory, Fig. 21-4(b). Hereafter, whenever we use a structural formula, we must keep well in mind that it represents an object actually having three dimensions.

In a similar fashion, the structure of a compound called n-pentane can be represented by the models shown in Fig. 21-11.

21-8 ROTATION ON CARBON BONDS

One other important aspect of structure in an organic compound is that a group in the molecule (some portion of it) can rotate relative to the rest of the molecule. That is, the group can turn, on an imaginary axis through the covalent bond, without weakening the carbon–carbon bond. In a ball-and-peg model this is equivalent to twisting one carbon atom, by allowing the peg to slip in its socket, so that the carbon turns in space relative to the carbon at the other end of the peg. They do not become separated (i.e., the bond does not break) because the peg does not leave the socket.

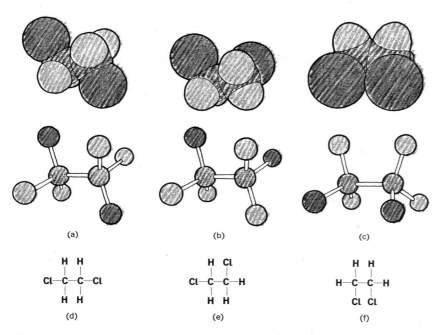

(a)   (b)   (c)

$$\begin{matrix} H & H \\ | & | \\ Cl-C- & C-Cl \\ | & | \\ H & H \end{matrix}$$

$$\begin{matrix} H & Cl \\ | & | \\ Cl-C- & C-H \\ | & | \\ H & H \end{matrix}$$

$$\begin{matrix} H & H \\ | & | \\ H-C- & C-H \\ | & | \\ Cl & Cl \end{matrix}$$

(d)   (e)   (f)

FIG. 21–12. Rotational forms of 1,2-dichloroethane. Three stages of rotation are shown in (a), (b), and (c), each represented by two types of models. Projection of these three forms yields the structural formulas (d), (e), and (f).

Bond rotation is illustrated in Fig. 21–12 for the molecule called 1,2-dichloroethane.*
The molecule could be as shown in Fig. 21–12(a). A moment later it could exist as shown in (b), after one carbon (and the three other atoms it holds) has rotated relative to the second carbon. By further rotation, the molecule could exist as in condition (c). There is abundant evidence to prove that these rotations occur in a molecule very frequently. The rotation is so easy that it happens, to some degree, every time one molecule collides with another. Therefore, we cannot isolate three different kinds of molecules, (a), (b), and (c), and call them three different compounds. At any given moment a sample of 1,2-dichloroethane contains all these forms (plus many other intermediate states of rotation) and one form is rapidly and easily changing to another. However, what *is* consistent about all molecules in the sample of 1,2-dichloroethane is the *structure*, the manner in which the atoms are bonded. At all times every molecule has one chlorine bonded to the number one carbon and another chlorine bonded to the number two carbon. (On the other hand, if we had a substance in which both chlorines were bonded to the number one carbon, this *would* be a different structure and hence a different compound with a different name, 1,1-dichloroethane. The

---

* *Dichloro* in the name indicates there are two chlorine atoms in the molecule and 1,2- means that if we call one of the carbon atoms in the molecule 1 and the other, 2, each one holds one of the chlorine atoms.

1,2-dichloroethane could not be changed to 1,1-dichloroethane by mere rotation of groups on the carbon–carbon bond.)

The whole point of this discussion is summarized in structural formulas (d), (e), and (f) of Fig. 21–12. These formulas would result if we just projected downward the models in (a), (b), and (c), respectively. *Therefore, we can use (d), (e), or (f): each represents 1,2-dichloroethane; one is as correct as the other.* This is *because all are molecules of the same compound.* The structural formulas (d), (e), and (f) only appear to be different at first glance. When we remember that they correspond to the three-dimensional models (a), (b), and (c), and that rotation is possible, we can understand that they all represent the same type of molecule.

◄ It is interesting to note that although various rotational forms are possible, they are not equally favorable. Form (c), Fig. 21–12, is least likely to exist because the bulky chlorine atoms are crowded when they are so close to one another. As a result, if the molecule gets flipped into form (c), it does not remain that way long. It will very soon rotate into a less crowded form. Correspondingly, form (a) is the most favorable, and (b) is intermediate. ►

21-9 WRITING STRUCTURAL FORMULAS

A structural formula written in the manner used in the previous sections may also be called a **valence bond structure,** because all the bonds in the molecule are shown. Once we have had a little experience with the valence bond structure and understand its relation to a model or to the real molecule, we will often find it convenient to write a more abbreviated structural formula. In general, most of the carbon valences in an organic molecule are occupied by hydrogen atoms. Since the hydrogens are so common and are also quite unreactive (as we will see in Section 22–4), a structural formula is often written in the style of Fig. 21–13(b). This is a **condensed structural formula.** In this form, all hydrogens bonded to a particular carbon are written beside the carbon, but their bonds are not shown; bonds to other atoms are shown, however.

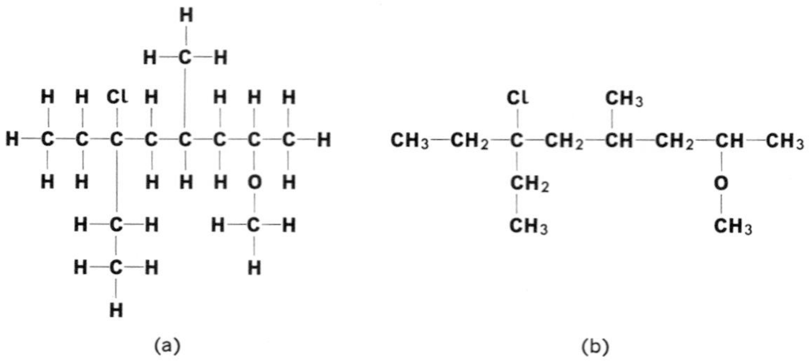

FIG. 21–13. Two types of structural formulas: (a) valence bond structure; (b) condensed structural formula.

The condensed structural formula can be written more rapidly and in less space than the valence bond structure. Also, the form of the carbon skeleton and the location of important groups (those other than hydrogens) can be more easily visualized from the condensed structural formula. This is readily apparent if we compare the valence bond structure of the organic compound (a) with its equivalent condensed formula (b) in Fig. 21–13.

Now let us consider some compounds having the molecular formula C_5H_{12}. It turns out that more than one isomer of this composition is possible. That is, if we had five carbon atoms and twelve hydrogen atoms, each with its normal valence, we could put them together into more than one structure. Although we cannot handle individual atoms in this fashion, we can find the answers by using ball-and-peg models or by describing the results on paper, using H— to represent each hydrogen with its covalent bond, and

$$-\overset{|}{\underset{|}{C}}-$$

for each carbon and its bonds.

Figure 21–14 shows a valence bond structure and a condensed structural formula for one isomer of C_5H_{12}; the corresponding models of the same molecule are pictured in Fig. 21–11. Another structural arrangement for five carbons and twelve hydrogens is represented by Fig. 21–15; this isomer is said to have a **branched** chain carbon skeleton. In contrast, the compound in Fig. 21–14 has an **unbranched** structure, often called a **straight** chain. If we inspect a model of the latter compound, Fig. 21–11, we see that the chain is not really straight in the geometric sense, but is a zigzag. Therefore the term *straight* is used in a special way for describing organic compounds; it really means *not branched*.

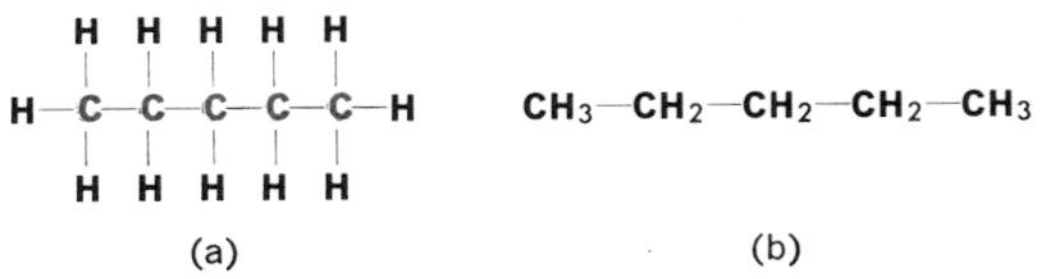

FIG. 21–14. An isomer of C_5H_{12} having a straight chain (an unbranched carbon skeleton): (a) valence bond structure; (b) condensed structural formula.

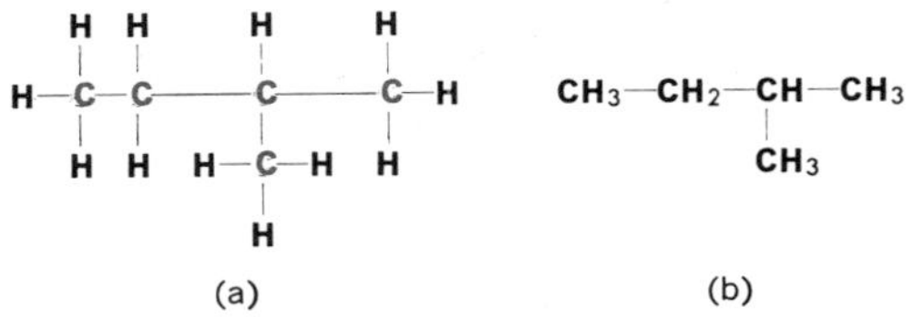

FIG. 21–15. An isomer of C_5H_{12} having a branched chain: (a) valence bond structure; (b) condensed structural formula.

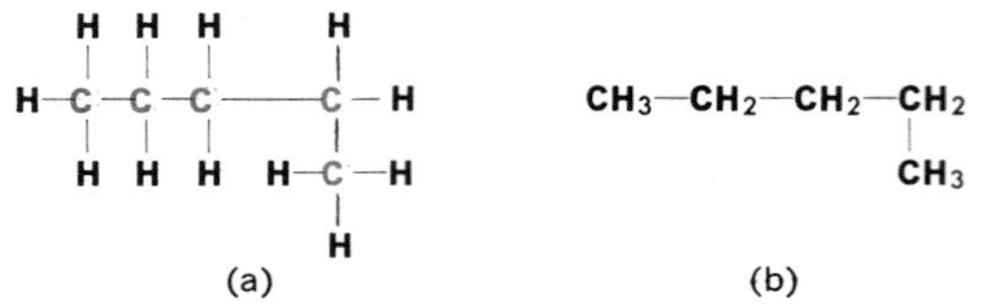

FIG. 21-16. A C_5H_{12} molecule having the same structure as that of Fig. 21-14, but in a different rotational form: (a) valence bond structure; (b) condensed structural formula.

One arrangement for C_5H_{12} that we might think of is diagrammed in Fig. 21-16. At first glance this seems to be different from the structures in either Fig. 21-14 or Fig. 21-15. It is indeed a different structure from that of Fig. 21-15. However, the molecule in Fig. 21-16 has the same structure as the one in Fig. 21-14. Every carbon atom in Fig. 21-16 is bonded to the same other atom as it is in Fig. 21-14. The two molecules are just different rotational forms of the same fundamental structure. (The situation is entirely analogous to the various rotational forms of 1,2-dichloroethane, described in Section 21-8). When the C_5H_{12} molecule of Fig. 21-14 collides with another object, rotation may occur at one of the bonds. The second carbon of the chain may rotate relative to the third carbon, carrying the —CH_3 group into the downward location. The molecule would then have the arrangement of Fig. 21-16. To convince yourself that this change is possible merely by rotation on one of the carbon-carbon bonds, test the theory with a ball-and-peg model and think about the relation between models and structural formulas.

The relationships between some possible isomers of C_5H_{12}, just described, can be summarized as follows: Molecules having the same molecular formula are isomers (different compounds) if their atoms are bonded differently, Figs. 21-14 and 21-15. On the other hand, if two molecules have only temporary differences in shape, due to rotation of groups on bonds, they are the same compounds, Figs. 21-14 and 21-16.

The existence of isomers creates a problem in naming the different compounds. Clearly, we need a distinctive name for each of the isomers of C_5H_{12}. This problem of nomenclature is discussed in Sections 22-2 and 22-3.

21-10 RING COMPOUNDS: STRUCTURES AND FORMULAS

We learned in Section 21-4 that two carbon atoms within the same chain could bond together, thus closing a ring. Such ring structures are of frequent occurrence in both natural and man-made compounds. Therefore, we should see how it is possible for ring compounds to exist if, as we have assumed (Section 21-6), the bonds around each carbon atom have a tetrahedral arrangement.

We will first examine the compound consisting of five carbon atoms in a ring, with ten hydrogen atoms to occupy the other carbon valences. A ball-and-peg model of the compound is shown in Fig. 21-17(a). In this arrangement all five carbons can be in one plane. If we look at the model from above, we see that the carbon skeleton forms a regular pentagon, represented in Fig. 21-17(c). Mathematically, we can calculate that the angles within a regular pentagon are each 108°. This is very close to the value of 109° for a tetrahedral

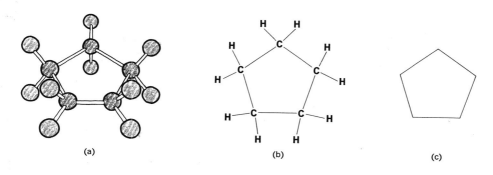

FIG. 21–17. The ring compound C_5H_{10}: (a) ball-and-peg model, (b) valence bond structure, (c) abbreviated structural formula, showing outline of carbon skeleton.

bond angle. Therefore the carbon atoms can adapt themselves quite readily to a five-membered ring. Furthermore, if we look again at the ball-and-peg model we see that the H—C—H bond angles around the edge of the ring can each be 109°. These possibilities apparently explain the fact that five-membered rings are quite stable and are easily and frequently formed.

Since it is not always convenient to make an accurate model or drawing of the compound C_5H_{10}, we can use the valence bond formula, Fig. 21–17(b). As usual, the written valence bond formula does not adequately portray the true three-dimensional nature of the real molecule. In this case, it does not show that the hydrogen atoms are either above or below the plane formed by the carbon atoms. However, it is easy to draw and is satisfactory once we clearly understand what it represents.

Sometimes it is convenient to use the pentagon of Fig. 21–17(c) as an abbreviated formula to represent the compound. When we do, we must imagine that there is one carbon at each corner of the pentagon and that each carbon is holding two hydrogens. In other words, in Fig. 21–17, (c) is an abbreviated version of (b).

Figures 21–18 and 21–19 imply that the bond angles of three- and four-membered rings must be distinctly different from those of a five-membered ring. Since a four-membered

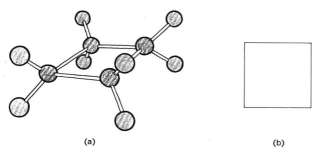

FIG. 21–18. The ring compound C_4H_8: (a) ball-and-peg model, (b) abbreviated structural formula.

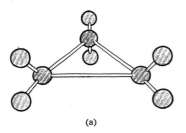
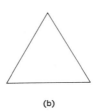

FIG. 21–19. The ring compound C_3H_6: (a) ball-and-peg model, (b) abbreviated structural formula.

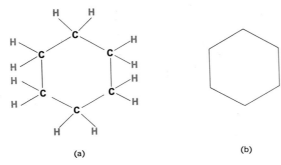

FIG. 21–20. The ring compound C_6H_{12}: (a) valence bond structure, (b) abbreviated structural formula.

ring produces a square, the carbon–carbon bond angles must be distorted away from their ideal value of 109°, down to 90°. In the case of the regular triangle formed by a three-membered ring, the carbon–carbon bond angles must be distorted way down to 60°! Experimentally, we find that although such structures can exist, the bond distortion causes strains in the molecules, making them less stable. A three-membered ring is sufficiently unstable to cause its chemical reactions to be modified. The strain can cause the ring to break open and react in a way that is not possible in the case of a five-membered ring.

For the ring compound C_6H_{12} we can write the formulas shown in Fig. 21–20. Although we will frequently use these formulas, we find once again that they do not reveal the correct shape of the molecule very well. If it is really a regular hexagon with all the carbon atoms lying in one plane, the carbon–carbon bond angles within the ring would have to be 120°. This is far enough from 109° so that we might expect this compound to be strained also.

Actually, the six-membered ring does not have to be planar (that is, with all the carbon atoms in the same plane); it can instead be puckered, as shown by the ball-and-peg model in Fig. 21–21(a). The rotations permitted by the carbon–carbon bonds allow the carbon skeleton to assume a zigzag shape (compare with Fig. 21–11). Consequently all the carbon bond angles can remain at their optimum value of 109° when the six-membered ring is formed. The ring is quite stable, even a little more stable than a five-membered ring.

Even larger rings can form because of the possibility of puckering. There can be some rotation at each carbon–carbon bond, permitting the skeleton to pucker into a shape which

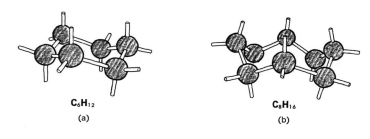

FIG. 21–21. Ball-and-peg models of puckered rings (hydrogen atoms not shown): (a) a six-membered ring, (b) an eight-membered ring.

will finally allow ring closure without straining any of the bond angles. Figure 21–21(b) shows one possible shape for an eight-membered ring. Rings containing 15, 20, or even 30 atoms are known. There is no theoretical reason why rings of almost any size cannot form.

IMPORTANT TERMS

Branched chain	Covalent bond	Organic substances
Carbon chain	Inorganic substances	Structural formula
Carbon ring	Isomers	Tetrahedral
Condensed structural formula	Molecular formula	

WORK EXERCISES

1. Two isomers having composition C_5H_{12} are shown in Section 21–9. How many other isomers, if any, are possible for C_5H_{12}? Draw their structural formulas (either valence bond or condensed formulas). If you are not certain about the total number of isomers from writing structural formulas, try ball-and-peg models. Check your answer in Section 22–2.

2. From all the formulas shown below, pick out the pairs or groups of formulas which actually represent the same compound.

   a) $CH_3CH_2CH_2CH_2CH_3$

   b) $CH_3CH_2CHCH_3$
                 |
                 CH_3

   c) $CH_2CH_2CH_2CH_3$
      |
      CH_3

   d) $CH_3CHCH_2CH_3$ with CH_3 attached above

   e) $CH_3CHCH_2CH_2CH_3$
         |
         CH_3

   f) $CH_3CH_2CH_2CHCH_2CH_3$
                 |
                 CH_3

g) $CH_3CH_2CH_2CHCH_3$
                      |
                     CH_2
                      |
                     CH_3

h) $CH_3\!-\!\underset{\underset{Br}{|}}{\overset{\overset{Br}{|}}{CH}}\!-\!CH\!-\!CH_3$

i) $CH_3\!-\!\underset{\underset{}{\overset{\overset{Br}{|}}{CH}}}\!-\!\underset{}{\overset{\overset{Br}{|}}{CH}}\!-\!CH_3$

j) $CH_3\!-\!\underset{}{\overset{\overset{Br}{|}}{CH}}\!-\!CH_2\!-\!CH_2\!-\!Br$

k) $CH_3\!-\!\underset{\underset{Br}{|}}{\overset{\overset{Br}{|}}{C}}\!-\!CH_2\!-\!CH_3$

l) $CH_3\!-\!\underset{\underset{CH_3}{|}}{\overset{\overset{Br}{|}}{CH}}\!-\!CH\!-\!Br$

3. Write structural formulas to show how many different structures are possible for the molecular formulas:

   a) C_4H_9Br b) $C_3H_6Cl_2$ c) $C_4H_{10}O$

SUGGESTED READING

Asimov, I., *A Short History of Chemistry*, Anchor Books, Doubleday, New York, 1965, pp. 93–96, 100–116. Describes the concepts of vitalism, isomers, valence, and structural formulas in the development of organic chemistry.

Asimov, I., *The New Intelligent Man's Guide to Science*, Basic Books, New York, 1965, pp. 433–438. An excellent brief summary of early organic chemistry, from vitalism until the development of structural formulas.

Asimov, I., *The Wellsprings of Life*, Abelard-Schuman, London-New York-Toronto, 1960, pp. 153–156. Summarizes the early controversy over inorganic versus organic substances.

Kurzer, F., and P. M. Sanderson, "Urea in the History of Organic Chemistry," *J. Chem. Educ.* **33**, 452 (1956). The authors state "The early history of urea provides a vivid impression of the slow and difficult beginnings of chemical science. . ."

Lipman, T. O., "Wöhler's Preparation of Urea and the Fate of Vitalism," *J. Chem. Educ.* **41**, 452 (1964).

Noller, C. R., *Textbook of Organic Chemistry*, 3rd ed., Chapters 1 and 4, W. B. Saunders, Philadelphia, 1966. Chapter 1 describes the nature and historical development of organic chemistry. Chapter 4 discusses isolation and analysis of organic compounds by both traditional and modern techniques.

Sanderson, R. T., "Principles of Chemical Bonding," *J. Chem. Educ.* **38**, 383 (1961). An extremely detailed outline for the student interested in exploring the concept more deeply.

Wasserman, E., "Chemical Topology," *Scientific American*, Nov. 1962 (Offprint #286). Chemists have succeeded in linking one ring compound through another ring. This article discusses the accomplishments and some of the intriguing possibilities.

Chapter 22 SATURATED HYDROCARBONS: The Alkanes

22–1 PETROLEUM, A SOURCE OF SATURATED HYDROCARBONS

Ancient civilizations in many areas of the world made use of the oily materials which they discovered oozing from cracks in the earth. In some localities the crude oil was quite fluid. In others, the seepage was chiefly asphalt (also called pitch or tar). In still other places natural gas escaped and frequently became ignited. These "eternal flames" gave rise to numerous myths and religious cults. Whether the materials were gas, oil, or pitch, they were all related and all arose from deposits of **petroleum** (L. *petra*, rock plus *oleum*, oil).

By 5000 B.C., the Egyptians were already using asphalt as one ingredient for embalming. Asphalt was also well known in the region of the Euphrates river before 4000 B.C., in cities such as Babylon, Ur, and Nineveh. Archeologists have discovered that asphalt was used there as a paint, as mortar to hold bricks, and as waterproofing for jars, baths, and boats. The Phoenician traders caulked their ships with asphalt 5000 years ago. The petroleum fields at Baku, on the Caspian Sea, have apparently been known since before recorded history and are still highly productive. Prior to 1000 B.C. the burning gas vents there attracted fire-worshipping cults. Marco Polo reported that oil from Baku was widely distributed for use as lamp fuel and as medicine for animals and humans.

The Chinese knew of petroleum more than 2000 years ago. They were perhaps the first to obtain it from drilled wells, although they may originally have been seeking water or salt. Both gas and oil were used for heat and light by the Chinese.

When Europeans began exploring the New World, they discovered that many Indian tribes were using petroleum products. Asphalt was an item of commerce among the Incas, who heated oil in immense clay vessels to obtain tar of the desired thickness. The material was used for embalming and for waterproofing clay pots. Petroleum was known to Indians in widely scattered areas of North America. Oil was used for war paint, for softening leather, and especially in the northeast, for medication. The Seneca Indians had such a well-estab-

FIG. 22–1. A modern oil pump and crude-oil storage tanks. [Courtesy of the Shell Oil Company.]

lished trade with other tribes that their oil used for the treatment of coughs, sores, and bruises was called Seneca oil.

In the United States and Canada the first oil wells were drilled during the period 1858–1860. Many others followed rapidly. From that time until 1900, the chief product isolated was kerosene, sold for use in lamps and cook stoves. Smaller amounts of lubricating oils were used. About the time that electric lamps might have put the oil companies out of business, automobiles appeared, causing a new spurt of growth in the oil industry. Refinery practice had to be altered for the production of gasoline.

During the period 1860–1900 chemists were learning that nearly all compounds in petroleum deposits were composed of nothing more than carbon and hydrogen. Whether from petroleum or elsewhere, compounds containing only carbon and hydrogen are called **hydrocarbons.** A compound is termed a **saturated hydrocarbon** if all its carbon atoms are saturated with hydrogen atoms; that is, hydrogens occupy all the carbon valence bonds, other than the minimum number of bonds required to link the carbons to one another in the chain. Because one chain can be composed of more carbons than are found in another chain, a whole series of saturated hydrocarbons is possible. Table 22–1 lists the first few members of the series. A complete list would show some molecules which contain as many as 10, 20, 50, or more carbon atoms linked together. Such a family of compounds can be found in deposits of petroleum. Saturated hydrocarbons usually constitute well over 90% of petroleum. The remainder often includes hydrogen sulfide and organic sulfur compounds, which have a strong odor. Small amounts of organic nitrogen or oxygen compounds may also be present. Petroleum from certain localities will contain several percent of aromatic compounds (Chapter 24), but many deposits have none. Some further remarks concerning petroleum products are found in Section 22–4.

**TABLE 22–1. Saturated Hydrocarbons—
the first four members in the series**

Name	Molecular Formula	Structural Formula
methane	CH_4	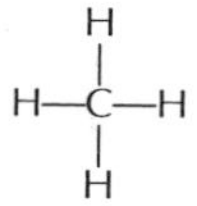 H—C—H with H above and H below
ethane	C_2H_6	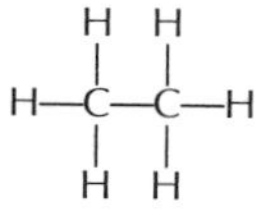 H—C—C—H with H's above and below
propane	C_3H_8	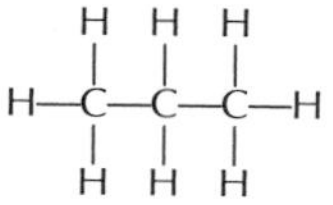 H—C—C—C—H with H's above and below
butane (*n*-butane)	C_4H_{10}	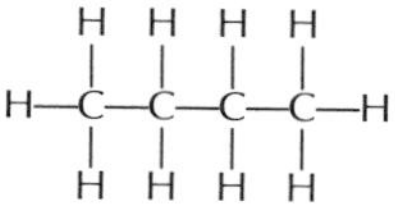 H—C—C—C—C—H with H's above and below

◄ A family of organic compounds, all of which have the same type of structure, is called a **homologous series** (Gr. *homos*, the same). In this book we will rarely have need to use the term again, but the *idea* of such a series of related compounds is important. Note (Table 22–1) that the molecular formula of any member differs from the one before it or after it by CH_2. Inspection of the structural formulas reveals the reason for this. To convert ethane to propane we need to lengthen the chain by one carbon, and in the process need to add only two new hydrogens. The change represented here is of course just a mental exercise, to help us under-

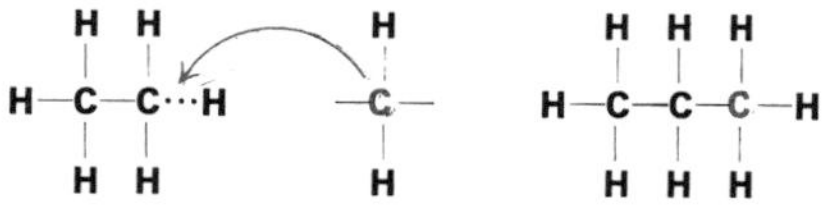

stand structural relations. We cannot pick up an individual molecule and manipulate it in this fashion. Nor can we carry out a reaction in the laboratory in quite this way. ►

22-2 DEVELOPMENT OF NAMES

When we get through the hydrocarbon series (Table 22–1) as far as butane, we encounter a problem of naming. A substance of molecular formula C_4H_{10} could also have this structure:

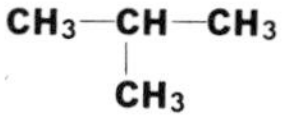

CH₃—CH—CH₃
|
CH₃

Since the latter is an isomer of butane, chemists years ago named it isobutane. To avoid any uncertainty, the unbranched butane (shown in Table 22–1) was designated *normal* butane, or *n*-butane.

The next member in the series is pentane. *Three* different structures, each having formula C_5H_{12} are possible. All three are real compounds; they have been isolated (from petroleum or other sources) and found to differ in their melting points, boiling points, and so forth. Therefore different names are needed for the isomeric pentanes. The unbranched one was again named *n*-pentane, and the one with the simpler branch was called isopentane. Since in this case there was yet another isomer, a "new" one, it was called neopentane (Gr. *neos*, new).

$$CH_3CH_2CH_2CH_2CH_3 \qquad CH_3CHCH_2CH_3 \qquad CH_3-\underset{\underset{CH_3}{|}}{\overset{\overset{CH_3}{|}}{C}}-CH_3$$
$$\qquad\qquad\qquad\qquad\quad |$$
$$\qquad\qquad\qquad\qquad CH_3$$

n-pentane   isopentane   neopentane

The situation becomes rapidly more complicated. There are five different structures having formula C_6H_{14}, nine having formula C_7H_{16}, 75 having formula $C_{10}H_{22}$, and 4347 having formula $C_{15}H_{32}$! It would become increasingly difficult to think up appropriate little syllables to designate the various isomers, and even more difficult to remember which one should represent which structure. Clearly, what is needed is a relatively simple, easily remembered, logical system for naming organic compounds. It should be general and inclusive enough that it could apply to any possible organic compound, including those not yet discovered. Such a method for assigning names to organic compounds has been developed through the cooperation of chemists from many different countries. Hereafter we will call such names the **systematic names.**

◄ By the 1880's this problem of organic nomenclature had become critical. Chemists had determined the structure of many natural products, including a few complex ones. Also, enough was known about organic reactions to permit the synthesis of completely new compounds, as well as the duplication of some of those discovered in nature. Consequently, the number of chemical structures known had surpassed any convenient method for naming them, and thereby readily communicating knowledge about them to others.

Work to fulfill the need for a systematic method of nomenclature was begun in 1889 by the International Congress of Chemists then meeting in Paris. A few members of the Congress were appointed to a study commission, to develop a set of rules for naming organic compounds. When the Congress next met in 1892 at Geneva, the recommendations of the commission were adopted by the approximately forty chemists present, and became known as the "Geneva rules." For the first time an adequate, internationally accepted system of nomenclature was available.

Thereafter, modifications had to be agreed upon occasionally, and a few new terms added to provide names for certain types of structure which had not been known previously. Some changes were accomplished at a meeting of the International Union of Chemistry (IUC) in 1930. The organization met again in 1949 under the name International Union of Pure and Applied Chemistry (IUPAC). At that time, and at subsequent meetings, the rules have been expanded. For a while the updated rules were called the IUC system and, more recently, the IUPAC system. At the present time it seems convenient to refer to the international nomenclature as *systematic names.* ►

22-3 THE SYSTEMATIC NAMES

In the systematic method of nomenclature, the saturated hydrocarbons, as a class, are called **alkanes.** Each individual member of the series has been assigned a name which represents the number of carbons in its chain, and ends with *-ane*. Thus, pent*ane* is an alk*ane* (saturated hydrocarbon) having five carbons. This name, used alone, designates only the *straight* chain (unbranched) isomer having formula C_5H_{12}. The systematic names for several alkanes are listed in Table 22–2. Except for the first four, nearly all the names were derived from the Greek names for numbers; *nonane* is of Latin origin.

TABLE 22-2. Names for alkanes

Molecular Formula	Name	Molecular Formula	Name
CH_4	methane	$C_{11}H_{24}$	undecane
C_2H_6	ethane	$C_{12}H_{26}$	dodecane
C_3H_8	propane		
C_4H_{10}	butane		
C_5H_{12}	pentane	$C_{16}H_{34}$	hexadecane
C_6H_{14}	hexane		
C_7H_{16}	heptane		
C_8H_{18}	octane	$C_{18}H_{38}$	octadecane
C_9H_{20}	nonane		
$C_{10}H_{22}$	decane		
		$C_{20}H_{42}$	eicosane
		$C_{25}H_{52}$	pentacosane

For a saturated hydrocarbon *ring* compound the term **cyclo** (Gr. *kyklos*, circle) is included in the name. The general name is *cycloalkane*. Individual compounds have the usual name designating the number of carbons. For example:

cyclopentane

One more bit of terminology is necessary in order to name *branched* skeleton hydrocarbons by the systematic method. An **alkyl group** is a unit of structure derived by removing (imaginarily) one hydrogen from an alkane, so that the group has a bond available for attachment to a different atom. Illustrations are given in Table 22–3. Any particular group is named by using the ending *-yl* in place of the *-ane* ending in the name of the parent alkane. When we wish to generalize, the symbol R is used to designate any alkyl group.

TABLE 22–3. Derivation of alkyl group names

alkane				R—H
	CH_4 methane	CH_3CH_3 ethane	$CH_3CH_2CH_3$ propane	alkane (general)
alkyl group				R—
	CH_3— methyl	CH_3CH_2— ethyl	$CH_3CH_2CH_2$— propyl	alkyl (general)

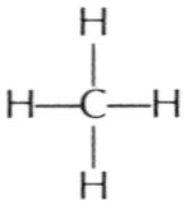

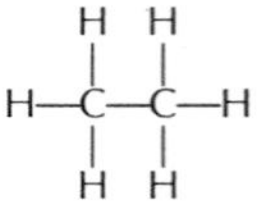

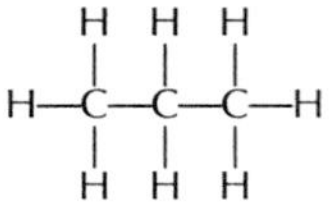

The rules for writing systematic names of alkanes may be summarized as follows:

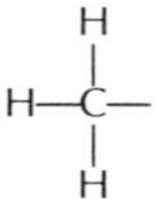

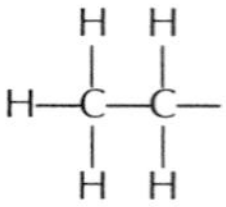

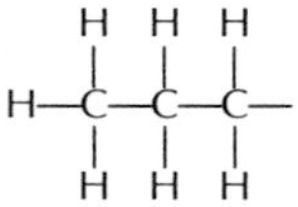

1) Name the longest carbon chain which can be found in the structure.
2) Preceding the longest-chain name, write down, in alphabetical order, the names of each of the kinds of alkyl groups which are attached to the main chain.
3) If there are several groups of the same kind attached to the main chain, list that group name only once, using the appropriate prefix such as *di-, tri-, tetra-,* etc., to indicate two, three, or four groups, respectively, of that kind.
4) Assign a number, as a prefix, to *each* of the alkyl groups in the name, to indicate the position of the group on the chain. For this purpose, start numbering the carbon atoms consecutively from either end of the chain, so that the attached groups will have the lowest numbers possible.

The rules are best illustrated by applying them, step by step, to some examples.

Example 1

1) pentane

2) ethyl methylpentane

[Rule (3) does not apply to this example.]

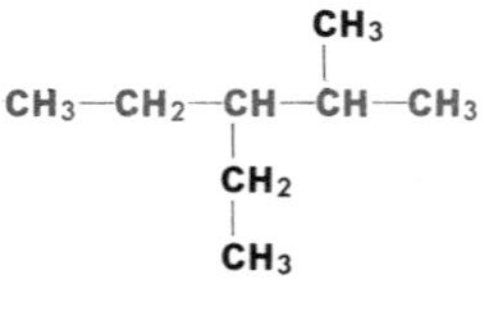

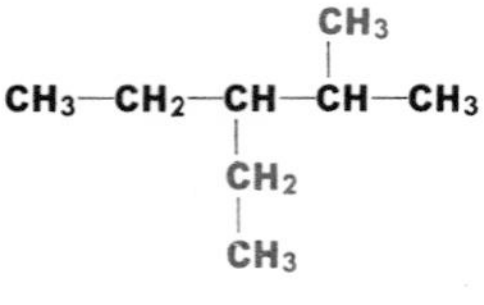

4) 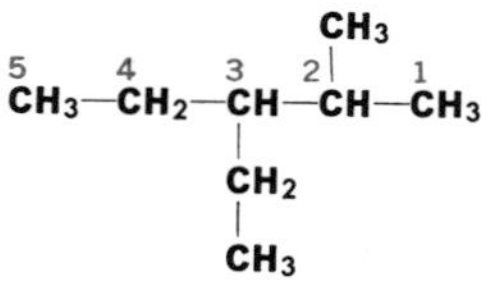 $\overset{5}{CH_3}-\overset{4}{CH_2}-\overset{3}{CH}-\overset{2}{\underset{|}{CH}}-\overset{1}{CH_3}$ 3-ethyl-2-methylpentane

with CH_3 above position 2, and below position 3:

$$\begin{array}{c} CH_2 \\ | \\ CH_3 \end{array}$$

(*Not* 3-ethyl-4-methylpentane, which would result if we counted from the other end of the chain.)

Example 2

1) 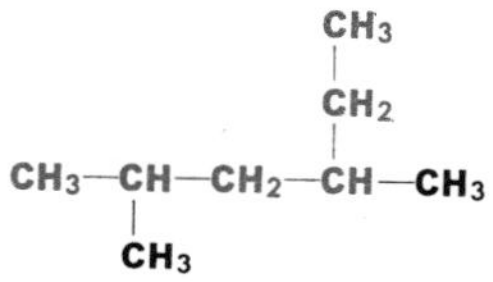 $CH_3-CH-CH_2-CH-CH_3$ hexane

with side chain $\begin{array}{c} CH_3 \\ | \\ CH_2 \end{array}$ above, and CH_3 below first CH

2) $CH_3\ \ CH-CH_2-CH-CH_3$ methylhexane

with side chain $\begin{array}{c} CH_3 \\ | \\ CH_2 \end{array}$ above, and CH_3 below

3)   See preceding structure.   dimethylhexane

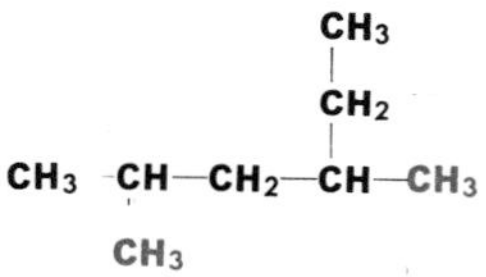

4) 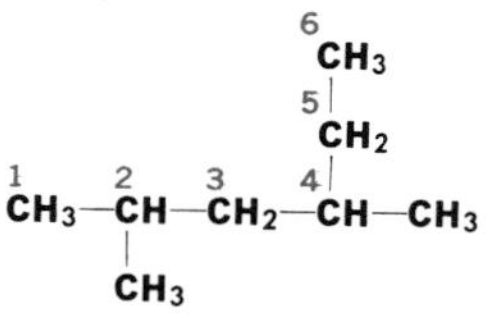 $\overset{1}{CH_3}-\overset{2}{CH}-\overset{3}{CH_2}-\overset{4}{CH}-CH_3$ 2,4-dimethylhexane

with side chain $\begin{array}{c} \overset{6}{CH_3} \\ | \\ \overset{5}{CH_2} \end{array}$ above, and CH_3 below

Example 3

1) 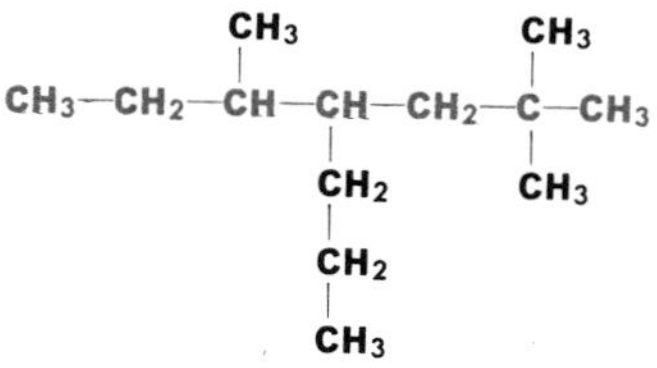 $CH_3-CH_2-CH-CH-CH_2-C-CH_3$ heptane

with CH_3 above third CH and CH_3 above sixth C, and below:

$$\begin{array}{cc} CH_2 & CH_3 \\ | & \\ CH_2 & \\ | & \\ CH_3 & \end{array}$$

2) $CH_3-CH_2-CH-CH-CH_2-C-CH_3$ methyl propylheptane

with CH_3 above third CH and CH_3 above sixth C, and below:

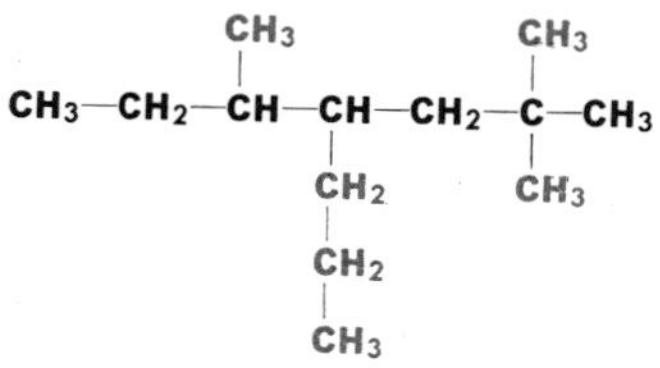

$$\begin{array}{cc} CH_2 & CH_3 \\ | & \\ CH_2 & \\ | & \\ CH_3 & \end{array}$$

3)   See preceding structure.   trimethyl propylheptane

4)

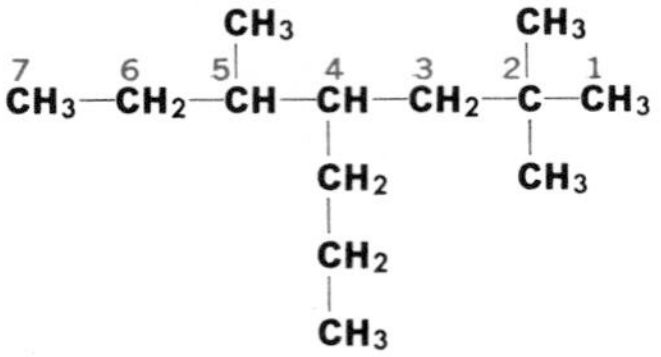

$$\underset{7}{CH_3}-\underset{6}{CH_2}-\underset{5}{CH}-\underset{4}{CH}-\underset{3}{CH_2}-\underset{2}{C}-\underset{1}{CH_3}$$

with CH₃ on carbons 5 and 2, and CH₂—CH₂—CH₃ below carbon 4, CH₃ below carbon 2.

2,2,5-trimethyl-4-propylheptane

The purpose of the name is to describe accurately to another person the structure we have in mind. If the naming rules are satisfactory (and are properly used) it should be impossible for him to interpret them in such a way that he could write a *different* structure than the one we had named.

Let us now apply the rules in the opposite manner, attempting to write a structure from a name.

Example 4

Given: the name 4,4-diethyl-2-methyloctane.

First, we see at the end of the name the word *octane*. Therefore we would write out a chain of eight carbons:

C—C—C—C—C—C—C—C

Next, we start reading at the beginning of the name and as we come to each group name we write carbons to represent it in the structure, meanwhile counting down the chain to be sure we put each group at the correct position.

The *4,4-diethyl* means two ethyl groups, both on the fourth carbon:

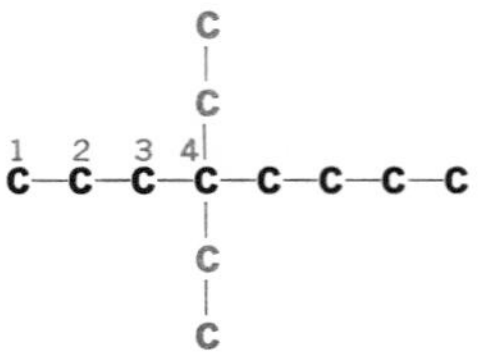

Now, *2-methyl* requires a methyl group on the second carbon; we must be sure to count in the same direction in which we counted the first time:

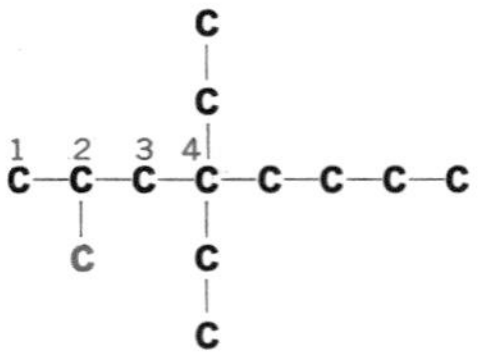

Finally, since we usually want to write a proper condensed structural formula, we can go back and put the required number of hydrogens at each carbon, keeping in mind that the covalence of carbon is 4:

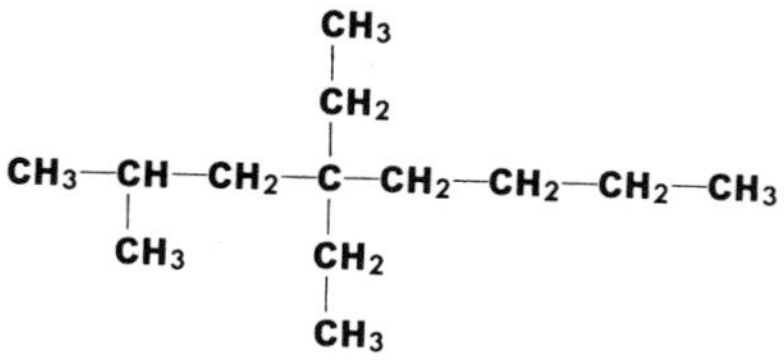

$$
\begin{array}{c}
\text{CH}_3 \\
| \\
\text{CH}_2 \\
| \\
\text{CH}_3-\text{CH}-\text{CH}_2-\text{C}-\text{CH}_2-\text{CH}_2-\text{CH}_2-\text{CH}_3 \\
\qquad\quad | \qquad\quad | \\
\qquad\quad \text{CH}_3 \quad\; \text{CH}_2 \\
\qquad\qquad\qquad | \\
\qquad\qquad\quad \text{CH}_3
\end{array}
$$

Note in Example 4 that the group name *ethyl* was mentioned only once; the prefix *di-* told us that there were two such groups. However, even though both are at the same position on the chain, the number must be given for *both* of them, thus: 4,4-. Had it been written only as *4-diethyl*, we would have been uncertain when writing the structure. Did the author really mean both are at 4? Or is this a typographical omission; should it have been 3,4-diethyl?

If we count all the atoms in the structure shown in Example 1, we find the molecular formula is C_8H_{18}; the compound is one of the isomeric octanes. Although we first wrote the word *pentane* as the basis of a name for this structure, it does not mean the compound is one of the pentane isomers. If we examine the *complete* name we see that it does indeed say "eight carbons." Ethyl means two, methyl is one more, and pentane means five, for a total of eight. It is wise to check for errors by counting the total in both the name and the structure, to see whether they agree.

It is also important to realize that an alkyl group, such as any of those shown in Table 22-3, is a strictly imaginary device, convenient for naming purposes. It is not necessarily true that an alkyl group is a real compound that we might find in nature or that we might make one by some chemical reaction and attach it to some other group.

All organic compounds have a carbon skeleton of some sort. They may also have certain groups attached to this skeleton: —OH, —NH₂, —Cl, and so forth. We can name compounds containing these groups merely by learning the term used to name each particular group. This term will be incorporated in the complete name, along with a position number, just as we used a name and number for each alkyl group. Once you have learned these few simple rules, you will know the important basis for naming organic compounds by the international system of nomenclature.

22-4 GENERAL PHYSICAL AND CHEMICAL PROPERTIES

Crude oil can be separated into various fractions by distillation, Fig. 22-2. Several familiar petroleum products thus obtained are listed in Table 22-4, along with the size of alkane molecules normally found in each of the products. Evidently there is a very simple relation between the size of the molecules and some of their physical properties. The table shows that small lightweight molecules have lower boiling points, which means they are more

FIG. 22-2. Distillation tower in an oil refinery. Crude oil enters via the large pipe at the lower right. Distilled fractions are drawn off through pipes at various levels in the tower, the most volatile material rising to the top. Streams of intermediate boiling range pass to smaller columns nearby, for further separation. [Courtesy of the Shell Oil Company.]

volatile. A larger molecule requires more energy to escape from the attraction of its neighbors in the liquid state and become a separate molecule in the vapor state. The temperature at which it boils is higher, corresponding to a greater energy requirement.

We are all aware of the fact that gasoline vaporizes more easily than does kerosene. Oils are even less volatile and paraffin wax is solid, at least until the melting point at 50°C

is reached. Methane or butane, whose molecules are very light, are gases at room temperature. Pentane, having a boiling point of 36°C, is the first alkane in the series which is liquid
at room temperature and pressure. Propane and butane (the two just lighter than pentane)
can easily be liquefied if compressed and kept in a tank under pressure; they are often
handled in this state and called liquefied petroleum gas (LPG).

It is also apparent from the list in Table 22–4 that the compounds consisting of heavier
molecules will be more viscous; compare gasoline, kerosene, oil, and petroleum jelly.

TABLE 22–4. Some common petroleum products

Product	Main Alkanes Present	Boiling Range, °C
natural gas	C_1	below 0°
liquefied petroleum gas (LPG); propane, butane	C_3—C_4	below 0°
petroleum ether; light naphtha (solvents and cleaning fluids)	C_5—C_7	30–100°
gasoline	C_5—C_{10}	35–175°
kerosene; jet fuel	C_{10}—C_{18}	175–275°
diesel fuel	C_{12}—C_{20}	190–330°
fuel oil	C_{14}—C_{22}	230–360°
lubricating oil	C_{20}—C_{30}	above 350°
mineral oil (refined; decolorized)	C_{20}—C_{30}	above 350°
petroleum jelly (Vaseline)	C_{22}—C_{40}	(m.p. 40–60°)
paraffin wax	C_{25}—C_{50}	(m.p. 50–65°)

Most of us have observed that oil floats on water; so does kerosene or gasoline. This
simple observation reveals two other physical properties of the alkanes: they are insoluble
in water and are less dense than water.

"Like dissolves like" is a general rule concerning solubilities. Water is a highly polar
substance which generally dissolves other polar or ionic compounds. This suggests that
an alkane, being insoluble in water, *is nonpolar*. Nonpolarity is an important characteristic
of hydrocarbon skeletons, one which influences the behavior of all organic compounds.

The reason an alkane is nonpolar can be understood if we examine a portion of its structure.

nonpolar bonds

We would expect the covalent bond between two carbon atoms to be nonpolar; since the atoms are identical, the electrons should be shared between them equally. It also happens that a hydrogen atom has just about the same tendency to attract electrons that a carbon atom does; that is, it has a similar electronegativity (Section 6–6). Consequently, electrons shared between a carbon atom and a hydrogen atom also form a nonpolar bond.

The nonpolar nature of alkanes makes them good *solvents* for other nonpolar or only slightly polar substances. However, because of their flammability, extreme caution must be observed if volatile hydrocarbons are used as solvents. Year after year, hundreds of people are seriously burned, and homes are destroyed because people were unwisely using gasoline to clean grease off a floor, an auto part, or a piece of clothing.

Alkanes are colorless. Recall that paraffin wax, kerosene, and the "white" gasoline used in camp stoves all lack color. The gasoline used in automobiles is orange because a little dye has been added as a warning that it contains tetraethyllead, a deadly poison. Common lubricating oils have a blue-green color because they still contain small amounts of colored substances originally present in the crude petroleum. These need not be removed for lubricants. The mineral oil used medically is essentially the same mixture of hydrocarbons, decolorized and refined.

Chemically, the distinctive feature of *an alkane* is that it *is generally inert*. There are only a very few chemical changes it will undergo. Most *compounds* which react (especially those studied in this book) are ionic or very polar substances. Consequently, the nonpolar alkanes do not react with them. A few examples are listed below, for it is as important to know what will *not* happen as it is to know what will.

$CH_3CH_2CH_2CH_3 + NaOH$
$CH_3CH_2CH_2CH_3 + HCl$
$CH_3CH_2CH_2CH_3 + H_2SO_4$
$CH_3CH_2CH_2CH_3 + Na$ $\Biggr\} \rightarrow$ no reaction
$CH_3CH_2CH_2CH_3 + KMnO_4$
$CH_3CH_2CH_2CH_3 + NaHCO_3$
$CH_3CH_2CH_2CH_3 + AgNO_3$

One important reaction of an alkane is its decomposition at high temperature, which will be discussed in Sections 23–2 and 24–9.

Alkanes do react with oxygen (combustion) and with chlorine or bromine. These reactions will be discussed in the next two sections. It is interesting to note that even these reagents do not attack an alkane under ordinary conditions at room temperature. For instance, kerosene or gasoline remain unchanged when exposed to air for a very long time. Combustion occurs only if a flame or spark provides the initial burst of high temperature to start the reaction with oxygen. The reaction, once started, is exothermic, so the high temperature is maintained and promotes the reaction of other molecules.

22–5 COMBUSTION

The combustion of methane is represented by Eq. (22–1).

$$H\overset{\displaystyle H}{\underset{\displaystyle H}{-}}\!\!C\!\!-\!\!H + 2O_2 \rightarrow CO_2 + 2H_2O + heat \qquad\qquad (22\text{--}1)$$

Energy, provided by the high temperature of a flame or spark, starts the reaction by breaking the covalent bonds of methane. Only then are the carbon and hydrogen atoms free to combine with oxygen. The formation of new bonds with oxygen releases even larger amounts of energy. The energy produced by the reaction of the first few molecules breaks covalent bonds in other methane molecules nearby, allowing them to react with oxygen. The reaction continues in this fashion until all the material is used up. At each step more energy is released than is required to initiate the combustion of adjacent molecules. The net result is the release of a tremendous amount of heat. Depending on conditions, a little of the energy may be dissipated as light.

Other alkanes react with oxygen in a similar manner. In each case the alkane molecule is completely broken up into separate hydrogen and carbon atoms which combine with oxygen to form water and carbon dioxide. This fact is used in writing a complete, balanced equation for such an oxidation. For example, if heptane burns, Eq. (22–2), we know the products will be CO_2 and H_2O. Furthermore, we can write down 7 molecules of CO_2, to account for all the carbons from heptane. Then we can write $8H_2O$ molecules to account for the 16 hydrogen atoms. Finally, we must provide enough O_2 molecules to accomplish these changes.

$$C_7H_{16} + 11O_2 \rightarrow 7CO_2 + 8H_2O \qquad\qquad (22\text{--}2)$$

If the amount of oxygen available to the burning hydrocarbon is not sufficient, carbon monoxide (CO) may be produced. Or, if some carbon atoms are not oxidized at all, they form the fine black particles called soot.

The largest consumption of alkanes is for the purpose of utilizing the energy released by combustion. Various sorts of engines have been designed to convert the heat energy to mechanical energy for doing work. Frequently, however, the heat may be used directly for heating homes and public buildings or for cooking. Some furnaces and cooking ranges operate on kerosene, others on butane, and so on. A heating fuel now widely used in the United States is natural gas. It is chiefly methane, with small amounts of other light hydrocarbons such as propane. Natural gas occurs in petroleum deposits, along with the mixture of liquid alkanes constituting the crude oil. The gas is carried by huge pipelines directly from the wells to most major cities in the United States.

Since carbon chains form the skeletons of organic compounds, nearly all the organic compounds will burn. Even solid organic substances are combustible; some familiar examples are wood, fats, cotton, and paraffin wax. How *easily* the compounds burn depends largely on their volatility. Gases and easily vaporized liquids, such as methane, butane, or octane, are readily ignited and burn vigorously.

22-6 SUBSTITUTION BY CHLORINE

Under ordinary circumstances an alkane does not react with chlorine. A reaction will start, however, if a mixture of alkane and chlorine is exposed to a high temperature (400°–500°C) or to ultraviolet light from a lamp or from direct sunlight. Equation 22–3 shows the results with methane.

$$
\overset{\overset{\displaystyle H}{|}}{\underset{\underset{\displaystyle H}{|}}{H-C-H}} + Cl-Cl \xrightarrow{\text{UV light}} \overset{\overset{\displaystyle H}{|}}{\underset{\underset{\displaystyle H}{|}}{H-C-Cl}} + H-Cl \tag{22-3}
$$

methane   chloromethane
                      (methyl chloride)

This is a **substitution reaction.** One chlorine atom has been substituted in place of one of the hydrogens originally bonded to the carbon. The displaced hydrogen atom has paired off with another chlorine atom to form hydrogen chloride.

Here again, as with combustion, we see that no reaction can occur unless some covalent bond is broken. Only after a hydrogen atom has been separated from the carbon atom can its place be taken by a chlorine atom. Indeed, it is also necessary to break the covalent bond between the two chlorine atoms in the Cl_2 molecule. The need for bond-breaking once again explains the purpose of the energy required to initiate the reaction. Ultraviolet light, which provides a larger amount of energy than does visible light, is sufficient to promote the reaction.

The reaction represented by Eq. (22–3) could be carried out by mixing methane gas and chlorine gas in a tank having a window through which we could shine ultraviolet light. As soon as a few molecules had reacted, some chloromethane would be present in the tank. It could react with the remaining chlorine in much the same way that the methane did; the result, Eq. (22–4), would be the substitution of a second chlorine atom onto the same carbon.

$$
\overset{\overset{\displaystyle H}{|}}{\underset{\underset{\displaystyle H}{|}}{H-C-Cl}} + Cl-Cl \xrightarrow{\text{UV light}} \overset{\overset{\displaystyle H}{|}}{\underset{\underset{\displaystyle Cl}{|}}{H-C-Cl}} + H-Cl \tag{22-4}
$$

                        dichloromethane

Of course, if this can happen, the substitution of a third chlorine atom and a fourth should also be possible. This is shown in Eqs. (22–5) and (22–6).

$$CH_2Cl_2 + Cl_2 \xrightarrow{\text{UV light}} \quad CHCl_3 \quad + HCl \tag{22-5}$$
$$\text{trichloromethane}$$
$$\text{(chloroform)}$$

$$CHCl_3 + Cl_2 \xrightarrow{\text{UV light}} \quad CCl_4 \quad + HCl \tag{22-6}$$
$$\text{tetrachloromethane}$$
$$\text{(carbon tetrachloride)}$$

These reactions occur step by step. Each one is a repetition of the same fundamental substitution reaction, and at each step one molecule of hydrogen chloride must be produced.

Consequently, when methane reacts with chlorine we obtain, in addition to the hydrogen chloride, a mixture of four different organic compounds. Fortunately the mixture can be separated by distillation, because the four compounds have distinctly different boiling points. Each time a chlorine atom is substituted on the carbon, the molecular weight increases by about 35. The heavier molecule has a higher boiling point. For example, trichloromethane boils at 61°C and tetrachloromethane at 76°C.

Alkanes other than methane can undergo substitution by chlorine. The chief difference is that a larger alkane yields a larger number of different chlorinated products. For example, when butane reacts with chlorine, the first stage of substitution (comparable to Eq. 22–3) can yield *two* isomeric chlorobutanes.

$$CH_3CH_2CH_2CH_3 + Cl_2 \xrightarrow{\text{UV light}} \begin{array}{c} CH_3-CH_2-CH_2-CH_2 + HCl \\ \qquad\qquad\qquad | \\ \qquad\qquad\qquad Cl \\ \text{and} \\ CH_3-CH_2-CH-CH_3 + HCl \\ \qquad\qquad | \\ \qquad\qquad Cl \end{array} \tag{22-7}$$

The chlorobutanes produced in Eq. (22–7) can react further with the chlorine in the reaction mixture to form *six* isomeric dichlorobutanes.

$$
\begin{array}{cc}
CH_3-CH_2-CH_2-CH_2 & CH_3-CH_2-CH-CH_3 \\
\qquad\qquad\qquad | & \qquad\qquad | \\
\qquad\qquad\qquad Cl & \qquad\qquad Cl
\end{array}
$$

$$\xrightarrow[\text{UV light} \;\; \text{more } Cl_2]{}$$

$$
\begin{array}{ccc}
\qquad\qquad Cl & & \\
\qquad\qquad | & & \\
CH_3-CH_2-CH_2-CH & CH_3-CH_2-CH-CH_2 & CH_3-CH-CH_2-CH_2 \\
\qquad\qquad\qquad | & \qquad\qquad | \;\; | & \qquad\; | \qquad\quad | \\
\qquad\qquad\qquad Cl & \qquad\qquad Cl \;\; Cl & \qquad\; Cl \qquad\quad Cl
\end{array}
$$

$$
\begin{array}{ccc}
& \qquad Cl & \\
& \qquad | & \\
CH_2-CH_2-CH_2-CH_2 & CH_3-CH_2-C-CH_3 & CH_3-CH-CH-CH_3 \\
| \qquad\qquad\qquad\quad | & \qquad\qquad | & \qquad\; | \;\; | \\
Cl \qquad\qquad\qquad\quad Cl & \qquad\qquad Cl & \qquad\; Cl \;\; Cl
\end{array}
$$

Repeated substitutions can produce trichlorobutanes, tetrachlorobutanes, and so on up to decachlorobutane, C_4Cl_{10}.

Because of differences in molecular weight, the dichlorobutanes as a group can be separated rather well by distillation from the chlorobutanes or the trichlorobutanes. The mixture of dichlorobutanes thus obtained might be useful as a solvent. For this purpose it would not matter that the various isomers present had different structures; the solvent ability of each molecule would be about the same. On the other hand, this substitution reaction would not be a good method by which to obtain, in pure condition, one particular compound, such as 1,3-dichlorobutane. It is difficult and expensive to separate one dichlorobutane isomer from another; all have the same molecular weight, so that the boiling point differences are slight.

Bromine reacts with alkanes in the same way that chlorine does, for example:

$$CH_3CH_3 + Br_2 \xrightarrow{\text{UV light}} CH_3CH_2Br + HBr$$

◄ 22-7 THE NATURE OF ALKANE REACTIONS

In describing the general chemical properties of alkanes, Section 22–4, we pointed out that alkanes do not participate in *ionic* reactions. Instead, when alkanes do react, the intermediate, reactive particle is a **radical,** that is, a group of atoms which has one unpaired electron to share and is in this sense comparable to an individual atom. The creation of radicals is due to the fact that when a nonpolar bond breaks, the tendency is for one electron to remain with each fragment. The appropriate energy can rupture a bond in this manner:

$$
\begin{array}{ccc}
\text{H} & & \text{H} \\
\ddot{} & & \ddot{} \\
\text{H}:\text{C}:\text{H} \rightarrow \text{H}:\text{C}\cdot & + & \cdot\text{H} \\
\ddot{} & & \ddot{} \\
\text{H} & & \text{H}
\end{array}
\qquad (22\text{-}8)
$$

$$
\begin{array}{cc}
\text{methyl} & \text{hydrogen} \\
\text{radical} & \text{atom}
\end{array}
$$

The fate of the resulting fragments then depends on the environment. If oxygen is present, the liberated hydrogen atoms combine with it to form water. Eventually the carbon atom, stripped of its hydrogens, also combines with oxygen, giving carbon dioxide and producing the familiar combustion reaction.

In chlorination, the energy supplied by ultraviolet light initiates the reaction by splitting a chlorine *molecule* into two separate chlorine atoms.

$$
:\!\overset{\cdot\cdot}{\text{Cl}}\!:\!\overset{\cdot\cdot}{\text{Cl}}\!: \xrightarrow{\text{UV light}} :\!\overset{\cdot\cdot}{\text{Cl}}\!\cdot \;\; + \;\; \cdot\overset{\cdot\cdot}{\text{Cl}}\!: \qquad (22\text{-}9)
$$

A chlorine atom, because of its unpaired electron, then attacks a methane molecule, picks off a hydrogen atom, and leaves a methyl radical.

$$
\begin{array}{ccc}
\text{H} & & \text{H} \\
\ddot{} & \ddot{} & \ddot{} \\
\text{H}:\text{C}:\text{H} \;\; + \;\; \cdot\text{Cl}: \rightarrow \text{H}:\text{C}\cdot + \text{H}:\text{Cl}: \\
\ddot{} & & \ddot{} \\
\text{H} & & \text{H}
\end{array}
\qquad (22\text{-}10)
$$

The methyl radical in turn promptly seeks an atom with which to share its unpaired electron. It picks one from a chlorine molecule, leaving a lone chlorine atom.

$$
\begin{array}{c}
\text{H} \\
\text{H} : \text{C} \cdot \\
\text{H}
\end{array}
\; + \; : \ddot{\text{Cl}} : \ddot{\text{Cl}} : \; \rightarrow \;
\begin{array}{c}
\text{H} \\
\text{H} : \text{C} : \ddot{\text{Cl}} : \\
\text{H}
\end{array}
\; + \; \cdot \ddot{\text{Cl}} :
\tag{22-11}
$$

The chlorine atom liberated by reaction (22–11) can also attack a methane molecule as in Eq. (22–10). Thus the sequence of reactions (22–10), (22–11), (22–10), (22–11), etc., can be repeated many times. The important points are that radicals are involved, not ions, and that energy was required in Eq. (22–9) to start the reaction sequence by breaking the first bond.

If no chlorine or oxygen is present when heat energy is applied to an alkane, some of its covalent bonds break anyway. The resultant radicals simply re-pair their unshared electrons in various ways to produce new compounds. Equations (22–12), (22–13), and (22–14) show one possible fate for butane at 500°C.

$$
\underset{\text{butane}}{\text{H}{-}\overset{\text{H}}{\underset{\text{H}}{\text{C}}}{-}\overset{\text{H}}{\underset{\text{H}}{\text{C}}}{-}\overset{\text{H}}{\underset{\text{H}}{\text{C}}}{-}\overset{\text{H}}{\underset{\text{H}}{\text{C}}}{-}\text{H}}
\rightarrow
\underset{\text{propyl}\atop\text{radical}}{\text{H}{-}\overset{\text{H}}{\underset{\text{H}}{\text{C}}}{-}\overset{\text{H}}{\underset{\text{H}}{\text{C}}}{-}\overset{\text{H}}{\underset{\text{H}}{\text{C}}}\cdot}
+
\underset{\text{methyl}\atop\text{radical}}{\cdot\,\overset{\text{H}}{\underset{\text{H}}{\text{C}}}{-}\text{H}}
\tag{22-12}
$$

$$
\underset{\text{propyl}\atop\text{radical}}{\text{H}{-}\overset{\text{H}}{\underset{\text{H}}{\text{C}}} : \overset{\text{H}}{\underset{\text{H}}{\text{C}}}{-}\overset{\text{H}}{\underset{\text{H}}{\text{C}}}\cdot}
\rightarrow
\underset{\text{methyl}\atop\text{radical}}{\text{H}{-}\overset{\text{H}}{\underset{\text{H}}{\text{C}}}\cdot}
+
\underset{\text{ethene}\atop\text{(an alkene)}}{\overset{\text{H}}{\underset{\text{H}}{\text{C}}} :: \overset{\text{H}}{\underset{\text{H}}{\text{C}}}}
\tag{22-13}
$$

$$
\underset{\text{methyl radicals}}{\text{H}{-}\overset{\text{H}}{\underset{\text{H}}{\text{C}}}\cdot \;+\; \cdot\overset{\text{H}}{\underset{\text{H}}{\text{C}}}{-}\text{H}}
\rightarrow
\underset{\text{ethane}}{\text{H}{-}\overset{\text{H}}{\underset{\text{H}}{\text{C}}}{-}\overset{\text{H}}{\underset{\text{H}}{\text{C}}}{-}\text{H}}
\tag{22-14}
$$

The net result of these three steps is that butane (C_4H_{10}) has been converted to ethene (C_2H_4) plus ethane (C_2H_6). The breakup of an alkane in this fashion is called **cracking;** its practical importance will be discussed in Section 23–2.

Although a radical is very reactive it is, like an atom, electrically neutral. For example, when chlorine has seven electrons in its valence shell it is a neutral atom. Only if it acquires one more electron does it become an ion having a negative charge.

$: \ddot{\text{Cl}} \cdot$ chlorine atom $: \ddot{\text{Cl}} :^{-}$ chloride ion

Similarly, the carbon in a methyl radical is neutral.

$$
\begin{array}{c}
\text{H} \\
\text{H} : \ddot{\text{C}} \cdot \\
\text{H}
\end{array}
\quad \text{methyl radical}
$$

The electrons in each carbon-hydrogen bond are shared; one electron is hydrogen's share and one is carbon's. Therefore, in a methyl radical, carbon can claim a total of four electrons for its valence shell. Since this is the number carbon should normally have, it is electrically neutral. ▶

22-8 NAMES OF ALKYL HALIDES

A compound having an alkane skeleton and a halogen in place of a hydrogen is called an **alkyl halide.** The general formula RX may be used for it. For an alkyl chloride we may use RCl; for an alkyl bromide, RBr. With the equations in Section 22-6 are given the systematic names for the four chlorine derivatives of methane; the additional names shown there in parentheses are common names.

To name an alkyl halide systematically we need only one new rule beyond those listed in Section 22-3: *an -o ending is used for a halogen group* (chloro, etc.), *and the group is given a smaller position number than is an alkyl group.*

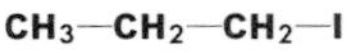

$$CH_3{-}CH_2{-}CH_2{-}I \qquad \underset{\substack{|\\Cl}}{CH_3{-}CH{-}CH{-}CH_3} \qquad \underset{\substack{|\\Br}}{CH_3{-}CH_2{-}CH{-}CH{-}CH_2{-}CH_2}$$

1-iodopropane 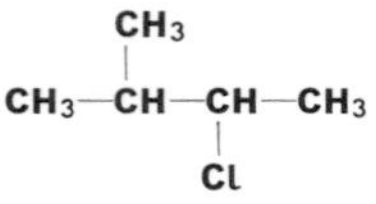   2-chloro-3-methylbutane 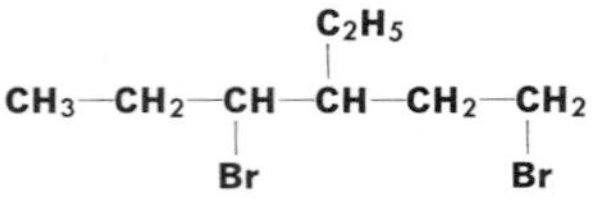   1,4-dibromo-3-ethylhexane

22-9 COMMON ORGANIC HALIDES

Although organic halogen compounds are very rare in nature, many can be synthesized. A few of the methods of synthesis will be mentioned in this text. Several useful halogen compounds are listed in Table 22-5; for each one the proper systematic name is listed first, followed by a common name or trademark names. Some of the examples are not *alkyl* halides because they have carbon skeletons containing double bonds or aromatic rings; these structures will be discussed in Chapters 23 and 24.

TABLE 22-5. Some organic halides

Formula	Name	Applications
CCl_4	**tetrachloromethane;** carbon tetrachloride; Carbona contains CCl_4 and benzene	dry-cleaning fluid; solvent for oils, fats, waxes; some insecticide use; in veterinary medicine, used against worms and flukes
$CHCl_3$	**trichloromethane;** chloroform	solvent; general inhalation anesthetic (safety margin between anesthetic dose and lethal dose very small; can damage liver)

TABLE 22–5 continued

Formula	Name	Applications
CHI_3	**triiodomethane;** iodoform	pale yellow solid; antiseptic and local anesthetic applied to small wounds, especially in veterinary practice
CF_2Cl_2	**dichlorodifluoromethane;** Freon-12	fluid used in refrigerators; propellant in aerosols for cosmetics, paints, etc., but not for foods
CH_3CH_2Cl	**chloroethane;** ethyl chloride	local anesthetic for minor surgery (freeze technique)
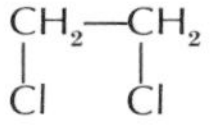 $\begin{array}{cc} CH_2 - CH_2 \\ \mid \quad \mid \\ Cl \quad Cl \end{array}$	**dichloroethane**	dry-cleaning fluid; solvent for fats, oils, waxes, resins, and especially rubber
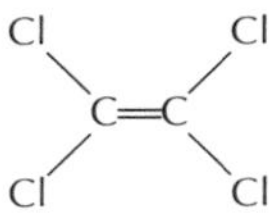 Cl,Cl,C=C,Cl,Cl	**tetrachloroethene**	dry-cleaning fluid, especially in coin-operated machines; metal degreasing; medically, in both humans and animals, against worms and flukes
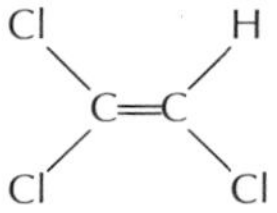 Cl,H,C=C,Cl,Cl	**trichloroethene;** Trilene	dry-cleaning fluid; metal degreasing; solvent; inhalation anesthetic, valuable for obstetrics and short operations
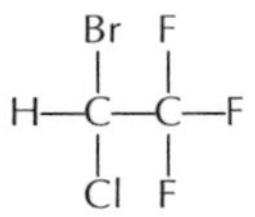 Br,F / H—C—C—F / Cl,F	**2-bromo-2-chloro-1,1,1-trifluoroethane;** halothane; Fluothane	inhalation anesthetic
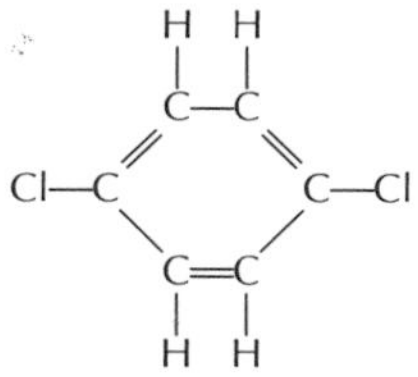 para-dichlorobenzene ring structure	**para-dichlorobenzene;** Dichloricide; Paramoth	kills moths in woolens (colorless crystals in flakes or lumps)
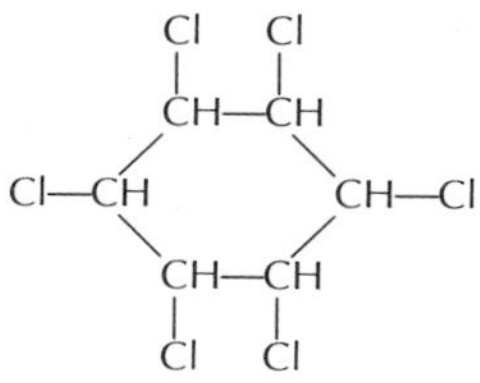 hexachlorocyclohexane ring structure	**hexachlorocyclohexane** $(C_6H_6Cl_6)$; Lindane; 666; Gammexane; BHC, benzene-hexachloride (erroneous)	very effective insecticide, wide agricultural use

It is of interest to note that most of the organic halogen compounds are similar in two types of properties. First, their biological effects seem to follow a general pattern. Depending on the particular halogen compound and its concentration, it may change the activity of individual cells; it may even kill them or a whole organism. The volatile halogen compounds, which can be inhaled, seem to affect the central nervous system, leading to unconsciousness if used in sufficient amounts. Large doses may cause death due to suspension of vital functions and/or permanent damage to certain tissues.

Second, the liquid organic halides are good solvents for many nonpolar or moderately polar organic compounds, such as alkanes, fats, waxes, and others. Some organic halides will dissolve a greater variety of substances than the alkanes will. In water, the organic halides are insoluble.

22-10 RELATION OF ALKANES TO OTHER ORGANIC COMPOUNDS

There are three reasons why it is convenient and logical to begin our study of organic chemistry with the alkanes. First, an alkane is chemically quite inert and provides a simple basis for studying the reactions of other organic compounds. For example, an *alkene* molecule, which we will discuss in the next chapter, may be regarded as a double-bond unit of structure plus an alkane skeleton.

an alkene $CH_3CH_2CH_2CH_2CH{=}CH_2$

                   alkane   functional
                   skeleton   group
                   (mainly inert) (reactive)

An alkene compound is very reactive due to the presence of a double bond between two of the carbons. *The double bond does something, or functions, and therefore that part of the structure is called a* **functional group.** While reactions are occurring at a functional group, the rest of the molecule, *the skeleton, survives unchanged.* This is a very important concept, and it simplifies the study of organic chemistry. For example, any compound having a C$=$C bond will have certain properties due to the reactivity of that bond. By learning what those properties are, we can predict the behavior of any of the thousands of different compounds in the series of alkenes. Similarly, the alcohols form a large series of compounds, each of which has an —OH group attached to an alkane skeleton. We can become acquainted with all alcohols by discovering what reactions to expect of an —OH group, and by keeping in mind that the alkane skeleton rarely reacts.

Second, the rules for naming alkanes (Section 22–3) provide the basis for naming carbon skeletons in other compounds having functional groups.

Finally, alkanes are important starting materials for synthesis because they are so abundant in petroleum. In succeeding chapters we will discuss methods for converting alkanes to other organic compounds.

In the next several chapters we will study, one by one, the various series, or families, of organic compounds. We will learn about the distinctive properties, the uses, the names, and the occurrence in nature of the compounds in each series.

IMPORTANT TERMS

Alkane   Hydrocarbon
Alkyl halide   Saturated hydrocarbon
Alkyl group   Substitution reaction
Cyclo-   Systematic name
Functional group   Unsaturated hydrocarbon

WORK EXERCISES

1. Show the condensed structural formula of

    a) 3-ethylpentane   b) 2,2-dimethylbutane
    c) 2-methyl-3-propylhexane   d) 2,2,4-trimethylpentane
    e) ethylcyclopentane   f) 1,3-dibromocyclohexane
    g) 4-ethyl-2,5-dimethyloctane   h) 3,5-dimethylheptane
    i) 2,3-dichloro-3-ethylhexane   j) 4,6-diethyl-3,4-dimethyl-6-propylnonane

2. Write condensed structural formulas for all isomers having the following molecular formulas:

    a) C_6H_{14} b) C_4H_9Cl c) $C_4H_8Cl_2$ d) $C_5H_{11}Br$

3. Write the systematic name for each structure in Problem 2. Are any of the names the same? If they are, look again to see whether the structures are really different. Is the naming system adequate—that is, does each structure have a unique name which applies to no other structure?

4. Name each structure in parts (a) through (j):

a) 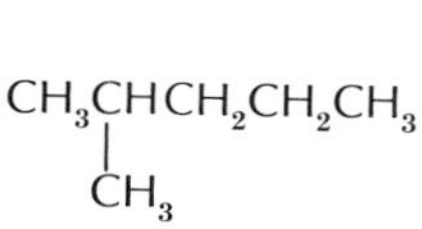 CH$_3$CHCH$_2$CH$_2$CH$_3$
       |
      CH$_3$

b) 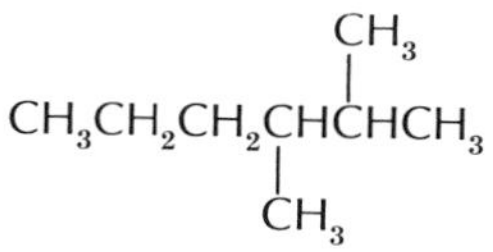   CH$_3$
                 |
    CH$_3$CH$_2$CH$_2$CHCHCH$_3$
                 |
                CH$_3$

c) 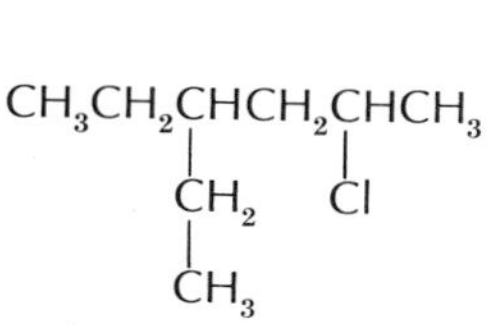 CH$_3$CH$_2$CHCH$_2$CHCH$_3$
             | |
            CH$_2$ Cl
             |
            CH$_3$

d) 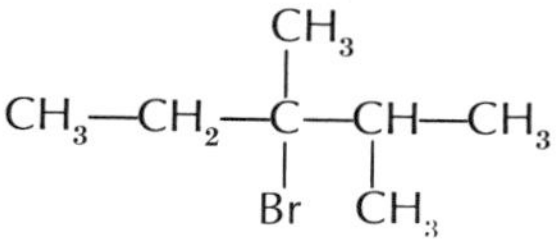   CH$_3$
                     |
   CH$_3$—CH$_2$—C—CH—CH$_3$
                 | |
                Br   CH$_3$

e) 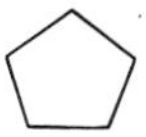 (cyclopentane)

f) 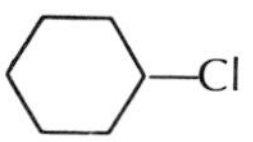 (cyclohexane)—Cl

g) 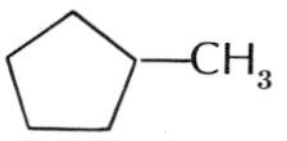 (cyclopentane)—CH$_3$

h) 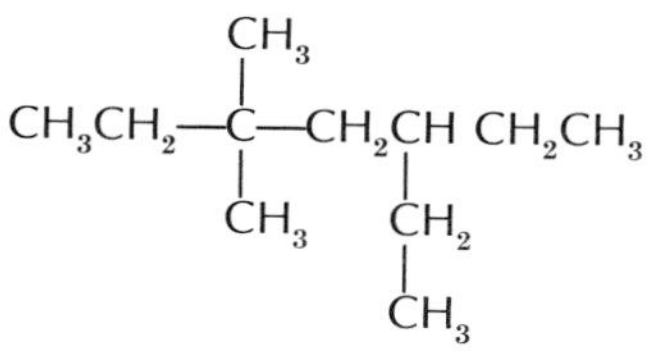   CH$_3$
                |
  CH$_3$CH$_2$—C—CH$_2$CH CH$_2$CH$_3$
               | |
             CH$_3$ CH$_2$
                   |
                 CH$_3$

i)
$$
\underset{\underset{CH_3}{|}}{CH_3CHCHCH_2}\overset{\overset{CH_3}{|}}{CHCHCH_2CH_3}
$$
with substituents CH₃, CH₃, CH₃, C₂H₅

i) $CH_3\underset{CH_3}{\overset{CH_3}{CHCHCH_2}}\underset{C_2H_5}{CHCHCH_2CH_3}$

j) $CH_3\underset{CH_2}{\overset{Br}{CHCHCH}}\underset{CH_2}{\overset{CH_3}{CHCH_2CH_3}}$
with CH_2, CH_2, CH_3, CH_2, CH_3

5. Give both a common name and a systematic name for:

   a) $CHCl_3$ b) CCl_4 c) $CH_3{-}\underset{CH_3}{CH}{-}CH_3$

   d) $CH_3{-}CH_2{-}\underset{CH_3}{CH}{-}CH_3$ e) CH_3Br

6. Write complete balanced equations for the reaction occurring in each mixture below, using structural formulas. If necessary, state "no reaction." If more than one reaction is possible in a given mixture, write equations for all of them.

   a) propane burning in a camp stove
   b) ethane and hydrogen chloride at 100°C
   c) methane and chlorine at high temperature
   d) isobutane and oxygen, heated
   e) cyclopentane and chlorine in ultraviolet light
   f) cyclohexane and air, heated
   g) pentane and concentrated sodium hydroxide
   h) methane and bromine in ultraviolet light
   i) dichloromethane and bromine in ultraviolet light

7. Name the compounds shown in Figs. 21–18 and 21–19.

8. Write a name and an abbreviated structural formula for the compounds shown in Fig. 21–21.

SUGGESTED READING

DeNevers, Noel, "Liquid Natural Gas," *Scientific American*, October, 1967. When natural gas is chilled to −162°C it becomes liquid and can be transported in containers other than pipelines. This new method of handling facilitates even wider distribution and use of natural gas.

DePuy, C. H. and K. L. Rinehart, Jr., *Introduction to Organic Chemistry*, Chapters 1 and 2, John Wiley, New York, 1967.

Evieux, E. A., "The Geneva Congress on Organic Nomenclature, 1892," *J. Chem. Educ.* **31,** 326 (1954).

Kimberlin, C. N., Jr., "Chemistry in the Manufacture of Modern Gasoline," *J. Chem. Educ.* **34,** 569 (1957).

Nelson, T. W., "The Origin of Petroleum," *J. Chem. Educ.* **31,** 399 (1954). A thorough, documented review.

Noller, C. R., *Textbook of Organic Chemistry*, 3rd ed., Chapter 5, W. B. Saunders, Philadelphia, 1966.

Rossini, F. D., "Hydrocarbons in Petroleum," *J. Chem. Educ.* **37,** 554 (1960).

Shoemaker, B. H., E. L. d'Ouville, and R. F. Marschner, "Recent Advances in Petroleum Refining," *J. Chem. Educ.* **32,** 30 (1955).

Chapter 23 UNSATURATED HYDROCARBONS: Alkenes and Alkynes

23-1 STRUCTURE AND OCCURRENCE OF ALKENES

In an **unsaturated hydrocarbon** the carbon skeleton holds *less* than the maximum number of hydrogens which it might hold. "Extra" covalent bonds can exist between some carbon atoms, because not all their valence electrons are occupied in bonds with hydrogens. An **alkene** is an unsaturated hydrocarbon having a carbon–carbon double bond; a good example is propene.

PROPENE

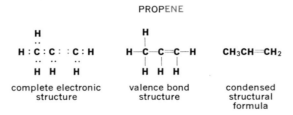

complete electronic structure   valence bond structure   condensed structural formula

The carbon–carbon double bond is very common in organic compounds. It is found in both chain and ring structures, in simple molecules and highly complex ones, in those produced within living cells, and in man-made substances.

A carbon atom having a double bond holds its attached groups at different angles than does a saturated carbon. Each doubly-bonded carbon is linked to only three other atoms, which move away from each other as far as possible. For example, in the molecule C_2H_4, called ethene, one particular carbon is bonded to two hydrogens and one other carbon. When these three atoms are spread out in space, we find bond angles of 120° (Fig. 23–1). Another result of this arrangement is that the molecule is planar; that is, the two carbons and their attached hydrogens lie in one plane.

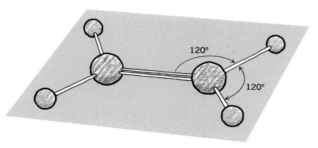

FIG. 23–1. Structure of the molecule $H_2C{=}CH_2$, ethene, showing all atoms in one plane and bond angles of 120°.

23-2 SOURCE AND USES OF ALKENES

The most economical way to obtain simple alkenes in large quantity is to **crack** alkanes from petroleum. For instance, if butane is heated to about 500°C the covalent bonds begin to break. Since any of the bonds is susceptible to fracture at this temperature, all the imaginable fragments are formed. (A more detailed explanation of the reaction is given in Section 22–7).

$$\text{H-C-C-C-C-H} \rightarrow \begin{cases} CH_3CH{=}CH_2 + CH_4 \\ CH_2{=}CH_2 + CH_3CH_3 \\ CH_3CH_2CH{=}CH_2 + H_2 \\ CH_3CH{=}CHCH_3 + H_2 \end{cases} \quad (23\text{--}1)$$

butane

Note in Eq. (23–1) that each time a segment is broken from the carbon chain there are insufficient hydrogens for all the carbon valences; consequently each break produces an alkene plus a saturated compound. The resultant mixture can be separated into its various components, each of which has a use. The cracking process is the industrial source of simple alkenes, because only small amounts exist originally in petroleum.

Alkenes which can be obtained inexpensively in this way are important intermediates for the synthesis of other organic compounds. For example, alkenes can be converted to alcohols, and these in turn to a wide variety of other organic materials.

Another important use of the cracking reaction is in the manufacture of gasoline. The hydrocarbons suitable for gasoline are chiefly octanes and other alkanes slightly smaller or larger (see Table 22–4). The amount of these found naturally in petroleum is seldom great enough to satisfy the demand for gasoline. Therefore an important part of any petroleum refinery is a cracking unit in which larger alkanes found in kerosene or fuel oil are broken into smaller molecules (Fig. 23–2). The cracking yields a great assortment of fragments, but the mixture can be distilled to yield several fractions, just as was the original petroleum. Fractions containing molecules too small or too large for gasoline are used for other purposes. The fraction of alkanes and alkenes in the C_5 to C_{10} size range constitutes "cracked gas." It has a superior octane rating and is blended with the natural gasoline.

FIG. 23–2. A catalytic cracking unit in an oil refinery. The reactor is in the center. The cracked products are piped from there to the tower at the right, a fractional distillation column which separates the material into gasoline, light oil, etc. [Courtesy of the Shell Oil Company.]

23–3 ALKENE NAMES

Table 23–1 shows the names of some representative alkenes. *Systematic names* have the ending *-ene* to designate the double bond. The position of the double bond in the carbon chain is indicated by a number placed just before the name for the chain; although the double bond is between two carbons, we need to tell only the number of the first carbon involved as we count down the chain.

CH₃CH₂CH=CHCH₃   2-pentene

If there are halogen atoms or alkyl groups attached to the chain, counting should be done from whichever end of the chain will allow *the lowest number for the double bond*.

We see in Table 23–1 several common names. These originated in the days before systematic names were developed. They are still with us because it is difficult to convince people to stop using common names for frequently encountered compounds. It is rather like trying to prevent a child's pals from calling him by a nickname. Unfortunately, some of the alkene common names are only slightly different from systematic names, which can

TABLE 23–1. Names of some alkenes

Structure	Systematic Name	Common Name
$CH_2\!=\!CH_2$	ethene	ethylene
$CH_3CH\!=\!CH_2$	propene	propylene
$CH_3CH_2CH\!=\!CH_2$	1-butene	α-butylene
$CH_3CH\!=\!CHCH_3$	2-butene	β-butylene
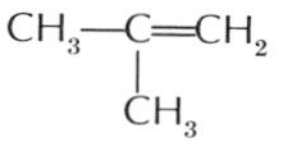 $CH_3\!-\!\underset{\underset{CH_3}{\mid}}{C}\!=\!CH_2$	methylpropene	isobutylene
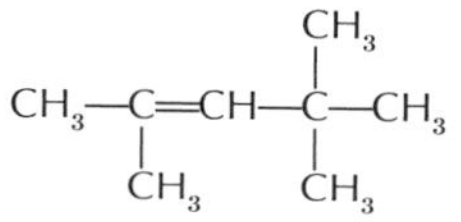 $CH_3\!-\!\underset{\underset{CH_3}{\mid}}{C}\!=\!CH\!-\!\overset{\overset{CH_3}{\mid}}{\underset{\underset{CH_3}{\mid}}{C}}\!-\!CH_3$	2,4,4-trimethyl-2-pentene	
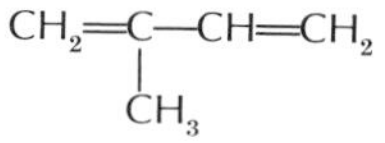 $CH_2\!=\!\underset{\underset{CH_3}{\mid}}{C}\!-\!CH\!=\!CH_2$	2-methyl-1,3-butadiene	isoprene
 (cyclopentene structure)	cyclopentene	
$R_2C\!=\!CR_2$ (general)	alkene	olefin

lead to confusion and misspelling. The common names are given in the table only so that you will be aware of the problem and can look up a name here if you see it used elsewhere. As much as possible we will use proper systematic names in this book; we urge you to do the same. In later chapters it will be necessary to learn a few common names because of their wide usage.

In common names, a double-bonded compound can be called an **olefin,** as a general term.

◄ That is, olefin is the common name equivalent to alkene. When "ethylene" gas was discovered in 1794, it was found to react with chlorine to form a water-insoluble oil. Hence it was called an olefiant gas (L. *oleum*, oil plus *-fiant*, making). Over the years the term evolved into the shorter olefin. ►

23-4 *CIS-TRANS* ISOMERS

When two carbon atoms are joined by a double bond, one carbon cannot rotate in relation to the other, under ordinary circumstances. An interesting consequence of this property is shown in Fig. 23–3; there are *two* different compounds corresponding to the name 2-butene! If the molecule has the methyl groups held on the same side, the compound is named *cis*-2-butene; if the two methyl groups are across from each other, the compound is

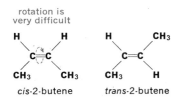

FIG. 23–3. The two isomers named 2-butene.

---

trans-2-butene. These are two distinctly different substances, each of which has its own physical properties. The double bond acts as a rigid barrier to rotation, thus restricting a methyl group in *cis*-2-butene from flipping over to produce a molecule of *trans*-2-butene.

◄ Strictly speaking, one should not say that rotation is *impossible* at a carbon–carbon double bond. However, because it can occur only if a bond is broken, we have said it will not take place under ordinary circumstances. If we supply enough energy (heat, for instance) to a molecule of *cis*-2-butene the extra bond in the double bond can be broken, for it is somewhat weaker than a carbon–carbon single bond. The bond-breaking is essentially a matter of unpairing the electrons. Once this happens, the carbons can then rotate, on the remaining single bond, into the shape of *trans*-2-butene. When the extra bond forms again (i.e., the electrons pair off again, releasing energy to the surroundings), a molecule of the *trans* compound results (Fig. 23–4). This is just another example of a chemical reaction: a bond has been broken and a new bond has been formed, yielding a different substance.

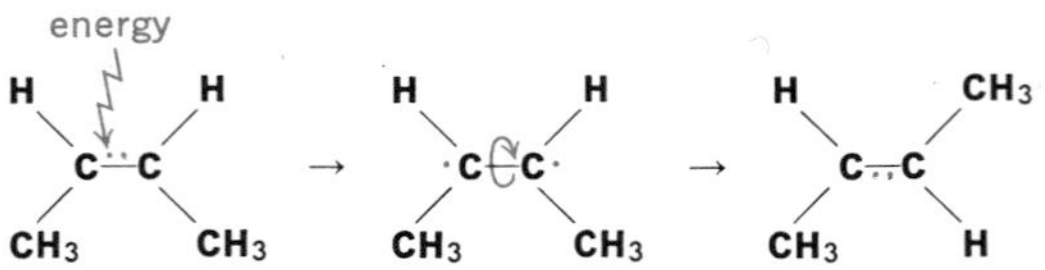

FIG. 23–4. Rotation at a double bond occurs only when a bond is broken by high energy.

Therefore it is quite proper to consider *trans*-2-butene as a different compound than *cis*-2-butene, even though one can be changed *chemically* to the other. It is possible to isolate a sample of each of the two compounds. Each will retain its specific form indefinitely, unless we purposely decide to carry out a chemical reaction to change one to the other. ►

Cis-trans isomerism is possible whenever there are enough different groups bonded around a carbon–carbon double bond. For example, there are *cis* and *trans* isomers of 1,2-dichloroethene or of 2-pentene (Fig. 23–5). However, *cis-trans* isomers of propene are not possible because one of the carbons at the double-bond holds two hydrogens (Fig. 23–6). Consequently the methyl group, whichever side it is on, will always be across from a hydrogen and beside a hydrogen.

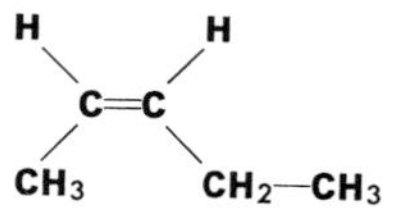

FIG. 23–5. Isomers of 2-pentene.

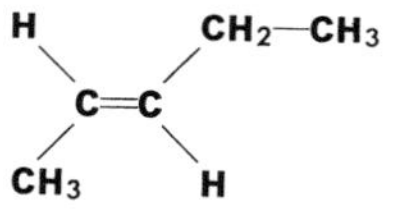

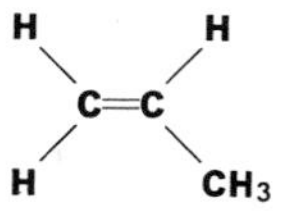

FIG. 23–6. Propene, no *cis-trans* isomers.

23–5 ALKENE REACTIONS

A. Introduction

The electrons in the "extra" bond of an alkene make it very reactive because they are loosely held and can be easily pulled into a different location to make new covalent bonds. Most reactions of alkenes fall into one category; they are **addition** reactions. Other atoms can be directly added to a double bond because valence electrons are available there: it is not necessary to displace atoms already present in order to make room for new atoms. (Recall that an alkane generally has to react by *substitution* because its valence bonds are already saturated with hydrogens.)

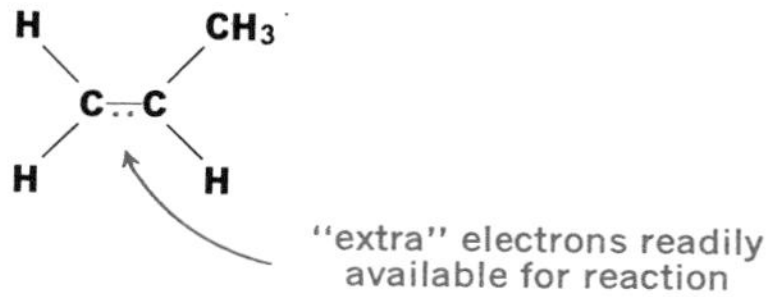

"extra" electrons readily
available for reaction

Alkenes can also be attacked by common ionic oxidizing agents ($KMnO_4$, and so forth). This reaction, too, depends on the readily available electrons. Oxidation amounts to loss of electrons, or at least displacement of electrons toward a new atom.

In this chapter the properties of a carbon–carbon double bond will be illustrated with simple alkenes. But keep in mind that even when a large molecule contains other functional groups, a double bond reacts in its own characteristic way. This is why we can study organic compounds by examining the properties of the various units of structure separately, and later predict the behavior of complex molecules having many functional groups. A molecule of citronellol* provides a simple illustration (Fig. 23–7).

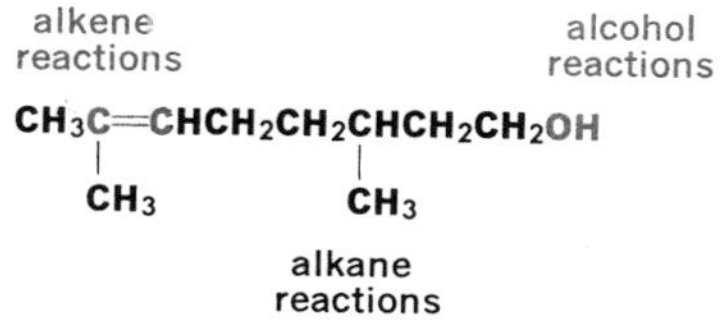

FIG. 23–7. Citronellol, 3,7-dimethyl-6-octene-1-ol.

Each of the types of structure present (alkene, alkane, alcohol) will behave in its own distinctive manner, and the chemical properties of citronellol will be the sum of all of these.

B. Addition of Hydrogen (Hydrogenation)

When an alkene is treated with hydrogen gas, in the presence of certain metal catalysts, it is converted to an alkane; the process is called **hydrogenation.**

$$
\begin{array}{c}
\text{H}\;\text{H}\;\text{H}\;\text{H}\;\text{H} \\
\mid\;\mid\;\mid\;\mid\;\mid \\
\text{H--C--C--C==C--C--H} \;+\; \text{H--H} \xrightarrow{\text{Ni}} \\
\mid\;\mid\quad\quad\mid \\
\text{H}\;\text{H}\quad\quad\;\text{H}
\end{array}
\qquad
\begin{array}{c}
\text{H}\;\text{H}\;\text{H}\;\text{H}\;\text{H} \\
\mid\;\mid\;\mid\;\mid\;\mid \\
\text{H--C--C--C--C--C--H} \\
\mid\;\mid\;\mid\;\mid\;\mid \\
\text{H}\;\text{H}\;\text{H}\;\text{H}\;\text{H}
\end{array}
\tag{23-2}
$$

2-pentene   hydrogen   pentane

The metals most successful as catalysts for hydrogenation are nickel, palladium, and platinum. Reaction occurs when both the alkene and hydrogen are adsorbed onto the surface of the metal. Since the amount of surface is important, the metal is used in a finely divided form; in this condition it is a black powder resembling charcoal. The reaction shown in Eq. (23–2) is carried out by adding a very small amount of nickel powder to some liquid pentene in a bottle or tank. The rest of the vessel is filled with hydrogen gas, and the mixture is shaken to keep the nickel powder dispersed. After ten or fifteen minutes the reaction is complete.

Such a reaction would not be the most practical way to get a simple alkane such as pentane, which is easily obtained from petroleum. Furthermore, we learned in Section 23-2 that the reverse procedure is more common; that is, a simple alkene is generally obtained *from* an alkane. However, hydrogenation might be very useful if we wanted to convert a segment of alkene structure in a more complex molecule to a saturated segment. For instance, cottonseed oil can be converted to a fat (Section 27–4), or maleic acid to succinic acid (Eq. 23–3).

$$
\text{HO--C--CH==CH--C--OH} + \text{H}_2 \xrightarrow{\text{Pt}} \text{HO--C--CH}_2\text{--CH}_2\text{--C--OH}
\tag{23-3}
$$

maleic acid   succinic acid

C. Addition of Chlorine or Bromine

Chlorine or bromine adds readily to a carbon–carbon double bond.

$$
\text{CH}_3\text{--CH}_2\text{--CH}_2\text{--CH}_2\text{--CH==CH}_2 + \text{Cl}_2 \rightarrow \text{CH}_3\text{--CH}_2\text{--CH}_2\text{--CH}_2\text{--CH--CH}_2
\tag{23-4}
$$

                                                          Cl   Cl

1-hexene   1,2-dichlorohexane

Reaction (23–4) can be carried out by simply bubbling chlorine gas into the liquid 1-hexene; no catalyst or heat is required.

Since chlorine is one of the few substances which can react with an *alkane*, it is especially important to note the differences in behavior of an alkene and an alkane with chlorine. *The alkene undergoes an addition reaction,* (23–4), *to give only one product.* Ordinary conditions are sufficient. In contrast, *an alkane reacts by substitution;* beside the organic products, HCl is always formed (Eq. 22–3). Drastic conditions are required: either ultraviolet light or a high temperature.

A reaction with bromine under ordinary conditions can be used as a simple laboratory test to detect the presence of unsaturation in a hydrocarbon.

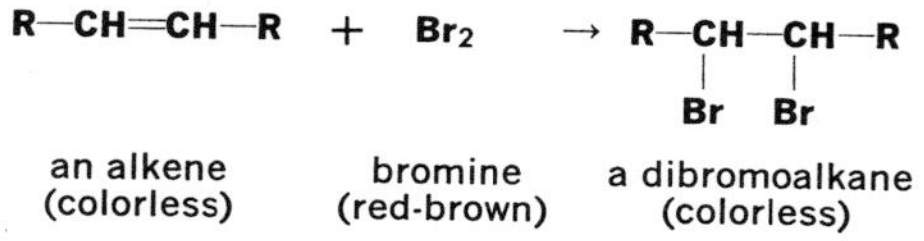

$$R-CH\!=\!CH-R \ + \ Br_2 \ \rightarrow \ R-CH-CH-R$$
$$\underset{Br \quad\ \ Br}{|\qquad\ |}$$

(23–5)

an alkene	bromine	a dibromoalkane
(colorless)	(red-brown)	(colorless)

Bromine itself has a dark red-brown color. If it is used up by addition to an alkene, the color disappears. However, if even one or two drops of bromine is mixed with an alkane, the solution takes on and continues to have a red-brown color because the bromine remains unchanged. Consequently, an alkene can be distinguished from an alkane by testing with bromine.

◄ It is convenient to use tetrachloromethane as a solvent for the test reaction, (Eq. 23–5), for several reasons. It is colorless and chemically inert to the bromine; it is a good solvent for all the substances involved; and very dilute solutions of bromine are sufficient. Thus we test a hydrocarbon by dissolving a drop of it in a few milliliters of tetrachloromethane in a test tube. To this we add, drop by drop, a solution containing 5% bromine in tetrachloromethane. If the color of the bromine solution disappears as fast as the drops enter the hydrocarbon solution, we assume an unsaturated hydrocarbon is present.

Although chlorine, too, reacts easily with an unsaturated compound, for practical reasons it is not used in a test. Chlorine is such a pale yellow-green color that in dilute solutions it is impossible to detect a color change. Also, chlorine is troublesome to handle because it is a gas. ►

D. Addition of Hydrogen Chloride

A number of acidic compounds will add to an alkene. We will mention the most common examples, one of which is hydrogen chloride.

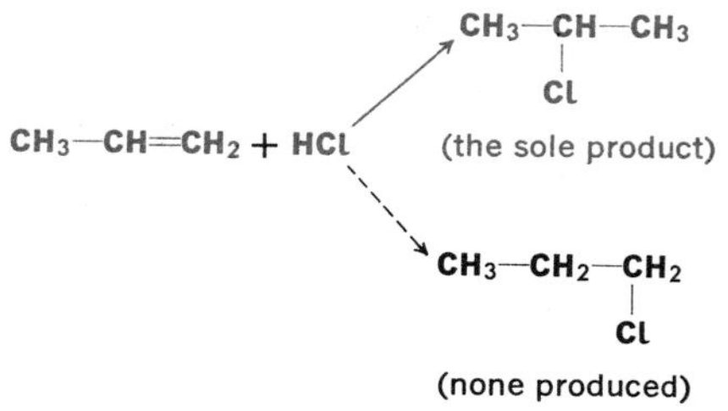

$$CH_3-CH\!=\!CH_2 + HCl$$

$$\nearrow \quad \underset{\underset{Cl}{|}}{CH_3-CH-CH_3}$$

(the sole product)

(23–6)

$$\searrow \quad \underset{\underset{Cl}{|}}{CH_3-CH_2-CH_2}$$

(none produced)

It is apparent (Eq. 23–6) that hydrogen chloride could add to propene in two different ways. Curiously, only one product is formed. This fact was first reported in 1869 by the Russian chemist Markovnikov. Somewhat paraphrased, **Markovnikov's rule** states that *when an acid adds to an alkene, the hydrogen becomes attached to the carbon already bearing the most hydrogens.*

◄ Markovnikov originally formulated this generality after observing the behavior of several alkenes. He had no idea *why* the results were thus. In the mid-1930's, Professor Frank Whitmore, of Pennsylvania State University, proposed a theory to explain how a reaction such as (23–6) occurs, and hence why Markovnikov's rule is correct. Briefly, the explanation is as follows: A Cl^- ion would be repelled by the extra electrons in the alkene double bond. The alkene is first attacked by an H^+ ion which is seeking electrons. An approaching positive ion can distort the electron pair in the "extra" bond of the alkene, pulling it into position to form a new covalent bond.

$$
\begin{array}{ccc}
\text{H} & \text{H} & \text{H} \\
| & | & | \\
\text{H}-\text{C}-\text{C}-\text{C}-\text{H} & \rightarrow & \text{H}-\text{C}-\text{C}-\text{C}-\text{H} \\
| & & | \quad + \quad | \\
\text{H} & & \text{H} \quad \text{H}
\end{array}
\qquad (23\text{–}7)
$$

H^+ (a carbonium ion)

The intermediate structure produced in Eq. (23–7) is a carbonium ion. It is a highly reactive ion which promptly combines with a chloride ion, as shown in Eq. (23–8).

$$
\text{H}-\text{C}-\text{C}-\text{C}-\text{H} + Cl^- \rightarrow \text{H}-\text{C}-\text{C}-\text{C}-\text{H}
\qquad (23\text{–}8)
$$

In the first step, the H^+ *might* have combined with propene, as shown in Eq. (23–9), producing a different carbonium ion.

$$
\begin{array}{ccc}
\text{H} & \text{H} & \text{H} \\
| & | & | \\
\text{H}-\text{C}-\text{C}-\text{C}-\text{H} & \rightarrow & \text{H}-\text{C}-\text{C}-\text{C}-\text{H} \\
| & & | \quad | \quad + \\
\text{H} & & \text{H} \quad \text{H}
\end{array}
\qquad (23\text{–}9)
$$

H^+ (a carbonium ion)

The nature of carbonium ions is such that the type produced in Eq. (23–7) is more stable and more easily formed than that shown in Eq. (23–9). In the competition, Eq. (23–7) wins, giving the results predicted by Markovnikov's rule.

During the years since Whitmore's first proposal it has become evident that carbonium ions are very common and important in certain organic reactions, especially those involving acids. As a result, chemists have studied carbonium ions intensively and have added significant details to Whitmore's original theory. Much research on the behavior of carbonium ions is still being conducted. ►

E. Addition of Sulfuric Acid

Sulfuric acid adds to an alkene, following Markovnikov's rule.

◄ In order to understand the structures resulting from this addition reaction, we should first examine the structure of sulfuric acid. The formula H_2SO_4 lists the atoms but tells nothing of the manner in which they are bonded. Actually, the four oxygens are clustered around the sulfur, and the hydrogens are bonded to oxygens.

SULFURIC ACID

$$
\begin{array}{ccc}
\ddot{:}\underset{..}{\ddot{O}}\ddot{:} & O & \\
H\underset{..}{:}\underset{..}{\ddot{O}}\underset{..}{:}S\underset{..}{:}\underset{..}{\ddot{O}}\underset{..}{:}H & H-O-\overset{\uparrow}{\underset{\downarrow}{S}}-O-H & HOSO_2OH \\
\underset{..}{:}\underset{..}{\ddot{O}}\underset{..}{:} & O & \\
\text{electronic} & \text{valence bond} & \text{condensed} \\
\text{structure} & \text{structure} & \text{structural} \\
& & \text{formula}
\end{array}
$$

Hereafter, in writing organic reactions, we will often use the condensed structural formula of sulfuric acid. ►

The addition of sulfuric acid to a double bond is illustrated in Eq. (23–10).

$$CH_3-CH=CH_2 + HOSO_2OH \rightarrow \quad CH_3-\underset{\underset{OSO_2OH}{|}}{CH}-CH_3 \tag{23–10}$$

propene   an alkyl hydrogen
                                      sulfate

The greatest use for the resulting alkyl hydrogen sulfate is to convert it to an alcohol. This is done by warming the compound in water:

$$CH_3-\underset{\underset{OSO_2OH}{|}}{CH}-CH_3 + H-O-H \rightarrow \quad CH_3-\underset{\overset{|}{OH}}{CH}-CH_3 \; + HOSO_2OH \tag{23–11}$$

2-propanol
(isopropyl alcohol)

Thus, reactions (23–10) and (23–11) constitute a two-step synthesis of an alcohol from an alkene.

F. Oxidation of Alkenes by Permanganate

An alkene is easily oxidized. It reacts, for example, with a dilute solution of potassium permanganate at room temperature.

$$3R-CH=CH-R + 2KMnO_4 + 4H_2O \rightarrow 3R-\underset{\overset{|}{OH}}{CH}-\underset{\overset{|}{OH}}{CH}-R + 2MnO_2\downarrow + 2KOH \tag{23–12}$$

        (purple)   (brown)

Reaction (23–12) is used chiefly as a test, which is possible because of the easily detected color changes. The permanganate is a *purple solution*, looking very much like grape juice.

When it reacts, its color disappears, and we see in its place a *dark brown precipitate* of manganese dioxide. A positive reaction *suggests* the presence of unsaturation in the organic compound; as a check we should also try the bromine test (Section 23–5C). Certain organic compounds other than unsaturated hydrocarbons can react with potassium permanganate.

◄ If an alkene is treated with *hot, concentrated* potassium permanganate solution, a more drastic change occurs. The alkene is split apart at the site of the double bond.

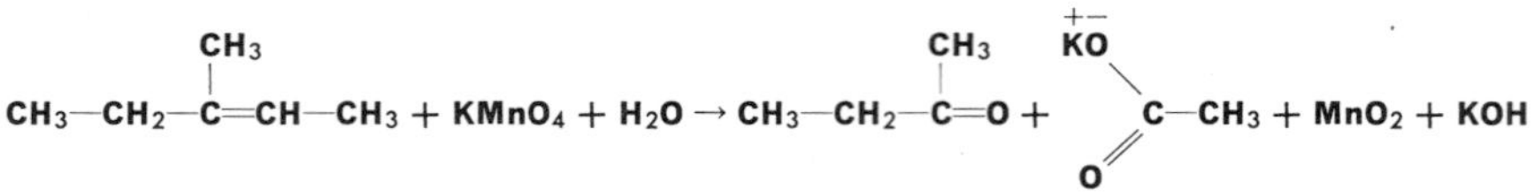

$$CH_3-CH_2-\underset{\underset{CH_3}{|}}{C}=CH-CH_3 + KMnO_4 + H_2O \rightarrow CH_3-CH_2-\underset{\underset{CH_3}{|}}{C}=O + \underset{\underset{O}{\parallel}}{\overset{\overset{CH_3 \quad \overset{+-}{KO}}{\diagdown}}{C}}-CH_3 + MnO_2 + KOH$$

(a ketone)   (a salt)

The fragments thus obtained are often well-known compounds which can be identified rather easily. If they are, we can deduce the structure of the original alkene, knowing that the functional groups in the fragments arose from the double bond.

Until about the time of World War II, oxidative cleavage was one of the most fruitful techniques employed by chemists to determine the structure of an organic compound. Now there are analytical instruments which reveal much information about a structure with less labor by the chemist. The instruments not only provide answers to simple problems rapidly, but enable the chemist to attack more complex problems such as the structure of antibiotics, vitamin B_{12}, or insulin. ►

G. Combustion

If a mixture of an alkene and oxygen is ignited, combustion occurs.

$$CH_3CH_2CH{=}CH_2 + 6O_2 \rightarrow 4CO_2 + 4H_2O$$

This behavior is not unique to alkenes. In fact, alkanes and practically all other organic compounds will also burn (Section 22–5). Therefore, in the remaining chapters, when we discuss each new series of compounds, we will not bother to mention that each one is combustible.

23–6 ALKYNES

Unsaturated hydrocarbons having a *triple* bond between two carbons are called **alkynes.** The ending *-yne* is used in a systematic name; the rest of the naming rules are the same as those for alkenes.

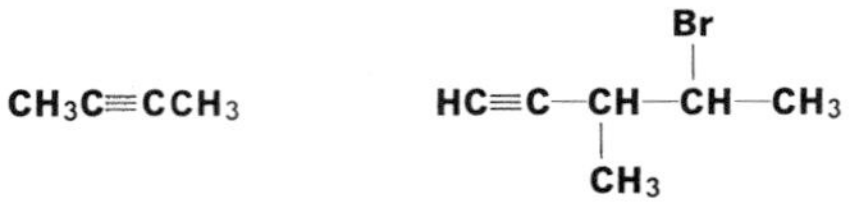

$$CH_3C{\equiv}CCH_3 \qquad\qquad HC{\equiv}C-\underset{\underset{CH_3}{|}}{CH}-\overset{\overset{Br}{|}}{CH}-CH_3$$

2-butyne   4-bromo-3-methyl-1-pentyne

Chemical reactions of alkynes are similar to those of alkenes, the chief difference being that the alkyne has *two* "extra" bonds which can react.

$$CH_3-CH_2-C\equiv CH + 2H_2 \xrightarrow{Ni} CH_3-CH_2-CH_2-CH_3$$

$$CH_3-CH_2-C\equiv CH + HCl \longrightarrow CH_3-CH_2-\underset{\underset{Cl}{|}}{C}=CH_2$$

Markovnikov rule applies

(1 mole)   (1 mole)

$$CH_3-CH_2-C\equiv CH + 2HCl \rightarrow CH_3-CH_2-\overset{\overset{Cl}{|}}{\underset{\underset{Cl}{|}}{C}}-CH_3$$

(1 mole)   (excess)

Alkynes also give positive results with the bromine test (Section 23–5C) and the permanganate test (Section 23–5F). The tests, therefore, cannot be used to distinguish an alkene from an alkyne. Instead, they are general for an unsaturated compound.

The structural formulas we have written for alkynes show quite accurately that each of the bond angles at a triple bond is 180°. This angle illustrates, once again,

180°

$$CH_3-\overset{\frown}{C}\equiv C-CH_3$$

the principle that the groups bonded to one particular carbon will get as far away from each other as possible.

23–7 ACETYLENE (Ethyne)

Ethyne, $HC\equiv CH$, requires some extra attention because of its tremendous practical importance. It is used widely and therefore is nearly always called by its common name, acetylene.

◄ The historical origin of the word acetylene is complicated and is more confusing than informative. Continued use of the word is also unfortunate, especially since the ending *-ene* suggests a double bond. ►

The production of acetylene in the United States is now well over one billion pounds a year. The oldest method of synthesis involves the following reactions:

$$3C + CaO \xrightarrow{2500°C} CaC_2 + CO \tag{23-13}$$

coke   lime   calcium   carbon
                  carbide   monoxide

$$(^-C\equiv C^-)Ca^{2+} + 2HOH \rightarrow HC\equiv CH + Ca(OH)_2 \tag{23-14}$$

calcium   acetylene
carbide

In an electric furnace, coke and lime are converted to calcium carbide, a solid (Eq. 23–13). It is essentially a salt, as shown in Eq. (23–14). Treatment of calcium carbide with water replaces the calcium ions with hydrogens, yielding acetylene.

◄ One of the raw materials for this process is limestone; when heated, it yields the lime required for reaction (23–13).

$$CaCO_3 \xrightarrow{heat} CaO + CO_2$$
limestone   lime

The calcium hydroxide produced by reaction (23–14) can be reconverted to lime by heating.

$$Ca(OH)_2 \xrightarrow{heat} CaO + H_2O$$

A choice between the two sources of lime depends on economic conditions.

The other key raw material is coke, obtained from coal as described in Section 24–9. ►

Slightly less than half of the acetylene manufactured in the United States now comes from a different raw material, natural gas (methane). Exposure to a very high temperature for less than one-tenth of a second converts the methane to acetylene.

$$2CH_4 \xrightarrow{1600°} HC\equiv CH + 3H_2 \tag{23-15}$$

◄ This is a radical reaction involving both cracking and recombination of fragments. Cracking of carbon–hydrogen bonds first produces methyl radicals. These may pair off to form ethane. Continued cracking of carbon–hydrogen bonds on the two-carbon skeleton eventually leads to acetylene.

$$CH_4 \rightarrow H\cdot + \cdot CH_3$$
$$CH_4 \rightarrow H\cdot + \cdot CH_3$$
$$\downarrow \quad\quad \downarrow$$
$$H_2 \quad\quad CH_3-CH_3 \xrightarrow[cracking]{continued} HC\equiv CH + 2H_2$$

All the steps are reversible. For instance, cracking of the carbon–carbon bond of ethane could reconvert it to methyl radicals. Reasonable yields of acetylene are produced because it is the most stable of all the possible products. One reason for the short reaction time is the very high temperature; even the acetylene would decompose if allowed to remain long at this temperature. ►

Combustion of acetylene, especially in the presence of oxygen rather than air, produces a very hot flame (near 2800°C). About 15% of the domestic production of acetylene is used in oxyacetylene torches for cutting and welding steel.

The rest of the acetylene goes into the synthesis of other organic compounds. The equations below show the most important synthetic uses of acetylene. Note that each one starts with an addition to the unsaturated bond of acetylene.

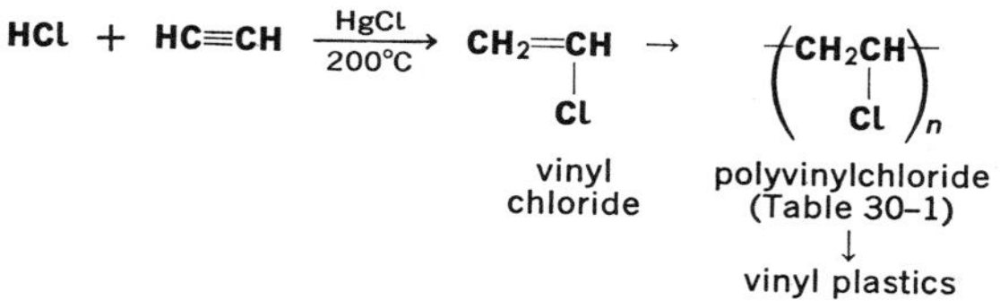

$$HCl + HC{\equiv}CH \xrightarrow[200°C]{HgCl} CH_2{=}CH \underset{Cl}{|} \rightarrow \left(CH_2CH \underset{Cl}{|}\right)_n \qquad (23\text{–}16)$$

vinyl chloride　　　polyvinylchloride
(Table 30–1)
↓
vinyl plastics

$$HCN + HC{\equiv}CH \xrightarrow{CuCl} CH_2{=}CH \underset{CN}{|} \rightarrow \left(CH_2{-}CH \underset{CN}{|}\right)_n \qquad (23\text{–}17)$$

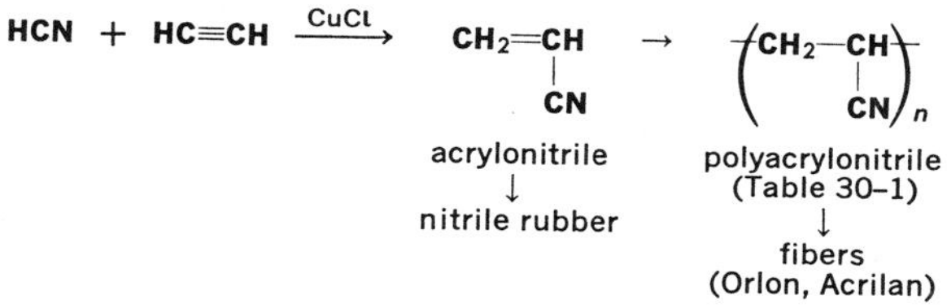

acrylonitrile　　　polyacrylonitrile
↓　　　　　　(Table 30–1)
nitrile rubber　　　　　↓
fibers
(Orlon, Acrilan)

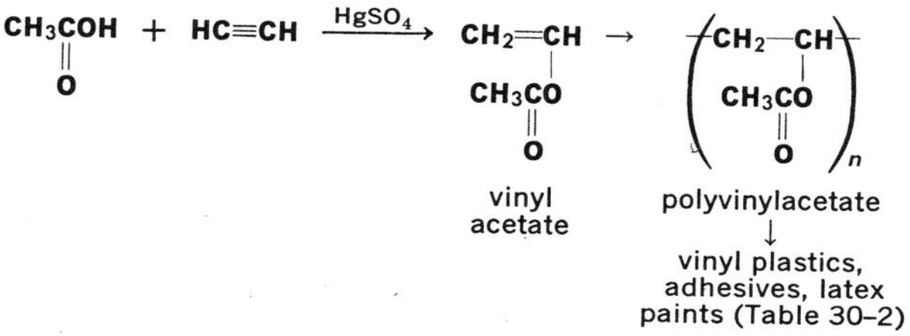

$$CH_3\underset{O}{\overset{\|}{C}}OH + HC{\equiv}CH \xrightarrow{HgSO_4} CH_2{=}CH \underset{CH_3\overset{\|}{\underset{O}{C}}O}{|} \rightarrow \left(CH_2{-}CH \underset{CH_3\overset{\|}{\underset{O}{C}}O}{|}\right)_n \qquad (23\text{–}18)$$

vinyl
acetate　　　polyvinylacetate
↓
vinyl plastics,
adhesives, latex
paints (Table 30–2)

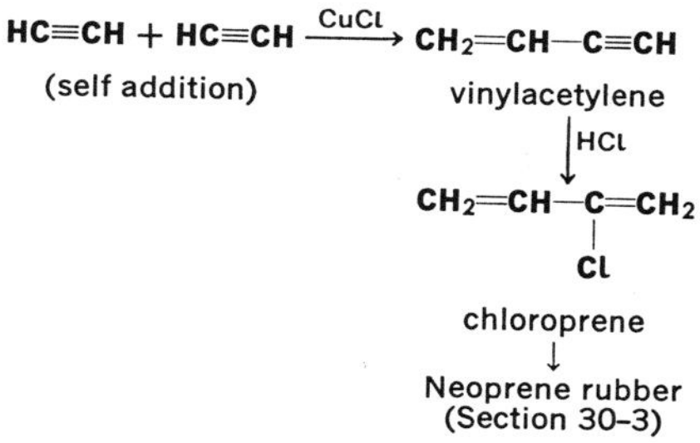

$$HC{\equiv}CH + HC{\equiv}CH \xrightarrow{CuCl} CH_2{=}CH{-}C{\equiv}CH \qquad (23\text{–}19)$$

(self addition)　　　vinylacetylene
↓ HCl
$$CH_2{=}CH{-}\underset{Cl}{\overset{|}{C}}{=}CH_2$$
chloroprene
↓
Neoprene rubber
(Section 30–3)

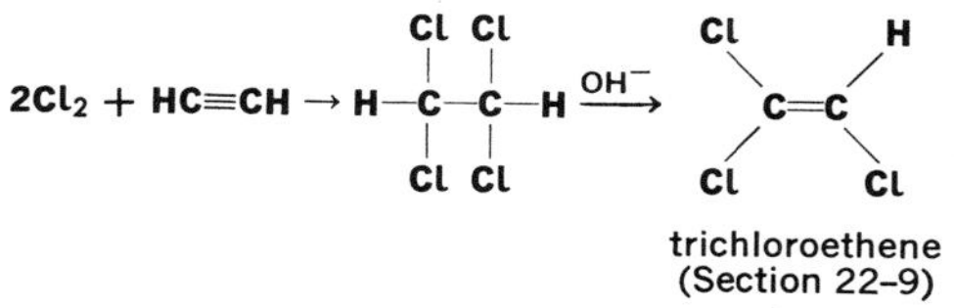

$$2Cl_2 + HC{\equiv}CH \rightarrow H{-}\underset{\underset{Cl}{|}}{\overset{\overset{Cl}{|}}{C}}{-}\underset{\underset{Cl}{|}}{\overset{\overset{Cl}{|}}{C}}{-}H \xrightarrow{OH^-} \underset{Cl}{\overset{Cl}{C}}{=}\underset{Cl}{\overset{H}{C}} \qquad (23\text{–}20)$$

trichloroethene
(Section 22–9)

$$\underset{Cl}{\overset{Cl}{C}}{=}\underset{Cl}{\overset{H}{C}} \xrightarrow{Cl_2} Cl{-}\underset{\underset{Cl}{|}}{\overset{\overset{Cl}{|}}{C}}{-}\underset{\underset{Cl}{|}}{\overset{\overset{Cl}{|}}{C}}{-}H \xrightarrow{OH^-} \underset{Cl}{\overset{Cl}{C}}{=}\underset{Cl}{\overset{Cl}{C}} \qquad (23\text{–}21)$$

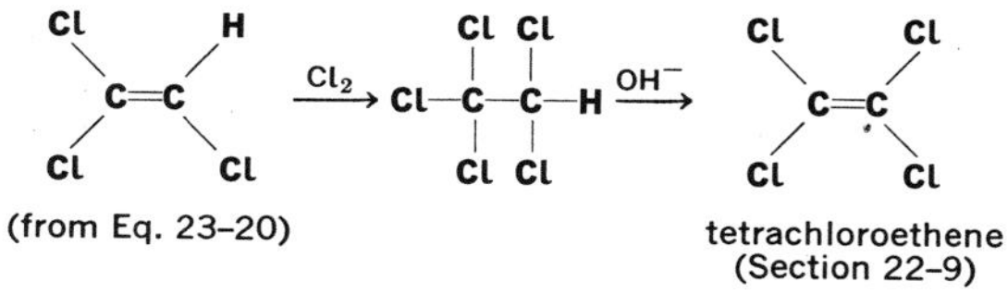

(from Eq. 23–20)　　　tetrachloroethene
(Section 22–9)

IMPORTANT TERMS

Addition reaction   Catalyst   Markovnikov rule
Alkene   Cis-trans isomers   Olefin
Alkyl hydrogen sulfate   Cracking reaction   Oxidation
Alkyne   Hydrogenation   Unsaturated hydrocarbon

WORK EXERCISES

1. Write the condensed structural formula and molecular formula for the following:

    a) hexane, 1-hexene, and cyclohexane .   b) heptane, 2-heptene, and cycloheptane
    c) 2-methylpentane; 2,3-dimethyl-2-butene; methylcyclopentane

2. Which compounds in Problem 1 are isomers? What generalization can you make about the relation between alkenes and cycloalkanes?

3. Write the structural formulas of all possible open-chain compounds (i.e., those whose carbon skeletons are not rings) that have the following molecular formulas:

    a) C_4H_8 b) C_5H_{10}

4. Write the structural formulas of all possible ring compounds having molecular formulas

    a) C_4H_8 b) C_5H_{10}

5. In view of your answers to Problems 3 and 4, give the total number of isomers of

    a) C_4H_8 b) C_5H_{10}

6. Write a systematic name for each compound in Problem 3.

7. Write the condensed structural formula for each of the following:

    a) 3-chloro-1-butene   b) trans-2-butene
    c) cyclohexene   d) 3-hexyne
    e) cis-4-methyl-2-pentene   f) 1-bromo-2-butyne

8. Briefly describe the principal method for obtaining alkenes in large quantities. What is the raw material? What processes and reactions are used to obtain an alkene from it?

9. Why are alkenes more reactive than alkanes?

10. Write a complete, balanced equation for the reaction occurring in each mixture below, using structural formulas. If necessary, state "no reaction."

    a) 1-butene, hydrogen, platinum   b) propene, bromine, 25°C
    c) 2-pentene burning in air   d) 1-butene, hydrogen chloride
    e) cyclopentene, chlorine, 25°C   f) cyclohexene, hydrogen, nickel
    g) 2-butene, concentrated sulfuric acid h) 1 mole of ethyne, 1 mole of hydrogen chloride
    i) propene, hydrogen chloride   j) propene, chlorine
    k) propyne, excess bromine   l) 1 mole propyne, 1 mole hydrogen chloride
    m) propyne burning in air

11. Which of the following would react with dilute permanganate solution at 25°C, causing its purple color to be replaced by a brown precipitate of MnO_2?

    a) propene   b) butane   c) cyclopentane
    d) butyne   e) 2-butene   f) cyclohexene
    g) 3-methyl-1-pentene   h) 2-chlorobutane

12. Show structural formulas of at least six compounds, not counting *cis-trans* isomers, which would result from the cracking of pentane at 500°C.

13. Consider the synthesis of chloroethane from ethane, on an industrial scale.

    a) What would be the source of the ethane?
    b) Write an equation to show how ethane could be converted to chloroethane in one step; i.e., by one reaction.
    c) Write equations to show how ethane could be converted to chloroethane by two steps.
    d) Suggest a reason why method (c) might be more satisfactory for producing pure chloroethane than method (b), despite the fact that (c) requires two steps.

SUGGESTED READING

DePuy, C. H. and K. L. Rinehart, Jr., *Introduction to Organic Chemistry*, Chapter 3. John Wiley, New York, 1967.

Hart, H. and R. D. Schuetz, *Organic Chemistry*, 3rd ed., Chapter 3. Houghton Mifflin, Boston, 1966.

Jones, J., "The Markovnikov Rule," *J. Chem. Educ.* **38**, 297 (1961). A fascinating account of the development of a scientific "law." Includes many details and special examples not described in this book.

Noller, C. R., *Textbook of Organic Chemistry*, 3rd ed., Chapter 6. W. B. Saunders, Philadelphia, 1966.

Chapter 24   AROMATIC HYDROCARBONS: Benzene and Related Compounds

24–1 TYPE OF STRUCTURE

Chemists long ago became intrigued by the fragrant oils produced by certain plants, such as clove oil, wintergreen oil, and almond oil. The compounds seemed to share so many similar properties that chemists thought of them as a particular class of substances. They became known as *aromatic* compounds because of their odors.

One simple aromatic compound is **toluene,** C_7H_8, obtained by heating the balsam formed in the bark of the South American *tolu* tree. Another is produced when the fragrant *benzoin gum* is decomposed to yield a volatile liquid, of formula C_6H_6, which was named **benzene.** Gradually chemists recognized that the compounds in their "aromatic" class all had a low ratio of hydrogens to carbons, had at least six carbons, and were apparently related to benzene. They also soon learned that "aromatic" was not a very accurate description. Many of the compounds which obviously belong in this class because of their structures and properties do *not* have odors; conversely, many substances having entirely different types of structure *are* fragrant. Although the old name has persisted, we now define an **aromatic compound** *as one having a characteristic structure like that of benzene.*

Clearly, it is important to learn *what* about the structure of benzene is so distinctive. For several decades chemists were baffled about how to write the structure of this compound. We shall not have time to review all the experimental observations and the numerous attempts to write structures consistent with the facts. Instead, we shall present the formulas which now seem to be the best representation of the structure of benzene.

Benzene, C_6H_6, has its six carbons joined in a ring, with one hydrogen on each carbon. This would require only three of the four valence electrons on each carbon, leaving one electron on each unshared, as shown in formula (a). It might seem then that an unshared electron could pair off with a similar one from an adjacent carbon, forming a structure such as (b) or (c).

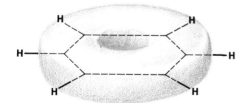

(a)   (b)   (c)

Formulas (b) and (c) raise some annoying questions, the most puzzling of which is the fact that *benzene does not have the chemical properties of an alkene.* We said that when a compound has a carbon–carbon double bond, and when we write this in its formula, we expect it to behave like a typical alkene. Since benzene does not behave in this way, neither formula (b) nor (c) seems to represent its true structure.

According to modern theory we believe that the "extra" electrons in a benzene ring do *not* pair off in specific locations, where they would be available to react as alkene double bonds. Instead, each electron interacts with the other unpaired electrons on *both* sides of it. The result is a continuous doughnut-shaped *electron-cloud* around the carbon skeleton of the benzene ring. All we know is that somewhere in the cloud there are six electrons. This is illustrated in the perspective diagram of Fig. 24–1. The ordinary covalent bonds forming the skeleton of the molecule are shown with dashed black lines; the electron cloud is in color.

FIG. 24–1. Electronic structure of benzene. The cloud represents the space occupied by six electrons.

It is possible, by means of complicated theoretical calculations, to show that this sort of electron cloud makes the molecule especially stable. It is stable because the charge of the electrons does not have to be concentrated in certain locations. We say the electrons are "delocalized," or spread out through the cloud. *Pairs* of electrons are not accessible for the type of addition reaction which is so easy for an alkene; nor are the electrons commonly attacked by an oxidizing agent. Consequently, we consider that benzene is not an unsaturated hydrocarbon, despite the fact that it has very few hydrogens and does have some "extra" electrons.

Although Fig. 24–1 gives a satisfactory picture of the distribution of the electrons in benzene, we are still left with the problem of how to write a simple formula using our standard symbols. It is inconvenient to draw a detailed picture such as Fig. 24–1 each time we want to write a chemical equation for benzene. Organic chemists now often use formula (d) or (e), in which the circle represents the continuous cloud of six electrons.

Formula (e) is the abbreviated style, in which we assume there is one carbon at each corner and each is holding one hydrogen. (Compare this formula with that for cyclohexane, Fig. 21–20.) In this book we shall use formula (e) for benzene. Another style, still found in many books, is to use a formula such as (c) or its abbreviated form f. The disadvantage of formula (c) or (f) is that you must remember that benzene does not *really* have double bonds. The three alternating "extra" bonds shown in (f) must be thought of as representing a total of six electrons held in a special way.

24–2 NAMES

A compound having an alkyl group attached to a benzene ring is named by prefixing the alkyl group name to the word benzene. Methyl benzene, however, is ordinarily called toluene.

The hydrocarbon names are used as the basis for naming other compounds. If two or more groups are attached to a ring, their relative positions are indicated by numbers. Since there is no "end" to the ring, we start counting at one of the groups.

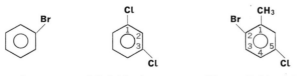

The hydrocarbon names are used as the basis for naming other compounds. If two or more groups are attached to a ring, their relative positions are indicated by numbers. Since there is no "end" to the ring, we start counting at one of the groups.

bromobenzene   1,3-dichlorobenzene   2-bromo-5-chlorotoluene

If *only* two groups are present, their relative positions can be designated by the terms *ortho, meta,* or *para,* abbreviated *o-, m-,* or *p-:*

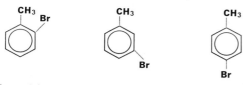

o-bromotoluene   *m*-bromotoluene   *p*-bromotoluene

It is necessary to realize that, for benzene structures, the distance between groups is the important factor in assigning names. For example, all the formulas below represent the same compound, even though the molecules are shown in different positions.

1,3-dibromobenzene or *m*-dibromobenzene

It is possible for a compound to be built from two or more fused benzene rings.

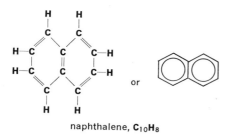

naphthalene, $C_{10}H_8$

◄ The numbering system for naphthalene derivatives is shown below. In case only one group is present, the positions are sometimes designated by the Greek letters α and β. ►

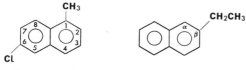

6-chloro-1-methylnaphthalene β-ethylnaphthalene
                                     2-ethylnaphthalene

The skeletons of a few of the other possible fused-ring aromatic hydrocarbons are shown below.

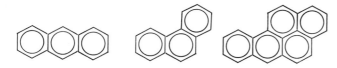

Some of the compounds composed of several rings induce the growth of cancer. One example is the last compound shown on page 325. Such compounds occur in coal tar and in cigarette tar.

In the examples of aromatic compounds shown so far, names have been written by naming the groups attached to the aromatic ring. Sometimes it is not convenient to do this, and it is easier to think of the ring as a group attached to some other carbon skeleton. In this situation, **phenyl** is the name used for the *group* obtained by removing one hydrogen from a benzene ring.

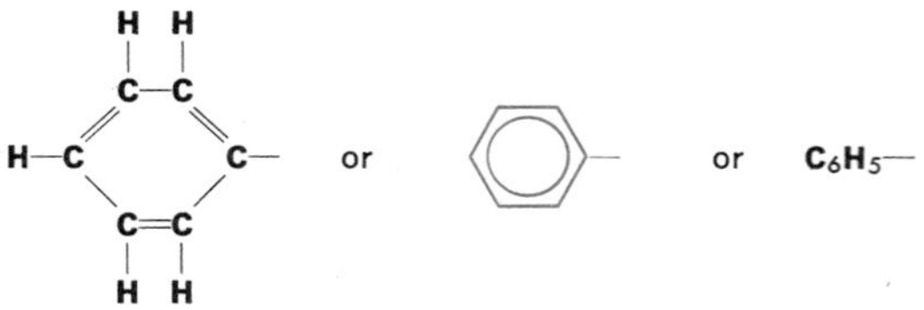

phenyl group

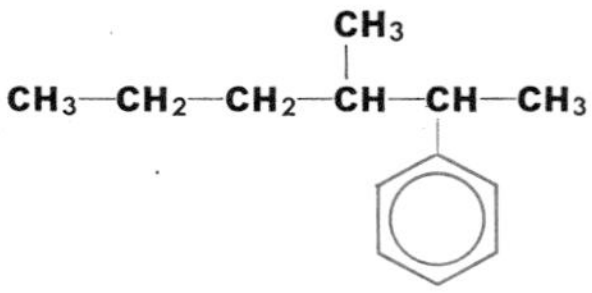

3-methyl-2-phenylhexane 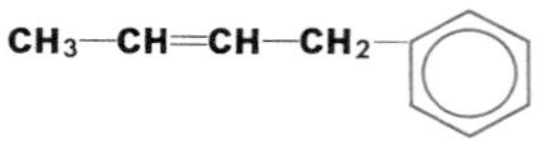   1-phenyl-2-butene

◄ Here is a case of an illogical mixture of names surviving from the past. During the 1840's the compound now known as benzene was called *phene*. Hence it was reasonable to call the related group *phenyl*. The name benzene for the parent compound gradually became accepted, so phene unfortunately died out, but phenyl did not! The name phene had been assigned to the compound because it and other aromatic compounds were associated with the manufacture of a type of illuminating gas (Gr. *phaino-*, shining). ►

In general, any group of this type is called an **aryl** group; the structures below are illustrations.

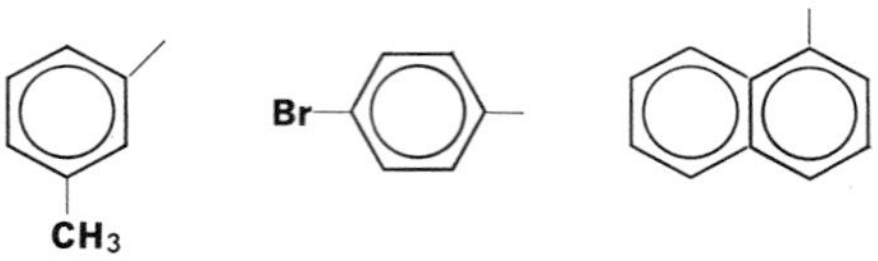

The symbol Ar- is used for an aryl group. Thus ArBr is an aryl bromide and ArH is an aromatic hydrocarbon.

24-3 GENERAL CHEMICAL PROPERTIES

We discovered in Section 24-1 that because benzene does not exhibit any of the customary alkene reactions it is necessary to develop a model, or picture, of benzene which truthfully represents these facts. The following list shows several of the reactions in which benzene does *not* participate.

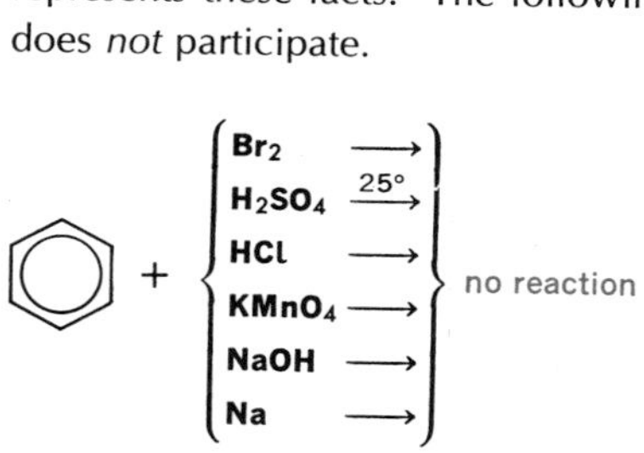

The concept to keep in mind is that the six electrons are very stable in the cloud around benzene. The cloud can rarely be broken up to make the electrons available for bonds to new atoms.

There are, however, a number of substances which react quite easily with benzene. Since addition reactions involving the electrons are not possible, apparently the only other parts of the molecule available for reaction are the hydrogen atoms. This is exactly the case. *The reactions typical of a benzene ring are substitutions*, in which a new group replaces a hydrogen. These substitutions are distinctly different from alkane substitutions. Neither a high temperature nor ultraviolet light is necessary for benzene substitutions. If the proper catalysts are provided, the reactions occur easily at moderate temperatures. Three important examples are described in the following sections.

24-4 REACTION WITH CHLORINE OR BROMINE

If we add some bromine to benzene, the bromine dissolves nicely in the liquid. However, no chemical change takes place; this was represented by the first equation of Section 24–3. If we then add to the solution a small amount of iron (a tack will do, or a chip of iron from a machine shop), some striking changes occur promptly. The solution becomes warm. Gas bubbles out and turns to white fumes when it reaches the moist air outside the flask. These fumes have a sharp, acid taste and odor, and they turn litmus red; complete analysis proves that they consist of hydrogen bromide. If we also analyze the liquid remaining in the flask we find bromobenzene, C_6H_5Br. Clearly, a chemical reaction has occurred which was apparently catalyzed by the iron. The products suggest that a bromine atom was *substituted* in place of a hydrogen on the benzene ring. We can write the reaction as shown in Eq. 24–1.

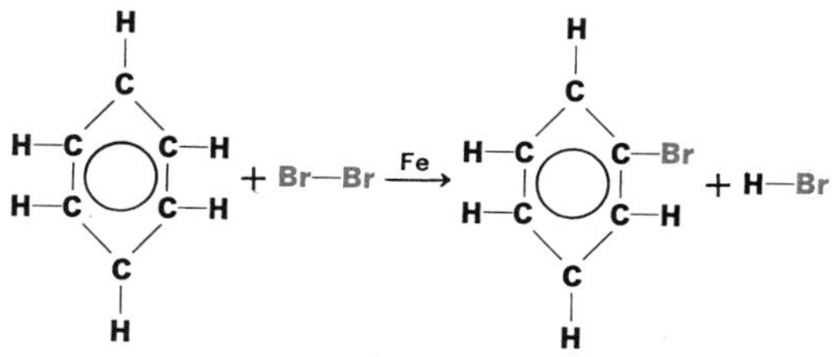

$$(24\text{-}1)$$

benzene   bromobenzene

Chlorine can react in the same way.

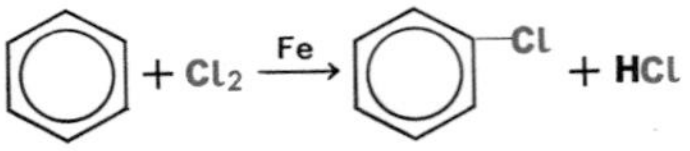

$$\bigcirc + Cl_2 \xrightarrow{\text{Fe}} \bigcirc\text{—Cl} + HCl \tag{24–2}$$

Equation 24–2 is actually balanced; remember that a hydrogen is present at each corner of the benzene ring even though it is not shown in the abbreviated formula.

Reactions of this type provide a simple means to obtain aryl chlorides or bromides.

The unique behavior of benzene is well illustrated by its reaction with chlorine or bromine. As we have noted, the reactions occur by substitution, not addition. Furthermore, the substitution does not require ultraviolet light or high temperature (which is necessary for halogen substitution onto an alkane); instead, the reaction is catalyzed by another chemical substance, in this case, iron.

24–5 REACTION WITH SULFURIC ACID

Concentrated sulfuric acid does not react with benzene at room temperature; in fact, the two liquids are immiscible. However, if the mixture is heated to a moderate temperature (130–150°C) a substitution reaction, called **sulfonation,** occurs.

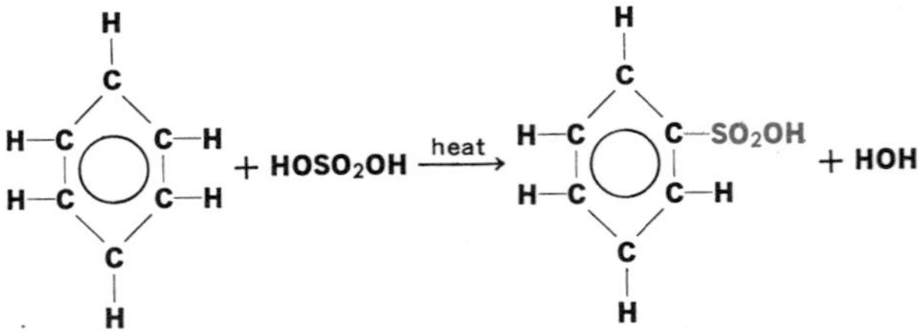

$$(24–3)$$

benzenesulfonic acid

Sulfonation, like the other benzene substitutions, requires a catalyst, despite the fact that in Eq. (24–3) none is apparent. Chemists have discovered that the reaction is self-catalyzed; one molecule of sulfuric acid promotes the reaction of another molecule.

Observe carefully the structure of the **benzenesulfonic acid.** There is a bond from a carbon to the sulfur (*not* to an oxygen). The three remaining oxygen atoms are all clustered around the sulfur. Review the structure of sulfuric acid discussed in Section 23–5E.

The structure of the sulfonic acid group is the same as that of sulfuric acid, except for the organic portion. Therefore, many of the properties of benzenesulfonic acid are similar to those of sulfuric acid. Benzenesulfonic acid is very soluble in water and is a highly ionized, strong acid (Eq. 24–4).

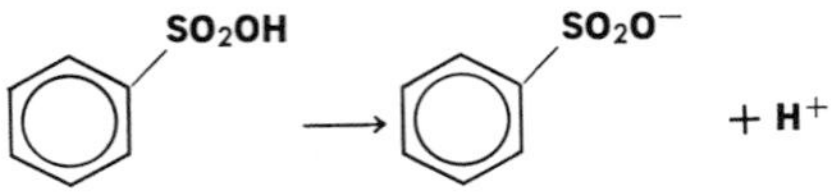

$$(24–4)$$

benzenesulfonate ion

It readily neutralizes bases (Eq. 24–5), and reacts with carbonates (Eq. 24–6).

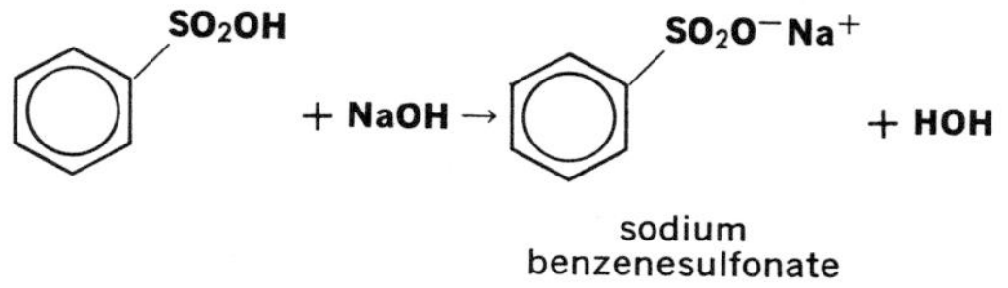

$$(24-5)$$

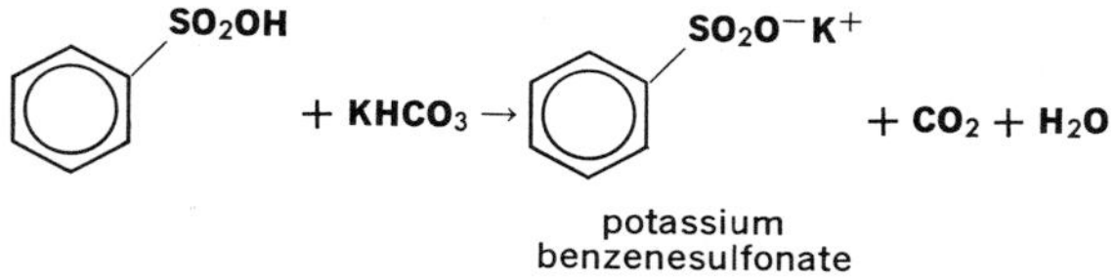

sodium
benzenesulfonate

$$(24-6)$$

potassium
benzenesulfonate

24-6 REACTION WITH NITRIC ACID

If benzene is treated with a solution containing both concentrated nitric acid and concentrated sulfuric acid, substitution begins even at room temperature. A **nitro group** from nitric acid is substituted onto the ring; the process is termed **nitration.**

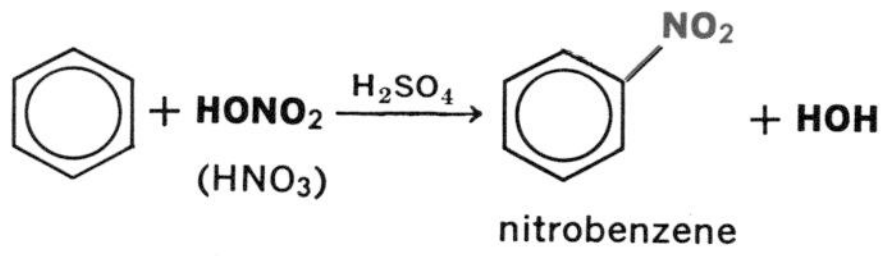

$$(24-7)$$

nitrobenzene

The sulfuric acid is written over the arrow in Eq. (24–7) because it is the catalyst. Although sulfuric acid is important to promote the reaction, substitution by nitro groups is much easier than by sulfonic acid groups; the nitrobenzene will *not* be contaminated with any benzene–sulfonic acid. In this connection, note that sulfonation (Eq. 24–3) requires a higher temperature than does nitration (Eq. 24–7).

The nitration reaction is used to prepare nitro compounds and is also one of the most frequently used methods for introducing other groups, indirectly, onto an aromatic ring. It will be shown in Section 28–3B that an aryl nitro compound ($ArNO_2$) can easily be converted to an aryl amine ($ArNH_2$). From the amine a great variety of other compounds can be made.

Compounds containing several nitro groups have explosive properties. Equation (24–8) shows how TNT can be made. Persons inexperienced in chemical procedures should not attempt this reaction because of the great danger involved.

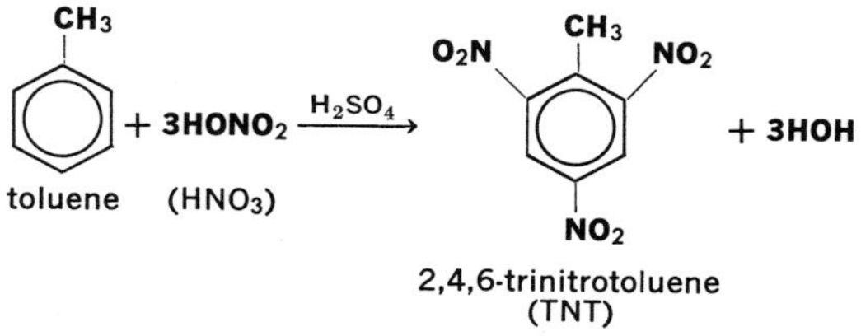

$$(24-8)$$

toluene   (HNO₃)

2,4,6-trinitrotoluene
(TNT)

24-7 OXIDATION OF SIDE CHAINS

An alkyl group attached to an aromatic ring is often called a **side chain.** Although the saturated hydrocarbon structure found in an alkyl group normally resists oxidation, an aromatic ring affects a side chain in such a way that it *can* be oxidized.

$$\text{C}_6\text{H}_5-\text{CH}_3 + 3[\text{O}] \xrightarrow{\text{KMnO}_4} \text{C}_6\text{H}_5-\underset{\text{OH}}{\overset{\text{O}}{\text{C}}} + \text{H}_2\text{O} \qquad (24\text{-}9)$$

benzoic acid
(an organic acid)

It is often convenient to write an organic oxidation reaction as in Eq. (24–9). The oxygen in brackets indicates oxidation, but does not mean that O_2 is the oxidizing agent. In effect, the oxygen is supplied by the inorganic oxidizing agent, which is written above the arrow. We do not attempt to show the change in the oxidizing agent nor include it in the balanced part of the equation; instead, we focus our attention on the changes in the organic substances. The equation is balanced as far as the oxygen and organic compounds are concerned. Actually, the $KMnO_4$ taking part in reaction (24–9) would be reduced to MnO_2, since the toluene is being oxidized.

If there is more than one side chain attached to a benzene ring, all of them can be oxidized. Also, other oxidizing agents can be used, as shown in Eq. (24–10).

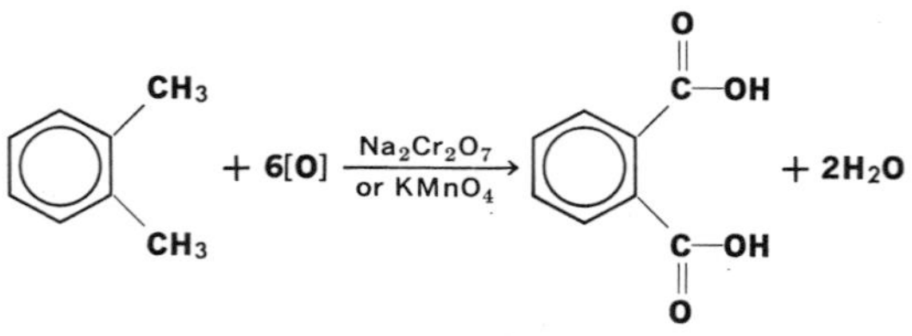

$$\underset{\text{CH}_3}{\overset{\text{CH}_3}{\text{C}_6\text{H}_4}} + 6[\text{O}] \xrightarrow[\text{or KMnO}_4]{\text{Na}_2\text{Cr}_2\text{O}_7} \underset{\underset{\text{O}}{\overset{||}{\text{C}}-\text{OH}}}{\overset{\overset{\text{O}}{\overset{||}{\text{C}}-\text{OH}}}{\text{C}_6\text{H}_4}} + 2\text{H}_2\text{O} \qquad (24\text{-}10)$$

phthalic acid

Longer side chains can likewise be oxidized (Eq. 24–11). In each case the oxidation starts at the carbon attached to the ring, emphasizing the fact that it is the ring which makes the alkyl side chain sensitive to attack. Once the oxidation begins, the rest of the carbons in the side chain are, as a rule, completely oxidized to carbon dioxide.

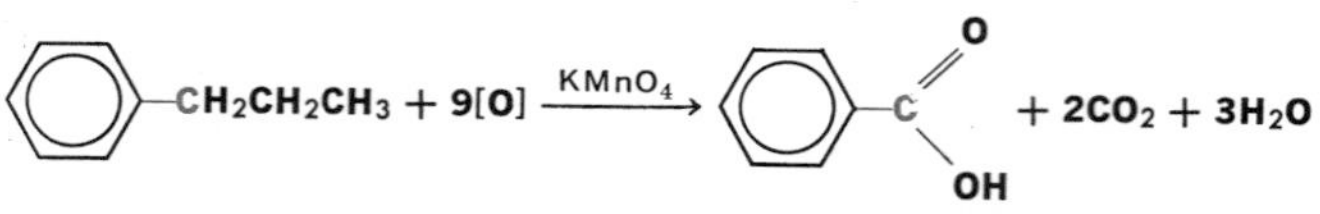

$$\text{C}_6\text{H}_5-\text{CH}_2\text{CH}_2\text{CH}_3 + 9[\text{O}] \xrightarrow{\text{KMnO}_4} \text{C}_6\text{H}_5-\underset{\text{OH}}{\overset{\text{O}}{\text{C}}} + 2\text{CO}_2 + 3\text{H}_2\text{O} \qquad (24\text{-}11)$$

Side-chain oxidation is useful for the preparation of an aromatic acid and for the identification of the original hydrocarbon.

24-8 HETEROCYCLIC COMPOUNDS

Many important compounds, both natural and synthetic, have ring structures in which there are some atoms other than carbons; hence they are called **heterocyclic** compounds (Gr. *hetero-*, other, different). The *hetero* atoms commonly found are nitrogen, sulfur, or oxygen. The ring may be saturated, unsaturated, or aromatic. Although heterocyclic compounds will be encountered occasionally later in the book, we will not attempt to discuss them in detail. It is important, however, to be aware that structures of this kind exist. Examples are shown below.

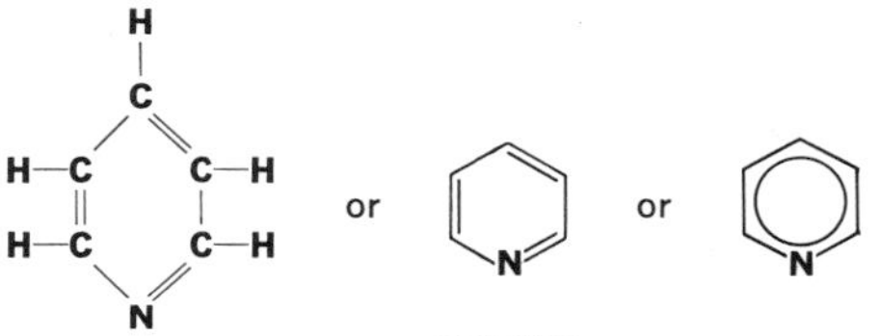

pyridine 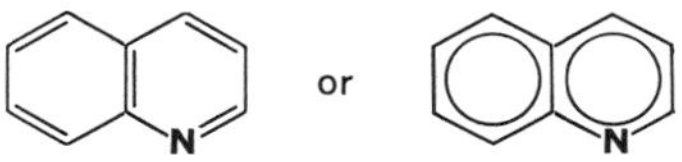   quinoline

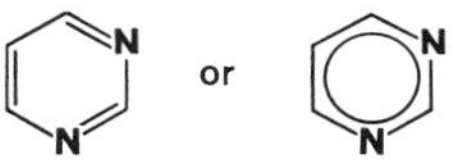

pyrimidine 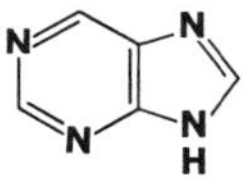   purine 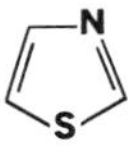   thiazole

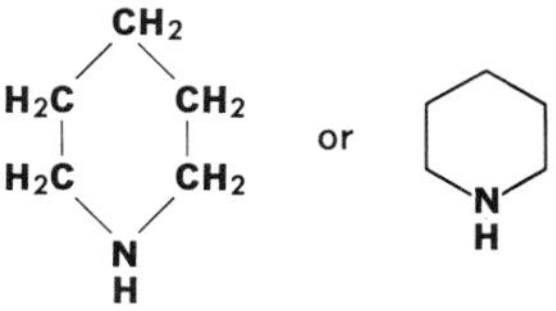

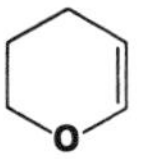

[Names of the structures in the last line need not be learned at this point.]

24-9 SOURCES OF AROMATIC COMPOUNDS

If coal is heated in the absence of air (so that it is not just burned up), a portion of the material vaporizes. The residue, called **coke,** is carbon plus small amounts of mineral impurities, mainly clay.

$$\text{coal} \xrightarrow{\text{heat}} \underset{\text{(residue)}}{\text{coke}} + \underset{\text{(volatile)}}{\text{coal tar}} \tag{24-12}$$

The hot vapors which escape are led to a cool chamber where they condense to become a thick liquid called **coal tar.** Coal tar is a valuable mixture composed of many different aromatic compounds, a few of which are listed in Table 24–1 to provide some idea of the

TABLE 24–1. Types of compounds in coal tar

Hydrocarbons

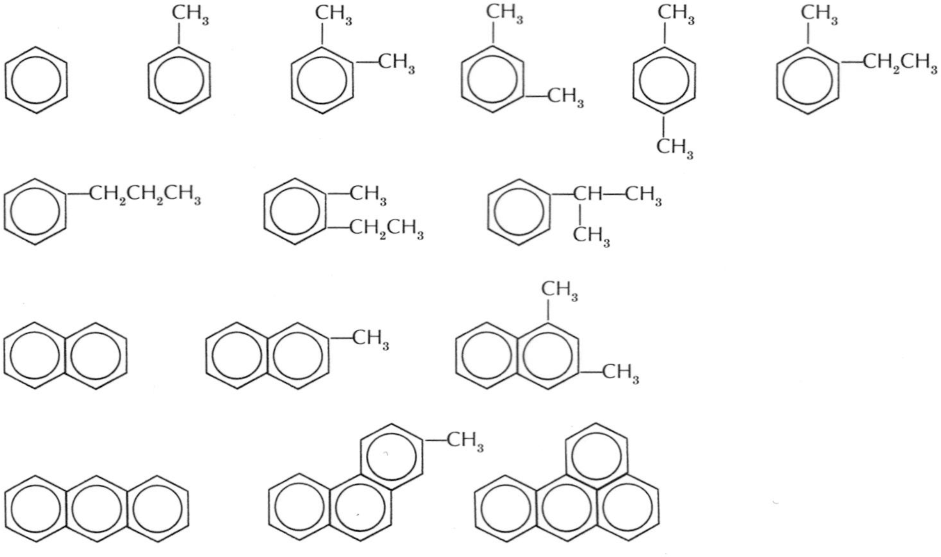

Phenols

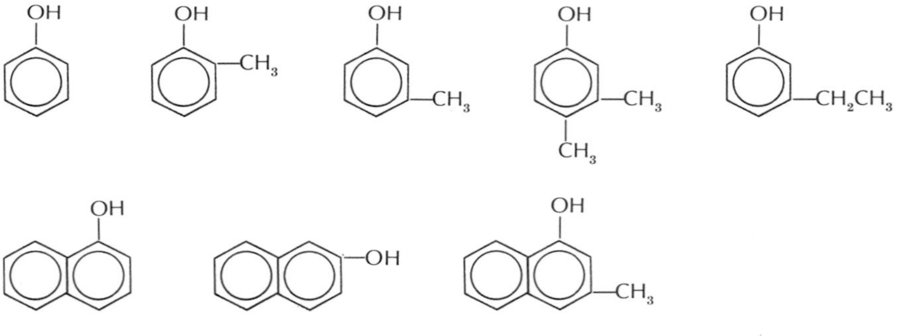

Nitrogen Heterocycles

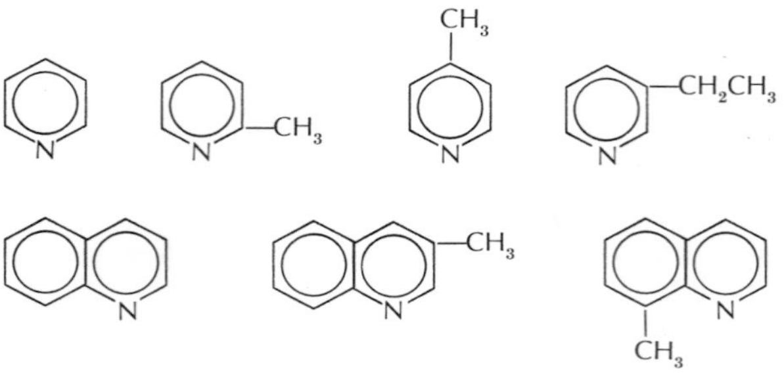

FIG. 24–2. A modern plant for the conversion of coal to coke and coal tar. Coal is stored in the concrete bin at the right. To its left is a battery of many coke ovens, each sixteen feet high. At the opposite end of the oven battery is an elevated pipe carrying the volatile coal gas and tar to the cooling towers at the left. At front center are two distillation columns for separation of the oils. [Courtesy of the Allied Chemical Corporation.]

variety present.   Although living plants and animals produce aromatic substances, they rarely yield large quantities of them. Consequently coal tar is the richest natural source of aromatic compounds.* (See Fig. 24–2.)

Of course, the coal tar mixture must be separated into various fractions before individual compounds can be obtained. Both chemical and physical methods of separation are used. The phenols, which are weakly acidic (Section 25–6), can be converted to water soluble salts with sodium hydroxide, and hence can be washed away from the rest of the coal tar. In a similar fashion the weakly basic nitrogen heterocycles (Section 28–2) can be extracted with sulfuric acid.

* Recall that petroleum has been mentioned as the ultimate source of *alkanes* (Section 22–1).

Each of the three groups—hydrocarbons, phenols, heterocycles—is then further separated by distillation into various fractions. Depending on the boiling range and the variety of compounds originally present, a particular fraction may be a single, relatively pure compound, or it may still contain several compounds of similar weight and physical properties. For instance, a fraction boiling at 136–144°C will contain ethylbenzene and the three dimethylbenzenes (xylenes). Even a fraction having a boiling range as narrow as 136–139°C will include all but one of these. Since they have similar structures and all have formula C_8H_{10}, their boiling points are nearly the same; it is difficult to separate one from the others.

Conversion of 1000 pounds of coal to coke (Eq. 24–12) yields only about 50 pounds of coal tar as a by-product. Since coke is used mainly for steel making, the demands of that industry determine the amount of coal tar available from this source. For many years the conversion of coal to coke has not supplied enough benzene and other simple aromatics to supply the great quantities used in the manufacture of dyes, drugs, plastics, and fabrics. It has been necessary to seek additional sources of aromatic hydrocarbons.

Petroleum is a natural resource from which simple aromatic hydrocarbons can be *manufactured*. Most petroleum deposits contain only very small quantities of aromatic compounds. However, certain of the petroleum alkanes can be chemically transformed to aromatic hydrocarbons by the **catalytic reforming** process. Alkane vapors are passed over a platinum catalyst at about 500°C. (See Fig. 24–3.) For example, a petroleum fraction containing primarily C_6 compounds is converted to benzene.

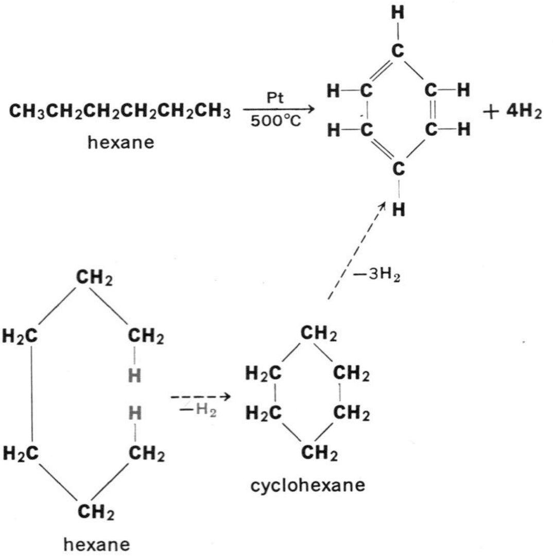

$$CH_3CH_2CH_2CH_2CH_2CH_3 \xrightarrow[500°C]{Pt} \text{benzene} + 4H_2$$

hexane

(24–13)

cyclohexane

hexane

The reaction (Eq. 24–13) involves loss of hydrogens, causing both ring closure and aromatization of the newly-formed ring. [The broken arrows in Eq. (24–13) show the intermediate steps.] The C_6 petroleum fraction initially contains substantial amounts of cyclohexane. However, we can see from Eq. (24–13) that all the cyclohexane present is converted to benzene as easily as is hexane.

FIG. 24–3. A catalytic reforming unit. Alkanes pass from a heater at the left into four reactors (right) containing platinum catalyst. The aromatic molecules produced there go to the tall distillation columns (center, rear) for separation into benzene, xylene, etc. [Courtesy of the Shell Oil Company.]

In an analogous manner, toluene can be formed from a C_7 petroleum fraction containing both heptane and methylcyclohexane.

$$\left. \begin{array}{l} \textbf{CH}_3\textbf{CH}_2\textbf{CH}_2\textbf{CH}_2\textbf{CH}_2\textbf{CH}_2\textbf{CH}_3 \\ \text{heptane} \\ \\ \text{methylcyclohexane} \end{array} \right\} \xrightarrow[\text{500°C}]{\text{Pt}} \quad \text{toluene} \; + \textbf{H}_2 \qquad (24\text{–}14)$$

Equation 24–14 indicates that an aromatic ring results even from heptane. This reaction occurs because a six-membered ring closes more easily than does a seven-membered ring, and once it does, the very stable benzene ring structure can be formed.

IMPORTANT TERMS

Aromatic compound	Coal tar	Nitro group
Aryl group	Heterocyclic compound	Ortho
Benzenesulfonic acid	Meta	Para
Catalytic reforming	Nitration	Phenyl group
		Sulfonation

WORK EXERCISES

1. Write a structural formula for

   a) toluene   b) ethylbenzene
   c) *para*dichlorobenzene   d) 1,2-dinitrobenzene
   e) 3-bromonitrobenzene   f) pyridine
   g) sodium benzenesulfonate

2. Give the structure and name of the products formed by the reaction of benzene with the reagents shown. If necessary, state "no reaction."

   a) concentrated sulfuric acid at 150°C   b) hot concentrated hydrochloric acid
   c) a mixture of concentrated nitric and sulfuric acids
   d) chlorine and iron   e) bromine at 25°C

3. Write the structure of the organic acid produced by the reaction of

   a) toluene with sodium dichromate
   b) ethylbenzene with potassium permanganate
   c) 1,2,4-trimethylbenzene with potassium permanganate
   d) *m*-bromotoluene with sodium dichromate

4. Describe briefly the following, and give an example of each.

   a) aromatic compound   b) heterocyclic compound

5. Briefly discuss the two chief sources of aromatic hydrocarbons.

6. Write the structural formulas to show how many trichlorobenzene ($C_6H_3Cl_3$) isomers are possible.

7. What are the three principal types of compounds found in coal tar?

SUGGESTED READING

DePuy, C. H. and K. L. Rinehart, Jr., *Introduction to Organic Chemistry,* Chapter 5. John Wiley, New York, 1967.

Hart, H. and R. D. Schuetz, *Organic Chemistry,* 3rd ed., Chapter 4. Houghton Mifflin, Boston, 1966.

Noller, C. R., *Textbook of Organic Chemistry,* 3rd ed., Chapter 20. W. B. Saunders, Philadelphia, 1966.

Chapter 25 ALCOHOLS, PHENOLS, AND ETHERS

25–1 INTRODUCTION

Nearly every primitive tribe has stumbled onto the fact that overripe fruits may undergo a pleasant type of spoilage (fermentation) which produces an intoxicating liquid. The more advanced societies discovered that by distillation they could isolate the intoxicating substance from the original liquid. During the Middle Ages this essence or spirit became known as alcohol in some European languages. (The word was derived from the Arabic *al kuh'l*, but with considerable alteration in meaning.) Scientists eventually learned that this organic compound contained not only carbon and hydrogen, but also oxygen. Furthermore, many other oxygen-containing substances, having different amounts of carbon, were found to be structurally related to alcohol. Consequently the term alcohol was used to designate all compounds having this type of structure, and also to name the one particular compound. Two other classes of compounds, the ethers and phenols, proved to be structurally related, each in a different way, to the alcohols.

In the water molecule (H—O—H) the two covalent bonds of oxygen hold hydrogen atoms. Either one or both of these bonds may instead be linked to organic groups. In an **alcohol** (R—O—H), the oxygen holds one alkyl group. In a **phenol** (Ar—O—H), the oxygen holds one aryl group. In an **ether,** the oxygen holds two alkyl or aryl groups which may be the same or different (R—O—R, R—O—R', R—O—Ar).

These oxygen structures may be found in such diverse materials as sugars, pain-relievers, disinfectants, plastics, and solvents. Vanillin, whose structure is shown on the next page, is the pleasant flavoring agent extracted from vanilla beans. Note that the compound has both an ether group and a phenol structure. Thymol, produced by the herb thyme, is used medically as a fungicide and also as a preservative for anatomical specimens. A few representative compounds are shown below.

CH_3-CH_2-O-H

ethanol
("alcohol," ethyl alcohol)

$CH_3-CH_2-O-CH_2-CH_3$

ethyl ether
(anesthetic "ether")

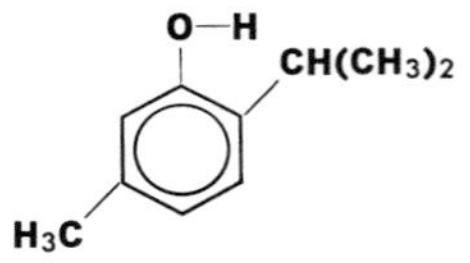

2-isopropyl-5-methylphenol
(thymol)

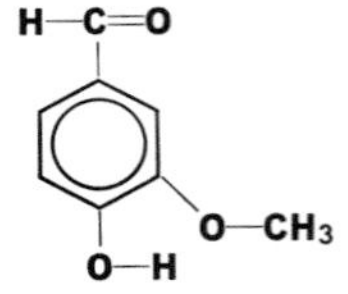

4-hydroxy-3-methoxybenzaldehyde
(vanillin)

25–2 ALCOHOL NAMES

In *systematic nomenclature* an alcohol is named by using the ending *-ol* in place of the final *-e* in the hydrocarbon name. Thus, the two-carbon alcohol is called ethanol. In most cases it is necessary to include a number to indicate the location of the hydroxyl group on the carbon chain. The hydroxyl, an important functional group, is assigned the lowest number possible for it, in preference to halogen or alkyl groups which may also be present. These rules are illustrated in the examples below.

Common names are also still used for many of the familiar alcohols. For these, a group name for the carbon skeleton is used, together with the word alcohol. In the examples, the common name is shown in parentheses.

$CH_3CH_2CH_2OH$

1-propanol
(*n*-propyl alcohol)

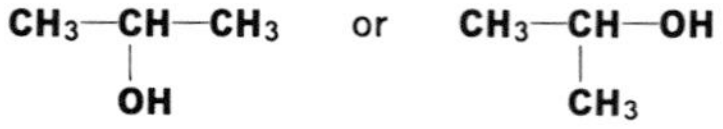

$CH_3-CH-CH_3$ or $CH_3-CH-OH$
with OH below first, CH_3 below second

2-propanol
(isopropyl alcohol)

$CH_3CH_2CH_2CH_2OH$

1-butanol
(*n*-butyl alcohol)

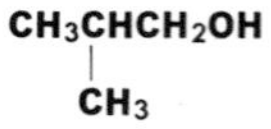

CH_3CHCH_2OH
with CH_3 below

2-methyl-1-propanol
(isobutyl alcohol)

$CH_3CH_2CH_2CH_2CH_2CH_2OH$

1-hexanol
(*n*-hexyl alcohol)

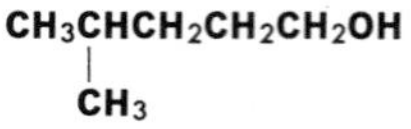

$CH_3CHCH_2CH_2CH_2OH$
with CH_3 below

4-methyl-1-pentanol
(isohexyl alcohol)

Note that the term *iso* is used to indicate a methyl branch in the chain at the end farthest from the functional group; it must not be used for groups branched elsewhere.

If we observe the reactions of the different butanol isomers, we find that their rates of reactions and kinds of products depend upon the position of the hydroxyl group in the molecule. Similar behavior of other isomeric alcohols leads to the generalization that their reactions depend not only upon the presence of the hydroxyl group but also upon the amount of branching in the carbon skeleton adjacent to the hydroxyl group. Consequently, we classify an alcohol as *primary, secondary,* or *tertiary* if there are, respectively, one, two, or three carbons directly bonded to the carbon holding the OH group.

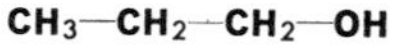

$$CH_3-CH_2-CH_2-OH$$

a primary alcohol

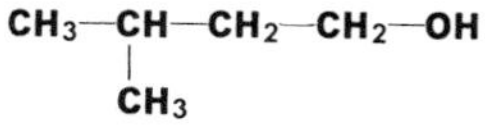

$$CH_3-CH-CH_2-CH_2-OH$$
$$|$$
$$CH_3$$

a primary alcohol

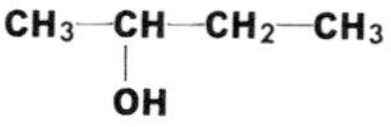

$$CH_3-CH-CH_2-CH_3$$
$$|$$
$$OH$$

a secondary alcohol

$$CH_3$$
$$|$$
$$CH_3-C-CH_2-CH_3$$
$$|$$
$$OH$$

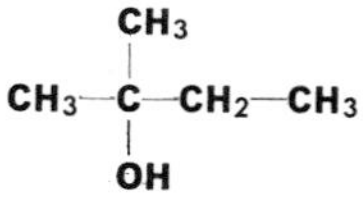

a tertiary alcohol

Note that the total number of carbons in the molecule, or branching elsewhere in the carbon skeleton, is not considered when we classify an alcohol as primary, secondary, or tertiary.

Some names for alkyl groups include the terms secondary (abbreviated *sec-*), or tertiary (abbreviated *tert-* or *t-*).

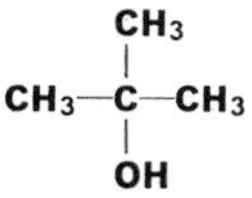

$$CH_3$$
$$|$$
$$CH_3-C-CH_3$$
$$|$$
$$OH$$

(tert-butyl alcohol)
2-methyl-2-propanol

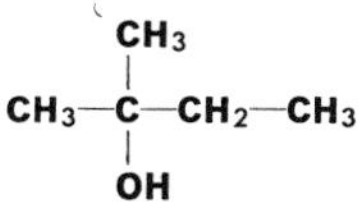

$$CH_3$$
$$|$$
$$CH_3-C-CH_2-CH_3$$
$$|$$
$$OH$$

(t-pentyl alcohol)
2-methyl-2-butanol

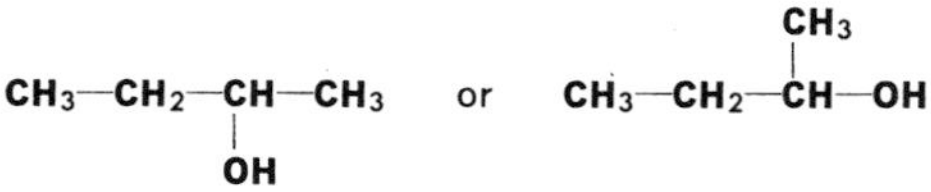

$$CH_3-CH_2-CH-CH_3$$
$$|$$
$$OH$$

or

$$CH_3$$
$$|$$
$$CH_3-CH_2-CH-OH$$

(sec-butyl alcohol)
2-butanol

Note carefully the difference between the sec-butyl group (shown just above) and the isobutyl group (shown on p. 338). Also note that a common group name, such as isohexyl, designates in this one name the total number of carbons and that there are no additional names for alkyl substituents.

Some molecules may have more than one hydroxyl group. The most familiar of these are shown below. Their systematic names are included for illustration, but their common names are nearly always used. (The term *glycol* is a general name for those alcohols having two OH groups, usually on adjacent carbons. The name ethylene glycol is derived from the fact that this compound can be made from ethylene).

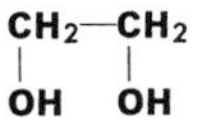

$$CH_2-CH_2$$
$$|\quad\ |$$
$$OH\ \ OH$$

(ethylene glycol)
1,2-ethanediol

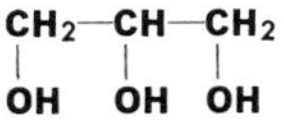

$$CH_2-CH-CH_2$$
$$|\quad\ |\quad\ |$$
$$OH\ \ OH\ \ OH$$

(glycerol)
1,2,3-propanetriol

25-3 COMMON ALCOHOLS

Methanol, also called *methyl alcohol,* or sometimes *wood alcohol,* was formerly obtained by destructive distillation* of wood. The product now manufactured synthetically is less expensive and so much purer that its industrial use has greatly increased. Each year tons of methanol are dehydrogenated (Section 25-5) to formaldehyde, which in turn is converted to phenol-formaldehyde, urea-formaldehyde, and melamine-formaldehyde polymers (Bakelite, Melmac, etc., Table 30-3) and to numerous other compounds. A nearly equal amount of methanol is used in automotive antifreezes. Methanol is also used as a solvent, and to build the structure of many dyes, drugs, and perfumes.

Methanol is a severe poison which can cause blindness and death. Even prolonged breathing of its vapor may be damaging; factory workers must be protected from the vapor by adequate ventilation.

Ethanol is the correct chemical name for the substance popularly known as alcohol. Some other common names for it are spirits of wine, spirits, grain alcohol, and ethyl alcohol.

Physiologically, alcohol induces relaxation, a feeling of well-being, poor coordination, a dulled sense of judgment, and if consumed in sufficient quantities, causes drowsiness and unconsciousness. A large quantity consumed within a short time can even cause death. However, because of the initial effects of alcohol, a fatal concentration in the body is rarely established.

Grapes, honey, milk, cactus sap, berries, or almost any other imaginable source of sugar can be fermented to alcohol by yeasts. Furthermore, the starch in rice, corn, oats, potatoes, rye, etc., can be biochemically broken down to sugar and then fermented to alcohol. Fermentation rarely produces an alcohol content in excess of 13%. Natural table wines are 11–13% alcohol. The higher percentages in strong liquors can be obtained only by distilling to concentrate the alcohol. *Proof* is a term used in the United States to designate the strength of alcoholic beverages. Numerically, proof is twice the percentage; for example, a 90-proof gin contains 45% alcohol; the remainder is water and trace amounts of flavoring substances.

In almost every nation the production of alcohol is closely regulated and is taxed, often heavily. Enough beverage alcohol is consumed to make this tax a very important source of revenue. Unfortunately, alcohol also frequently creates medical and sociological problems.

Great quantities of alcohol are used industrially, in the form of **denatured alcohol.** This is alcohol to which a small amount of a poisonous substance has been added to make it unfit for drinking. The additive also usually has a disagreeable odor and taste. Some of the common denaturing agents are methanol, benzene, gasoline, and isopropyl alcohol. Denatured alcohol is used to avoid the heavy beverage tax. In the United States, the current price for a gallon of 95% (190 proof) denatured alcohol is about 70 cents, when purchased in large quantity. The same amount of alcohol with the beverage tax included costs $20.70!

In both laboratory and industry, 95% alcohol is used extensively. This is the highest concentration which can be obtained by ordinary distillation; it is pure enough for many

---

* In destructive distillation a material is heated (in the absence of air) to a very high temperature, so that it decomposes and releases volatile substances.

purposes. If, by special means, the last 5% of water is removed, the pure, water-free alcohol is called **absolute alcohol.**

Part of the industrial alcohol is obtained by fermentation of molasses, or sometimes of potatoes. Most is synthesized from ethene, obtained as usual from petroleum sources. The two-step process described in Section 23–5E is utilized in some factories.

$$CH_2{=}CH_2 + HOSO_2OH \rightarrow CH_3CH_2OSO_2OH$$
ethene   sulfuric acid   ethyl hydrogen sulfate

$$CH_3CH_2OSO_2OH + HOH \xrightarrow{heat} CH_3CH_2OH + HOSO_2OH$$
                                     ethanol

In many factories the conversion from ethene to ethanol is accomplished in *one* operation by passing steam and ethene through a hot tube containing phosphoric acid adsorbed on an inert material.

$$CH_2{=}CH_2 + HOH \xrightarrow[300°C]{H_3PO_4} CH_3CH_2OH$$

Ethanol is used for the synthesis of other organic compounds, as a component of lotions, perfumes, and cosmetics, and as a solvent.

Isopropyl alcohol is most familiar as the compound in "rubbing alcohol." Other applications are in hand lotions, after-shave lotions, or cosmetics, and in quick-drying inks and paints. The largest quantities of isopropyl alcohol are converted to acetone by the dehydrogenation reaction (Section 25–5). The isopropyl alcohol required for all these needs is synthesized from propene by the two-step hydration process, utilizing sulfuric acid (Section 23–5E).

Ethylene glycol is an excellent automotive antifreeze because it is nonvolatile. It is also used in hydraulic brake fluids, printer's inks, stamp-pad inks, ball-point pens, and as a solvent for certain paints, plastics, and other materials. Large quantities are converted to the polymers constituting Dacron fibers, Mylar film, and alkyd paints.

Glycerol, also called glycerin, is a constituent of all fatty foods and is readily used by the human body. This is interesting in view of the fact that other small alcohols, including ethylene glycol, are toxic.

Most countries obtain glycerol entirely as a by-product of soap-making. In the United States additional quantities are made synthetically because of the great demands for it. (One authority has reported more than 1500 uses for glycerol!) The synthesis, developed by the Shell companies, uses propene from petroleum as the starting material.

Glycerol is a good humectant (moisture-retaining agent). This property makes it useful in the manufacture of tobacco, candy, cosmetics, skin lotions, inks, dentifrices, and pharmaceuticals. Eye corneas, blood cells, and other live tissues are often treated with glycerol for frozen storage. A few of the materials synthesized from glycerol are alkyd paints and other polymers, the explosive nitroglycerin, and monoglycerides and diglycerides used as emulsifiers and softening agents.

25–4 PHYSICAL PROPERTIES OF ALCOHOLS, PHENOLS, AND ETHERS

The volatility of an organic compound is directly related to its molecular weight. We found that alkanes of low molecular weight are gases at room temperature, those of higher weight are liquids, and the heaviest are solids (Section 22–4). We also know that within the group of alcohols a larger molecule has a higher boiling point than does a smaller one. We might expect, then, that methanol and ethanol would be gases, and would have very low boiling points. Instead, both are liquids. Evidently some factor other than weight is also affecting the volatility of alcohols. We now believe that most physical properties of alcohols are influenced by hydrogen bonds.

Hydrogen bonds may be formed from one alcohol molecule to another, because of the highly polar covalent bond between oxygen and hydrogen, Fig. 25–1.

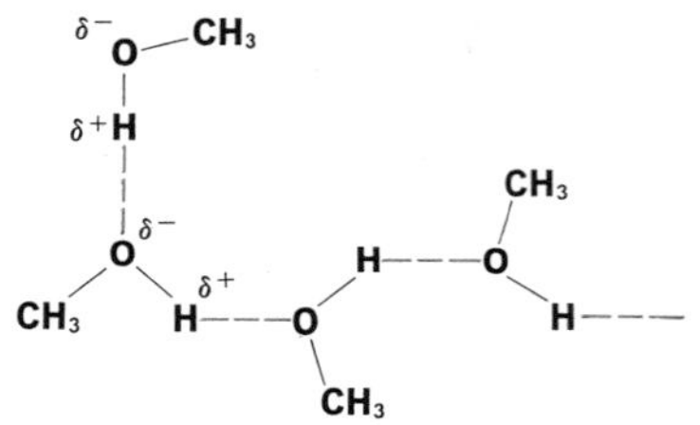

FIG. 25–1. Hydrogen bonds (color) create strong attractions between alcohol molecules.

Just as hydrogen bonds do in the case of water (Section 10–7), these strong intermolecular attractions have a profound effect on the physical properties of **alcohols.**

First, an alcohol has a *higher boiling point* than does an alkane hydrocarbon of about the same weight and size. This is illustrated by the data for 1-butanol and *n*-pentane, given in Table 25–1. Because of the hydrogen bond attractions between alcohol molecules, it is difficult for a molecule to break away from its neighbors in the liquid and exist as an individual molecule in the gas state. Therefore the alcohol requires more energy (higher temperature) for vaporization than does the hydrocarbon.

TABLE 25–1. Relation of boiling point to structure

Compound	Molecular Weight	Structure	Boiling Point, °C
n-pentane	72	$CH_3CH_2CH_2CH_2CH_3$	36
1-butanol	74	$CH_3CH_2CH_2CH_2OH$	118
ethyl ether	74	$CH_3CH_2OCH_2CH_3$	35

Second, the simple alcohols are much *more soluble in water* than are the hydrocarbons of similar size. This solubility is due to the fact that when an alcohol is mixed with water it can form hydrogen bonds to water molecules, and hence be pulled into the water, as indicated in Fig. 25–2.

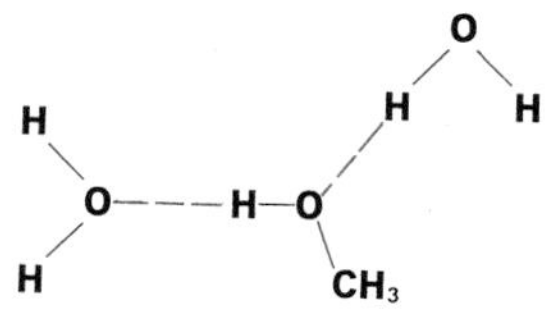

FIG. 25-2. Methanol dissolves in water because water molecules are attracted to it by hydrogen bonds (color).

We find, however, that a long-chain alcohol such as 1-octanol,

$$CH_3CH_2CH_2CH_2CH_2CH_2CH_2CH_2OH,$$

is practically insoluble in water. We explain this by saying that the attraction of the polar OH group toward water molecules is not sufficient to pull such a large hydrocarbon chain into solution; the 1-octanol behaves nearly the same as does nonpolar octane. Alcohols of medium size, of course, have intermediate solubilities. The data in Table 25-2 show that the longer the carbon chain, the less soluble the alcohol is in water.

TABLE 25-2. Solubility of alcohols in water

Alcohol	Solubility at 20°C (g ROH/100 g H_2O)
methanol	completely miscible
ethanol	completely miscible
1-propanol	completely miscible
1-butanol	8
1-pentanol	2.7
1-hexanol	0.6

Although long-chain alcohols are insoluble in water, they do dissolve in octane or other hydrocarbons. The bulk of the long-chain alcohol molecule is the nonpolar hydrocarbon group, which readily associates with solvents similar to it in structure. Alcohol solubility is nicely summarized by the statement "like dissolves like."

◄ In hot, dry locations tremendous amounts of water are lost from reservoirs through evaporation. Because of its solubility properties, octadecanol ($C_{18}H_{37}OH$) has been used successfully to reduce this loss. When octadecanol is thrown on the water, the OH group is attracted to the water but is unable to pull such a long hydrocarbon group into solution. Consequently, the octadecanol molecules line up side by side on the surface, with the OH groups in the water and the long hydrocarbon "tails" sticking out of the water vertically. A continuous film (just one molecule thick!) forms on the surface, greatly hindering the evaporation of water molecules. ►

Alcohols can, in turn, act as solvents for *other* compounds; their ability to do this depends on the principles just discussed. Ethanol is a good solvent for alkanes and aromatic hydrocarbons as well as for polar compounds such as benzoic acid, acetone, and other alcohols. Methanol is a poorer solvent for alkanes, but dissolves the polar compounds and even some ionic salts.

Phenols follow the same solubility principles as do alcohols. Phenols are more water-soluble and have higher boiling points than do aromatic hydrocarbons of similar size. However, since even the smallest phenol has a skeleton of six carbons, phenols are only moderately soluble in water. Those having large carbon-skeletons are more soluble in hydrocarbons such as benzene. Most phenols are quite soluble in ethanol.

We note in Table 25–1 that the boiling point of **ethyl ether** is almost identical to that of n-pentane. This similarity is due to the fact that hydrogen bonding cannot exist between two ether molecules. In an ether, all the hydrogens are held on carbon atoms (Fig. 25–2). Since the carbon-hydrogen covalent bonds are *nonpolar*, a hydrogen atom of one molecule does not attract an oxygen atom in another molecule. Hydrogen bonding is important only when a hydrogen atom is caught between two very negative atoms, such as two oxygens, Fig. 25–1. Since hydrogen bonds do not exist between ethyl ether molecules, their volatility is very similar to that of n-pentane.

Ethyl ether, the most common ether, forms a separate layer when mixed with water. In a practical sense it is, therefore, often regarded as insoluble. Actually, some of the ether dissolves (about 7 g/100 g of water), but the amount is not easily observed by the eye. Ether is completely miscible with alkanes.

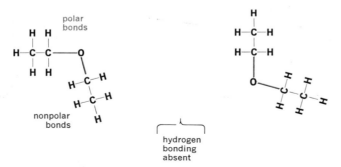

FIG. 25–3. There are no hydrogen-bond attractions between ether molecules because their hydrogen atoms are held by nonpolar bonds.

Ether can dissolve a wide variety of organic structures because of its own intermediate character; the alkyl portion of the molecule is typically nonpolar, but the oxygen bonds are moderately polar (Fig. 25–3). Consequently, ether associates with and dissolves nonpolar compounds such as alkanes, benzene, and fats, as well as moderately polar compounds such as phenol or acetic acid. The compounds which fail to dissolve in ether are chiefly those having several very polar groups, such as sugars, glycerol, or ethylene glycol. The chemical inertness of ether, Section 25–7, is another factor making it a desirable solvent for organic compounds. On the other hand, the great flammability of ether makes it very dangerous.

25–5 CHEMICAL PROPERTIES OF ALCOHOLS

A. Covalent Functional Group

First of all, we should keep in mind that in an alcohol molecule such as H—O—CH$_3$, all the bonds, including those from oxygen to carbon and from oxygen to hydrogen, are *covalent*. Although the oxygen bonds are quite *polar* covalent bonds, they are not ionic. Therefore, the alcohol is *not* a strong base like NaOH which releases separate hydroxide ions, HO$^-$, into solution. The functional group of an alcohol may be called a hydrox*yl group*, but not a hydrox*ide ion*. Although the alcohol functional group does not ionize, in many other respects it is quite reactive, and hence an alcohol may be converted to a variety of other substances. Several important chemical properties of alcohols are discussed in the following paragraphs.

B. Dehydrogenation; Oxidation

When vapors of an appropriate alcohol are passed over a hot copper catalyst, Eqs. (25–1) and (25–2), hydrogen is lost, and an aldehyde or ketone is produced.

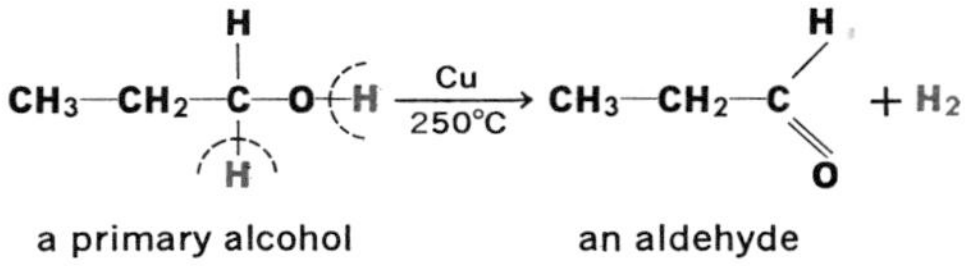

$$\text{CH}_3\text{—CH}_2\text{—}\overset{\overset{\text{H}}{|}}{\underset{\underset{\text{H}}{|}}{\text{C}}}\text{—O—H} \xrightarrow[250°C]{\text{Cu}} \text{CH}_3\text{—CH}_2\text{—C}\overset{\text{H}}{\underset{\text{O}}{\Big\langle}} + \text{H}_2 \tag{25–1}$$

a primary alcohol   an aldehyde

$$\text{CH}_3\text{—CH}_2\text{—}\overset{\overset{\text{CH}_3}{|}}{\underset{\underset{\text{H}}{|}}{\text{C}}}\text{—O—H} \xrightarrow[250°C]{\text{Cu}} \text{CH}_3\text{—CH}_2\text{—C}\overset{\text{CH}_3}{\underset{\text{O}}{\Big\langle}} + \text{H}_2 \tag{25–2}$$

a secondary alcohol   a ketone

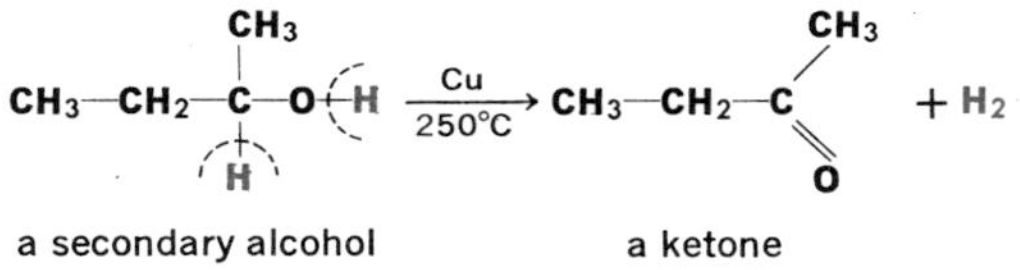

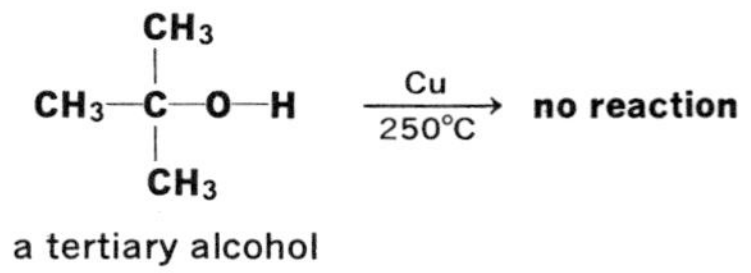

$$\text{CH}_3\text{—}\overset{\overset{\text{CH}_3}{|}}{\underset{\underset{\text{CH}_3}{|}}{\text{C}}}\text{—O—H} \xrightarrow[250°C]{\text{Cu}} \text{no reaction} \tag{25–3}$$

a tertiary alcohol

The reaction is termed **dehydrogenation** because it involves *removal of hydrogens* from the molecule; in this case, one from the oxygen and one from the carbon adjacent. Since the adjacent carbon in a tertiary alcohol does not hold a hydrogen, the reaction is not possible, Eq. (25–3).

The dehydrogenation reaction is important for at least three reasons:

1) It demonstrates the structural relations among the organic compounds involved. Note that a primary alcohol is converted to an aldehyde, a secondary alcohol becomes a ketone, and a tertiary alcohol is unchanged.

2) Dehydrogenation also occurs in vital biochemical reactions. In such cases, the reaction must take place at body temperature, and the catalyst is an enzyme.

3) This reaction provides a valuable synthetic method for making aldehydes or ketones from the readily available alcohols. It is adaptable to either laboratory or factory use. Aldehydes and ketones are discussed further in Chapter 29.

Dehydrogenation is in a sense equivalent to *oxidation:* the aldehyde or ketone product is in a state of higher oxidation than was the alcohol. This fact can be demonstrated experimentally by showing that the results are similar when alcohols are treated with the ionic oxidizing agents commonly used in the laboratory. In Eq. (25–4) below, the oxygen in brackets, [O], represents an oxygen atom supplied in solution by an ionic oxidizing agent such as $KMnO_4$ or $Na_2Cr_2O_7$. Note that this oxygen atom combines with the two hydrogens removed from the alcohol.

$$CH_3-CH_2-\overset{\overset{\displaystyle CH_3}{|}}{\underset{\underset{\displaystyle H}{|}}{C}}-O-H + [O] \rightarrow CH_3-CH_2-\overset{\overset{\displaystyle CH_3}{|}}{C}\underset{\displaystyle O}{\diagup\diagdown} + H_2O \qquad (25\text{–}4)$$

Such a reagent is rarely useful for preparing an aldehyde from a primary alcohol, because the aldehyde is easily oxidized further to an organic acid:

$$CH_3-\overset{\overset{\displaystyle H}{|}}{\underset{\underset{\displaystyle H}{|}}{C}}-O-H \xrightarrow[\text{[O]}]{} CH_3-\overset{\displaystyle H}{C}\underset{\displaystyle O}{\diagup\diagdown} + H_2O \xrightarrow[\text{[O]}]{\text{more}} CH_3-\overset{\displaystyle OH}{C}\underset{\displaystyle O}{\diagup\diagdown} \qquad (25\text{–}5)$$

(difficult   organic acid
to isolate)

In contrast, the dehydrogenation reaction is generally an excellent method for synthesizing aldehydes as well as ketones.

Combustion occurs with alcohols, as it does with most other organic compounds, when they are exposed to oxygen at a sufficiently high temperature. The resultant complete oxidation yields the usual products, carbon dioxide and water:

$$CH_3CH_2OH + 3O_2 \xrightarrow{\text{heat}} 2CO_2 + 3H_2O$$

C. Reaction with Active Metals

Sodium metal displaces hydrogen from the oxygen in an alcohol.

$$2Na + 2H-O-CH_3 \rightarrow \quad 2\overset{+}{Na}\overset{-}{O}-CH_3 \quad + H_2\uparrow \qquad (25\text{–}6)$$

methanol   sodium methoxide

In this respect the alcohol is behaving like water, a covalent compound related to it.

$$2Na + 2H-O-H \rightarrow \quad 2\overset{+}{Na}\overset{-}{O}-H \quad + H_2\uparrow$$

sodium hydroxide

The chief difference is one of degree: sodium reacts less violently with an alcohol than with water. Furthermore, the sodium alkoxide ($\overset{+}{Na}\ \overset{-}{O}R$), resulting from an alcohol, is a strong base, just as is sodium hydroxide ($\overset{+}{Na}\ \overset{-}{O}H$). Note also the same type of names: hydroxide, alkoxide, methoxide, etc. Reactive metals such as potassium, magnesium, calcium, and aluminum will similarly react with alcohols to form alkoxides, Eq. (25–7).

$$Mg + 2HOCH_2CH_3 \rightarrow \quad Mg(OCH_2CH_3)_2 \quad + H_2 \uparrow \tag{25-7}$$
$$\text{magnesium ethoxide}$$

D. Reactions with Acids

Alcohols are dehydrated when they are treated with strong acids such as sulfuric or phosphoric. The water lost may be split out from one alcohol molecule, in which case an alkene results, Eq. (25–8); or it may be split out between two molecules, so that an ether results, Eq. (25–9).

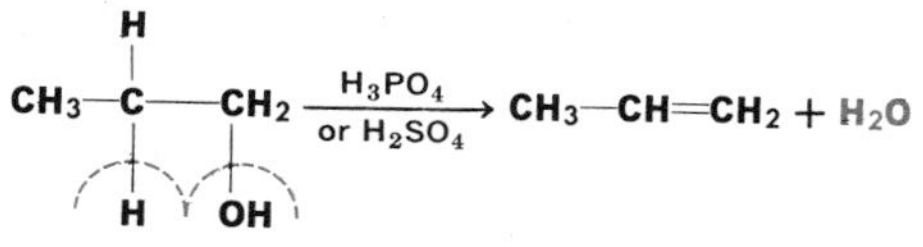

$$\begin{array}{c} H \\ | \\ CH_3-C-CH_2 \\ | \quad | \\ H \quad OH \end{array} \xrightarrow[\text{or } H_2SO_4]{H_3PO_4} CH_3-CH=CH_2 + H_2O \tag{25-8}$$

1-propanol   propene

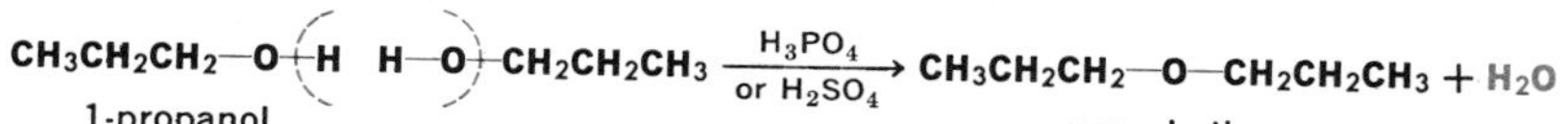

$$CH_3CH_2CH_2-O \mid H \quad H \mid O-CH_2CH_2CH_3 \xrightarrow[\text{or } H_2SO_4]{H_3PO_4} CH_3CH_2CH_2-O-CH_2CH_2CH_3 + H_2O \tag{25-9}$$
1-propanol   propyl ether

Which product results depends on the reaction conditions and the particular alcohol used. A number of both alkenes and ethers have been synthesized in this fashion. Ethyl ether is manufactured by this reaction or a modification of it.

Concentrated halogen acids convert alcohols to organic halides, Eq. (25–10).

$$ROH + HBr \rightarrow RBr + H_2O \tag{25-10}$$

$$\begin{array}{c} CH_3CHCH_3 + HCl \rightarrow \\ | \\ OH \end{array} \quad \begin{array}{c} CH_3CHCH_3 \\ | \\ Cl \end{array} \quad + H_2O$$

2-propanol   2-chloropropane

Alcohols react with organic acids to form compounds called esters.

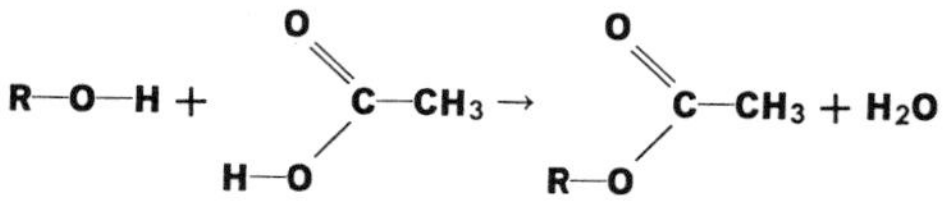

$$R-O-H + \quad \overset{\displaystyle O}{\underset{H-O}{\overset{\|}{C}-CH_3}} \rightarrow \quad \overset{\displaystyle O}{\underset{R-O}{\overset{\|}{C}-CH_3}} + H_2O$$

an ester

The esters, of interest both chemically and biologically, will be discussed in Chapters 26 and 27.

Under the proper conditions, concentrated nitric acid changes an alcohol to an alkyl nitrate. The most familiar example of this reaction, Eq. (25–11), occurs in the manufacture of glyceryl trinitrate, an explosive used as an ingredient of blasting mixtures and of propellants in ammunition. Glyceryl trinitrate is also used for treatment of coronary attacks.

$$
\begin{array}{llll}
CH_2OH & & CH_2ONO_2 & \\
| & & | & \\
CHOH & +\ 3HONO_2 \rightarrow & CHONO_2 & +\ 3H_2O \\
| & & | & \\
CH_2OH & & CH_2ONO_2 &
\end{array}
\qquad (25\text{–}11)
$$

glycerol   nitric acid   glyceryl trinitrate
                           ("nitroglycerin")

◄ The product in Eq. (25–11) is often called *nitroglycerin*, a confusing and erroneous name. Structurally, it is a nitrate compound; there are three oxygens around the nitrogen, and the carbon is bonded to an oxygen. Compare this structure with that of a true nitro group such as that in nitrobenzene or trinitrotoluene (Section 24–6), in which there are two oxygens around nitrogen, and the carbon is directly bonded to the nitrogen.

Another explosive, cellulose nitrate (nitrocellulose) is obtained when the cellulose of cotton or wood pulp is treated with nitric acid. There are alcoholic OH groups in cellulose, Section 33–5, so the reaction with nitric acid is the same as that shown in Eq. (25–11). Working with either cellulose nitrate or glyceryl trinitrate is extremely hazardous; early attempts to use them ended in disaster. Finally, in 1867, the Swedish chemist and industrialist Alfred Nobel patented dynamite, a mixture of glyceryl trinitrate with diatomaceous earth. He had found that glyceryl trinitrate could be safely handled in this condition. A decade later Nobel discovered that a mixture of glyceryl trinitrate and cellulose nitrate formed a colloidal mass which, curiously, stabilized both of them. This gelatin could be used for blasting purposes or, in a modified form, in guns. We can also stabilize cellulose nitrate by treating it with alcohol-ether solvent to render it colloidal, then forming it into grains, and finally removing the solvent. Nobel's invention of a detonator for these stabilized explosives was equally important. Explosives are of little use if they cannot be set off when desired.

Either cellulose nitrate alone, or a mixture of glyceryl and cellulose nitrates is called *smokeless powder*. (Ancient gunpowder was a mixture of potassium nitrate, charcoal, and sulfur.) Nitrate materials of this kind are widely used in guns, rockets, and missiles. The explosives are tremendously useful in mining, road building, etc.; they are cruelly destructive in military use. Advances in technology very often present mankind with dilemmas.

Alfred Nobel acquired a large fortune from oil fields and from manufacturing explosives. He willed funds to the establishment of the Nobel Prizes for peace, chemistry, physics, literature, and physiology or medicine. The first prizes were awarded in 1901, five years after his death. ►

25-6 PHENOLS

The term **phenol** is used to name this whole class of compounds, as well as the simplest example in the group. (The term phen*ol* implies a hydroxyl derivative of phene; the origin of the word *phene* is mentioned in Section 24–2.)

ArOH

general formula for a phenol   phenol (carbolic acid)

All phenols are weakly acidic and able to react with sodium hydroxide, Eq. (25–12). Most, however, are unable to react with sodium hydrogen carbonate. (In contrast, alcohols do not react even with sodium hydroxide.)

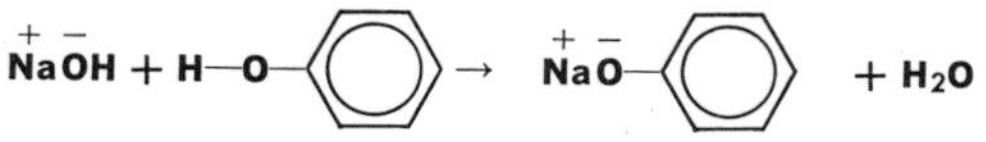

$$NaOH + H-O-\!\!\bigcirc \rightarrow NaO-\!\!\bigcirc + H_2O \qquad (25\text{--}12)$$

phenol   sodium phenoxide

This acidic property is reflected in some of the names. An aqueous solution of phenol is still occasionally called "carbolic acid." Picric acid is an especially acidic phenol.

The structures and names of several phenols are shown below.

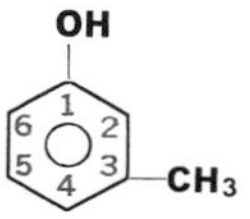

3-methylphenol
(m-cresol)

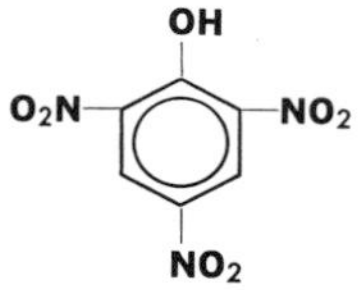

2,4,6-trinitrophenol
(picric acid)

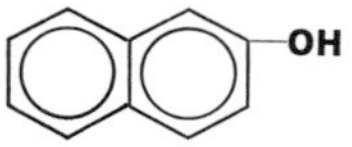

2-naphthol
(β-naphthol)

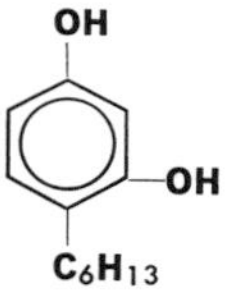

(hexylresorcinol)

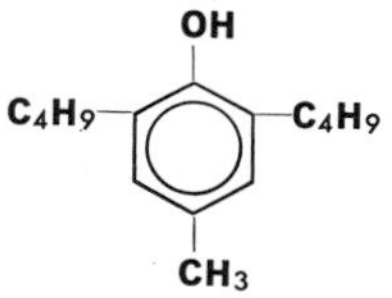

2,6-di-t-butyl-4-methylphenol
BHT

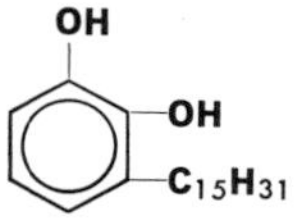

(urushiol)
the irritant in poison ivy
and poison oak*

Phenols have interesting physiological properties. Phenol itself is a disinfectant used on floors and apparatus. If strong solutions are spilled on the skin they will kill (burn) some of the tissue. Similarly, the germicidal properties of creosote (a crude mixture, obtained from coal tar, of aromatic hydrocarbons, cresols, and other phenols) make it a good wood preservative. Hexylresorcinol is used in humans and animals to combat intestinal worms

---

* Urushiol is actually a mixture of closely related compounds in which the C_{15} side-chains have varying numbers of double bonds.

and urinary infections. Butylated hydroxytoluene, BHT, is now used extensively as an anti-oxidant in foods, rubber, plastics, petroleum products, and soaps. It prevents deterioration caused by exposure to air.

Phenol is manufactured into important polymers, chiefly the phenol-formaldehyde and epoxy types. Thousands of pounds of dyes are made annually from naphthol. Alizarin, a phenolic compound found in madder root, has been used as a dye since ancient times. It is now made synthetically.

The phenols used in quantity are often obtained from coal tar, Section 24-9; for some, the supply is augmented by synthesis from petroleum materials.

25-7 ETHERS

An ether group occurs as a unit of structure in a variety of compounds produced by living organisms. However, the role, if any, that the ether unit plays in crucial biochemical re-actions is not apparent. Possibly its chief contribution is to provide a molecule with the proper physical characteristics, such as size or solubility. This situation may be related to the fact that ethers are chemically very inert, in much the same way that alkanes are. Combustion occurs with oxygen, and chlorine will substitute onto the alkyl portion of an ether in the presence of ultraviolet light. However, hydrogen, strong bases, reactive metals, or strong reducing agents have no chemical effect on an ether. Some strong acids and oxidizing agents may attack an ether at high temperatures, but these, too, are without effect at moderate temperatures.

Therefore, except when studying the structure of natural products, we are usually con-cerned with only a very few simple ethers. By far the most common of these is ethyl ether, sometimes called diethyl ether, but most often simply ether. It is used mainly as a solvent (Section 25-3) and to some extent as an anesthetic.

In 1846, William Morton, a dentist, tested ether as an anesthetic while extracting a tooth. About two weeks later he was the first to make public its effectiveness, by administer-ing it to a patient during surgery. The use of ether had been suggested to Morton by a chemist, Charles Jackson, who had experimented with inhalation of ether. Before this time surgery was an agonizing procedure. The patient was strapped to a table and (if he was lucky) soon lost consciousness due to pain. Ethanol had some value as a relaxant, but only by the use of ether and other anesthetics could surgery develop to its present state, involving kidney and heart transplants.

Ether is a very useful anesthetic. A safe level of unconsciousness can be achieved with-out depressing respiration or circulation. The amount of ether required is not toxic. Some disadvantages of using ether are that most patients experience prolonged and unpleasant recovery, and that ether is highly flammable. A number of other agents, or combinations of agents, have now replaced ether in many cases.

Ethene, cyclopropane, and vinyl ether ($CH_2{=}CH{-}O{-}CH{=}CH_2$) are also successful anesthetics, but share with ether a high flammability. Trichloromethane, commonly called chloroform, Table 22-5, is effective and nonflammable. It must be administered with great care, however, to avoid overdosage or liver damage, but is used in many parts of the world. Another halogen compound, halothane, Table 22-5, was developed in 1956 specifically for anesthesia, and by 1966 had become widely accepted. The inorganic compound nitrous oxide (N_2O) is a weak anesthetic often used as a supplement to others. It is also effective in conjunction with intravenous administration of thiopental sodium, a heterocyclic compound, Section 24–8.

IMPORTANT TERMS

Alcohol	*Hydroxyl group*
Alkoxide	*Primary alcohol*
Dehydrogenation	*Phenol*
Ether	*Secondary alcohol*
Hydrogen bond	*Tertiary alcohol*

WORK EXERCISES

1. Show the structure of all possible alcohols having the molecular formula $C_4H_{10}O$.

2. Write a systematic name for each isomer shown in Question 1.

3. Label each isomer in Question 1 as primary, secondary, or tertiary.

4. Show the product that each alcohol in Question 1 would give with copper at 250°C.

5. Show the structure of:

   a) 2-propanol   b) phenol   c) isobutyl alcohol
   d) 4-methyl-2-pentanol   e) potassium methoxide   f) sec-butyl alcohol
   g) *m*-nitrophenol   h) sodium ethoxide   i) 5-bromo-2-methyl-3-hexanol
   j) two different secondary alcohols having formula $C_5H_{12}O$
   k) 3-ethyl-2-phenyl-1-pentanol
   l) 3-chloro-4-isopropyl-2-heptanol   m) cyclohexanol

6. Methyl ethyl ether, $CH_3OCH_2CH_3$, has mol. wt. 60 and is a gas (b.p. 10°C), whereas ethylene glycol, $HOCH_2CH_2OH$, has about the same mol. wt. (62), but has b.p. 197°C.

   a) Explain why ethylene glycol has such a high boiling point.
   b) Why is the high boiling point an advantage when ethylene glycol is used as antifreeze in an automobile engine?

7. Write complete equations for these reactions. If necessary, state "no reaction."

   a) 1-butene and cold concentrated sulfuric acid   b) product from (a) plus warm water
   c) ethanol and sodium metal   d) ethanol and copper at 250°C
   e) 3-pentanol and copper at 250°C   f) phenol and sodium hydroxide
   g) 2-butanol and warm potassium permanganate solution
   h) methanol and aluminum

8. Show how 2-propanol (rubbing alcohol) could be manufactured, starting with petroleum as the raw material.

SUGGESTED READING

Beecher, H. K., "Anesthesia," *Scientific American*, Jan. 1957. A fascinating review of the history of anesthesia, from early to recent times.

Clevenger, S., "Flower Pigments," *Scientific American*, June 1964 (Offprint #186). Despite the wide range in color from red to blue, these pigments are phenolic compounds with many similarities in structure.

DePuy, C. H. and K. L. Rinehart, Jr., *Introduction to Organic Chemistry*, Chapter 6. John Wiley, New York, 1967.

Greenberg, L. A., "Alcohol in the Body," *Scientific American*, Dec. 1953. A thorough discussion of the biochemical reactions and physiological effects of alcohol.

Hart, H. and R. D. Schuetz, *Organic Chemistry*, 3rd ed., Chapters 5 and 6. Houghton Mifflin, Boston, 1966.

Lesser, M. A., "Glycerin—Man's Most Versatile Chemical Servant," *J. Chem. Educ.* **26,** 327 (1949). A survey of some of the history and uses of glycerol, but out-of-date in terms of new applications in recent years.

Chapter 26 ORGANIC ACIDS

26–1 INTRODUCTION

Some of the most abundant and well-known organic compounds are acids. Of equal importance and familiarity are the fats, which are made up of organic acids chemically combined with the alcohol glycerol. For centuries man used tart fruits, sour milk, and vinegar, even though he was not acquainted with the individual compounds responsible for the sour tastes. When men did finally begin to isolate and identify separate acids (starting mostly in the 18th century), they usually named them after some familiar source, as shown in Table 26–1. Formic acid is the irritant in the sting of red ants, bees, and nettle plants. Butyric acid occurs in rancid butter, aged cheese, and human perspiration; it is the chief cause of their strong, offensive odor.

As a class, the acids shown in Table 26–1 are most properly called **carboxylic acids.** The functional group characteristic of the class is a **carboxyl group;** in this group the four covalent bonds of carbon may be represented as follows:

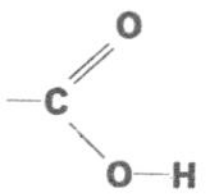

carboxyl group

In most cases the structure should be carefully written out, as shown above. For the sake of brevity, the group is sometimes written —COOH (especially in the printing of books); when it is represented thus, be sure to remember the actual pattern of bonding. In abbreviated form, the acids themselves may be represented by RCOOH or ArCOOH.

TABLE 26–1. Some common organic acids (carboxylic acids)

Common Name	Origin of Name	Structure	Systematic Name
formic acid	L. *formica*, ant	HCOOH	methanoic acid
acetic acid	L. *acetum*, vinegar	CH_3COOH	ethanoic acid
propionic acid	Gr. *pro(tos)*, first + *pion*, fat	CH_3CH_2COOH	propanoic acid
butyric acid	L. *butyrum*, butter	$CH_3CH_2CH_2COOH$	butanoic acid
caproic acid	L. *caper*, goat	$CH_3CH_2CH_2CH_2CH_2COOH$	hexanoic acid
lactic acid	L. *lactis*, milk	$CH_3\text{—}\overset{\displaystyle |}{\underset{\displaystyle OH}{CH}}\text{—}COOH$	2-hydroxy-propanoic acid
benzoic acid	obtained from benzoin, a plant gum	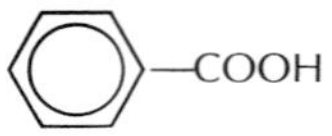 C$_6$H$_5$—COOH	benzoic acid
salicylic acid	obtained from the willow tree L. *salix*; Fr. *salicine*	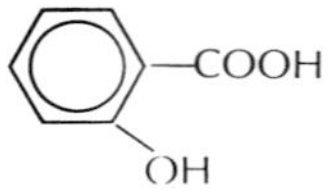 C$_6$H$_4$(OH)—COOH	2-hydroxy-benzoic acid

The whole carboxyl group should be regarded as *one* functional group with its own distinctive properties. These unique properties are due to the fact that the OH portion and the C=O portion of the carboxyl group interact with each other strongly. Consequently, the carboxyl group has few chemical properties in common with a hydroxyl group, OH (Chapter 25), or with a carbonyl group, C=O (Chapter 29).

The systematic names for carboxylic acids follow the usual pattern: To the name for a carbon skeleton we add an ending for the carboxyl group by replacing the final -e with -*oic* *acid*. Thus, the five-carbon acid is called pentanoic acid. In the systematic nomenclature *benzoic acid* is used as a parent name for aromatic carboxylic acids, Table 26–1.

26-2 ACIDIC PROPERTIES; Salt Formation

Acetic acid is a good example to use in beginning our discussion of chemical properties. By the mid-1700's chemists could isolate acetic acid in fairly pure condition from the distillation of vinegar. By the mid-1800's many of the properties of acetic acid had been carefully observed. The customary analysis indicated that the molecular formula was $C_2H_4O_2$. The substance had the sour taste thought to be typical of acids, and it neutralized caustic soda (sodium hydroxide). The resultant salt had the formula $C_2H_3O_2Na$. Even if an excess of caustic soda was used, only one of the four hydrogens of acetic acid could be replaced by sodium. Various other observations were made, including some which suggested that the two oxygens were bound to one carbon. To be consistent with all the experimental observations, and with the ideas of valence becoming accepted at that time (with $C = 4$, $O = 2$, $H = 1$), acetic acid was written this way:

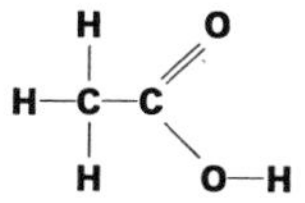

Over the years this has proven to be a satisfactory structural formula for acetic acid; that is, none of the more recent experimental facts have indicated that the atoms are bonded in some different pattern.

All the bonds of acetic acid are covalent. However, the nature of the carboxyl group is such that the oxygen–hydrogen bond is even more intensely polar than is the oxygen–hydrogen bond of water or of an alcohol. In fact, when acetic acid is dissolved in water an occasional acid molecule is able to ionize; the hydrogen escapes from the oxygen, to become an H^+ ion in solution. At any one time in a 0.1 M solution, only about one acetic acid molecule out of every thousand exists in the ionized condition. The arrows in Eq. (26–1) are meant to show that most acetic acid molecules are in the non-ionized form.

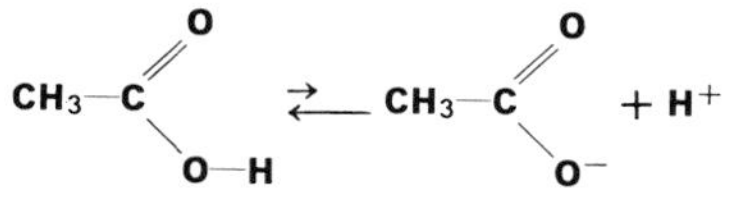

$$(26-1)$$

Recall that when HCl dissolves in water, *all* the molecules become ionized, yielding separate H^+ and Cl^- ions. By comparison, *acetic acid is termed a weak acid* because its water solution contains only a few hydrogen ions at any one time. However, the presence of even such a small number of hydrogen ions is enough to give the solution *typical acid properties:* it changes the color of litmus paper, etc.

If sodium hydroxide is added to acetic acid, the hydroxide ions pull hydrogen ions away from nearly all the acetic acid molecules (rather than from just one out of a thousand, as water does). As usual, this acid-base reaction Eq. (26–2) produces a salt.

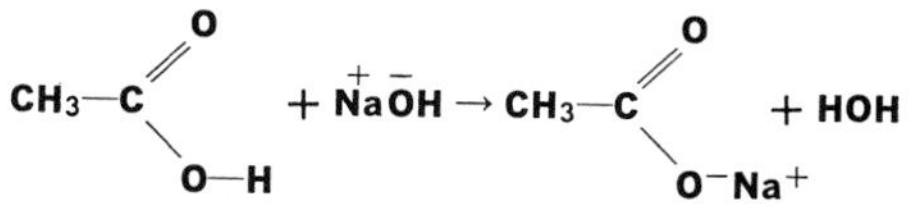

$$(26-2)$$

The reaction occurs very rapidly, actually as fast as one can stir the solutions together. A second, very important feature of the reaction is that one gram molecular weight of acetic acid can convert one gram molecular weight of sodium hydroxide to a salt. In other words, molecule by molecule, a weak acid (e.g., acetic) has as much *capacity* to neutralize a base as does a strong acid (e.g., hydrochloric).

However, acetic acid, when alone in a dilute water solution, releases only a few hydrogen ions at any moment. Since the typical acidic properties are due to the hydrogen ions, the solution of acetic acid in water is not strongly acidic. This property of organic acids is important in biological systems. The tissues may need to have available a large supply of some acid, but at any given time a high concentration of hydrogen ions cannot be tolerated. The organic acids, being only slightly ionized, satisfy these conditions very nicely.

For the same reason, if we wish to halt the caustic effects of a strong base which has been spilled, vinegar or some other weak acid is a desirable neutralizing agent. If we used a strong acid, it might cause as much damage as the base we were trying to neutralize.

This whole situation can be dramatically summarized by considering another example. A 1 M solution of hydrochloric acid is much more strongly acid than is a 10 M solution of acetic acid. (In fact, the hydrochloric acid solution is about 100 times as acidic!) Yet, a given volume of the acetic acid solution has the *capacity* to neutralize ten times as much sodium hydroxide as does the hydrochloric acid solution.

The reaction of carboxylic acids with bases is quite general. Other bases such as KOH, $Mg(OH)_2$, or $Al(OH)_3$ could be involved. Also, the acidity of nearly all carboxylic acids is about the same, despite rather wide structural variations elsewhere in the molecule. Benzoic acid has almost exactly the same acid strength as does acetic acid. Here are some further examples of acid-base reactions:

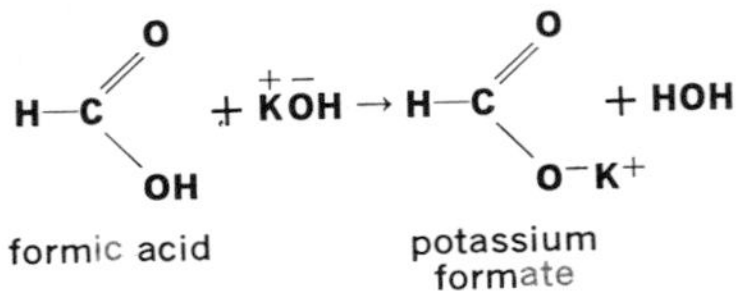

$$H-C\overset{O}{\underset{OH}{\Big<}} + \overset{+\ -}{KOH} \rightarrow H-C\overset{O}{\underset{O^-K^+}{\Big<}} + HOH$$

formic acid   potassium formate

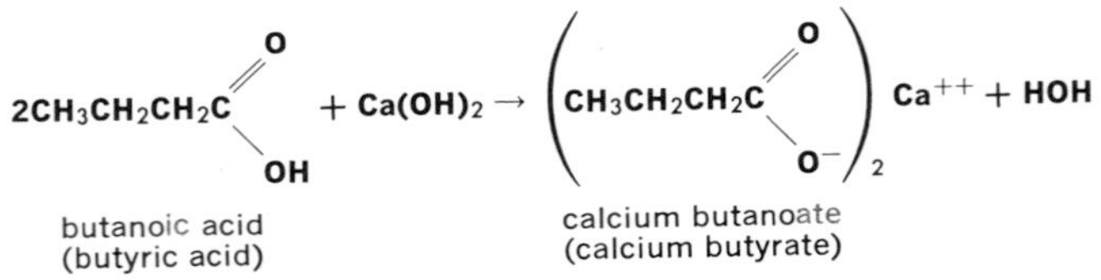

$$2CH_3CH_2CH_2C\overset{O}{\underset{OH}{\Big<}} + Ca(OH)_2 \rightarrow \left(CH_3CH_2CH_2C\overset{O}{\underset{O^-}{\Big<}}\right)_2 Ca^{++} + HOH$$

butanoic acid   calcium butanoate
(butyric acid)   (calcium butyrate)

As shown above, the salts of carboxylic acids are named by changing the *-ic* ending of the acid name to *-ate* for the salt. This applies whether we are using common names or systematic names.

In a carboxylate salt, such as $RCOO^-Na^+$, the functional group has an ionic bond. Therefore the compound has properties similar in many ways to those of an inorganic salt. The carboxylate salts are often quite soluble in water and conduct an electric current in solution. They form relatively hard crystals and have high melting points.

When a piece of limestone ($CaCO_3$) or a little baking soda ($NaHCO_3$) is dropped into vinegar, a distinct fizzing occurs. Water solutions of other carboxylic acids give the same results. Proper testing reveals that the gas being evolved is carbon dioxide. Evidently a carboxylic acid is capable of donating a hydrogen ion to a carbonate or hydrogen carbonate ion, Eqs. (26–3) and (26–4). (Incidentally, this means that the carboxylic acid is a considerably stronger acid than is a phenol, Section 25–6.)

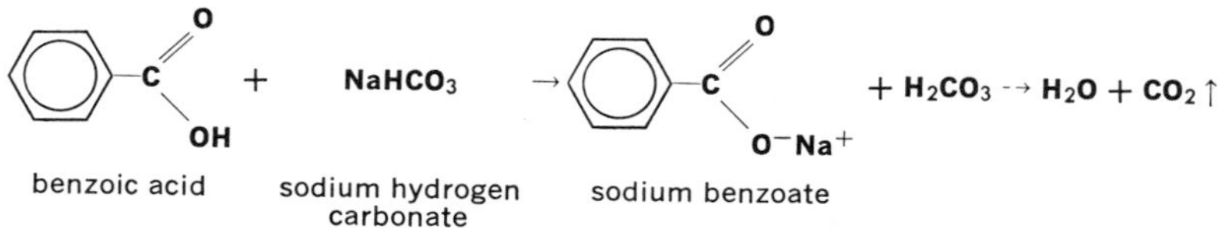

benzoic acid   sodium hydrogen   sodium benzoate
                  carbonate

$$2CH_3CH_2COOH + K_2CO_3 \rightarrow 2CH_3CH_2COO^-K^+ + H_2CO_3 \rightarrow H_2O + CO_2 \uparrow \qquad (26\text{--}4)$$

propanoic   potassium   potassium
  acid   carbonate   propanoate

Thus, the reaction of carboxylic acids with carbonates or hydrogen carbonates is another means by which salts are created.

If we add hydrochloric acid to an aqueous solution of sodium benzoate, a white precipitate of benzoic acid appears. (This acid happens to be a solid compound.) Or, if we add sulfuric acid to a solution of sodium butyrate, we promptly note the strong odor of butyric acid.

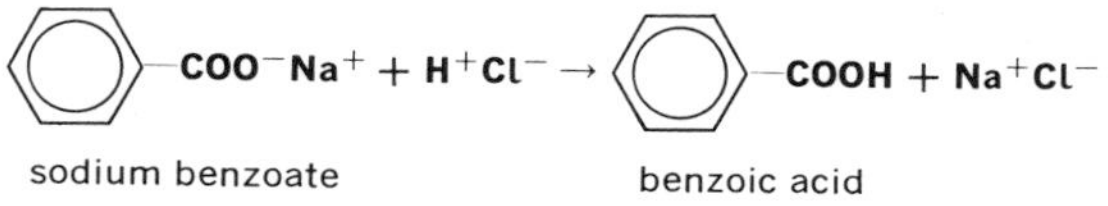

sodium benzoate   benzoic acid

$$2CH_3CH_2CH_2COO^-Na^+ + (H^+)_2SO_4{}^{2-} \rightarrow 2CH_3CH_2CH_2COOH + (Na^+)_2SO_4{}^{2-} \qquad (26\text{--}6)$$

sodium butyrate   butyric acid

In general, we find that mineral acids will convert carboxylate salts to the corresponding carboxylic acids. Our explanation of this is simply that the carboxylic acids are weak acids, so that the strong mineral acids are capable of forcing hydrogen ions onto carboxylate ions, Eqs. (26–5) and (26–6).

To summarize, carboxylic acids have acidic properties for the same reason that inorganic acids do: they release hydrogen ions. The difference is one of degree; organic acids are weak acids because they are only slightly ionized. Like the inorganic acids, they form salts by reaction with metallic hydroxides, oxides, or carbonates.

26–3 WATER SOLUBILITY OF CARBOXYLIC ACIDS AND SALTS

In the preceding paragraph we mentioned sodium benzoate and benzoic acid, Eq. (26–5). Sodium benzoate is quite soluble in water (61 g will dissolve in 100 g of water at 25°C). On the other hand, benzoic acid is only slightly soluble (about 0.25 g of benzoic acid will dissolve in 100 g of water at 25°C), so most of it is precipitated from the solution. In general, this relationship exists for carboxylic acids and their alkali metal salts; although the salt may be either fairly soluble or very soluble in water, the acid is less soluble, often much less so. The alkali salts are more water-soluble because they are ionic; the fully developed charges on ions strongly attract polar water molecules, causing solution. The carboxylic acids, however, are chiefly non-ionized. In order to dissolve, they must depend upon hydrogen-bond attractions between their carboxyl groups, which are polar, and the water molecules, Fig. 26–1. These attractions due to *partially* developed charges in polar molecules are less strong than the attractions to ions.

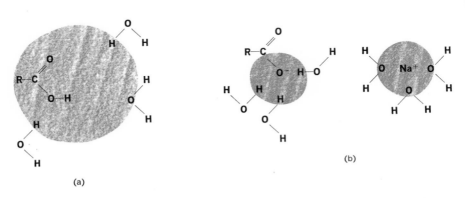

(a)

(b)

FIG. 26–1. Comparison of solvent action of water on polar and ionic substances: (a) moderate attraction between water molecules and a polar acid molecule, RCOOH; (b) strong attraction between water molecules and the ionic salt, $RCOO^-Na^+$.

The result is that the solubility of carboxylic acids in water is about like that of alcohols; the smallest acids are very soluble, those of five and six carbons are slightly soluble, and the larger molecules are "insoluble." In contrast, most sodium or potassium carboxylate salts are quite soluble in water.

26–4 REACTION WITH ALCOHOLS: ESTERIFICATION

Before 1800, a few chemists had discovered that if they heated an organic acid with alcohol, in the presence of sulfuric acid, two products resulted: water and an oily, water-insoluble liquid usually having a pleasant, fruitlike odor. During the same era it was also observed that by proper treatment the fragrant oil could be converted back to the original acid and alcohol. Clearly, this new kind of compound seemed to be some combination of alcohol with an organic acid, achieved by splitting out water. During the 1800's, this reaction was found to be very generally applicable to a great variety of acids in combination with many different alcohols. Eventually the products were called **esters** (apparently a made-up name), and this method of preparing them was termed **esterification** (literally, ester-formation).

The necessity for logically relating the structures of the alcohol, the acid, and the ester played an important part in the development of the concepts of organic structural formation (Section 21–4). We are now able to write the esterification reaction as in Eq. 26–7.

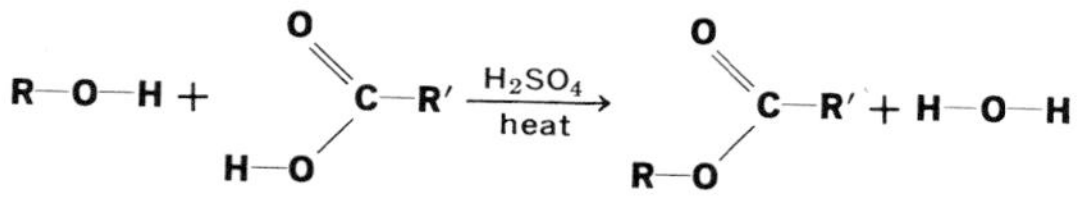

$$R-O-H + \underset{\text{alcohol} \quad \text{carboxylic acid}}{\overset{O}{\underset{H-O}{\parallel}}} C-R' \xrightarrow[\text{heat}]{H_2SO_4} \underset{\text{ester}}{\overset{O}{\underset{R-O}{\parallel}}} C-R' + \underset{\text{water}}{H-O-H} \tag{26-7}$$

$$CH_3CH_2-O-H + \underset{\text{ethyl alcohol} \quad \text{acetic acid}}{\overset{O}{\underset{H-O}{\parallel}}} C-CH_3 \xrightarrow[\text{heat}]{H_2SO_4} \underset{\text{ethyl acetate}}{\overset{O}{\underset{CH_3CH_2-O}{\parallel}}} C-CH_3 + H-O-H \tag{26-8}$$

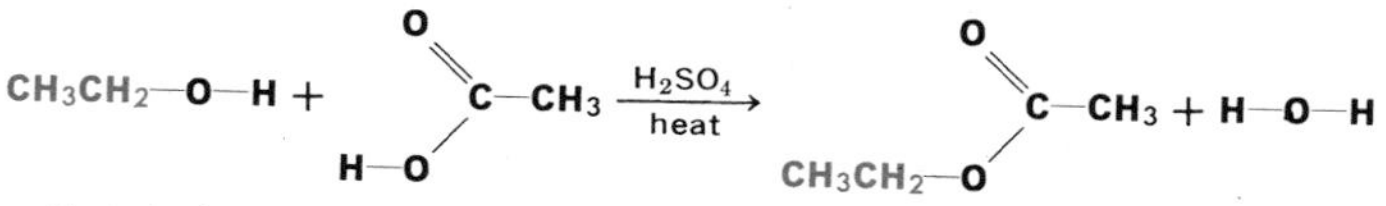

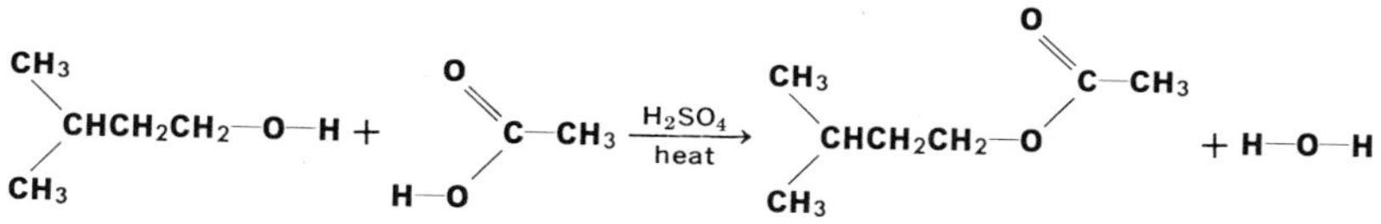

$$\underset{\text{isopentyl alcohol}}{\overset{CH_3}{\underset{CH_3}{}} CHCH_2CH_2-O-H} + \underset{\text{acetic acid}}{\overset{O}{\underset{H-O}{\parallel}}} C-CH_3 \xrightarrow[\text{heat}]{H_2SO_4} \underset{\text{isopentyl acetate}}{\overset{CH_3}{\underset{CH_3}{}} CHCH_2CH_2-O} \overset{O}{\overset{\parallel}{C}}-CH_3 + H-O-H \tag{26-9}$$

Note that the structure of an ester is described in its name. The group name for the alcohol portion is stated first, followed by the name of the acid component, with its -ic ending changed to -ate.

◄ When the hydrogen of a carboxylic acid is replaced by an alkyl group, yielding an ester, the ester name ends with -ate. Recall that this is the same system used to name an organic *salt*, in which a metal ion has replaced the hydrogen. Thus, acet*ic* acid (CH_3COOH) yields sodium acet*ate* (CH_3COONa). The same is true for *inorganic* oxygen-containing acids and salts: sulfur*ic* acid (H_2SO_4) gives sodium sulf*ate* (Na_2SO_4). Of course, in chemical *structure* an ester differs from a salt in one very important manner: the alkyl group of the ester is *covalently* bound to the oxygen, whereas the metal in a salt exists as an *ion*. ►

Aromatic carboxylic acids undergo the esterification reaction as readily as do the alkanoic acids, for example,

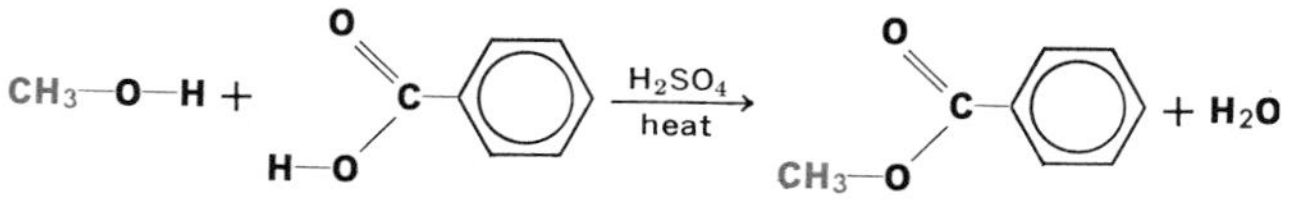

$$CH_3-O-H + \underset{\text{methanol} \quad \text{benzoic acid}}{\overset{O}{\underset{H-O}{\parallel}} C}\bigcirc \xrightarrow[\text{heat}]{H_2SO_4} \underset{\text{methyl benzoate}}{\overset{O}{\underset{CH_3-O}{\parallel}} C}\bigcirc + H_2O \tag{26-10}$$

26-5 COMMON ESTERS, NATURAL AND SYNTHETIC

The odors of flowers and fruits are due to mixtures of several organic compounds. It was not until chemists developed skillful techniques that they were able to separate such mixtures into individual compounds and determine their structures. (Some of the more complicated mixtures are still being investigated.) Eventually, chemists found in plant materials a few esters which were identical with those synthesized in the laboratory by the esterification reaction, Eq. (26–7). **Isopentyl acetate,** Eq. (26–9), was detected in bananas, apples, and some other fruits. It is often called *banana oil* (or *amyl* acetate, an old common name). Since it is a good solvent for certain lacquers, cements, and plastics, large quantities are made industrially by the esterification reaction. **Isopentyl butanoate** occurs in cocoa oil, along with several other compounds; by itself it has a distinctly sweet, fruity odor resembling pears. **Ethyl acetate,** Eq. (26–8), is found in wine, pineapples, and other fruits. It is a valuable solvent used in nail polish removers and in the manufacture of perfumes, plastics, paints, and photographic films.

Methyl benzoate, Eq. (26–10), occurs in a few plant oils; its odor is somewhat medicinal rather than sweet. Another example of an ester derived from an aromatic acid is methyl salicylate (Section 26–9D).

Several other simple esters, not known to occur in fruits or flowers, have nevertheless been prepared and used for decades by manufacturers of artificial flavors and scents. **Methyl butanoate** resembles the scent of apples. **Butyl butanoate** has a fine odor useful in pineapple essence. **Ethyl butanoate** is used in artificial peach flavor, as well as in pineapple and apricot. **Pentyl propanoate** resembles apricot essence.

The effects of vapors on the human nose are intriguing, but not well understood. For instance, the sweet, fruity odors of the simple esters present a marked contrast to the odors of the acids from which they are derived. Methanoic (formic) acid and ethanoic (acetic) acid have pungent, stinging odors. The larger acids, butanoic, hexanoic, and octanoic, have goatlike or rancid odors. Propanoic acid, of intermediate size, has some of both the pungent and the rancid qualities. Acids larger than about decanoic are so slightly volatile that we detect very little odor in their presence.

The esters discussed so far have been derived from alcohols. Esters of phenols are also of frequent occurrence in nature and in the laboratory. One example of a phenolic ester is **phenyl acetate;** note very carefully the structural difference between this ester and methyl benzoate, Eq. (26–10).

phenyl acetate

The phenols will not react directly with a carboxylic acid to form an ester (another case in which phenols differ from alcohols). However, esters of phenols are easily synthesized by an indirect method discussed in Section 26–7.

All told, the ester group is very common in nature. It occurs in fats, to be discussed in Chapter 27, and in many simple compounds, as we have seen in this chapter. The ester group may also appear in a complex molecule, along with several other functional groups, as shown by the structures below.

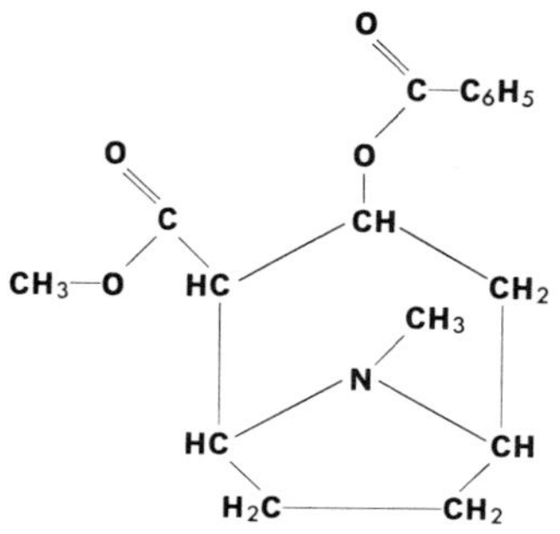

cocaine

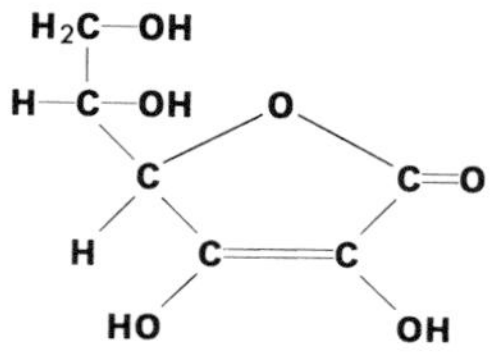

vitamin C

Cocaine, produced by the coca bush of Bolivia and Peru, is a habit-forming narcotic if taken internally. In medicine it is used as a surface anesthetic. Note that cocaine has two different ester groups and a basic amine group (Section 28–2). Note also the interesting location of the ester group in **vitamin C.**

26–6 HYDROLYSIS AND SAPONIFICATION OF ESTERS

In Section 26–4, we learned that after chemists discovered esters they also discovered how to split them into the component alcohol and acid. From the beginning, this has been a useful, frequently-applied manipulation. One method for accomplishing the cleavage is now called hydrolysis; another is saponification.

An ester can be cleaved by heating it in water containing a little strong acid.

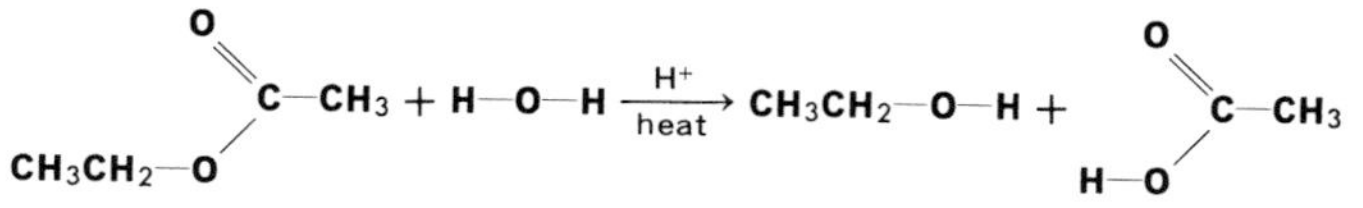

$$CH_3CH_2-O-\overset{\overset{O}{\|}}{C}-CH_3 + H-O-H \xrightarrow[\text{heat}]{H^+} CH_3CH_2-O-H + \overset{\overset{O}{\|}}{\underset{H-O}{C}}-CH_3 \qquad (26\text{–}11)$$

an ester   water   an alcohol   a carboxylic acid

A chemical decomposition, such as this one, due to reaction with water is termed **hydrolysis** (Gr. *hydro*, water plus *lysis*, loosen, break away). In this particular case, the catalyst is a strong acid. Any of the common mineral acids are effective, for example, hydrochloric, sulfuric, or phosphoric acid.

The ester-hydrolysis reaction just written, Eq. (26–11), looks suspiciously like the equation for esterification written backward, Eq. (26–7). Furthermore, we find experimentally that *complete* hydrolysis is not achieved in the reaction mixture; some of the alcohol and the carboxylic acid molecules thus produced combine with each other to recreate some ester molecules and water. We often show in one equation, Eq. (26–12), the relation between these two easily reversible reactions:

$$CH_3CH_2-O-\overset{O}{\overset{\|}{C}}-CH_3 + H-O-H \underset{B}{\overset{A}{\underset{\longleftarrow}{\overset{H^+\text{ heat}}{\longrightarrow}}}} CH_3CH_2-O-H + H-O-\overset{O}{\overset{\|}{C}}-CH_3 \qquad (26-12)$$

As written here, the forward reaction, A, would be hydrolysis; the reverse reaction, B, would be esterification. The heat and catalyst have the same influence on both reactions, merely speeding up the action. This observation, and many others, causes us to believe that exactly the same events of bond-breaking and bond-making occur as the reactions proceed in either direction.

On a practical basis, we can carry out either a hydrolysis or an esterification, depending on which materials we put into the flask. However, because the products can react with each other to give back the starting materials, we never get complete conversion. That is, if we attempt to hydrolyze an ester to an alcohol plus a carboxylic acid, we will obtain *chiefly* those products; but we must expect that there still will be *some* ester in our reaction mixture. Similarly, if we attempt an esterification reaction, Eqs. (26–12B) or (26–7) the conversion to ester will not be a complete one.

A second method for cleaving an ester is to treat it with an aqueous solution of a metallic hydroxide, most often sodium hydroxide. The reaction can be conducted at room temperature within a reasonable time, but as usual can be hastened by heat.

$$CH_3-O-\overset{O}{\overset{\|}{C}}-R + \overset{+\ -}{Na}OH \longrightarrow CH_3OH + \overset{O}{\overset{\|}{C}}-R \qquad (26-13)$$

an ester	sodium hydroxide (in water)	an alcohol	sodium salt of an acid

Because of the base used, one of the products of this reaction is a salt of an acid rather than the acid itself; the other cleavage product is an alcohol, as in the hydrolysis reaction, Eq. (26–11).

If the R-group in this example happens to have a long, straight chain (12 to 18 carbons), the salt produced is a soap. Indeed, we will see in Section 27–5 that treatment with sodium hydroxide solution is used to produce soap from fats (a special class of esters). The term **saponification** (literally, soap making) is now applied quite broadly to the reactions of hydroxides with any kind of ester, Eq. (26–13).

Although the *salt* of an acid is produced by saponification, mere acidification of the reaction mixture (for example, with hydrochloric acid) immediately converts the salt to the corresponding acid.

$$R-\overset{O}{\overset{\|}{C}}\underset{O^-Na^+}{} + H^+Cl^- \longrightarrow R-\overset{O}{\overset{\|}{C}}\underset{O-H}{} + Na^+Cl^- \qquad (26-14)$$

With this simple after-treatment, saponification can give the same net result as hydrolysis; an ester can be split into its component alcohol and carboxylic acid. Indeed, saponification may often be the preferred method because the cleavage is complete; the salt of the carboxylic acid cannot recombine with the alcohol to give back some of the ester.

26–7 FORMATION AND REACTIONS OF ACID CHLORIDES

A carboxylic acid can be converted to an acid chloride by treatment with phosphorous trichloride, for example:

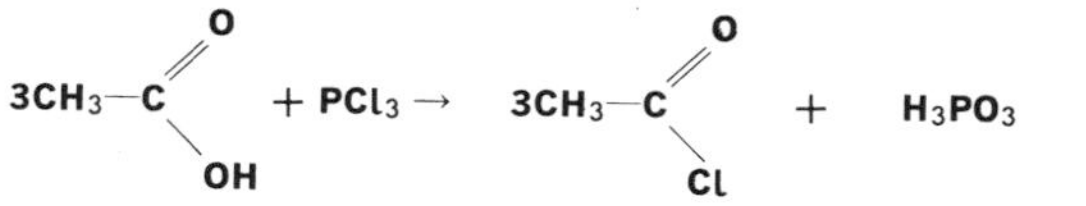

$$3CH_3-\overset{\displaystyle O}{\underset{\displaystyle OH}{C}} + PCl_3 \rightarrow 3CH_3-\overset{\displaystyle O}{\underset{\displaystyle Cl}{C}} + H_3PO_3 \qquad (26\text{–}15)$$

acetic acid   acetyl chloride   phosphorous
                   (an acid chloride)   acid

The acid chloride is a highly reactive substance which can be converted to still other acid derivatives. For example, it reacts with an alcohol to produce an ester:

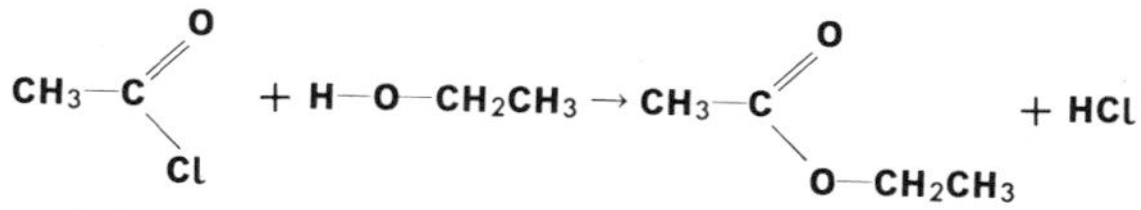

$$CH_3-\overset{\displaystyle O}{\underset{\displaystyle Cl}{C}} + H-O-CH_2CH_3 \rightarrow CH_3-\overset{\displaystyle O}{\underset{\displaystyle O-CH_2CH_3}{C}} + HCl \qquad (26\text{–}16)$$

acetyl chloride   ethanol   ethyl acetate

An advantage of this indirect, two-step pathway from the acid to the ester, Eqs. (26–15) and (26–16), is that both steps give complete conversion to the desired products. This may be important if either the alcohol or the acid is expensive. Of course, the ester could also have been produced in one step by direct reaction of the alcohol with acetic acid (esterification), Eq. (26–8). However, the conversion to ethyl acetate would not be very high because esterification is a reversible reaction (Section 26–6).

The reactive acid chloride also provides a method for synthesizing an ester of a phenol.

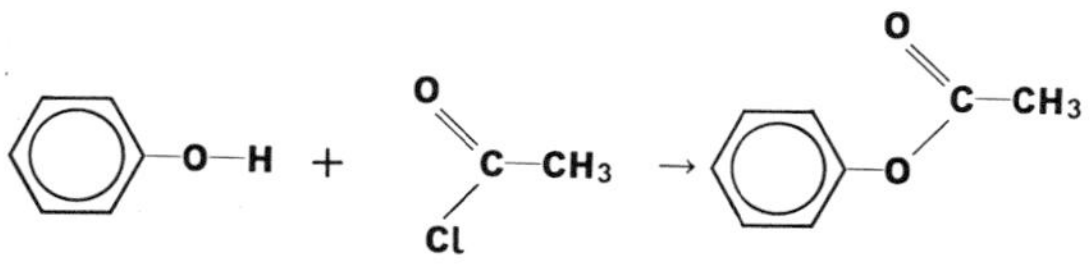

$$(26\text{–}17)$$

phenol   acetyl chloride   phenyl acetate

Direct esterification of a phenol with a carboxylic acid is not possible.

Amides are another type of acid derivative which can be synthesized via acid chlorides (Section 28–4).

26–8 SOURCES OF ACIDS

Carboxylic acids may be synthesized by a great variety of methods. A few of the common procedures will be discussed in this section. Other methods are of interest primarily to professional chemists.

Often the acids may be obtained by oxidation of other organic compounds, on either a laboratory or an industrial scale. Primary alcohols, as well as aldehydes, may be oxidized to acids, Eqs. (26–18) and (26–19).

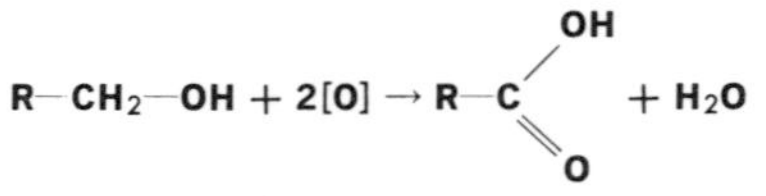

$$R\text{—}CH_2\text{—}OH + 2[O] \rightarrow R\text{—}C\overset{OH}{\underset{O}{\diagdown}} + H_2O \tag{26–18}$$

$$R\text{—}C\overset{H}{\underset{O}{\diagup}} + [O] \rightarrow R\text{—}C\overset{OH}{\underset{O}{\diagdown}} \tag{26–19}$$

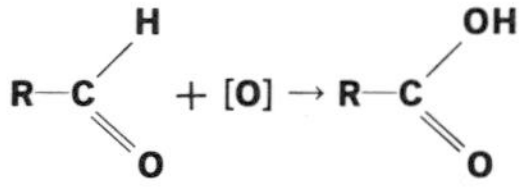

In the laboratory these oxidations are usually accomplished by reagents such as sodium dichromate or potassium permanganate.

For commercial production it is desirable to use an inexpensive oxidizing agent such as oxygen from air. With this modification the two conversions above, Eqs. (26–18) and (26–19) are used for manufacturing acetic acid. In one process, manganese acetate catalyzes the air-oxidation of acetaldehyde. (Sources of acetaldehyde are discussed in Section 29–2).

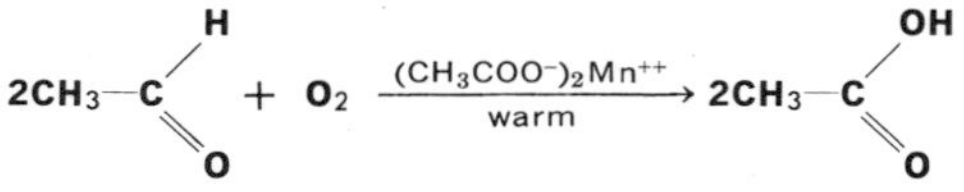

$$2CH_3\text{—}C\overset{H}{\underset{O}{\diagup}} + O_2 \xrightarrow[\text{warm}]{(CH_3COO^-)_2Mn^{++}} 2CH_3\text{—}C\overset{OH}{\underset{O}{\diagdown}}$$
$$\text{(air)} \qquad\qquad\qquad \text{acetic acid}$$

This is the main source of pure (*glacial*) acetic acid (Section 26–9A).

When only dilute solutions of acetic acid are required, as in food use, vinegar can be obtained by an oxidative fermentation of ethanol.

$$CH_3CH_2OH + O_2 \xrightarrow{\text{bacteria}} CH_3COOH + H_2O$$

The required ethanol is in turn obtained from the fermentation, by yeasts, of blackstrap molasses, an inexpensive by-product of the sugar industry.

We learned in Section 24–7 that an alkyl benzene can be oxidized to benzoic acid. For industrial production, a vanadium pentoxide or manganese acetate catalyst makes possible the use of air for the oxidation. Nearly all benzoic acid is obtained in this way from toluene, Eq. (26–20).

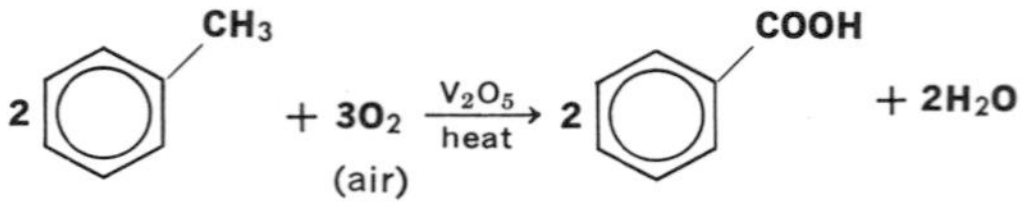

$$2\,\underset{}{\bigcirc}\text{—}CH_3 + 3O_2 \xrightarrow[\text{heat}]{V_2O_5} 2\,\underset{}{\bigcirc}\text{—}COOH + 2H_2O \tag{26–20}$$
$$\text{(air)}$$

Certain other aromatic carboxylic acids are produced in the same manner from different starting materials.

From fats one may obtain a mixture of octadecanoic acid (stearic acid) and a few other long-chain acids (Section 27–1).

26–9 OTHER ACIDS, ESTERS, AND SALTS OF INTEREST

A. Acetic Acid

Dilute solutions of acetic acid (vinegar) have been used from antiquity and are still being used to preserve meat, fish, pickles, and other foods. Acetic acid arrests the growth of various microorganisms, preventing spoilage of the food to which it is added.

Acetic acid which is nearly pure, and undiluted by water, is called *glacial* acetic acid, so named because it freezes at about 16°C. Industrially, it is as important among organic compounds as sulfuric acid is among the inorganics. A weak acid, it is a useful acidulant in the dyeing and processing of textiles and in the coagulation of rubber latex. Acetic acid is one of the intermediates essential for the manufacture of cellulose acetate film, acetate textile fibers, and innumerable pharmaceuticals. The insecticide Paris green is a mixture of copper acetate, $Cu(CH_3COO)_2$, and copper arsenite, $Cu(AsO_2)_2$.

B. Benzoic Acid

Benzoic acid is an intermediate for the synthesis of many drugs and dyes. Increasing amounts are being used to improve the quality of alkyd enamels. Sodium benzoate, C_6H_5COONa, has long been used as a food preservative. It is most satisfactory in somewhat acid foods (pH 4 or lower), particularly in fruit juices, catsup, pickles, pie fillings, jams, and margarine. Sodium benzoate is an effective bactericide at the customary concentration of 0.1%, and is tasteless and nontoxic. It is also a preservative for drugs, cosmetics, toothpastes, gum, and starch.

C. Dicarboxylic Acids

In a number of organic compounds we may find two or more carboxyl groups in one molecule. The simplest example is **oxalic acid,** HOOC—COOH, which is just two carboxyl groups bonded together. Its name arises from the fact that it is the sour material in wood sorrel, botanically called oxalis (Gr. *oxys*, acid). Since both the hydrogens in oxalic acid can be neutralized by a base, it can form either normal salts such as NaOOC—COONa, sodium oxalate, or acidic salts such as HOOC—COOK, potassium hydrogen oxalate. It is the latter form which occurs in sorrel plants, rhubarb, and spinach. Apparently the amount of rhubarb or spinach we eat, or the manner in which we eat it, does not provide a harmful dose of oxalic acid. However, the acid and its salt are definitely toxic. Livestock have died because of its presence in the poisonous weed halogeton. Oxalic acid can be used in some circumstances to remove ink stains and rust. It is quite effective for cleaning the rusty scale from the insides of auto radiators.

Although many dicarboxylic acids are well known, we will mention just one more for now. **Succinic acid,** $HOOC—CH_2—CH_2—COOH$, apparently occurs in almost all plants and animals. It was first mentioned in 1550 by Agricola, who isolated some from amber (L. *succinum*). The acid is an important intermediate for the manufacture of numerous pharmaceuticals and polymers. The salt sodium succinate is an antidote for poisoning by heavy metals or by barbiturate drugs.

D. Hydroxy Acids

Yet another structural variation occurs because a molecule may have both hydroxyl and carboxyl functional groups. We have already mentioned, Section 26–1, that sour milk contains **lactic acid** (2-hydroxypropanoic acid). This acid may also occur in fatigued muscle tissue.* Lactic acid is a common acidulant for food products because its mild acid taste does not overpower other flavors; a few examples of its use are in soups, olives, beer, soft drinks, cheese, and sherbets. The lactic acid for these purposes is commercially obtained by the action of *lactobacillus* organisms on molasses or starch.

Tartaric acid, a by-product of wine-making, is structurally dihydroxysuccinic acid:

$$HOOC—CH—CH—COOH$$
$$\quad\quad\;\; OH\;\; OH$$

During the aging of wine, a substance, originally present in the grape juice, crystallizes on the inside of the barrel. The medieval Greeks called this hard crust tartaron; in modern English it is tartar. The purified material, being white, is called *cream of tartar*. We now know that this is the potassium hydrogen salt of tartaric acid. Cream of tartar is widely used in baking powders. It is only slightly soluble at room temperature. However, at baking temperatures it dissolves and reacts with the sodium hydrogen carbonate also present in the baking powder, releasing bubbles of carbon dioxide. Tartaric acid itself may be obtained when desired by treating crude tartar with sulfuric acid. Tartaric acid is used in some foods, soft drinks, and metal polishes.

Citric acid (L. *citrus*) is a more complex substance having three carboxyl groups and one alcohol group.

$$CH_2—COOH$$
$$HO—C—COOH \quad\quad \text{citric acid}$$
$$CH_2—COOH$$

This acid occurs in several berries and other fruits, but especially in lemons, oranges, etc. In fact, it is present in very small amounts in all living cells which derive energy from the

---

* The breakdown of glucose, through a complex series of reactions, releases the energy needed for movement and body heat. Under certain circumstances, lactic acid may be one of the end products of glucose metabolism.

metabolism of carbon compounds. In food processing, citric acid is used more than any other solid organic acid because it is nontoxic, very soluble in water, and has a pleasant, mildly sour taste. A few of its applications are in fruit and vegetable juices, candies, desserts, jellies, frozen fruits, soft drinks, and effervescent tablets; others are in cosmetics, hair rinses, rust and scale removers, and bottle-washing mixtures. It is usually the most satisfactory acidulant for drug preparations.

Although citric acid was formerly isolated from citrus wastes, since about 1925 it has been produced more economically by growing a fungus, *aspergillus niger*, in a glucose solution. Citric acid is a metabolic product elaborated by the fungus as it consumes the glucose. The mat of fungus is then filtered off, and the citric acid is crystallized from the solution.

The salt sodium citrate, in conjunction with citric acid, is valuable for its buffering ability in jellies, ice cream, candy, gelatin desserts, and whipping cream; the setting of these foods depends on the proper pH. The sodium citrate-citric acid mixture is likewise the most desirable buffer for medicines. In samples of human blood collected for transfusion, the mixture acts as a buffer and anticoagulant.

Salicylic acid and its derivatives are an interesting family. They constitute about half of all the "coal tar" drugs (i.e., benzenoid and related compounds) manufactured in the United States.

salicylic acid   methyl salicylate   acetyl salicylic acid
                        "oil of wintergreen"   "aspirin"

Salicylic acid, a better disinfectant than phenol, is a common ingredient of topical ointments for skin diseases. It causes the outer layer of skin to flake off, but does not kill the underlying tissue.

The ester methyl salicylate is a fragrant oil occurring in numerous plants, especially wintergreen. It is a flavoring agent for candy, gum, foods, and dentifrices, and a constituent of some antiseptics and perfumes. Methyl salicylate is used in liniments as a counterirritant. The mild surface inflammation it creates affects the circulation in a manner which relieves sore muscles. Commercial quantities of methyl salicylate are produced by esterification of salicylic acid with methanol.

Aspirin is the most widely used synthetic drug because it is cheap, relatively safe, easily available, and quite effective in reducing fever and in relieving headaches or similar discomforts. Recently, enough aspirin has been produced in the United States each year to provide every person in the country with about 200 of the standard 5-grain tablets; this amounts to nearly 40 tons per day! Note in the structure of aspirin that the phenolic group has been converted to an acetate ester.

E. Waxes

Waxes are produced by a number of plants and animals. The wax in our ears and beeswax are typical of those produced by animals. Carnuba wax, from the leaves of certain Brazilian palm trees, makes an excellent polish for floors and automobiles. These waxes, although often mixtures of compounds, are chiefly esters in which both the acid portion and the alcohol portion have very long chains. A common example is $C_{27}H_{55}COOC_{30}H_{61}$. The simple term *wax* is usually reserved for these ester compounds. Modified names are used for other substances having waxy properties. For instance, recall that paraffin wax is a mixture of long-chain hydrocarbons.

IMPORTANT TERMS

Acid chloride	*Carboxylate salt*	*Ester*	*Hydrolysis*
Alkanoic acid	*Carboxylic acid*	*Esterification*	*Saponification*

WORK EXERCISES

1. Give the structural formula of
   a) propanoic acid
   b) hexanoic acid
   c) benzoic acid
   d) sodium acetate
   e) potassium benzoate
   f) ethyl benzoate
   g) isopropyl acetate
   h) 3-chlorobenzoic acid
   i) a wax

2. Write complete equations for the following reactions:
   a) formic acid, sodium hydroxide
   b) acetic acid, sodium hydrogen carbonate
   c) benzoic acid, ethanol, H_2SO_4, heat
   d) sodium benzoate, HBr
   e) ethyl butanoate, H_2O, H_2SO_4, heat
   f) butanoic acid, isopentyl alcohol, H_2SO_4, heat
   g) methyl benzoate, dilute NaOH, heat

3. Show how
   a) butanoic acid could be obtained from 1-butanol
   b) benzoic acid could be obtained from toluene

4. Write the equation for the reaction of methanol with *p*-bromobenzoic acid to produce an ester.
   a) Which would you estimate would be less expensive, the methanol or the *p*-bromobenzoic acid?
   b) If you were to prepare this ester in the laboratory, what conditions, concentrations, etc., would you use to make maximum use of the more expensive component?

SUGGESTED READING

Collier, H. O. J., "Aspirin," *Scientific American*, Nov. 1963 (Offprint #169). There is now a better understanding of the reasons for the dramatic effectiveness of the most widely used drug.

DePuy, C. H. and K. L. Rinehart, Jr., *Introduction to Organic Chemistry*, Chapter 11, John Wiley, New York, 1967.

Hart, H. and R. D. Schuetz, *Organic Chemistry*, 3rd ed., Chapter 9, Houghton Mifflin, Boston, 1966.

Jacobson, M. and M. Beroza, "Insect Attractants," *Scientific American*, Aug. 1964 (Offprint #189). The sex attractants excreted by insects are being isolated so that the chemical structure can be determined. If an attractant can be synthesized, it can be used to lure insects to traps. The structures discovered so far include alcohols, esters, and other types.

Noller, C. R., *Textbook of Organic Chemistry*, 3rd ed., Chapters 11 and 27, W. B. Saunders, Philadelphia, 1966.

Chapter 27   THE CHEMISTRY OF FATS

27-1 STRUCTURE AND HYDROLYSIS OF FATS

Typical fats, such as bacon fat or beef tallow, can be hydrolyzed to glycerol and a mixture of fatty acids. From detailed studies of the hydrolysis fragments and of the other properties of fats, it is certain that fats *are esters of glycerol with fatty acids*.

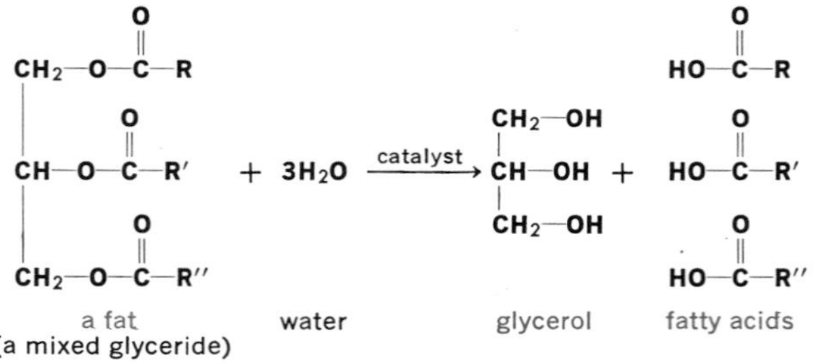

$$
\begin{array}{c}
\underset{\substack{\text{a fat}\\ \text{(a mixed glyceride)}}}{
\begin{array}{l}
\text{CH}_2\!-\!\text{O}\!-\!\overset{\overset{\text{O}}{\|}}{\text{C}}\!-\!\text{R}\\[4pt]
\text{CH}\!-\!\text{O}\!-\!\overset{\overset{\text{O}}{\|}}{\text{C}}\!-\!\text{R}'\\[4pt]
\text{CH}_2\!-\!\text{O}\!-\!\overset{\overset{\text{O}}{\|}}{\text{C}}\!-\!\text{R}''
\end{array}}
\;+\;\underset{\text{water}}{3\text{H}_2\text{O}}\;\xrightarrow{\text{catalyst}}\;
\underset{\text{glycerol}}{\begin{array}{l}\text{CH}_2\!-\!\text{OH}\\[4pt]\text{CH}\!-\!\text{OH}\\[4pt]\text{CH}_2\!-\!\text{OH}\end{array}}
\;+\;\underset{\text{fatty acids}}{\begin{array}{l}\text{HO}\!-\!\overset{\overset{\text{O}}{\|}}{\text{C}}\!-\!\text{R}\\[4pt]\text{HO}\!-\!\overset{\overset{\text{O}}{\|}}{\text{C}}\!-\!\text{R}'\\[4pt]\text{HO}\!-\!\overset{\overset{\text{O}}{\|}}{\text{C}}\!-\!\text{R}''\end{array}}
\end{array}
\tag{27-1}
$$

The term **glyceride** is a special name designating an ester of glycerol; the term triglyceride is also frequently used (Section 35–3). Since there is a variety of different acids combined in a natural fat, it is often called a **mixed glyceride.** The arrangement of R-groups in the fat structure shown above is just one typical example. In another molecule from the same sample of fat the arrangement might be R', R, R'' or R', R, R or R, R'', R, etc. Therefore, a fat is not a pure compound by the usual chemical definition that all the molecules in a sample are identical. (See Table 27–2.)

In the laboratory, hydrolysis of a fat can be accomplished with a mineral acid, such as hydrochloric or phosphoric, acting as catalyst.

◄ The chemical reaction taking place during the digestion of fatty food in the intestines of man or an animal is another example of the hydrolysis reaction, Eq. (27–1). The catalyst for the reaction is an enzyme.

In certain tissues of plants and animals, *biosynthesis* of fats occurs.

$$\text{fatty acids} + \text{glycerol} \xrightarrow{\text{enzyme}} \text{fat} + \text{water} \tag{27–2}$$

This synthesis is the reverse of the hydrolysis reaction, Eq. (27–1). Plants first synthesize fatty acids and glycerol from very simple molecules and then combine them, Eq. (27–2), to produce a fat. Animals can do the same, but they also obtain large amounts of fatty acids and glycerol from digested food. ►

27–2 FATTY ACID CONSTITUENTS

Since the glyceride structure is common to all fats, the variations in properties from one type of fat to another must be due to differences in their fatty-acid components. It is therefore convenient to describe fats in terms of the fatty acids present.

In general, *a natural fatty acid has a skeleton composed of an even number of carbon atoms in a long, unbranched chain.* A chain length of sixteen or eighteen carbons is predominant. Carbon–carbon double bonds are common. The most typical acids found in fats are listed in Table 27–1. Common names, rather than systematic names, are often used for these acids; origins of the names are discussed in Section 35–2.

Note that each of the common unsaturated acids, oleic, linoleic, and linolenic, has an eighteen-carbon skeleton like that of stearic acid, but a different number of carbon–carbon double bonds. Consequently, in this family one formula differs from the next by two hydrogens, (see the last four formulas in Table 27–1).

TABLE 27–1. Common fatty acids

Structural Formula and Common Name	Abbreviated Formula
$CH_3(CH_2)_{10}COOH$ lauric acid	$C_{11}H_{23}COOH$
$CH_3(CH_2)_{12}COOH$ myristic acid	$C_{13}H_{27}COOH$
$CH_3(CH_2)_{14}COOH$ palmitic acid	$C_{15}H_{31}COOH$
$CH_3(CH_2)_{16}COOH$ stearic acid	$C_{17}H_{35}COOH$
$CH_3(CH_2)_7CH\!=\!CH(CH_2)_7COOH$ oleic acid	$C_{17}H_{33}COOH$
$CH_3(CH_2)_4CH\!=\!CHCH_2CH\!=\!CH(CH_2)_7COOH$ linoleic acid	$C_{17}H_{31}COOH$
$CH_3CH_2CH\!=\!CHCH_2CH\!=\!CHCH_2CH\!=\!CH(CH_2)_7COOH$ linolenic acid	$C_{17}H_{29}COOH$

TABLE 27-2. Composition of some fats and oils

Fat or Oil	Fatty Acid Present, % by Weight[a]						
	lauric C_{12} sat'd	myristic C_{14} sat'd	palmitic C_{16} sat'd	stearic C_{18} sat'd	oleic C_{18} one C=C	linoleic C_{18} two C=C	linolenic C_{18} three C=C
lard		1–2	25–30	12–16	40–50	5–10	1
beef tallow		3–5	25–30	20–30	40–50	1–5	
mutton tallow		1–5	20–25	25–30	35–45	3–6	
butterfat (cow)[b]	2–5	8–14	25–30	9–12	25–35	2–5	
coconut fat[c]	45–48	16–18	8–10	2–4	5–8	1–2	
palm kernel fat[d]	43–47	15–20	8–9	2–5	10–18	1–3	
palm oil or fat		1–3	35–45	4–6	40–50	8–11	
peanut oil			8–10	3–5	55–60	25–30	
sardine oil		5–6	12–16	2–3	(75–82)[e]		
olive oil			8–16	2–3	70–85	5–15	
cottonseed oil		1	20–25	1–2	20–30	45–50	
soybean oil			10	3	25–30	50–55	4–8
safflower oil			6	3	13–15	75–78	
linseed oil					20–35	15–25	40–60
tung oil			4–6		5–10	9–12	(76–82)[f]

[a] The approximate range of typical values for each fat is indicated by these figures which were compiled from various sources.

[b] Also 3–4% butyric and 1–3% each of C_6, C_8, C_{10} acids.

[c] Also 5–9% each of C_8 and C_{10} acids.

[d] Also 4% C_8 and 4–8% C_{10} acids.

[e] Total unsaturated acids, 75–82%, including 10–15% palmitoleic, $CH_3(CH_2)_5CH=CH(CH_2)_7COOH$; some as large as C_{24} with up to six C=C.

[f] Tung oil contains eleostearic acid rather than linolenic; the three C=C are in different locations.

◄ The curious fact that nearly all natural fatty acids possess an even number of carbon atoms was explained by experiments in the 1950's, Section 40–3. It was found that most organisms capable of synthesizing fatty acids do so by using acetate groups (CH_3COO^-), which are two-carbon building blocks. There are a few exceptions. It has been discovered that certain bacteria can produce fatty acids having methyl branches and an odd number of carbons. One such organism is *mycobacterium tuberculosis*. Branched-chain or odd-numbered acids are apparently rare in higher plants and animals.

Acids containing fewer than twelve carbons, or more than twenty, occur in some fats but are less common. ►

The composition of a particular fat can be determined by hydrolyzing it, Eq. (27–1), and then analyzing the resultant mixture of fatty acids. The percent, by weight, of each acid present in various fats is listed in Table 27–2.

27–3 FATS AND OILS

It has become customary to call a glyceride a fat if it is solid, or an oil if it is liquid, at ordinary temperatures. This differentiation of course is arbitrary and depends on the climate. The differences in melting points of the glycerides are due chiefly to the varying numbers of double bonds present; the more of these there are, the lower the melting point. For example, olive oil and cottonseed oil have considerably higher percentages of unsaturated acids than do lard and tallow, Table 27–2.

Palm oil or fat represents an interesting borderline case. It is usually called an oil because it is a liquid as it originates in the tropics. However, in the temperate regions it may be a semisolid. In palm oil the total percentage of unsaturates (oleic plus linoleic) is only slightly higher than that of lard or tallow, Table 27–2.

◄ The *length* of the fatty acid chains can also influence the melting point. As in other series of organic compounds, shorter chains mean lower melting points. Although coconut fat and palm kernel fat are highly saturated, they soften at a lower temperature than does lard because of their high percentage of lauric acid. Another interesting example is butter. Although it is quite saturated, it is not as stiff as tallow because butter has a moderate number of short chain acids. There are few other examples of this effect among the glycerides because most of them are constituted of C_{16} and C_{18} acids. ►

The data in Table 27–2 suggest that animal glycerides are usually fats, while plant glycerides are usually oils. However, this differentiation does not always hold since the environmental temperature of the organism does have an effect on the form of the glyceride. Thus, for example, the sardine glycerides are oils. On the other hand, the tropical plants (coconut, palm) produce higher-melting glycerides. Experiments have shown that when two groups of the same plants or animals are raised at different temperatures, the group raised at the lower temperature produces more unsaturated glycerides, Section 40–4. In general, however, the oils are found in plants or in animals living in cold environments.

Animal fats may slowly become rancid if exposed to air at room temperature. The attack of oxygen on unsaturated groups produces smaller acids and aldehydes, many of which have foul odors. Although plant oils are more unsaturated, they are less susceptible to rancidity. They normally contain significant amounts of tocopherols (vitamin E) which inhibit the oxidation. Animal fats may be protected by the addition of an anti-oxidant such as BHT, Section 25-6.

When the term *oil* is used in connection with plant products, it refers to the glycerides which are structurally esters. Petroleum oil, however, consists of hydrocarbons, Section 22-4.

27-4 HYDROGENATION OF OILS

For some purposes, solid fats rather than liquid oils are preferred. Oils, which are more unsaturated, can be "hardened" to higher-melting solids by the addition of hydrogen to their double bonds. The hydrogenation reaction, first described for alkenes, Section 23-4B, can be applied to oils:

An oil
(lower melting;
liquid at room temperature)

A fat
(higher melting;
solid at room temperature)

$$
\begin{array}{l}
CH_2-O-\overset{\overset{O}{\|}}{C}-(CH_2)_{16}CH_3 \\[2mm]
CH-O-\overset{\overset{O}{\|}}{C}-(CH_2)_7CH=CHCH_2CH=CH(CH_2)_4CH_3 + 3H_2 \xrightarrow[\text{heat}]{\text{Ni}} \\[2mm]
CH_2-O-\overset{\overset{O}{\|}}{C}-(CH_2)_7CH=CH(CH_2)_7CH_3
\end{array}
\qquad
\begin{array}{l}
CH_2-O-\overset{\overset{O}{\|}}{C}-(CH_2)_{16}CH_3 \\[2mm]
CH-O-\overset{\overset{O}{\|}}{C}-(CH_2)_{16}CH_3 \\[2mm]
CH_2-O-\overset{\overset{O}{\|}}{C}-(CH_2)_{16}CH_3
\end{array}
\qquad (27\text{-}3)
$$

glyceryl tristearate

Note that in this example of an oil molecule there are two unsaturated side chains, one oleic and one linoleic. In the resultant fat, all three groups are stearic, so the product is called glyceryl tristearate.

The reaction is carried out by bubbling hydrogen into a tank of the hot oil. A little powdered nickel is dispersed in the oil to catalyze the hydrogenation—the nickel can be removed later.

In this manner cheap, abundant vegetable oils, such as cottonseed or soybean oils, can be converted to oleomargarine, cooking greases (Crisco, Spry, etc.), or stocks to be further processed into soap, Section 27-5. The hydrogenation can be controlled to provide the degree of firmness most suitable for the product desired. For oleomargarine a certain amount of milk, vitamins A and D, emulsifying agents, flavors, and yellow food colors are added to the hardened oil. It should be noted that the same coloring agents are frequently added to butter to improve its appearance. When cows are not on fresh pasture the color of the butter is pale and the vitamin A content decreases by about half.

27-5 SAPONIFICATION

It was shown in Section 26-6 that a typical ester can be cleaved either by water or by a sodium hydroxide solution. Since fats are esters, they display the same behavior. Cleavage of a fat by water was described in Section 27-1; cleavage by hydroxide, also called saponifica-

FIG. 27–1. A soap kettle used for the traditional saponification reaction. This is a view at the top of the kettle, which may be 20–30 ft high. [Courtesy of Procter and Gamble Company.]

tion, is illustrated in Eq. 27–4.

$$
\begin{array}{c}
CH_2-O-\overset{\overset{\displaystyle O}{\|}}{C}-C_{17}H_{35} \\[4pt]
CH-O-\overset{\overset{\displaystyle O}{\|}}{C}-C_{17}H_{35} \;+\; 3NaOH \;\rightarrow\;
\begin{array}{c}CH_2-OH \\ CH-OH \\ CH_2-OH\end{array}
\;+\; 3\;\overset{\overset{\displaystyle O}{\|}}{\underset{NaO}{C}}-C_{17}H_{35} \\[4pt]
CH_2-O-\overset{\overset{\displaystyle O}{\|}}{C}-C_{17}H_{35}
\end{array}
\qquad (27\text{–}4)
$$

a fat   glycerol   (sodium stearate)
                                                   a soap

An alkali metal carboxylate salt having a chain of 12 to 18 carbons has cleansing properties and is called a **soap;** the most common example is sodium stearate.

Ordinary hand soap has for many years been manufactured by the chemical reaction shown in Eq. (27–4). The ingredients are sodium hydroxide (caustic soda) and a natural fat such as tallow or a hardened vegetable oil; these are heated together with water in a large vessel called a soap kettle, (Fig. 27–1). When the reaction is complete, salt is added to the mixture, causing precipitation of the soap. After the soap has been collected, the valuable glycerol, Section 25–3, can be separated from the saltwater solution.

FIG. 27–2. The tower (foreground) is a hydrolyzer used in the continuous process for soapmaking. [Courtesy of Procter and Gamble Company.]

FIG. 27–3. Soap is formed in this neutralizer tank when a stream of fatty acids from the hydrolyzer (Fig. 27–2) is mixed with a stream of alkali. [Courtesy of Procter and Gamble Company.]

Soap is still manufactured in kettles by the saponification reaction, Eq. (27–4), in most parts of the world. In the United States a new process utilizing the hydrolysis reaction, Eq. (27–1), has been developed. Fats are treated in a tall tower, Fig. 27–2, under pressure, with very hot water. The resultant fatty acids pass out through a pipe at the top of the tower and glycerol, in water, is drawn off at the bottom. After purification, the fatty acids are carried to a neutralizer tank, Fig. 27–3, where treatment with exactly the correct amount of alkali converts the acids to soap, Eq. (27–5). The advantages of this process for soap-making are

$$R{-}COOH + NaOH \rightarrow RCOONa + HOH \qquad (27\text{–}5)$$
fatty acids   soap

that it is rapid, it can be run continuously, and it permits more efficient separation and purification of glycerol and the fatty acids.

By using potassium hydroxide in the manufacturing process, a potassium soap can be prepared. It is more expensive but is desirable for a liquid soap or shaving cream because it is more soluble and produces a softer lather. Sodium stearate ($C_{17}H_{35}COONa$) produces a firm lather and has excellent cleansing properties, but dissolves best in hot water. Coconut and palm kernel fats, having a higher percentage of C_{12} and C_{14} acids, Table 27–2, yield soaps which are more soluble. These are often blended with soap mixtures made from lard or tallow.

◄ The Romans of the first century A.D. were well acquainted with the art of soap-making. It is believed that they learned it from the Greeks. During the Middle Ages the process became known throughout the Mediterranean countries. Animal fats or olive oil were boiled in a kettle with water and ashes from wood or seaweed. The ashes provided potassium and sodium bases derived from the minerals originally present in the plants. It was not until about 1850 that people learned that glycerol was present as a by-product and was useful for other purposes. ►

27–6 THE SOLUBILITY AND CLEANSING ACTION OF SOAPS

A sodium carboxylate salt ($R{-}COO^-Na^+$) is highly ionic and usually quite water-soluble because of the strong attraction of water molecules to the charges on the ions, Section 26–3. Let us now consider how this behavior might be modified in the case of a soap, in which the R-group is a *long* hydrocarbon chain. The structure of sodium stearate, a typical soap, is written out in Fig. 27–4. Beneath it is a diagram symbolizing the two important features of the structure. The circle represents the ionic carboxylate end of the molecule and the long line represents the nonpolar hydrocarbon chain. The nonpolar hydrocarbon group

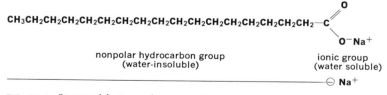

FIG. 27–4. Structural features of a soap molecule.

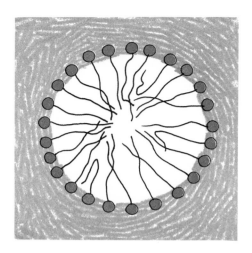

FIG. 27–5. A soap micelle; about 100 soap molecules clustered together and surrounded by water.

is not soluble in water, but water would be attracted to the ionic groups and hence *tend* to dissolve the molecules.

The outcome of these conflicting tendencies is illustrated in Fig. 27–5. When soap molecules are placed in water, the hydrocarbon portions will not permit themselves to be exposed to water. Instead, they are attracted to each other, forming a cluster in which they are literally dissolved in each other. This grouping allows the ionic groups at the ends of the soap molecules to be attracted to the surrounding water molecules. The result is that the soap molecules are, in a sense, able to "dissolve" in the water. However, this is a colloidal solution, not a true solution.

The droplet of soap molecules surrounded by water, illustrated in Fig. 27–5, is called a *soap micelle*. Experimental measurements indicate that there are about 100 soap molecules in each cluster. The alignment of the hydrocarbon groups is random and frequently changing, as is typical in a liquid. In particular, the hydrocarbon chains must be bent, because of the crowding that would result at the center of the cluster if all were straight. The liquid soap micelles dissolved in liquid water constitute one example of an emulsion, one of the types of colloidal solutions, Section 14–3.

◄ Recall that in a true solution each dissolved ion or molecule is separately and completely surrounded by solvent molecules. (Examples would be potassium bromide ions in water, hexane molecules in ether, or iodine molecules in ethyl alcohol.) However, the "solution" of soap in water is designated as a colloidal solution because each bit of dissolved material is a cluster of *many* solute molecules. Although each cluster or micelle is fairly large, they do not coalesce and settle out. The most important factor in keeping the micelles dispersed throughout the water is the negative electrical charge, from carboxylate ions, on the surface of each micelle. When two of the micelles approach each other they are repelled by their like charges and hence do not coalesce into a larger globule. ►

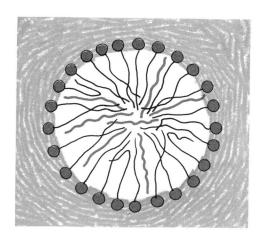

FIG. 27–6. Grease molecules dissolved inside soap micelle.

Figure 27–6 shows how soap can pull into solution (emulsify) oil and dirt particles which alone would not be soluble in water. The interior of the soap micelle is essentially the same as a liquid alkane mixture, such as kerosene. It is therefore a good solvent for materials similar to it in structure, namely nonpolar or slightly polar substances.

When a soap solution is splashed over a dirty dish, an automobile, or a fabric, soap molecules spread over the surface of the object, loosening any oily material. Agitation helps jar the oil from the surface and disperse it into tiny droplets. More and more soap molecules surround the oil, until it becomes incorporated within a soap micelle, as illustrated in Fig. 27–6. Particles of dirt often cling to an object because of an oily film. Once the oil is emulsified and removed by the soap, the dirt particles are also loosened. The very small particles may even be trapped inside the soap micelle.

◄ From the standpoint of human civilization, it is interesting to note that the carboxylate salts obtainable from natural fats, Eq. (27–4), have just the right properties to make them good cleansing agents. If the carbon chain is longer than eighteen carbons, the salt is not sufficiently water-soluble to be useful. If it contains less than ten carbons it does not emulsify oil. ►

27–7 SYNTHETIC DETERGENTS

It was shown in the previous section that a soap has cleansing properties because it can emulsify an oil in water. This action depends on the structural features shown in Fig. 27–4. In more general terms, any molecule will show cleansing and emulsifying behavior if it possesses the necessary combination of two different structural units: a large nonpolar, hydrocarbon group and a water-soluble end group. In addition to the soaps, there are numerous other compounds, both natural and synthetic, which fulfill these structural requirements.

The term **detergent** (L. *detergere*) means simply cleansing agent. Soap is just one of many compounds in this group. However, in everyday language when a person speaks of a detergent he is usually thinking of a modern synthetic detergent. The old familiar soap is still often regarded as being in a separate class.

The sulfonate salt shown below is a synthetic detergent which has excellent cleansing ability and is therefore widely distributed for both household and commercial use. Some common brand names are Tide, Fab, Cheer, and Trend. (In general, synthetic detergents of this type are called alkylbenzenesulfonates.)

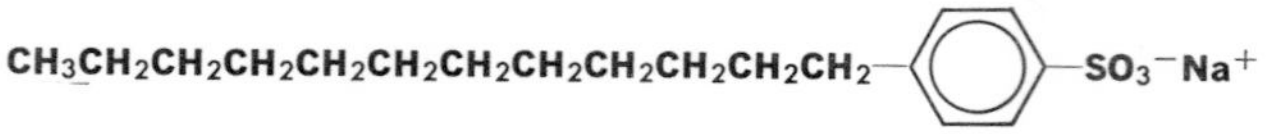

$$CH_3CH_2CH_2CH_2CH_2CH_2CH_2CH_2CH_2CH_2CH_2CH_2 \text{—} \bigcirc \text{—} SO_3^- Na^+ \quad \text{a common synthetic detergent}$$

sodium *n*-dodecylbenzenesulfonate

This sulfonate salt is synthesized commercially by the route outlined in Fig. 27–7, starting from petroleum raw materials. Appropriate chemical changes yield *n*-dodecylbenzene. A typical sulfonation reaction, Eq. (24–3), then substitutes a sulfonic acid group onto the benzene ring *para* to the alkyl group. The resultant sulfonic acid is finally neutralized with a base to obtain the detergent.

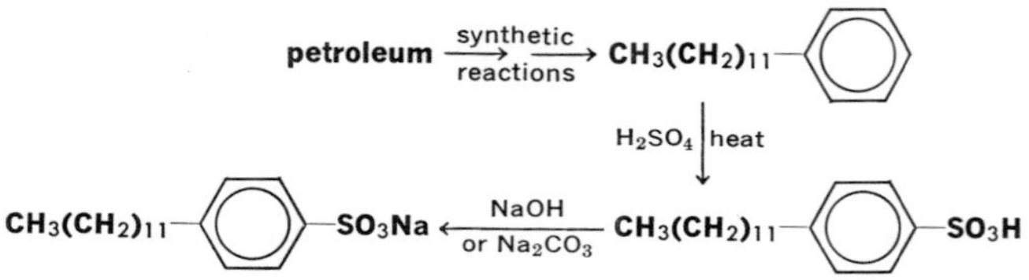

FIG. 27–7. Synthetic route to a typical sulfonate detergent.

The alkylbenzenesulfonate detergent shown above is said to be *biodegradable;* that is, it can be decomposed by microorganisms in a sewage plant or septic tank. Before 1965 the alkylbenzenesulfonates being manufactured had highly *branched* alkyl groups which were not easily degraded. The metabolism of microorganisms is adapted to straight-chain alkyl groups, such as those found in soap or natural fats. Consequently, the nondegraded detergents caused serious problems of foaming and contamination in the water released from sewage plants. Research chemists provided a solution to the problem. The manufacturing process has been changed so that a straight-chain alkyl group is built into the detergent molecule (Fig. 27–7).

Another useful detergent is the sodium alkyl sulfate shown below. Note that it has the two features of structure previously described as being essential for cleansing action.

$$CH_3(CH_2)_{10}CH_2OSO_2O^- Na^+$$

It is also possible for a detergent molecule to have a water-soluble end with a *positive* charge (rather than a negative charge as in the previous examples). Such a compound is therefore sometimes called an *invert soap*. Here is one example:

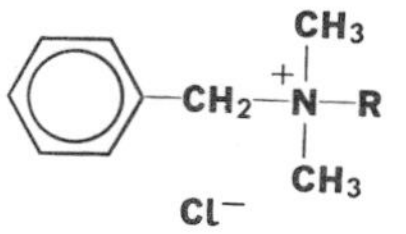

This type of compound is known as a quaternary ammonium salt, Section 28–3A. Since it is not only a good washing agent but also has germicidal properties, it is especially suitable for use in hospitals, etc.

It is not even necessary that the end group of a detergent be ionic, so long as it is water soluble. Polar covalent structures, if there are enough of them, can provide the required solubility. This is illustrated in the examples below.

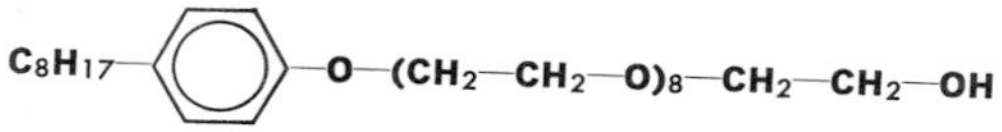

C_8H_{17}—⬡—O—$(CH_2$—CH_2—$O)_8$—CH_2—CH_2—OH

R—$\overset{\displaystyle O}{\underset{\displaystyle \|}{C}}$—$O$—$(CH_2$—$CH_2$—$O)_8$—$CH_2$—$CH_2$—$OH$ the R group is from a typical fatty acid

Compounds of this type, known as *non-ionic detergents*, are used extensively in dishwashing liquids, in low-sudsing products for clothes washers, and in special applications in which the absence of inorganic ions is desirable.

27–8 HARD WATER

Much of the water used in homes and factories is *hard* water, containing appreciable amounts of iron, magnesium, and calcium ions. These accumulated in the water as it percolated through soils and rock strata. Ions of this type interfere with the washing action of a soap because they form an insoluble precipitate with the soap; for example,

$$2CH_3(CH_2)_{16}COO^-Na^+ + Mg^{2+} \rightarrow [CH_3(CH_2)_{16}COO]_2Mg \downarrow + 2Na^+ \qquad (27\text{--}6)$$

The resultant precipitate appears as sticky curds in the water; some of it forms a ring as it clings to the side of the washbowl or bathtub. This film of course represents waste. Enough soap must be used to precipitate all the magnesium ions before any dissolved soap is available for washing action. Furthermore, the presence of the curdy precipitate interferes with the cleansing ability of the additional soap which is used.

An important advantage of a synthetic detergent such as the alkylbenzenesulfonate is that it does *not* form an insoluble precipitate with magnesium or calcium ions. It is therefore a very good washing agent even in hard water.

Naturally *soft* water can be obtained by collecting fresh rain water before it runs through the soil. Hard water may be softened by treating it in some way to remove the undesirable ions (Section 10–15).

27-9 DRYING OILS

A drying oil is the essential ingredient causing a paint or varnish to become a tough, protective coating. A good drying oil must be highly unsaturated. Tung oil and linseed oil are excellent examples, Table 27-2. When such oil is spread out in a thin layer, air attacks the unsaturated groups, causing the formation of covalent bonds from one carbon chain to another. A vast network of crosslinks develops, transforming the oil into a tough film. (See Section 30-7 for other examples of cross-linked materials.) In this sense, the "drying" is actually a chemical change, not merely an evaporation of solvent.

Paint consists of a drying oil, a pigment, a drier, and a thinner.

◄ The **pigment** contributes the color and enough opaqueness for good hiding quality. The most important white pigments (because of their hiding power) are oxides of zinc, titanium, or antimony, and lead oxide, carbonate, or sulfate. A desired color is achieved by adding to these varying amounts of other inorganic compounds: chromium oxide (green), cadmium sulfide (yellow, orange, red), iron oxides (yellow, red, maroon, brown), lead chromate (yellow), or complex iron cyanides (blue). Colored organic compounds are used in certain paints, but do not withstand sunlight well. The principal black pigment is carbon.

A **drier** is a catalyst which hastens the reaction of the drying oil with air. Carboxylate salts of cobalt, manganese, and lead are effective for this purpose.

The **thinner** is a solvent used in sufficient amounts to make the paint flow evenly over the surface. Paint thinners usually consist of *mineral spirits* (a mixture of C_9 and C_{10} hydrocarbon isomers from petroleum) and turpentine (C_{10} hydrocarbons produced by pine trees). The thinner evaporates soon after the paint is applied to the surface. Subsequent drying of the paint involves the reaction with air, described above. ►

IMPORTANT TERMS

Detergent	Hard water	Mixed glyceride	Triglyceride
Drying oil	Hydrogenation	Oils	Unsaturated chains
Fats	Hydrolysis	Saponification	
Glyceride	Micelle	Soap	

WORK EXERCISES

1. Write the structure of
   a) an ester containing oleic, palmitic, and stearic acids combined with glycerol. With these components is more than one structure possible? What general name is given to such a compound?
   b) a fat   c) an oil   d) a soap
   e) a synthetic detergent   f) a drying oil

2. Write a complete equation, using structural formulas, for each reaction and tell the name used for that type of reaction.

   a) glyceryl tripalmitate, sodium hydroxide solution, heat
   b) glyceryl trioleate, hydrogen, nickel, heat
   c) glyceryl tristearate, water, hydrochloric acid, heat

3. Which of these compounds would you expect to be solid, and which liquid, at room temperature? Check your answers in a chemical handbook.

   a) glyceryl trioleate   b) glyceryl tristearate   c) glyceryl tributyrate

4. What type of structure must an organic compound have to be a good cleansing agent?

5. Discuss briefly the process for manufacturing oleomargarine. In general, how do you think its nutritional value compares with that of butter?

SUGGESTED READING

DePuy, C. H. and K. L. Rinehart, Jr, *Introduction to Organic Chemistry*, Chapter 11, John Wiley, New York, 1967.

Hart, H. and R. D. Schuetz, *Organic Chemistry*, 3rd ed., Chapter 11, Houghton Mifflin, Boston, 1966.

Levey, M., "The Early History of Detergent Substances," *J. Chem. Educ.* **31,** 521 (1954).

Noller, C. R., *Textbook of Organic Chemistry*, 3rd ed., Chapter 12, W. B. Saunders, Philadelphia, 1966.

Snell, F. D., "Soap and Glycerol," *J. Chem. Educ.* **19,** 172 (1942). An excellent discussion, although it lacks a description of the modern continuous process of soap making.

Snell, F. D., and C. T. Snell, "Syndets and Surfactants," *J. Chem. Educ.* **35,** 271 (1958). A good survey of the types, properties, and manufacturing of synthetic detergents.

Chapter 28 AMINES

28-1 THE RELATIVES OF AMMONIA

The amines are structurally related to ammonia. Whereas in ammonia the nitrogen holds three hydrogens, in an amine it is bonded to at least one organic group.

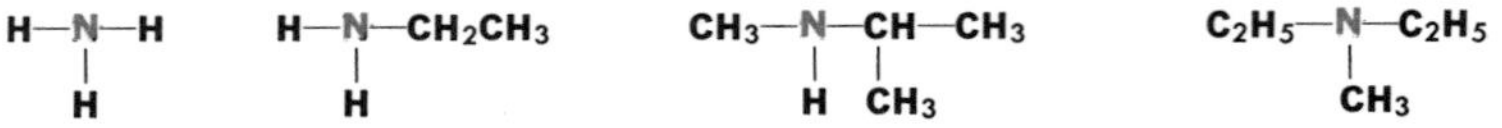

$$H—\overset{\displaystyle |}{\underset{\displaystyle H}{N}}—H \qquad H—\overset{\displaystyle |}{\underset{\displaystyle H}{N}}—CH_2CH_3 \qquad CH_3—\overset{\displaystyle |}{\underset{\displaystyle H}{N}}—\overset{\displaystyle |}{\underset{\displaystyle CH_3}{CH}}—CH_3 \qquad C_2H_5—\overset{\displaystyle |}{\underset{\displaystyle CH_3}{N}}—C_2H_5$$

ammonia   ethylamine   methylisopropylamine   diethylmethylamine

The easiest method for naming the amines, shown above, is simply to name the organic groups bonded to the nitrogen. However, doing so may not be convenient if the organic group is complex. In such cases, illustrated below, an —NH_2 can be regarded as a *group* attached to a carbon skeleton. The name **amino** is used to indicate that the —NH_2 group is present.

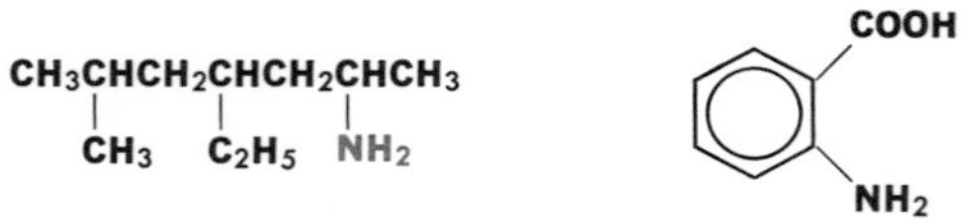

$$CH_3\overset{\displaystyle |}{\underset{\displaystyle CH_3}{CH}}CH_2\overset{\displaystyle |}{\underset{\displaystyle C_2H_5}{CH}}CH_2\overset{\displaystyle |}{\underset{\displaystyle NH_2}{CH}}CH_3$$

2-amino-4-ethyl-6-methylheptane   o-aminobenzoic acid

The aryl amines are named as derivatives of aniline, the simplest amine in the aromatic class.

aniline   methylaniline*   p-chloroaniline

---

* Another, more precise, name for this compound is N-methylaniline. The capital N indicates that the methyl group is definitely on the nitrogen atom, not on the ring.

◄ As might be expected, several of the properties of amines are similar to those of ammonia. The smaller amines, such as methylamine, dimethylamine, or ethylamine, are gases which are quite soluble in water and have a pungent odor very much like the odor of ammonia. The larger the carbon skeleton of an amine, the less soluble it is in water. Medium-sized amines (butyl, pentyl, etc.) have fishy odors. Two of the decomposition products found in decaying flesh are amines having foul, putrid odors; they have been given the descriptive names putrescine and cadaverine. ►

$H_2NCH_2CH_2CH_2CH_2NH_2$ $H_2NCH_2CH_2CH_2CH_2CH_2NH_2$
     putrescine   cadaverine

28-2 BASIC PROPERTIES

We found in Section 12–5 that an ammonia molecule behaves as a base because it has an electron pair which it readily shares with a hydrogen ion.

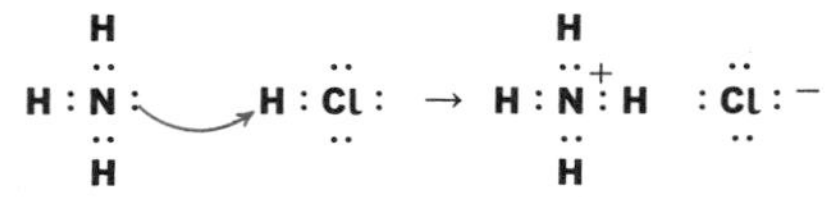

$$\text{H:N + H:Cl} \rightarrow \text{H:N:H :Cl:}^- \tag{28-1}$$

ammonia   hydrogen   ammonium chloride
           chloride

Any amine also is a base; it, too, has an electron pair available, Eq. (28–2).

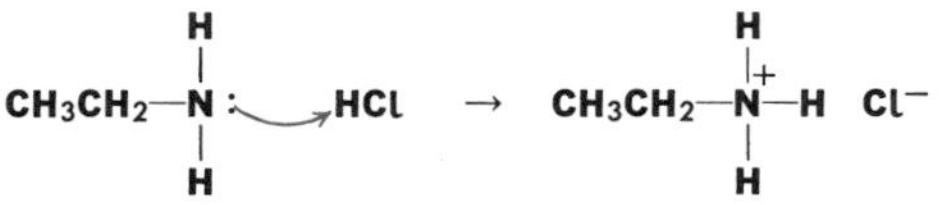

$$\text{CH}_3\text{CH}_2\text{—N: + HCl} \rightarrow \text{CH}_3\text{CH}_2\text{—N—H Cl}^- \tag{28-2}$$

ethylamine   hydrogen   ethylammonium chloride
         chloride

$$\text{CH}_3\text{—N: + HOOC—CH}_3 \rightarrow \text{CH}_3\text{—N—H }^-\text{OOC—CH}_3$$

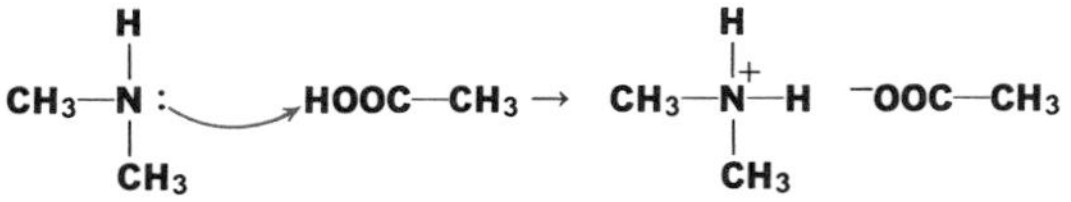

dimethylamine   acetic acid   dimethylammonium acetate

The salts which result from these acid-base reactions are named as **substituted ammonium salts,** as shown above. Since the basic property of an amine is due to the pair of available electrons, an amine of the type R_3N : reacts as a base, too, Eq. (28–3).

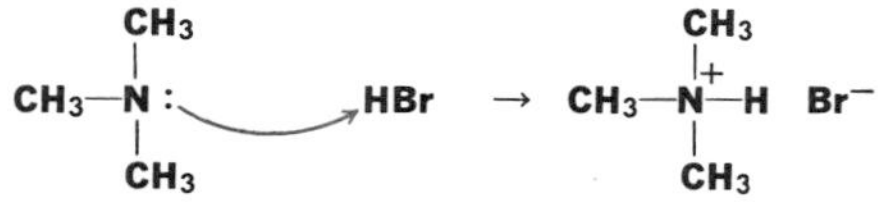

$$\text{CH}_3\text{—N: + HBr} \rightarrow \text{CH}_3\text{—N—H Br}^- \tag{28-3}$$

trimethylamine   hydrogen   trimethylammonium
          bromide   bromide

For the same reason, the heterocyclic nitrogen compounds, Section 24–8, are likewise basic, despite the fact that the nitrogen is held in the ring.

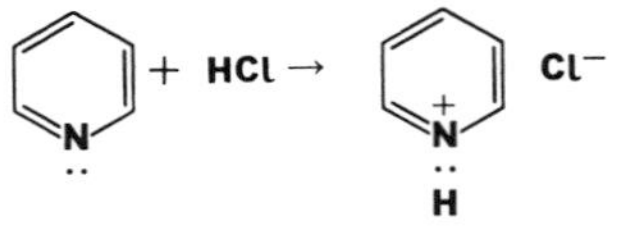

pyridine   pyridinium chloride

28-3 PREPARATION OF AMINES

A. Alkyl Amines

A common method for the synthesis of an *alkyl* amine involves the reaction of an alkyl halide with ammonia, often in the presence of a stronger base such as sodium hydroxide.

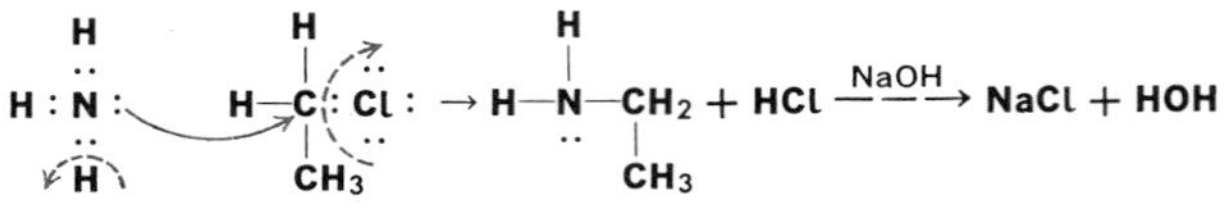

$$H:N: \quad H-C: Cl: \rightarrow H-N-CH_2 + HCl \xrightarrow{NaOH} NaCl + HOH \qquad (28-4)$$

ammonia   ethyl   ethylamine
             chloride

This is another reaction which depends upon the electron pair of nitrogen. When the pair of electrons attacks the alkyl group, a halide ion (for example, Cl⁻) is displaced off the other side of the carbon being attacked, Eq. (28–4). Following the substitution of the alkyl group onto nitrogen, a hydrogen ion can be lost from the nitrogen. Indeed, the reaction is promoted if a strong base is present to pull the hydrogen ion off the nitrogen. From this method of formation we see that an amine can truly be regarded as a substitution product of ammonia.

Further substitution occurs if an amine is allowed to react with more alkyl halide, Eqs. (28–5) and (28–6). The nitrogen of an amine still has a pair of electrons available, so it can react in the same way that ammonia does.

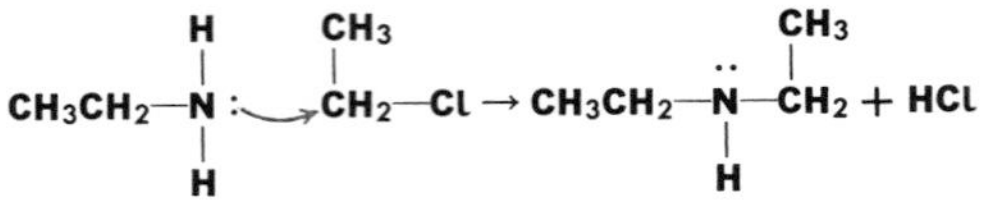

$$CH_3CH_2-N: \quad CH_2-Cl \rightarrow CH_3CH_2-N-CH_2 + HCl \qquad (28-5)$$

ethylamine   diethylamine

$$C_2H_5-N: \quad CH_2-Cl \rightarrow C_2H_5-N-C_2H_5 + HCl \qquad (28-6)$$

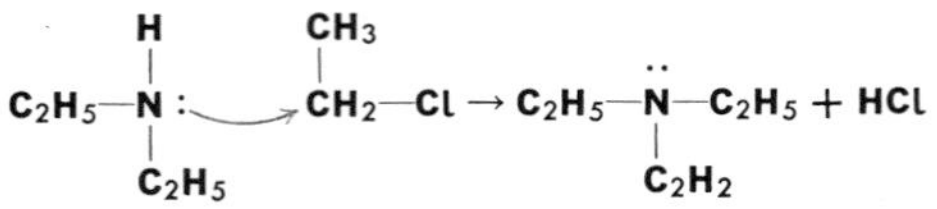

diethylamine   triethylamine

In fact, even a trialkylamine can react, because it too has an electron pair available, Eq. (28–7). However, in this case, there is no hydrogen to be lost from the nitrogen so the product is an ionic salt:

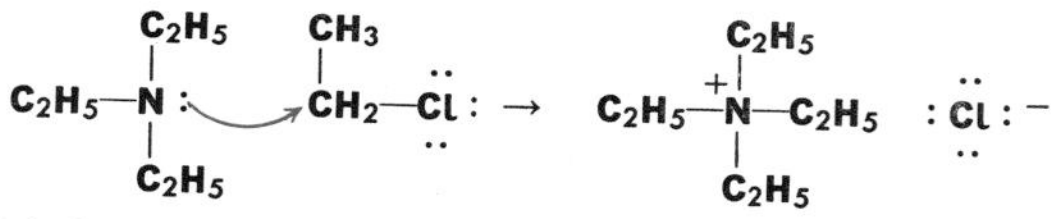

$$(28-7)$$

triethylamine   tetraethylammonium chloride

Since this final product ($\overset{+}{N}R_4\overset{-}{Cl}$) is a completely substituted ammonium salt (compare $\overset{+}{N}H_4\overset{-}{Cl}$), it is named accordingly. A compound of the type $\overset{+}{N}R_4\overset{-}{Cl}$ is also called, in general, a **quaternary ammonium salt** because of the four organic groups present.

Another variation of this synthetic method is to treat some amine with an alkyl halide having a different group.

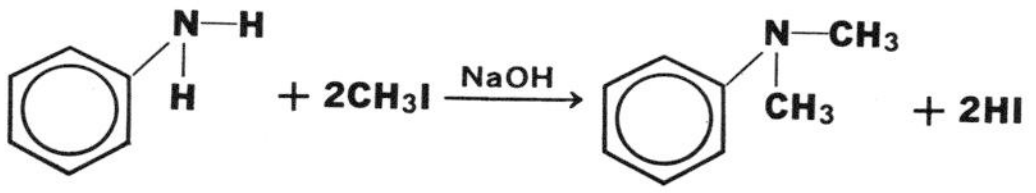

aniline   dimethylaniline

B. Aryl Amines

A different synthetic method is usually employed to prepare *aryl* amines. A nitro group can be reduced to an amino group by hydrogens produced from the action of an acid on a metal. Iron or tin are commonly used.

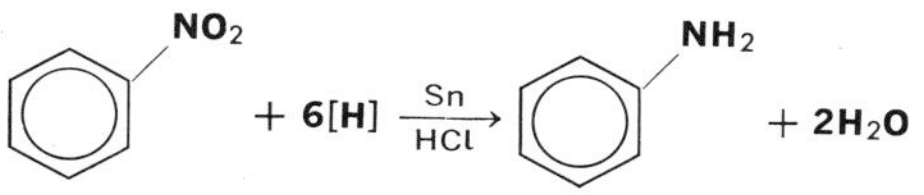

$$(28-8)$$

nitrobenzene   aniline

$$(28-9)$$

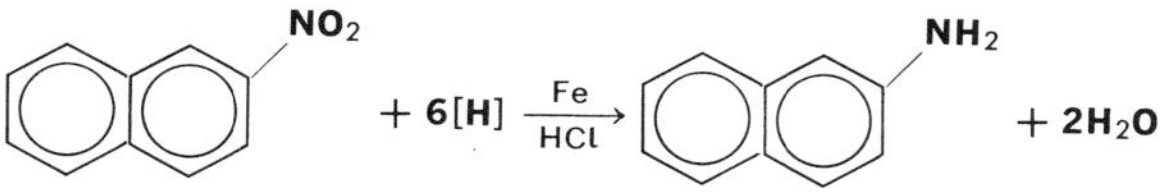

2-nitronaphthalene   2-naphthylamine

The reactions shown in Eqs. (28–8) and (28–9) are particularly useful because the nitro group is so easily substituted onto an aromatic ring, Section 24–6. This in turn means that a great variety of aryl amines can be synthesized. For example, consider the following synthetic route:

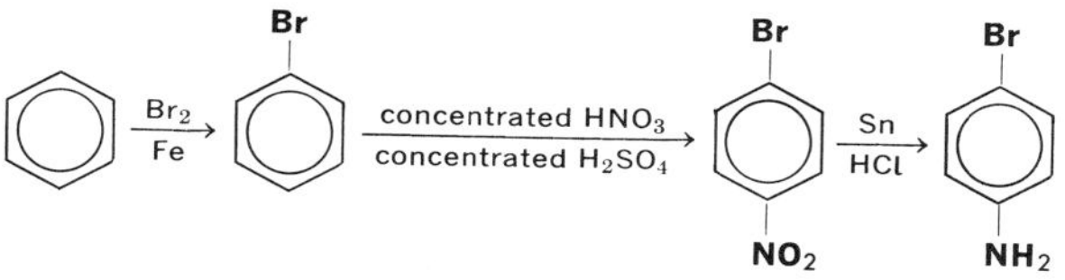

28–4 CONVERSION OF AMINES TO AMIDES

An acid chloride reacts rapidly with ammonia to form an amide. A particular amide is named according to the acid group from which it is derived.

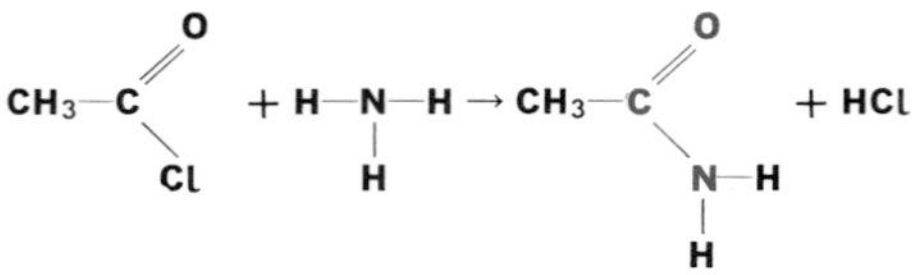

acetyl chloride   acetamide   (28-10)

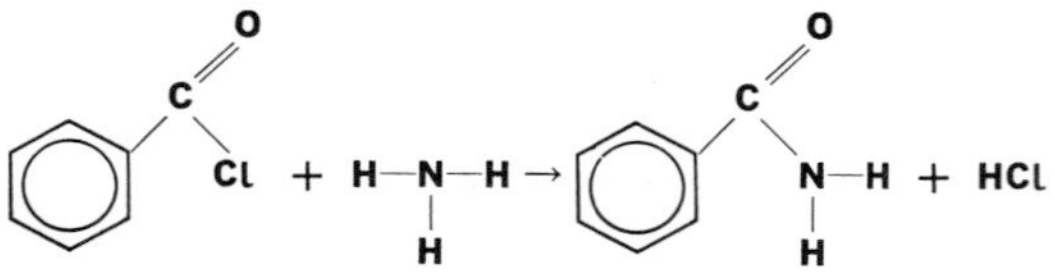

benzoyl chloride   benzamide

This reaction with ammonia, Eq. (28–10), is analogous to the reaction of an acid chloride with an alcohol, Section 26–7. Acid chlorides react also with amines, Eq. (28–11), provided at least one hydrogen is available for displacement; the trialkylamines therefore do not react.

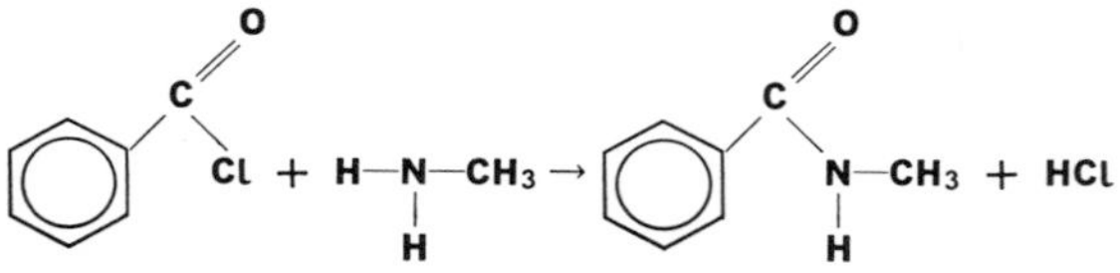

N-methylbenzamide   (28-11)

N,N-diethylacetamide

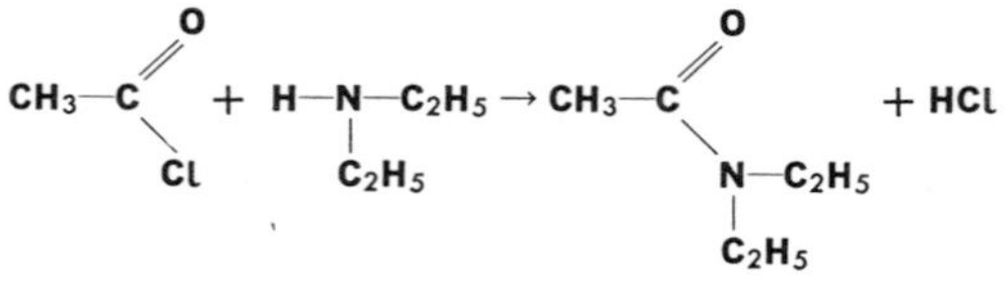

no reaction

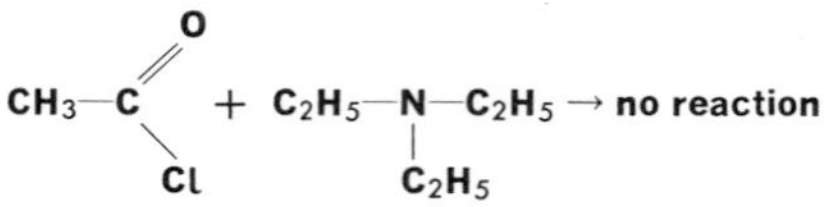

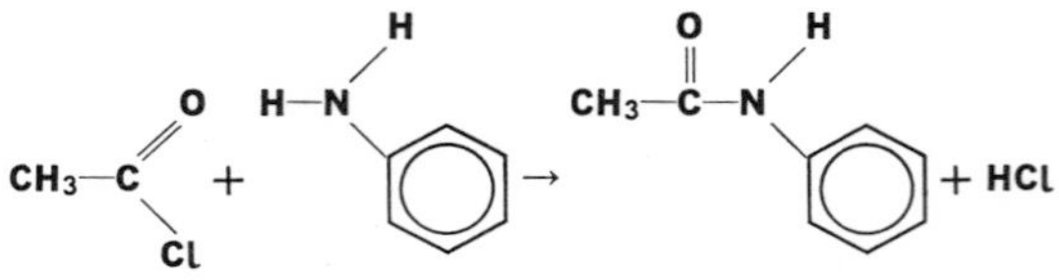

acetyl chloride   aniline   acetanilide

Amides can also be formed from the carboxylic acids themselves, Eq. (28–12). However, heat is required because a carboxylic acid is less reactive than an acid chloride.

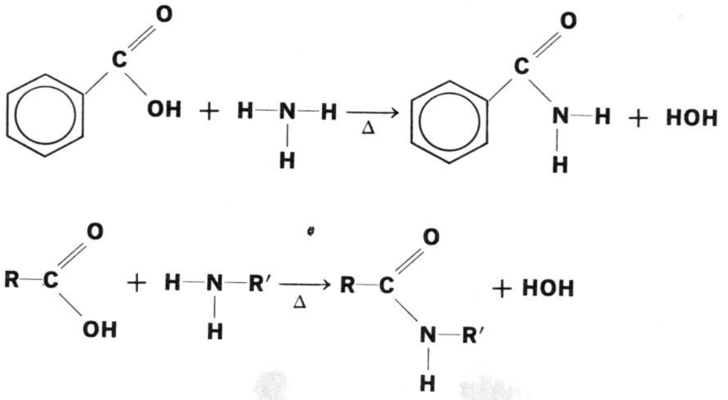

$$\text{C}_6\text{H}_5\text{—C(=O)—OH} + \text{H—N(H)—H} \xrightarrow{\Delta} \text{C}_6\text{H}_5\text{—C(=O)—N(H)—H} + \text{HOH} \tag{28–12}$$

$$\text{R—C(=O)—OH} + \text{H—N(H)—R}' \xrightarrow{\Delta} \text{R—C(=O)—N(H)—R}' + \text{HOH}$$

Reaction 28–12 is comparable to the esterification reaction of an acid with an alcohol, Section 26–4 and, like it, is very slow unless heat is used. Furthermore, the reverse reaction
is possible, Eq. (28–13); an amide can be hydrolyzed (a mineral acid catalyst helps), just
as can an ester, Section 26–6.

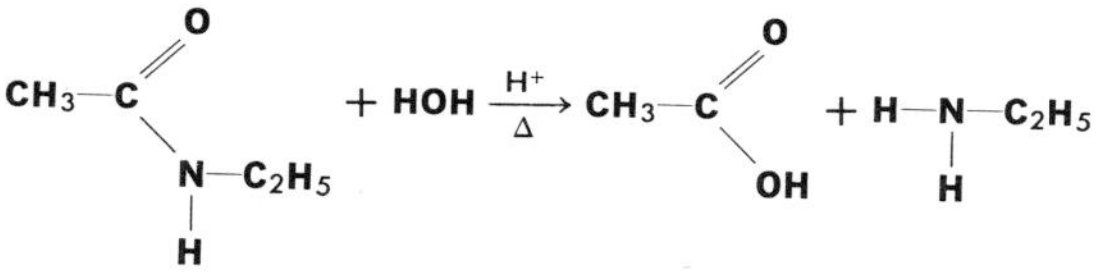

$$\text{CH}_3\text{—C(=O)—N(H)—C}_2\text{H}_5 + \text{HOH} \xrightarrow[\Delta]{\text{H}^+} \text{CH}_3\text{—C(=O)—OH} + \text{H—N(H)—C}_2\text{H}_5 \tag{28–13}$$

The formation and hydrolysis of amide bonds are not only frequent laboratory procedures
but are also essential to the chemistry of peptides and proteins, Chapter 34. In the latter
case, enzymes in the living cells catalyze the reactions so that they occur easily at body
temperature, provided energy sources are available.

The amides are essentially "neutral" substances, in contrast to the basic amines. Although the nitrogen in an amide still has an extra pair of electrons, the rest of the structure
affects it in such a way that the electrons are not readily shared with a hydrogen ion. Since
basicity depends on donation of an electron pair, to a hydrogen ion, for example, we say
that the amide is not a base.

28–5 SULFONAMIDES

The sulfonamides are related to sulfonic acids just as amides are related to carboxylic acids.

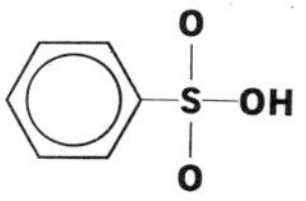

benzenesulfonic acid 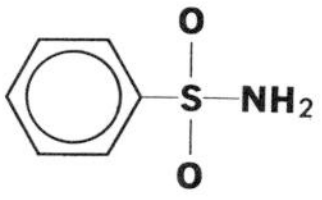   benzenesulfonamide

A sulfonamide is best prepared via the corresponding acid chloride. For example, benzenesulfonyl chloride, Eq. (28–14), is the acid chloride of benzenesulfonic acid. Treatment of a sulfonyl chloride with ammonia converts it to a sulfonamide.

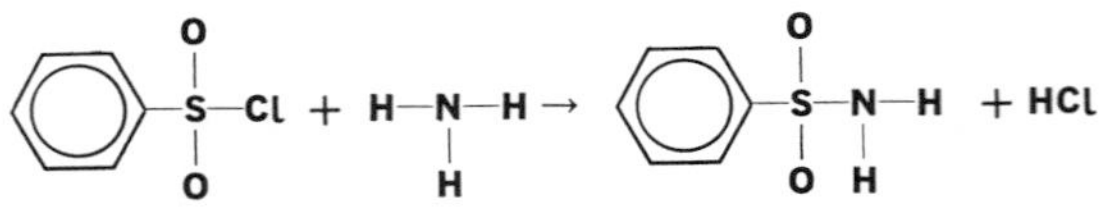

benzenesulfonyl chloride

benzenesulfonamide

$$(28-14)$$

The sulfonamides are widely used by chemists for identification purposes and for theoretical studies. They also provide the **sulfa drugs,** which are effective against bacterial infections. The simplest of these is **sulfanilamide,** shown below along with some of its derivatives. The sulfa names are generic drug names; relatively short names such as this are usually assigned to drugs because they are more convenient for everyday use than the complete systematic chemical names.

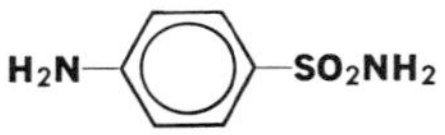

sulfanilamide
(*p*-aminobenzenesulfonamide)

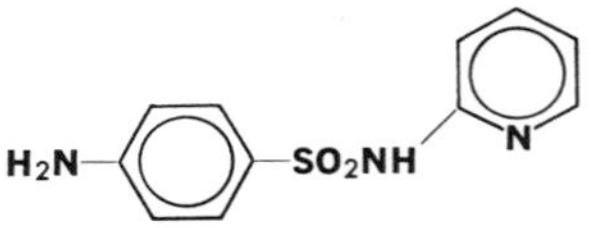

sulfapyridine

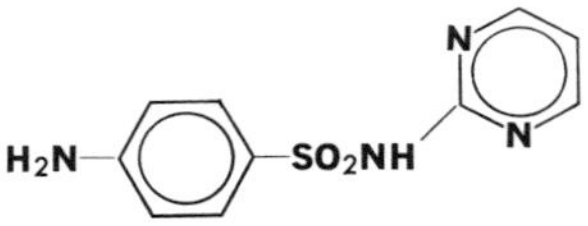

sulfadiazine

The structural variations in the sulfas are achieved by carrying out the synthesis with some amine, $ArNH_2$, in place of ammonia, Eq. (28–14). Altogether, hundreds of differently substituted sulfanilamides were prepared by chemists for testing by physicians. Some compounds proved to be especially potent against certain organisms, and others more effective against different organisms. The drugs differ also in their side effects on the patient.

◄ The sulfa drugs, developed largely during the period 1935–1945, were the first widely used compounds which specifically halted bacterial growth. Before the advent of such drugs, medical treatment of infections was largely confined to reducing fever and treating other symptoms, with the hope that the patient's own resistance would then fight the infection more vigorously.

Many men benefited in World War II because of the sulfa drugs. Their diseases or wounds would otherwise have been severely crippling or even fatal. Although there are still appropriate applications of the sulfa drugs, for many purposes they have been replaced by the even more effective antibiotics which became available during the 1950's. ►

28-6 MORE COMPOUNDS OF INTEREST

A. Vitamins

Several (but not all) of the vitamins have nitrogen atoms in either amide groups or amine groups. Quite often the basic amino nitrogen is part of a heterocyclic ring. **Niacin** is a very important vitamin but is the simplest in structure. It has one basic nitrogen in a pyridine ring, plus a neutral nitrogen in an amide group. Most vitamins have a more complex structure, such as that of **thiamine** (vitamin B_1).

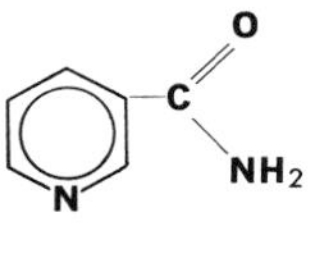

niacin 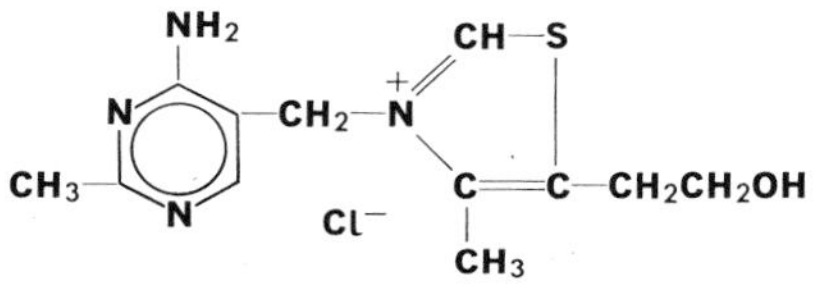   thiamine (vitamin B_1)

Note in thiamine that the five-membered heterocyclic ring contains both a nitrogen and a sulfur, with the nitrogen in the form of a quaternary ammonium salt, Section 28-3A.

B. Alkaloids

A number of plants produce nitrogen-containing substances which are moderately basic and are therefore called alkaloids (alkali-like). Most of these compounds have striking effects on the nervous systems of animals; some may even be fatal. Structurally, the nitrogens present in alkaloids are most often in heterocyclic rings. The simplest alkaloid is **coniine,** which occurs in the poison hemlock plant (see Fig. 28-1). In Section 26-5 the alkaloid **cocaine** was described. Two other familiar examples are shown in Figs. 28-2 and 28-3.

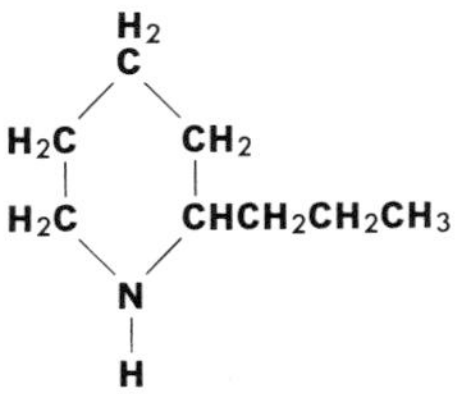

coniine

FIGURE 28-1

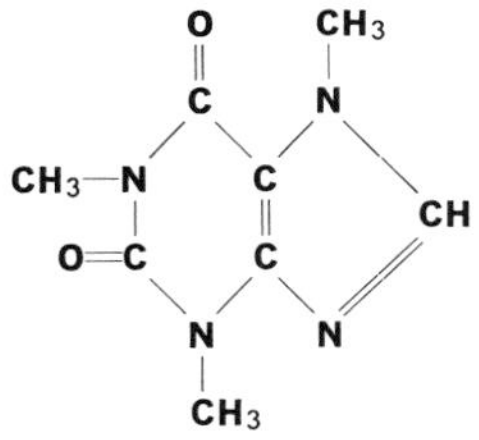

caffeine

FIGURE 28-2

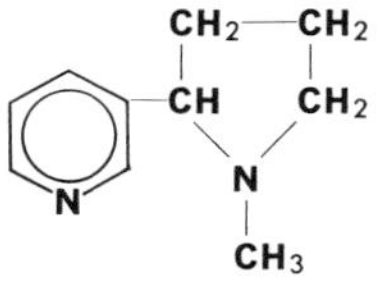

nicotine

FIGURE 28-3

Caffeine is present in tea, coffee, cola nuts, and a number of other plants. The compound is a stimulant. Apparently rather large amounts are necessary to cause death; no fatalities from caffeine have been reported.

More than ten different alkaloids have been found in tobacco leaves, but **nicotine** constitutes three-fourths of the weight of alkaloids present. Nicotine is highly toxic to animals and has considerable use as an insecticide. In very small amounts, as might be inhaled from smoking tobacco, it causes brief stimulation.

Ergot, a fungus disease of rye, produces several different amides of **lysergic acid.**

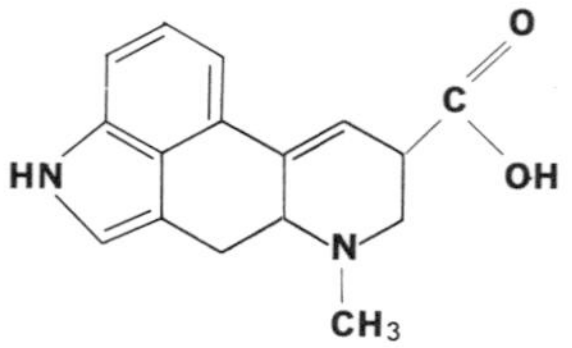

lysergic acid

A synthetic modification of these alkaloids is a hallucinogenic drug called LSD, which represents *lysergic acid diethylamide*. Appropriate treatment of the natural materials can yield lysergic acid. Its carboxyl group, by standard procedures, can react with diethylamine to become a diethylamide structure.

◄ Many alkaloids have even more complicated structures than those shown above. One example is **quinine,** which is moderately effective in suppressing malaria infections. **Strychnine** is a poison causing convulsions and death. A certain species of poppy plant produces the drug **morphine. Codeine** is a slight modification of morphine. Both are habit-forming, but when properly administered in controlled amounts are medically useful as pain relievers and sedatives. Another modification of morphine is **heroin,** which is so addicting that its use even for medical purposes is illegal in the United States. ►

C. Urea

Economically and biologically, urea is important. It is a colorless, odorless, crystalline, water-soluble compound playing a significant part in the balance of life between plants and animals. Chemically, it is the amide of carbonic acid; the structural relations are shown in the scheme below.

$$\begin{array}{ccc} H_2O + CO_2 & & \\ \downarrow\uparrow & & \\ HO{-}\underset{\underset{O}{\|}}{C}{-}OH \;+\; 2NH_3 & \rightleftharpoons & H_2N{-}\underset{\underset{O}{\|}}{C}{-}NH_2 + 2H_2O \\ \text{carbonic acid} \quad \text{ammonia} & & \text{carbamide} \\ & & \textbf{urea} \end{array} \tag{28–15}$$

Like other amides, urea can be *hydrolyzed* to yield ammonia plus the parent acid; the hydrolysis reaction is represented by Eq. (28–15) if you read from right to left. Since carbonic acid is unstable, it decomposes to carbon dioxide and water. In the opposite direction, urea can be *formed* from carbon dioxide and ammonia, as represented by Eq. (28–15) if you read from left to right.

Metabolism of proteins by an animal could potentially release ammonia into his body. The ammonia would be harmful if it accumulated. Many animals dispose of the amine group by combining it with carbon dioxide to form urea. [They carry out Eqs. (28–15), in effect, in several steps promoted by enzymes. See Section 39–5 for details of the conversion.] The urea is then excreted. In the soil the enzymes of certain bacteria hydrolyze the urea, thus reversing Eq. (28–15) and releasing the ammonia, which is then available for plants to rebuild into new proteins.

Urea can also be obtained by conducting in a factory the reaction shown in Eq. (28–15). Ammonia, carbon dioxide, and a little water are mixed under pressure at about 180°C. The resultant urea can be isolated as a granular solid by evaporating the water present. Recent production of urea in the United States has exceeded one million tons per year. About 80% of this is used for fertilizers; the rest goes into urea-formaldehyde plastics and adhesives, a few pharmaceuticals, and miscellaneous other products.

◄ Urea is one of the essential ingredients for the synthesis of the **barbiturate** drugs. The other component is an ethyl malonate ester bearing two substituents. (Ethyl malonate itself is C_2H_5OOC—CH_2—$COOC_2H_5$, the ester of a diacid, malonic acid.) During the reaction, Eq. (28–16), two new amide bonds are formed, closing a ring.

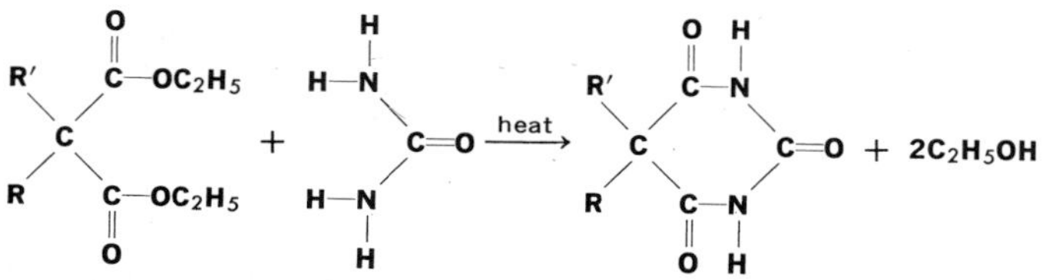

$$(28–16)$$

substituted ethyl malonate 	urea 	a barbiturate

In general, the barbiturates are effective sedatives and soporifics. They can be used to induce sleep, calm epileptic patients, provide sufficient unconsciousness for minor surgery, etc. Many variations of the drugs are possible because different substituents (R, R') can be built into the compounds. These variations provide differences in depth of relaxation, effective time, and so forth. Of the dozens which have been synthesized and tested, a few of the most common are listed in Table 28–1. ►

TABLE 28–1. Some common barbiturates

Substituents R	R'	Generic Name	Some Brand Names
CH_3CH_2—	CH_3CH_2—	barbital	Veronal, Barbitone, Dormonal
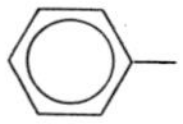 ⬡—	CH_3CH_2—	phenobarbital	Luminal, Gardenal, Barbenyl
$CH_3CHCH_2CH_2$— 　　$\vert$ 　　CH_3	CH_3CH_2—	amobarbital	Amytal, Somnal, Isomytal

D. Aniline and Related Compounds

Thousands of tons of aniline and naphthylamine are manufactured annually by the type of reduction shown in Eq. (28–9). For commercial purposes, scrap cast iron is the least expensive metal to use as the source of hydrogen. Aniline and its derivatives are used largely for the manufacture of dyes and compounds for rubber processing. Smaller quantities are converted to photographic chemicals and important pharmaceuticals.

◀ Aniline has always been closely associated with important dyes. Its name is derived from *anil*, a term used in southern Europe for indigo, because in 1826 aniline was obtained from the decomposition of the natural dye indigo. For many years this source supplied most of the aniline, which remained a rare compound until about 1845 when chemists became aware that aniline could be prepared by reducing nitrobenzene. Aniline was soon to become associated with not only certain natural dyes, but also synthetic dyes.

In 1856 the English chemist William Perkin, then only eighteen years old, attempted to synthesize quinine. In the process he treated aniline with sodium dichromate, a strong oxidizing agent. The result at first appeared to be a useless, tarry mess. However, Perkin discovered (while trying to clean the flask) that alcohol dissolved out of the mess a beautiful purple substance. This proved to be a satisfactory dye for fabrics and became known as *mauve*. With his father and brother, Perkin went into the business of manufacturing the dye. Mauve became so popular and so successful commercially that it set off a rash of trial-and-error experimentation; people mixed this and that with aniline or related amines, hoping to discover an equally lucrative dye. Surprisingly, a number of fairly useful dyes were developed in this way.

It was nearly 1860 before the first structural formulas for organic compounds were written. It was during the 1860's (while mauve was in vogue) that structural formulas began to be applied with great success to a wide variety of organic compounds. Several German chemists insisted that the dyes too should be examined structurally. They reasoned that if a person could learn what types of structure were present in good dyes, then he could more sensibly plan reactions which might lead to similar structures. This attitude was eventually justified. By the end of the century the synthetic dye industry in Germany far surpassed that in England. Indeed, there had been a vigorous growth in all aspects of the German chemical industry.

Thus the development of compounds derived from aniline, in particular some of the dyes, greatly stimulated the discovery of fundamental knowledge about organic compounds. This development also gave organic chemists confidence to attempt the synthesis of organic structures, whether they were duplicates of molecules found naturally or entirely new molecules. Incidentally, the synthesis of quinine, which Perkin had originally attacked, proved to be a very difficult one. This synthesis was not achieved until nearly a century later, in 1944.

It was inevitable that sooner or later chemists would attempt to duplicate synthetically the lovely blue indigo dye produced by *Indigofera* plants. For aniline had been obtained as a decomposition product from indigo, and many of the new dyes had been built up from aniline or closely related compounds. Note the place of aniline in the structure of indigo, shown below.

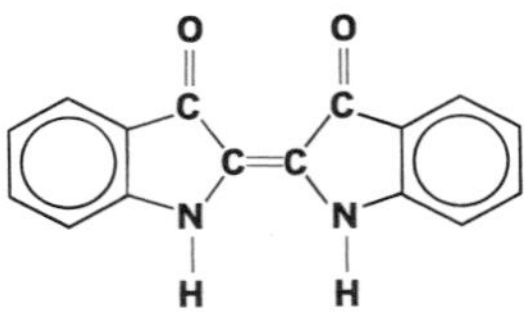

indigo

In 1880 the German chemist Baeyer reported a laboratory synthesis of indigo from relatively simple organic compounds. Unfortunately, some of the intermediate steps required expensive reactants. For factory production it was necessary to find a different series of reactions utilizing cheap materials. Not until 1897 was synthetic indigo put on the market at a price lower than that of the natural product. The economic repercussions were immediate. Frequently a technological change of this sort has a devastating effect on certain groups in society; in this case it was the indigo farmers of India. Indigo is still the most used blue dye. It is cheap and is a "fast" color; that is, it does not fade easily during washing or upon exposure to light.

Aniline is now essential for the manufacture of a great variety of dyes, produced at a rate of thousands of tons per year. ▶

IMPORTANT TERMS

Amide   Quaternary ammonium salt
Amine   Substituted ammonium salt
Amino group

WORK EXERCISES

1. Name these compounds:

    a) $CH_3CH_2NHCH_2CH_3$

    b) 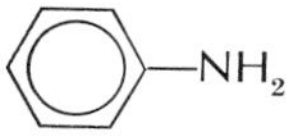 —NH_2

    c) $CH_3CHCH_2NH_2$
        |
        CH_3

    d) $CH_3NH_3{}^+$ Br^-

2. Give the structural formula of

    a) trimethylamine   b) ammonia
    c) ethyl-*n*-propylamine   d) *o*-nitroaniline
    e) 3-amino-2,4-dimethylpentane   f) *p*-aminophenol
    g) triethylammonium chloride   h) benzamide

3. Using structural formulas, show clearly how methylamine can behave as a base in reacting with hydrogen bromide.

4. Write complete equations for the following reaction mixtures. If necessary, state "no reaction."

    a) one mole of methyl bromide, one mole of ammonia
    b) trimethylamine, hydrogen chloride
    c) methylamine, acetyl chloride
    d) methyl chloride, trimethylamine
    e) *p*-nitrotoluene, tin, hydrochloric acid
    f) acetyl chloride, trimethylamine
    g) benzoic acid, ethylamine, heat

5. Using RCOOH to represent lysergic acid, show the structure of the diethylamide derived from it.

SUGGESTED READING

Amundsen, L. H., "Sulfanilamide and Related Chemotherapeutic Agents," *J. Chem. Educ.* **19,** 167 (1942). An interesting, readable account written at the time when sulfa drugs were most important.

Asimov, I., *The New Intelligent Man's Guide to Science*, Basic Books, New York, 1965, pp. 447–462. A fascinating account of the contributions from organic synthesis.

Asimov, I., *A Short History of Chemistry*, Anchor Books, Doubleday, New York, 1965, pp. 168–182. Description of the rise of synthetic and structural organic chemistry, including dyes, drugs, explosives, and proteins.

DePuy, C. H. and K. L. Rinehart, Jr., *Introduction to Organic Chemistry*, Chapter 8, John Wiley, New York, 1967.

Gates, M., "Analgesic Drugs," *Scientific American*, Nov. 1966 (Offprint #304). A discussion of morphine and the search for related drugs which would provide the same benefits without the undesirable effects.

Hart, H. and R. D. Schuetz, *Organic Chemistry*, 3rd ed., Chapter 12, Houghton Mifflin, Boston, 1966.

Kurzer, F. and P. M. Sanderson, "Urea in the History of Organic Chemistry," *J. Chem. Educ.* **33,** 452 (1956). The authors state, "The early history of urea provides a vivid impression of the slow and difficult beginnings of chemical science . . ."

Robinson, T., "Alkaloids," *Scientific American*, July 1959. Most alkaloids have a profound effect on animals and humans, but their function in plants is obscure.

Chapter 29   CARBONYL COMPOUNDS

29-1 NAMES AND STRUCTURES

A carbonyl group has a carbon with a double bond to oxygen.

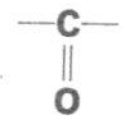

$$\begin{matrix} -\overset{\textstyle |}{\underset{\textstyle \|}{C}}- \\ O \end{matrix}$$ carbonyl group

If both of the other bonds from the carbon hold organic groups, the compound is a **ketone;** if one of the bonds holds a hydrogen, the compound is an **aldehyde.**

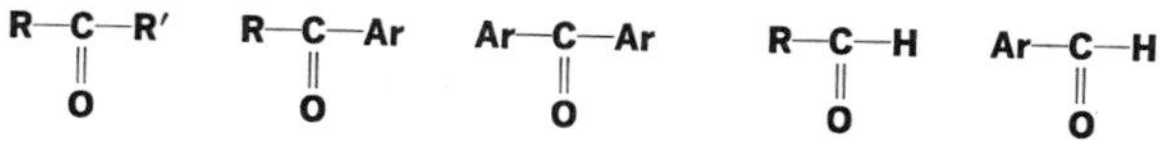

$$R-\overset{\|}{\underset{O}{C}}-R' \qquad R-\overset{\|}{\underset{O}{C}}-Ar \qquad Ar-\overset{\|}{\underset{O}{C}}-Ar \qquad R-\overset{\|}{\underset{O}{C}}-H \qquad Ar-\overset{\|}{\underset{O}{C}}-H$$

ketones   aldehydes

◄ A carboxylic acid

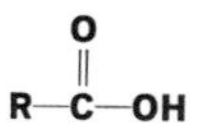

$$R-\overset{\overset{\textstyle O}{\|}}{C}-OH$$

is not generally included in the class of carbonyl compounds because its functional group rarely gives the same reaction products that a carbonyl group does, Section 26-1. ►

Names for typical carbonyl compounds are shown in Table 29-1. In a systematic name, the ending -*one* is used for a ketone. As usual, a number is assigned to indicate where in the carbon skeleton this functional group is located. (Note that numbers are not really necessary for propanone or butanone.) The systematic ending for aldehyde is -*al;* it is unnecessary to assign the number *1* to the aldehyde group because if the carbonyl group were at a different position in the chain (say, 2 or 3), the compound would be a ketone, not an aldehyde.

TABLE 29–1. Nomenclature of aldehydes and ketones

Structure	Common Name	Systematic Name
$CH_3\!-\!C\!-\!CH_3$ $\quad\ \ \ \overset{\|}{O}$	acetone	propanone
$CH_3\!-\!C\!-\!CH_2\!-\!CH_3$ $\quad\ \ \ \overset{\|}{O}$	methyl ethyl ketone	butanone
$CH_3\!-\!CH_2\!-\!C\!-\!CH\!-\!CH_2\!-\!CH_3$ $\qquad\qquad \overset{\|}{O}\ \ \overset{\|}{CH_3}$	ethyl *sec*-butyl ketone	4-methyl-3-hexanone
$H\!-\!C\!-\!H$ $\quad\ \overset{\|}{O}$	formaldehyde	methanal
$CH_3\!-\!C\!-\!H$ $\quad\ \ \ \overset{\|}{O}$	acetaldehyde	ethanal
$CH_3\!-\!CH_2\!-\!C\!-\!H$ $\qquad\qquad \overset{\|}{O}$	propionaldehyde	propanal
$\overset{CH_3}{\overset{\|}{CH_3\!-\!CH\!-\!C\!-\!H}}$ $\qquad\qquad \overset{\|}{O}$	isobutyraldehyde	2-methylpropanal

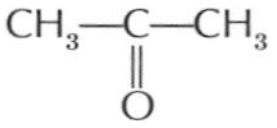

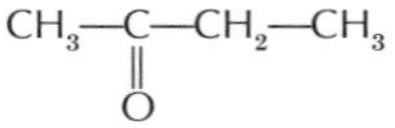

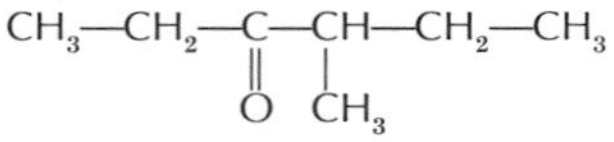

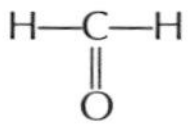

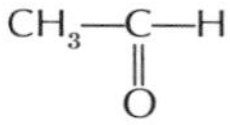

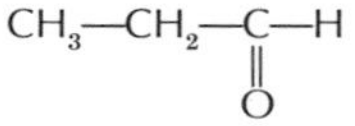

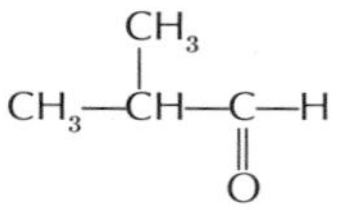

29–2 SYNTHESIS FROM ALCOHOLS

Chemists have devised a great number of methods for building aldehyde or ketone groups into a variety of molecules. We will consider the one most general method of synthesis. Primary or secondary alcohols can be dehydrogenated to aldehydes and ketones, respectively. This reaction is summarized in Eq. (29–1) and was discussed in detail in Section 25–5B.

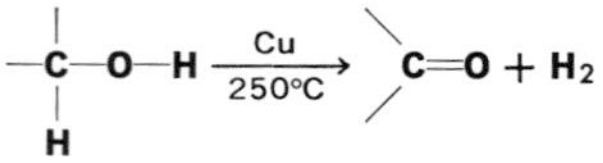

$$-\overset{\displaystyle |}{\underset{\displaystyle H}{C}}\!-\!O\!-\!H \xrightarrow[250°C]{Cu} \ \ \diagdown\!\!C\!\!=\!\!O + H_2 \tag{29-1}$$

A specific example of the dehydrogenation reaction is the following:

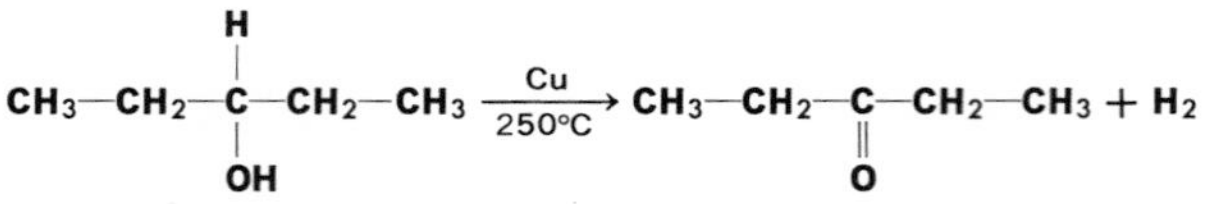

$$CH_3\!-\!CH_2\!-\!\overset{\displaystyle H}{\underset{\displaystyle OH}{C}}\!-\!CH_2\!-\!CH_3 \xrightarrow[250°C]{Cu} CH_3\!-\!CH_2\!-\!\overset{\displaystyle}{\underset{\displaystyle O}{C}}\!-\!CH_2\!-\!CH_3 + H_2$$

3-pentanol   3-pentanone
                             (diethyl ketone)

Many of the aldehydes and ketones which are manufactured in large amounts are made by this procedure, or a slight variation of it (e.g., silver catalyst is sometimes used in place of copper). Examples of compounds prepared in this fashion are acetone, methyl ethyl ketone, formaldehyde, and acetaldehyde.

29-3 COMPOUNDS OF INTEREST

Many aldehydes and ketones can be manufactured inexpensively by the methods shown in the previous section. They are, in turn, frequently used to synthesize still other organic materials. Thus, **acetaldehyde** is converted to acetic acid, polymers, chemicals for the processing of rubber, and baits to kill snails and slugs. Approximately a million tons of **formaldehyde** are manufactured in the United States annually; nearly all is made into polymers for adhesives or plastic molding materials (Bakelite, Melmac). A solution of formaldehyde in water, called *formalin*, is used to preserve biological specimens. It reacts with the protein in such a way that decay is inhibited, and the tissue becomes firmer. Formaldehyde is also used in embalming. **Acetone** is the starting material for a variety of organic intermediates and solvents, including those manufactured into epoxy polymers and polymethacrylates (Lucite, Plexiglass). Another ketone, **cyclohexanone,** is an intermediate in the synthesis of nylon.

In addition, numerous ketones are effective solvents for materials such as lacquers, fingernail polish, waxes, adhesives, and plastics. **Acetone** (propanone) and **methyl ethyl ketone** (*MEK*; butanone) are the two used most extensively as solvents.

Acetone is also biologically important. Abnormal metabolism in individuals having diabetes causes the production of acetone, Section 38–10; it is then excreted in the urine, or in severe cases even exhaled in the breath.

Many compounds produced by plants or animals have aldehyde or ketone functional groups. The examples listed in Table 29–2 give some idea of the wide variety possible and the complexity of some of them.

29-4 CHEMICAL REACTIONS

Aldehydes and ketones are reactive compounds which can be transformed to a wide variety of other useful substances. Many of these chemical changes are of interest primarily to the professional chemist. We will consider just two reactions, hydrogenation and oxidation.

A. Hydrogenation

Hydrogen will add to a carbonyl group in much the same fashion that it adds to an alkene double bond, Section 23–4B. Catalysts such as nickel, palladium, or platinum are necessary to promote the addition reaction, another example of hydrogenation. If we consider specific examples, we note once again the structural relation of aldehydes to primary

TABLE 29–2. Some carbonyl compounds found in nature

Structure	Name	Comments
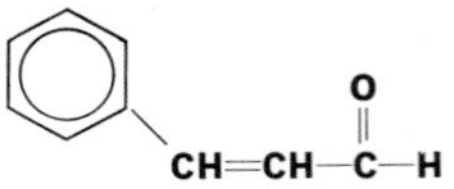	cinnamaldehyde	in cinnamon bark; causes the odor and flavor
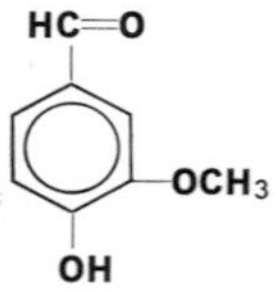	vanillin	in vanilla beans
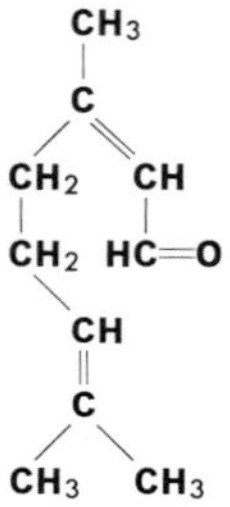	citral	in the rinds of citrus fruits and several other plants; characteristic lemon odor
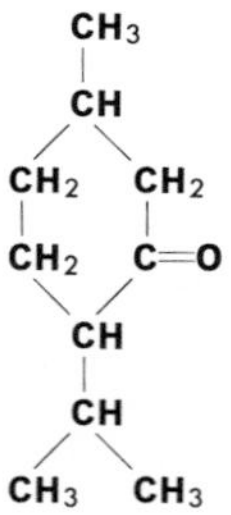	menthone	in mint leaves along with menthol, the related alcohol
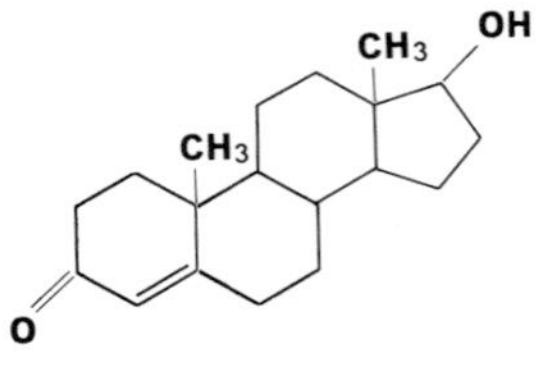	testosterone	a male sex hormone
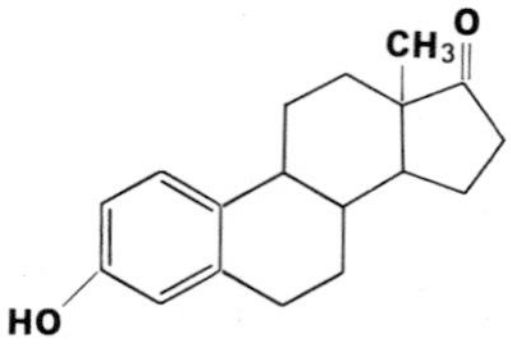	estrone	a female sex hormone

alcohols and of ketones to secondary alcohols:

$$\underset{/}{\overset{\backslash}{C}}=O + H_2 \xrightarrow{Ni} -\underset{\underset{H}{|}}{\overset{|}{C}}-O-H \qquad\qquad (29\text{-}2)$$

$$CH_3CH_2\underset{\underset{O}{\|}}{CH} + H_2 \xrightarrow{Ni} CH_3CH_2\underset{\underset{OH}{|}}{CH_2}$$

$$CH_3\underset{\underset{O}{\|}}{C}CH_3 + H_2 \xrightarrow{Ni} CH_3\underset{\underset{OH}{|}}{CH}CH_3$$

Further, we see that the hydrogenation reaction, Eq. (29–2), is just the reverse of dehydrogenation, Eq. (29–1).

Hydrogenation of carbonyl compounds, Eq. (29–2), is seldom used to synthesize common alcohols. Instead, the alcohols are usually the source of the carbonyl compounds, Section 29–2. However, the hydrogenation reaction may often be important in preparing a more unusual alcohol or in establishing structural relations. An example of the latter is the hydrogenation of menthone to menthol.

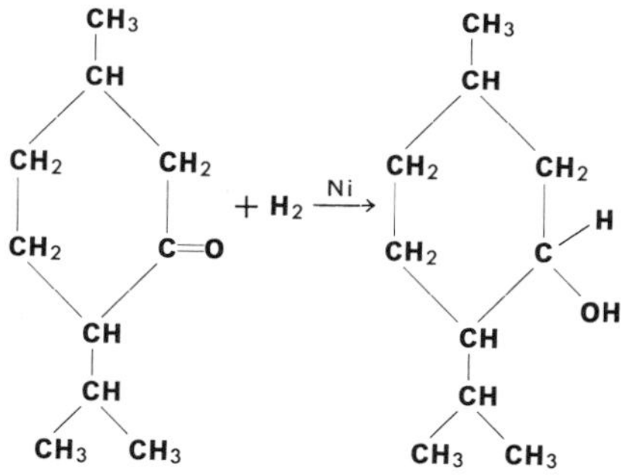

menthone   menthol

B. Oxidation

Under ordinary conditions ketones resist attack by the common ionic oxidizing agents. Aldehydes, on the other hand, are very easily oxidized to carboxylic acids.

$$RCH_2-\underset{\underset{O}{\|}}{C}-CH_2R + [O] \xrightarrow{KMnO_4} \text{no reaction} \qquad RCH_2-\underset{\underset{O}{\|}}{C}-H + [O] \xrightarrow{KMnO_4} RCH_2-\underset{\underset{O}{\|}}{C}-OH$$

The oxidation involves attack at the *hydrogen* bonded to the carbonyl group. However, *carbons* bonded to the carbonyl group are resistant to attack, which explains why the ketone is unchanged.

This difference in behavior has been used as the basis of qualitative tests to distinguish an aldehyde from a ketone. One such test is provided by **Tollen's reagent,** a solution of silver nitrate in aqueous ammonia:

$$\underset{O}{R-\overset{\|}{C}-H} + 2Ag^+ + 3NH_3 + H_2O \rightarrow \underset{O}{R-\overset{\|}{C}-O^-} + Ag\downarrow + 3NH_4^+ \tag{29-3}$$

While the aldehyde group is being oxidized to a carboxyl group, the silver ion is reduced to silver metal, thus providing a change which can be seen. The metallic silver precipitates in very fine black particles or coats the surface of the glass vessel with a bright silver mirror. A carbonyl compound which behaves in this way is presumed to be an aldehyde; if it does not cause the formation of metallic silver, a ketone is suspected.

Tollen's reagent is used not only as a qualitative test but also for the manufacture of mirrors. For the latter purpose, the aldehyde required, Eq. (29-3), may be either formaldehyde or a sugar such as glucose.

◄ Glucose is an aldehyde and like all simple sugars, Section 33-2, has an OH group on the carbon adjacent to the carbonyl group. This structure is especially reactive toward Tollen's reagent. Two similar reagents, originally developed to test for sugars, are **Fehling's solution** and **Benedict's solution.** Both contain copper(II) ions (bright blue solution) which are reduced to copper(I) oxide (brick red precipitate).

$$\underset{O}{R-\overset{\|}{C}-H} + 2Cu^{2+} + 5OH^- \rightarrow \underset{O}{R-\overset{\|}{C}-O^-} + Cu_2O + 3H_2O \tag{29-4}$$

Benedict's solution, for example, is often used to detect sugar in urine and is quite satisfactory for this purpose. The Fehling and Benedict solutions are also frequently applied to simple aldehydes or ketones; however, the results are apt to be misleading. For instance, butanal does *not* give positive results with Fehling's solution.

The alert reader may wonder why OH$^-$ ions in the same solution with Cu^{2+} ions do not cause precipitation of insoluble Cu(OH)$_2$. This reaction is prevented by including citrate ions or tartrate ions (not shown in Eq. 29-4) in the solution. These ions form a "complex" with Cu^{2+} which protects it from combination with OH$^-$. ►

IMPORTANT TERMS

Aldehyde	*Ketone*
Dehydrogenation	*Oxidation*
Hydrogenation	

WORK EXERCISES

1. Name each structure:

   a) CH_3CH_2CH
   $\overset{\|}{O}$

   b) $CH_3CH_2CCH_3$
   $\overset{\|}{O}$

   c) ⟨benzene ring⟩$-C-CH_2CH_3$
   $\overset{\|}{O}$

   d) $CH_3CHCH_2CHCH_2CH$
   $\quad\quad\overset{|}{Cl}\quad\overset{|}{CH_3}\quad\overset{\|}{O}$

2. Write an equation to show how each of the following could be synthesized from the appropriate alcohol.

   a) 2-pentanone   b) formaldehyde   c) acetaldehyde   d) cyclohexanone

3. Show the structure that would result when each of these compounds is treated with hydrogen and nickel catalyst. [Consult Table 29–2 for structures.]

   a) 3-pentanone   b) vanillin   c) citral   d) testosterone

4. Show how butanone (methyl ethyl ketone) could be synthesized from an alkene. [More than one step is required.]

5. Benzaldehyde, C_6H_5CHO, is a liquid. After it has been exposed to air for some time, a white solid appears at the mouth of the bottle. As time goes on, more and more of the solid settles to the bottom of the bottle. The solid is not soluble in water, but does dissolve readily in dilute sodium hydroxide solution. Suggest a probable structure for the white solid and a reason for its formation.

SUGGESTED READING

DePuy, C. H. and K. L. Rinehart, Jr., *Introduction to Organic Chemistry*, Chapter 9, John Wiley, New York, 1967.

Hart, H. and R. D. Schuetz, *Organic Chemistry*, 3rd ed., Chapter 8, Houghton Mifflin, Boston, 1966.

Chapter 30   POLYMERS

30-1 POLYMERS, NATURAL AND SYNTHETIC

As we have seen, the concept of structure in covalent compounds led to a vigorous development of organic chemistry from 1860 onward. Chemists became skilled at synthesizing compounds because, as a rule, they could reliably predict the outcome of reactions. They also became adept at proving the structures of the molecules, both natural and synthetic, with which they worked. Some of these molecules were highly complex and moderately large. However, it was not until the 1920's that chemists began to realize that the covalent structures so characteristic of organic substances could lead to the formation of *extremely* large molecules called **polymers** (meaning *many parts*). A single polymer molecule contains not thirty or one hundred or two hundred atoms, but *thousands* of atoms linked together covalently.

Most of the very stuff of life is polymeric material. Aside from water, a large amount of an animal body consists of proteins, which are polymers. The proteins make up not only the soft tissues but also such structures as hair, feathers, cartilage, horns, fingernails, and turtle shells. Starch, the chief food storage material of plants, is a polymer. Cellulose, the structural material of many plants, is a polymer. In wood the cellulose fibers are further strengthened by being cemented together by lignin, another polymer. Plant cells, like animal cells, contain protein. Nucleic acids, which play one of the most critical roles in living material, are also polymers. The nucleic acids carry the genetic information from one generation to the next and dictate the construction of the protein polymers which carry on many of the other functions of life.

In addition to consuming plants and animals for food, man has for ages adapted many of the natural polymers for other useful purposes. Some notable examples are wood, cotton, linen, hemp, wool, and silk. Rubber has found widespread application only within the past hundred years. Not until 1930 were chemists able to make completely new *synthetic* polymers. The resultant plastics, elastomers (synthetic rubbers), adhesives, fibers, and coatings (paints and enamels) have profoundly affected our technology and standard of living.

In this chapter we will discuss a number of the common synthetic polymers. Several of the natural polymers will be discussed later in the text, in terms of their biochemical functions.

30-2 ADDITION POLYMERS

Under the influence of the proper catalyst, one molecule of a substituted alkene, such as vinyl chloride, Eq. (30-1), can use its "extra" electrons to form a covalent bond to a second molecule of vinyl chloride, which can in turn link to a third molecule, and this to a fourth, and so on, to form an immensely long chain of such units. The gigantic molecule thus produced is a polymer. In Eq. (30-1) the n represents a very large number, from several hundred up to a few thousand.

$$n \ CH{=}CH_2 \ \xrightarrow{\text{peroxide}} \ \left(CH{-}CH_2 \right)_n$$
$$\quad\ \ | \qquad\qquad\qquad\qquad |$$
$$\quad\ \ CL \qquad\qquad\qquad\quad CL$$

vinyl chloride poly(vinyl chloride)
a **monomer**   a **polymer**

$$(30\text{-}1)$$

The number n is called the degree of polymerization. Each of the small molecules from which the polymer is built is called a monomer (meaning *one part*). A structural formula for the polymer is written by drawing one portion of the structure in parentheses. The n beside the parentheses indicates that this portion of structure, called the repeating unit, is repeated n times. Note that there is a definite structural relation between the repeating unit and the monomer from which it is derived. For one particular polymer molecule the value of n may differ from that of another molecule in the same sample. It is not possible to determine n accurately, but experiments can tell us that for a certain polymer, n has a value of 1000–1400, for example.

Poly(vinyl chloride) is one example of an addition polymer, one of the two fundamental types of polymers. An **addition polymer** is so named because it is formed by an addition reaction, similar in some respects to other addition reactions of alkenes, Section 23–4. The structural characteristic of an addition polymer is that its backbone is a chain of carbon atoms built up during the polymerization reaction. One addition polymer differs from another in the nature of the groups—alkyl, aryl, or functional groups—which may be attached at alternate carbons along the chain.

◄ The manner in which a polymerization reaction occurs is now reasonably well understood. The formation of poly(vinyl chloride) and many other polymers can be initiated by a peroxide catalyst. Figure 30-1 summarizes the stages in such a polymerization. First, the peroxide decomposes to form radicals, Section 22–7. A radical, R·, is highly reactive; it can become more stable if it finds one more electron to pair with its one odd electron. In the presence of an alkene, the radical can make use of one of the two electrons in the extra bond of the alkene. This, however, leaves one odd electron at the other end of the former alkene bond. Consequently, the newly-formed particle is a radical also. As soon as it collides with another alkene molecule it binds one electron, once again leaving one unpaired. Thus, the stage is set for an indefinite number of repeated reactions, whereby the growing polymer chain adds to itself one monomer molecule after another.

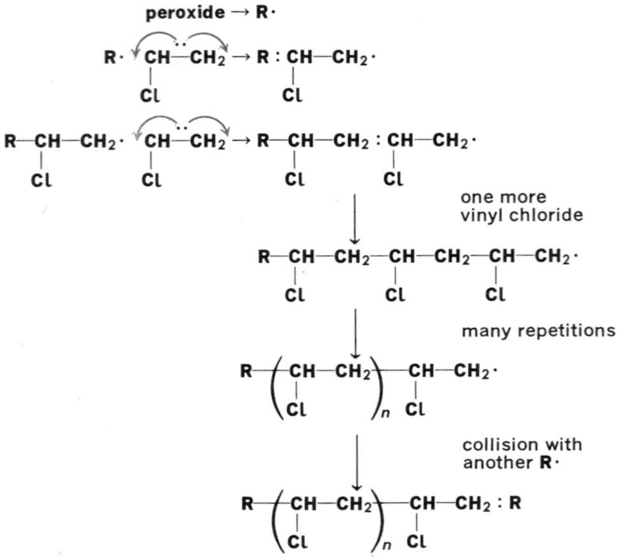

FIG. 30–1. Mechanism of a typical addition polymerization catalyzed by peroxide; vinyl chloride converted to poly(vinyl chloride).

It is apparent from Fig. 30–1 that at each stage of the polymerization a reactive site (in this example, a radical) is produced at the end of the growing chain. In fact, it might appear that the polymer chain would stop growing only when all the monomers had been used. If so, it would contain not a thousand or two but billions and billions of repeating units. The reason the polymer chain stops growing is that occasionally the odd electron at the end of the growing polymer chain will encounter another radical, R·, with which it can form a covalent bond *without* generating a new reactive site. Because only a trace of peroxide is added to the alkene monomer, only a few radicals are present at any given time. Therefore the growing polymer radical may typically collide with, and add, about a thousand alkene molecules before a collision with another radical causes termination. Still other radicals, released by the decomposing peroxide, simultaneously initiate the growth of numerous other polymer chains. In general, the greater the number of radicals supplied to the mixture, the faster will be the rate of polymerization, because more polymer chains will be growing at any given moment. The greater concentration of radicals will also cause the formation of shorter polymer chains (that is, n will be smaller);

FIG. 30–2. Clear, flexible film of polyethylene, an addition polymer, is widely used for food packaging. [Courtesy of Eastman Chemical Products, Inc.]

FIG. 30–3. A molded bottle cap of polypropylene, an addition polymer. [Courtesy of Eastman Chemical Products, Inc.]

chain growth will terminate sooner because there will be a greater chance that the reactive site will encounter another radical.

Polymerization of an alkene can also be initiated by either a positive ion, Eq. (30–2), or a negative ion, Eq. (30–3), rather than by a radical. However, in every case the attack of the reactive particle on an alkene generates a particle having the same kind of reactive site. The

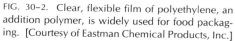

$$\text{R}^+ \text{CH--C} \rightarrow \text{R}:\text{CH}_2-\text{C}^+ \rightarrow \text{etc.} \qquad (30\text{–}2)$$

$$\text{R}:\text{CH--CH}_2 \rightarrow \text{R}:\text{CH--CH}_2:^- \rightarrow \text{etc.} \qquad (30\text{–}3)$$

new particle then tries to stabilize itself by attacking another alkene molecule, but in the process only generates a new reactive site, and so on. ►

It is possible to synthesize a great variety of polymers, each having different properties, by starting with different alkene monomers. For example, polystyrene is a stiff, relatively brittle plastic used to mold toys, model trains, knobs for radios, and inexpensive picnic spoons and cups. In contrast, polypropylene, although rigid, is extremely tough, impact-resistant, tear-resistant, and in thin sections is quite flexible. A contoured chair having the

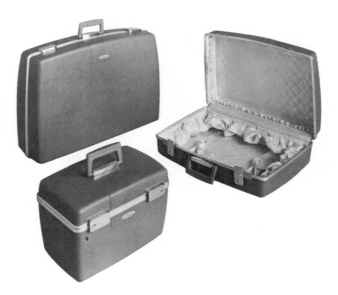

FIG. 30–4. Sturdy, attractive luggage can be fashioned from tough polypropylene. [Courtesy of Eastman Chemical Products, Inc.]

FIG. 30–5. Teflon, the familiar "non-stick" lining for cooking utensils, is also an effective electrical insulator. In this instrument used to guide jet aircraft, the printed circuit (dark lines in center and upper section) is embedded within a sheet of Teflon 0.01 in. thick. [Courtesy of du Pont de Nemours.]

seat and back all in one piece can be fashioned from polypropylene. A complete box with hinge and lid can be molded in one operation from polypropylene. At the hinge the polypropylene is simply molded paper-thin so that it will be flexible. The hinge is so tough that it can be bent back and forth a great many times (probably more than a million) without breaking. Despite the flexibility of the hinge, the box and lid, being thicker, are rigid.

Several other common varieties of addition polymers are described in Table 30–1.

TABLE 30–1. Some common addition polymers

Structure	Chemical Name	Common Name or Brand Name	Uses
$\left(\begin{array}{c} CH-CH_2 \\ | \\ Cl \end{array}\right)_n$	poly(vinyl chloride)	PVC, "vinyl"	floor tile; pipes; wire covering; clear film for food packaging
$\left(\begin{array}{c} CH-CH_2 \\ | \\ C_6H_5 \end{array}\right)_n$	polystyrene	"styrene"	toys and models; household articles; instrument panels and knobs; styrofoam insulating material; hot drink cups, picnic jugs, etc.
$\left(\begin{array}{c} CH-CH_2 \\ | \\ CH_3 \end{array}\right)_n$	polypropylene		pipes; valves; packaging film; sterilizable bottles for babies and hospitals; utility boxes; fish nets; waterproof carpeting
$(CH_2-CH_2)_n$	polyethylene		squeeze bottles; flexible cups and ice cube trays; clear, soft film for food bags and clothes packages; weather balloons; moisture barriers in buildings
$(CF_2-CF_2)_n$	polytetrafluoroethylene	Teflon	linings for cooking pans; electrical insulation; gaskets, valves, and machine parts; heat- and chemical-resistant pipes and sheets
$\left(\begin{array}{c} CH-CH_2 \\ | \\ CN \end{array}\right)_n$	polyacrylonitrile	Acrilan, Orlon	fabrics and knitted goods
$\left(\begin{array}{c} CH_3 \\ | \\ C-CH_2 \\ | \\ COOCH_3 \end{array}\right)_n$	poly(methyl methacrylate)	"acrylic," Lucite, Plexiglass	airplane windows; models; light fixtures; costume jewelry; dental fillings and false teeth; tooth brush and hair brush handles; reflectors; automobile taillights

30-3 DIENE POLYMERS

A **diene** is an organic compound having *two* carbon–carbon double bonds somewhere in its structure. Of particular value in polymerization reactions are compounds such as 1,3-butadiene,

$$CH_2{=}CH{-}CH{=}CH_2$$

in which the two double bonds are separated from each other by one single bond.

A polymer prepared from such a diene is just another example of an addition polymer.

Neoprene, Eq. (30–4), was the first diene polymer successfully commercialized and the first synthetic rubber developed in the United States. Neoprene has been manufactured since the late 1930's for use in shoe soles, coverings for electric wires, and for rubber hoses,

$$n CH_2{=}\underset{\underset{CL}{|}}{C}{-}CH{=}CH_2 \xrightarrow{\text{peroxide}} \left(CH_2{-}\underset{\underset{CL}{|}}{C}{=}CH{-}CH_2 \right)_n \qquad (30\text{-}4)$$

chloroprene
2-chloro-1,3-butadiene

polychloroprene
Neoprene

gaskets, and fittings which must withstand attack by oil or gasoline. Neoprene is superior to natural rubber in its toughness and its resistance to weathering and to oil. This polymer would make excellent tires, but is too expensive for this purpose.

It is important to note that when chloroprene or a similar diene polymerizes, Eq. (30–4), each monomer is linked into the polymer chain by the opposite ends of the original diene unit, and that a double bond remains in each repeating unit of the polymer.

◀ The manner in which the diene becomes bonded at its opposite ends is shown in Eq. (30–5). There is a shift of electrons on all four carbons of the diene skeleton. Consequently,

$$R\cdot \; CH_2{-}\underset{\underset{CL}{|}}{C}{-}CH{-}CH_2 \rightarrow R:CH_2{-}\underset{\underset{CL}{|}}{C}{-}CH{-}CH_2\cdot \; \rightarrow \text{etc.} \qquad (30\text{-}5)$$

the new reactive site (an odd electron) appears at the end of the chain. However, this process is just a variation of the fundamental addition reaction (compare with Fig. 30–1). ▶

Natural rubber is a polymer of isoprene, Eq. (30–6).

$$n CH_2{=}\underset{\underset{CH_3}{|}}{C}{-}CH{=}CH_2 \xrightarrow{\text{catalyst}} \left(CH_2{-}\underset{\underset{CH_3}{|}}{C}{=}CH{-}CH_2 \right)_n \qquad (30\text{-}6)$$

isoprene
2-methyl-1,3-butadiene

polyisoprene
natural rubber

A number of plants, especially *Hevea* trees, can produce rubber, using enzymes to catalyze the synthesis. For years all attempts to form rubber in the laboratory, by polymerizing isoprene, failed. Then during the early 1950's, Karl Ziegler in Germany and Giulio Natta in

Italy conducted extensive research on new types of catalysts which regulate reactions in a special way. Because of the fundamental principles they established during these and subsequent studies, Ziegler and Natta shared the Nobel Prize for chemistry in 1963. By applying their principles, chemists at the Firestone Rubber Company and at Goodrich-Gulf developed methods which would, in the laboratory or factory, polymerize isoprene into a material virtually identical to natural rubber. The Firestone product has the brand name Coral Rubber; the Goodrich-Gulf material is called Ameripol. These rubbers are now manufactured in large quantities for use in tires or in any of the other applications for natural rubber.

◄ The synthetic polyisoprene described above is truly a synthetic *rubber*, in that it is a manufactured material which actually duplicates the substance produced by rubber trees. The other materials commonly called "synthetic rubber" are really different compounds which have elastic, rubbery properties. It is less ambiguous to call them *synthetic elastomers*.

Isoprene can be manufactured readily from petroleum. A method for polymerizing chloroprene was developed in the 1930's. Why, then, did it take until the mid-1950's before a catalyst could be found which would produce a polyisoprene that was a true duplicate of natural rubber? This is another case in which the *shape* of the molecule is a critical factor. Note that the repeating unit of natural rubber, Eq. (30–6), still contains one double bond. The portions of carbon skeleton attached to the double bond could be in either a *cis* or a *trans* arrangement. In natural rubber, all the double bonds throughout the polymer chain have the *cis* configuration. This can be duplicated synthetically only with a special catalyst which maintains close control over the growing polymer chain, forcing it to assume the *cis* configuration at each step.

A number of the catalysts used to polymerize chloroprene or the alkenes *will* convert isoprene to a polymer. However, they produce a polymer chain having both *cis* and *trans* bonding randomly distributed. The polymer is therefore not equivalent to natural rubber and its properties are not especially useful. Recently still other catalysts have been discovered which will produce all-*trans* polyisoprene. This material is very stiff, in contrast to the highly elastic quality of all-*cis* polyisoprene, be it natural or synthetic. ►

Polybutadiene can be prepared from its monomer, Eq. (30–7), by the same catalysts

$$n\text{CH}_2\!\!=\!\!\text{CH}\!-\!\text{CH}\!\!=\!\!\text{CH}_2 \xrightarrow{\text{catalyst}} \left(\text{CH}_2\!-\!\text{CH}\!\!=\!\!\text{CH}\!-\!\text{CH}_2\right)_n \qquad (30\text{–}7)$$

butadiene   polybutadiene

used for polymerization of isoprene. Polybutadiene is more elastic and has a better bounce than natural rubber. It is the component of the toy "superballs" which bounce so high.

30–4 COPOLYMERS

When a mixture of *different* monomers is polymerized the product is a **copolymer.** By varying the kinds of monomers used and the percentage of each in the mixture, a chemist can often create a polymer having some property, such as toughness or heat stability, required for a certain application. Table 30–2 lists some of the copolymers presently being manufactured. These are further examples of addition polymers. Figures 30–6 and 30–7 illustrate how these materials can be utilized.

TABLE 30-2. Examples of (addition) copolymers

Monomer Components	Polymer Name	Uses
vinyl chloride, vinyl acetate	"vinyl," vinylite	phonograph records; shower curtains, rain wear
vinyl chloride vinylidene chloride	Saran	"Saran wrap" for food; fibers for auto seat covers; pipes
vinyl chloride, acrylonitrile	Dynel, Vinyon	fibers for clothing
ethylene, propylene	EPR, ethylene-propylene rubber	tires
styrene, butadiene	SBR, styrene-butadiene rubber	tires
isobutylene, isoprene	butyl rubber	inner tubes
acrylonitrile, butadiene, styrene	ABS	crash helmets; women's spike heels; luggage; pipes; parts and cases for batteries, telephones, and other instruments; knobs and handles

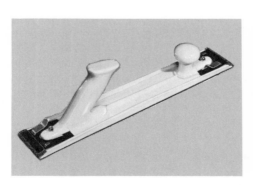

FIG. 30-6. Body and handle of a tool molded from acrylonitrile-butadiene-styrene (ABS), a copolymer. [Courtesy of the Marbon Chemical Division, Borg-Warner Corporation.]

FIG. 30-7. Since ABS plastic can be chrome-plated, it is used for decorative parts in cars and homes. Shown here is a lavatory faucet. [Courtesy of the Marbon Chemical Division, Borg-Warner Corporation.]

30–5 CONDENSATION POLYMERS

The second fundamental type of polymer is a condensation polymer, formed by a **condensation reaction.** A small molecule such as water or methanol is split out as each unit is added to the polymer chain. Structurally, condensation polymers are distinguished by the fact that there are almost always functional groups *within* the polymer backbone. (In contrast, the backbone of an addition polymer consists of carbon atoms, Section 30–2).

Nylon is a good illustration of a condensation polymer. It is formed by the reaction of two monomers, a diamino compound and a dicarboxylic acid, Eq. (30–8).

$$NH_2(CH_2)_6NH_2 \ + \ \underset{\substack{\parallel \quad \parallel \\ O \quad O}}{HOC(CH_2)_4COH} \ \rightarrow \ \underset{}{\overset{H_2O \qquad H_2O \qquad H_2O}{\cdots NH(CH_2)_6NHC(CH_2)_4CNH(CH_2)_6NHC(CH_2)_4C\cdots}}$$

1,6-diaminohexane   1,6-hexanedioic acid   nylon
(adipic acid)

(30–8)

The amino groups react with the carboxylic acid groups in the usual way, Eq. (28–9), forming amide groups. Note that the amide functional groups become part of the polymer backbone, and that for each amide link formed one molecule of water is split out.

It is apparent from Eq. (30–8) that for a condensation reaction of this type to lead to a polymer, each participating monomer must have *two* functional groups. Thus, after one end of the diamine has reacted with an acid molecule, the amino group at the opposite end is available for reaction with another acid molecule. Since the acid molecule also has another functional group at the opposite end, it can react with yet another diamine molecule. Consequently, innumerable repetitions of the reaction are possible. It would be good practice for the reader to rewrite Eq. (30–8) step by step, to see how the polymer chain grows.

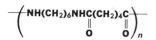

FIG. 30–8. The structural formula of nylon (a polyamide).

In Eq. (30–8) a moderately long section of the polymer chain was written out in order to show the nature of the reaction. Fig. 30–8 is a structural formula for the nylon polymer written in the usual more abbreviated form. Since two different monomers go into the structure of nylon, a repeating unit in the polymer formula must show each of them. In general, nylon is called a **polyamide** because amide functional groups are the links holding the polymer together.

Nylon makes strong, long-wearing fibers particularly suitable for hosiery, sweaters, and other articles of clothing. It was the first completely synthetic fiber marketed,* and to a

---

* The manufacture of rayon began at an earlier date. Rayon is natural cellulose which has been *modified* by chemical reactions. The process depends on the fact that the polymer backbone of rayon was present originally in the cellulose. The structural changes are made only in the groups attached to the backbone.

 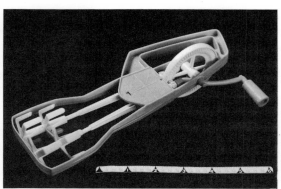

FIG. 30-9. Articles molded of nylon: left, machine gears; right, gears and blades of a beater. The frame and handle of the beater are of ABS. [Courtesy of du Pont de Nemours.]

very large extent has replaced silk which it resembles in many of its properties. Nylon is superior to silk in most respects, and it is cheaper to produce. It is not entirely coincidental that silk and nylon have similar properties. Silk is a protein and all proteins are polyamides, Chapter 34. Nylon can be molded into solid articles (see Fig. 30-9). It is quite strong and has a slippery surface; gears made of nylon need no lubrication. It is also frequently used for glides on drawers and zippers on clothing, for combs and cups, and for knobs and handles of various sorts. In the United States the production of nylon during 1967 reached the astounding total of one billion pounds.

The most common type of nylon has the structure shown in Fig. 30-8. Other nylon polymers having somewhat different properties can be made by using a diamine or a dicarboxylic acid having a different carbon skeleton.

Another type of condensation polymer is a **polyester;** as the name implies, the functional groups repeated in this polymer chain are esters. The most familiar polyester is poly(ethylene terephthalate), fibers of which are known as Dacron or Terylene. The polymer is formed, Eq. (30-9), by the reaction of ethylene glycol with the methyl ester of terephthalic acid. In the process, a molecule of methanol is split out for each new ester group formed; the net result is that teraphthalic acid (a *di*carboxylic acid) is transformed from one type of ester to another. A polymer results because ethylene glycol, the alcohol forming the new ester groups, is also a *di*functional molecule.

$$n\text{HOCH}_2\text{CH}_2\text{OH} + n\text{CH}_3\text{OC}-\!\!\!\bigcirc\!\!\!-\text{COCH}_3 \rightarrow \left(\!\!-\text{OCH}_2\text{CH}_2\text{OC}-\!\!\!\bigcirc\!\!\!-\overset{}{\underset{}{\text{C}}}\!\!\right)_n + 2n\text{CH}_3\text{OH} \qquad (30\text{-}9)$$

ethylene glycol   methyl terephthalate   poly(ethylene terephthalate)
(Dacron, Mylar)

Polyester fibers, such as Dacron, are used extensively in fabrics for clothing and other goods. The material can also be extruded into clear, tough films having excellent tear resistance and dimensional stability. One application is in Cronar motion-picture film. Another is the Mylar film and sheets used for recording tapes and other purposes.

30–6 THERMOPLASTIC versus THERMOSET POLYMERS

In the previous sections, polymers were classified on the basis of chemical structure as either addition or condensation types. It is also convenient to classify polymers into two different groups on the basis of their behavior when exposed to heat, which profoundly affects their uses. **Thermoplastic** polymers become plastic (that is, moldable) when heated. They can be repeatedly heated until soft and remolded. In contrast, a **thermoset** polymer hardens or sets when heated. It can be molded only once; thereafter it is rigid and heat will not soften it.

Polyethylene is a good example of a thermoplastic polymer. It can be heated and molded over and over again. A Melmac dish is a thermoset polymer. It remains rigid even when placed directly in a flame, but would soon char and decompose at such a high temperature.

All the polymers, both addition and condensation, described in the previous sections are *thermoplastic*. However, it is also possible to make a *thermoset* polymer utilizing either the addition or the condensation type of linkage. The essential difference is that a thermoset polymer is cross-linked, whereas a thermoplastic polymer is not. The phenomenon of cross-linking is described in the next section.

30–7 CROSS-LINKED POLYMERS

We discovered in Section 30–5 that a condensation reaction can lead to a polymer only if each monomer component has *two* functional groups. Now let us see what can happen if at least one of the components has *three* functional groups on each molecule. One common mixture of this type consists of phthalic acid and glycerol. When the mixture is heated, the acid and the glycerol react with each other to form ester bonds and release water, Fig. 30–10. Long polymer molecules result. Although this product is similar in many ways to the polyester molecule shown in Eq. (30–9), it differs in one essential feature. Each glycerol molecule has three hydroxyl groups, only two of which are needed to form the ester links holding the polymer backbone together. The third hydroxyl group on each glycerol unit is available to react with phthalic acid, and frequently does so.

Figure 30–10 represents the initial stage of reaction between phthalic acid and glycerol, and shows two polymer chains. This stage can be achieved by proper control of reaction conditions; for example, moderate heat can be maintained for a limited time. We note however, that in each polymer chain carboxyl and hydroxyl groups are still available. If the mixture is heated further, these remaining functional groups react to form additional ester bonds, linking one polymer chain to another. The result, shown in Fig. 30–11, is a vast network in which each polymer chain is covalently bonded to many others. Indeed,

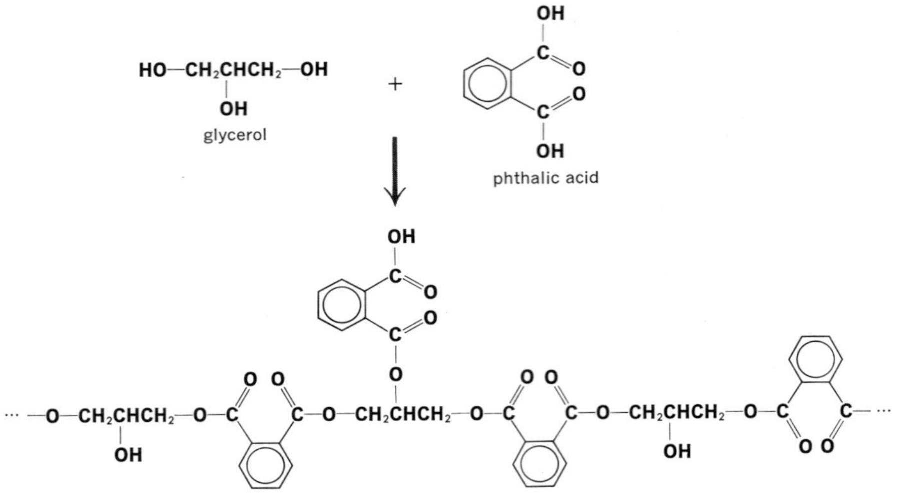

FIG. 30-10. The initial stage of reaction between glycerol and phthalic acid.

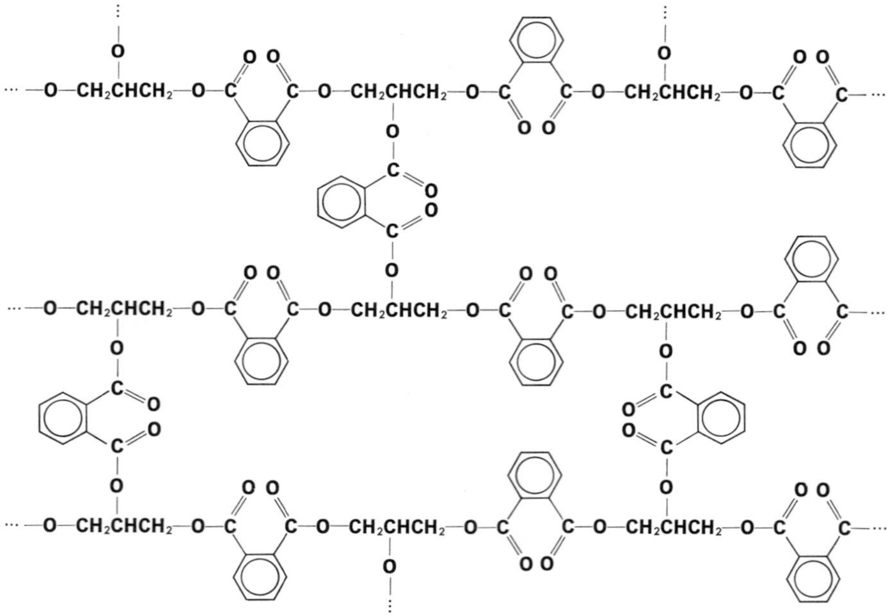

FIG. 30-11. The structure of glyptal, a thermoset polymer. The final stage of reaction between glycerol and phthalic acid produces a highly cross-linked, rigid material.

since each chain is bonded to others, and these in turn to others, the whole mass of material could be considered as one giant molecule. After the final stage of reaction the polymer is said to be highly **cross-linked.** Physically, it has become rigid.

The initial polymer prepared from glycerol and phthalic acid has very few cross links, Fig. 30–10. It is a slightly viscous liquid which can be poured into a mold or treated in some other way. After one thorough heating the material becomes a rigid, cross-linked polymer which can never again be melted or remolded. We see now that cross-linking creates a thermoset polymer. In contrast, a thermoplastic polymer is said to have a linear structure, because each molecule is just one long chain.

Glyptal is the common name for the glycerol-phthalic acid polyester, Figs. 30–10 and 30–11. Vast quantities of the material are used for baked enamels on automobiles and household appliances, and much smaller amounts for molded articles. For enameling, the first-stage glyptal polymer is mixed with pigments and sprayed onto a metal surface. Exposure to a bank of infrared heat lamps then causes the cross-linking leading to the thermoset polymer.

A variety of well-known thermoset polymers are listed in Table 30–3. All have one feature in common: they are cross-linked polymers.

TABLE 30–3. Some common thermoset (cross-linked) polymers

Monomer Components	Polymer Name	Uses
glycerol, phthalic acid	glyptal	baked enamels; molded articles
phenol, formaldehyde	phenol-formaldehyde resin, phenolic, Bakelite, Formica, Micarta	table tops; wall panels; resin bond for plywood; radio and appliance cabinets; washing machine agitators; handles; dials; drawer pulls
urea, formaldehyde	urea-formaldehyde resin	translucent light panels in homes and cars; decorative wall panels; bottle caps; adhesives; enamels; housings for radios and appliances
melamine, formaldehyde	melamine-formaldehyde resin, Melmac	dishes; panel boards; buttons; cases for hearing aids

30–8 THE SOCIAL IMPORTANCE OF SYNTHETIC POLYMERS

One of the distinctly human traits is man's ability to construct useful and beautiful objects. Centuries ago he started using the materials he could find in nature, such as wood, silver, gold, clay, leather, horn, and plant fibers. Gradually he developed more complex processes for obtaining useful materials. He discovered new metals that could be isolated by heating certain rocks (ores), and found that a mixture of sand and alkali subjected to very high temperatures yielded glass, an *inorganic* polymer. Only within the last few decades has man learned to synthesize organic polymers, thereby providing himself with a host of new structural materials.

With synthetic polymers, man has an immense new field for creative expression, both artistic and utilitarian. The synthetic polymers have properties different from those of any natural material previously employed; in many cases they are profoundly different. Moreover, man understands that the polymerization reaction is a very general process. By the proper choice of monomers one can create a new material having, within reason, almost any property desired.

This flood of new materials has had a tremendous effect upon our culture within a short period of time. As recently as 1940 the only synthetic polymer often encountered by the average citizen was Bakelite. Nylon hosiery, Neoprene rubber soles, and Plexiglas were relatively new. We now take for granted a wide variety of polymers used in fabrics, toys, gadgets, machinery, construction materials, and art objects—paintings, jewelry, dishes, and sculptures.

30-9 CONSERVATION OF ORGANIC RAW MATERIALS

We must bear in mind that nearly all the valuable synthetic organic compounds—polymers, medicines, dyes, etc.—are derived from two natural resources: coal and petroleum. At present the greatest quantities of both these resources are simply burned up to provide heat. Coal and petroleum are becoming so important as sources of material that we cannot afford much longer to waste them in combustion. Within a few generations man must develop other sources of energy, before these critical sources of carbon compounds are completely exhausted.

IMPORTANT TERMS

Addition polymer	*Diene*	*Polymer*
Condensation polymer	*Monomer*	*Repeating unit*
Copolymer	*Natural rubber*	*Synthetic rubber*
Cross-linked	*Polyamide*	*Thermoplastic*
Degree of polymerization	*Polyester*	*Thermoset*

WORK EXERCISES

1. Give the name and structure of the monomer from which each of the polymers in Table 30-1 can be prepared.

2. Using any one of the examples from Table 30-1, write an equation for the formation of the polymer showing the catalyst, the degree of polymerization, and the repeating unit.

3. In Section 30-3 it was stated that all the double bonds in natural rubber (polyisoprene) have the *cis* configuration. Draw a portion of a rubber molecule in the correct *cis* arrangement.

4. Write a fairly long section of structure for styrene-butadiene rubber, keeping in mind that there will not necessarily be a regular alternation of monomer components as the polymer chain develops.

5. Write out, step-by-step, a fairly long segment of Dacron structure (Eq. 30–9), so that you see how the polymer chain grows. What small molecule is eliminated as each new covalent bond forms? What type of polymer is Dacron?

SUGGESTED READING

Asimov, I., *The New Intelligent Man's Guide to Science*, Basic Books, New York, 1965, pp. 462–486. A highly readable account of polymers, plastics, fibers, and rubbers.

Asimov, I., *A Short History of Chemistry*, Anchor Books, Doubleday, New York, 1965, pp. 182–188. Discussion of polymers.

Ayres, E., "The Fuel Situation," *Scientific American,* Oct. 1956. Discusses the rapidity with which our fossil fuels are being consumed.

Crick, F. H. C., "Nucleic Acids," *Scientific American*, Sept. 1955. This entire issue of *Scientific American* is devoted to polymers, both natural and synthetic. Other articles in this edition are "Giant Molecules," by H. F. Marks; "How Giant Molecules Are Made," by G. Natta; and "Proteins," by P. Doty.

DePuy, C. H. and K. L. Rinehart, Jr., *Introduction to Organic Chemistry*, Chapter 4, John Wiley, New York, 1967.

Fisher, H. L., "New Horizons in Elastic Polymers," *J. Chem. Educ.* **37,** 369 (1960). A comprehensive but readable survey of the field, with many references.

Fisher, H. L., "Rubber," *Scientific American*, Nov. 1956. Discussion of synthetic rubbers and a brief history of natural rubber.

Lessing, L. P., "Coal," *Scientific American*, July 1955. Coal is more important as a raw material than as a fuel.

Levinthal, C., "Molecular Model-Building by Computer," *Scientific American*, June 1966 (Offprint #1043). The activity of biologically important giant molecules is profoundly influenced by the shapes into which they can twist. The possibilities can be studied with a computer.

Mark, H. F., "The Nature of Polymeric Materials," *Scientific American*, Sept. 1967. An excellent discussion of the properties of both natural and synthetic polymers and the possibilities of tailoring these molecules for new uses.

Price, C. C., "The Geometry of Giant Molecules," *J. Chem. Educ.* **36,** 160 (1959).

Chapter 31 STEREOISOMERS

31–1 INTRODUCTION

This chapter deals with the fascinating isomers, called *stereoisomers*, which can exist because of particular spatial arrangements within the molecules. Since we have already encountered a few examples of one type, the *cis-trans* isomers, we will begin by investigating additional examples of *cis-trans* isomers. Then it will be possible to define some important terms and describe a very different type of isomer within the large category of stereoisomers.

31–2 *CIS-TRANS* ISOMERS: ADDITIONAL EXAMPLES

We discovered, in Section 23–4, that there could be both a *cis* and a *trans* isomer of an alkene such as 2-butene. The two isomers can exist because the rotation of groups about the double bond is restricted. A similar situation arises in substituted cycloalkanes, whose carbon skeletons fall approximately in a plane, with attached groups held either above or below the plane of the ring. For example, *cis*-1,3-dichlorocyclopentane and *trans*-1,3-dichlorocyclopentane (Fig. 31–1) are two different compounds. The two chlorine atoms can both be below the plane of the ring, or one can be above the plane and one below. In this case, it is the ring itself which acts as a more or less rigid structure, preventing part of the skeleton in one isomer from rotating to produce the other isomer. Although each bond in the skeleton of the compound is a single bond, the carbon atoms are linked in a ring. Therefore, one carbon cannot rotate relative to the others without breaking a bond and tearing the ring open. So the situation is the same as it is with the *cis-trans* isomers of alkenes: a *cis* compound can be changed to its *trans* isomer only by way of a chemical reaction involving bond-breaking and bond-formation.

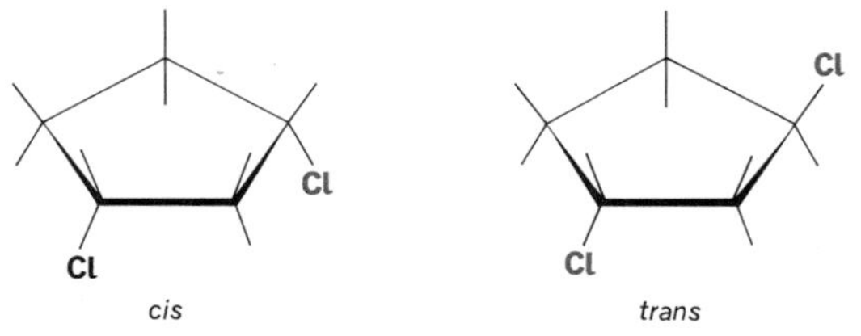

FIG. 31–1. Two different molecules of 1,3-dichlorocyclopentane.

31–3 STEREOISOMERS: DIFFERENCES IN CONFIGURATION

For any given pair of *cis-trans* isomers (for example, Fig. 31–1), the *cis* compound has the same *structure* as the *trans* compound. The **structure** *of a molecule refers to which atom is bonded to which other atom, and to the type of bonds involved.* A *trans* isomer differs from a *cis* isomer only in the arrangement in space of its atoms. We say it is their configurations which differ. **Configuration** *refers to spatial arrangement.* Compounds differing in this fashion constitute a particular class of isomers: **stereoisomers** *have the same structure, but different configurations.* The *cis-trans* isomers represent just one type of stereoisomers, whose differences in configuration are due to some rigid structure in the molecule (a double bond or a ring). The other type of stereoisomers, to be described below, are called *optical isomers;* their configurations depend upon a different factor.

31–4 THE STRANGE ISOMERS OF LACTIC ACID

Lactic acid occurs in a great variety of natural materials, including sour milk and sore muscles. It has a sour taste much like that of vinegar and other organic acids. Analysis of lactic acid reveals that its molecular formula is $C_3H_6O_3$; two of the oxygens are in a carboxyl group and the third is in a hydroxyl group. Furthermore, there is abundant evidence to prove that the hydroxyl group is on the carbon adjacent to the carboxyl group. Therefore, we are required to write the structural formula as in Fig. 31–2.

CH₃—CH—COOH
      |
     OH

FIG. 31–2. The structure of lactic acid.

For many compounds this would appear to be a satisfactory formula. Not so in this case. Lactic acid seems to have two different isomers, both of which, however, must have the same *structure* (Fig. 31–2). Although there are many sources for the different kinds of lactic acid, one kind can be obtained conveniently from certain bacteria, another kind from muscle tissue. The properties of the two are listed in Table 31–1.

TABLE 31–1. **Properties of the two isomeric lactic acids**

Property	Isomer *A*	Isomer *B*
source	muscle	bacteria
melting point	26°C	26°C
rotation of polarized light	+3.8° (to the right)	−3.8° (to the left)
other physical properties	*A* and *B* behave identically	
chemical properties	reactions correspond to the structural formula (Fig. 31–2); *A* and *B* behave identically	
assigned name	(+)-lactic acid	(−)-lactic acid

In *nearly* all respects the two kinds of lactic acid are identical. Are we justified in suggesting that they are different compounds? In one unusual property, their effect on the rotation of polarized light, the two kinds of lactic acid are curiously similar and yet different. Each affects the polarized light to the same extent, rotating it 3.8°. However, the results are exactly opposite. In one case it is a positive value (rotation to the right), while in the other case it is a negative value (rotation to the left). Indeed, it is remarkable that lactic acid has *any* effect on polarized light; many organic compounds do not. For this reason we have never before bothered to mention this particular physical property, as we have properties such as boiling point, density, or solubility. The nature of polarized light will be discussed in the next section. For now, we will say that because the distinctive feature of the lactic acids involves light they were called **optical isomers.*** We shall soon see that numerous other organic compounds exhibit the same behavior.

In order to have names to designate each of the optical isomers of lactic acid, chemists have called them simply (+)-lactic acid and (−)-lactic, referring to their effects on light.

The idea that the two lactic acids really arᵉ different compounds is further supported by their behavior upon melting. Once again they are curiously similar yet different. Each type of lactic acid, when pure, melts (or freezes) at 26°C. However, if we mix a small amount of (+)-lactic acid with (−)-lactic acid, it melts at a temperature *lower* than 26°C. This suggests that the (+)-isomer is behaving as a foreign substance toward the (−)-isomer; that is, the molecules of the (+)-isomer must be different than those of the (−)-isomer. Recall that, whereas pure water freezes at 0°C, if we dissolve in it a different compound, such as salt or sugar, the water freezes at a lower temperature (Section 11–9).

Although the two varieties of lactic acid are exactly the same in most properties, there are these few differences which suggest that they are not the same compound. At least we

---

* Optics is a branch of physics concerned with light. The term was derived from the Greek word *optikos*, relating to the eye or vision.

will assume they are different compounds until we find out more about them. Even more important, we should try to discover what is causing this behavior. But before we do, we should learn a little more about polarized light.

31–5 POLARIZED LIGHT AND OPTICAL ACTIVITY

Many of the properties of light may be described by regarding it as wave motion (Fig. 31–3). That is, as a ray of light moves along in one direction, there are vibrations of an electromagnetic field in a direction perpendicular to the direction of travel. In the diagram only one wave is shown; an end view of its plane of vibration would appear as a line. In ordinary light the vibrations may be in *any* direction perpendicular to the line of travel. Therefore, we must imagine that the planes of vibration of other waves could be tilted at various angles, so that in the end view there are many lines.

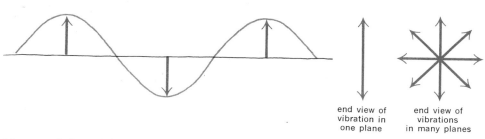

end view of vibration in one plane   end view of vibrations in many planes

FIG. 31–3. Ordinary light as wave motion.

When ordinary light, vibrating in many different planes, passes through certain materials, the only light which gets through is confined to vibrating entirely in one plane. Light having only one plane of vibration is called plane-polarized light, or more briefly, **polarized light.** One material which has polarizing ability is calcite, a clear, crystalline form of calcium carbonate. The arrangement of atoms in the calcite crystal is such that light passing through it is forced to align its vibrations into one plane.

A **polarimeter** is an instrument designed to measure the effect of substances on polarized light. It is a long cylinder holding various bits of apparatus; from the outside it usually looks like a telescope. Figure 31–4 shows the functioning parts of a polarimeter, in diagram form. The front end of the cylinder holds a calcite crystal, called a *polarizer*. This converts the ordinary light entering the instrument to polarized light. The light then passes through a tube containing the sample being studied. If the sample is a compound such as lactic acid, it can rotate the plane of vibration of the polarized light. The light will still be vibrating entirely in one plane, but the plane will be tilted so that it lies at a different angle than it did originally. At the back end of the instrument is another calcite crystal, the same as the first, but called an *analyzer*. Before the sample is placed in the instrument, the analyzer is carefully lined up with the polarizer, so that the polarized light vibrating in a vertical plane can pass on through the analyzer. However, if polarized light which passes through the sample is no longer aligned in a vertical direction, it is blocked by the analyzer. In order to allow the light to pass, we must rotate the analyzer until it is tilted at the same angle as the polarized light from the sample. The analyzer is attached to a round dial marked off in degrees, like a protractor. Therefore we can read on the dial the number of degrees through which we need to turn the analyzer to get it properly aligned with the polarized light.

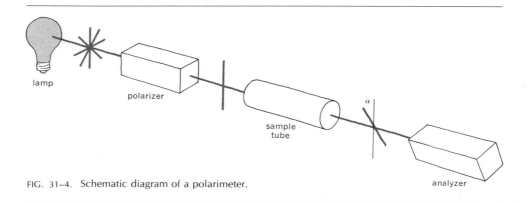

FIG. 31–4. Schematic diagram of a polarimeter.

◄ The ability to rotate polarized light is a property of individual molecules. Therefore the amount of rotation observed in the polarimeter will be greater if the polarized light encounters more solute molecules by passing through a more concentrated solution or through a longer tube. Meaningful rotation values can be obtained only if we compare one with another under a standard set of conditions. The value used, called the **specific rotation** and symbolized by [α], is the *amount of rotation given by a pure liquid or a solution at a concentration of one gram per milliliter, in a sample tube one decimeter long.* Very often the measurement will be observed using a tube of a different size or a solution of different concentration. In this case [α] can easily be calculated by the following equation:

$$[\alpha] = \frac{\alpha}{lc},$$

where [α] = the specific rotation,
 α = the observed rotation in degrees,
 l = the tube length in decimeters (dm),
 c = the concentration in g/ml.

Thus if a 2-dm tube is used for a certain sample, α (the degrees of rotation actually observed on the polarimeter dial) would be twice as great as it would have been for the same sample in a 1-dm tube. But when one substitutes 2 for l in the equation, α is divided and brought back to the standard conditions, giving [α]. ►

We say that lactic acid is *optically active* because it affects the polarized light. **Optical activity** *is the ability to rotate the plane of vibration of polarized light.* Acetic acid, ethanol, acetone, and many other organic compounds do not rotate polarized light at all; these we

TABLE 31–2. Comparison of optically active and inactive organic compounds

Optically Active	Optically Inactive
CH_3—CH—COOH OH 2-hydroxypropanoic acid (lactic acid)	CH_3—CH_2—COOH propanoic acid

CH_3—CH_2—CH—CH_3
             OH
2-butanol
	CH_3—CH_2—CH_2—CH_2
	              OH
	1-butanol

CH_3—CH_2—CH_2—CH—CH_3
                 OH
2-pentanol
	CH_3—CH_2—CH—CH_2—CH_3
	            OH
	3-pentanol

CH_3—CH—COOH
        NH_2
2-aminopropanoic acid
	CH_2—CH_2—COOH
	    NH_2
	3-aminopropanoic acid

CH_3—CH—CH_2—COOH
        Cl
3-chlorobutanoic acid
	CH_3—CH—CH_2—COOH
	        CH_3
	3-methylbutanoic acid

say are optically inactive. If the rotation caused by an optically active compound is to the right (clockwise), the compound is said to be *dextrorotatory* (L. *dexter*, right). When writing the numerical value, we give it a positive sign, thus: +3.8°. Conversely, a *levorotatory* substance (Fr. *lévo*, L. *laevus*, left) rotates the light to the left (counterclockwise) and its numerical value is given a negative sign.

One characteristic of an optically active compound is that somewhere, somehow, there can always exist a companion which behaves exactly like it in all respects but one: the companion rotates polarized light the same number of degrees but in the *opposite* direction. Thus we think of optical isomers as existing in pairs which somehow are opposites, like a right hand and a left hand. Even though we may first encounter only the right hand, sooner or later we will locate the left hand.

Quite a variety of organic compounds can display optical activity; a few examples are listed in Table 31–2. Surprisingly, many other organic compounds are optically inactive, despite the fact that they are similar to some of the active ones.

31-6 TETRAHEDRAL CARBON TO THE RESCUE

So far all we have done is to describe the observed properties of optical isomers. The big question is: *Why* are they that way? If they exist as pairs of different substances, yet have the same structure, how can we write two different formulas? Or, more properly, can the

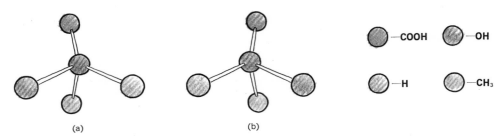

FIG. 31–5. Two nonsymmetric arrangements are possible when tetrahedral carbon holds four different groups. If lactic acid is the example, the groups would be: —COOH, —OH, —H, —CH₃.

atoms somehow be assembled in two ways which will make most properties the same yet have opposite effects on light? Furthermore, why are other organic compounds, apparently rather similar, *not* optically active?

Louis Pasteur was aware of this problem as long ago as 1860; he had been studying optically active salts of tartaric acid, obtained from the sediment in wine kegs. Despite his genius, there was not sufficient chemical knowledge at that time to make it possible for him to see an answer to the puzzle. He did surmise, however, that an optically active compound must have its atoms arranged in some kind of nonsymmetric pattern, and that there would be a companion pattern in which the nonsymmetric arrangement was laid out in the opposite order. Examples of such nonsymmetric objects are a right hand and a left hand or a clockwise and a counterclockwise helix (a coil). These pairs have the same structure; they differ only in the arrangement of their parts in space.

The answer to the problem was proposed by two young men independently and almost simultaneously in 1874. One was a Dutch chemist, Jacobus van't Hoff, age twenty-two; the other was a Frenchman, Joseph le Bel, age twenty-seven. They perceived that *if* a carbon atom holds four different groups and *if* its bonds have a tetrahedral structure (Section 21–6), then the arrangement of atoms around the carbon will automatically be nonsymmetric. And precisely because it is nonsymmetric, one other (and *only* one other) arrangement is possible, which is nonsymmetric in the opposite sense. The three-dimensional models pictured in Fig. 31–5 illustrate this principle.

The two possible spatial arrangements for lactic acid (Fig. 31–5) are related to each other in the way that an object is related to its mirror image. That is, if we hold one of the models up to a mirror, the image we see in the mirror looks like the *other* model; the image is the opposite or reflected arrangement. Equally important, these two arrangements (configurations) are *different*. Regardless of how we turn one model in space it will never have the same configuration as its mirror-image companion. (Of course, we must not take the model apart and rebuild it.) A pair of hands illustrates this concept nicely. A right hand has a nonsymmetric arrangement in space. A left hand has the same *structure:* it has fingers of the same length attached to the hand by the same kind of bones at the same angles. The left hand differs only in its spatial arrangement, which is an opposite nonsymmetric pattern.

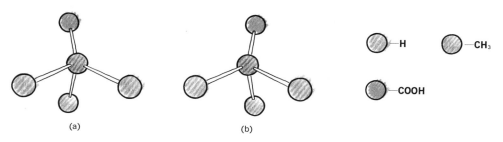

FIG. 31–6. A molecule of propanoic acid and its mirror image, which is identical.

If we hold a right hand up to a mirror, the image we see there is a left hand! Furthermore, the hands are nonidentical. We cannot make a right hand become a left hand by merely turning it upside down or backward. To return now to the two different molecules of lactic acid, a pair of isomers related in this way are called enantiomers. **Enantiomers** *are compounds which are nonidentical mirror images.*

The fact that four different groups are important to make enantiomers possible is further emphasized if we examine a molecule of propanoic acid, CH_3CH_2COOH. This compound is the same as lactic acid except that it lacks a hydroxyl and therefore has *two* hydrogens bonded to the central carbon. We can make a model of the propanoic acid molecule. Like any object, this model has a mirror image (Fig. 31–6). However, in this case the object and its mirror image are *identical*. That is, there can be only one kind of object having this structure. This uniqueness is due to the fact that both the object and its mirror image are symmetric; this symmetry, in turn, depends on the presence of two groups of the same kind (in this case, two hydrogens) attached to the central carbon atom.

Soon after van't Hoff grasped the idea that a tetrahedral carbon could possibly account for optical isomers, such as the lactic acids, he checked his hypothesis with many of the organic compounds that had been described in the chemical journals of his time. (For a few selected illustrations, see Table 31–2). He found that compounds having one carbon holding four different groups were indeed optically active. However, a few of the compounds then listed as being optically active did *not* have four different groups at one carbon. Van't Hoff was confident enough to predict that these samples were contaminated with other compounds which were optically active. Because of the keen interest in the new concept, various chemists reexamined these "exceptions" and before long proved that van't Hoff's predictions were true. There is now no doubt that the explanation of optical isomerism offered by van't Hoff and le Bel is correct. It is supported by experimental evidence from thousands of compounds.

We say then that optical isomers have the same structure but different configurations. Their differences in configuration depend upon nonsymmetric patterns within the molecules. Since optical isomers differ only in configuration, they fall within the class of stereoisomers (Section 31–3).

31-7 FORMULAS FOR OPTICAL ISOMERS

Once again we are confronted by the problem of developing a written formula which will adequately represent a three-dimensional molecule. In fact, for optical isomers the problem is especially acute because their very nature depends entirely upon the subtle differences in spatial arrangement. Certain methods for writing formulas of optical isomers, shown below, have proved to be quite satisfactory and are widely used by chemists.

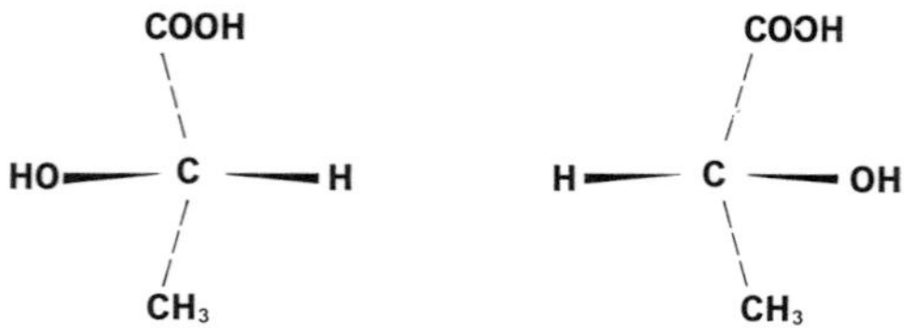

COOH   COOH

HO$-$C$-$H   H$-$C$-$OH

CH$_3$ CH$_3$

FIG. 31-7. Perspective formulas of the lactic acid enantiomers.

A perspective formula (Fig. 31-7) is easy to draw and effectively portrays the three-dimensional arrangement of groups in a molecule. It is evident that this formula is a close approximation to a picture of a three-dimensional model; compare Figs. 31-5 and 31-7. In a perspective formula the tapered bond lines imply that the two groups at the side are out in front of the central carbon atom, closer to the viewer. Also, it is understood that the other two groups, attached by broken lines, are behind the central carbon.

It is even possible to write a satisfactory valence bond formula for an optical isomer (Fig. 31-8), *provided* we understand exactly what it represents and how to use it properly. By arbitrary convention chemists have agreed that in a valence bond formula the groups written at the sides of the central carbon project forward toward the viewer, whereas the other two groups extend backward behind the central carbon. In other words, the lactic acid formulas in Fig. 31-8 represent the same configurations as those shown in Figs. 31-7 and 31-5.

A perspective formula is drawn in such a way that we can easily see the three-dimensional arrangement of groups. But when we look at a valence bond formula we must *imagine* the spatial arrangement; it is very important that we visualize the arrangement correctly, following the rule agreed upon. For example, one might be tempted to argue that con-

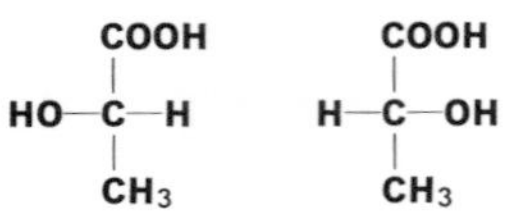

COOH   COOH
 | |
HO$-$C$-$H   H$-$C$-$OH
 | |
CH$_3$ CH$_3$
 (a)   (b)

FIG. 31-8. Valence bond formulas of the lactic acid enantiomers, corresponding to the formulas shown in Fig. 31-7.

figuration (b) in Fig. 31–8 is really identical to that in (a); it just looks different because of the way it was written. After all, if (b) were just lifted off the paper and flipped over it would look the same as (a). The error in this argument results from ignoring the rule that one must assume the groups written at the sides are projecting *forward*. If (b) were flipped over, the groups at the side would then project to the *rear* and (b) would *not* coincide with (a). To say it another way, although a valence bond formula *appears* to be flat, it represents a molecule which actually has three dimensions. When we inspect the models (Fig. 31–5) or the perspective formulas (Fig. 31–7) of the two lactic acid configurations we realize that (b) is really different than (a).

◄ Whenever valence bond formulas are used it is essential to remember that they represent three-dimensional objects. It is important that we all follow the same rule as to *how* we visualize the spatial arrangement of groups. All the rule really says is that whenever we write a valence bond formula for a configuration we will always view it from the same direction. The real molecules, or models of them, can of course be moved anywhere in space. However, when we wish to compare one with another and write their formulas, it is just a matter of convenience to view them always from the same direction. ►

31–8 RACEMATES

In Section 31–4 we found that lactic acid could be obtained from a variety of natural sources. Lactic acid can also be made synthetically, Eq. (31–1), by catalytic hydrogenation of pyruvic acid. The product thus obtained is called *racemic* lactic acid.

$$CH_3-\underset{\underset{O}{\|}}{C}-COOH + H_2 \xrightarrow{Ni} CH_3-\underset{\underset{OH}{|}}{CH}-COOH \qquad (31-1)$$

pyruvic acid   *racemic* lactic acid

Is this yet a third type of lactic acid, differing from either the (+)-lactic acid or the (−)-lactic acid described in Table 31–1? Yes and no. The chemical properties of *racemic* lactic acid are identical to those of (+)- or (−)-lactic acid. However, it has a different solubility: its melting point is 18°C, and it is optically inactive ($[\alpha] = 0$).

Chemists have discovered that *racemic* lactic acid is composed of exactly 50% (+)-lactic acid and 50% (−)-lactic acid. Such a mixture, called a racemate, can be formed by any pair of optical isomers. A **racemate** *is composed of exactly equal amounts of a pair of enantiomers*. A racemate is optically inactive because there are just as many molecules rotating the polarized light to the left as there are to the right; hence the net rotation observed in a polarimeter is zero.

When lactic acid is *synthesized* in the laboratory from pyruvic acid, *why* is a racemate produced? In contrast, some living organisms can build exclusively (+)-lactic acid and others, the (−) enantiomer. The laboratory reaction can be explained by considering the spatial arrangement of the molecules involved (Fig. 31–9). The starting material, pyruvic acid, is a symmetric molecule and hence is optically inactive. The molecule is flat; that is, the three groups attached to the central carbon all lie in one plane. In the diagram this

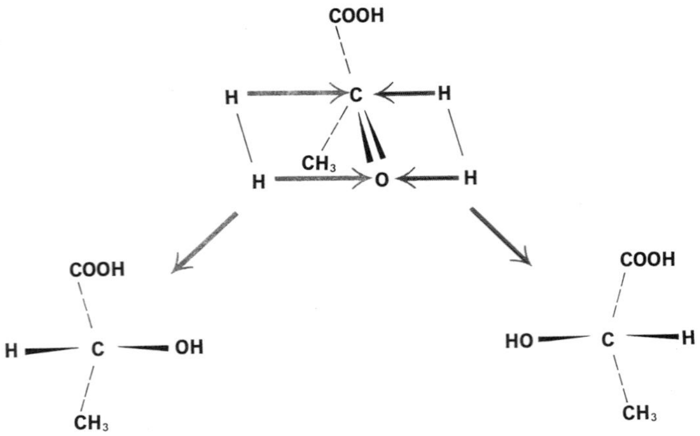

FIG. 31–9. A hydrogen molecule can add to either side of a pyruvic acid molecule, yielding either en-antiomer of lactic acid with equal probability. The product thus obtained is a racemate.

---

plane is perpendicular to the page; the oxygen is nearest the viewer and the methyl and carboxyl groups are to the rear. Now when a hydrogen molecule adds to the double bond, it has an exactly equal chance to approach the flat pyruvic acid molecule from either side. Thus of the billions of molecules reacting, sheer chance will dictate that half of them will produce one enantiomer of lactic acid and the other half will produce the opposite en-antiomer. Consequently, the product *as obtained in the reaction flask* is optically inactive; it is a racemate. This will always be the case, regardless of the type of reaction used. When-ever optically inactive materials are converted by chemical synthesis to new compounds, the resultant products are still optically inactive. Even though nonsymmetric configurations are created in the new molecule, the mixture as a whole will be a racemate.

If the two enantiomers constituting the racemate are separated from each other, then each will be optically active when alone. However, such a separation can *not* be accom-plished by ordinary methods such as distillation or crystallization. Since the enantiomers have the same chemical and physical properties, both will show identical behavior during such treatment. A racemate can be separated into its component enantiomers only by the use of some other compound, which is already optically active, as a reagent or catalyst to influence the process.* In other words, we can generate new optically active material only if we use material which is already optically active! This is similar to the chicken-and-egg dilemma and the answer to it is similar: this is part of the mystery of life. The optically active material necessary to start the process must be obtained from a living organism.

To summarize, enantiomers behave differently from each other in the presence of another compound which is nonsymmetric (optically active). This is the second way in which enantiomers differ from each other. Their effect on polarized light is the other property in which they differ (Section 31–4).

---

* The exact details of such a process are described in more comprehensive texts on organic chemistry.

We have just seen that an optically active reagent can be used to *separate* a racemate into two enantiomers, each of which will then be optically active. New optically active material can also be produced if an optically active catalyst or reagent is present at the time that new, nonsymmetric molecules are being formed. This optically active agent, being nonsymmetric, favors the formation of one enantiomer in preference to the other. A laboratory synthesis can be controlled by an optically active substance; the great majority of biochemical syntheses occur in this manner. We will discuss a biochemical example in the next section.

31–9 OPTICAL ISOMERS IN LIVING ORGANISMS

Muscle tissue can convert pyruvic acid to lactic acid. This reaction, Eq. (31–2) is a bio-

$$CH_3 - \overset{\displaystyle |}{\underset{\displaystyle \overset{||}{O}}{C}} - COOH + 2H \xrightarrow[\text{(muscle tissue)}]{\text{enzyme}} HO - \overset{\displaystyle \overset{COOH}{|}}{\underset{\displaystyle \underset{CH_3}{|}}{C}} - H \qquad (31-2)$$

pyruvic acid   (+)-lactic acid

synthesis. The crucial difference between it and the chemical synthesis, Eq. (31–1) is that the biosynthesis produces only *one* enantiomer, (+)-lactic acid. In Eq. (31–2) the two hydrogen atoms added to the double bond come not from H_2 gas, but from an organic compound in the tissue. This difference, however, happens to be unimportant in determining which optical isomers will be produced. The important factor in Eq. (31–2) is the catalyst, an enzyme.

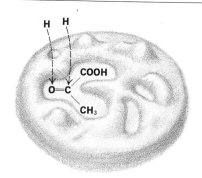

FIG. 31–10. An enzyme holding a pyruvic acid molecule, only one side of which is available for reaction. (The enzyme, represented schematically in color, is a complex organic molecule which would be much larger, in proportion, than suggested here.)

The enzyme catalyzes the reaction because it binds the pyruvic acid to itself and weakens the double bond, thereby facilitating the addition of hydrogen. The enzyme is a nonsymmetric molecule. (Incidentally, this of course makes it optically active.) Consequently, the enzyme acts as a pattern; a pyruvic acid molecule can fit onto its surface aligned in only one way (Fig. 31–10). Hydrogen atoms can then be added to the pyruvic acid from just *one* direction, thus yielding only one enantiomer of lactic acid.

As we have seen, certain other organisms may produce the opposite enantiomer of lactic acid. This just means that they have a different enzyme to promote the biosynthesis of lactic acid. Still different organisms may form both enantiomers, i.e., an optically inactive racemate. The significant point is that living organisms *can* produce single enantiomers (optically active) by means of their enzymes which are optically active molecules. In fact, in those biochemical reactions which are most crucial in sustaining life, organisms nearly always produce specifically one optical isomer. For example, amino acids are the essential units from which all proteins are built. Every amino acid molecule used for this purpose must have the configuration shown below; the opposite enantiomer will not suffice.

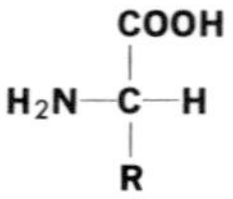

$$\begin{array}{c} \text{COOH} \\ | \\ \text{H}_2\text{N}-\text{C}-\text{H} \\ | \\ \text{R} \end{array}$$

31–10 MORE COMPLEX OPTICAL ISOMERS

A carbon atom holding four different groups is often called an **asymmetric carbon,** meaning literally, *not symmetric*.* For instance, in Fig. 31–11 the C shown in color designates the asymmetric carbon in a molecule of 2-butanol. Because of the asymmetric carbon, 2-butanol can assume two different configurations. In a written valence bond formula, when the carbon skeleton is stretched out vertically, only two arrangements for the H and OH groups are possible: the OH can be either to the right or to the left.

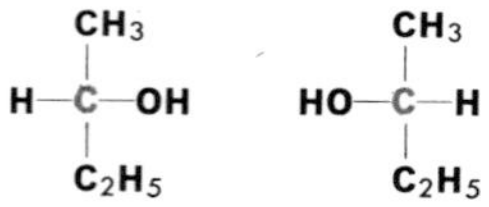

$$\begin{array}{cc} \begin{array}{c} \text{CH}_3 \\ | \\ \text{H}-\text{C}-\text{OH} \\ | \\ \text{C}_2\text{H}_5 \end{array} & \begin{array}{c} \text{CH}_3 \\ | \\ \text{HO}-\text{C}-\text{H} \\ | \\ \text{C}_2\text{H}_5 \end{array} \\ \text{(a)} & \text{(b)} \end{array}$$

FIG. 31–11. The two enantiomers of 2-butanol.

Now suppose we add to the 2-butanol molecules one more asymmetric carbon, making 2,3-pentanediol (Fig. 31–12). Starting with one of the 2-butanol configurations (Fig. 31–11a) one could add to it, at the upper end, another asymmetric carbon in either of two ways, with the OH to the right or to the left (Fig. 31–12a,b). Similarly, a new asymmetric carbon can be added in two ways to the other configuration of 2-butanol (Fig. 31–11b) giving 31–12c,d. In this fashion, four different configurations of 2,3-pentanediol are possible.

In Fig. 31–12, compounds (a), (b), (c), and (d) are all optical isomers of each other. Furthermore, (a) and (d) are enantiomers; they are mirror images but are not identical. Compounds (b) and (c) make up another pair of enantiomers. A fifty-fifty mixture of (b) and (c)

* The term *asymmetric carbon* is convenient, although strictly speaking the carbon itself cannot be asymmetric. It is the carbon plus its four groups which creates a nonsymmetric arrangement.

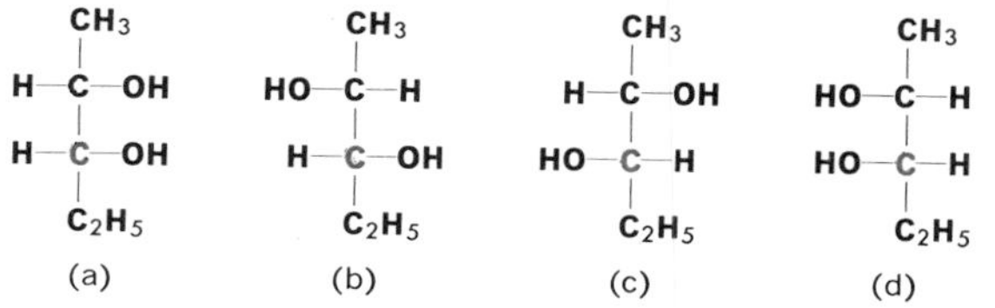

$$
\begin{array}{cccc}
\text{CH}_3 & \text{CH}_3 & \text{CH}_3 & \text{CH}_3 \\
\text{H}-\text{C}-\text{OH} & \text{HO}-\text{C}-\text{H} & \text{H}-\text{C}-\text{OH} & \text{HO}-\text{C}-\text{H} \\
\text{H}-\text{C}-\text{OH} & \text{H}-\text{C}-\text{OH} & \text{HO}-\text{C}-\text{H} & \text{HO}-\text{C}-\text{H} \\
\text{C}_2\text{H}_5 & \text{C}_2\text{H}_5 & \text{C}_2\text{H}_5 & \text{C}_2\text{H}_5 \\
(a) & (b) & (c) & (d)
\end{array}
$$

FIG. 31–12. The four configurations of 2,3-pentanediol.

would constitute a racemate. A fifty-fifty mixture of (a) and (d) would yield another racemate having solubility, melting point, etc., different from the racemate of (b) and (c).

A further examination of the configurations in Fig. 31–12 reveals some additional facets of optical isomerism. Since (b) and (c) are enantiomers, they have identical melting points, boiling points, solubilities, etc. Even their rotation of polarized light is the same in amount, although of opposite sign. But what is the relation between (b) and (a)? They are **diastereomers;** *they are optical isomers but are not mirror images.* Compounds (b) and (a) have *different* melting points, boiling points, solubilities, etc. Each is optically active, but (b) rotates polarized light to a very different extent than does (a). Since (a) and (b) both have OH functional groups, they will have the same type of chemical properties. However, the *rate* at which they react may be different. To summarize, each configuration in Fig. 31–12 has one companion which is its enantiomer, its mirror image. But either of the other two configurations will be diastereomers of it. Thus, (a) and (b) are diastereomers of each other; so also are (a) and (c), (b) and (d), or (c) and (d).

Many organic compounds, both natural and synthetic, have *several* asymmetric carbon atoms. How many optical isomers can we expect in such cases? We know that if there is 1 asymmetric carbon, 2 configurations are possible. Then if there are 2 asymmetric carbons, each of the first two possibilities is multiplied by 2 (Fig. 31–12). Hence, if there are three different asymmetric carbons, there would be $2 \times 2 \times 2$, or 2^3, or 8 possible configurations. In general, the number of different configurations will be 2^n, where n is the number of different asymmetric carbons. (This is often called *van't Hoff's rule,* for he was the first one to state the principle.) This simple mathematical relation leads to some astounding results. Glucose, a sugar occurring in humans and in many other organisms, has four asymmetric carbons. This means there are 2^4 or 16 compounds having the same structure but different configurations. One of these is glucose; another is its enantiomer. The other 14 compounds in this family of optical isomers are all diastereomers of glucose.

The important compound cholesterol has molecular formula $C_{27}H_{46}O$. Of these 27 carbon atoms, only 8 are asymmetric. However, $2^8 = 256$! The enzymes controlling the formation of cholesterol are so specific that only the one compound, out of 256 possible isomers, is formed by living organisms!

◄ The number of different configurations predicted by the 2^n rule is the *maximum* number possible. When all the asymmetric carbons in a molecule are of different type, the maximum will be realized. Occasionally two of the asymmetric carbons will be similar, in the sense that the four groups bound to one carbon are the same as the four groups bound to another carbon. In this case not so many combinations will be possible, and the total number of configurations will be less than 2^n. ►

31–11 SUMMARY OF TYPES OF ISOMERS

Isomers are different compounds having the same molecular formula.

a) **Structural isomers** have different structures.

$CH_3-CH_2-CH=CH_2$ and $CH_3-CH=CH-CH_3$

CH_3-O-CH_3 and CH_3-CH_2-OH

b) **Stereoisomers** have different configurations, but the same structure.

1. **Cis-trans isomers** have different configurations because of rigid structures in the molecules. (These are also called *geometric isomers*.)

2. **Optical isomers** have different configurations because of nonsymmetric patterns in the molecules.

Enantiomers are nonidentical mirror images.

A **racemate** is composed of exactly equal amounts of a pair of enantiomers.
Diastereomers are optical isomers which are not mirror images of each other.

31-12 CONCLUSION: THE IMPORTANCE
OF STRUCTURE AND CONFIGURATION

From our first encounter with organic substances, in Chapter 21, to these final discussions of organic chemistry, the importance of isomers has been apparent. Covalent bonds give organic compounds specific structures and configurations, which in turn establish their chemical and physical properties. In fact, we can go one step further. Subtle differences in the shape and structure of organic molecules are of prime importance to life itself. The function of organic compounds in living cells falls within the field of *biochemistry*, our next broad topic for study.

IMPORTANT TERMS

Configuration   Optical activity   Polarized light
Enantiomers   Polarimeter   Tetrahedral carbon atom

[See also the terms in Section 31-11.]

WORK EXERCISES

1. Which of these structures could exist in an optically active form?

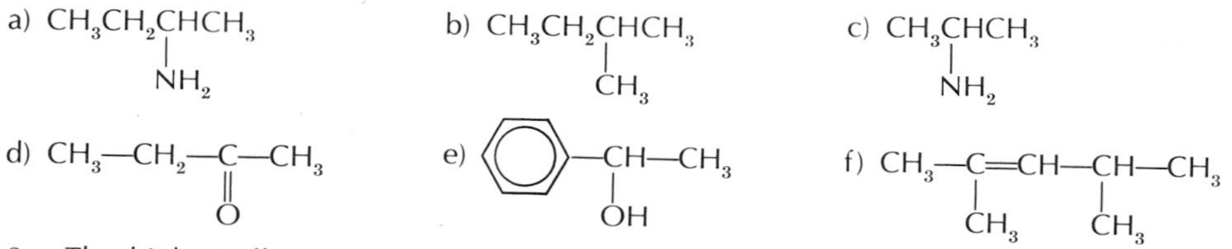

a) $CH_3CH_2CHCH_3$
                    |
                    NH_2

b) $CH_3CH_2CHCH_3$
                    |
                    CH_3

c) CH_3CHCH_3
            |
            NH_2

d) $CH_3-CH_2-\overset{\displaystyle O}{\overset{\displaystyle \|}{C}}-CH_3$

e) ⟨◯⟩$-CH-CH_3$
              |
              OH

f) $CH_3-C=CH-CH-CH_3$
           | |
           CH_3 CH_3

2. The biologically important sugar ribose has the structure shown below. How many optical isomers (different configurations) are possible for this structure?

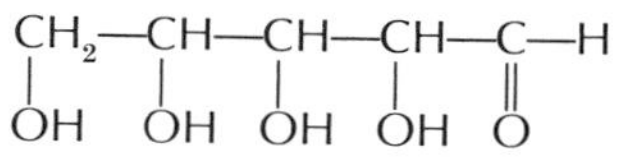

$CH_2-CH-CH-CH-C-H$
 | | | | ‖
OH OH OH OH O

3. For each pair of molecules below, tell what type of isomerism is involved, *if any*.

a)
CH_3 CH_3
    \   /
     $C=C$
    /   \
H H

CH_3 H
    \   /
     $C=C$
    /   \
H CH_3

b) $CH_3CH_2CH_2CH$
                 ‖
                 O

$CH_3CH_2CCH_3$
           ‖
           O

c)
        CH_3
          |
$H-C-Br$
          |
        CH_2
          |
        CH_3

        CH_3
          |
$Br-C-H$
          |
        CH_2
          |
        CH_3

d) CH$_3$CHCH$_2$COOH   CH$_3$CH$_2$CH$_2$COOH
     |
     CH$_3$

e)
$$H-\underset{\underset{CH_3}{|}}{\overset{\overset{CH_3}{|}}{C}}-Cl \qquad\qquad Cl-\underset{\underset{CH_3}{|}}{\overset{\overset{CH_3}{|}}{C}}-H$$

f)
$$\underset{Br}{\overset{CH_3CH_2}{\diagdown}}C=C\underset{H}{\overset{H}{\diagup}} \qquad\qquad \underset{CH_3CH_2}{\overset{Br}{\diagdown}}C=C\underset{H}{\overset{H}{\diagup}}$$

g)
$$CH_3-\underset{\underset{NH_2}{|}}{\overset{\overset{H}{|}}{C}}-COOH \qquad\qquad CH_3-\underset{\underset{H}{|}}{\overset{\overset{NH_2}{|}}{C}}-COOH$$

h)

4. Review Problem 3, Chapter 21. In the light of your present knowledge of stereoisomers, what is the *total* number of isomers possible for each molecular formula?

SUGGESTED READING

Asimov, I., *A Short History of Chemistry*, Anchor Books, Doubleday, New York, 1965, pp. 116–124. Concerns optical isomerism and tetrahedral carbon.

DePuy, C. H. and K. L. Rinehart, Jr., *Introduction to Organic Chemistry*, John Wiley, New York, 1967, pp. 117–124.

Dubos, R., *Pasteur and Modern Science*, Chapters 2 and 3, Anchor Books, Doubleday, New York, 1960. Describes Pasteur's exciting work with nonsymmetric crystals of tartaric acid salts and his astounding discovery that the racemic material could be separated into two kinds of crystals which were optically active but of opposite rotation.

Hart, H. and R. D. Schuetz, *Organic Chemistry*, 3rd ed., Chapter 13, Houghton Mifflin, Boston, 1966.

Noller, C. R., *Textbook of Organic Chemistry*, 3rd ed., Chapter 17, W. B. Saunders, Philadelphia, 1966.

Roberts, J. D., "Organic Chemical Reactions," *Scientific American*, Nov. 1957 (Offprint #85). This article is very good at this stage of your study. It will provide both some new insights and a review of some of the important ways in which organic molecules react.

Chapter 32 INTRODUCTION TO BIOCHEMISTRY

32-1 DEVELOPMENT OF BIOCHEMISTRY

It is difficult to set a date for the beginning of the study of biochemistry. Discoveries of facts, proposals of classifications, and the development of the theories we now recognize as comprising the body of knowledge of modern biochemistry were made by many persons. Fundamental discoveries were made by persons we would now call chemists, physiologists, physicians, and many others who would be difficult to classify. For a long time all these people were held back by the doctrine that special vital forces were needed for biological reactions, and that these reactions could not be understood by men. However, some men either from bravery, foolhardiness, or perhaps because they did not realize that what they were doing was supposed to be impossible began to study biochemical questions. Even before the Renaissance many studies were made of the composition of various parts of plants and animals, of the chemistry of the soil, fertilizers, and the requirements for plant growth.

Theophrastus Bombastus von Hohenheim, better known as Paracelsus, who lived from 1493 to 1541, brought together much of the old alchemical mystique and added new ideas of his own. He believed, among other things, that food contained both poisonous and wholesome parts and that digestion separated the two parts. His theory was that when the digesting agent, the *Archaeus,* was not working properly, the poisonous elements were not separated and eliminated, so the person became ill. Medicines were given to restore the *Archaeus* to its normal state. Some of the medicines used were poisonous salts (mercury II chloride and lead acetate); others were extracts from plants. Among the latter were extracts made by distillation, sometimes a distillate from fermented material which contained ethanol.

437

The temporarily beneficial effects of ethanol no doubt led to widespread acceptance of the remedies of Paracelsus. The ideas of Paracelsus and his followers were interesting and stimulated much experimentation. Probably many of their patients died not so much from their illnesses as from the "cures" prescribed. However, the ways of approaching and looking at the chemistry of living things proposed by Paracelsus led to better theories.

Another early scientist who was interested in the individual reactions taking place in living organisms was the Frenchman, Louis Pasteur. He helped to develop the idea that fermentation of grapes (we know now that it was actually the sugar in the grapes) to produce alcohol really involved a series of chemical reactions, and that these reactions occurred in living yeast cells. He further realized that the products formed in these reactions could be changed if different types of cells (either different yeasts or bacteria) were present. A further step was taken when the Buchner brothers showed in 1896 that fermentation did not require whole cells, as Pasteur had believed, but that cell-free yeast juices which contained a "ferment" could bring about certain reactions. It was later realized that the "ferment" was not a single substance but was really a mixture of many biological catalysts which came to be called enzymes. When these catalysts were extracted and purified, and as highly purified forms of the reactants became available to scientists, the road was opened for the investigation of the reactions that take place in living organisms.

FIG. 32–1. Methods of separation and analysis of mixtures by chromatography and electrophoresis.

(a) Paper chromotography. In paper chromatography a mixture of substances is applied to a spot on a piece of filter paper. The paper is then placed in a container with a solvent mixture which either rises on the paper by capillary action or is allowed to flow down the paper from a solvent reservoir. If this procedure does not separate all components (as with C and D above) a second solvent mixture can be used in a direction at right angles to that of the first solvent mixture. This gives a two-dimensional chromatogram. Thin-layer chromatography is similar to one-dimensional paper chromatography except that a plate of glass coated with a thin layer of absorbent material is used.

(b) Column chromatography. In column chromatography a mixture is applied to the top of a glass column filled with a powdered adsorbent substance, and a solvent mixture is allowed to flow through the column. This produces a separation of substances in the mixture. If test tubes are moved under the column at given intervals by the use of a turntable, the different components can be separated.

(c) Gas (gas-liquid) chromatography. In gas chromatography a mixture of substances is injected into the instrument. A current of helium or other inert gas carries the mixture through a small tube packed with an adsorbent material. The tube is heated to help in separation of the components of the mixture. As the components leave the instrument they are detected by some type of device and a curve is plotted. From such curves both the number of components and the relative amount of each may be seen. Some gas chromatographs have arrangements for trapping the individual components as they leave the instrument. These trapped materials can then be analyzed by other methods.

(d) Paper electrophoresis. In paper electrophoresis the mixture is applied to a filter paper or other similar material which is then placed in an electrophoresis cell having an anode at one end and a cathode at the other. Electricity is allowed to flow, and the components of the mixture migrate in the electric field. In the illustration, substances A and B are anions (they migrate toward the anode) and D and E are cations. C has not migrated.

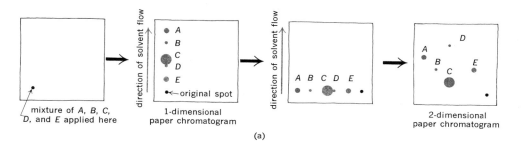

mixture of A, B, C, D, and E applied here
direction of solvent flow
A
B
C
D
E
original spot
1-dimensional paper chromatogram
direction of solvent flow
A B C D E
D
A
B
E
C
2-dimensional paper chromatogram

(a)

mixture added to column
solvent (from reservoir)
E
D
C
A
B

(b)

detector
(exit)
sample injected
helium tank
C
E
A
D
B
gas chromatogram

(c)

mixture applied here
anode
cathode
+
+
+
+
−
−
−
−
A B C D E
electrophoretogram

(d)

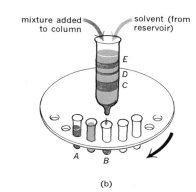

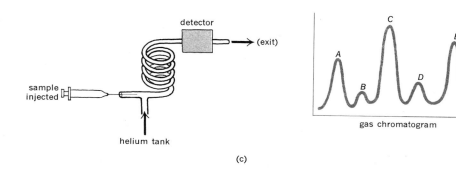

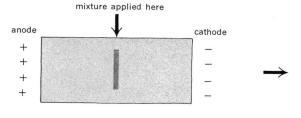

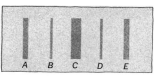

As investigation led to greater understandings, the early biochemists were nagged by a fear that the reactions observed when parts of plants or animals were placed in a glass container (*in vitro*) might not be the same as those that actually occurred in a living plant or animal (*in vivo*). Another difficulty some of the clearer thinkers recognized was that the substances isolated and purified from natural products might have been modified by the processes they used and thus might no longer be exactly the same as they were in the starting material. Whether or not they are producing "isolation artifacts" and the "*in vitro-in vivo*" problem still plague modern biochemists.

The past few decades have seen an extremely rapid increase in biochemical knowledge, and predictions for the future make the older science fiction seem mild. Why is our knowledge of biochemistry growing so rapidly? There are many answers. One is that the United States government has been and is supporting biochemical research. Another reason for the rapid growth is the discovery and development of new techniques, particularly those for separating and analyzing biochemical compounds. Researchers are purifying and separating substances of importance to biochemistry by using the techniques of **chromatography.** Either solid material packed in columns, paper, or the process of gas-liquid chromatography (popularly called "gas" chromatography) has been especially useful. Chromatographic techniques have made it possible to separate individual amino acids from complex mixtures— a task that previously had been almost impossible. Some of these analytical techniques are shown in Fig. 32–1. These separations have led to knowledge of the composition and structure of many of the compounds most important to life. Analytical methods which involve the absorption of infrared and ultraviolet radiation, as well as other techniques, have made it possible to analyze a sample consisting of only a few milligrams of material. The availability of radioactive isotopes, particularly the radioisotope of carbon, carbon-14 (C-14), has led to amazing progress in the study of biochemical reactions. Now specific molecules can be labeled with C-14 and their "fate" in an animal or plant shown by determining which excretion products are labeled. Thus, finding labeled carbon dioxide in the air expired by a rat given glucose which contained carbon-14 is evidence that glucose is converted, *in vivo*, to carbon dioxide by the rat (Fig. 32–2). By administering very small quantities of radio-isotopes to humans, medical researchers can sometimes diagnose, and in other instances (usually with larger doses) treat, various diseases.

Many of the early, and some of our modern discoveries in biochemistry have resulted from accidental discoveries in a research laboratory. Discovery of things not searched for, which is called serendipity, has been responsible for countless biochemical developments. For instance, the important discovery by the Buchners that cell extracts could carry out the reactions of fermentation was made not as the result of an experiment planned for this purpose, but came about as the result of their attempts to produce a "yeast juice" that they hoped would have medicinal value. When Eduard Buchner added a solution of sugar to the yeast juice with the hope that it would act as a preservative, he observed that fermentation was occurring, and concluded that units smaller than the whole cells (which Louis Pasteur insisted were necessary) could carry out fermentation. The cell is so complex that studies of how it works are only now being done. However, the realization that smaller units—the "ferments" that we now call enzymes—could serve as catalysts was a significant biochemical advance. Discoveries such as this require a trained, perceptive scientist, accurate observa-

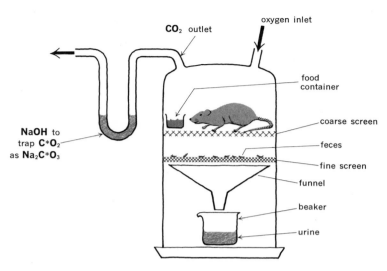

FIG. 32–2.   Diagram of an apparatus used to measure metabolism of radioactive substances in an animal. An animal that has been fed or injected with a radioactive substance is placed in the apparatus shown above. Gases he exhales as well as feces and urine can be collected and analyzed. (The asterisk is used to indicate radioactive atoms.)

tions of unexpected results, and the correct interpretation of these observations. It is interesting to speculate as to when—or whether—antibiotics would have been developed if Alexander Fleming had merely discarded his culture of staphylococcus that had been "contaminated" by a penicillin-producing mold.

Although such accidental discoveries are important to the progress of science, most of the discoveries and most of the development of new products have been made as the result of well-planned experiments. While researchers are always looking for the unexpected event in their routine work, this prospect does not provide the only motive for biochemical research. Biochemists are usually driven by at least two other motives in their research. For some, the desire to know how living organisms function—just for the pleasure of knowing —is the major motive. Others are more concerned with practical results—curing or preventing diseases. To most researchers, of course, both motives are important.

Although it is interesting to know how biochemistry developed and to realize some of the difficulties it faces, the major question, "What is biochemistry?" has not yet been discussed.

The simplest definition of biochemistry is that it is the chemistry of living plants and animals. Chemistry, as we have learned, is concerned with the composition, structure, and reactions of various types of matter. Biochemistry is the study of the composition and structure of those materials found in living organisms and the substances derived from them. Further, it is concerned with the *reactions* which occur in living organisms.

32–2 BIOCHEMICAL COMPOSITION

Life exists in many varieties from the unicellular algae through the simpler animals and plants to the giant redwood trees and whales. In spite of their obvious differences, there is a remarkable similarity in the compounds which are found in these varied types of organisms. All living matter, as well as all inanimate matter, is composed of the approximately one hundred naturally occurring chemical elements. About half of these elements are found in measurable amounts in the human body and in most other organisms that have been studied. Of these fifty elements, less than half have some known function in the human body. Those elements for which no function is known may be present simply because they became incorporated in the organism passively—just because they happened to be in the environment. The other possibility is that further research will discover their function.

TABLE 32–1. Chemical elements found in the human body*

oxygen	65 %	potassium	0.35%
carbon	18.5	sulfur	0.25
hydrogen	9.5	chlorine	0.20
nitrogen	3.3	sodium	0.15
calcium	1.5	magnesium	0.05
phosphorus	1.0		

* Data from Best and Taylor, *The Living Body*, 4th ed., New York, Holt, Rinehart, and Winston, 1958.

Only eleven chemical elements make up any appreciable percentage of the tissues of plants and animals. These elements are carbon, hydrogen, oxygen, nitrogen, sulfur, phosphorus, sodium, potassium, calcium, magnesium and chlorine. The first three of these elements, carbon, hydrogen, and oxygen, are present in virtually all the compounds found in living plants or animals, just as they are in almost all organic compounds. Nitrogen is also a major component of biochemical compounds; sulfur and phosphorus are present in many instances. Sodium, potassium, calcium, and magnesium are often referred to as "mineral elements," and are usually found either as ions or in relatively simple, "inorganic" compounds even though they are an important part of any living organism. Table 32–1 shows the composition of the human body.

Although one must begin by discussing the elements found in biochemical substances, these elements are present primarily in the form of compounds. A real understanding of biochemistry, therefore, must involve a description of compounds. If one were to attempt to answer the question, "What compounds are found in living organisms?", the list of such compounds would be extremely long.

When scientists are confronted with such a long list, they usually look for similarities and differences and, on the basis of these, they develop a system of classification. While no simple system of classification can include all the compounds found in living matter, biochemists have developed a system which includes the large majority of these compounds, with the usual qualifications that some compounds may belong to two or more classifications, and that there be a classification of "miscellaneous."

The most abundant compound in all living organisms is water. The percentage of water varies from well over 90% in some of the simpler aquatic animals to about 50% in a severely dehydrated camel. Various parts of any plant or animal will contain different amounts of water. Muscle tissue is about 70% water, human blood is 80%, and even the proverbially dry bony tissue is about 40% water. The importance and functions of this simple but remarkable compound were discussed in Chapter 12.

If we remove the water from any biochemical substance, we find that the dehydrated material contains three major types of compounds. The relative amounts of these three types of compounds may vary widely, but all plants and animals contain at least small amounts of each and together these three account for almost all the "dry weight" of a plant or animal.

TABLE 32–2. Approximate composition of materials from plants and animals

	Water	Carbo-hydrate	Protein	Lipid	Nucleic* Acid	Ash†
mammalian muscle (lean)	72–80%	1%	17–21%	5%	0.3%	1%
brain	79	1	8–10	10	0.2	—
hen's egg	74	1	13	11	—	1
cow's milk	87	5	3	4	—	0.7
rat liver	69	4	16	5	0.3	1.4
fish, cod	83	0	16	0.4	—	1.2
bananas	75	23	1.2	0.2	—	0.8
rice	12	80	7.6	0.3	—	0.4
peanuts (roasted)	2.6	24	27	44	—	2.7
honey	20	80	0.3	0	—	0.2
potatoes, white	78	19	2	0.1	—	1.0
potatoes, sweet	68	28	2	0.7	—	1.1
spinach	93	3.2	2.3	0.3	—	1.5
beer (4% alcohol)	90	4.4	0.6	0	—	0.2
soybeans, dry	7.5	35	35	18	—	4.7

* Figures for nucleic acid content are, in general, not available for foods and other animal products. It is interesting to note that some viruses, the bacteriophages, may contain from 12 to 61% DNA, and that tobacco mosaic virus has from 5 to 6% RNA.
† The value given as ash indicates the amount of material remaining when all organic matter has been oxidized. It is an indication of the amount of mineral elements present.

As early as 1827, William Prout classified food substances as either saccharine, albuminous, or oily. With increasing knowledge came the realization that not only foods, but all animal and plant tissues contained these three types of compounds. We now use the terms carbohydrates, proteins, and lipids to describe these compounds which were originally differentiated so long ago. A fourth type of compound—the nucleic acids—is present in much lesser quantities, but is a vital component of living organisms.

Table 32–2 gives the approximate composition of several substances of interest to biochemists.

Since the carbohydrates, proteins, lipids, and nucleic acids are complex compounds, although made of simple building blocks, it is important to know their structures. Most of the naturally occurring representatives of these compounds, with the exception of the lipids, may be considered to be polymers. The two-dimensional structure of many of these substances has been studied for some time; however, the three-dimensional structure is known for only a few of these important polymers and is a subject of research at the present time. Separate chapters are devoted to the description of the composition and structure of the carbohydrates, the proteins, the lipids, and the nucleic acids.

In addition to substances in these four groups, there are other compounds of major importance in biochemistry. Although these compounds make up less than 1% of most organisms, they may be extremely important for the continued life of the organism. Some of these groups of compounds are the vitamins, the porphyrin-containing compounds such as hemoglobin and chlorophyll, various plant pigments, and the medically important substances, the alkaloids.

32-3 BIOCHEMICAL REACTIONS

When we understand the composition and structure of the basic biochemicals, we are ready to consider their reactions. The similarities of reactions in various types of organisms are much more striking than are their differences. The term used by biochemists to describe the reactions which take place in living organisms is **metabolism.** Metabolism is subdivided into a "building" aspect called **anabolism** (anabolic reactions), and a process of degradation or "tearing-down" of compounds called **catabolism** (catabolic reactions).

Since the basic reactants in metabolic reactions are organic chemical compounds, biochemical reactions are much like organic reactions. There are, however, some important differences. If organic reactions are to proceed at an appreciable rate, it is often necessary that the reactants be heated or that acidic or basic catalysts be added to the reaction mixture. Since high temperatures and acidic or basic conditions almost always result in the death of any living thing, another milder method is utilized to bring about biochemical reactions.

Almost all biochemical reactions, both catabolic and anabolic, are catalyzed by enzymes. An enzyme is itself a protein, and may be defined as a catalyst of biological origin or alternately as a catalytically active protein. A further discussion of enzymes and of the energy relationships of biochemical reactions is given in Chapter 37, "Biochemical Reactions."

32-4 THE CELL AND ITS PARTS

The various compounds just described are found as parts of structures in living organisms. Although there is extracellular material, the cell is the basic unit of all living things. Cells may be combined to make tissues, groups of tissues to make organs, and organs to make organisms. While most aspects of these organizations are the subject matter of physiology, biochemists are concerned with the basic structures of cells.

The modern idea of a cell is that it is composed of many small parts called *organelles.* See Fig. 32-3. The nucleus has long been recognized as an important part of any living cell. More recently, however, small units called the mitochondria, microsomes, and lyso-

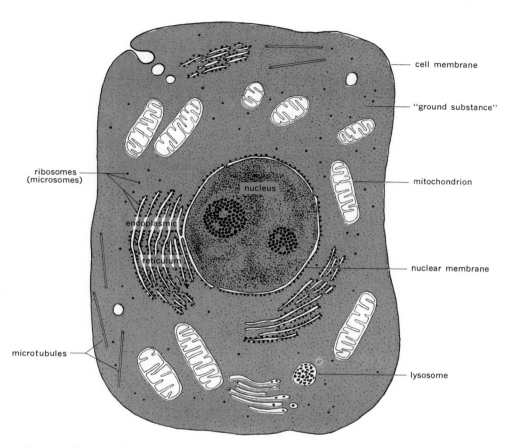

FIG. 32–3. Drawing of a typical animal cell, showing subcellular units (organelles) believed to be present, according to studies of electron micrographs. Not all these organelles are observed in every cell. See Fig. 32–4 for an electron micrograph showing these structures.

somes have been identified as subcellular organelles. These different organelles can be recognized in electron micrographs (Fig. 32–4), and can often be separated as relatively pure units by centrifugation. If we remove the liver from an animal, cut it, and then grind it with sand or disrupt the tissue in a blender or homogenizer, we get a thick semisolid much like a milkshake in consistency. This mixture is called a *homogenate*, and when it is spun in a centrifuge, we can separate the different units or organelles which make up the cells. This separation is possible because the subcellular units are of different sizes. Figure 32–5 shows the way such particles would be distributed after a short period of centrifugation. By centrifuging at definite speeds and pouring off the unsedimented fraction (the supernatant fraction), we can obtain relatively pure preparations of cell nuclei, the mitochondria and

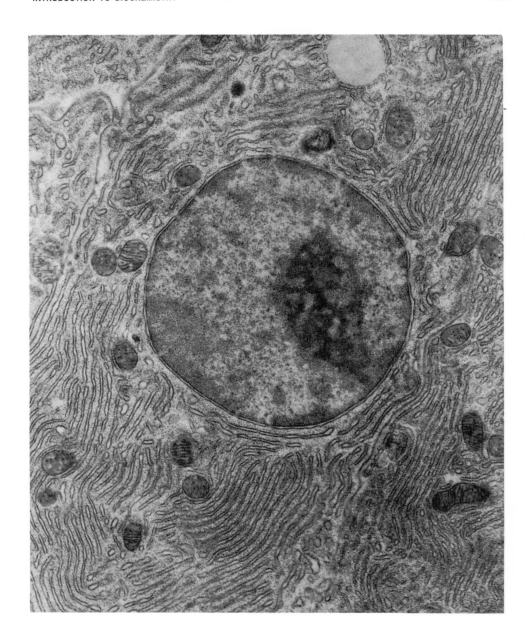

FIG. 32–4. An electron microscope photograph of the nucleus and part of the cytoplasm of a cell from the pancreas of a bat (magnified 18,000 times). The double-layered nuclear membrane, ribosomes lining channels that probably serve for secretion, and many mitochondria are clearly seen. [From John W. Kimball, *Biology,* Addison-Wesley, Reading, Mass., 1965. Photograph courtesy of Dr. Don W. Fawcett.]

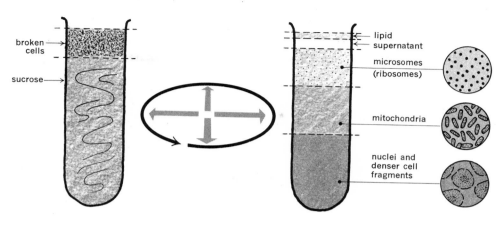

FIG. 32-5. Diagram showing separation of subcellular fractions by centrifugation. [Adapted from an illustration of a centrifuge by the Fisher Scientific Company.]

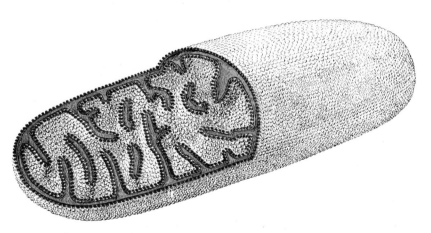

FIG. 32-6. Cross section drawing of a typical mitochondrion. This represents an idealized view based on electron micrographs. There are many small particles attached to the inner membrane. [From "The Mitochondrion" by David E. Green. Copyright © 1964 by Scientific American, Inc. All rights reserved.]

microsomes. The clear supernatant liquid from which all organelles have been removed is a rich source of enzymes—as are all the other fractions.

The **mitochondrion,** Fig. 32–6, even though extremely small, is a complex unit, the site of many of the metabolic reactions that release and store the energy from foods. It has been postulated that the enzymes which catalyze a series of reactions are arranged in sequence on the cristae (inner membranes) of mitochondria. Thus a molecule may be metabolized by passing from one enzyme to another on a mitochondrial assembly or, perhaps more correctly, a disassembly line.

The name **microsomes** was given to a preparation isolated by centrifuging a cell homogenate at a high speed after the nuclei and mitochondria had been removed. The microsome fraction contains the ribosomes and some of the threads of material that tie these small spherical bodies together. The *ribosomes,* so named because they are rich in ribonucleic acids (RNA), are important in the synthesis of proteins by the cell.

By other techniques we can isolate **lysosomes,** which contain enzymes that catalyze the decomposition of many important compounds in the cell. It is believed that these "suicide bags" are ruptured after the death of a cell and are responsible for the process of self-destruction—*autolysis*—of dead cells. Articles further discussing these fascinating subcellular organelles are listed at the end of this chapter. In the following chapters, the involvement of these organelles in specific reactions or series of reactions will be given.

32-5 SUMMARY

In this chapter we have traced briefly the beginnings of biochemistry and have indicated some of the answers to the question, "What is biochemistry?" Another possible answer to this question might be, "Biochemistry is the things a biochemist does." While this is less satisfactory as a formal definition of biochemistry, perhaps it is the best one. For biochemistry is still a growing, developing science. What it will be a few years from now depends on what the biochemists and their colleagues who call themselves biophysicists, molecular biologists, or cytochemists find interesting enough to experiment with and to speculate about. Like the living things with which it deals, biochemistry is changing. If we would really understand it, we must know not only what it seems to be today, but what it has been and the direction in which it seems to be going.

Biochemistry is a fascinating science because it is the chemistry of living things—plants and animals. Most of us are primarily concerned about one particular kind of animal—the human. There are, of course, many ways of answering the question, "What is a man?" The biochemical answer presents a picture in which some areas are well-defined and often highly complex while others are still hidden by the mists of ignorance. Nevertheless, the whole picture makes a beautiful kind of sense. In the next several chapters we will try to show you this biochemical way of looking at life. It is not a view that can be really understood after a brief, superficial glimpse. Some concentration on details is demanded if you would eventually see at least a bit of the grand design of life as seen by the biochemist.

IMPORTANT TERMS

Anabolism	*Fermentation*	*Metabolism*
Biochemistry	*In vitro*	*Microsome*
Catabolism	*In vivo*	*Mitochondrion*
Chromatography	*Isolation artifacts*	*Ribosome*
Enzyme	*Lysosome*	

SELECTED READING

Biochemistry Texts. The reader may wish further details on many of the items discussed throughout the section on biochemistry. The following list represents a selection of basic biochemistry texts containing different degrees of detail.

Cheldelin, V. H. and R. W. Newburgh, *The Chemistry of Some Life Processes*, Reinhold, New York, 1964. A short, paperback guide to biochemistry.

Conn, E. E. and P. K. Stumpf, *Outlines of Biochemistry*, 2nd ed., John Wiley, New York, 1966. A brief textbook of biochemistry filled with formulas and equations.

Harrow, B. and A. Mazur, *Textbook of Biochemistry*, 9th ed., W. B. Saunders, Philadelphia, 1966. One of the standards among the shorter biochemistry texts. The present edition is up to date and well written.

Mahler, H. R. and E. H. Cordes, *Biological Chemistry*, Harper and Row, New York, 1966. A comprehensive biochemistry text. A good, detailed basic reference.

White, A., P. Handler, and E. L. Smith, *Principles of Biochemistry*, 3rd ed., McGraw-Hill, New York, 1964. A good, extensive biochemistry text written primarily for medical students.

Other Reading. The following references are both more general and, in some instances, more specific.

Asimov, I., *The Chemicals of Life*, Signet Science Library Book, New American Library, New York, 1962. A highly readable, elementary discussion of biochemistry by Mr. Asimov, a biochemist with many other interests.

Asimov, I., *A Short History of Biology*, Natural History Press, Garden City, New York, 1964. A well-written introduction to many biochemical topics.

Baker, J. J. W. and G. E. Allen, *The Study of Biology*, Addison-Wesley, Reading, Mass., 1967. A modern presentation of biology for those who want additional background for their study of chemistry.

Baldwin, E., *An Introduction to Comparative Biochemistry,* 4th ed., Cambridge University Press, London, 1964. The fourth edition of a classic in the area of comparative biochemistry—the study of differences in biochemistry found in different kinds of animals.

Borek, E., *The Atoms Within Us*, Columbia University Press, New York, 1962. This amazing book contains an interesting discussion of biochemistry and biochemical principles without using a single structural formula.

Brachet, J., "The Living Cell," *Scientific American*, Sept. 1961 (Offprint #90). The key article in an issue devoted to the topic of cells.

deDuve, G., "The Lysosome," *Scientific American*, May 1963 (Offprint #156). A discussion of a cell organelle which sometimes digests the cell itself.

Green, D., "The Mitochondrion," *Scientific American*, Jan. 1964 (Offprint #175). A discussion of the molecular architecture and function of this important cellular component.

Jevons, R., *The Biochemical Approach to Life*, Basic Books, New York, 1964. A well-written discussion of biochemistry, its relation to other sciences, and its significance.

Kamen, M. D., "Tracers," *Scientific American*, Feb. 1949 (Offprint #100). An introduction to the technique of using isotopes to trace biochemical processes.

Kennedy, D., *The Living Cell*, W. H. Freeman, San Francisco, 1965. The book includes twenty-four articles reprinted from the *Scientific American*, nine of them from the Sept., 1961, issue devoted to the cell.

Morrison, J. H., *Functional Organelles*, Reinhold, New York, 1966. A readable but detailed discussion of mitochondria, chromosomes, and other subcellular organelles.

Scientific American Book, *The Physics and Chemistry of Life*, Simon and Schuster, New York, 1955. Although this book is a bit outdated, it includes many basic articles from the *Scientific American*.

Siekevitz, P., "Powerhouse of the Cell," *Scientific American*, July 1957 (Offprint #36). An older discussion of the mitochondrion.

Stein, W. H., and S. Moore, "Chromatography," *Scientific American*, Mar. 1951 (Offprint #81). A good introduction to technique that is so important in biochemistry today.

Zamecnik, P. C., "The Microsome," *Scientific American*, Mar. 1958 (Offprint #52). Somewhat outdated, but a basic discussion of this subcellular organelle.

Chapter 33 THE CHEMISTRY OF CARBOHYDRATES

33–1 INTRODUCTION

When we heat a sugar in a test tube we observe several successive changes. The sugar melts and then begins to darken and finally, after prolonged heating, there is a black residue, which seems to be carbon, in the tube. Water condenses on the upper walls of the tube during the heating. From this experiment we might deduce that sugar can be decomposed into carbon and water, so that we could classify sugar as a hydrate of carbon or a carbohydrate. If we found a variety of compounds which behave similarly when heated, we could classify these compounds as carbohydrates. Chemical analysis of sugar and similar compounds would show that sugar and the other carbohydrates are composed only of carbon, hydrogen, and oxygen, and that their formulas can be expressed as $C_x \cdot (H_2O)_y$. In many cases x would be equal to y ($C_6H_{12}O_6$) while in others ($C_{12}H_{22}O_{11}$) accurate analysis would be required to show that x and y were not really equal.

Relatively early in the development of biochemistry as the result of experiments like those listed above, certain compounds were classified as carbohydrates. Further observations have shown, however, that it is inaccurate to describe those compounds we know as carbohydrates as "hydrates of carbon." Not only do the hydrogen and oxygen atoms of carbohydrates fail to exhibit the properties of water of hydration, but the way these compounds react leads to the conclusion that there are alcohol and either aldehyde or ketone functional groups in the carbohydrate molecule. The modern definition for the classification known as **carbohydrates** is that the compounds are polyhydroxy aldehydes or ketones. This definition is usually expanded to include polymers and other compounds derived from, or closely related to, the polyhydroxy aldehydes and ketones.

A nutritionist often describes the carbohydrates as the sugars and starches. This description is incomplete, however, since it does not include the many polysaccharides other than starch. Sugars, which biochemists usually define as sweet-tasting carbohydrates, are the simplest carbohydrates. Their names usually contain the suffix -ose. The starches, which may be defined as the complex, granular or powdery carbohydrates found in seeds, bulbs, and tubers of plants, represent only one of a group of complex carbohydrates—the polysaccharides—which includes glycogen, cellulose, the pectins, and many other compounds. Carbohydrates are usually classified as follows: (1) monosaccharides, (2) oligosaccharides, (3) polysaccharides, and (4) derived or related compounds.

33-2 MONOSACCHARIDES

The monosaccharides may be described as those carbohydrates that cannot be further degraded by hydrolysis. They contain a single chain of carbon atoms. Compounds containing three carbon atoms, the *trioses,* are the simplest monosaccharides.

The general names for the monosaccharides are formed from a prefix indicating the number of carbon atoms and the suffix *-ose* which we have already mentioned. Thus we have trioses, tetroses, pentoses, hexoses, and heptoses containing 3, 4, 5, 6, and 7 carbon atoms, respectively. Those monosaccharides which contain an aldehyde group are **aldoses,** those with a ketone group, **ketoses.** The indication that a sugar contains a ketone group may also be made by including the letters *-ul-* in the name of the compound. Thus we may speak of *aldopentoses, ketoheptoses,* and *heptuloses,* the latter two terms being synonymous.

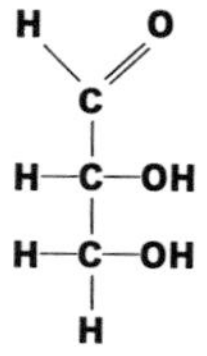

D-glyceraldehyde 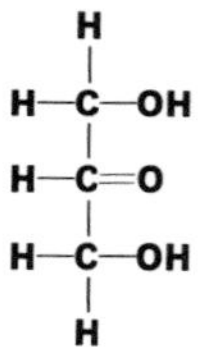   dihydroxy acetone

The two trioses are glyceraldehyde, which may exist in either of two optically active forms, and dihydroxyacetone. Glyceraldehyde is especially important because most of the common sugars may be considered as being derived from it, a derivation which results when carbon atoms are added to lengthen the three-carbon chain, although biosynthesis of sugars does not follow this course. Sugars are designated as D- or L-sugars, depending upon whether the asymmetric carbon atom farthest from the aldehyde or ketone group is similar to the D-form or the L-form of glyceraldehyde. (In the stuctures shown below, asymmetric carbons are shown in color. (See Sections 31–5, 31–7.)

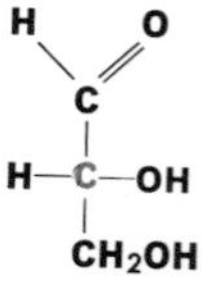

D-glyceraldehyde 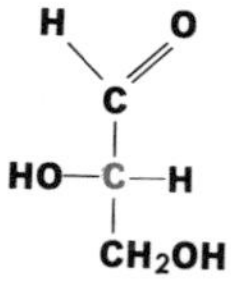   L-glyceraldehyde 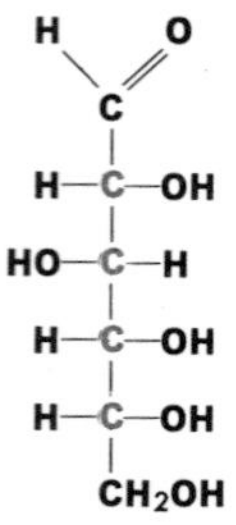   D-glucose 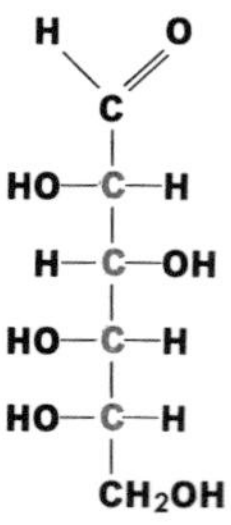   L-glucose 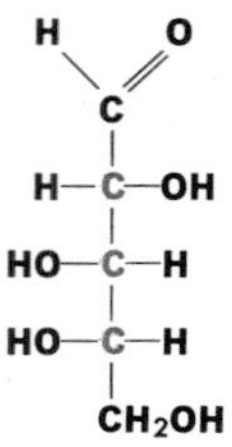   L-arabinose

Although D-glyceraldehyde rotates plane-polarized light to the right (i.e., it is *dextro-rotatory*) and L-glyceraldehyde rotates plane-polarized light to the left (hence it is *levo-rotatory*), compounds which are derived from these parent compounds may have different rotations, since they usually contain other asymmetric carbon atoms. In the examples above, glucose has four asymmetric carbon atoms and arabinose has three. The form of the keto-hexose, *fructose*, which is related to D-glyceraldehyde and is thus D-fructose, rotates po-larized light to the left. To designate this rotation of polarized light, we use the plus (+) sign for dextrorotatory compounds and the minus (−) sign for those compounds that are levorotatory. Thus fructose may be classified as D(−) fructose, the D indicating that it is related to D-glyceraldehyde, and the (−) indicating that it rotates plane-polarized light to the left.

The most abundant monosaccharides are the hexoses and pentoses. Since these com-pounds may contain several asymmetric carbon atoms, many isomers are possible. In general, these isomers have been given common or trivial names which often reflect the source or a property of the sugar. Structures of the more common monosaccharides are shown below.

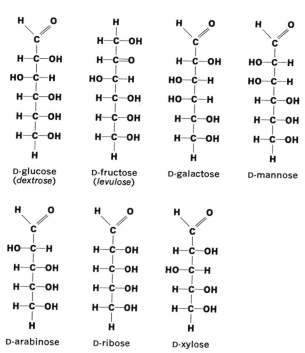

D-glucose (*dextrose*)　　D-fructose (*levulose*)　　D-galactose　　D-mannose

D-arabinose　　D-ribose　　D-xylose

◀ The name *glucose* which is derived from a Greek word for sweet wine, reflects the fact that this sugar was originally isolated from grapes. The alternative name, *dextrose*, resulted from the observation that the common form of this sugar rotates polarized light to the right. The name *fructose* is derived from the Latin word for fruit, *fructus*; and the other common name for this sugar, *levulose*, indicates its levorotatory property. *Galactose* (a component of the disaccharide lactose) is found in milk and owes its name to the Greek prefix *galact-*, meaning milk. *Lactose* is derived from the Latin prefix *lact-*, meaning milk. The name *mannose* reflects the fact that its related hexahydric alcohol, *mannitol*, was found in the dried juice of the manna tree. *Arabinose* is produced from gum arabic, an exudate from certain types of acacia trees. Apparently the name *ribose* was coined by selection and rearrangement of the letters in arabinose, which is appropriate, since the two are isomers. *Xylose* is found in woody parts of plants; its name is derived from the Greek word, *xylon*, meaning wood. The name *sucrose* is derived from the French word for sugar, *sucre*, and *maltose* is named for its source, malt, which is formed in germinating cereals. The word *saccharide* is derived from words for sugar that are similar in Arabic, medieval Latin, and Greek. ►

The formulas given for the pentoses and hexoses are called *open-chain formulas*. They were proposed by the great German chemist, Emil Fischer. Further study of the properties of these sugars, especially properties of sugars in solution, led to the conclusion that the carbonyl group of the sugars reacts with one of the alcohol groups. The reaction involves the shift of one hydrogen atom from an alcohol group to the carbonyl group, with the formation of a bond between the oxygen of the alcohol and the carbonyl carbon to give a ring structure. When it forms this ring structure the carbonyl carbon becomes asymmetric, and two isomers are possible. Rather than giving a totally new name to each form, we call these isomers the *alpha* (α) and *beta* (β) forms. These structures can be represented in either one or the other of the following ways.

β-D-glucose

α-D-glucose

or

β-D-glucose

α-D-glucose

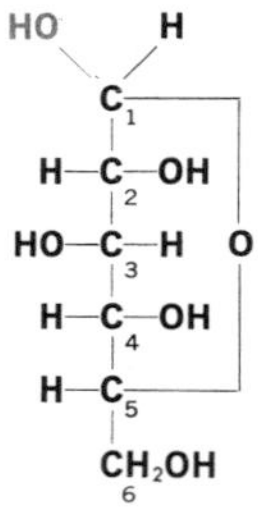

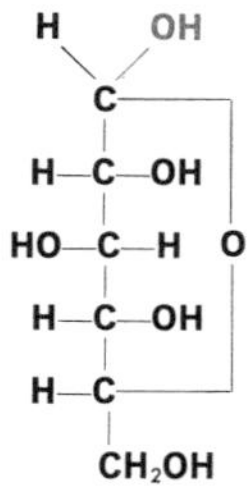

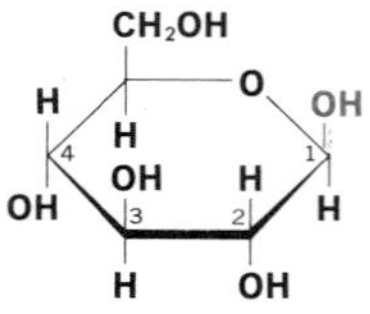

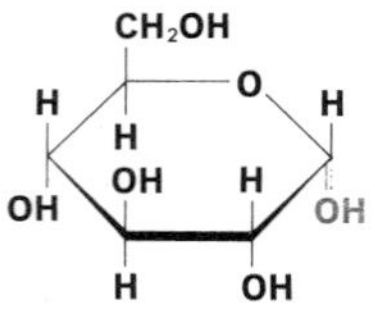

The two representations on the right are called *Haworth structures*. The most common forms of the monosaccharides (using the Haworth formulas) are

α-D-glucose

β-D-fructose

β-D-galactose

β-D-ribose

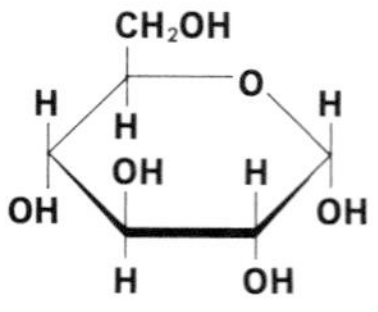

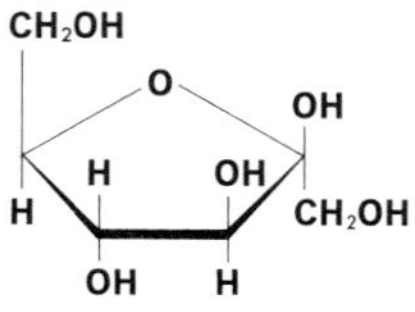

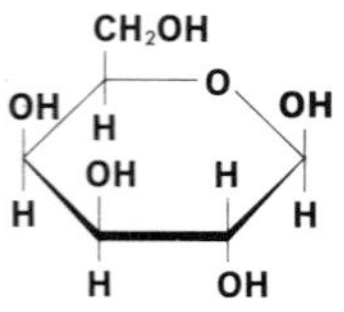

The monosaccharides as such are not found in any appreciable quantity in nature. A monosaccharide is usually found combined with other monosaccharides in the form of polymers called *polysaccharides*, such as starch or cellulose. In some cases, monosaccharides are combined with compounds other than carbohydrates, such as ribose is in ribonucleic acid (RNA).

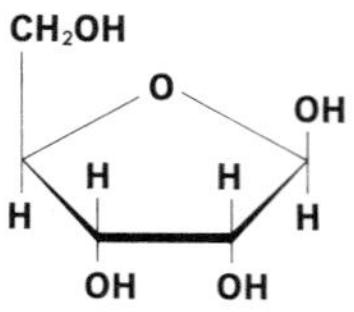

Many fruits, berries, and plant juices do, however, contain some free monosaccharides. Glucose was first found in grapes, which may contain as much as 27% glucose. However, most fruits contain much less glucose, and animals contain very little. The proportion of glucose in human blood, for example, is approximately 100 mg/100 ml. Even though the concentration is low, it must be maintained very near this level; persons with levels below normal go into *hypoglycemic* (low blood sugar) shock, and *hyperglycemia* (excess sugar in the blood) can result in coma.

Fructose, like glucose, is found in small quantities in many fruits. Honey contains relatively large amounts of both glucose and fructose. The other monosaccharides are generally found as components of other compounds.

Monosaccharides may be isolated from their natural sources by various extraction procedures. They are more commonly prepared by the hydrolysis of polysaccharides. Commercial preparation of glucose, for instance, is accomplished by the hydrolysis of starch. Although most of the monosaccharides have been synthesized in small amounts for theoretical purposes, such as the need to prove a certain structure or to establish the relationship of a given monosaccharide to other compounds, chemical synthesis is not commercially profitable.

Monosaccharides are colorless, crystalline solids. Crystallization is often difficult because of the presence of small amounts of impurities in the original solution. Since sugars are so similar to one another in chemical and physical properties, it is hard to separate them, and a small amount of fructose present as an impurity in a solution of glucose prevents formation of glucose crystals.

Solutions of sugars are viscous and have a sweet taste. While most of the common monosaccharides belong to the D-category, the actual (observed) rotation may be either to the right or to the left. Measuring the degree of rotation of plane-polarized light by a solution is a technique that may be used to find the amount of a sugar in the solution, provided only one sugar or only one optically active compound is present.

The chemical properties of monosaccharides are those of the aldehydes and the alcohols. Heat, catalysts, and strong acids, bases, or other reagents are usually required if we wish to observe these chemical properties in the laboratory.

Oxidation of Monosaccharides

Monosaccharides can be oxidized by hot alkaline solutions of certain metallic ions. In the process, the metallic ions are reduced. Since the sugars are the reducing agents, they are often referred to as **reducing sugars.** Such reactions are used to identify monosaccharides. Fehling's and Benedict's tests, for example, use an alkaline solution of copper (II). In both cases the test is positive if it results in a yellow or red compound of copper (I).

glucose $+$ Cu^{2+} $\rightarrow$ oxidized glucose $+$ Cu^{+}
**   (blue)   (yellow-red)**

These reactions can be adapted to test for the presence of glucose either in the urine or blood. A qualitative test is used on the urine of persons suspected to have diabetes. Quantitative tests (ones that tell how much of a substance is present) based on the reducing properties of sugars are routinely used to determine the concentration of glucose in blood. Tollens' test uses a solution containing silver ions (Ag^+). A test is considered positive if a silver mirror forms on the wall of the test tube. In fact, before aluminum was used as the reflective substance for mirrors, a reaction similar to Tollens' test was used in the manufacture of mirrors.

These oxidations usually convert glucose to a mixture of various oxidization products.

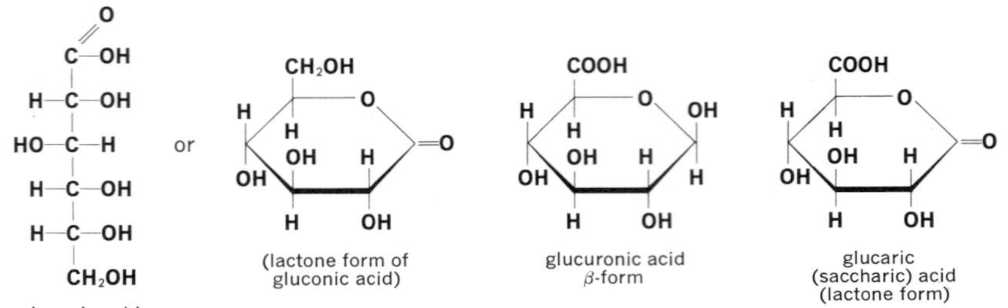

gluconic acid (Fischer formula)

(lactone form of gluconic acid)

glucuronic acid β-form

glucaric (saccharic) acid (lactone form)

Oxidization processes which are catalyzed by enzymes yield products in which specific alcohol or aldehyde groups are oxidized. Similar compounds result from the oxidation of other monosaccharides. Complete oxidation of monosaccharides yields CO_2 and H_2O.

Condensation of Monosaccharides

Two monosaccharide molecules can react to form a disaccharide.

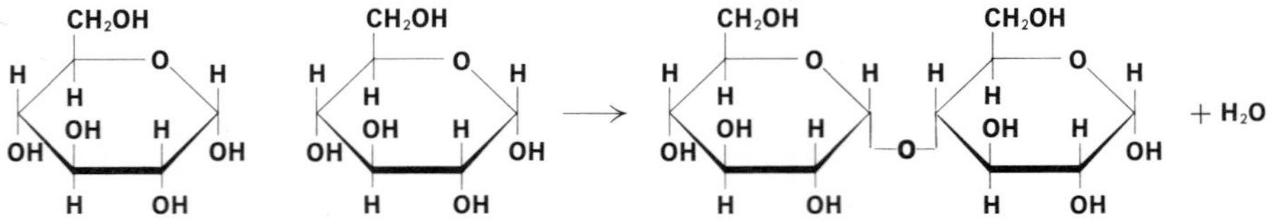

α-D-glucose α-D-glucose α-maltose

The most common bonding in such sugars is from carbon number 1 of one unit to the carbon number 4 of the other, as shown above. However, 1-6, 1-3, and other linkages are possible. If the carbon number 1 is in the alpha form (as illustrated), the linkage between the units is an **alpha linkage. Beta linkages** are formed when the beta form of the monosaccharide reacts. The product of the reaction of two molecules of β-glucose is β-cellobiose.

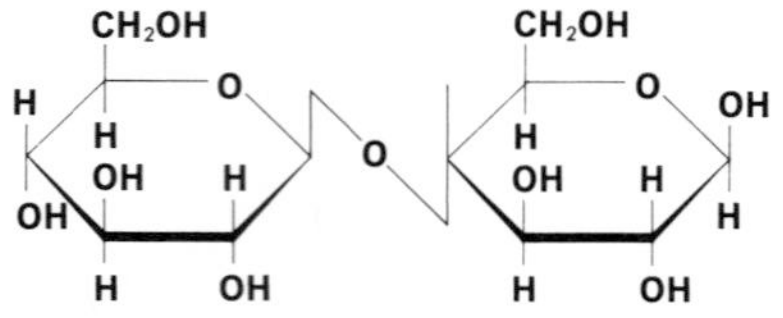

β-cellobiose

If this condensation process continues, trisaccharides, tetrasaccharides, and eventually, polysaccharides, may be formed.

Formation of Phosphate Esters

A structure of great biochemical importance is formed when either an alcohol or aldehyde group of a sugar is converted to a phosphate ester.

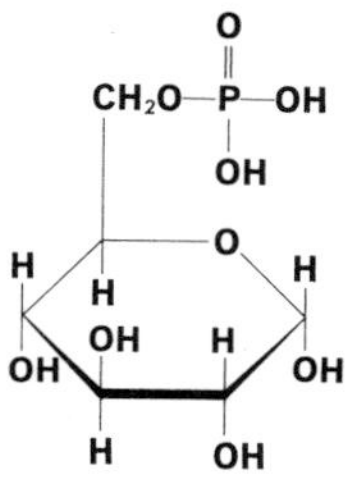

glucose-6-phosphate 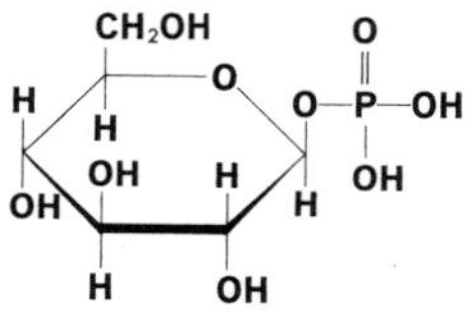   glucose-1-phosphate

For simplicity, the phosphate group is often indicated by the symbol Ⓟ as shown below.

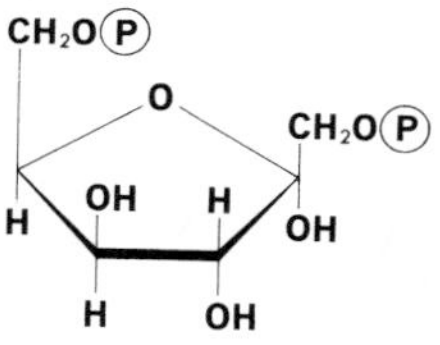

fructose-1,6-diphosphate 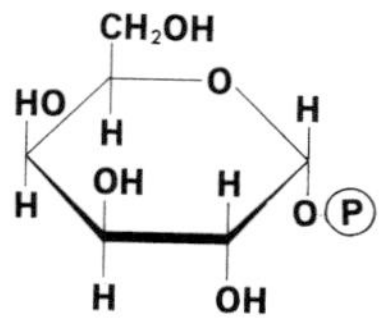   galactose-1-phosphate

In living organisms the source of the phosphate group in most such reactions is adenosine triphosphate (ATP) rather than phosphoric acid. In such reactions the ATP is converted to ADP (adenosine diphosphate).

glucose + ATP → glucose-6-phosphate + ADP

(See Chapter 36 for the formula for ATP.) The phosphorylation of glucose with ATP is probably the only important reaction of glucose in the human body.

33-3 COMPOUNDS RELATED TO MONOSACCHARIDES

Some compounds which are similar to carbohydrates do not fit the definition since they lack certain groups or contain others. Since these compounds are similar in structure to the monosaccharides and may occur as units in polymeric carbohydrates, they are usually included in a discussion of carbohydrates.

The compound 2-deoxyribose is found as a constituent of the deoxyribonucleic acids (DNA), which are important in the transmission of inherited characteristics. Other deoxy sugars are also known.

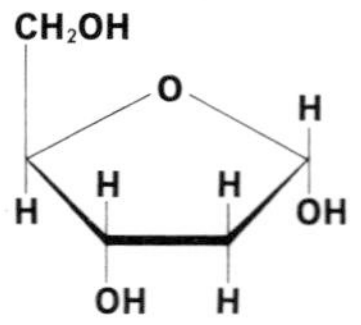

CH₂OH

2-deoxy ribose

Glucosamine is a compound having an amino group in place of the alcohol group on carbon 2 of glucose. It is an important component of the polymer that makes up the tough outer covering (exoskeleton) of insects. Those compounds which can be regarded as oxidized monosaccharides, such as gluconic and galacturonic acids, are components of polymers which will be discussed in greater detail in the section on polysaccharides.

33-4 OLIGOSACCHARIDES

Oligosaccharides are those carbohydrates which, when hydrolyzed, give two or more monosaccharide units. The prefix *oligo-* means few, and the upper limit of this classification is indefinite, but most authorities indicate that not more than ten or twelve monosaccharide units are found in oligosaccharides. While the number of possible oligosaccharides is great, only a few have been found in plants and animals. The most common oligosaccharides are the disaccharides.

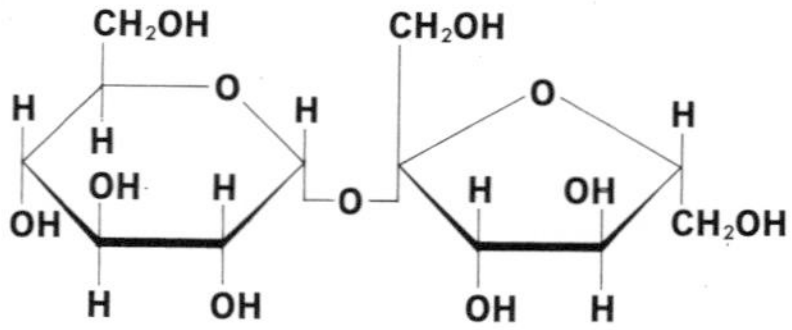

sucrose

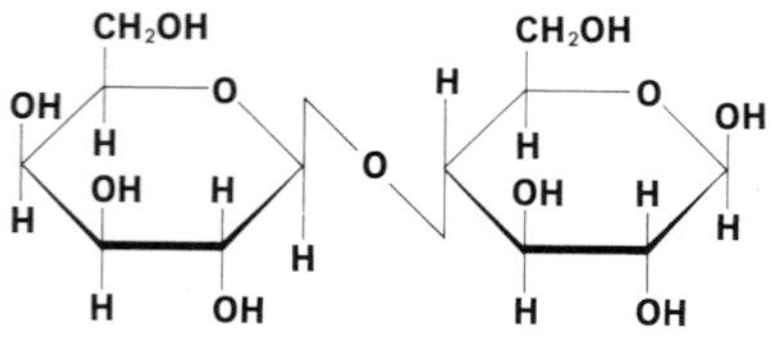

β-lactose

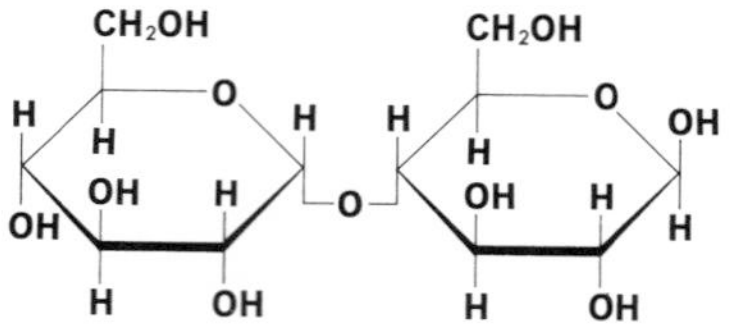

β-maltose

Sucrose is especially abundant in sugar beets, and in sugar and sorghum canes. It is also found in most common fruits and vegetables. Lactose is found primarily in milk. The milk from cows and goats is about 5% lactose; human milk contains from 6 to 7% of this sugar. The other disaccharides are not found in appreciable amounts in natural products. While tri- and tetra-saccharides are apparently present in many plants, they have not been studied extensively, and the higher oligosaccharides are apparently quite rare.

The disaccharides are obtained commercially by isolation from natural products. Sucrose is commercially important and has the distinction of being one of the few chemically pure substances that can be obtained in a grocery store. Maltose is present, along with other substances, in corn syrup which is made by the hydrolysis of corn starch. Maltose is also found in germinating seeds where enzymes have produced it from the polysaccharide, starch.

Biosynthesis of the disaccharides involves the synthesis of monosaccharides and finally the coupling of two monosaccharides (or their phosphate esters) to give the disaccharides. Only small amounts of disaccharides have been made this way in the laboratory; as with monosaccharides, the synthesis is not commercially feasible.

Both the chemical and physical properties of the disaccharides are similar to those of the monosaccharides. Table 33–1 shows the solubility and relative sweetness of common sugars. The measurement of sweetness involves the use of human tasters who determine the dilution that can be made before a solution no longer tastes sweet. Because they tend to form supersaturated solutions, the exact solubility of sugars is difficult to measure. It is interesting to note that there is a correlation between solubility and sweetness.

TABLE 33–1. Solubility and relative sweetness of sugars

	Solubility (g/100 ml of H_2O)	Sweetness
sucrose	179	100
glucose	83	74
galactose	10	32
fructose	very soluble	173
xylose	117	40
lactose	17	16
maltose	108	33
saccharin*	—	55,000

* Saccharin, which is not a sugar, is included for comparison.

Disaccharides can be hydrolyzed to give monosaccharides. This process is easily catalyzed by either strong acid or enzymes. The hydrolysis of sucrose is especially interesting. Since the aldehyde group of glucose and the ketone group of fructose are combined to make the bond between these two molecules in sucrose, there is no reducing group present, and sucrose does not reduce Fehling's or Benedict's reagents. After hydrolysis, however, molecules of glucose and fructose are present and the hydrolyzed solution is now "reducing." Since a mixture of fructose and glucose is actually sweeter than one of sucrose alone, hydrolysis of a solution of sucrose increases its sweetness.

Sucrose has an optical rotation of +66.5°; glucose has a rotation of +52.7°; and fructose, −93°. Consequently, when one molecule of sucrose is hydrolyzed to yield one each of glucose and fructose, the net rotation of the mixture is to the left. This change in rotation has been called inversion, and hydrolysis of sucrose is sometimes called **inversion of sucrose.** An equimolar mixture of glucose and fructose is called *invert sugar;* the enzyme which catalyzes this hydrolysis is often referred to as *invertase* instead of by its systematic name, *sucrase.*

Food preparation or cooking that involves exposing sucrose solutions to high temperatures under acid conditions produces hydrolysis. While this may make the food concerned a bit sweeter, it is more likely that the real purpose of the cooking is to produce a mixture of sugars. Such a mixture is less likely to crystallize (as when a jelly "sugars") than a pure solution.

Sucrose is commercially the most important of the disaccharides. It is an important item of world trade because of its desirability as a sweetening agent. Before the advent of synthetic noncaloric sweeteners, each person in the United States consumed an average of 100 pounds of sucrose per year. Although other countries consume less sucrose, more than 35 million tons are produced in the world each year. Approximately one-third of this sugar comes from beets and two-thirds from cane.

Lactose is found in the milk of mammals. It can be purified and has some commercial uses but has never been used as widely as a sweetener because of its low solubility and because it is not nearly so sweet as sucrose.

33–5 POLYSACCHARIDES

The polysaccharides, which contain many monosaccharide units linked together, are the most abundant carbohydrates. It is difficult to determine experimentally exactly how many such units there are in a polysaccharide chain. Molecular weights ranging from several thousand to values in the millions have been reported for various polysaccharides. It is generally assumed that the higher molecular weights represent the true molecular weight of the polysaccharide as it occurs in the plant, and that the lower weights are caused by degradation of the polymers during purification. However, we cannot totally disregard the possibility that some polymerization occurs during the purification process. Probably the best conclusion is that the number of units may vary somewhat without affecting the overall properties of the polysaccharide. There is a possibility that the molecular weight of a polysaccharide is characteristic of the species of plant or animal in which it is found.

One difference in structure which is of great biological significance is the one between the alpha- and beta-linked polysaccharides. Those polysaccharides containing the alpha form of monosaccharide units are much more digestible than β-linked polymers. Animals use α-linked starch as a major source of food, but only a few animals can digest the β-linked cellulose. Actually the cellulose-utilizing animals, such as cattle and sheep, and even the lowly termite, are able to use this β-linked polymer only because of microorganisms in their digestive tract which actually perform the hydrolysis of cellulose to glucose for them.

Compare the structures of starch and cellulose which are shown below:

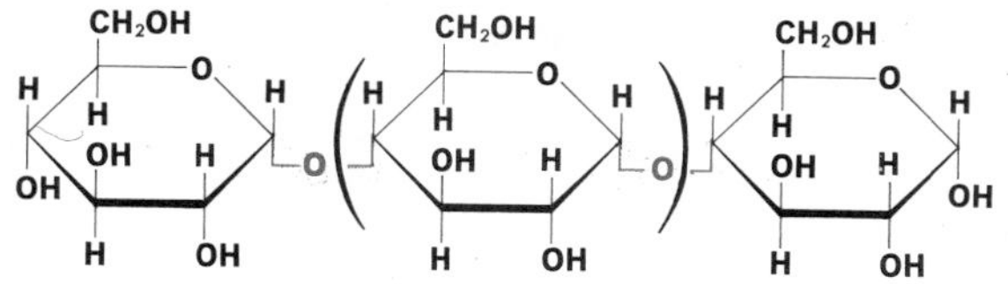

starch (α-linked)

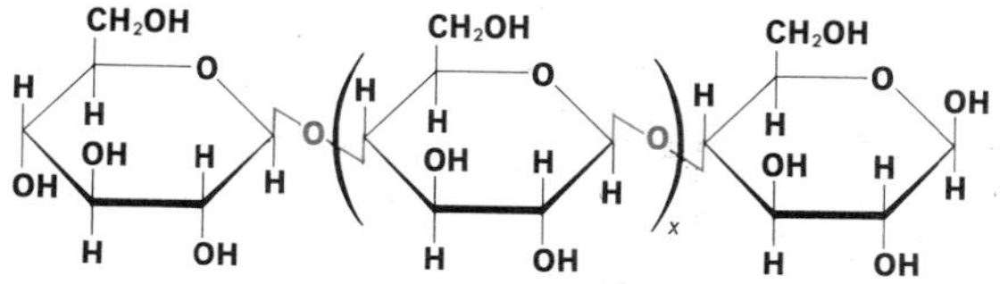

cellulose (β-linked)

The polysaccharides make up between 60% and 90% of the dry weight of plants, where they serve both as structural materials and as reserve food supplies. They are found in much smaller amounts, usually less than 1% of the total weight, in animals. Typical polysaccharides are starch, which may be obtained from the seeds and tubers of a variety of plants; cellulose, the structural material of plants; and glycogen, which is found in small amounts in animals.

The polysaccharides are noncrystalline, white solids which are only slightly soluble in water. In contrast to the mono- and oligosaccharides, the polysaccharides are not sweet-tasting. Nor are the polysaccharides very reactive chemically, both because of their insolubility and the fact that their most active groups (the aldehyde and ketone groups) are tied up in the linkage between monosaccharide units. Strong acids or enzymes are required to catalyze the hydrolysis of polysaccharides to give monosaccharide units.

Polysaccharides composed of pentose units are called **pentosans.** They are found in wood, straw, and leaves of plants. The gums from some trees are the richest sources of relatively pure pentosans. Pentosans are not very useful commercially since most animals cannot digest them; however, chemical degradation can give furfural which is used commercially for the manufacture of nylon and in the refining of petroleum.

The most important and abundant polysaccharides are polymers of the hexoses and are called **hexosans.** Glucose is the only monomeric unit of most of the abundant and important polysaccharides.

Starch

Various kinds of starch are found in the cereal grains and in many kinds of tubers. The starch from each type of plant has a characteristic form of granule. Experienced persons can tell the source of the starch by examining a sample microscopically (see Fig. 33–1).

Chemically, all forms of starch are quite similar; all are composed totally of glucose. Most sources of starch yield two fractions, amylose and amylopectin (Fig. 33–2). These two forms are very similar and separation is difficult. While both kinds of starch contain alpha 1-4 links between monosaccharide units, the amylopectin molecules contain many more glucose units, are highly branched (1-6 linkages), and are somewhat more soluble in water.

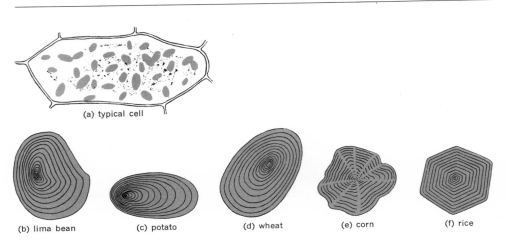

(a) typical cell

(b) lima bean   (c) potato   (d) wheat   (e) corn   (f) rice

FIG. 33–1. Characteristic starch grains. Starch grains are scattered throughout the cytoplasm of many plant cells. (a) In the sketch of a typical cell the starch grains are indicated as black bodies. Drawings of enlarged starch grains of typical plants are shown in (b) through (f). [Adapted from *Principles of Plant Physiology* by Arthur W. Galston and James Bonner. W. H. Freeman and Company. Copyright © 1952.]

The starches in the form of rice, potatoes, and wheat or cereal products supply about 70% of the world's food. In many cultures starch makes up much more than 70% of the diet, since most highly starchy foods are relatively inexpensive to buy or relatively easy to grow.

Glycogen

Glycogen is found in the liver and muscles of animals, and it is often called "animal starch." Glycogen is similar to the amylopectin fraction of starch in that it is made totally of glucose and is highly branched. Since animals do not synthesize starch, glycogen represents the only form in which they can store excess glucose. The total amount of glycogen in an animal is small; about 1% of the muscle and between 1.5 and 4% of the liver is glycogen. However, this small amount is extremely important in maintaining the correct level of glucose in the blood and in supplying the muscles with a source of energy.

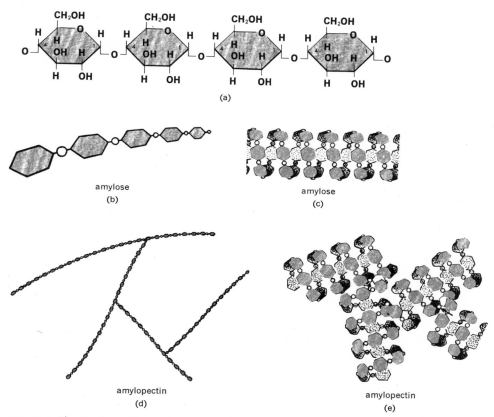

FIG. 33–2. The structure of the amylose and amylopectin components of starch. The structure of amylose can be represented as (a) or as simplified in (b). The three-dimensional structure of amylose is given in (c). A simplified representation of a part of a molecule of amylopectin is shown in (d), and a three-dimensional diagram of amylopectin is represented in (e). [Adapted from *Principles of Plant Physiology* by Arthur W. Galston and James Bonner. W. H. Freeman and Company. Copyright © 1952.]

Cellulose

Cellulose is the most abundant organic compound. It has been estimated that 50% of all carbon atoms in the vegetation on the earth is tied up in cellulose molecules. Like starch and glycogen, cellulose is made exclusively of glucose units, but unlike them, the glucose units are β-linked. This β-linked polymer of glucose is extremely tough and indigestible, and for this reason is an effective structural material both within plants and, in turn, for man who uses many materials which contain cellulose. The woody part of plants contain large amounts of cellulose. Cotton is 98% cellulose. Cellulose-containing materials such as lumber, cotton, and rayon (which is a chemically-modified cellulose) are important commercially.

Chitin

The tough outer covering of many insects and of crustaceans like crabs and lobsters is made of another β-linked polymer. In this instance, however, the monomeric unit is not glucose but glucosamine, and the substance is called chitin. Complete hydrolysis of chitin yields both glucosamine and acetic acid, and apparently the monomeric structural unit is N-acetyl glucosamine.

33-6 HETEROPOLYSACCHARIDES

Those polysaccharides discussed so far have been made of a single kind of monosaccharide. There are other polysaccharides which usually contain two different monosaccharides, and occasionally more than two monomeric units. These are the heteropolysaccharides. In many cases the linkage seems to be from the number 1 carbon of one unit to the 2, 3, or 6 carbon of the other unit, instead of the more common 1-4 linkage found in starch, glycogen, and cellulose. These materials have not been studied so extensively as the homopolysaccharides, but they seem to play important roles in the chemistry of living things. Among the more important heteropolysaccharides are the pectic acids, which are polymers of the uronic acids combined with other substances. They are responsible for the solidity of many fruits, and are used commercially in making jams and jellies. Another group comprises the mucopolysaccharides which are usually found associated with proteins. The principal products obtained following hydrolysis of these polysaccharides are the amino sugars and the "uronic" acids. Some examples of substances which contain mucopolysaccharides are heparin, a naturally occurring anticoagulant of blood; cartilage; and hyaluronic acid which has been called the "cement" or ground substance between cells.

33-7 SUMMARY

The carbohydrates are found primarily in polymeric form in the structural parts of plants. Although the basic monosaccharide unit contains the relatively active aldehyde or ketone group, these groups are involved in linking the monosaccharide units into the polymeric form and do not influence the chemical properties of the polysaccharides to any extent. The way in which monosaccharides are linked determines not only the shape of the polymer, but also influences the possibility of hydrolyses that are catalyzed by enzymes. The β-linked polysaccharides, particularly cellulose, are insoluble, tough polymers that are not attacked by most digestive enzymes of animals.

The more active, relatively soluble monosaccharides function as intermediate compounds in the breakdown and synthesis of polysaccharides. The monosaccharides formed from the hydrolysis of polysaccharides are a major source of energy for the life of all animals. The concentration of glucose in the blood of animals is of major significance. Without the monosaccharide, glucose, life as we know it would not be possible.

IMPORTANT TERMS

Aldose	*Hexose*	*Oligosaccharide*	*Sugar*
Carbohydrate	*Hyperglycemia*	*Pentose*	
Cellulose	*Hypoglycemia*	*Polysaccharide*	
Glycogen	*Ketose*	*Starch*	

WORK EXERCISES

1. Define the following terms: ketotetrose, triose, aldopentose, octulose, deoxysugar.

2. Draw the structural formulas for (a) all possible aldopentoses (indicate asymmetric carbon atoms with asterisks); (b) L-glucose; (c) a trisaccharide; (d) two galactose molecules with a β-1-4 linkage between them; (e) a molecule of glucosamine linked β-1-3 to a molecule of β-glucuronic acid.

3. Explain what is meant by (a) D (−) fructose, (b) a reducing sugar, (c) a β-linkage between monosaccharides.

4. Using structural formulas write equations for

   a) the hydrolysis of sucrose,

   b) the complete oxidation of glucose, of gluconic acid, of glucaric (saccharic) acid.

5. How is a fruit jelly that has been boiled for ten minutes different from the uncooked mixture of ingredients?

6. What is the nutritional significance of the β-linkage between the units of a polysaccharide?

7. What reason might be deduced for the fact that starch does not taste sweet?

8. Benedict's test is used to see whether glucose is present in the urine of persons with *diabetes mellitus*. During the period of time a mother produces milk after the birth of a child, she may excrete lactose or galactose in the urine. Would urine containing either lactose or galactose give a positive Benedict's test?

9. Consult a general biochemistry text to find the following:

   a) the formulas for mucopolysaccharides not given in the previous chapter,

   b) the names and formulas of hexoses other than glucose, galactose, mannose, and fructose.

Chapter 34 PROTEINS

34-1 INTRODUCTION

Many important parts of the body are largely made of protein. Muscle, blood, and the nonmineral part of bone are protein. The enzymes, those vital catalysts without which biological reactions would be too slow to support life, are also proteins.

The first definition of proteins was given in Gerardus Johannes Mulder's *General Physiological Chemistry*, published in 1844–1851:

"There is present in plants as well as animals a substance which . . . performs an important function in both. It is one of the very complex substances, which under various circumstances may alter their composition, and serves . . . for the regulation of chemical metabolism . . . It is without doubt the most important of the known components of living matter, and it would appear that, without it, life would not be possible. This substance has been named protein."

While Mulder was investigating the compounds that he finally called **protein,** apparently the name (derived from the Greek word *proteios,* which means of the first rank or importance), was suggested to Mulder in 1838 by the great Swedish chemist, J. J. Berzelius.

Later, more precise studies of the substance Mulder called protein indicated that it was not just one substance as he and others believed, but that it was composed of many substances, each differing slightly from the others. When faced with complexities of this sort, scientists can discard the classification, but they usually try to save it by separating and classifying the individual members of the group. By 1907 the British Physiological Society proposed a classification of proteins based on solubility. The new classification included

1) albumins: proteins soluble in water and salt solutions;

2) globulins: proteins slightly soluble in water, soluble in dilute salt solutions;

3) prolamines: proteins insoluble in water, but soluble in 70–80% ethanol;

4) glutelins: proteins insoluble in water and ethanol, but soluble in acid or base,

5) scleroproteins: proteins insoluble in aqueous solvents.

Other classifications could be added to this list, but only the first two names, albumin and globulin, are still widely used to describe types of proteins.

While classification of proteins by solubility was relatively easy and provided the basis for a simple classification, it did not give real insight into the nature of proteins. Elemental analysis had shown that proteins contained nitrogen. This knowledge was useful in describing proteins but was not adequate for defining them, since many other biochemical substances also contained nitrogen. Modern biochemists know that the formula for lactoglobulin, the globulin obtained from milk, is approximately $C_{1864}H_{3012}N_{468}S_{21}O_{576}$. Since this is a representative protein, not really one of the larger ones, it is easy to see that writing the formula for a protein is both cumbersome and probably useless as a device for describing or understanding the nature of these compounds.

How, then, can we characterize the proteins? We saw that the hydrolysis of carbohydrates gives certain basic building blocks, the monosaccharides. What happens when we hydrolyze proteins? When hydrolysis is done under acid conditions we get a mixture of about twenty different amino acids. All proteins so treated give a similar mixture. Some proteins give other substances also, but they *all* give amino acids. Here, then, is the common characteristic of proteins—amino-acid building blocks. Our current definition of proteins is that *they are high-molecular weight substances which, upon hydrolysis, yield amino acids.* Any attempt to understand the nature of proteins, therefore, must begin with a discussion of the amino acids.

34–2 AMINO ACIDS

The amino acids, as their name implies, are organic compounds which contain both an acid and an amino group. There are hundreds of possible amino acids, but only twenty are found in appreciable quantities in proteins. These are all α-amino acids—that is, the amino group is on the α carbon—the carbon next to the carboxyl carbon. A list of the formulas and names of some of the common amino acids is given in Fig. 34–1.

◄ Except for those amino acids containing an additional acid group which are named as acids, the names of amino acids end in the suffix -ine.

Cystine was first found in bladder stones in 1810. Its name is derived from the Greek *kystis*, meaning a pouch or bladder. Cystine is one of the least soluble amino acids and is still occasionally found in the form of stones in the urinary bladder.

The simplest amino acid, glycine, was one of the first to be isolated by hydrolysis of proteins. Since it has a slightly sweet taste, it was named from the Greek word for sweet, *glykys*.

When leucine was isolated as white, glistening plates, its name was chosen as a derivative of *leukos*, the Greek word for white. Isoleucine was named for its structural analogy to leucine.

The silk protein sericin (from the Latin word for silk) yields large amounts of serine. Cheese (*tyros* in Greek) was the first source of tyrosine. The amide asparagine is found in asparagus, and its hydrolysis product is aspartic acid. Arginine was named because it forms silver (L., *argentum*) salts. Proline derives its name from its chemical similarity to pyrrolidine; valine is named for its similarity to valeric (pentanoic) acid; and glutamic acid for its similarity to the dicarboxylic acid, glutaric acid. ►

Although small quantities of amino acids are found in the blood after the digestion of a protein-containing meal, they are found primarily in the form of their polymers, the proteins. It is from the naturally occurring proteins that commercial quantities of amino acids are produced. Plants can synthesize amino acids from ammonia and carbon dioxide. Animals, however, have to use larger units for making amino acids, and usually take an amino group from one compound and transfer it to a keto-acid. Green plants can synthesize all the amino acids they require for the production of protein, but most animals can make only approximately half of the amino acids they require. Consequently, they must get the others from their diet to build the proteins of muscles, enzymes, and blood components.

An interesting, but commercially unfeasible, process for synthesizing amino acids was discovered by Miller and Urey, working at the University of Chicago. They were able to find very small quantities of amino acids after passing an electric spark through a mixture of methane, ammonia, water, and hydrogen. Other experimenters have proved that the gases used as starting materials can be varied somewhat and that very small amounts of amino acids are relatively easy to produce. These experiments are interesting because the gases used, often called the *primitive* gases, are the ones we believe are present in the atmospheres of the other planets, and were the ones probably present on the primitive earth. These experiments indicate a way amino acids may have been synthesized on a lifeless earth. Even more important, these discoveries led to the realization that amino acids are stable compounds and that any reactions that supply large amounts of energy to hydrogen compounds of carbon, nitrogen, and oxygen are likely to synthesize amino acids.

◄ By adding hydrocyanic acid (HCN) to mixtures of primitive gases, pyrimidine and purine bases like those of the nucleic acids can be produced. When phosphates are also present, ATP can be produced. When phosphates are also present, ATP can be produced. Other researchers have produced protein-like substances by heating mixtures of amino acids with phosphate or other catalysts. Methane, carbon dioxide, hydrogen, and ammonia are prevalent in the atmospheres of the planets of our solar system and HCN has been detected in the tails of comets. Thus, we could predict that we should find most of the building blocks of life in materials from the surface of Mars and perhaps from moon dust which, we hope, our astronauts will bring back soon. Chemical analysis of these materials is an exciting prospect. ►

FIG. 34–1 (pp. 469–473). The common amino acids. The names, symbols, R-groups, and a photograph of a Courtauld space-filling model are given for the common amino acids. The R-groups are indicated in color. [Adapted from Snell, Shulman, Spencer, and Moos, *Biophysical Principles of Structure and Function*, Addison-Wesley, 1965.]

Name	Symbol	R-group	Model
Glycine	Gly	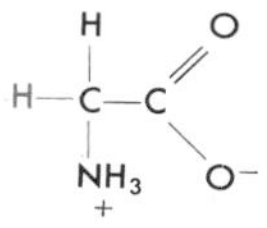	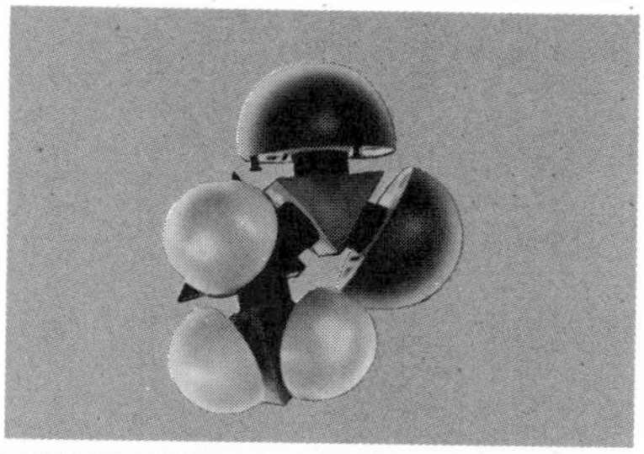
Alanine	Ala	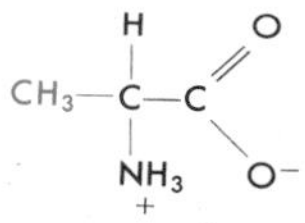	
Valine	Val	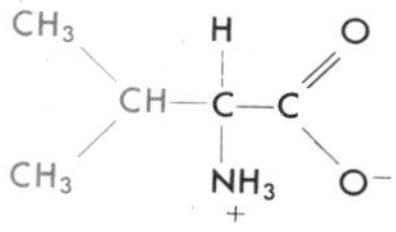	
Leucine	Leu	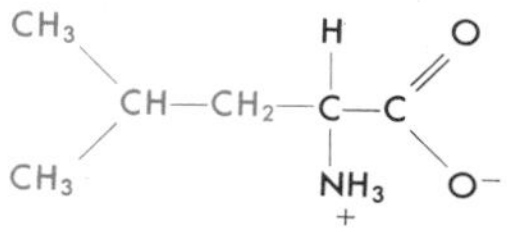	
Isoleucine	Ileu or Ile	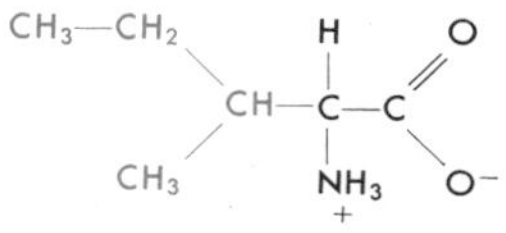	

Name	Symbol	R-group	Model

Serine   Ser

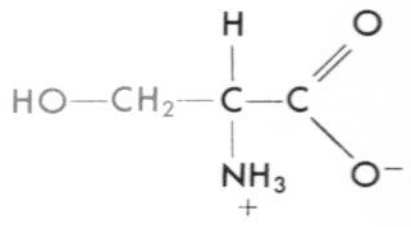

$$HO-CH_2-\overset{\overset{\displaystyle H}{|}}{\underset{\underset{\displaystyle NH_3^+}{|}}{C}}-\overset{\overset{\displaystyle O}{\parallel}}{C}-O^-$$

Threonine   Thr

$$\overset{\displaystyle HO}{\underset{\displaystyle CH_3}{}}CH-\overset{\overset{\displaystyle H}{|}}{\underset{\underset{\displaystyle NH_3^+}{|}}{C}}-\overset{\overset{\displaystyle O}{\parallel}}{C}-O^-$$

Phenylalanine   Phe

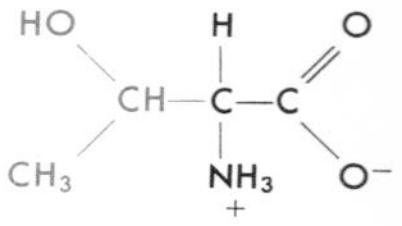

$$-C-CH_2-\overset{\overset{\displaystyle H}{|}}{\underset{\underset{\displaystyle NH_3^+}{|}}{C}}-\overset{\overset{\displaystyle O}{\parallel}}{C}-O^-$$

Tyrosine   Tyr

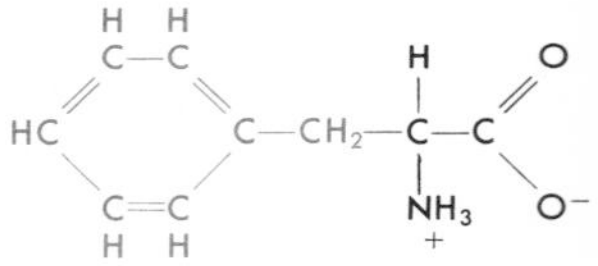

$$HO-C-\ \cdots\ -C-CH_2-\overset{\overset{\displaystyle H}{|}}{\underset{\underset{\displaystyle NH_3^+}{|}}{C}}-\overset{\overset{\displaystyle O}{\parallel}}{C}-O^-$$

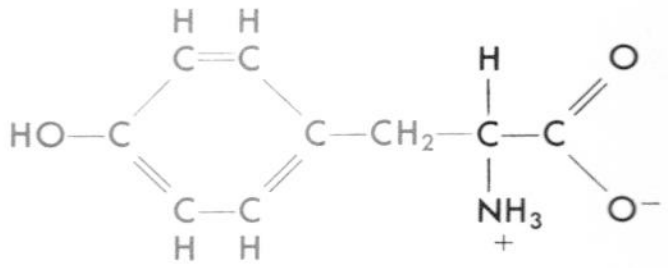

Tryptophan   Try

$$-C-CH_2-\overset{\overset{\displaystyle H}{|}}{\underset{\underset{\displaystyle NH_3^+}{|}}{C}}-\overset{\overset{\displaystyle O}{\parallel}}{C}-O^-$$

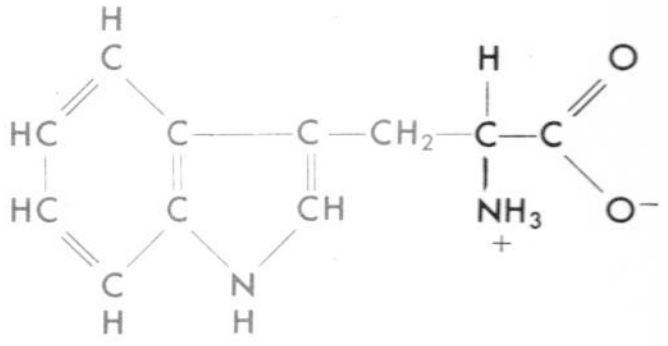

Name	Symbol	R-group	Model

Cystine   (CyS)$_2$

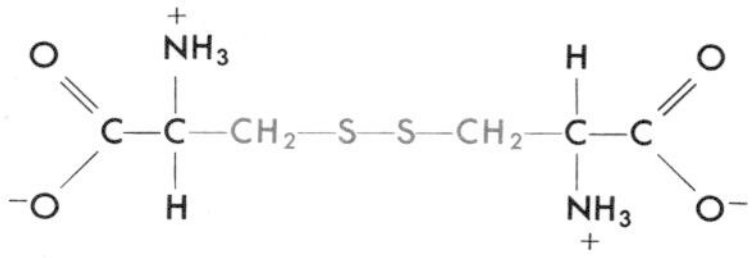

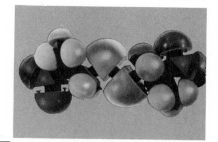

Cysteine   CySH

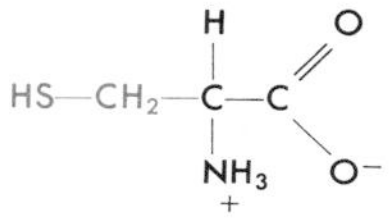

HS—CH$_2$—C with H, C=O, O$^-$, NH$_3^+$

Methionine   Met

CH$_3$—S—CH—CH$_2$—C with H, C=O, O$^-$, NH$_3^+$

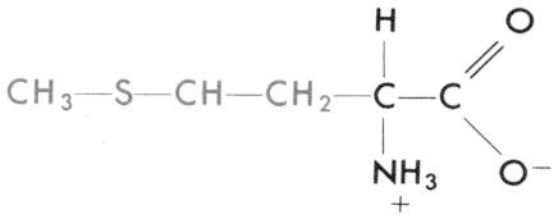

Proline   Pro

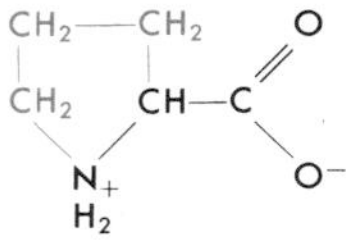

Hydroxyproline   Hyp

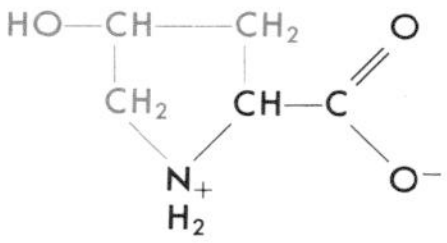

Name	Symbol	R-group	Model
Aspartic Acid	Asp		
Glutamic Acid	Glu		
Asparagine	Asp-NH$_2$ or Asn		
Glutamine	Glu-NH$_2$ or Gln		
Histidine	His		

Name	Symbol	R-group	Model
Arginine	Arg		

$$H_2N$$
$$C-NH-CH_2-CH_2-CH_2-\overset{\overset{\displaystyle H}{|}}{C}-\overset{\displaystyle O}{C}$$
$$H_2N \qquad\qquad\qquad \underset{+}{NH_3} \quad O^-$$

| Lysine | Lys | | |

$$\underset{+}{H_3N}-CH_2-CH_2-CH_2-CH_2-\overset{\overset{\displaystyle H}{|}}{C}-\overset{\displaystyle O}{C}$$
$$\underset{+}{NH_3} \quad O^-$$

Physical Properties of the Amino Acids

The amino acids are white, crystalline solids, and most are quite soluble in water. They have relatively high melting points for compounds of low molecular weight. These properties suggest that the amino acids resemble the inorganic salts and probably exist as polar molecules. Measurement of the properties of amino acids in solutions confirms the fact that they are indeed charged molecules and also that their charge may change from negative to positive or vice versa with changes in the acidity of the solution. This change in charge is accompanied by a change in chemical and physical properties. At pH values near neutral, most amino acids have both a negative and a positive charge, and thus are dipolar ions. In acid solutions they tend to have a proton attached to their negative group and are cations, while in basic solutions they are usually anions. The pH at which a protein will not migrate when placed in an electrical field is called the *isoelectric point.* (See Fig. 34–2) The isoelectric point is the pH at which the negative charges on the protein molecule exactly balance its positive charges. This point varies for the different amino acids and provides a method of separating one amino acid from all others, or at least all others having different isoelectric points.

ionic forms of the amino acid alanine

in an acid solution   in a neutral solution   in a basic solution

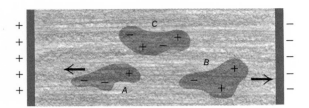

FIG. 34–2. Migration of charged particles in an electric field. This drawing shows how various amino acids or protein molecules can be separated by electrophoresis. Substance A which has an excess of negative charges migrates toward the anode; substance B has an excess of positive charges and thus is a cation. Substance C, although it has charged groups, has equal numbers of positive and negative charges and will not migrate when placed in an electrical field. Substance C is at its isoelectric point.

Since amino acids take up hydrogen ions (protons) in acid solutions and release them in basic solutions, they resist changes in the pH of a solution and are good buffers. The alpha carbon of amino acids usually has four different groups attached to it. We could predict, therefore, that the amino acids are optically active. This is indeed true with most of the naturally occurring amino acids having the L-configuration.

Chemical Properties of the Amino Acids

Several biochemical reactions are common to all amino acids. Among these are formation of peptide bonds, transamination, oxidative deamination, and decarboxylation.

When the amino group of one amino acid reacts with the acid group of another amino acid, a compound called a **peptide** is formed. The group

$$
\begin{array}{c}
\quad\ \ \text{O} \\
\quad\ \ \parallel \\
-\text{C}-\text{NH}-
\end{array}
$$

is called the *peptide bond*. It is a substituted amide bond.

$$
\underset{\text{alanine}}{
\begin{array}{c}
\text{O} \\
\parallel \\
\text{C}-\text{O}^{(-)} \\
| \\
\overset{\oplus}{\text{H}_3\text{N}}-\text{C}-\text{H} \\
| \\
\text{CH}_3
\end{array}}
\ + \
\underset{\text{glycine}}{
\begin{array}{c}
\text{O} \\
\parallel \\
\text{C}-\text{O}^{(-)} \\
| \\
\overset{\oplus}{\text{H}_3\text{N}}-\text{C}-\text{H} \\
| \\
\text{H}
\end{array}}
\ \longrightarrow \
\underset{\text{alanylglycine}}{
\begin{array}{c}
\text{O} \quad\ \text{H} \ \ \overset{\text{O}}{\overset{\parallel}{\text{C}}}-\text{O}^{(-)} \\
\parallel \quad\ | \quad | \\
\text{C}-\text{N}-\text{C}-\text{H} \\
| \qquad\quad \text{H} \\
\overset{\oplus}{\text{H}_3\text{N}}-\text{C}-\text{H} \\
| \\
\text{CH}_3
\end{array}}
\ \ \text{or} \ \
\underset{\text{glycylalanine}}{
\begin{array}{c}
\text{O} \quad\ \text{H} \ \ \overset{\text{O}}{\overset{\parallel}{\text{C}}}-\text{O}^{(-)} \\
\parallel \quad\ | \quad | \\
\text{C}-\text{N}-\text{C}-\text{H} \\
| \qquad\quad \text{CH}_3 \\
\overset{\oplus}{\text{H}_3\text{N}}-\text{C}-\text{H} \\
| \\
\text{H}
\end{array}}
$$

In addition to the two dipeptides given above, alanylalanine, glycylglycine, or tri-, tetra- or polypeptides may be produced whenever two amino acids react to produce peptides. The *chemical* synthesis of a specific peptide is difficult; it usually requires that the amino group of one amino acid and the carboxyl group of the other one be "blocked" so that only one reaction takes place. The *biological* synthesis of peptides is more specific and often gives only one product because of those remarkable catalysts—the enzymes. Although there is only one peptide bond in alanylglycine, the compound is called a **dipeptide.** Three amino acids, when combined, give a **tripeptide.** The combination of many amino acids gives first polypeptides, and finally the extremely high-molecular-weight compounds, the proteins.

The structure of peptides may be indicated by names, as was done for alanylglycine. A shorter method is routinely used, however, whereby the three-letter symbols for each amino acid, Fig. 34–1, are strung together. It is understood that the free amino group is at the left end and the free carboxyl group at the right. However, the symbols (NH_2) and (COOH) can be used for unambiguous presentation. Thus alanylglycine is shown as ala · gly or (H_2N) ala · gly (COOH).

The reaction of an amino acid with a keto acid in the presence of an enzyme called a transaminase gives a different amino acid and a different keto acid. The process is called **transamination** since the amino group is transferred from one carbon chain to another one.

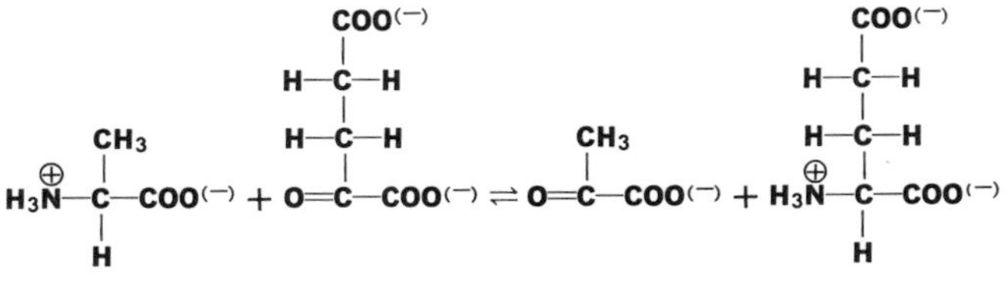

alanine α-ketoglutaric   pyruvic   glutamic
                  acid   acid   acid

The reaction is easily reversible, and at equilibrium there are appreciable quantities of both reactants and products. This reaction provides a method for synthesis of amino acids when the corresponding keto acid is available. Although it is generally said that certain amino acids are essential, i.e., they cannot be synthesized in a given animal, it is really the keto acid or the basic carbon skeleton which is essential. The reaction given above shows that either glutamic acid or alanine can be synthesized when α-ketoglutaric acid or pyruvic acid are present along with a source of amino groups. Since α-ketoglutaric acid, pyruvic acid, and amino groups are common in the bodies of animals, glutamic acid and alanine are synthesized by most animals and, therefore, are not essential amino acids.

Amino acids may also be converted to keto acids by the process of **oxidative deamination.** This is a two-step process which involves first a loss of two hydrogen atoms, followed by the addition of a molecule of water. (For simplicity, the formulas for the amino acids are written in a non-ionic form.)

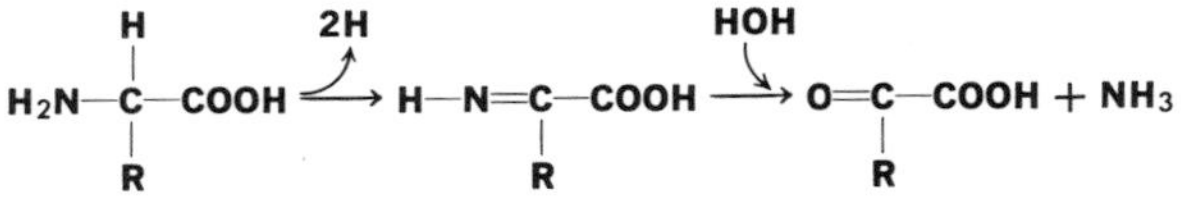

Unlike transamination, this series of reactions is not readily reversible. The overall reaction releases appreciable amounts of energy from the amino acid, and the reverse reaction cannot serve as a source of amino acids in animals. A process essentially the reverse of this, **reductive amination,** is used by plants for synthesis of amino acids.

Amino acids may react to produce carbon dioxide and an amine by the process of **decarboxylation.**

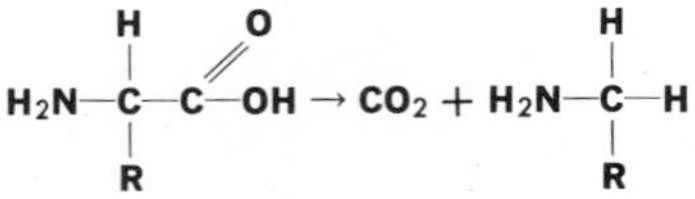

$$H_2N-\overset{\overset{\displaystyle H}{|}}{\underset{\underset{\displaystyle R}{|}}{C}}-\overset{\overset{\displaystyle O}{\|}}{C}-OH \rightarrow CO_2 + H_2N-\overset{\overset{\displaystyle H}{|}}{\underset{\underset{\displaystyle R}{|}}{C}}-H$$

The extent to which such reactions occur in humans is probably slight, but histamine may be synthesized from histidine in this way. Histamine produces allergic reactions and promotes the motility of the stomach. The decarboxylation products of lysine and ornithine give the vile-smelling amines which have been given the expressive names of putrescine and cadaverine.

In addition to the general reactions which can occur with all amino acids, there are specific reactions. These are reactions of the side chain of the amino acid. Some illustrations are given below.

The hydrolysis of arginine to give urea and ornithine is a major source of urea in animals. Urea, which is found in the urine, is the major nitrogen-containing excretion product of the metabolism of amino acids. (See Chapter 39–5.)

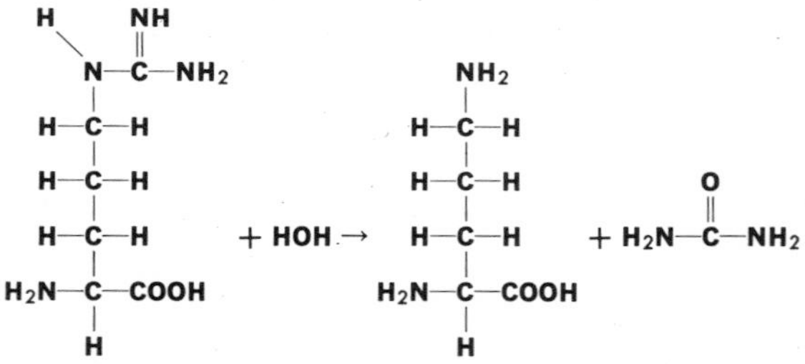

arginine   ornithine   urea

Two molecules of cysteine can be oxidized to form the disulfide cystine. This reaction is important in forming cross linkages between polypeptide strands in proteins. Mild reducing conditions can convert cysteine to cystine.

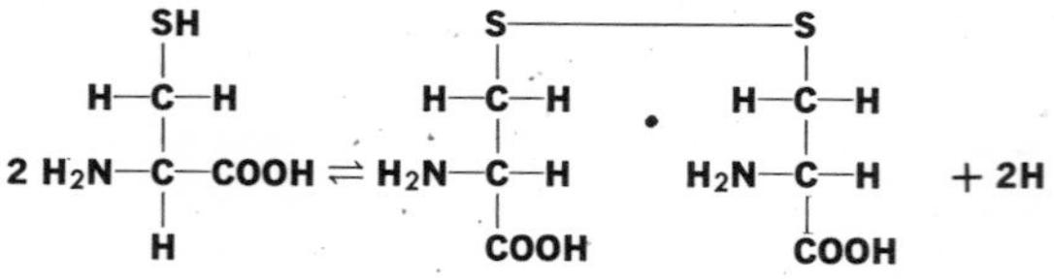

cysteine   cystine

A combination of general and specific reactions occurs in the conversion of the amino acid phenylalanine to the hormone epinephrine which is also known as adrenalin. This conversion involves a series of reactions and illustrates how a normal dietary component is converted to a substance of vital importance to the continued life of the animal.

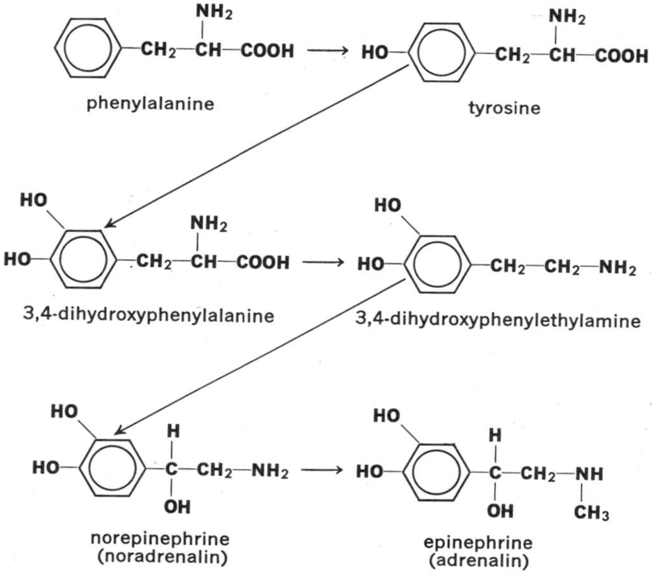

Although amino acids can be converted to many relatively simple compounds which are of vital importance, their major function is to serve as building blocks for proteins.

34-3 PROTEINS

Compounds characterized as proteins are found throughout all living things. Muscles which are major structural material in all animals are proteins. While blood is about 80% water, the remaining 20% is largely protein. Almost all biochemical reactions require enzymes as catalysts if they are to proceed at a rate sufficient to maintain life. The enzymes may contain other compounds, but they are basically protein. The nucleic acids-which form an important part of the hereditary material in the nucleus of the cell and which occur in the viruses are always found in close association with specific types of protein. Even the nonmineral matrix of the bone is protein. It has been estimated that probably 700 different proteins are known and that between 200 and 300 have been studied. Approximately 150 proteins have been obtained in crystalline form. These figures will, no doubt, soon be much too low as research in the area of protein chemistry continues.

While some proteins are extremely stable, such as those found in the hide of cattle which can be converted to a tough, durable leather, others are very delicate. Merely passing a current of air through a solution of some enzymes is sufficient to alter them so much that they can no longer function as catalysts. The protein hemoglobin is remarkable for its ability to bind oxygen strongly enough so that it can be carried from the lungs to all parts of the body, and then to release the oxygen (and pick up carbon dioxide) in the tissues. The alteration of only 1 of the amino acids—in the more than 150 found in one of the polypeptide chains of hemoglobin—from a glutamic acid to a valine unit changes the properties of hemoglobin drastically. Persons having this altered hemoglobin (called sickle-cell hemo-globin) instead of normal hemoglobin suffer from sickle-cell anemia which is a fatal disease. This and other hereditary diseases are discussed in greater detail in Chapter 42.

The principal problem of protein chemistry is to explain in terms of structure or physical and chemical properties just how the proteins function.

The Structure of Proteins

The exact boundary between polypeptides and proteins is not precisely defined. However, it is generally accepted that 100 or more amino acids must be in the chain for a peptide to be called a protein. (See Fig. 34-3)

Although the strongest bond between the amino acids in a protein is the peptide bond, experimental evidence indicates that there are other bonds holding the chains of amino acids to one another. This bonding is similar to the cross-linking which is found in many synthetic polymers. Hydrogen bonds and disulfide bonds have been shown to be responsible for forming these cross-links in protein molecules. Hydrogen bonds are found between a keto group of one chain and an amino group (and its hydrogen) of another chain, and between the side chains of some amino acids. Disulfide bonds are formed when a cysteine molecule in one chain reacts with the cysteine molecule of another chain.

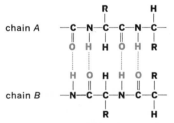

hydrogen bonds between amino acid chains

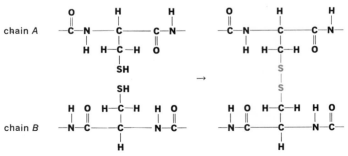

formation of disulfide bonds between protein chains

FIG. 34–3. A pentapeptide. The structure of this peptide is shown in the diagram and models of two of its possible configurations are shown above the diagram. [Adapted from Snell, Shulman, Spencer, and Moos, *Biophysical Principles of Structure and Function*, Addison-Wesley, 1965.]

Hydrogen bonds are weak and are easily ruptured. They are important, however, since there are so many of them in each protein molecule. Disulfide bonds are covalent bonds and are much stronger. There are probably other types of cross-linkages between polypeptide chains, such as secondary peptide bonds (between an amino acid which as an additional acid group and one which has an amino group in its side chain). Bonds which involve the linkage of the —OH groups of two serines by a phosphate group may also be present.

While cross-linkages can form between two separate chains, it is also possible for bonds, particularly hydrogen bonds, to form between the proper groups in a single chain. This type of linkage causes the chain to coil into a spiral or helix. X-ray diffraction studies indicate that many proteins exist in this helical form. Recent studies of the structure of the proteins hemoglobin and myoglobin indicate that part, but not all, of their structure is in the spiral form. Studies of insulin indicate that the helical structure is present there to only a small extent. (See Figs. 34–4, 34–5, and 34–6.)

Hydrogen bonds between polypeptide chains are relatively easy to break. Many procedures of protein chemistry probably involve changing the number and nature of hydrogen bonds between chains. The disulfide bonds are harder to break. Most of the processes for "permanent waving" of the hair involve first the rupture and then the reestablishment (in different relative positions) of disulfide bonds in the proteins of hair.

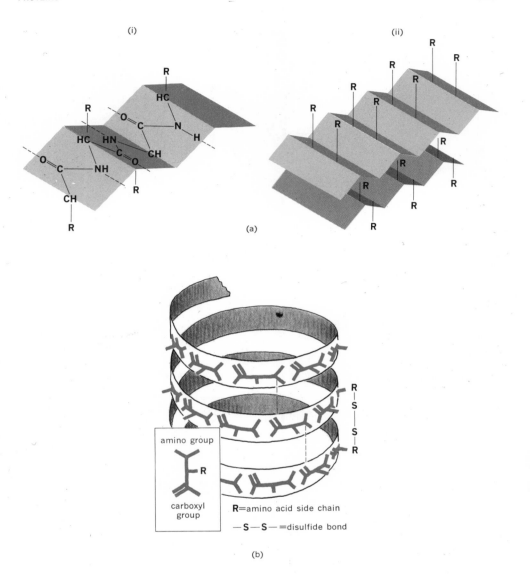

FIG. 34–4. Three-dimensional forms of polypeptides. Peptide chains in proteins are held together by secondary bonds, especially hydrogen bonds. Two forms of protein structures that are known to exist are the pleated sheet shown in (a) and the alpha-helix shown in (b). In (a), the pleated sheet form, the chains are linked together by the hydrogen bonds between the carbonyl groups of one chain and the amino groups of the other. Because of the natural bond angles, a structure such as this forms a pleated sheet. Several sheets may be held together as shown on the right. [Adapted from Setlow and Pollard, *Molecular Biophysics*, Addison-Wesley, 1962.] The alpha-helix shown in (b) represents another possible configuration of a polypeptide chain. The dotted lines between amino acid units represent hydrogen bonds. The covalent disulfide bonds are also shown. Other bonds are possible. X-ray diffraction studies show that many proteins contain the alpha-helix in parts of their structure. [Adapted from Baker and Allen, *Matter, Energy, and Life*, Addison-Wesley, 1965.]

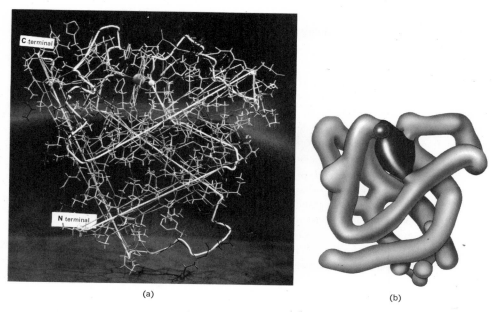

(a)

(b)

FIG. 34–5. The protein myoglobin: (a) photograph of a model of myoglobin from the sperm whale, (b) drawing of a molecule of myoglobin. In (b) the dark, disc-shaped portion is the heme group. [Photograph courtesy of Professor John C. Kendrew, drawing adapted from Epstein, *Elementary Biophysics*, Addison-Wesley, 1963.]

FIG. 34–6. The protein hemoglobin. Each of the four subunits of hemoglobin contains one heme group. The *a*-chains are represented in white; the *b*-chains in black. The model on the left shows two black *b*-chains and one white *a*-chain. The basic peptide backbone is shown by the white and black lines. The model on the right shows the complete hemoglobin molecule containing two *a*-chains and two *b*-chains. Two heme groups are shown; the other two are on the opposite side of the molecule. In this model oxygen is shown attached to the heme groups. [From *Nature* **185,** 416 (1960). Photographs courtesy of Dr. M. F. Perutz.]

Protein Synthesis

Because of their great complexity and of the difficulties involved in synthesizing individual dipeptides and tripeptides, proteins have not yet been chemically synthesized. Insulin, which contains 51 amino acids, has been synthesized, however, as has ACTH which contains 39 amino acids, but these substances are near the polypeptide-protein border of classification. The immense amount of time and labor that is required for the synthesis of insulin means that except for special purposes, such syntheses are not feasible.

Proteins are, of course, synthesized by all living things. This process again is complex since it involves the linking of hundreds of specific units in a specific way. It can be calculated that there are approximately 1.35×10^{167} (135 followed by 165 zeros) possible arrangements of the amino acids found in the relatively small protein molecule of hemoglobin. This number is much greater than the number of atoms in the universe. The ability of a cell to synthesize just the right kind of proteins is truly remarkable.

The process of protein synthesis *in vivo* is under hereditary control. Although some of the details remain to be discovered, it now appears that the master plan for protein synthesis is found in the DNA (deoxyribonucleic acid) in the nucleus of the cell. This plan or code is transferred to the RNA (ribonucleic acid) which actually serves as the pattern for the extremely complex task of making just the right kind of protein. Several hereditary disorders are now known in which an individual is unable to synthesize one kind of protein. In some anemias there is a change in only one amino acid in the hemoglobin molecule. A similar "inborn error of metabolism" is responsible for the condition known as phenylketonuria which, if untreated, produces idiocy in persons with the defect. The deficiency in this case is in a specific enzyme required for the metabolism of the amino acid phenylalanine. (See Chapter 42 for a further discussion of these hereditary defects.)

Physical Properties of Proteins

From the large molecular weights of the proteins, which range from about twelve thousand to hundreds of thousands, we would expect these molecules to be insoluble in water. Many proteins are, in fact, insoluble in water, but many very important ones are quite water soluble. This solubility is probably due to the charged nature of the protein molecule. Although most of the amino and acid groups are tied up in the peptide bond, other groups of the amino acids (their side chains) are often in a charged state. The additional acid groups in glutamic acid and aspartic acid, the amino groups in lysine and arginine, as well as other side chains can be charged. As with the primary amino and acid groups, the state of charge of the side chains depends upon the pH of the solution. When the net charges on a protein are at a minimum, i.e., when the negative charges are equal to the positive charges, the protein will not migrate when placed in an electrical field. The process of placing a protein solution on paper or some other relatively inert substance and allowing the proteins present to migrate toward the anode or cathode is called electrophoresis (see Fig. 34–2). This technique is used to separate individual proteins from mixtures. It is now finding wide application for studying the various proteins in blood serum. (See Fig. 34–7.)

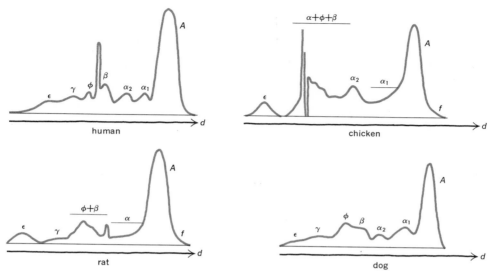

FIG. 34–7. Electrophoretic patterns of the blood plasma from the human, the rat, the chicken, and the dog. Albumin is identified by an A, fibrinogen by ϕ, and the various globulins by the letters, α, β, γ, and ϵ. [Adapted from an article by H. F. Deutsch, *J. Biol. Chem.*, **161**, 1, 1945.]

The pH value at which a protein will not migrate when placed in an electrical field is called its **isoelectric point.** This is the point of minimal solubility for that protein. We can make use of such knowledge in separating it from other proteins, or in helping us decide which protein (or proteins) are present in a solution.

Chemical Properties of Proteins

The chemical reactions of the proteins—particularly those of greatest importance—are difficult to study. In most cases only a relatively small part of the huge protein molecule is actually changed or undergoes a reaction. It is now believed that only a small part of the molecule of an enzyme, called its active site, is involved when the enzyme catalyzes a reaction. The combination of the iron-containing protein hemoglobin with oxygen is believed to involve the iron atom and one of the histidine molecules in the protein chain. Biochemists are only beginning to understand the true nature of the chemical reactions of proteins. More knowledge in this fascinating area will bring us much closer to understanding the chemical nature of living processes.

Other, *in vitro*, chemical reactions of proteins are used for their identification and characterization. In some cases a colored product is produced, as in the xanthoproteic reaction in which proteins are treated with nitric acid, or in the biuret test which uses a copper salt in conjunction with a basic solution of the protein. Other tests involve the

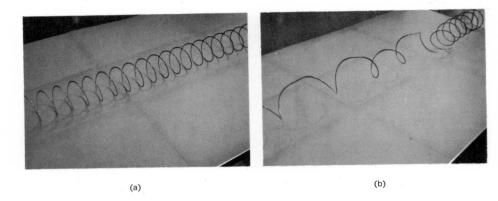

(a)   (b)

FIG. 34–8. Denaturation of proteins. (a) The coiled spring toy known as a "slinky" is used to represent the helical structure of a protein. When the elastic limit of the helix is exceeded, the shape is irreversibly altered as shown in (b). This is analogous to irreversible denaturation of a protein. [From Baker and Allen, *Matter, Energy, and Life,* Addison-Wesley, 1965.]

precipitation of the protein by heat or salts. A simple method for differentiation of the albumins from the globulins is based on the fact that the former stay in solution and the latter precipitate when in a solution that is half saturated with ammonium sulfate.

Most of these reactions used to identify proteins result in the gross alteration of the protein. The term **denaturation** has been used to describe these changes. While there is some disagreement as to the use of the term denaturation, it is best defined as *any change in any property of a protein that does not involve rupture of the basic peptide bonds.* Some of these changes can be reversed, as when a globulin that has been "salted out" of solution is redissolved. Others, such as the heat treatment of egg albumin, cannot be reversed, i.e., you can't "unboil" an egg. (See Fig. 34–8.) Some biochemists restrict the definition of denaturation to those processes which are irreversible. Denaturation, of course, causes a loss of biological activity.

Purification of Proteins

The purification of proteins has played an important role both in the study of these vital compounds and in the uses of the purified substances. Before determining the composition of a protein, the chemist must be sure that it is pure, i.e., that he has only one specific protein. The study of the exact nature of catalysis by enzymes also requires pure substances. Since any foreign protein that is injected into an organism usually produces antibodies to that protein, it is essential that any material that is to be injected be highly purified. For these reasons it is necessary that insulin, which is used to treat diabetes, and the polypeptide ACTH, which is sometimes used to treat local inflammations, as well as many other proteins be as pure as possible. Oral administration of proteins is ineffective since digestion breaks them down into individual amino acids.

Protein purification is based on a knowledge of the physical properties of the proteins. The proteins may be separated from lipids and carbohydrates on the basis of their solubility and of their charged state. If relatively crude materials are used, the material is first fractionated by spinning it in a centrifuge. Proteins have different solubilities. The differential solubility of the various proteins in salt solutions or in solutions containing organic solvents such as ethanol or acetone form the basis for many separations. Other purifications can be made by passing the material through a column of a chromatographic absorber which utilizes the differences in affinity of the various proteins for the adsorbent. Electrophoresis uses the difference in migration rate of proteins as influenced by their charged state which is, in turn, influenced by the pH of the solution. This method is useful in purifying relatively small amounts of proteins. (See Fig. 32–1.) All purification procedures particularly those with organic solvents, are preferably done at low temperatures and with the use of other precautions to prevent irreversible denaturation of the protein. Since proteins are large molecules, they can be separated from salts and other small soluble molecules by dialysis. In this process a sac of semipermeable membrane retains the protein while the smaller particles escape into a surrounding liquid. By using a variety of these techniques it is possible to separate the proteins of blood so that dried serum or gamma globulin become available for medical uses.

Importance of Proteins

Proteins play many vital roles in the living organism. Their importance in enzymatic catalysis, as oxygen carriers, and as structural materials have already been mentioned. While it is impossible in an elementary text to discuss all the important functions of proteins, a few more significant ones are given below.

Since animals synthesize their body proteins from amino acids, and especially since they can synthesize only half of these amino acids, it is extremely important that their diets include adequate amounts of the ones that are not made in their own bodies. The major source of these essential amino acids is the proteins of the diet. One of the greatest nutritional problems is that much of the world's population does not eat enough of the kind of protein that provides the critical amino acids. This topic is discussed further in Chapter 41, "Nutrition."

In addition to hemoglobin, the blood contains many other proteins. There are albumins which serve to maintain sufficient osmotic pressure to help water and other nutrients pass freely through the walls of the capillaries. The particular kind of globulin that has been called gamma globulin constitutes one of our major supplies of antibodies for resisting some diseases. The proteins fibrinogen and prothrombin are essential for the formation of the clump of red blood cells called a clot. Clotting is useful when it prevents excessive loss a blood, but clots can also form in the blood vessels of the heart or brain, causing a type of heart attack or stroke.

Many of the hormones which serve as important regulators of the processes of the body are proteins. Most of the hormones of the master gland, the pituitary, are protein-containing. Two of them, vasopressin and oxytocin, are octapeptides; others are either glycoproteins (compounds containing both protein and carbohydrate) or pure proteins. The widely used

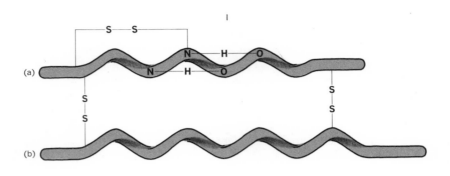

II [the primary sequence of amino acids]

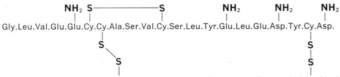

FIG. 34–9. Two representations of the structure of insulin. The lower diagram shows the sequence of amino acids in two protein chains called the a- and b-chains. These two chains are linked together with disulfide bonds. The upper representation is a drawing of the insulin molecule showing both the disulfide bridges and possible hydrogen bonds. The disulfide bridge in the a-chain links two parts of that chain and does not serve to bind two polypeptide chains together as do the other disulfide bonds. [Adapted from C. B. Anfinsen, *The Molecular Basis of Evolution*, Wiley and Sons, New York, 1963, second edition.]

hormone, insulin, contains 51 amino acids and may be classed as either a large polypeptide or a very small protein (See Fig. 34–9). The discovery and extraction of insulin and its use in the treatment of diabetes makes a dramatic chapter in the story of man's conquest over disease. Thousands of persons, whose days would have been limited, now live normal lives because large quantities of highly purified insulin are available. The use of a growth hormone has met with only limited success. Further study and purification of other hormones can be expected to lead to longer and better lives for some of those persons who today suffer from hormone insufficiency.

The importance of proteins in our lives may be traced from the time a sperm cell (made up of nucleic acids and proteins) unites with an ovum. In animals, the fertilized egg develops through stages of differentiation which are largely influenced by a succession of enzymes, to the birth of the individual. Birds' eggs, which provide nutrition for the embryo birds, are especially rich in proteins. The gradual growth of a person is due to the increase in bone and muscle under the control of the proteinaceous hormones and with the help of the enzymes. The production of new sperm and ova under the influence of other protein-containing hormones leads to the perpetuation of the species. The continued life and health of the individual depends on sufficient nutrition by proteins (along with other foods) and on his ability to manufacture sufficient enzymes to catalyze the essential reactions and sufficient antibodies to resist infections. The failure of any of these protein-influenced systems or, in some cases, the overactivity of some of these processes leads to the death of the individual.

While the importance of other classes of compounds cannot be forgotten, Mulder's statement that protein "is without doubt the most important of the known components of living matter, and it would appear that, without it, life would not be possible" is still true.

The basic ideas in the following statement are still valid, although the quotation is from a book published in 1959 and is already perhaps out-of-date because of the rapid progress being made in biochemistry.

"In essence, the problem of protein chemistry is to explain the special physiological functions of these large complex molecules in terms of their structure. Since no protein has yet been synthesized, the approach to these problems consists largely in examination of the parts of the molecules and probably arrangement of these parts in individual proteins, and the chemical and physical behavior of the intact proteins. These problems are formidable and present tremendous technical difficulties because of the enormous diversity and complexity of proteins. Nevertheless, the rewards to be gained are rich ones, for, with an understanding of the chemistry of the proteins, we can begin to approach the fundamental objective of all the biological sciences, the explanation of the properties of living matter in physical and chemical terms."*

IMPORTANT TERMS

Albumin	Electrophoresis	Hemoglobin	Polypeptide
Amino acid	Essential amino acid	Hormone	Protein
Deamination	Gamma globulin	Peptide	Salting out
Decarboxylation	Globulin	Peptide bond	Transamination
Denaturation			

WORK EXERCISES

1. List the common dicarboxylic amino acids.
2. List the common amino acids containing more than one amino group.
3. What functional groups other than the carboxyl and amino groups are found in the side chains of proteins?
4. List several natural products that are primarily or largely composed of protein.
5. Write all possible charged states of cystine, of glutamic acid, of lysine.

---

* Abraham White, et al., *Principles of Biochemistry*, 2nd ed., McGraw-Hill, New York.

6. Write equations for each of the following reactions and name all the products of the reactions.

   a) the reaction of glycine and serine to form a dipeptide
   b) the transamination of alanine with alpha ketoglutaric acid
   c) the decarboxylation of histidine, of ornithine
   d) the complete hydrolysis of lysylphenylalanylasparagine
   e) the oxidative deamination of aspartic acid, of alanine

7. Write the structures for glycylcysteinylalanine and for threonylcysteinylproline, and show possible cross-linkages between these peptides.

8. Write the complete structure for the peptides indicated below:
   a) (H_2N)-tyr-ala-ser(COOH)   b) (H_2N)-gly-gly-met-phe(COOH)

9. Why is insulin injected rather than taken orally in the treatment of diabetes?

10. A substance containing the elements C, H, O, N, and S, having a high molecular weight, was dissolved in water. Addition of sufficient ammonium sulfate to make the solution 50% saturated did not result in precipitation of the substance. What can you conclude about the substance? What test or tests would be necessary to confirm your identification?

11. From a general biochemistry text (see list at the end of Chapter 32) find the answer to the following:

   a) What is the structure of glutathione?.
   b) List several dipeptides of biological importance.
   c) Using the simplest method possible, write the complete structure of ribonuclease and of insulin.

SUGGESTED READING

Altschul, A. M., *Proteins, Their Chemistry and Politics*, Basic Books, New York, 1965. As indicated in the title, this book discusses both the chemical characteristics of the proteins and their importance in world food problems.

Although the following four articles are slightly outdated, they present basic discussions of the important aspects of proteins.

Doty, P., "Proteins," *Scientific American*, Sept. 1957 (Offprint #7).

Fruton, J. S., "Proteins," *Scientific American*, June 1950 (Offprint #10).

Pauling, L., R. B. Corey, and R. Hayward, "The Structure of Protein Molecules," *Scientific American*, July 1954 (Offprint #31).

Stein, W. H. and S. Moore, "The Chemical Structure of Proteins," *Scientific American*, Feb. 1961 (Offprint #80).

In the following, the stories of the determination of the structure of the proteins, insulin, myoglobin, hemoglobin, and the polypeptide ACTH, are told by the workers who were active in this research. The illustrations in these articles are excellent.

Kendrew, J. C., "The Three-Dimensional Structure of a Protein Molecule," *Scientific American*, Dec. 1961 (Offprint #121).

Li, C. H., "The ACTH Molecule," *Scientific American*, July 1963 (Offprint #160).

Perutz, M. F., "The Hemoglobin Molecule," *Scientific American*, Nov. 1964 (Offprint #196).

Thompson, E. O. P., "The Insulin Molecule," *Scientific American*, May 1955 (Offprint #42).

Phillips, D. C., "The Three-Dimensional Structure of An Enzyme Molecule," *Scientific American*, Nov. 1966. This article not only discusses the structure of a protein as do those above, but has the added fascination of discussing the structure in terms of the way in which this enzyme works as a catalyst.

Chapter 35   CHEMISTRY OF THE LIPIDS

35–1 INTRODUCTION

If we separate the water, carbohydrates, and proteins from a cell or from a total organism, the major component left is **lipid.** In practice the procedure used is just the opposite of that given above—the lipids are separated from all other biochemical materials by extracting them in ethyl ether, ethanol, chloroform, or similar solvents or mixtures of these solvents. This procedure is the basis for our definition of lipids as *biochemical substances that are soluble in nonpolar organic solvents.* The lipids are commonly known as fats; biochemists, however, reserve the name "fat" for one particular kind of lipid.

Since lipids are defined in terms of solubility, and since many types of compounds are soluble in the lipid solvents, we find the lipids include many, heterogeneous compounds. They are not made of one particular kind of building block as are the proteins and carbohydrates, and almost no lipids are really polymers.

35–2 CLASSIFICATION OF LIPIDS

Since the lipids lack a really basic building block, the only way to study the lipids systematically is by a classification based on solubility and hydrolysis products. As you may expect, there are different systems of classifications. It is especially difficult to classify those lipids that yield two or more characteristic hydrolysis products. The following classification is widely accepted and is sufficient for a basic understanding of the lipids:

a) triglycerides   b) phospholipids (phosphatides)   c) waxes
d) steroids   e) terpenes   f) miscellaneous

TABLE 35–1. Common fatty acids

SATURATED ACIDS

Name	Formula	Common Source
acetic acid	CH_3COOH	vinegar
butyric acid	C_3H_7COOH	butter
caproic acid	$C_5H_{11}COOH$	butter
caprylic acid	$C_7H_{15}COOH$	butter
capric acid	$C_9H_{19}COOH$	butter, coconut oil
lauric acid	$C_{11}H_{23}COOH$	coconut oil
myristic acid	$C_{13}H_{27}COOH$	coconut oil
*palmitic acid	$C_{15}H_{31}COOH$	animal and vegetable fats
*stearic acid	$C_{17}H_{35}COOH$	animal and vegetable fats
arachidic acid	$C_{19}H_{39}COOH$	peanut oil
lignoceric acid	$C_{23}H_{47}COOH$	brain and nervous tissue
cerotic acid	$C_{25}H_{51}COOH$	beeswax, wool fat

UNSATURATED ACIDS

Name	Formula	Number of Double Bonds	Common Source
*palmitoleic acid	$C_{15}H_{29}COOH$	1	animal and vegetable fats
*oleic acid	$C_{17}H_{33}COOH$	1	animal and vegetable fats and oils
linoleic acid	$C_{17}H_{31}COOH$	2	linseed oil, vegetable oils
linolenic acid	$C_{17}H_{29}COOH$	3	linseed oil
arachidonic	$C_{19}H_{31}COOH$	4	brain and nervous tissue

* Acids indicated with an asterisk are among the most widely distributed.

The placement of a lipid in one of the categories above depends primarily on its hydrolysis products. Although there are many kinds of molecules in these hydrolysis products, as would be expected in a group of compounds defined only in terms of solubility, there is more similarity than one might expect. In fact, we find present in lipids relatively few of the thousands of possible organic compounds. This natural economy comes about because of the great similarity in synthetic pathways in different organisms. We must not forget that the composition of biochemical substances is the result of the synthetic processes in plants and animals.

The most common hydrolysis products or building blocks of the lipids are the mono-carboxylic organic acids which are commonly called the fatty acids. Of all possible fatty acids, we find that only those having an even number of carbon atoms occur to any appreciable extent. Although there is some variation as to the number of double bonds (degree of unsaturation) in these acids, branched chains and ring compounds are rare in the fatty acids. The commonly found fatty acids are given in Table 35–1.

◄.The word *acid* is derived from the Latin *acere*, meaning to be sour, and is a good description of many acids. The term is appropriate, for example, for acetic acid, but it becomes less accurate as the chain-lengths increase, thus decreasing solubility and ionization so that the higher fatty acids do not taste sour. In addition, the vile odors and tastes of some of the fatty acids far overshadow their sourness. The higher fatty acids, oleic and stearic, are a fatty oil and a rather slippery solid, respectively, and the name fatty is an adequate description, but the term *acid* indicates only that the acid group (—COOH) is found in all these molecules. These are weak acids; the hydrogen is only slightly ionized; and the acids are not sour.

The Latin word for vinegar is *acetum*, and thus acetic acid is appropriately named as the sour substance from vinegar. Butyric acid derives its name from its source, butter, which is *butyrum* in Latin. Caproic, caprylic, and capric acids are vile-smelling acids which can be found in rancid butter, especially that made from goats' milk. These acids are also responsible for the odor associated with goats, so their derivation from the Latin, *caper* or *capri*—which means goat—is fitting. It should be emphasized that while in an esterified form, particularly in a triglyceride, these acids do not have their characteristic odors. Normally these acids are found as essentially odorless esters; it is only when bacteria and molds act upon butter and cheese that the vile odors are produced. Small amounts of these acids in cheeses such as Camembert and Roquefort are not objectionable to many, but actually add to the flavor.

Lauric acid, which is found in coconut oil, is also obtained from berries of the laurel, *Laurus nobilis*, for which it is named. Palmitic acid is named for the source of the coconuts from which it is extracted—the palm tree. Before the characterization of palmitic acid, the name palmic acid was used to describe a component of castor oil, so the slightly more complex name, palmitic, was coined for the fatty acid.

The Greek word, *stear*, is used to designate stiff fat or tallow which is derived from beef animals, one variety of which we call a steer; so we get the name stearic acid for the acid found in beef fat. Arachidic acid was found originally in peanut oil; the generic name of the peanut plant, *Arachis hypogoea*, which itself was derived from the Greek, *arachos*, meaning a legumi-nous weed, was used in naming two C_{20} acids, arachidic and arachidonic acids. Although biochemists think of lignoceric acid as being found primarily in the brain and nervous tissues, its isolation from beechwood tar led to the derivation of its name from *lignum*, the Latin word for wood, and *cera*, which is Latin for waxy. The name cerotic acid is listed as being derived from the Greek word *keros* meaning waxy, but the Latin word is similar, and describes a waxy acid—one found, in a combined form, in beeswax.

Oleic acid, which is found in so many oils, derives its name from the Latin, *oleum*, which means oil. Linoleic and linolenic acids are named by combining the prefix lin- from the Latin word for flax, *linum*, and oleum. The names reflect the source of these acids, linseed oil, which is made from the seeds of the flax plant. Palmitoleic is an obvious hybridized name for a sub-stance having characteristics of palmitic (16 carbons) and oleic (one double-bond) acids.

Obviously, the names of the fatty acids have been derived almost directly from their sources. It should perhaps be emphasized that they are not present as free acids but in the form of esters, primarily glycerol esters, in their natural sources. ▶

In addition to the fatty acids, certain other components are found in many lipids. The more common are glycerol, choline, and aminoethanol.

glycerol   choline   aminoethanol

Other lipids contain structural units which are related to isoprene. The isoprene units exist both in chain form

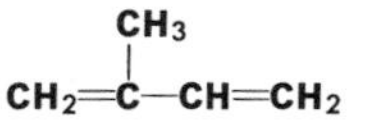

$$CH_2{=}\overset{\overset{\textstyle CH_3}{|}}{C}{-}CH{=}CH_2 \quad \text{isoprene}$$

and in a ring structure as in β-carotene.

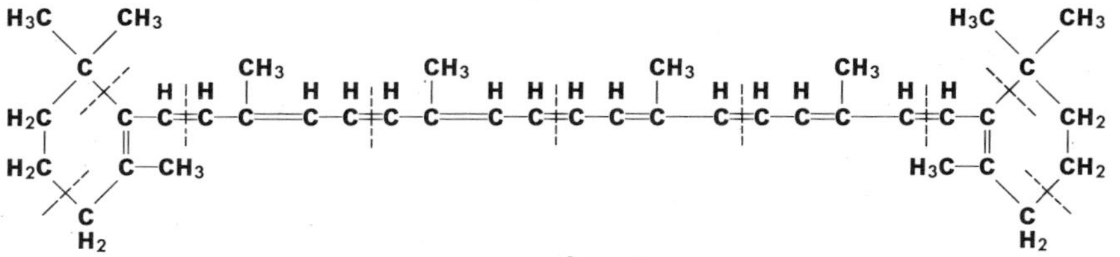

β-carotene

The dotted lines indicate isoprene units in this complex structure. Rubber is a polymer made of isoprene units, Eq. (30–6). Although it is more difficult to see, the complex structure known as the steroid nucleus contains several isoprene units. The biological synthesis of cholesterol involves the combination of several such units.

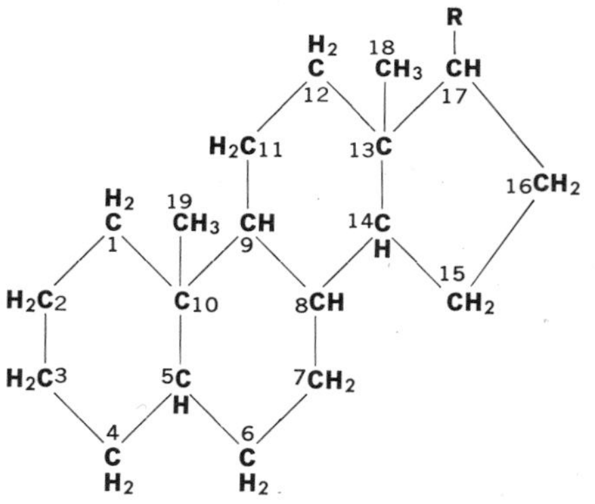

steroid nucleus 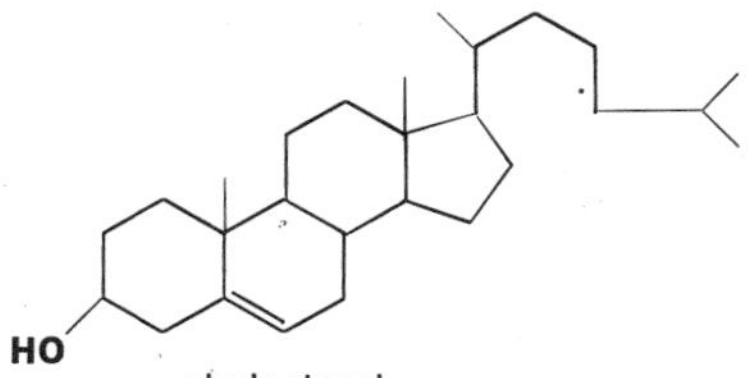   cholesterol

35–3 TRIGLYCERIDES

The name triglyceride is used by biochemists to describe those esters of glycerol which contain three fatty acids. The triglycerides, which are commonly called the fats and oils, are the most abundant lipids. Animals accumulate fats when their food intake exceeds energy output. Although plants accumulate some fats and oils, particularly in their seeds, they usually store excess energy in the form of carbohydrates. The basic chemistry of the glycerides was discussed in Chapter 27. Here we will add details that are of special interest to biochemists.

The separation of most fats and oils from their natural sources usually involves only a physical process. Olive and cottonseed oils are separated by pressing, and butter by churning cream which contains the butterfat. Lard is separated from various fatty tissues of the swine by heating to melt the fat which is then filtered while hot to remove it from proteins and carbohydrates. In biochemical preparations, fats are usually extracted, along with the other lipids, by adding a mixture of organic solvents (usually ethanol and ethyl ether) to a natural product. Triglycerides are then separated from the other lipids by the use of other solvents, and finally by saponification. Since many lipids are not esters, they are not subject to alkaline hydrolysis (saponification). Consequently they may be separated from the soaps (which are water soluble) by extracting the unsaponified lipids in organic solvents. (See Section 27–6 for a discussion of saponification and soaps.)

Pure triglycerides are colorless, odorless, and tasteless. Characteristic tastes, odors, and colors of butter, olive oil, and cod liver oil are caused by compounds other than triglycerides. Many of the physical properties of the triglycerides depend upon length or degree of unsaturation of the carbon chain of the esterified fatty acids; see Section 27–3.

The major biochemical reaction of triglycerides is hydrolysis. Enzymes which catalyze the hydrolysis are commonly called *lipases*. Other reactions may occur at double bonds in the fatty-acid chain but these reactions, which include oxidation and addition of halogens, do not normally occur in living systems. These reactions are used primarily to identify and characterize lipids.

Butter and other triglycerides that have been left at warm temperatures for long periods of time tend to develop obnoxious odors and tastes. We say they have become **rancid.** The odors are due to free fatty acids (butyric acid in butter) and aldehydes. These free acids are formed as a result of two of the characteristic reactions of the triglycerides, oxidation of double bonds and hydrolysis of the ester bond. The hydrolysis which releases odorless glycerol in addition to the vile smelling acids is often catalyzed by enzymes present in bacteria. Oxidation of fatty acids occurs principally at the double bonds. Exposure to the oxygen of air at warm temperatures induces oxidation which results in the rupture of double bonds to form free aldehyde groups. These aldehydes have odors similar to those of the fatty acids and, in fact, are readily converted to fatty acids by oxidation. Oxidative processes are the primary causes of rancidity in most foods.

Triglycerides are of major importance because they represent the primary energy storage compounds in animals. The fact that they provide insulation both from heat loss and mechanical shock also makes them useful. An insulating layer of fatty tissues just below the skin helps the human body maintain its required temperature of 98.6°. Many vital internal organs, such as the kidneys, are encased in a thick layer of fat which helps to protect the animal against mechanical shock. Subcutaneous fat also performs this function.

35–4 PHOSPHOLIPIDS

Many lipids contain the element phosphorus in addition to carbon, hydrogen, and oxygen. These phospholipids are found in many parts of living organisms, but are especially prevalent in the brain and nervous tissue. Liver and egg yolks also contain appreciable amounts of a particular type of phospholipid—lecithin. The outer membranes of most cells contain phospholipids.

Many phospholipids are considered derivatives of phosphatidic acid. The R-groups are those of relatively long-chain fatty acids.

$$
\begin{array}{c}
\text{H}_2\text{—C—O—C}\!\!\!\overset{\displaystyle \text{O}}{\diagup}\!\!\!\text{—R} \\
\text{R}'\text{—C}\!\!\!\overset{\displaystyle \text{O}}{\diagup}\!\!\!\text{—O—C—H} \\
\text{H}_2\text{C—O—P}\!\!\!\overset{\displaystyle \text{O}}{\diagup}\!\!\!\text{—OH} \\
\text{OH}
\end{array}
$$

phosphatidic acid

Phosphatidic acid does not occur as such in living animals. In derivatives of phosphatidic acid the phosphate group is generally esterified with an OH group of a nitrogen-containing alcohol. Substances most commonly esterified here are choline, ethanolamine, and the amino acid serine.

$$
\begin{array}{c}
\text{H}_2\text{C—O—C}\!\!\!\overset{\displaystyle \text{O}}{\diagup}\!\!\!\text{—R} \\
\text{R}'\text{—C}\!\!\!\overset{\displaystyle \text{O}}{\diagup}\!\!\!\text{—O—C—H} \\
\text{H}_2\text{C—O—P}\!\!\!\overset{\displaystyle \text{O}}{\diagup}\!\!\!\text{—O—CH}_2\text{—CH}_2\text{—N}^{\oplus}\text{—(CH}_3)_3 \\
\text{O}^{\ominus}
\end{array}
$$

a lecithin

In fact, further classification of phospholipids, derivatives of phosphatidic acid, depends on the basic alcohol present. Lecithins contain choline; cephalins contain either ethanolamine or serine; and the plasmalogens contain an unsaturated long-chain ether and either choline or ethanolamine. Phospholipids which are not derivatives of phosphatidic acid are also known.

The phospholipids, particularly the lecithins, are large molecules having both a nonpolar component and a highly polar one. Thus, we would expect them to be good detergents (see Section 27–7). Apparently the major biochemical function they perform is in associating the water-insoluble lipids and the water-soluble components of any living organism. It has been proposed that phospholipids help in the transport of lipids in the blood stream (which is basically water). As a matter of fact, tiny fat globules are present in the blood after digestion of a meal containing fat. It is interesting to speculate about whether the phospholipids are responsible for keeping these globules small enough so that they do not block the small blood vessels. Less vital uses of lecithins are as emulsifying agents to keep the fat, chocolate, and other components of many candies from separating. Egg yolks which are rich in lecithins are used to emulsify vinegar and salad oil into a mayonnaise or salad dressing.

The prevalence of phospholipids in brain and nervous tissue leads us to wonder about their significance in these important tissues. While it may be they are present only inadvertently, some biochemists are strongly influenced by the belief that "nature probably does nothing without a purpose," and they are trying to find the purpose or function of the phospholipids in these areas. At present, we can say only that their function is not yet fully understood.

35-5 WAXES

The esterification of a fatty acid with a simple alcohol (i.e., one having only a single OH group rather than three as in glycerol) gives a wax. Examples were mentioned in Section 26–9E. Whale oil (which is not truly an oil, but a wax) contains cetyl palmitate, and beeswax contains myricyl palmitate.

$$CH_3(CH_2)_{14}-\overset{\displaystyle O}{\overset{\|}{C}}-O-(CH_2)_{15}-CH_3$$

cetyl palmitate

$$CH_3(CH_2)_{14}-\overset{\displaystyle O}{\overset{\|}{C}}-O-(CH_2)_{29}-CH_3$$

myricyl palmitate

35-6 STEROIDS

The term **sterol** means solid alcohol. Cholesterol was isolated from gallstones in 1775, and the prefix *chole* indicates its relation to the bile (*chole* is the Greek word for bile). We now know that cholesterol is present in many tissues of the body, especially in brain and nervous tissue. Cholesterol was only the first of a great variety of compounds having a steroid nucleus. Steroids having an —OH group are called *sterols*. (See Section 35–2 for the formula for cholesterol).

The steroid nucleus is generally a flat structure. If we consider the nucleus to be in the plane of the page of this book, substituent groups will be either above or below the ring. When we draw the structure, we use a solid line to indicate that the substituent is above or in front of the ring, and a dotted line to show it is below or to the back.

Since sterols are primarily hydrocarbons with a high molecular weight, they are soluble in the nonpolar organic solvents, and are classified as lipids. Modern biochemistry has found other relationships between the fatty acids and cholesterol that indicate the propriety of their being classified together. Acetate, in its active form (known as acetyl coenzyme A) is the starting material not only for the synthesis of fatty acids and cholesterol, but for many other lipids. The physiological function of cholesterol is not known, but there seems to be some correlation between the level of cholesterol in the blood and a tendency toward certain types of heart attacks. The presence of cholesterol in gallstones represents an instance of an unnatural concentration of a normal body constituent.

There are many steroids that have well-known specific functions. Testosterone, the male hormone, is responsible for secondary sexual development in the male, and estradiol and other related compounds perform a similar (although different) function in the female.

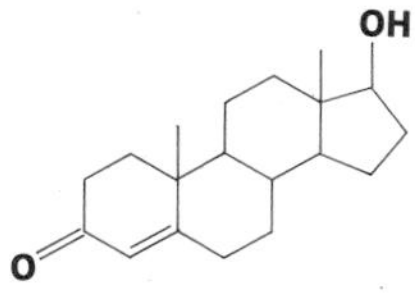

testosterone 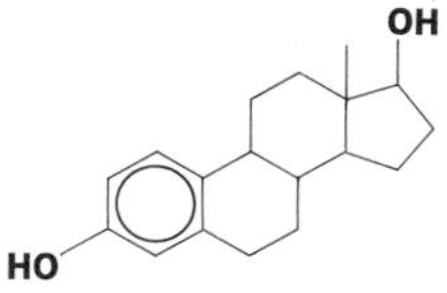   estradiol

The hormones of the adrenal gland, such as cortisone and aldosterone, as well as the hormone progesterone, are steroids. Progesterone helps to maintain pregnancy in the female, and is known to inhibit the release of ova. Cholesterol is the precursor of many of these sterols.

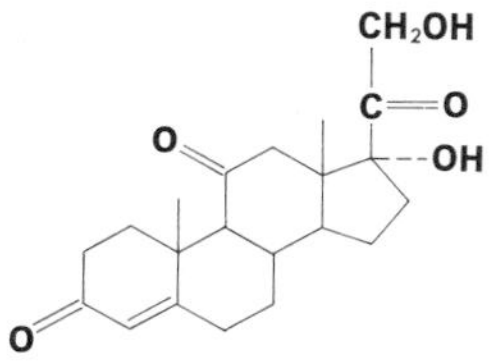

cortisone 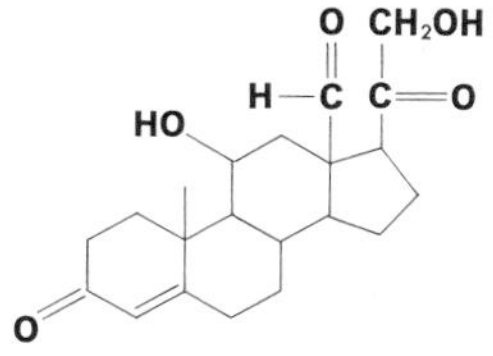   aldosterone 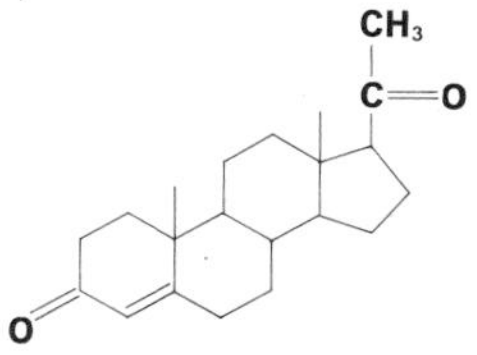   progesterone

A group of steroids which has recently received a great deal of attention comprises the oral contraceptives. Several compounds are used for this purpose, but they fall into two classes—the analogs of progesterone and those of the natural estrogens such as estradiol. Norethindrone and mestranol are widely used as oral contraceptives. Comparison of their formulas to those of progesterone and estradiol shows the obvious similarities.

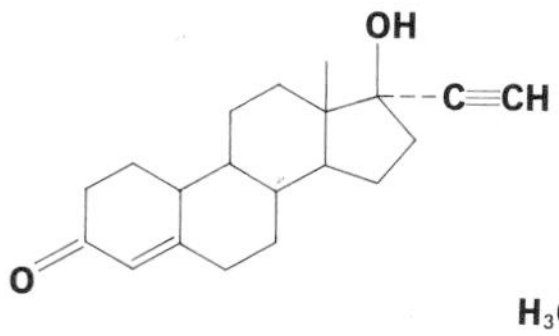

norethindrone 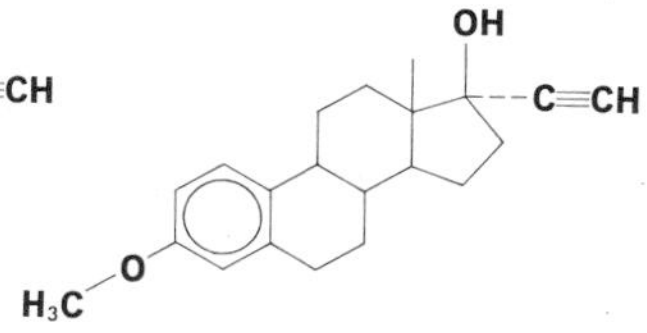   mestranol

When these two steroids are given either in a single pill or in separate pills at different times during the menstrual cycle they result in essentially normal menstruation with the exception that no ova (eggs) are released from the ovary. Similar results are produced by administering progesterone and estradiol; however, these hormones are relatively ineffective when given orally and must be injected for maximal effects. Thus we can see that a slight difference in chemical structure allows a steroid taken orally to function in a manner similar to one normally produced by the body. While estrogens are produced regularly following puberty, progesterone is normally produced only during pregnancy. The combination of the two steroids inhibits ovulation and prevents conception in a manner similar to that occurring during normal pregnancy. While the oral contraceptives are widely used, some bad side-effects have been reported. These drugs are currently available only upon prescription and should be taken under the supervision of trained medical personnel.

Vitamin D is not truly a steroid, since one of the rings of this compound has been ruptured, but it is closely related to the steroids. It is produced by the action of ultraviolet radiation on 7-dehydrocholesterol.

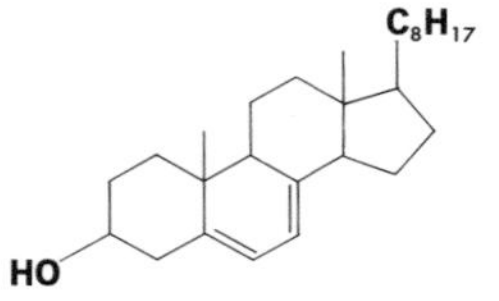

7-dehydrocholesterol

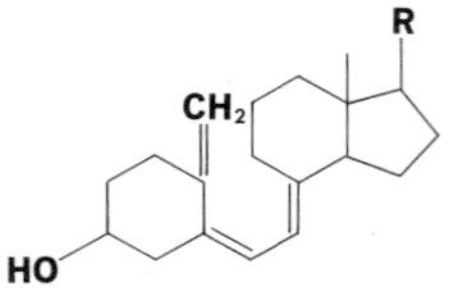

vitamin D

(If R is C_9H_{17}, the compound is vitamin D_2. If R is C_8H_{17}, the compound is vitamin D_3.)

The bile acids, which are necessary for the digestion of lipids, also contain a steroid nucleus. These acids are usually combined with an amino acid derivative when functioning biochemically.

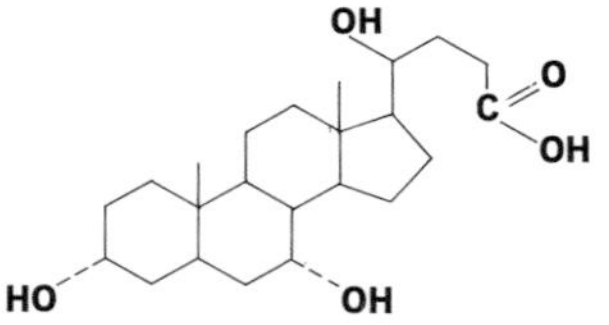

cholic acid

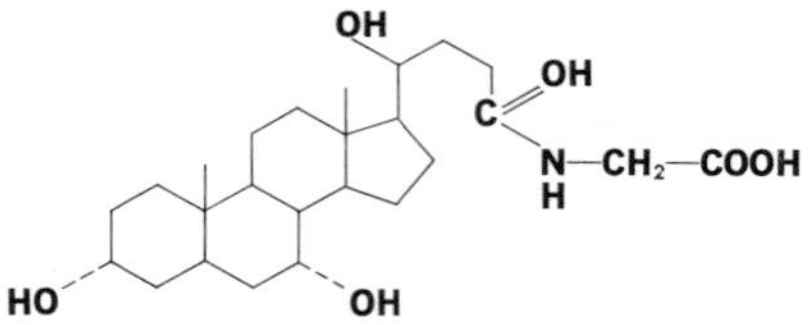

glycocholic acid (glycine derivative of cholic acid)

35–7 TERPENES

The substance we call turpentine can be obtained from the resin or gum of pine and fir trees. A great number of other compounds are related to turpentine in terms of both odor and chemical structure. As a group, these compounds are called terpenes, a name derived from an ancient spelling for turpentine.

The terpenes have a distinctive fragrance and can be isolated from natural sources by steam distillation. They are responsible for the odors of pine trees, citrus fruits, geraniums, and many other plants. Chemically, they can be considered as being derived from two isoprene units (which can, in turn, be derived from acetate); they contain 10 carbon atoms. Other similar compounds containing 15, 20, and 30 carbon atoms are called the sesquiterpenes, diterpenes, and triterpenes. Typical examples of terpenes are shown in the following structures:

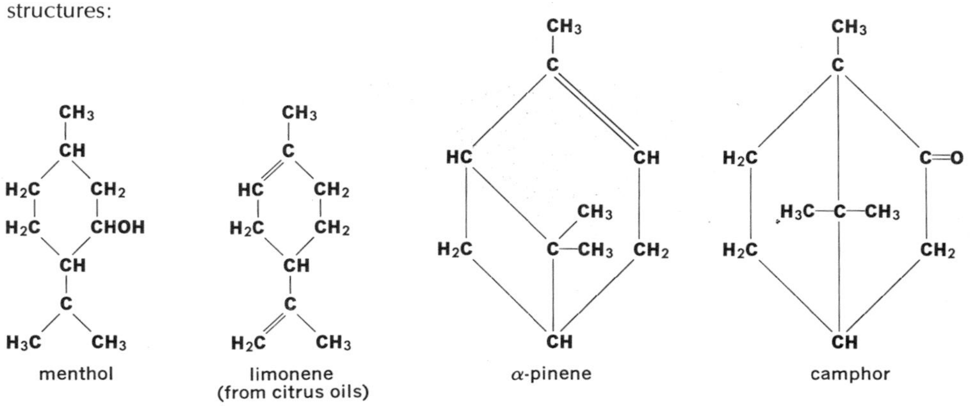

menthol   limonene   α-pinene   camphor
(from citrus oils)

The carotenes, the orange pigment found in many green plants as well as in carrots, are related to the terpenes. Vitamin A also belongs to this classification although its molecular weight is sufficiently high to keep it from having the characteristic terpene odor.

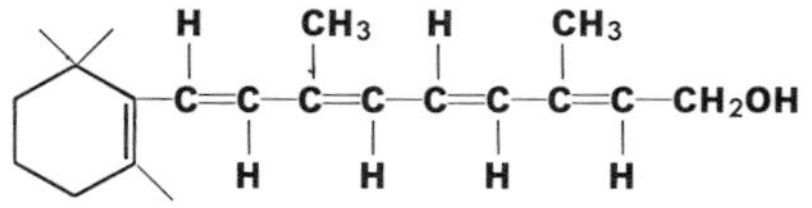

vitamin A (all *trans* form)

The odorous members of the terpenes apparently attract insects and thus aid in the fertilization of plants. In photosynthesis the carotenes probably play some role in the absorption of light energy. Vitamin A has several functions in the human. It is present, for example, in rhodopsin (visual purple) and apparently plays an important role in vision (see Chapter 41).

35-8 SUMMARY

From the foregoing we can see that the classification lipid includes many different types of compounds. The triglycerides are probably of greatest importance, from a quantitative aspect, to most animals. These compounds provide energy when eaten, and serve as compounds in which energy can be stored for future use. The phospholipids are also widely distributed in the animal body. The role they play is not yet well understood. Cholesterol is found in many places in animal tissues and is especially prevalent in the brain. Although found in only relatively small quantities, the steroid-derived vitamin D and the steroid hormones such as testosterone, estradiol, and cortisone are vital. When there is a deficiency or excessive amounts of them, the consequences are severe and may even be fatal.

Other lipids—particularly the terpenes—are of significance to plants, but only a few of them, such as vitamin A, are of biochemical importance to humans. However, the social and economic importance of these compounds, especially of rubber, is great.

IMPORTANT TERMS

Fat	*Phospholipid*	*Triglyceride*
Lipase	*Saponification*	*Unsaturation*
Lipid	*Steroid*	*Wax*
Oil	*Terpene*	

WORK EXERCISES

Before you do the following exercises, you may wish to review Chapter 27.

1. List the hydrolysis products of
   a) triglycerides   b) phospholipids   c) waxes
   d) steroids   e) terpenes

2. Draw the structure of
   a) a triglyceride containing stearic, palmitic, and lauric acids. Is there more than one possible answer to this question?
   b) a highly unsaturated triglyceride
   c) a fat
   d) a lecithin containing lignoceric and arachadonic acids
   e) cetyl stearate

3. Write equations for the
   a) hydrolysis of myristyloleyllaurin
   b) addition of bromine to palmitoleic acid
   c) saponification of a triglyceride

4. Indicate whether you think each of the following triglycerides would be a fat or an oil:
   a) tripalmatin   b) triolein   c) tributyrin
   [You may wish to check your predictions by consulting a handbook of chemistry.]

5. Would you expect fats or oils to have the greater tendency to become rancid?

6. On the basis of the two causes of rancidity, how might you protect triglycerides from developing this undesirable characteristic?

7. Cow's milk produced when cattle are grazing on green pastures is usually appreciably yellower than that produced when they are fed dried alfalfa or other dry food. Can you give a reason for this?

8. What information can you find on labels of various food products that are high in lipids, such as cooking oils, oleomargarines, and butter, about the source and content of lipids in these foods?

9. From a general biochemistry text,
   a) Find the formulas and significance of steroids other than those discussed in this chapter.
   b) List the formulas and explain the significance of other terpenes.

SUGGESTED READING

Dole, V. P., "Body Fat," *Scientific American*, Dec. 1959. A discussion of depot fat and obesity.

Fieser, L. F., "Steroids," *Scientific American,* Jan. 1955 (Offprint #8). A survey article written by an authority in the field of steroids.

Chapter 36   CHEMISTRY OF THE NUCLEIC ACIDS

36-1 INTRODUCTION

The carbohydrates, proteins, and lipids, along with the mineral elements and water, constitute about 99% of most living organisms. The remaining 1%, however, includes some of the most important biochemical compounds. Without these compounds, cells would be unable to exist for any appreciable length of time and could never reproduce.

Probably the most important of these minor constituents are the nucleic acids. These compounds were so named because they were originally found in the nuclei of cells. We now know that they are also found in the cytoplasm and that there is some difference both in location and function of the two basic kinds of nucleic acids. Deoxyribose nucleic acid (DNA) is found almost totally in the nucleus, and ribose nucleic acid (RNA) is found both in the nucleus and in the cytoplasm of cells. From the names it is obvious that the presence or absence of an oxygen in a ribose component of the nucleic acid molecule is a chemical difference between DNA and RNA. There are other differences as will be pointed out later. While the functions of RNA and, to some extent, of DNA still are not totally known, it seems that DNA plays a primary role in transmission of hereditary information from one cell to its daughter cells, and that the functions of RNA are secondary.

36-2 COMPOSITION AND STRUCTURE OF THE NUCLEIC ACIDS

The hydrolysis of a pure sample of a nucleic acid yields phosphoric acid, a pentose (either ribose or 2-deoxyribose), and a mixture of organic compounds that have the properties of bases. (See Figs. 36–1 and 36–2.) The five most common bases are adenine, guanine, thy-

β-D-ribose 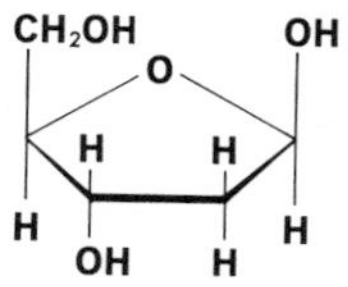   β-2-deoxy-D-ribose

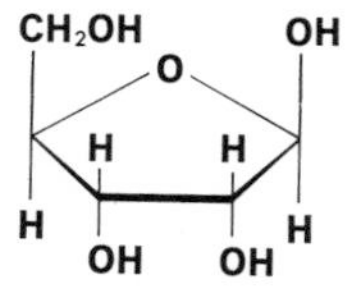

FIG. 36–1. Structures of the pentoses found in nucleic acids.

mine, cytosine, and uracil. Adenine and guanine are called **purine bases** because of their relation to purine, and similarly thymine, cytosine, and uracil are **pyrimidine bases.**

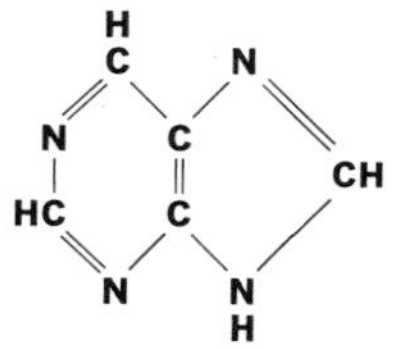

purine 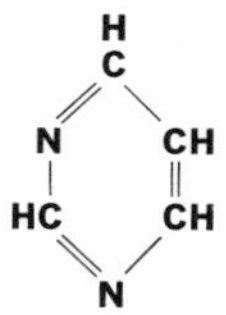   pyrimidine

Other bases such as 5-methylcytosine and 5-hydroxymethylcytosine are found in small amounts in some nucleic acid hydrolysates. Although the amounts of the different components vary somewhat, there is always one phosphate group and one pentose for each base. In most kinds of DNA the amount of purines is equal to the amount of pyrimidines, the amount of adenine equal to that of thymine, and the amount of guanine to that of cytosine. This ratio of bases is not usually found in RNA.

Although some false assumptions were originally made concerning the structure of DNA, when it was determined that the molecular weight of DNA was very high, it became obvious that DNA was a polymer of a basic unit containing a base, deoxyribose, and a phosphoric acid group. This monomeric unit is a **nucleotide.** The structures containing only the base and the sugar are called **nucleosides.** The structures of a nucleotide and a nucleoside are shown in the accompanying diagram. See also Table 36–1.

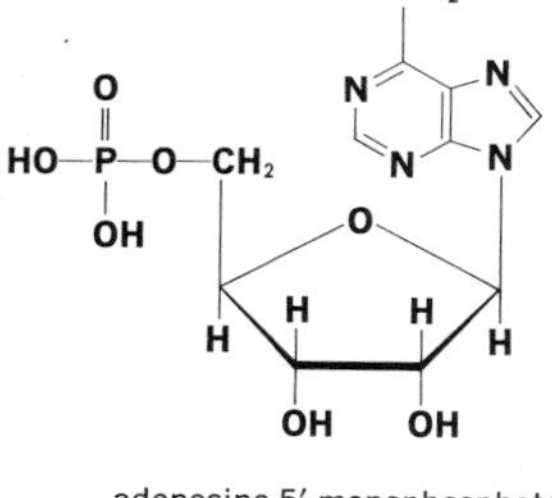

adenosine 5'-monophosphate
or adenylic acid
(a nucleotide)

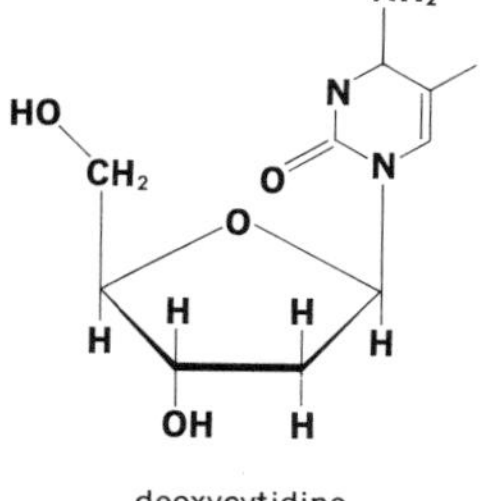

deoxycytidine
(a nucleoside)

In general, DNA exists as a double-stranded polymer with hydrogen bonds holding adenine of one strand to a thymine in another strand, with cytosine and guanine similarly

Formula	Model

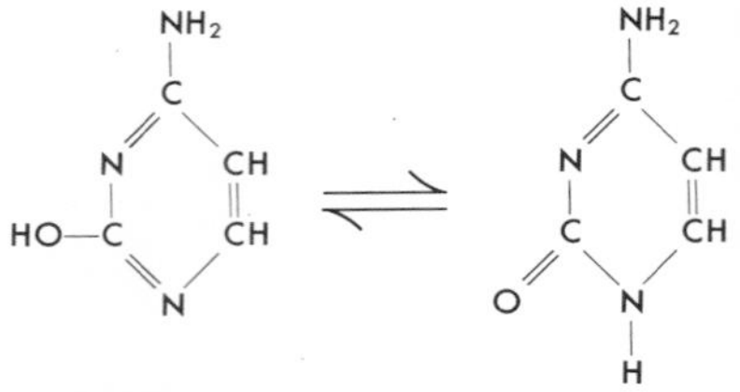

enol form   keto form
cytosine

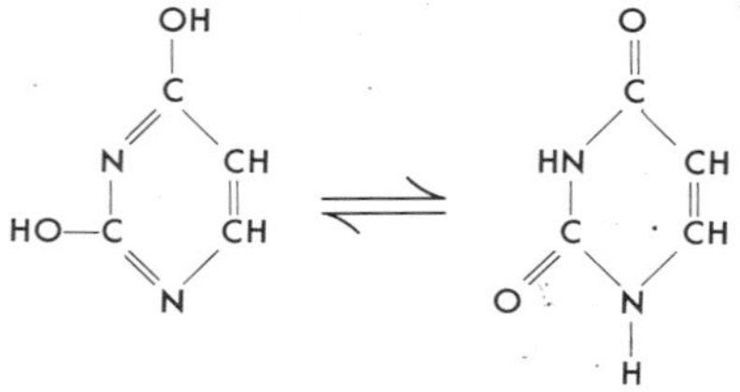

enol form   keto form
uracil

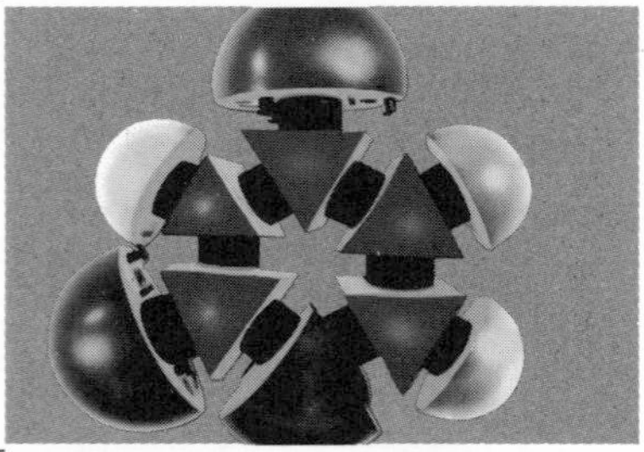

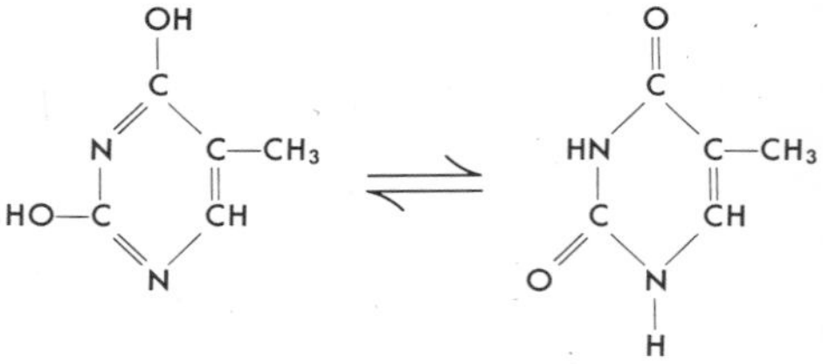

enol form   keto form
thymine

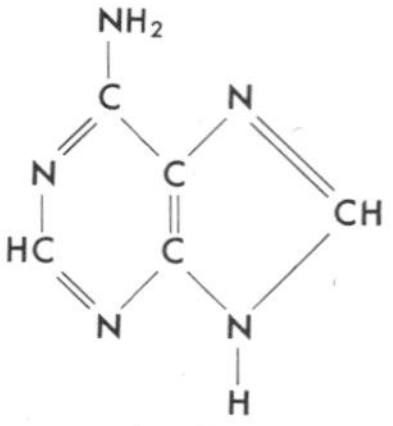

adenine

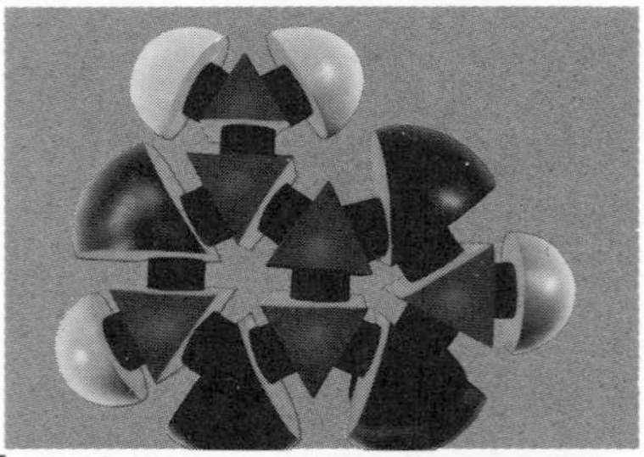

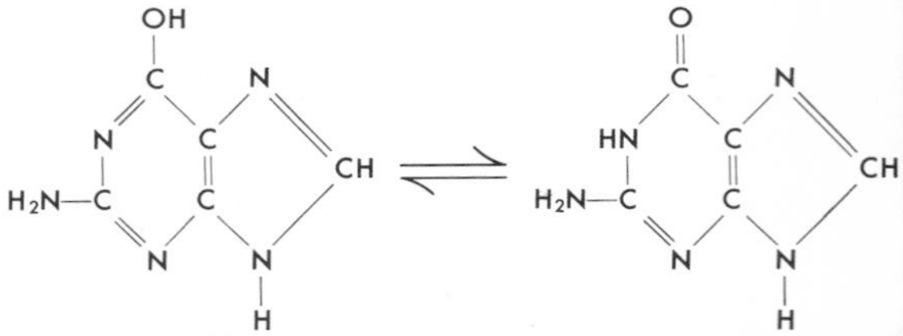

enol form   keto form
guanine

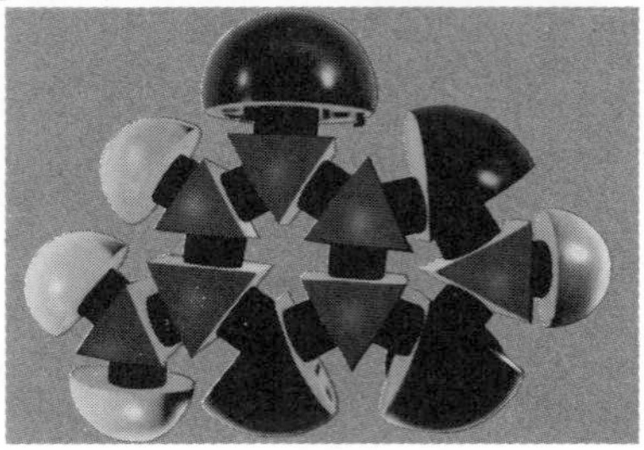

TABLE 36–1. Names of nucleotides and nucleosides

Base	Nucleoside	Nucleotide
cytosine	cytidine or deoxycytidine	cytidylic or deoxycytidylic acid
uracil	uridine or deoxyuridine	uridylic or deoxyuridylic acid
thymine	thymidine*	thymidylic acid*
adenine	adenosine or deoxyadenosine	adenylic or deoxyadenylic acid (adenosine phosphate)
guanine	guanosine or deoxyguanosine	guanylic or deoxyguanylic acid

* In nature thymine is always combined with deoxyribose, not ribose. Thymidine and thymidylic acid contain ribose, not deoxyribose.

bonded. (See Fig. 36–3.) Single-stranded DNA is found in some viruses; however, such single-stranded forms now seem to be a minor exception to the rule that DNA is double-stranded. Three hydrogen bonds are possible between cytosine and guanine, while only two are present in the adenine-thymine pair. This finding correlates well with the fact that more energy is required to separate the two strands of DNA (a process called *melting*) when the guanine-cytosine content of the DNA is high. See Fig. 36–4. When DNA solutions are heated, the hydrogen bonds between strands are disrupted, and the strands separate as shown in (b). Slow recooling permits essentially normal double-stranded DNA. Rapid chilling produces some intrastrand bonds as well as some interstrand bonds.

The three-dimensional structure of the nucleic acids was established on the basis of X-ray diffraction studies. We now know that DNA is a double-stranded, spiral (helical) molecule. For convenience, adenine, thymine, guanine, and cytosine are designated by the first letters of their names in the representation of the structure of DNA shown in Fig. 36–5. Other visualizations of the DNA structure are shown in Fig. 36–6.

In addition to the obvious difference in having ribose instead of deoxyribose, RNA contains uracil and does not contain thymine. Since its molecular weight is usually lower than that of DNA, and since there seems to be no uniform ratio of bases, we could postulate that RNA is only single-stranded. Although pure samples of RNA are difficult to obtain and studies of structure are difficult to make and interpret, it seems that most forms of RNA are single-stranded and have a helical structure in only part of their molecules. There seem to be at least three types of RNA that can be separated by essentially physical means: messenger RNA, ribosomal RNA, and soluble or transfer RNA. The names given these forms of RNA reflect the function they are believed to play in protein synthesis. The role of nucleic acids in protein synthesis is presented in Chapter 39.

FIG. 36–2 (opposite). Structures of pyrimidine and purine bases of nucleic acids. [Adapted from Snell, Shulman, Spencer, and Moos, *Biophysical Principles of Structure and Function,* Addison-Wesley, 1965.]

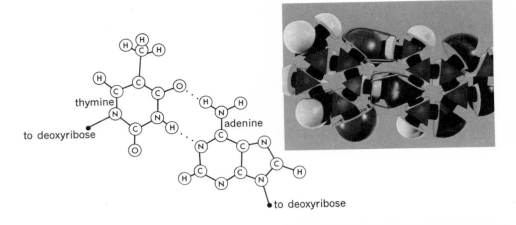

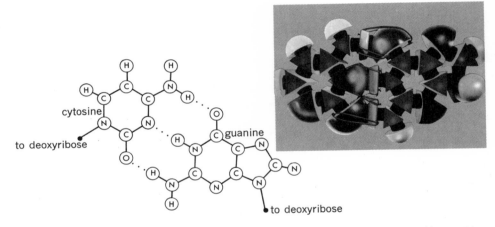

FIG. 36–3. Hydrogen bonds between the adenine: thymine and cytosine: guanine pairs of bases. Note that there are two bonds between adenine and thymine and three between guanine and cytosine. [Photographs from Snell, Shulman, Spencer, and Moos, *Biophysical Principles of Structure and Function*, Addison-Wesley, 1965.]

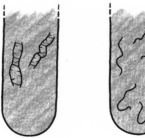

DNA solution

(a)

DNA solution heated above denaturation (melting) temperature (Note separation of the strands.)

(b)

Recombination produced by sudden chilling

(c)

FIG. 36–4. A representation of the separation and recombination of DNA strands.

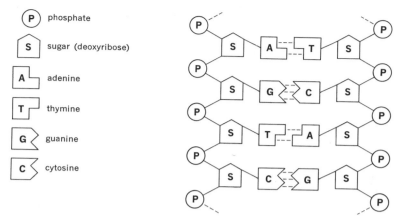

FIG. 36–5. A representation of the structure of a segment of DNA.

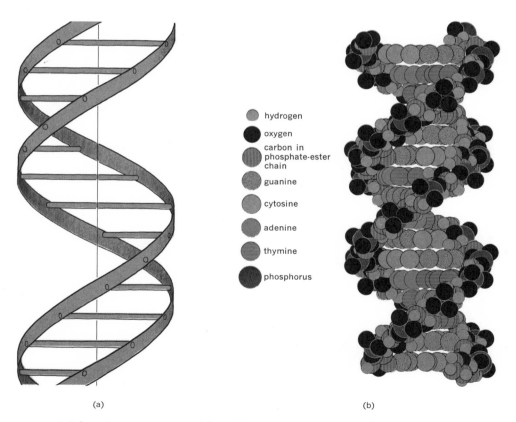

(a)

(b)

FIG. 36–6. Schematic representations of the molecule of DNA: (a) a simplified model showing the two strands linked by ladderlike steps formed by the base pairs, (b) a more complex representation of the same structure. [(b) is reprinted by permission from American Cancer Society and Dr. L. D. Hamilton; *CA, A Bulletin of Cancer Progress* **5,** 163 (1955) from material provided by Dr. W. E. Seeds and Dr. H. R. Wilson, Wheatstone Physics Laboratory, King's College, London.]

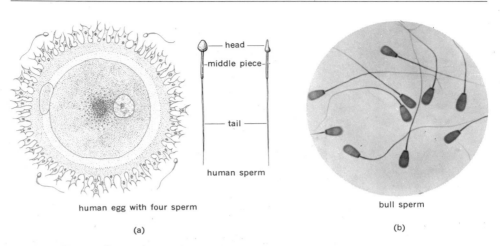

human egg with four sperm

head
middle piece
tail

human sperm

bull sperm

(a)

(b)

FIG. 36-7. Sperm cells. (a) shows a drawing of a human egg and sperm cells and (b) is reproduced from a microscopic slide of the sperm of a bull. [Adapted from Baker and Allen, *The Study of Biology*, Addison-Wesley, 1967.]

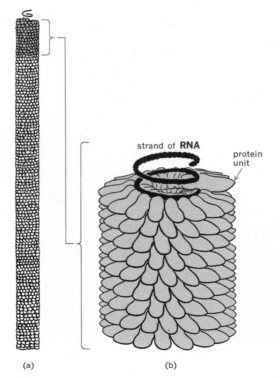

strand of **RNA**

protein unit

(a)   (b)

FIG. 36-8. Diagrammatic representation of the structure of the tobacco mosaic virus (TMV): (a) is a drawing of a complete virus particle (note similarity to photomicrograph of TMV in Fig. 36-9; (b) shows an enlarged diagram of part of the TMV particle with a single coiled strand of RNA emerging from the stack of spirally arranged protein units which surround it. Each protein unit is identical to all others and contains 158 amino acids in a sequence which is known. The complete TMV particle has 2200 of these protein units. [Adapted from a model in *Viruses and the Nature of Life* by W. M. Stanley and E. G. Valens.]

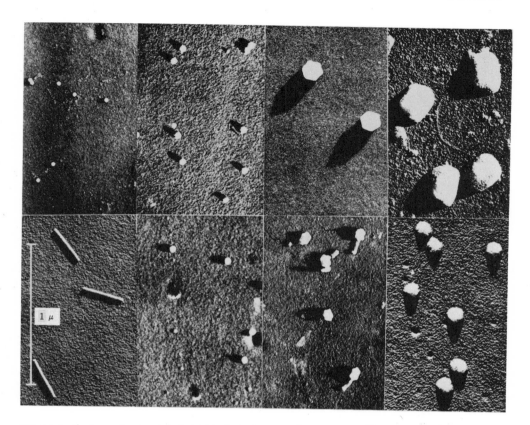

FIG. 36–9. Electron micrographs of eight typical viruses at the same magnification. Top (left to right): poliomyelitis, small bacteriophage, *Tipula irridescens* (an insect virus showing individual particles, not crystals), vaccinia (the virus that causes smallpox). Bottom: tobacco mosaic virus, rabbit papilloma, large bacteriophage, influenza virus. [Courtesy of the Virus Laboratory, University of California, Berkeley.]

36–3 OCCURRENCE OF NUCLEIC ACIDS

Nucleic acids are defined as those complex biochemical substances which yield, upon hydrolysis, purine and pyrimidine bases, ribose or deoxyribose, and phosphate. They are found in all living cells where they are usually present at a level of less than 1% of the total net weight of the cell. Yeast cells and some bacterial cells may contain up to 5% nucleic acid. The bacteriophages may contain as much as 60% DNA. It has been estimated that if all the DNA in an average adult human were uncoiled and laid out in a straight line it would reach five billion miles. This long string would, however, be only one or two angstroms wide.

In almost all instances the nucleic acids are found in combination with proteins in the form of nucleoproteins. Many of the functions of nucleic acids are performed only poorly, if at all, when the specific protein they ordinarily are associated with is missing. Sperm cells are composed of a DNA nucleoprotein. (See Fig. 36–7.) Viruses contain either DNA or RNA surrounded by a protein coating. (See Figs. 36–8 and 36–9.) In some cases it has been possible to separate the protein outer coat from the inner thread of the virus and then to recombine the two fractions into a virus which is able to infect living cells.

36-4 SYNTHESIS OF NUCLEIC ACIDS

The nucleic acids can be synthesized from simple materials by most organisms. Some bacteria require adenine or other bases in order to synthesize their nucleic acids, but most organisms can synthesize the pentoses and bases, and combine them with phosphate from their diet to assemble the nucleic acids required. While each kind of organism makes its own specific kind of DNA, the RNA from different species seems to be quite similar. Some polymers that can function in place of natural RNA have been synthesized *in vitro*. The synthesis, however, requires an enzyme as a catalyst. Other enzymes can catalyze the synthesis of DNA when provided with the proper starting materials and a small amount of already-formed DNA as a primer. The synthesized DNA is similar in physical properties to the DNA of the primer, but until recently such synthetic DNA's had not been shown to have biological activity. Late in 1967, Kornberg and his co-workers reported the synthesis of a viral DNA that could infect microorganisms. Although it is probably incorrect to describe these experiments as the creation of life in a test tube, they do represent a major advance in the synthesis of biologically active molecules. Synthetic DNA may some day be used to change hereditary characteristics. The synthesis, or replication, of DNA is shown in Fig. 36–10.

36-5 PHYSICAL PROPERTIES OF THE NUCLEIC ACIDS

Samples of DNA have been found to have an extremely high molecular weight. Values in the millions have been found. Some lower values have also been reported, but it is likely that the samples were torn apart in the process of separating them from other cell components. The alternate possibility, that the high molecular weight components were aggregations of smaller molecules present in the intact cell seems less likely, but cannot be ignored. It is probable that all the DNA in some bacterial and viral cells is represented by one single molecule. There are many forms of RNA, some of which have molecular weights as low as 75,000 while others have weights probably extending into the million range.

Because of their many polar groups and in spite of their high molecular weight, nucleic acids are water-soluble. The bases of the nucleic acids absorb ultraviolet radiation in the 250- to 290-millimicron range. This property is commonly used to identify and measure the amount of nucleic acids in a sample.

36-6 CHEMICAL PROPERTIES OF THE NUCLEIC ACIDS

The hydrolysis of nucleic acids is catalyzed either by acids, bases, or by enzymes. Enzymes which catalyze the hydrolysis of only RNA (RNA-ases) or DNA (DNA-ases) are widely used in studies of nucleic acids. The first products of hydrolysis of the nucleic acids are nucleotides, but these can be further hydrolyzed to give nucleosides, and finally to give the bases, pentose and phosphate. Each step in the hydrolysis requires a specific type of enzyme.

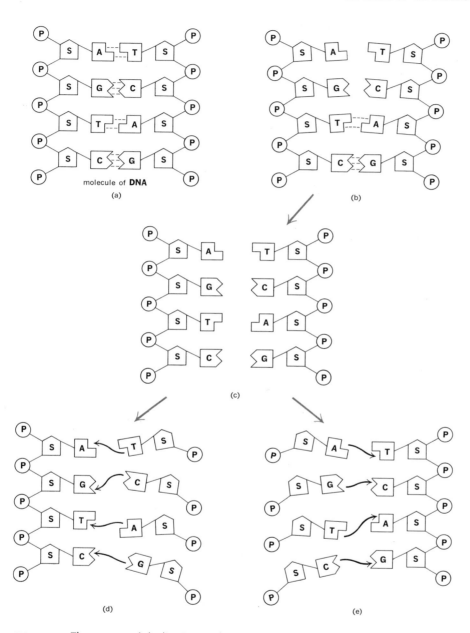

FIG. 36-10. The process of duplication (replication) of DNA. (a) shows part of the molecule of DNA (see Fig. 36-5 for identification of components). In (b) the two strands have begun to separate and in (c) they are completely apart. (d) shows how individual nucleotides join with the left strand of the DNA to form another double-stranded molecule, and (e) shows a similar process for the right strand of the original DNA. Since each half of the original DNA molecule has now produced a molecule identical to the original DNA molecule, duplication has occurred. This process occurs in the chromosomes of the cell nucleus prior to cell division.

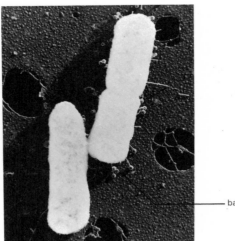

FIG. 36–11. A photomicrograph showing several bacteriophages attached to one of the two cells of the bacterium *E. Coli.* [Courtesy, Thomas F. Anderson, Francois Jacob, Elie Wollman.]

36-7 THE IMPORTANCE OF NUCLEIC ACIDS

The role nucleic acids play in heredity and in protein synthesis is discussed in Chapters 39 and 42. A third important role played by nucleic acids is in the action of viruses. We tend to think of viruses as causing diseases, which they do, but they are of biochemical interest also. A virus represents a kind of bridge between living and nonliving materials. Many viruses have been isolated as crystallized nucleoproteins. In this form they can be stored in bottles on shelves for long periods of time. Yet, when added to living organisms or to cultures containing living cells, the virus can take over the function of the living cell so that it produces new virus particles instead of new cells. So far scientists have not been able to get viruses to reproduce even in a medium containing all known nutritional requirements of cells unless living cells are also present.

One type of virus, the bacteriophages, which are viruses that attack bacteria, has been studied extensively. These viruses consist of an inner core of nucleic acid surrounded by an outer coat of protein. They attach themselves to the wall of a bacterium and inject their nucleic acid into the bacterium. (See Fig. 36–11.) The injected nucleic acid then takes over the metabolism of the cell and so directs it that thousands of new virus particles, each capable of infecting other bacteria, are produced. In other instances the virus is apparently present in the bacterial cell in an inactive or latent form and the virus is, in fact, reproduced along with other cell components for several generations. When this infected cell is exposed to some kind of shock, such as ultraviolet irradiation or certain chemical agents, the virus becomes active and directs the cell towards its own destruction by production of virus particles.

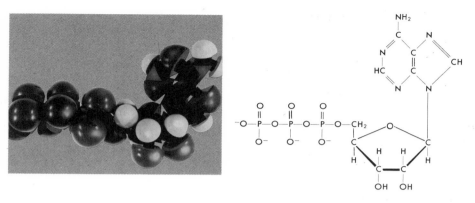

FIG. 36–12. The structure of ATP (adenosine triphosphate). [From Snell, Shulman, Spencer, and Moos, *Biophysical Principles of Structure and Function*, Addison-Wesley, 1965.]

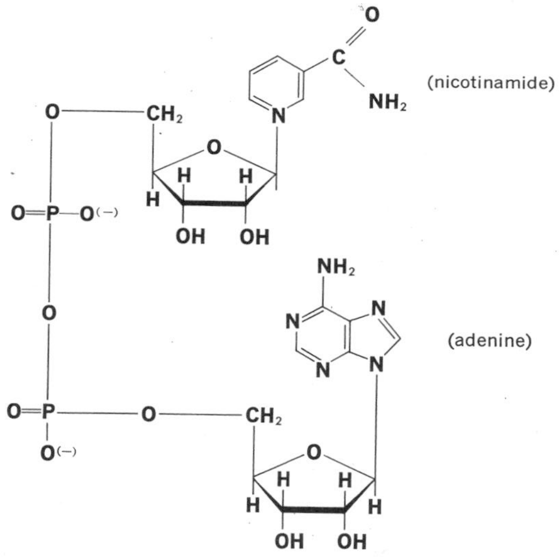

FIG. 36–13. ·The structure of NAD (nicotin-amide adenine dinucleotide).

Some forms of cancer are caused by viruses. In fact, the Nobel prize-winning scientist, Dr. Wendell Stanley, stated many years ago that he believed all cancer was caused by viruses. Other scientists have speculated that many humans carry inactive viruses which can cause cancer when irradiated or otherwise stimulated. These hypotheses are still largely conjectures, and proof must wait for further research on the way nucleic acids function. The development of new research techniques coupled with a better knowledge of the bio-chemistry of nucleic acids may lead to the understanding of cancer and to cures or controls for this disease.

Nucleotides have been discussed as the monomeric units from which the polymeric nucleic acids were made. Nucleotides which are present as such, not as polymers, also

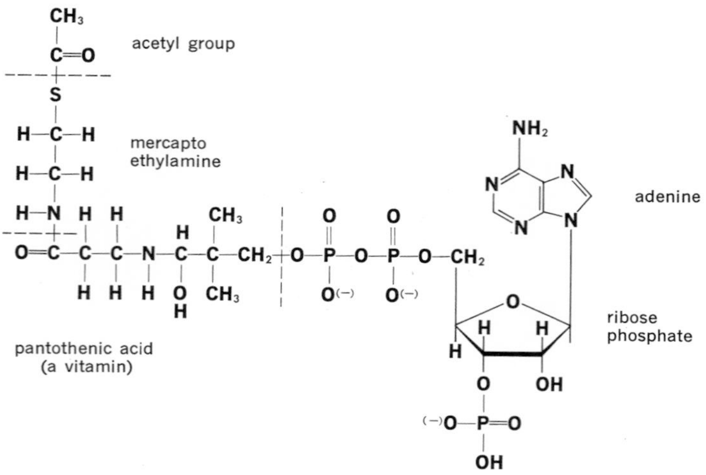

FIG. 36–14. The structure of coenzyme A (CoA). An acetyl group is shown attached to the CoA to give acetyl CoA.

play an important role in biochemical reactions. Adenosine triphosphate (ATP), a nucleotide with two additional phosphate groups, serves as the energy source for hundreds of biochemical reactions (Fig. 36–12). When either of the two end phosphate groups is removed by hydrolysis, a large amount of energy is made available for driving energy-requiring reactions. Such diverse reactions as synthesis of proteins, muscular contraction, and the production of light by fireflies all require ATP as an energy source. Triphosphates of guanine and other bases serve similar roles.

The active form of many of the vitamins is a nucleotide. In some cases the vitamin itself is the base, combined with a ribose and phosphate unit; in others, adenine or some other base is required. (See Figs. 36–13 and 36–14.)

The reason why a nucleotide "handle" is so widely found in the structure of extremely important biochemical compounds is not known. While it may be only accidental or coincidental that the base-pentose-phosphate combination is so widespread, this apparent coincidence is the kind of observation that makes a biochemist want to track down the significance of this chemical structure.

IMPORTANT TERMS

Bacteriophage
Deoxyribonuclease (DNA-ase)
Deoxyribonucleic acid (DNA)
Nucleic acid
Nucleoprotein

Nucleoside
Nucleotide
Primer DNA
Purine base

Pyrimidine base
Ribonuclease (RNA-ase)
Ribonucleic acid (RNA)
Virus

WORK EXERCISES

1. Draw the formulas for the following:

   a) deoxycytidine   b) uridylic acid   c) thymidylic acid
   d) deoxyguanosine   e) adenosine diphosphate (ADP)

2. List the major hydrolysis products of each of the following:

   a) DNA   b) RNA   c) deoxyuridine   d) adenylic acid   e) guanine

3. Draw the structure for the trinucleotides specified by the symbols CGA and GGT. Locate possible hydrogen bonds between these nucleotides. What is the maximum number of hydrogen bonds possible between these two trinucleotides?

4. What would be the expected products if

   a) DNA-ase were added to a sample of nucleic acids purified from a specimen of liver?

   b) RNA-ase were added to a purified sample of DNA?

5. What are the major differences between DNA and RNA?

Consult a standard biochemistry text for answers to the following:

6. What bases other than guanine, adenine, cytosine, thymine, and uracil are found in the nucleic acids? What percentage of total bases is represented by these "other" bases?

7. What techniques are used to separate and analyze the components of the nucleic acids?

SUGGESTED READING

Crick, F. H. C., "Nucleic Acids," *Scientific American*, Sept. 1957 (Offprint #54). A basic article by one of the pioneers in establishing the structure of nucleic acids.

Hoagland, M. B., "Nucleic Acids and Proteins," *Scientific American*, Dec. 1959 (Offprint #68). A discussion of the basic role of nucleic acids in protein synthesis. See the references at the end of Chapter 39 for further articles relating to this topic.

Holley, R. W., "The Nucleotide Sequence of a Nucleic Acid," *Scientific American*, Feb. 1966. A report of the first determination of structure of a molecule of RNA by the scientist who supervised the work.

Horne, R. W., "The Structure of Viruses," *Scientific American*, Jan. 1963. This article, which is illustrated with electron micrographs of virus particles, discusses the general structure of a variety of viruses.

Chapter 37 BIOCHEMICAL REACTIONS

37–1 INTRODUCTION

With the exception of energy from radioisotopes, all energy used on earth comes from the sun. The energy released from petroleum and coal was trapped long ago; that from wood and from food we eat left the sun only a relatively short time ago. Devices for making direct use of the sun's energy through solar cells are now being developed.

For millions of years plants have used chlorophyll and other pigments to trap radiation from the sun and convert this energy into the potential energy of chemical compounds. This ancient process of energy conversion has only recently been scientifically investigated, and there are still many unanswered questions concerning the nature of photosynthesis. As the name implies, **photosynthesis** involves synthesis of all the different compounds found in plants utilizing the energy of sunlight. The synthesis of glucose is often summarized as

$$6CO_2 + 6H_2O \rightarrow C_6H_{12}O_6 + 6O_2$$

The special biochemistry of plants and particularly of photosynthesis will be discussed in Chapter 43. Here in this chapter ways are discussed in which animals use the energy stored in food for the many processes that are required for life.

Although animals absorb some radiation from the sun, energy for the real work of the body is provided by the food the animal eats. The green plant is the original source of this useful energy; for flesh-eating organisms, the energy of the plant has been converted to energy stored in meat of the animal which is eaten. (See Fig. 37–1.) The processes by which an animal utilizes food have been categorized as ingestion, digestion, assimilation, followed by the elimination of unused material and waste products. Biochemists are concerned with digestion and especially with assimilation of digested materials. In some cases, they are interested in the excretions, particularly the urine, for evidence of the abnormal functioning of an animal.

radiant energy

plants make food

cow eats plants,
produces milk

man drinks milk
or eats meat

FIG. 37-1. A biological food chain. Energy from the sun is trapped by a plant and converted into the potential energy of its leaves, seeds, and fruit. An animal, such as a cow, eats the plants and converts the energy stored in plants to that in its body or in the milk which it produces. A man may derive energy either by drinking the milk produced by the cow or by eating the flesh of the animal as steak or hamburger. At each step some of the energy is converted to heat or is lost to the surroundings by other means.

37-2 DIGESTION

Following ingestion of food there is often some physical separation of the food particles. The alternative to some form of chewing used by mammals and insects is the search for small morsels of food by those having lesser developed mouth parts. In most animals, chewing also results in moistening and lubricating the food with saliva. In the human, as well as in many other animals, the saliva contains enzymes which catalyze the first steps in the process of digestion.

The **digestive system,** or **gastrointestinal tract,** is essentially a partially filled tube extending between the mouth and the anus. (See Fig. 37-2.) Food in the tract, which is called the alimentary canal, is not really "inside" the body. It becomes part of the body only when it is absorbed through the intestinal wall. We can describe the process briefly by saying that as the food passes through this hollow tube, various secretions are added, some material escapes into the body via either the blood or lymph, waste products are added to the indigestible food residue, bacteria act upon the contents of the intestine, and finally the remaining material, the feces, is excreted.

Chemically, digestion is the hydrolysis of ingested food into smaller molecules. Polysaccharides are converted to monosaccharides, proteins to amino acids, and the triglycerides are broken down into fatty acids and glycerol. The function of digestion seems to be the production of molecules small enough to be absorbed through the intestinal wall. The hydrolyses of digestion are catalyzed by enzymes. These digestive enzymes are secreted by a variety of organs and are added to the food at strategic points in its passage through the digestive tract. The systematic names for enzymes are formed by adding the suffix -ase to the name of the substance whose transformation is catalyzed by the enzyme. Thus a peptidase acts on a peptide, an amylase acts on starch (both amylose and amylopectin parts), and sucrase acts on sucrose.

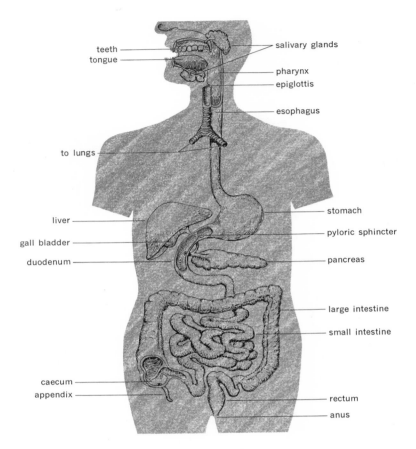

teeth
tongue
salivary glands
pharynx
epiglottis
esophagus
to lungs
liver
gall bladder
duodenum
stomach
pyloric sphincter
pancreas
large intestine
small intestine
caecum
appendix
rectum
anus

FIG. 37–2. The digestive system of the human. [From John W. Kimball, *Biology,* Addison-Wesley, 1965.]

It is true, in one respect, that "we are what we eat"—that is, we use the amino acids and monosaccharides and other components of our food to build our own bodies. However, human fat and human proteins are different from those of the flour, butter, and steak we eat. Since only simple units of the proteins, carbohydrates, and lipids are absorbed through the intestinal wall and since we are able to assemble the units only in our own way, a good analogy to digestion is that of a complex brick building being demolished—the mortar being dissolved, and the simplest units, the bricks, small pieces of wood, or steel being reused for construction of another building.

The digestive process in the human is complex, but it can be simply described to provide a background for the biochemistry of this important series of events. Detailed discussions of the digestion of specific biochemical compounds are given in Chapters 38, 39, and 40. As we have already noted, when food is chewed it is mixed with saliva which both lubricates the food and contains the enzyme (salivary amylase) which initiates digestion of starch. The esophagus serves mainly as a connecting tube between the mouth and the stomach. It produces no digestive enzymes. When food reaches the stomach, action of salivary amylase is stopped by acidity which comes from the hydrochloric acid secreted by the stomach.

Food normally stays in the stomach for a few hours while both hydrochloric acid and pepsin catalyze the hydrolysis of food, particularly of the proteins and carbohydrates. Pepsin, in contrast to salivary amylase, functions only in an acid solution and is well adapted to the pH of 1.0 to 2.5 which prevails in the stomach. Pepsin, which is found in birds, fish, and reptiles as well as in mammals, catalyzes the hydrolysis of proteins to yield a mixture of smaller polypeptides. Other digestive enzymes have been found in the stomach, but they are not effective at the pH of the stomach, and it has been speculated that perhaps these enzymes are holdovers from infancy when their secretion into a less acid stomach (characteristic of infants) may have been effective. Alternatively, they may become effective in the lower tract where the pH is neutral or slightly alkaline.

TABLE 37-1. Digestive enzymes

Site of Secretion	Enzyme	Site of Action	Substrate Acted Upon	Products of Action
mouth	salivary amylase	mouth	starches	maltose, dextrins
stomach	pepsin	stomach	proteins	polypeptides (peptone)
pancreas	pancreatic amylases	small intestine	starches	maltose
pancreas	trypsin	small intestine	proteins, polypeptides	small peptides
pancreas	chymotrypsin	small intestine	proteins, polypeptides	small peptides
pancreas	pancreatic lypase	small intestine	tryglycerides	fatty acids, glycerol
small intestine	disaccharidases	small intestine	disaccharides	monosaccharides
small intestine	nucleotidases	small intestine	nucleotides	nucleosides, phosphate

As the partially digested food enters the small intestine, it is met with a large number of catalysts for the digestive process. From the gall bladder come the nonenzymatic bile acids which aid in emulsification of lipids; from the pancreas comes a mixture of amylases, the peptidases trypsin and chymotrypsin, at least one lipase, cholesterol esterase which catalyzes the hydrolysis of esters of cholesterol, and perhaps other, yet to be discovered, enzymes. Finally, the intestine itself secretes several enzymes. Among these are various disaccharidases, peptidases, nucleosidases, and nucleotidases. In addition to the enzymes and bile acids, the various secretions contain sufficient alkaline materials to neutralize the acid of the stomach. It is believed that the secretions added to the food in the intestine are sufficient to do a complete job of digestion and in fact many persons digest food reasonably well following removal of large portions of their stomachs. However, they must eat more frequently and follow some dietary restrictions for adequate digestion. Digestive enzymes are outlined in Table 37-1.

Digested foods pass through the intestinal walls into the blood or lymph. Lipids, in particular, are absorbed by the lymph. Undigested foods, along with bacteria which find the intestine a good home and breeding place, are passed into the large intestine or colon where water and perhaps some other substances are absorbed. The contents of the large intestine are finally discharged as the feces.

The other major way the body rids itself of waste products is through the urine, but this represents a different type of excretion. Urine is produced by the kidneys, which may be thought of as a filter for the blood. In addition to water, urine contains waste products produced by the further reactions of materials absorbed through the intestinal wall. The urine is a much better indicator of the kinds of reactions going on in the body than are feces, since it contains only the end products of the vital reactions of the body, and does not contain undigestible substances which might be present merely by chance. Consequently urinalysis is much more important than analysis of feces in diagnosis of the state of health of a person.

37-3 FURTHER METABOLISM

The word **metabolism** is used to describe the sum total of all reactions that occur in a living organism. The study of metabolism emphasizes those reactions which follow the absorption of digested food; strictly speaking, however, digestion is also a part of metabolism. Those molecules which are absorbed into the body may either be built into more complex molecules in reactions described as **anabolic,** or degraded into smaller molecules in **catabolic** reactions. Anabolic reactions require energy and are characterized as **endergonic,** and catabolic reactions liberate energy and are **exergonic** reactions. Any chemical substance that is involved in metabolic reactions is a **metabolite.**

37-4 ENERGETICS

There are many ways of measuring the amount of energy released in or required for a chemical reaction. The most meaningful expression of biochemical energy is **free energy.** This term is defined as the energy available for doing useful work. Chemical reactions occur spontaneously when substances containing relatively high amounts of energy are converted into substances having less energy. Compounds with less energy are therefore less likely to react, i.e., they are more stable. Thus a spontaneous chemical reaction may be defined as a process in which matter proceeds to more stable states. Carbon dioxide contains less energy than carbon and oxygen, and water contains less potential energy than its component elements.

Since chemical substances tend to proceed to states in which their energy is released and they are more stable, the obvious question arises, "Why doesn't a potentially combustible substance, such as wood, start to burn spontaneously in air?" In this case, we know that the wood must first reach its kindling temperature. Speaking in more general terms, an **energy of activation** must be supplied before even a potentially spontaneous reaction will proceed. For some reactions, such as the burning of phosphorus in air, normal room temperature is sufficient to initiate the reaction.

A useful analogy to the energy of activation is provided by the water in a lake high on a mountain. Normally the water would run downhill until it reached sea level, but some barrier, perhaps a beaver dam or a landslide, prevents the water from running downhill and releasing the energy—energy which might be used to drive turbines and give rise to electrical energy. If we supply energy by using a pump, we can raise the water over the barrier and let it flow downhill. The pump is analogous to a device for providing the energy of activation. Ways in which energy can be stored, converted, and released are shown in Figs. 37–3, 37–4, and 37–5.

Although glucose does not burn at body temperature even when placed in pure oxygen, animals have systems for converting glucose, as well as other foods, into carbon dioxide and water. The oxidation of glucose which initially requires an energy of activation, takes place in many steps. At some of these steps, small amounts of energy are released. The release of all the energy of a molecule of glucose in a single reaction would be similar to the effect of placing a simple waterwheel at the base of Niagara Falls. Living organisms cannot utilize such large amounts of energy. Using the waterfall analogy, we can say that organisms divert the flow of water around a precipitous waterfall, and by using several small waterwheels at the bottom of small waterfalls, they are capable of trapping the energy in small, useful packets. (See Fig. 37–6.)

Some energy so released is used to drive the anabolic reactions of the organisms. Some energy is used to keep the heart beating, move food through the digestive tract, and move the animal from one place to another. The problem that living organisms have solved, that of release of large amounts of energy in small units, is similar to the problem still faced by nuclear scientists who are trying to make the tremendous energy from the fusion of hydrogen useful to drive generators or automobiles instead of functional only as a bomb blast.

Plants and animals are able to store and use the energy of metabolic reactions largely because of the compound adenosine triphosphate (ATP). This compound, which was discussed in Chapter 36, represents the principal "currency" of most living organisms. The energy of food is stored by the conversion of adenosine diphosphate to adenosine triphosphate, and the reverse reaction is used to drive energy-requiring reactions. (See Fig. 37–7.) The amount of free energy released in the conversion of ATP to ADP and phosphate is probably between 10,000 and 12,000 cal (10–12 kcal) per mole.*

ATP + HOH → ADP + phosphate + 8 to 12 kcal

---

* The exact amount of energy released in a living organism by the conversion of ATP to ADP and phosphate is not accurately known. The reaction under certain specific conditions known as standard conditions, *in vitro*, yields less energy, a value nearer 8 kcal/mole.

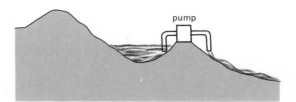

FIG. 37-3. Release of stored energy. The water in a mountain lake is analogous to chemical compounds which contain stored energy. Some of the energy can be released when the water runs downhill; however, the dam, which represents an energy barrier similar to the energy of activation in a chemical reaction, may prevent the water from flowing toward sea level. If a pump is installed to lift the water over the dam, however, release of energy can then take place spontaneously.

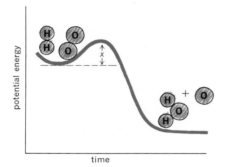

FIG. 37-4. Diagram of the energy relationships between hydrogen and oxygen gases and water. The end products have less energy than the reactants; thus, the reaction releases energy after the initial energy of activation (represented by x) is supplied. The energy barrier is relatively small. [Adapted from Baker and Allen, *Matter, Energy, and Life*, Addison-Wesley, 1965.]

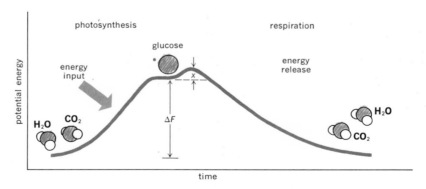

FIG. 37-5. An energy diagram showing the conversion of water and carbon dioxide to glucose, followed by the oxidation of glucose. Energy from the sun is "stored" in the "uphill" process of photosynthesis. This energy is released in respiration. The difference in free energy between glucose and the two substances, water and carbon dioxide, is represented by ΔF. The value x represents the energy of activation necessary for the oxidation of glucose. This energy is supplied by ATP. [Adapted from Baker and Allen, *Matter, Energy, and Life*, Addison-Wesley, 1965.]

FIG. 37–6. Waterfall analogy to biochemical energetics. When water falls over a high waterfall it generates tremendous amounts of energy. A waterwheel placed at the bottom of such a fall would be smashed. If, instead of one precipitous waterfall, the stream is diverted into a series of smaller falls, each one having a water wheel, the energy which the water loses can be converted into useful energy. When biochemical reactions that yield large amounts of energy proceed in a series of reactions, each of which can synthesize ATP, the same principle is shown.

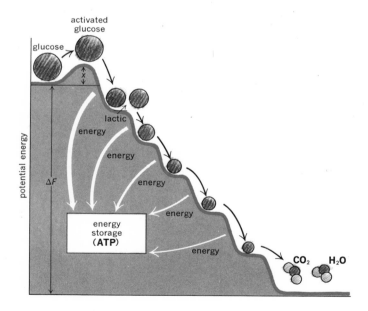

FIG. 37–7. The energetics of the oxidation of glucose. The diagram shows how glucose must first be activated (by ATP) before its energy is released. The release of this energy is shown as occurring in a series of steps, each of which generates ATP from ADP and phosphate. [Adapted from Baker and Allen, *The Study of Biology*, Addison-Wesley, 1967.]

37-5 ELECTRON TRANSPORT

The energy contained in foods is released primarily in the process of oxidation of the hydrogen atoms contained in the food. Hydrogen atoms, or, speaking more precisely, the electrons of these atoms are passed from one compound to another in the series of reactions known as electron transport. The enzymes and coenzymes necessary for electron transport are localized in the mitochondria of cells.

Electrons may take several different routes, and certain intermediates are not really known, but the scheme involving nicotinamide adenine dinucleotide (NAD), flavine adenine dinucleotide (FAD), and the cytochromes is probably the most important such system. The formulas for these compounds are given in Fig. 37-8. The substance nicotinamide adenine dinucleotide phosphate (NADP), which functions much as NAD does, contains an additional phosphate on the ribose unit attached to nicotinamide. There are several cytochromes all having structures similar to cytochrome c (See Fig. 37-9).

In this system, two electrons along with one proton are passed from an energy-rich molecule to NAD. Thus NAD is reduced, and the donor molecule is oxidized. In turn, $NADH_2$ passes the electrons to FAD which oxidizes the $NADH_2$, reduces the FAD, and releases energy. Then $FADH_2$ passes the electrons to the cytochromes. The cytochromes are complex molecules which contain iron in the 3+ state which is reversibly reduced to the 2+ state by the electrons it receives from $FADH_2$. One of the cytochromes eventually passes electrons to an oxygen atom which also acquires two protons, and the end product of the

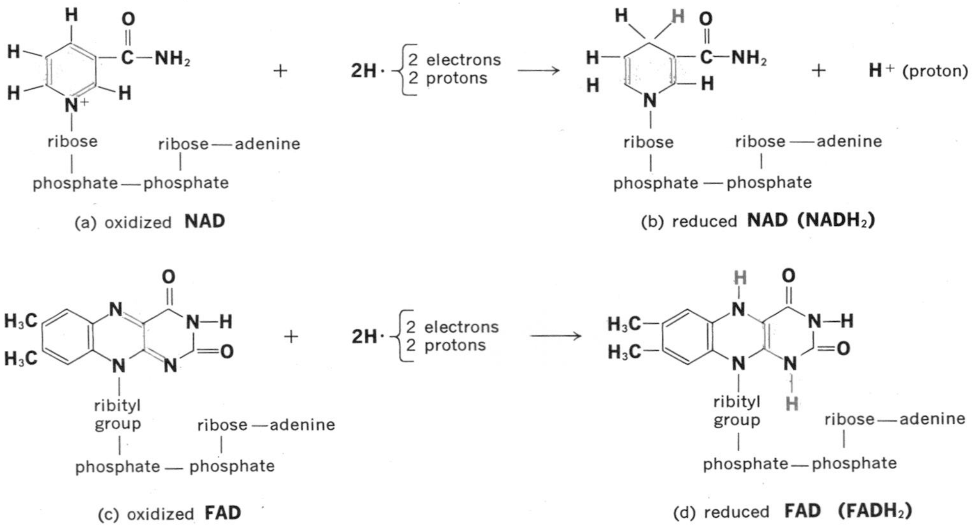

FIG. 37-8. Formulas of electron acceptors in the electron transport system: (a) shows oxidized NAD (see Fig. 36-13 for complete structure), (b) reduced NAD ($NADH_2$), (c) oxidized FAD, (d) reduced FAD ($FADH_2$).

series of reactions is water. In this series of reactions the combination of hydrogen with oxygen to produce water, a process that releases large amounts of energy, has been broken into several steps, and the potentially destructive or unusable amounts of energy are made available in useful-size packets. There are more intermediate compounds than those given above and in Figs. 37–8 and 37–10. However, the exact role played by each is not so firmly established as is that of NAD, FAD, and the cytochromes. For this reason and for simplification, these other compounds have not been included in this presentation.

We can summarize the process of electron transport as follows:

1) The substrate loses two electrons and one proton to NAD, converting it to $NADH_2$, and releasing a hydrogen ion (proton) to the surroundings.

2) The $NADH_2$ gives two electrons and one proton to FAD. In addition, the FAD acquires a proton from its surroundings and becomes $FADH_2$.

3) Since each molecule of the cytochromes can accept only one electron, two molecules are required to accept the two electrons from $FADH_2$. The two protons lost in the transformation of $FADH_2$ to FAD are released into the surroundings.

4) An atom of oxygen acquires two electrons from two molecules of a cytochrome, oxidizing the cytochrome and reducing the oxygen.

5) The oxygen acquires two protons to form water.

This process is given diagrammatically in Fig. 37–10.

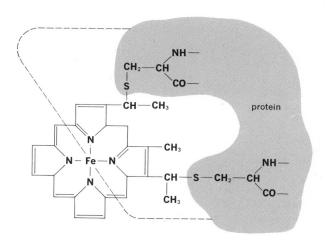

FIG. 37–9. The structure of cytochrome c. The heme group is bound to the protein molecule by sulfide linkages to the amino acid cysteine which is part of the protein. [Adapted from Baker and Allen, *The Study of Biology*, Addison-Wesley, 1967.]

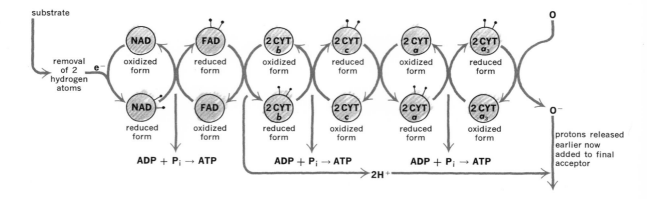

FIG. 37–10. A summary of electron transport. The diagram shows the removal of the two hydrogen atoms from an oxidizable substrate, the transport of the electrons, and the final acceptance of the electrons and two protons by an atom of oxygen to give water. The energy released is trapped in the synthesis of ATP from ADP and inorganic phosphate (P_i). [Adapted from Baker and Allen, *The Study of Biology*, Addison-Wesley, 1967.]

During the process of hydrogen transport, in a way still not fully understood, ATP is synthesized from ADP and phosphate. If NAD is the original electron acceptor there are usually three molecules of ATP synthesized for every two electron pairs (or two hydrogen atoms) or for every molecule of water formed. If FAD is the original electron acceptor, only two molecules of ATP are synthesized in the formation of water. Thus, by the process of electron transport, any chemical substance that can yield electrons (which are almost always released in combination with protons as hydrogen atoms) can result in the synthesis of ATP and the storage of energy. The synthesis of ATP, as well as electron transport, occurs primarily in the mitochondria of cells.

To illustrate, ethanol is oxidized to give acetic acid (probably in the form of acetyl coenzyme A) by two reactions, both of which involve NAD.

ethanol + NAD → NADH$_2$ + acetaldehyde

acetaldehyde + H$_2$O + NAD → NADH$_2$ + acetic acid

◄ An alternative pathway involves the oxidation of acetaldehyde, with FAD as the hydrogen acceptor. Thus ethanol can yield a molecule of acetic acid with the resultant synthesis of either six molecules of ATP (if both reactions use NAD) or five molecules of ATP (if one reaction uses NAD and the other FAD).

The complete oxidation of acetic acid involves a more complex process and can yield a total of twelve molecules of ATP.

CH$_3$COOH + 2O$_2$ → 2CO$_2$ + 2H$_2$O

The energy stored as the result of the complete biological oxidation of ethanol can be compared with the amount of energy released when ethanol is oxidized *in vitro*, as follows. The *in vivo* oxidation of one molecule of acetate is known to yield 12 molecules of ATP, and the conversion of ethanol to acetate gives either 5 or 6 molecules of ATP depending upon the pathway taken. If we use an average total value of 17.5 moles of ATP synthesized as the result of the oxidation of one mole of ethanol, and multiply this by 12 (the energy stored when one ADP is converted to an ATP), we get a total of 210 which is the number of kilocalories of energy stored when one mole of ethanol is oxidized *in vivo*. The *in vitro* oxidation of ethanol yields 312 kcal/mole. To determine the efficiency of storage of the energy released, we divide 210 by 312 and get 67%. If we use 8 kcal as the energy stored per mole of ATP, the efficiency is 140/312 or 45%. Even this lower figure is appreciably better than the efficiency with which an internal combustion engine converts the energy of fuel to other forms of energy. ▶

37–6 ENZYMES

In many respects biochemical reactions are similar to the chemical reactions occurring *in vitro*. They follow the laws of conservation of mass and energy and most require an energy of activation. The products formed are similar to those formed in organic reactions. Like many nonbiochemical reactions, they require catalysts in order to proceed at any appreciable rate. Although a few reactions that occur in living organisms proceed without catalysts, the greatest number require the biochemical catalysts, enzymes. An enzyme is usually defined in just these terms, as a catalyst of biological origin. All known enzymes contain protein. Some are composed only of protein; others require some cofactor other than protein in order to function. FAD and NAD are cofactors, usually called coenzymes, and function primarily in conjunction with a particular enzyme. (See Fig. 37–11.)

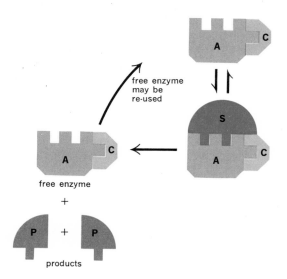

FIG. 37–11. A diagram showing the involvement of a coenzyme in an enzymatic reaction. The protein part of an enzyme (apoenzyme) combines with its coenzyme. The substrate molecule then attaches to the completed enzyme and is converted into the products of the reaction with the regeneration of the free enzyme. Not all enzymes require coenzymes. [Adapted from Baker and Allen, *Matter, Energy, and Life,* Addison-Wesley, 1965.]

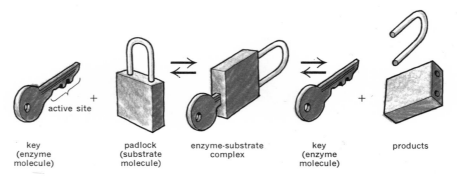

key   padlock   enzyme-substrate   key   products
(enzyme   (substrate   complex   (enzyme
molecule)   molecule)   molecule)

FIG. 37–12. The lock-and-key model for picturing the interaction of substrate and enzyme. [From Baker and Allen, *Matter, Energy, and Life*, Addison-Wesley, 1965.]

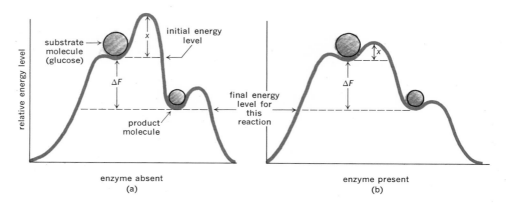

FIG. 37–13. The effect of an enzyme on the activation energy. The amount of activation energy is represented by x and the change in free energy by ΔF. The uncatalyzed reaction (on the left) requires a greater energy of activation. In reactions that proceed in a series of stepwise reactions, each reaction has its energy of activation. [Adapted from Baker and Allen, *Matter, Energy, and Life*, Addison-Wesley, 1965.]

Enzymes are remarkable catalysts in that they can accelerate the rate of reactions without either an increase in temperature or a major change in pH. They differ from most other catalysts since usually only one reaction is promoted and by-products are not formed. The exact way enzymes function is still the subject of active research. It is generally believed that the **substrate,** the substance reacting, is bound in some way to the surface of an enzyme. The binding site is apparently quite specific and can bind only one or only one kind of substrate molecule. This specificity has been compared to a lock and key. The enzyme (the key) functions only when a certain specific lock (substrate) or perhaps a certain type of lock is available. (See Fig. 37–12.)

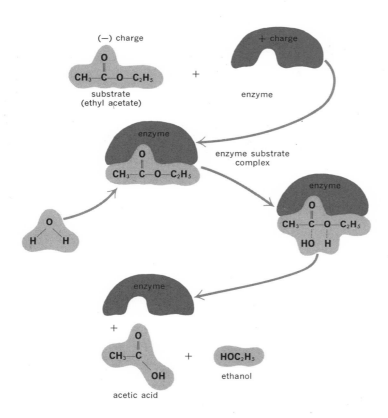

FIG. 37-14. A diagrammatic representation of an enzymatic reaction in which the enzyme makes the substrate more vulnerable to attack by the reacting molecule. In this reaction, the substrate (ethyl acetate) is bound to the enzyme both by complementary shapes and by opposite charges. This binding facilitates the hydrolysis of the ester bond by a molecule of water.

TABLE 37-2. Types of enzymes

Enzymes	Reaction Catalyzed
1. oxidoreductases	oxidation and reduction
2. transferases	transfer of a chemical grouping from one compound to another
3. hydrolases	hydrolytic reactions
4. lyases	nonhydrolytic addition or removal of groups
5. isomerases	conversion of a substance into one of its isomers
6. ligases	syntheses or, more specifically, the formation of various types of bonds

One way of answering the question, "What is it that enzymes really do?" is to say that they influence the course of a reaction so that less energy of activation is required. They *do not,* however, provide this energy. Enzymes cannot make *impossible* reactions proceed; the energy driving the reaction is still the difference between reactants and products. Enzymes, in common with other catalysts, only hasten the rate of attainment of equilibrium in a chemical reaction. (See Fig. 37–13.)

Another way of answering the question of what enzymes do is to say that they hold reactants at sites on the enzyme surface so that reactions which would otherwise require random collisions can take place more often. It has also been postulated that when enzymes bind substrates, they actually stretch the molecule somewhat as the rack stretched the victims of this instrument of torture. This tension makes it easier for specific bonds to be·broken. Perhaps this stretching exposes a specific bond (e.g., an ester bond) so that it is more easily attacked by another molecule (e.g., a water molecule) to bring about a reaction (e.g., the hydrolysis of an ester). (See Fig. 37–14.)

To discuss enzymes we must have methods for naming them. Originally enzymes were given trivial names, and we still use the names pepsin, catalase, and steapsin for enzymes that catalyze the hydrolysis of proteins, the decomposition of H_2O_2, and a mixture of lipid-hydrolyzing enzymes. A better nomenclature consisted of adding the suffix -*ase* to the name of the substrate upon which an enzyme acted, and we still use the names sucrase, urease, and arginase for enzymes that catalyze reactions involving sucrose, urea, and arginine. Since one substrate may undergo any one of several possible reactions, however, we now find it better to include not only the name of the substrate but also the type of reaction catalyzed when naming the enzyme.

The most recent system for naming enzymes is based on the type of reaction they catalyze. The categories used are given in Table 37–2. The complete name of the enzyme in this system includes the name of the substrate (or the general type of compound to which it belongs), as well as the type of reaction catalyzed. Under this system urease belongs to class 3, the hydrolases, and is called *urea amidohydrolase,* which indicates that the substrate urea is hydrolyzed and that the reaction is the hydrolysis of an amide. Sucrase is named as a β-D-*fructofuranoside fructohydrolase,* that is, an enzyme that hydrolyzes a fructose group from a compound which contains D-fructose in a beta linkage and in the furanose form. The basic classifications are broken down into subgroups and we can refer to an enzyme by a series of numbers. Urease, for instance, is 3.5.1.5. For the purposes of this book, many aspects of the formal nomenclature are too specific, so we will use trivial names as a general rule, sometimes with explanations as to the exact reaction catalyzed.

37–7 FAILURE OF METABOLIC REACTIONS

Metabolism has been characterized as a series of conversions from one compound to another, each conversion requiring an enzyme. We can illustrate the process as follows:

Compound A $\xrightarrow{\text{A-ase}}$ Compound B $\xrightarrow{\text{B-ase}}$ Compound C

C-D-ase ↙   ↘ C-E-ase

Compound D   Compound E

In this illustration, as long as sufficient compound A is available in the ingested food and as long as all enzymes are present and functioning normally, the reactions will proceed with the production of compounds D and E. (In reality, a better illustration would go as far as compounds X, Y, and Z.) If there is an inadequate amount of compound A in the diet, all other compounds would be deficient, unless perhaps B or C happened to be included in the diet. Such dietary deficiencies can be quickly corrected when they are detected.

More serious consequences result when an enzyme does not function. Failure of an enzyme may come about for several reasons: an organism may be unable to synthesize the enzyme either because of lack of components or because of some hereditary defect which prevents the synthesis. Normal enzymes may also fail to function when inhibitors are present. Many inhibitors of enzyme action are known. Many of the potent poisons such as cyanide and fluoride act as enzymatic inhibitors. Enzymes may also be inhibited by an excess of a normal metabolite other than their normal substrate.

In the illustration above, if the enzyme B-ase were absent or not functioning normally, we would find a deficiency of compounds C, D, and E. If these were vital compounds, such as the hormones adrenalin or thyroxine, the organism would function abnormally and might die. Another effect of the malfunction of B-ase would be that large amounts of B and perhaps of A (depending upon the reversibility of the conversion of A to B) would accumulate. This accumulation might result only in increased excretion of B which might go almost unnoticed unless B were colored or especially odorous. If, however, large amounts of B inhibited the reaction in another metabolic sequence (for instance, the conversion of compound M to compound N) here again the result might be extremely deleterious or even fatal.

37–8 HORMONES

A major problem faced by any organism is the control of the *rates* of the various reactions which are constantly taking place within the organism. While the enzymes are very important in this control, a further role is played by hormones. A **hormone** *may be defined as a product of an endocrine gland.* There are several such glands, such as the pituitary, the thyroid, parts of the pancreas, the adrenals, and parts of the ovaries or testes. (See Fig. 44–4.) The products of these glands are secreted directly into the blood stream and distributed to all parts of the body of an animal. Some of the glands listed above are also exocrine glands— they produce some secretions that flow through ducts to a definite site of action.

Hormones of higher animals are usually found to be either protein-containing or steroids. In many cases nonprotein matter is associated with the proteinaceous hormones. Insulin, which is the hormone of the pancreas, is a polypeptide which normally contains small amounts of the metal zinc. The hormones of the pituitary, such as the growth hormone, the thyroid-stimulating hormone, the hormones which influence the ovary and testes, as well as others from this source, are primarily proteins or polypeptides. The sex hormones produced by the ovary or testes as well as most of the hormones of the adrenal gland are steroid hormones. (See Section 35–6.) The hormones of the thyroid gland and of the medulla of the adrenal gland are derivatives of amino acids.

Although the physiological effects of the hormones, such as the increase of the basal metabolic rate by thyroxine or the effect of testosterone on the secondary sexual characteristics in the male are well known, the exact manner in which hormones exert their control on body processes is not known. Recent research indicates that hormones function by increasing the rate of synthesis of certain proteins, perhaps by first increasing the rate of synthesis of ribonucleic acid (RNA) which, in turn, influences the rate of protein synthesis. If the protein synthesized is an enzyme, the effects on metabolism are obvious.

A great deal of interrelation exists between the various hormones. One of the simplest examples is that between the thyroid-stimulating hormone of the pituitary and the thyroid hormone thyroxine and/or triiodothyronine. The thyroid-stimulating hormone induces the thyroid gland to produce its hormone thyroxine. Thyroxine, in turn, influences the pituitary gland and inhibits the production of the stimulating hormone. This kind of process has been called "feedback." If the thyroid gland cannot produce sufficient thyroxine because of a lack of iodine in the diet, excessive amounts of thyroid-stimulating hormones are produced, causing an enlargement of the thyroid gland, which is called a goiter.

There are many other feedback relationships between various endocrine glands, some of them extremely complex. For example, the sexual cycles in females, the production of inflammation and wound healing, and the control of the level of glucose in the blood are all influenced by relationships of endocrine glands and their hormones.

37–9 SUMMARY OF METABOLISM

The reactants and products formed in metabolic reactions are remarkably similar in all organisms which have been studied. These reactions, which occur in a number of small sequential steps, involve conversion of one substance to another within living organisms. The presence of a number of steps in an overall reaction not only aids in trapping energy from foods, but also transforms reactions requiring large amounts of energy to a series of small reactions, each of which can be driven by available energy. The introduction of a number of small steps also makes possible more sensitive control of reactions.

Each metabolic reaction is catalyzed by an enzyme. Failure of an enzyme to function normally usually causes a deficiency of some substance or substances and an accumulation of other substances. These deficiencies or excesses may have serious or fatal consequences for living organisms.

Anabolic reactions require energy which is provided by catabolic reactions, particularly oxidations. The ATP helps transfer energy to energy-requiring (endergonic) from energy-releasing (exergonic) reactions. Any substance that can be oxidized by NAD or FAD usually brings about the synthesis of ATP from ADP and phosphate. A molecule of reduced NAD normally yields three molecules of ATP, while one of FAD yields only two molecules of ATP when complete oxidation has taken place.

Both anabolic and catabolic reactions are going on all the time in all living organisms. Although an animal may maintain a given weight for a long time, the molecules of which he is composed are constantly being changed. When animals are given isotopically labelled foods, we soon find these isotopes incorporated in their body tissues. They then begin to be eliminated slowly. We characterize this condition as being a dynamic equilibrium. It is not like a chemical equilibrium, because new molecules are constantly being added and eliminated. The situation is better illustrated (Fig. 37–15) if we picture a vessel of water that maintains a constant level even though water is constantly entering and leaving.

FIG. 37–15. An illustration of dynamic equilibrium. In the illustration, water flows from a faucet into a container that has an overflow outlet. Although the amount of water in the container remains constant, individual molecules are constantly being added from the faucet and removed from the overflow. If we added a dye to the water, we would see that it would gradually be washed away. Essentially, this is what we see when we give radioactive isotopes to a plant or animal and note their disappearance even though the plant or animal is neither growing nor shrinking in size.

We often speak of a **metabolic half-life.** This is the time it takes to replace half of a given body component. Half of the protein in the liver of a rat is replaced in 7 days so we say that rat-liver protein has a metabolic half-life of 7 days.

The next several chapters are concerned with the metabolism of various types of compounds. We will discuss specific instances that led to the generalizations we have stated in this chapter. We will examine normal catabolic and anabolic reactions and trace the effects of blockages of such pathways or abnormal reactions, and the relation of these abnormalities to disease.

IMPORTANT TERMS

ATP	Chymotrypsin	FAD	Nucleosidase
Alimentary canal	Coenzyme	Free energy	Nucleotidase
Amylase	Cytochromes	Ingestion	Pepsin
Anabolic	Digestion	Inhibitor	Peptidase
Assimilation	Endergonic	Lymph	Photosynthesis
Bile	Energy of activation	Metabolite	Saliva
Catabolic	Enzyme	Metabolism	Substrate
Chlorophyll	Exergonic	NAD	Trypsin

WORK EXERCISES

1. Write equations for the digestion of

   a) sucrose   b) a triglyceride   c) ethyl acetate

2. List the enzymes necessary for the complete digestion of

   a) a protein   b) a triglyceride   c) a polysaccharide

3. What type of organic compound is being hydrolyzed in the digestion of (a) a protein, (b) a triglyceride, (c) a polysaccharide?

4. Substance *A* gives 200 kcal/mole when completely oxidized *in vitro*. Its metabolism to the same end products results in the synthesis of 15 moles of ATP from ADP and phosphate. What is the efficiency of conversion of the energy of compound *A* to the energy stored in ATP?

5. How do enzymes differ from other catalysts?

6. Name the enzyme catalyzing each of the following reactions:

   a) triglyceride + water → fatty acids + glycerol
   b) maltose + water → glucose
   c) RNA + water → organic bases + ribose + phosphate
   d) adenylic acid + water → adenosine + phosphate
   e) adenosine + water → adenine + ribose

7. Some persons secrete little or no hydrochloric acid in their stomachs. How would their digestion differ from that of a normal person? What treatment might be used for these persons?

8. Why must the growth hormone be administered by injection rather than by mouth in order to be effective?

9. How does an enzyme affect the equilibrium of a reaction?

10. Using electron dot formulas, show the actual number of electrons in the oxidized and reduced part of the riboflavin molecule that changes when FAD → $FADH_2$.

Consult a basic biochemistry text to find the answers to the following:

11. What are some urine tests that are of metabolic significance?

12. What are the digestive hormones, and how do they function?

SUGGESTED READING

Changeux, J. P., "The Control of Biochemical Reactions," *Scientific American*, Apr. 1965 (Offprint #1008). The author discusses the control of enzymes which in turn control other syntheses—a complex theory is involved, but is well explained in this article.

Chappell, G. S., *Through he Alimentary Canal with Gun and Camera,* Dover, New York, 1963. A humorous account of a totally imaginary, pseudoscientific trip.

Kleiber, M., *The Fire of Life—An Introduction to Animal Energetics*, John Wiley, New York, 1961. The title explains the book, but does not indicate that it is well written and interesting.

Lehninger, A. L., *Bioenergetics.* W. A. Benjamin, New York, 1965. A modern, readable (paperback) introduction to the processes of energy transfer in living systems.

Lehninger, A. L., "How Cells Transform Energy," *Scientific American*, Sept. 1961 (Offprint #91).

Lehninger, A. L., "Energy Transformation in the Cell," *Scientific American*, May, 1960 (Offprint #69).

Mayerson, H. S., "The Lymphatic System," *Scientific American*, June 1963 (Offprint #158). This well-illustrated article describes the function of this important circulatory system.

Racker, E., "The Membrane of the Mitochondrion," *Scientific American*, Feb. 1968. The process of oxidative phosphorylation, the place where it occurs, and the inner membrane of the mitochondrion are discussed in this well-illustrated article.

Stumpf, P. K., "ATP," *Scientific American*, Apr. 1953 (Offprint #41). For further information about this important molecule we recommend this article.

Chapter 38   METABOLISM OF CARBOHYDRATES

38-1 INTRODUCTION

Carbohydrates that are ingested by an animal are usually in the form of high-molecular-weight polymers, principally the starches and cellulose. The animal is then faced with two major problems: first, that of degrading the polymer into units small enough to be absorbed through the wall of the intestine, and second, that of releasing the energy of the carbohydrate and converting it into a useful form. Some of the degraded carbohydrate is reconverted to the polymer glycogen which is then stored in the liver and muscles, but this result accounts for only a relatively small amount of the carbohydrates digested by animals. Most digested carbohydrates are oxidized to carbon dioxide and water with the release of energy or are converted to lipids and stored.

Plants metabolize carbohydrates quite differently. Instead of ingesting polymeric carbohydrates, green plants make their own carbohydrates through the process of photosynthesis. Some of this carbohydrate may be oxidized to yield energy for energy-requiring reactions in the plant. The remainder of the saccharide units are polymerized to yield starches and cellulose. Plant biochemistry and photosynthesis are discussed in detail in Chapter 43. The following discussion is concerned primarily with the metabolism of carbohydrates in animals.

38-2 DIGESTION OF CARBOHYDRATES

The digestion of starch begins in the mouth where salivary amylase is added to food as it is being chewed. **Amylases** catalyze the hydrolysis of starch to give molecules of the disaccharide, maltose, and smaller starchlike molecules called dextrins. (See Fig. 38-1 for a representation of the action of an amylase.) The action of salivary amylase continues

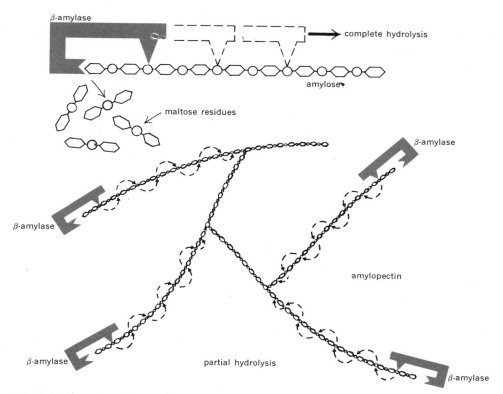

FIG. 38–1. The action of an amylase on starch. The enzyme β-amylase aids in the digestion of starch by catalyzing the hydrolysis of every second α 1–4 linkage in a starch molecule. This reaction yields maltose which must be further digested under the influence of maltase to yield glucose. Since β-amylase catalyzes the hydrolysis of only α 1–4 linkages, its action stops when a 1–6 branch is reached. A starch molecule in which degradation has stopped at the 1–6 branches is called a dextrin. [Adapted from *Principles of Plant Physiology* by Arthur W. Galston and James Bonner, W. H. Freeman and Company. Copyright © 1952. Reprinted from an original article by W. Z. Hassid and R. M. McCready, *J. A. Chem. Soc.* **65**, 1943, p. 1159.]

as food passes through the esophagus but stops when the food is exposed to the acidity of the stomach. The extremely low pH of the stomach stops the action of salivary amylase; however, the hydrogen ions themselves serve as catalysts for hydrolysis of bonds between saccharide units. These acid-catalyzed hydrolyses tend to act at random sites in the starch molecules and produce a mixture of mono-, di-, tri-, and higher saccharides. Following most normal meals, only part of the starches are converted to the monosaccharide level by the time the food leaves the stomach and passes into the small intestine.

In the small intestine, pancreatic amylases attack the remaining starch molecules, and the disaccharidase, maltase, completes the digestion by converting maltose to glucose.

Disaccharides such as sucrose are not digested by enzymes until they reach the small intestine where the disaccharidases convert them to monosaccharides. Monosaccharides are not digested but are absorbed in the same form in which they were eaten.

The carbohydrate cellulose is not digested by higher animals. In most animals, cellulose is excreted as such; it makes up the so-called roughage of the diet and contributes to the bulk of the feces. Cattle, sheep, and similar animals, however, are able to use the cellulose of their diet. Those animals have several food pouches or stomachs; the first of them contains various microorganisms, some of which can convert cellulose to glucose. Since this conversion occurs long before the food enters the intestine, the glucose produced by the hydrolysis of cellulose can be absorbed and utilized by ruminants.

◄ The name *ruminant* is derived from the name given to the first food pouch—the rumen. This group of animals includes goats, antelopes, giraffes, deer, and camels, in addition to sheep and cattle. These animals swallow their food without really chewing it, and later, while resting, regurgitate the food and chew it in a process described as chewing their cud. The process seems to mix saliva and microorganisms from the rumen with the food prior to its being carried to another food pouch, the abomasum, where it is acted upon by the acid gastric juice. ►

One other type of animal—the insect called the termite—can also make use of cellulose. This is, of course, why termites are so destructive. They eat their way through wooden structures using the cellulose of the wood for energy. Again it is not the termite itself, but a microorganism, a protozoan, living in the gut of the termite that contains the enzymes necessary to degrade cellulose into a useful form—glucose.

38-3 ABSORPTION AND FURTHER METABOLISM OF CARBOHYDRATES

After complete digestion has converted carbohydrates into monosaccharides, they are absorbed through the wall of the intestine into the blood stream. The portal vein carries the absorbed monosaccharides to the liver where they may be either synthesized into glycogen, oxidized to CO_2 and H_2O, or perhaps released as monosaccharides and allowed to circulate to other parts of the body. Although other organs are capable of metabolizing glucose, the liver is responsible for much of the carbohydrate metabolism. Under the influence of the pancreatic hormone, insulin, and other factors, the liver regulates the amount of glucose in the circulating blood. When the level of glucose in the blood is high, as it is after digestion of a meal rich in carbohydrates, the liver synthesizes large amounts of glycogen. When the amount of blood glucose is low, as it would be following intensive exercise, glycogen is depolymerized to yield glucose. Thus the liver, under the influence of insulin and other hormones, keeps the level of glucose in the blood relatively constant. The digestion and further metabolism of carbohydrates can be summarized as follows:

$$\text{polysaccharides} \xrightarrow{\text{digestion}} \text{monosaccharides} \xrightarrow[\substack{\text{intestinal} \\ \text{wall}}]{\substack{\text{absorption} \\ \text{through}}} \text{monosaccharides} \longrightarrow CO_2 + H_2O$$
$$\downarrow$$
$$\text{glycogen}$$

The concentration of glucose in the blood is extremely important for proper functioning of the human body. The normal fasting level of glucose is between 70 and 90 mg/100 ml. (Some methods of analysis which measure other compounds in addition to glucose give slightly higher values.) A concentration of glucose below the normal range is called *hypoglycemia*, and one higher than the normal level is called *hyperglycemia*. (See Fig. 38-2.)

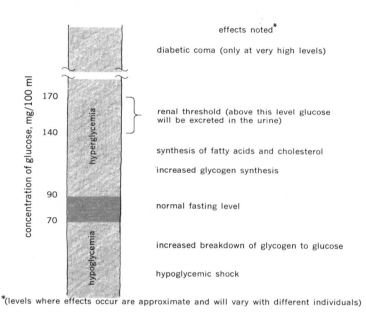

*(levels where effects occur are approximate and will vary with different individuals)

FIG. 38-2. Effects noted at various levels of blood glucose.

Extreme hypoglycemia produces a series of reactions known as shock. The symptoms may include the trembling of muscle, a feeling of weakness, and a whitening of the skin. Serious hypoglycemia can cause unconsciousness and lowered blood pressure, and may result in death. Loss of consciousness is probably due to the lack of glucose in the brain which depends on this sugar for most of its energy. Extreme hypoglycemia is usually due to the presence of excessive amounts of insulin. Some individuals who suffer from hyperinsulinism (overproduction of insulin) are subject to hypoglycemia if they eat a meal rich in carbohydrates. The most common cause of hypoglycemia is probably the injection of excessive amounts of insulin by diabetics; most diabetics carry candy or other glucose-rich substances with them to eat if they feel the onset of hypoglycemia. It is interesting to note that insulin shock has been used in treatment of mental diseases.

Research on hyperglycemia has shown that at levels higher than normal, the conversion of glucose to glycogen is stimulated. At these higher levels, fatty acids and cholesterol are synthesized from glucose. At some level, between 140 and 170 mg/100 ml for most people, glucose is excreted in the urine. The concentration of glucose necessary for the appearance of glucosuria (glucose in the urine) is called the *renal threshold*. Actually, glucose is always filtered into the urine in the kidneys but is reabsorbed before the urine leaves the kidney. Thus glucosuria represents not so much an abnormal filtering out of glucose but rather an inability of the kidney tubule cells to reabsorb the glucose. Extremely high levels of blood glucose are observed in cases of diabetic coma; factors other than hyperglycemia are probably responsible for the coma, however.

A variety of hormones controls the level of blood glucose. Insulin (from the pancreas) lowers blood glucose and enhances the conversion of glucose to glycogen. Adrenalin (epinephrine), one or more pituitary hormones, and a second pancreatic hormone—glucagon —all tend to raise the concentration of glucose in the blood. All these factors, acting together, keep the blood glucose level within certain limits beyond which the animal could not survive.

38–4 GLYCOGEN SYNTHESIS AND BREAKDOWN

The major intermediates in the conversion of glucose to glycogen are glucose 6-phosphate and glucose 1-phosphate. The same two intermediates are involved in the conversion of glycogen to glucose, but there are at least two instances where the conversions take different pathways. We can think of the situation as being similar to going between city *A* and city *D* with cities *B* and *C* being intermediate points, where there are oneway roads for part, but not all, of the way.

◄ The phosphate required to convert glucose to glucose 6-phosphate, as well as the energy required for the reaction, is provided by ATP. The reaction may be catalyzed by an enzyme known as hexokinase. Glucose 6-phosphate is then converted to glucose 1-phosphate. In glycogen synthesis, glucose 1-phosphate next reacts with uridine triphosphate (UTP) to give the compound UDP-glucose. Then UDP-glucose condenses to give glycogen, and the UDP is set free. The synthesis of glycogen requires a small amount of preformed glycogen to act as a pattern or primer, and also requires another enzyme or set of enzymes to make the 1-6 branches which are important in the glycogen molecule.

When glycogen is converted to glucose 1-phosphate in the process of glycogenolysis, the enzyme catalyzing this reaction is different from the glycogen synthetase which catalyzed its formation. The enzyme catalyzing the degradation is a phosphorylase, i.e., an enzyme that uses phosphoric acid to cleave a larger molecule. Although this enzyme can catalyze the synthesis of glycogen, equilibrium lies in the direction of the formation of glucose 1-phosphate. This glucose phosphate is then isomerized to glucose 6-phosphate which can then enter a variety of metabolic sequences.

The transformation of glucose 6-phosphate to glucose involves an enzyme called a phosphatase. The reaction gives glucose and phosphoric acid. It does not result in the synthesis of ATP from ADP and phosphate, so the reaction is not the reverse of that catalyzed by hexokinase. (The symbol ℗ is used to indicate a phosphate group.) These reactions may be summarized as follows:

The effects of deficiencies of the enzymes that catalyze these reactions are discussed in Section 38–11. ▶

The irreversibility of parts of the scheme for the reversible conversion of glucose to glycogen is an illustration of the generalization that synthetic and degradative pathways may use the same general intermediates but do not follow the same paths. A further reference to this is made in Section 40–5.

38-5 DEGRADATION OF GLUCOSE

The conversion of glucose to carbon dioxide and water, with the release of much of the energy contained in the glucose molecule, is essentially an oxidation. The amount of free energy released in the complete oxidation of one mole of glucose is about 690 kcal.

glucose + oxygen → carbon dioxide + water + 690 kcal

This amount of energy is much greater than the amount that can be stored effectively in a molecule of ATP. From the discussion of the previous chapter, we would expect that the degradation and oxidation of glucose proceeds in a series of steps, some of which are capable of yielding energy that can be stored in ATP. This is true, and we now know a great number of intermediates involved in the process. For convenience, we generally think of one series of reactions as leading from glucose to either pyruvic* or lactic acid. We call this series of reactions **glycolysis.** The second series of reactions involves the conversion of pyruvic acid or lactic acid to acetic acid, and finally to carbon dioxide and water. This series is referred to as **aerobic metabolism** and involves the **citric acid cycle** or the *Krebs cycle*.

---

* Lactic, pyruvic, and acetic acids are weak acids and ionize only slightly; however, at the pH of the body, these substances are present as lactate, pyruvate, and acetate ions. Acetate is present in most biological systems as acetyl coenzyme A. Throughout the biochemistry section of this book, the term acid may be used to refer to a molecule, but should not be understood as meaning that the substance is actually present as the acid.

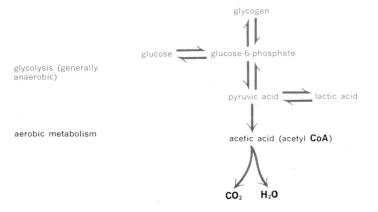

FIG. 38–3. A summary of the metabolism of glucose.

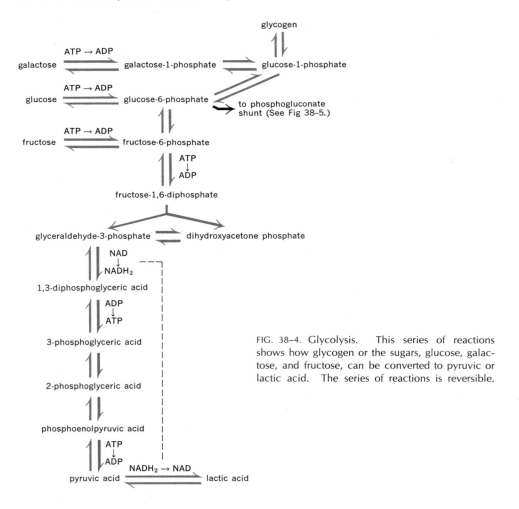

FIG. 38–4. Glycolysis. This series of reactions shows how glycogen or the sugars, glucose, galactose, and fructose, can be converted to pyruvic or lactic acid. The series of reactions is reversible.

The term *aerobic* means in the presence of air. Actually, it is the oxygen of the air that is required for aerobic reactions. Anaerobic reactions do not require oxygen. In some cases, oxygen inhibits anaerobic processes, while in others the presence of oxygen has no effect on the reactions. The degradation of glucose is summarized in Fig. 38–3.

38-6 GLYCOLYSIS

Since the prefix *glyco-* is used to designate carbohydrates generally and not only glycogen, the term glycolysis means the lysis or degradation of carbohydrates. The reactions of glycolysis can proceed without oxygen to yield lactic acid. They may also proceed in the presence of oxygen, and in this case the end product is pyruvic acid.

```
glucose ⎫
        ⎬ glucose 6-phosphate  ──with oxygen──→ pyruvic acid
glycogen ⎭                     ──without oxygen──→ lactic acid
```

Glycolysis results in the splitting of a 6-carbon compound into two 3-carbon compounds, and the synthesis of ATP. The reactions of glycolysis are summarized in Fig. 38–4 and discussed in detail in the following paragraphs.

◄ We may consider glycolysis as starting with either glucose or glycogen. The first step in either case involves addition of a phosphate group. Ordinary phosphate is sufficient for phosphorylation of glycogen, but ATP is required to phosphorylate glucose. Glucose 6-phosphate is formed in one step from glucose, and after two steps when glycogen is the starting material.

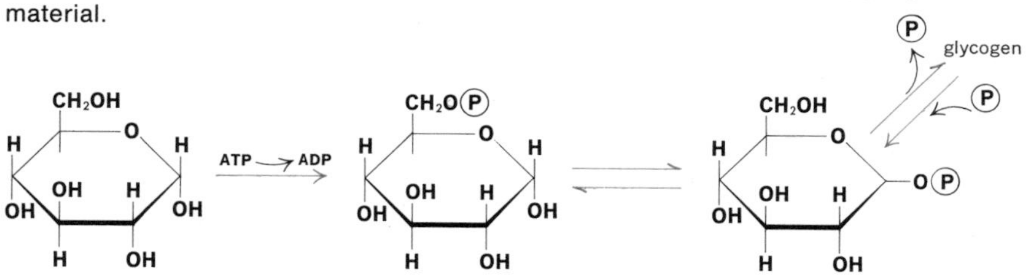

glucose   glucose 6-phosphate

By an isomerization, glucose 6-phosphate is converted to fructose 6-phosphate: This reaction is best shown using straight-chain or Fisher formulas.

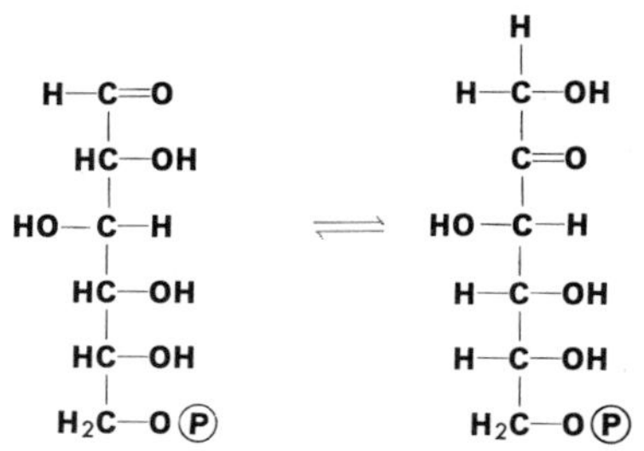

glucose 6-phosphate   fructose 6-phosphate

At this point another molecule of ATP is required to transform fructose 6-phosphate to fructose 1,6-diphosphate. This diphosphofructose is then split to give two 3-carbon compounds, glyceraldehyde 3-phosphate, and dihydroxy-acetone phosphate.

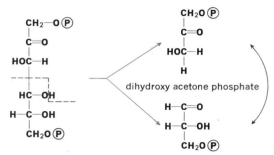

fructose 1,6-diphosphate   glyceraldehyde 3-phosphate

Dihydroxy acetone phosphate represents a dead end in this metabolic pathway; only the fact that the enzyme triosephosphate isomerase can catalyze the conversion of dihydroxyacetone phosphate to glyceraldehyde 3-phosphate prevents the loss of half the energy of the glucose molecule. We can say that the net effect of the splitting of one molecule of fructose diphosphate is the formation of two molecules of glyceraldehyde 3-phosphate. So far the glycolytic scheme has required an energy input in the form of two molecules of ATP, but has not yet released any of the energy of glucose.

The next step in glycolysis, the conversion of glyceraldehyde 3-phosphate to 1,3-diphosphoglyceric acid, is a complex reaction. It involves the addition of a phosphate and the oxidation of the molecule from an aldehyde to an acid. This oxidation results in the formation of reduced NAD ($NADH_2$).

glyceraldehyde   phosphoric   1,3-diphospho-
3-phosphate   acid   glyceric acid

We will discuss the fate of this reduced NAD later, since we wish to follow the general course of glycolysis which involves the further reaction of 1,3-diphospho-glyceric acid.

One bond between the phosphoric acid and glyceric acid in 1,3-diphosphoglyceric acid is an anhydride linkage, and as such its rupture provides sufficient energy to synthesize a molecule of ATP from ADP and phosphate. The other product of the hydrolysis of 1,3-diphosphoglyceric acid is 3-phosphoglyceric acid.

1,3-diphospho-   3-phospho-
glyceric acid   glyceric acid

The compound 3-phosphoglyceric acid is converted to its isomer, 2-phosphoglyceric acid. Removal of a molecule of water from the latter compound gives the enol form of phosphopyruvic acid.

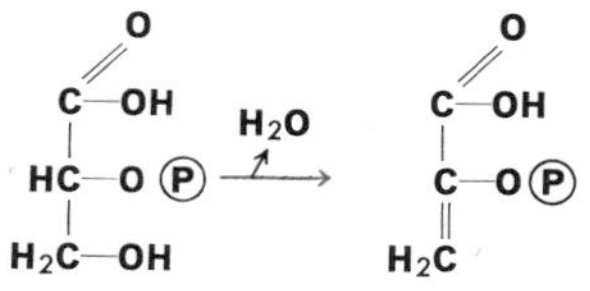

2-phospho-   phosphoenol-
glyceric acid   pyruvic acid

Hydrolysis of phosphoenolpyruvic acid again gives both the phosphate and sufficient energy to result in the synthesis of ATP from ADP.

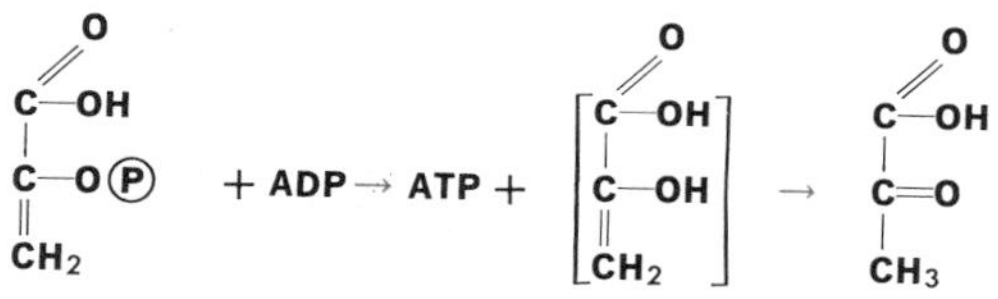

phosphoenol-   pyruvic acid   pyruvic acid
pyruvic acid   (enol form)   keto form

With the removal of the phosphate we are left with the nonphosphorylated compound pyruvic acid. It is of interest to note that phosphorylated carbohydrates are found almost always within cells, and the nonphosphorylated compounds, glucose, pyruvic acid, and lactic acid are found in the blood stream. ►

The splitting of glucose to two 3-carbon compounds results in the formation of reduced NAD. Pyruvic acid is the end product of glycolysis if oxygen is present and the reduced NAD (formed in the conversion of glyceraldehyde 3-phosphate to 1,3-diphosphoglyceric acid) is oxidized through an electron-transport chain to give water. When glycolysis occurs in the absence of oxygen, it is necessary that some other agent be found for oxidizing the reduced NAD. The oxidized form of NAD is an essential catalyst; without it, glycolysis would stop with the accumulation of glyceraldehyde 3-phosphate. The compound which oxidizes NAD in anaerobic glycolysis is pyruvic acid itself. In this process, the pyruvic acid is reduced to give lactic acid. Thus we say that lactic acid is the normal end product of anaerobic glycolysis.

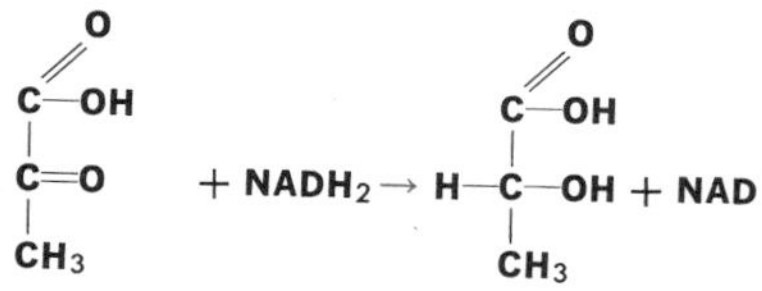

pyruvic acid   lactic acid

Monosaccharides other than glucose are also metabolized in glycolysis. Fructose makes up half of the sucrose molecule, and is a product of digestion of any sucrose-containing foods. Fructose is phosphorylated to give fructose 6-phosphate, which is a normal glycolytic intermediate. Lactose, commonly known as milk sugar, produces one molecule of glucose and one of galactose when hydrolyzed in the digestive process. Full utilization of the energy of lactose requires that galactose be metabolized.

◄ The route by which galactose enters the glycolytic pathway involves phosphorylation to give galactose 1-phosphate. This compound is then converted to its isomer glucose 1-phosphate by a change in configuration of the alcoholic OH group on carbon number 4.

galactose 1-phosphate   glucose 1-phosphate

The glucose 1-phosphate so formed cannot be distinguished from that formed from glycogen or glucose, and it is metabolized via the glycolytic reactions. ►

The glycolysis of one molecule of glucose requires the investment of two molecules of ATP, and results in the synthesis of four molecules of ATP. (There are two reactions which yield ATP, but one molecule of glucose gives two molecules of each of the reactants, and hence two molecules of ATP at each of the steps.) Thus the net energy gain in anaerobic glycolysis is the formation of two molecules of ATP per molecule of glucose. The $NADH_2$ which is generated is oxidized to NAD by the conversion of pyruvate to lactate.

Aerobic glycolysis gives more ATP synthesis since the oxidation of each $NADH_2$, with the formation of H_2O, gives an average of three ATP's (Section 37–3); there are two reduced NAD molecules per molecule of glucose, so we get six ATP's from this source. When we add these to the two that are obtained whether or not oxygen is present, the net energy trapping in aerobic glycolysis is eight molecules of ATP per molecule of glucose.

◄ The free energy resulting from complete oxidation of some glycolytically significant compounds is

glucose, 690 kcal/mole   pyruvic acid, 275 kcal/mole   lactic acid, 315 kcal/mole.

From these data we see that there is more potential energy in lactic acid than in pyruvic acid. Since two moles of either pyruvic or lactic acid are formed from one mole of glucose, the energy differences are

690 − 2(275) or 140 kcal/mole for the conversion of glucose to pyruvic acid, and
690 − 2(315) or 60 kcal/mole for the conversion of glucose to lactic acid.

From this calculation we see that 140/690 or about 20% of the energy of glucose is released when glycolysis is aerobic and the end products are pyruvic acid and water. Only 60/690 or about 9% of the energy is released when glycolysis is anaerobic and lactic acid is formed as the only end product.

We can calculate the efficiency with which the released energy is trapped in ATP as follows. The formation of pyruvic acid and water results in the conversion of 8 molecules of ADP to ATP. If we multiply 8 by 12 kcal, which is the energy stored when a mole of ADP is converted to one of ATP, we get 96 kcal of energy stored. Since 140 kcal of energy is released and 96 are trapped, the efficiency is about 96/140 or 70% for aerobic glycolysis. Anaerobic glycolysis results in the synthesis of only 2 ATP's per molecule of glucose, so we have a storage of only 24 kcals of energy. The amount of the energy of glucose released is 60 kcal, so the efficiency of trapping of the released energy in anaerobic glycolysis is only 24/60 or 40%. Thus we can see that not only does anaerobic glycolysis release less of the energy of glucose than does aerobic glycolysis, but that it also traps the released energy much less efficiently. ▶

Glycolysis results in the conversion of the energy of glucose to ATP. Only a small part of the energy of glucose is released; most of it is still in the lactic acid or pyruvic acid which is left at the end of the process. However, this amount of energy is apparently sufficient to support life and growth of anaerobic bacteria. Some of these bacteria are characterized as lactobacilli because of the lactic acid they produce. Human muscles, particularly those working with inadequate amounts of oxygen, can use anaerobic glycolysis as a source of energy and they, too, produce lactic acid. Lactic acid in their growth media eventually prevents further growth of bacteria. Lactic acid in the muscles of animals may be the cause of cramps. A more beneficial scheme would result in the release of a greater percentage of the energy of the glucose and would end with products such as carbon dioxide and water that were nontoxic and easy to eliminate. Such a system exists and will be discussed, after a few digressions, in the section on aerobic metabolism. ▶

◀ 38-7 THE PHOSPHOGLUCONIC ACID SHUNT

Not all glucose 6-phosphate is metabolized by being converted to fructose 6-phosphate. An alternative pathway involves the oxidation of glucose 6-phosphate to 6-phosphogluconic acid. The series of reactions resulting from this conversion is called the *phosphogluconate shunt*. The term shunt indicates a bypass, and in some ways this pathway is a bypass to glycolysis. The phosphogluconate pathway is shown in Fig. 38–5.

The pathway provides oxidations in the first two reactions and thus provides energy. The energy here is transferred to nicotinamide adenine dinucleotide phosphate (NADP), a compound much like NAD but containing an additional phosphate group. Reduced NADP is an important energy source for some biosynthetic reactions, particularly for lipid synthesis. Enzymes for the phosphogluconate pathway are found in tissues that synthesize lipids. In addition to producing $NADPH_2$, this pathway results in the synthesis of pentoses, and is probably the major source of the ribose and deoxyribose needed for nucleic acid synthesis.

Many tissues, particularly the liver, have enzymes for both glycolysis and the phosphogluconate series of reactions. These tissues can metabolize glucose by either pathway, and the pathway chosen probably depends on conditions such as the availability of oxygen and the level of $NADPH_2$ or of pentoses in the cells or in the circulating blood that moves through the tissues. Muscle and brain tissue apparently use the glycolytic pathway exclusively for metabolism of carbohydrates, since they do not contain the enzymes necessary for the phosphogluconate pathway. Some bacteria use reactions similar to this pathway. It is interesting to note that the photosynthesis of carbohydrates involves many of the intermediate compounds found in the phosphogluconate reaction sequence. It also involves NADP. ▶

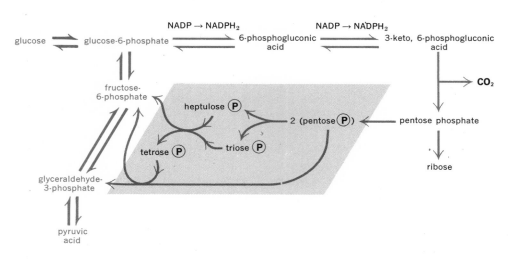

FIG. 38-5. The phosphogluconate shunt. This series of reactions is an alternative to those of glycolysis. The shaded area represents various possible condensations that may be used to convert pentose phosphate molecules to glyceraldehyde phosphate or fructose 6-phosphate. Glycolytic reactions are also shown for reference.

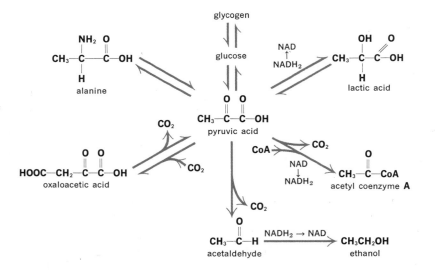

FIG. 38-6. Metabolism of pyruvic acid. Pyruvic acid represents a major branching point in metabolism. Some of the important products derived directly from pyruvic acid are shown.

38–8 METABOLISM OF PYRUVIC ACID

Pyruvic acid may undergo any of several alternate reactions, and thus represents a major branching point in metabolism. Some of these reactions lead to other series of reactions, and some represent metabolic dead ends. Figure 38–6 summarizes these reactions.

Addition of an amino group transforms pyruvic acid to the amino acid alanine. The reverse reaction also occurs and represents one method for conversion of amino acids into carbohydrates. Addition of carbon dioxide, perhaps not to pyruvic acid itself but to phosphoenolpyruvic acid, gives the dicarboxylic acid oxaloacetic acid whose significance will be shown later. The reversible conversion of pyruvic acid to lactic acid has been discussed previously. This conversion represents a metabolic dead end, and lactic acid, if it is to be further metabolized, must first be changed back to pyruvic acid. In normal muscle tissue when there is an adequate supply of oxygen, it is doubtful that any lactic acid is formed. Pyruvic acid may, by a reversal of glycolysis, be converted to glucose or glycogen.

Pyruvic acid may lose a molecule of carbon dioxide in either of two ways. These two different methods lead to quite different pathways and represent a major difference in metabolism in different kinds of organisms. In the simpler process, carbon dioxide is lost and acetaldehyde is formed:

$$\underset{\text{pyruvic acid}}{CH_3-\overset{\overset{\displaystyle O}{\|}}{C}-COOH} \rightarrow \underset{\text{acetaldehyde}}{CH_3-\overset{\overset{\displaystyle O}{\|}}{C}-H} + CO_2$$

The acetaldehyde may then be reduced to yield ethanol. This pathway is found primarily in yeasts, and is the basis of alcoholic fermentation. In this process yeasts metabolize glucose through the anaerobic glycolytic pathway with the formation of pyruvic acid. They do not, however, oxidize the reduced NAD by transforming pyruvic acid to lactic acid. Instead, they use the reduced NAD to convert acetaldehyde to ethanol:

$$\underset{\text{acetaldehyde}}{CH_3-\overset{\overset{\displaystyle O}{\|}}{C}-H} + NADH_2 \rightarrow \underset{\text{ethanol}}{CH_3-\overset{\overset{\displaystyle H \quad OH}{\diagup}}{\underset{\underset{\displaystyle H}{|}}{C}}} + NAD$$

Thus the alcoholic fermentation of carbohydrates yields as end products carbon dioxide and ethanol. The series of reactions may be summarized as

$$C_6H_{12}O_6 \rightarrow 2C_2H_5OH + 2CO_2$$

The process does not involve oxygen, and the amount of energy trapped by the yeasts is small (two ATP molecules per molecule of glucose), but is sufficient to support their growth and reproduction. Eventually the ethanol formed by the yeasts results in a medium that will not support further growth, and they are thus inhibited by one of the products of their metabolism.

◄ Alcoholic fermentations have been known and widely used since prehistoric times. The widespread availability of both carbohydrates and yeasts has led to a variety of alcoholic beverages. Starches of wheat and barley yield beer, sugar of grapes gives wine, fermented honey gives mead—the list of conversions is almost endless. When alcohol is removed from the fermentation mixture by distillation, we get vodka, saki, brandy, whiskey, and other beverages. While all these beverages contain large amounts of alcohol, the differences between them are due to compounds other than alcohol which either distill over with the alcohol or are added later.

The process of fermentation has been explained in many ways. The Greeks described it as the god Dionysius acting upon grape juice; Pasteur realized that the fermenting agents were yeasts; we now describe fermentation as being the enzymatically catalyzed conversion of carbohydrates to ethanol and carbon dioxide. The process of alcohol production has always fascinated man. However, he has undoubtedly been more concerned with the effects achieved by consumption of the products than he has with understanding the process of the formation of alcohol.

An interesting abnormality, recently reported in the press, involved a Japanese man who was repeatedly accused of drunkenness even though he maintained that he had not consumed any alcoholic beverages. He was found to have, as the result of a previous injury, an extra pouch in his stomach. This pouch, which was protected from the effects of the acid gastric juice, was harboring a colony of yeasts which were very efficiently producing ethanol. He then, quite unconsciously, absorbed the alcohol with the usual results. It is not likely, however, that similar pouches are present in the stomachs of others who protest in the face of overwhelming evidence to the contrary that they have not consumed alcohol. ►

The other way pyruvate may lose carbon dioxide is by a complex reaction. In this reaction or series of reactions, carbon dioxide is formed. The resulting acetaldehyde-like intermediate is indirectly oxidized by an enzyme using NAD as a hydrogen acceptor, and acetic acid in the form of acetyl coenzyme A (acetyl CoA) is formed. This series of reactions is not reversible; in other words, acetyl CoA is not carboxylated to yield pyruvic acid. There are several possible fates for acetyl CoA; the most common one is the series of reactions known as the citric acid cycle.

38-9 AEROBIC METABOLISM—THE CITRIC ACID CYCLE

The series of aerobic reactions in animals is variously called the *Krebs cycle, tricarboxylic acid cycle,* and the *citric acid cycle.* We will use the latter name since it seems to be the most descriptive. This series of reactions is not restricted to the metabolism of carbohydrates; it is also important in the metabolism of both lipids and proteins. Any substance that can be converted to acetyl CoA may enter the cycle. In this cyclic series of reactions a 2-carbon unit, the acetyl group, is completely converted to carbon dioxide and water. The cycle requires oxygen to oxidize (through the electron transport system) the $NADH_2$, $NADPH_2$, and $FADH_2$ which accepted hydrogen atoms (electrons) from the intermediates in the cycle. Although there are minor variations, the cycle is used by almost all plants and animals that have been studied. Anaerobic organisms, of course, do not use it.

The citric acid cycle is summarized in Fig. 38-7, and discussed in detail in the following paragraphs.

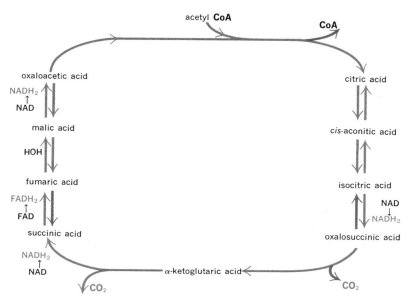

FIG. 38–7. The citric acid cycle. This series of reactions, which is also known as the Krebs cycle, converts an acetate group to carbon dioxide and water. The water is formed indirectly by the oxidation of $NADH_2$ and $FADH_2$ through the electron transport system.

◀ In the first reaction of the cycle an acetyl CoA unit is condensed with an oxaloacetate molecule to give citric acid.

O=C—COOH　　　　　　O　　　　　H—C—COOH
|　　　　　　　　　　　‖　　　　　　|
H—C—COOH + CH₃—C—CoA → HO—C—COOH + CoA
|　　　　　　　　　　　　　　　　　|
H　　　　　　　　　　　　　　　　H—C—COOH
　　　　　　　　　　　　　　　　　|
　　　　　　　　　　　　　　　　　H

oxaloacetic　　acetyl CoA　　citric acid
acid

Actually, the citric acid formed is in equilibrium with *cis*-aconitic acid and isocitric acid, but the equilibrium favors the formation of citric acid.

H　　　　　　　　　　H　　　　　　　　　H
|　　　　　　　　　　|　　　　　　　　　|
H—C—COOH　H₂O　H—C—COOH　H₂O　H—C—COOH
|　　　　　　　　　‖　　　　　　　　　|
HO—C—COOH ⇌　　C—COOH ⇌　　H—C—COOH
|　　　　　　　　　‖　　　　　　　　　|
H—C—COOH　H₂O　H—C—COOH　H₂O　HO—C—COOH
|　　　　　　　　　|　　　　　　　　　|
H　　　　　　　　　　　　　　　　　　H

citric　　　　*cis*-aconitic　　　isocitric
acid　　　　　　acid　　　　　　　acid

Because of this reversibility citric acid would seem to be a poor substance for the initiation of a series of reactions. However, the reaction by which it is formed from oxaloacetic acid and acetyl CoA is virtually irreversible, and there are no other significant biological reactions of citric acid. The dehydrogenation of isocitric acid to give oxalosuccinic acid causes an imbalance in the equilibrium. As would be expected from the law of mass action, the net effect is the series of reactions leading from citric acid to oxalosuccinic acid.

In the formation of oxalosuccinic acid, two hydrogen atoms are removed from isocitric acid to give reduced NAD (or NADP in some organisms) and oxalosuccinic acid:

$$
\begin{array}{c}
\text{H} \\
| \\
\text{H--C--COOH} \\
| \\
\text{H--C--COOH} \\
| \\
\text{HO--C--COOH} \\
| \\
\text{H}
\end{array}
+ \ \text{NAD} \ \rightarrow \
\begin{array}{c}
\text{H} \\
| \\
\text{H--C--COOH} \\
| \\
\text{H--C--COOH} \\
| \\
\text{O=C--COOH}
\end{array}
+ \ \text{NADH}_2
$$

isocitric   oxalosuccinic
acid   acid

In the next reaction of the citric acid cycle, this compound loses carbon dioxide to give α-ketoglutaric acid:

$$
\begin{array}{c}
\text{H} \\
| \\
\text{H--C--COOH} \\
| \\
\text{H--C--COOH} \\
| \\
\text{O=C--COOH}
\end{array}
\ \rightarrow \
\begin{array}{c}
\text{H} \\
| \\
\text{H--C--COOH} \\
| \\
\text{H--C--H} \\
| \\
\text{O=C--COOH}
\end{array}
+ \ \text{CO}_2
$$

oxalosuccinic α-ketoglutaric
acid   acid

The following reaction, the conversion of α-ketoglutaric acid to succinic acid is complex, and includes both an oxidation and a decarboxylation. It is similar to the conversion of pyruvic acid to acetyl CoA, in that it requires both NAD and coenzyme A. This reaction, or perhaps to be completely accurate we should call it a series of reactions, is almost completely irreversible.

$$
\begin{array}{c}
\text{H} \\
| \\
\text{H--C--COOH} \\
| \\
\text{H--C--H} \\
| \\
\text{O=C--COOH}
\end{array}
+ \ \text{NAD} \ \rightarrow \
\begin{array}{c}
\text{H} \\
| \\
\text{H--C--COOH} \\
| \\
\text{H--C--H} \\
| \\
\text{O=C--OH}
\end{array}
+ \ \text{CO}_2 + \text{NADH}_2
$$

α-ketoglutaric   succinic
acid   acid

Succinic acid is dehydrogenated under the influence of an FAD-containing enzyme to give fumaric acid. Fumaric acid is then hydrated to give malic acid which is dehydrogenated, in a reaction which requires NAD, to yield oxaloacetic acid.

$$
\begin{array}{c}
\text{COOH} \\
| \\
\text{CH}_2 \\
| \\
\text{CH}_2 \\
| \\
\text{COOH}
\end{array}
\ \xrightarrow{\text{FAD} \rightarrow \text{FADH}_2} \
\begin{array}{c}
\text{H--C--COOH} \\
|| \\
\text{HOOC--C--H}
\end{array}
\ \xrightarrow[\text{HOH}]{} \
\begin{array}{c}
\text{H--C--OH} \\
| \\
\text{CH}_2 \\
| \\
\text{COOH}
\end{array}
\ \xrightarrow{\text{NAD} \rightarrow \text{NADH}_2} \
\begin{array}{c}
\text{COOH} \\
| \\
\text{C=O} \\
| \\
\text{CH}_2 \\
| \\
\text{COOH}
\end{array}
$$

succinic   fumaric   malic   oxaloacetic
acid   acid   acid   acid

The oxaloacetic acid unites with an acetate unit to give citric acid, and the cycle begins again. Of course, with a cyclic series of reactions there is really no beginning and no end, but the general availability of acetyl CoA and the significance of having sufficient oxaloacetate to react with it makes this an especially important reaction in the cycle, and a good point to start and stop any discussion of the cycle. ▶

In the citric acid cycle a molecule of acetyl CoA, or more precisely of a 2-carbon unit, is converted to two molecules of CO_2 and four of H_2O. The energy contained in the acetyl CoA is converted to ATP via the intermediates NAD (or NADP), FAD, and the cytochrome system.

◀ One turn of the citric acid cycle results in the formation of three molecules of $NADH_2$ and one of $FADH_2$. This reaction results in the synthesis of eleven molecules of ATP from ADP and phosphate (three from each $NADH_2$ and two from the $FADH_2$). In addition, the energy released in the conversion of α-ketoglutaric acid to succinic acid, perhaps through the involvement of coenzyme A, is sufficient to synthesize another molecule of ATP. The total number of molecules of ATP synthesized per acetate unit is twelve. ▶

We can summarize the amount of ATP synthesized in the complete oxidation of glucose to carbon dioxide and water as follows:

aerobic glycolysis	8 ATP
conversion of 2 moles of pyruvic acid to 2 moles of acetyl CoA	6 ATP
oxidation of 2 moles of acetyl CoA	24 ATP
total	38 ATP

Using 12 kcal as the energy stored in an ATP molecule, we have 12×38 or 456 kcal of energy stored in ATP. Since the total free energy change in the conversion of glucose to carbon dioxide and water is 690 kcal (Section 38–5), the series of reactions results in trapping 456/690 or 66% of the energy of glucose.

These calculations are based on an energy storage of 12 kcal per mole of ATP. It may be that the real value of this energy is only 8 kcal per mole. If such is the case, the efficiency of storage is only 44%, rather than 66%.

38-10 SUMMARY OF METABOLISM OF CARBOHYDRATES

Carbohydrates are usually ingested in the form of starch and cellulose. Small amounts of sucrose, glucose, and fructose are also present in many foods. Lactose (milk sugar) is an important component in the diet of babies, children, and many adults. The process of digestion degrades all digestible carbohydrates to monosaccharides, and the indigestible carbohydrates such as cellulose are excreted unchanged. The products of digestion, the monosaccharides, are absorbed into the bloodstream and carried to various organs where they are utilized. Utilization may involve anabolic reactions leading to glycogen in animals and starch or cellulose in plants. For the purpose of simplification, catabolism of carbo-hydrates is usually divided into several series of reactions: glycolysis, the phosphogluconate pathway, and the citric acid cycle. The latter serves for the metabolism of proteins and lipids as well as for carbohydrates.

Other series of reactions are known to involve metabolites of the carbohydrates, but the three metabolic schemes listed seem to be the most important ones. It is possible to list more intermediate compounds in each of the series of reactions given in the glycolytic, phosphogluconate, and citric acid pathways. The degree of detail given in Figs. 38-4, 38-5, and 38-7, however, is sufficient and perhaps extravagant for a basic understanding of the process.

Although remarkable similarity is observed in the reactions in organisms ranging from the yeasts and bacteria to man, there are some differences. Many microorganisms use anaerobic glycolysis and release only small amounts of the potential energy of the carbo-hydrates they ingest. Since they are essentially nonmotile, perhaps they need less energy. It is possible that formation of excess ATP might even be deleterious for them. The growth of these microorganisms is, in fact, inhibited by the products of their own metabolism—ethanol and lactic acid. Other microorganisms, the aerobes, not only get more energy from each molecule of glucose, but also produce nontoxic carbon dioxide and water as waste products.

Multicellular organisms, particularly those which move from place to place, often at rapid rates, use aerobic pathways. Certain of their tissues, such as the muscle tissues which in order to insure survival must often work under conditions of low oxygen concentration, retain the glycolytic system. This system uses NAD to allow oxidation reactions to proceed even in the absence of oxygen. When this happens, pyruvic acid is converted to lactic acid, and we say that the animal has incurred an "oxygen debt." The "debt" is repaid by rapid breathing, even after violent exercise has stopped. The rapid breathing results in (1) in-creased oxygenation of the blood flowing to the tissues, (2) the conversion of lactic acid to pyruvic acid and NAD to $NADH_2$, and (3) the oxidation of $NADH_2$ through the electron transport system.

38-11 ABNORMALITIES OF CARBOHYDRATE METABOLISM

Several diseases are caused by abnormalities of the carbohydrate metabolism. We will discuss briefly those that are best understood—*diabetes mellitus,* galactosemia, glycogen-storage disease, and glucose 6-phosphate dehydrogenase abnormalities.

Diabetes Mellitus

The word *diabetes* means excretion of large amounts of urine; *mellitus* means sweet. There-fore, the term *diabetes mellitus* signifies that a sweet urine—actually a urine containing glucose—is excreted in large amounts. Other forms of diabetes, such as *diabetes insipidus* are known, and it is not totally wrong to describe the increased excretion of urine following ingestion of large amounts of beer as a temporary diabetes.

The condition we know as *diabetes mellitus* was probably known to the ancient Egyptians. The Greek scientist Celsus, who lived from 30 B.C. to 50 A.D., described a disease producing "polyuria without pain but with emaciation and danger," and a Chinese physician, about 200 A.D., described the condition as a "disease of thirst." About 1500, Paracelsus evaporated the urine of a diabetic and recovered "salt," which must have been a mixture of urea, salts, and sugar. Even in primitive societies it was known that ants were attracted to the urine of diabetics because of its sweetness.

From the dawn of civilization until the 1920's *diabetes mellitus* was fatal. No effective treatment was known. In severe cases, the patient could expect to live less than a year after discovery of his condition. The outlook then for diabetics is analogous to the prognosis today for people who develop leukemia.

Diabetes mellitus is characterized by the presence of glucose and three other abnormal substances—acetone, acetoacetic acid, and B-hydroxybutyric acid in the urine. The glucose found in the urine is a reflection of the high level of glucose in the blood stream. The high level of blood glucose (hyperglucosemia) is due to the fact that the normal metabolism is severely impaired in the diabetic. He apparently cannot convert glucose either to glycogen or to carbon dioxide and water at anything like the normal rate. Since glucose cannot be utilized, it accumulates following digestion of a carbohydrate-containing meal, and is only slowly excreted. The variation in normal metabolism of glucose can be shown by a glucose-tolerance test. The person undergoing the test fasts for at least 12 hours, and then drinks a solution containing a large amount of glucose. Blood samples are withdrawn after specific time intervals and analyzed for glucose. While both normal and diabetic persons will show a rise in blood glucose under the conditions of the test, the concentration of glucose in the blood will be higher and the rate of decrease will be slower in the diabetic than in the normal person. Typical glucose tolerance curves are shown in Fig. 38–8.

The other unusual urinary components of diabetics, acetoacetic acid, β-hydroxybutyric acid, and acetone, are believed to accumulate because the diabetic is unable to oxidize acetyl CoA.

Thus we can say that, in the absence of glucose metabolism, acetyl CoA tends to accumulate. It has been postulated that the real deficiency here is in oxaloacetic acid, and that this deficiency is caused by the lack of pyruvic acid which can lead to the formation of oxaloacetic acid by a carboxylation reaction. This possibility has not yet been definitely shown to be true, and perhaps it is best merely to say that three abnormal metabolites, all probably

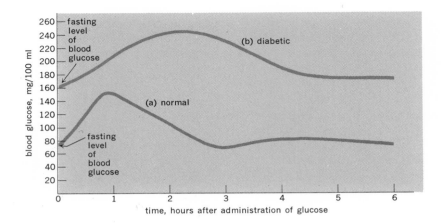

FIG. 38–8. Glucose tolerance curves. A glucose tolerance curve shows the amount of blood glucose at various intervals after an individual has consumed a large amount of glucose. Curve (a) is a normal curve. It shows a rise followed by a decrease and sometimes reaches a level slightly below the normal fasting level before returning to normal. Curve (b) represents results obtained when the test is made on a diabetic person. His fasting level is higher than normal and administration of glucose increases the blood glucose level to values that usually exceed the renal threshold. The typical "diabetic" curve falls off only slowly, and abnormally high values are found several hours after administration of the glucose.

derived from acetyl CoA are present in the urine of diabetics. Acetone is also excreted with the air expired from the lungs of persons with severe, untreated diabetes.

In 1921, the Canadian scientists Frederick Banting and Charles Best (who was only a medical student at the time), proved that a substance that alleviated the symptoms of *diabetes mellitus* could be extracted from the pancreas. This substance, now known to be a hormone, is called *insulin*. Normally it is produced by special cells in the pancreas and released into the bloodstream and from the bloodstream absorbed by many tissues. Injections of insulin lead to the disappearance of all symptoms of *diabetes mellitus.*

How does insulin work? We really don't know. It has the net effect of promoting the metabolism of glucose. The best theory is that insulin promotes the absorption of glucose into cells. Until glucose is inside a cell, it cannot be metabolized. Absorption of glucose into a cell may involve its reaction with ATP to yield glucose 6-phosphate, but it is not certain that this is the reaction influenced by insulin.

Insulin is now extracted from pancreases of beef, swine, and sheep, and made available in a highly purified form. It must be injected into the diabetic, since ingestion as a pill would result in the digestion of the polypeptide, insulin, and reduce it to its component amino acids. Insulin is a treatment, not a cure, for diabetes. A cure would have to increase the ability of the pancreas to manufacture and release insulin.

Mild cases of diabetes, those that develop in later life, can be treated with various chemical substances which can be administered orally. These drugs do not contain insulin, and are effective only in mild cases—those in which the patient is able to produce some but an insufficient amount of insulin. These drugs, whose trade names are Orinase and Diabinese, apparently function by stimulating the secretion of the insulin that the diabetic person can still make.

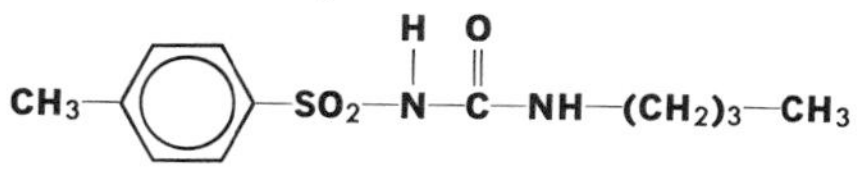

$$CH_3-\bigcirc-SO_2-\underset{H}{N}-\underset{O}{C}-NH-(CH_2)_3-CH_3$$

tolbutamide (Orinase)

$$Cl-\bigcirc-SO_2-\underset{H}{N}-\underset{O}{C}-\underset{H}{N}-(CH_2)_2-CH_3$$

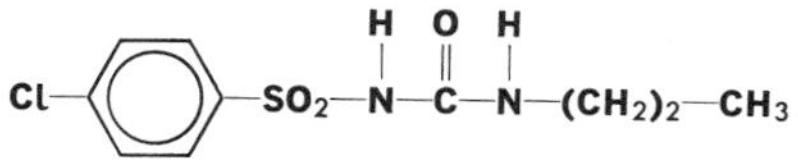

chlorpropamide (Diabinese)

Diabetes mellitus can be characterized as a disorder of carbohydrate metabolism. The exact nature of the defect is not known. The treatment of diabetes did not come from an understanding of the chemistry of the disease, but as the result of careful observation and a hunch on the part of Dr. Banting. In other disorders, treatment has been suggested only after the biochemical nature of the disease was understood.

Galactosemia

Galactosemia is a disease of infants. It is characterized by a high level of galactose in the blood. Galactose is also found in the urine. This condition becomes evident soon after the birth of affected children. They vomit whenever milk is feed to them, fail to gain weight, their liver enlarges, and in severe cases, they may die. Untreated survivors of this condition tend to be dwarfed, mentally retarded, and may have cataracts in their eyes. Fortunately, this disease is relatively rare and can be treated effectively.

When it was realized that the disease was caused by the inability to metabolize the galactose which was derived from the lactose present in milk, the treatment was obvious— restriction of the intake of the milk and milk products which produce lactose. If this treatment is begun during the first few weeks of life, all symptoms disappear and there are no long-term effects.

It is now known that galactosemia is caused by a hereditary deficiency of the enzyme responsible for the conversion of galactose 1-phosphate to glucose 1-phosphate. As the children grow older they usually develop an alternate pathway for metabolizing galactose, and thus the need to restrict milk is not permanent.

With the understanding of the cause and treatment of this condition, the problem becomes one of detection. Unfortunately, the early symptoms of galactosemia are similar to those of many other diseases of infants. Careful observation and examination of the urine and blood for the presence of galactose can lead to prompt diagnosis and treatment. Ignorance is the only reason for the prevalence of this disorder.

◄ Glycogen Storage Disease

A much more serious situation is involved in glycogen storage disease. Actually, several forms of this disorder are known, each probably involving the failure of a specific reaction in the reversible conversion of glucose to glycogen. The disease is characterized by an accumulation of glycogen in the liver, heart, or skeletal muscle. These conditions are hereditary and rare, but are usually fatal, with death often the result of decreased resistance to infections.

One form of glycogen-storage abnormality, known as Von Gierke's disease, involves the absence of the enzyme necessary to convert glucose 6-phosphate to glucose. No treatment has been found to be really effective. Other forms of these diseases involve the enzyme responsible for forming branches or for debranching the glycogen molecule—that is, a lack of the enzyme involved in the formation or disruption of 1-6 bonds between glucose units. A summary of the blocks involved in various types of glycogen storage disease is given in Fig. 38–9.

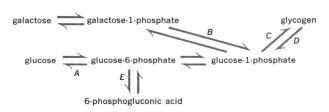

FIG. 38–9. Site of enzymatic deficiencies in disease of carbohydrate metabolism: *A*, site of defect in von Gierke's disease; *B*, site of defect in galactosemia; *C*, site of defect in diffuse glycogenolysis (Type III); *D*, site of defect in glycogen storage disease of liver and muscle (Type IV); *E*, site of defect in drug-induced hemolytic anemia and favism.

Disorders Involving Glucose 6-phosphate Dehydrogenase

The administration of certain drugs, namely phenacetin and some of the sulfonamides, causes the rupture of blood cells (hemolysis) and a subsequent anemia in some persons. In severe cases, half of the hemoglobin may be destroyed in this way. Although hemoglobin is normally synthesized by these persons, and blood transfusions may be given to persons with this defect, this disorder is still a serious one. A related condition is caused when sensitive persons eat fava beans. The defect in these disorders involves the enzyme glucose 6-phosphate dehydrogenase, the enzyme involved in entrance of glucose 6-phosphate into the phosphogluconate shunt. It is quite likely that persons having these disorders are somewhat more resistant to malaria than are normal persons, so the condition is not without its advantages. Since this trait is widely found in African Negroes, it has apparently helped them to survive in a malarial area and has consequently been transmitted to their offspring. We say that such traits have "positive survival value." ►

The hereditary diseases discussed above seem to be rare. There is some tendency for *diabetes mellitus* to be inherited, although the mode of inheritance is not completely understood. It is highly likely that other hereditary diseases involving irregularities in carbohydrate metabolism will be found. In some cases, such as in galactosemia, understanding the disease has led to an obvious and effective treatment. In others, as in the glycogen storage diseases, no effective treatment has yet been found. The study of defects in metabolism or "metabolic" diseases has only begun, and 'represents a real challenge for the medical biochemist. This type of disease is discussed further in Chapter 42, "The Chemistry of Heredity."

IMPORTANT TERMS

Adrenalin	Disaccharidase	Hypoglycemia
Aerobic	Galactosemia	Insulin
Amylase	Glucagon	Phosphogluconate shunt
Anaerobic	Glucosuria	Phosphorylase
Citric acid cycle (Krebs cycle)	Glycolysis	Phosphorylation
Diabetes mellitus	Hyperglycemia	

WORK EXERCISES—Part A

1. How does the metabolic oxidation of glucose differ from the reaction when a small amount of sugar is burned in a flame? In what ways are the reactions similar?

2. Which glycolytic intermediates have no phosphorus in their structure?

3. Describe how the level of glucose in the blood is kept within a narrow range.

4. What is the source of blood glucose in an animal that has eaten no carbohydrates for a long period of time?

5. Summarize the digestion of a molecule of a highly branched polysaccharide.

6. Does glucosuria always mean that a person has *diabetes mellitus?*

7. Compare and contrast the three major metabolic pathways by which a molecule of glucose can be metabolized—glycolysis, phosphogluconate shunt, and the citric acid cycle.

In solving problems 8, 9, and 10, assume that the free energy "stored" when a mole of ADP is converted to one of ATP is 12 kcal.

8. The complete oxidation of acetic acid to carbon dioxide and water using a bomb calorimeter yields approximately 200 kcal of free energy per mole of acetic acid. Compare this energy with the amount of energy stored as ATP when acetic acid is oxidized via the citric acid cycle.

9. Fluoroacetic acid occurs in the leaves of poisonous plant (*Dichapetalum cymosum*). The toxicity of this substance is due to the fact that it combines with oxaloacetic acid to form fluorocitric acid which acts as an inhibitor of the dehydration of citric acid in the citric acid cycle. Assuming that the further reactions of citric acid are completely blocked, but that no other reactions are blocked, how many ATP molecules would you estimate could be produced per molecule of glucose fed to an animal poisoned

with fluoroacetic acid? How does this amount of ATP compare to that normally obtained in an unpoisoned animal?

10. Malonic acid is poisonous. Apparently the toxicity is due to the fact that it inhibits the dehydrogenation of succinic acid in the citric acid cycle. Assuming (for ease of calculation) that the free energy of the conversion of glucose to CO_2 and H_2O is 700 kcal/mole, estimate what percentage of the free energy of the glucose would normally be trapped as ATP in an animal poisoned with malonate. How does this figure compare with the amount of energy produced by glucose in an unpoisoned animal?

The Use of Isotopes in Biochemistry

The reactions by which the carbohydrates are metabolized have been studied by using isotopes. In these studies, a labeled compound (one containing the isotope) is administered to an animal either by injection or by feeding, and later some part of the animal or his waste products is analyzed for the isotope. Individual enzymatic reactions may be studied by adding isotopic substrates to purified enzyme systems.

The radioactive isotope carbon-14 (^{14}C) is probably the most widely used, but the non-radioactive isotopes deuterium (^2H), nitrogen-15, and oxygen-18 are often used instead. The radioactive isotopes tritium (^3H), phosphorus-32, and iodine-131 can also be used.

Some isotopic compounds are uniformly labeled (for example, all the carbon atoms may contain ^{14}C) while in other compounds only one carbon atom is isotopic. Using an asterisk to indicate labeled carbon atoms (which should not be confused with the use of an asterisk for indicating asymmetry in optically active compounds), we can differentiate between uniformly and specifically labeled pyruvic acid as follows:

$$H_3C^*—\overset{\overset{\textstyle O}{\|}}{C^*}—C^*OOH \qquad\qquad H_3C—\overset{\overset{\textstyle O}{\|}}{C}—C^*OOH$$

uniformly labeled pyruvic acid   carboxyl-labeled pyruvic acid

In performing and interpreting experiments involving isotopes, we make the following assumptions:

1) The labeled compound is metabolized in the same manner as a nonlabeled compound.

2) The label stays with the atom which was originally labeled, and this atom maintains its position in a complex molecule. Care must be taken when labeling hydrogen atoms since the fact that the hydrogen of acids dissociates from its original molecule makes interpretation of results difficult.

3) When symmetrical compounds are formed, the results are the same as if the isotopic label were distributed between similar atoms. Thus if succinic acid is labeled in only one of the noncarboxylic carbons ($HOOC—CH_2—C^*H_2—COOH$), it behaves as if the label were distributed over the two similar carbons ($HOOC—C^*H_2—C^*H_2—COOH$). Metabolism of this succinic acid to give the nonsymmetrical malic acid (in the citric

acid cycle) would produce both

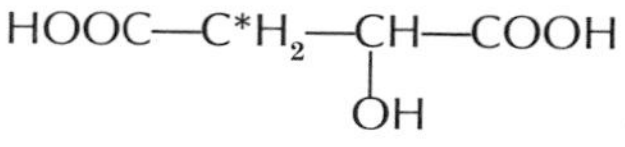

$$HOOC-C^*H_2-CH-COOH \quad \text{and} \quad HOOC-CH_2-C^*H-COOH$$
$$OH OH$$

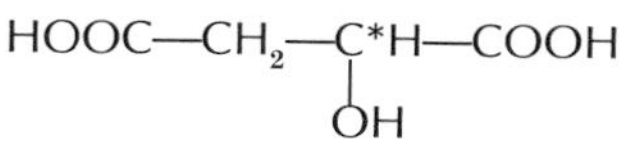

and analysis of such a mixture would give results indicating that the labeling was spread over both the noncarboxyl carbons:

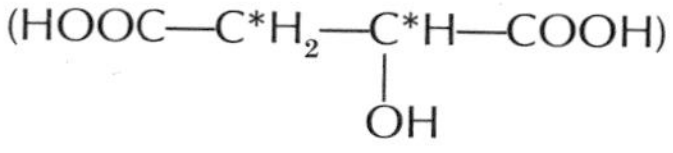

$$(HOOC-C^*H_2-C^*H-COOH)$$
$$OH$$

The carboxyl carbons, however, would not be labeled. There is one important exception to this rule about labeling as it applies to symmetrical compounds. Although citric acid is symmetrical, research indicates that the enzyme that catalyzes its metabolism in the citric acid cycle treats the citric acid as if it were nonsymmetrical, and

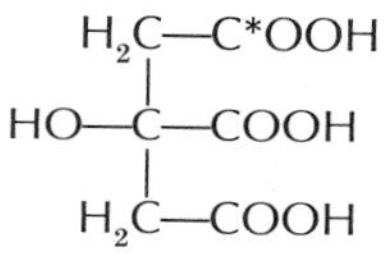

$$H_2C-C^*OOH$$
$$HO-C-COOH$$
$$H_2C-COOH$$

gives α-keto glutaric acid labeled only in one carboxyl group,

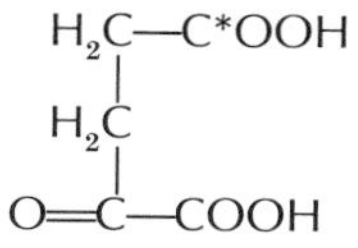

$$H_2C-C^*OOH$$
$$H_2C$$
$$O=C-COOH$$

WORK EXERCISES—Part B

On the basis of this discussion, do the following work exercises:

11. List five radioactive compounds that might be isolated from a rat or his excretion products following the injection of pyruvic acid with the carboxyl carbon labeled with carbon-14. Locate the position of the radioactive carbon in each.

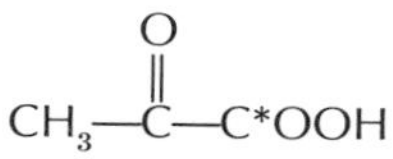

$$\overset{\displaystyle O}{\overset{\displaystyle \|}{CH_3-C-C^*OOH}}$$

12. What compounds which are normal metabolites of pyruvic acid would you expect to have no radioactivity when carboxyl-labeled pyruvic acid was administered to rats?

13. If carboxyl labeled pyruvic acid had been added to a culture of yeast, which products of yeast fermentation would be radioactive and which products would not contain carbon-14?

14. One of the major reactions of pyruvate is its conversion to acetyl CoA. This reaction could be studied by the following experiments:

The enzymes and cofactors known to be necessary for the conversion of pyruvic acid to acetyl coenzyme A are used in both experiments. In Experiment 1, the addition of pyruvate labeled in the methyl or carbonyl carbon gave acetyl CoA containing radioactivity. In Experiment 2 the addition of acetate labeled in both carbon atoms did not result in the formation of labeled pyruvic acid.

What can you conclude about the reversibility of this reaction?

15. Glucose was synthesized to contain carbon-14 in the fourth carbon and later given to a white rat. The following compounds were later isolated from the animal: glucose, fructose-1,6-diphosphate, pyruvic acid, acetyl CoA, α-ketoglutaric acid. Indicate the position of the carbon-14 (if present) in each of these compounds.

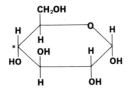

SUGGESTED READING

Levine, R., and M. S. Goldstein, "The Action of Insulin," *Scientific American*, May 1958. This article discusses glucose metabolism and the function of insulin.

Wolf, G., *Isotopes in Biology*, Academic Press, New York, 1964. This paperback book gives a wealth of information on the use of isotopes for the study of biochemical processes.

Chapter 39 METABOLISM OF PROTEINS

39–1 INTRODUCTION

The digestion of proteins is necessary in order to convert them into amino acids which can be absorbed across the intestinal wall. Undigested proteins are potent antigens and bring about the production of antibodies (that are themselves proteins) which produce allergic reactions. These body defenses against foreign proteins means that absorption of proteins without digestion would produce severe allergic shock reactions following each meal. It is possible that some proteins are absorbed through the intestine without bad effects during the first few days of a baby's life. In this way the mother's milk probably provides the child with preformed antibodies which will serve until he can manufacture his own. The permeability of the intestine is rapidly lost within a few days after birth.

Following digestion and absorption, the amino acids of proteins may either be catabolized to yield energy or built into one of the thousands of proteins necessary for the life and well-being of the organism. The process of protein synthesis is extremely complex. Each protein is made of at least a hundred amino acids in a highly specific sequence. The regular misplacement of just one amino acid can lead to serious consequences. At the same time that the exact structure is being formed, energy must be provided for this anabolic process.

This chapter discusses first the digestion of proteins and then the reactions of the amino acids that result either in their degradation to yield energy or in their synthesis into larger molecules, especially the proteins which play a vital role in the life of any organism.

39–2 PROTEIN-DIGESTING ENZYMES

The digestion of proteins to yield amino acids is catalyzed by a variety of enzymes all of which may be called **peptidases,** since the bond hydrolyzed is the peptide linkage between the amino acids. The word **proteolytic** is also used to describe these enzymes. The reaction may be written as follows:

$$H_3\overset{+}{N}-\underset{\underset{H}{|}}{\overset{\overset{R_1}{|}}{C}}-\overset{\overset{O}{||}}{C}-\underset{H}{N}-\underset{\underset{H}{|}}{\overset{\overset{R_2}{|}}{C}}-\overset{O}{C}-\overset{-}{O} + HOH \rightarrow H_3\overset{+}{N}-\underset{\underset{H}{|}}{\overset{\overset{R_1}{|}}{C}}-\overset{O}{C}-\overset{-}{O} + H_3\overset{+}{N}-\underset{\underset{H}{|}}{\overset{\overset{R_2}{|}}{C}}-\overset{O}{C}-\overset{-}{O}$$

a dipeptide   +   water   amino acid   +   amino acid

There are many varieties of peptidases. **Exopeptidases** act on peptide bonds nearest to the end of a long protein chain. They may be either **aminopeptidases** or **carboxypeptidases** depending upon whether or not they exert their action nearest the end of the protein (or polypeptide) chain having the free amino or carboxyl group. **Endopeptidases** catalyze the hydrolysis of peptide bonds that are not near the end of a chain. **Dipeptidases** act only upon dipeptides. Many of the peptidases are specific, for example, endopeptidases might catalyze hydrolyses only at places where a tyrosine residue was present in the polypeptide chain; others seem to work for only a limited number of similar amino acids.

All the proteolytic enzymes that have been carefully studied to date are secreted in inactive forms. Pepsin, for instance, is produced as an inactive protein **pre-pepsin** (also called pepsinogen*). Its conversion to pepsin involves the hydrolysis of some of its own peptide bonds. This hydrolysis is catalyzed by hydrogen ions or by pepsin itself. Two questions are immediately suggested: "How does hydrolysis of peptide bonds convert an inactive protein into an active enzyme?" and "Why are these enzymes secreted in an inactive form?" "How" questions are much easier to answer than "Why" questions, but answers have been proposed for both. Conversion of inactive pre-pepsin to pepsin probably involves the removal of an inhibitor and perhaps a "masking" group. The "masking" group is used to describe a part of the pre-pepsin molecule that covers or masks the active site of the enzyme much as a sheath masks a knife—although in this case the masking group is much smaller than the active agent. Pre-pepsin has a molecular weight of 42,600 and pepsin of 34,500, indicating that the inhibitor and other peptides removed have a weight of approximately 8000.

The answer to the question concerning the reason for production of inactive precursors (sometimes called **zymogens,** or enzyme generators) is suggested by the realization that the cells that manufacture these enzymes are themselves proteins. It would be inefficient or even disastrous if these proteolytic enzymes destroyed the very tissues that made them. The basic question "Why doesn't the stomach or intestine digest itself?" has plagued scientists for some time. Apparently the answer is that most of the stomach and intestinal wall is protected by a lining of polysaccharide-protein complex (a mucopolysaccharide) called mucus which is relatively indigestible but which does, however, slough off continuously—much as do the outer layers of our skin. The second part of the answer is that the really unprotected part of the stomach, the glands that manufacture pepsin, are protected because they make an inactive form of the enzyme. The same explanation can be used to describe the manufacture of pre-trypsin and pre-chymotrypsin by the pancreas.

---

* The name pepsinogen is most commonly used. The International Union of Biochemistry recommends pre-pepsin. They make similar recommendations for the precursors of trypsin and chymotrypsin.

39–3 PROTEIN DIGESTION

Protein digestion does not start until the food reaches the stomach. Here the combination of HCl and the endopeptidase, **pepsin,** initiates protein digestion. Complete action by pepsin results in the hydrolysis of about 10% of the bonds of typical proteins and leaves particles having molecular weights of between 600 and 3000. Such a mixture is also produced *in vitro* (using pepsin, of course) and sold as *peptone* for use in bacterial growth media.

In the small intestine, the partially digested proteins are exposed to the action of the endopeptidases **trypsin** and **chymotrypsin,** and carboxypeptidases from the pancreas. Aminopeptidases and dipeptidases are probably secreted from the intestinal wall. Trypsin and chymotrypsin are secreted as pre-trypsin and pre-chymotrypsin, and it is probable that the exopeptidases are also secreted as inactive zymogens. As the result of the action of the various peptidases, proteins are converted into amino acids and these are absorbed through the intestinal wall into the blood stream.

Some proteolytic enzymes are extracted from their natural sources and used for various purposes. Papain, which comes from the papaya fruit, is used in meat tenderizers where its action partially digests the meat. Other proteolytic enzymes have been used to aid in freeing the lens of the eye prior to its removal in surgery for cataract and to facilitate regrowth of nerve cells that have been cut.

39–4 METABOLISM OF AMINO ACIDS

The digestion and the eventual fate of amino acids absorbed into the blood stream may be summarized as follows:

proteins → amino acids
1. synthesis into protein,
2. removal of amino group to give a keto acid, which may:
   a) be converted to glucose or glycogen,
   b) be converted to CO_2 and water,
3. participation in a pathway peculiar to a given amino acid

Protein Synthesis

The synthesis of protein is an extremely rapid process when one considers the complexity of the protein being synthesized. Only minutes after the injection of radioactive amino acids into an animal, radioactive protein can be found in that animal, indicating that the synthesis occurs rapidly. We also know from other studies with isotopes that there is a continual degradation and resynthesis of all the proteins in any organism. The white rat replaces half of its proteins in 17 days. The human takes 80 days to do the same. These figures are somewhat misleading, however, since not all proteins are degraded and resynthesized (the term protein turnover is used to describe the process) at the same rate. Half of the proteins in the blood serum are turned over in 10 days, liver proteins require only 20 to 25 days, but the turnover in the protein of bone (collagen) is slow.

The problem of exactly how an organism synthesizes protein has intrigued scientists for many years. How does a cell put together just the right amino acid, in the right sequence to give a protein that may serve as an enzyme, an antibody against bacteria, or perhaps a

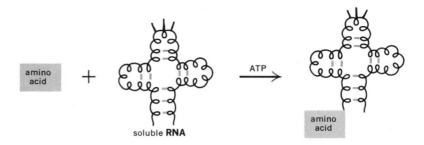

FIG. 39-1. The activation and binding of an amino acid to soluble RNA. In the reaction shown above a single enzyme is responsible for both activating an amino acid and binding it to the specific soluble RNA that will carry it to the ribosome.

hormone? Since the number of possible arrangements of the 20 amino acids in even a small protein is greater than the number of atoms in the known universe, protein synthesis cannot be just a random synthesis, but must be under strict control from some kind of "director."

The realization that the kinds of proteins an organism synthesizes depends upon its heredity led to speculation that DNA was probably involved in some way and might serve as the "director" or source of information. This assumption we now know to be true. In fact, both DNA and RNA are involved in the synthesis of proteins. Three kinds of RNA, each having different physical characteristics, are involved in protein synthesis. These three forms are called (1) **soluble (transfer) RNA,** (2) **ribosomal RNA,** and (3) **messenger (template) RNA.** Each plays a specific role in protein synthesis.

The general scheme of protein synthesis has only recently been proposed. It is probable that our ideas about the processes involved will change as more research is done. The following descriptions represent the process as it is now understood.

The first step in the synthesis of proteins involves a reaction of a given amino acid with ATP. This reaction produces a compound having a structure that can be summarized as adenine-ribose-phosphate-amino acid. The amino acid is said to be "activated" in this process. (See Fig. 39-1.) This activated amino acid is then transferred to a specific kind of soluble RNA. There is at least one kind (and perhaps more than one) of soluble RNA for each amino acid. The structures of the soluble RNA's that bind to some of the amino acids have now been established, and it is hoped that more such molecules will soon be analyzed and perhaps even synthesized (Fig. 39-2).

FIG. 39-2 (opposite). Models of the soluble RNA that transfers alanine. The models shown represent possible shapes of alanine-transferring RNA. Regions of hydrogen bonding between strands are indicated by the closeness of the strands. Note that in most RNA there are bases other than the four found in the greatest quantity. The triplet I-G-U is presumed to be the part of the molecule that matches with messenger RNA. [Adapted from R. W. Holley et al., "Structure of a Ribonucleic Acid," *Science,* **147,** 19 Mar. 1965, pp. 1462–1465. Copyright, 1965, by the American Association for the Advancement of Science.]

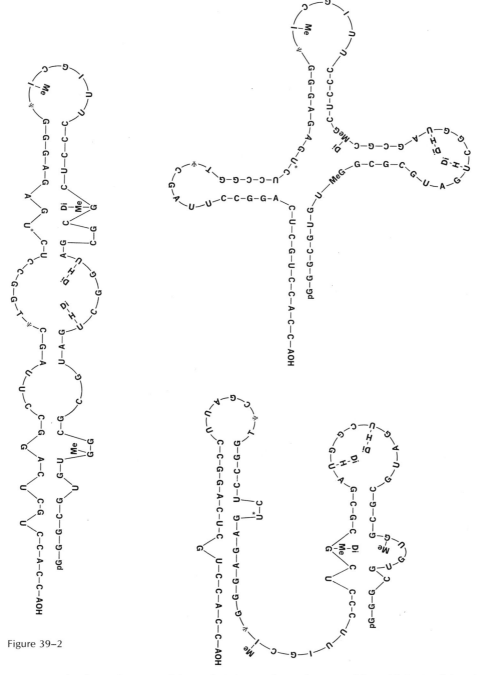

Figure 39–2

Key: A = adenylic acid, C = cytidylic acid, G = guanylic acid, U = uridylic acid, I = inosinic acid, U* indicates a mixture of uridylic acid and dihydrouridylic acid, and Ψ = pseudo-uridylic acid. The presence of additional hydrogen atoms or methyl groups is also shown (MeG and Di-H-U indicate methyl guanylic and dihydrouridylic acids, respectively).

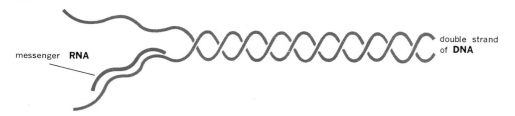

messenger **RNA**

double strand
of **DNA**

FIG. 39–3. Synthesis of messenger RNA. It is believed that DNA strands in the nucleus of the cell un-
wind sufficiently for a given strand to serve as a pattern for the synthesis of messenger RNA. The messenger RNA then carries the instructions contained in the DNA to the ribosomes.

The soluble-RNA-amino-acid complex then travels to the ribosome (a small organelle
within the cell) where the amino acid is added to other amino acids to form polypeptide
chains and eventually proteins. The soluble RNA then leaves the ribosome and picks up
another molecule of its particular kind of amino acid. The order in which the amino acids
which are brought to the ribosome by soluble RNA are linked together in a peptide chain is
specified by messenger RNA.

Messenger RNA, as well as other known kinds of RNA, is believed to be synthesized
in the nucleus of the cell under the influence of DNA. Apparently DNA not only duplicates
itself (as described in Chapter 36) but also serves as a pattern for the synthesis of a specific
kind of messenger RNA. In DNA duplication, a guanine in one strand of DNA serves as a
guide for adding a cytosine to a forming chain of DNA, and adenine is the guide for thymine.
Since RNA contains uracil instead of thymine, it is probable that an adenine in a DNA
molecule directs the placement of a uracil (actually a uridylic acid molecule) in a chain
of messenger RNA. (See Fig. 39–3.) Thus, we can summarize the synthesis of RNA from DNA
as follows:

DNA chain: —**G**—**C**—**A**—**G**—**G**—**C**—**T**—**A**—·····
RNA chain: —**C**—**G**—**U**—**C**—**C**—**G**—**A**—**U**—·····

Messenger RNA then travels from the nucleus to the ribosome, carrying in its structure the
message describing, in a type of code, a particular protein molecule. Messenger RNA and
the soluble-RNA-amino-acid combination meet at the ribosome (which itself is made of
RNA and protein). In some way messenger RNA specifies the kind of amino acid to be
placed at each part of a forming protein chain. Presumably it does so by matching some
specific part of the soluble RNA. In the illustration shown below only a small area of the
soluble RNA exactly matches the messenger RNA.

ribosome
messenger RNA: —**C**—**G**—**U**—**C**—**C**—**G**—**A**—**U**—·····
  soluble RNA: —**A**—**A**—**U**—**G**—**G**—**C**—**A**—**G**—·····

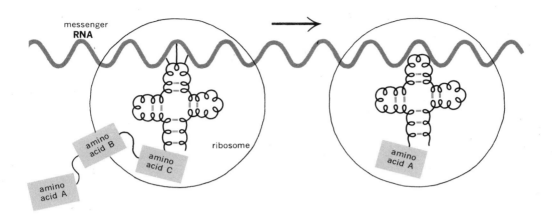

FIG. 39–4. Synthesis of protein at the ribosome. The ribosome apparently has two major active areas. In one, messenger RNA is held so that transfer RNA having the correct sequence of nucleotide bases can match it. When the matching takes place, the activated amino acid is positioned over the area where peptide bonds are generated between amino acids to give the protein chain.

We believe that the code requires three bases to specify an amino acid. In the illustration above the sequence —C—C—G— in messenger RNA is being matched with the complementary G—G—C located somewhere on the soluble RNA which is carrying the amino acid proline. When this situation occurs, the amino acid is in the right position to be added to the polypeptide chain. In other words, C—C—G is the code for proline. (See Fig. 39–4.)

Many types of polymers resembling messenger RNA have now been synthesized (using enzymes as catalysts), and the types of protein made when these synthetic messengers are added to a mixture of ribosomes, soluble RNA amino acids and other factors, have led to the proposal of a 3-nucleotide "code" for each amino acid. We know, for instance, that when polyuridylic acid is added to a system capable of synthesizing protein, only polyphenylalanine is formed. Research indicates that there is more than one code for each amino acid. The codes for the various amino acids are given in Table 39–1.

Evidence indicates that messenger RNA from one kind of organism can be used with ribosomes and soluble RNA amino acids from another, and that the kind of protein synthesized is characteristic of the messenger RNA. If this theory proves to be true it may indicate the method by which nucleic acids from viruses can "take over" the synthetic systems of the cell. It would also explain why viruses require whole cells—not just an assortment of nutrients if they are to grow and reproduce.

Messenger RNA molecules are depolymerized after being used only once or, at most, a few times. The messenger RNA of higher plants and animals seems to be more stable than that of bacteria. While this destruction of messenger RNA seems wasteful, it provides a sensitive means of controlling the kind of protein synthesized. Bacteria usually need to respond to more environmental changes than do the cells of higher plants or animals. Bac-

TABLE 39–1. The genetic code

This table gives the trinucleotides (codons) that are believed to contain the information for incorporating a given amino acid into a polypeptide chain. Although the code is degenerate in that more than one trinucleotide codes for a given amino acid, there is a general similarity in two of the bases in the codons for an amino acid. The codons UAA and UAG may serve the purpose of stopping peptide synthesis, and thus may be *terminator* codons. The data in the table are from the reports of a number of investigators.

Amino Acid	Codons	Amino Acid	Codons
alanine	GCA, GCC, GCG, GCU	leucine	CUA, CUC, CUG, CUU, UUA, UUG
arginine	CGA, CGC, CGG, CGU, AGA, AGG	lysine	AAA, AAG
asparagine	AAC, AAU	methionine	AUG, AUA(?)
aspartic acid	GAC, GAU	phenylalanine	UUC, UUU
cystine	UGC, UGU	proline	CCA, CCC, CCG, CCU
glutamic acid	GAA, GAG	serine	UCA, UCC, UCG, UCU, AGC, AGU
glutamine	CAA, CAG	threonine	ACA, ACC, ACG, ACU
glycine	GGA, GGC, GGG, GGU	tryptophan	UGA, UGG
histidine	CAC, CAU	tyrosine	UAC, UAU
isoleucine	AUA, AUC, AUU	valine	GUA, GUC, GUG, GUU

teria that stop making a protein they no longer need are more efficient and tend to be successful in their never-ending struggle to survive and reproduce.

There are many unsolved problems having to do with protein synthesis. For example: What determines which part of the DNA in the nucleus is used for the pattern of messenger RNA at a given time? What triggers the release of protein chains from the ribosome? How are secondary linkages within the protein produced?

Amino Acid Degradation

The basic biochemical reactions of amino acids were described in Chapter 34, "Proteins," as peptide synthesis, transamination, deamination, and decarboxylation. We have seen that the process of peptide bond formation with the synthesis of proteins is a significant one for all organisms. The extent to which the other reactions play a role in any given animal is an important aspect of the biochemistry of the animal.

To determine the extent to which transamination actually occurs in an animal, we can feed him any one amino acid that has been labeled with the nonradioactive isotope nitrogen-15 in the amino group. Later when we examine the various tissues of the animal we find that nitrogen-15 is present in the amino acids, both free and in proteins, with the exception of lysine. If we make our examination only a short time after feeding the animal the isotopic amino acid, we find that the greatest amount of ^{15}N is still in the amino acid administered, with lesser amounts in glutamic acid and aspartic acids, and still lesser amounts in the other amino acids, except lysine, of course, which contains no ^{15}N. These findings lead to the conclusion that the keto acids corresponding to the amino acids, glutamic acid and aspartic acid, are the most important "amino acceptors" in transamination reactions. It is not surprising to find that these keto acids, α-ketoglutaric and oxaloacetic acids, are found as reactants in the citric acid cycle.

Another approach to finding the extent of transamination is made by feeding an animal the keto analogs of amino acids. We know that a supply of certain amino acids is essential for a given animal, a white rat, for example, because the animal cannot synthesize these amino acids at a sufficient rate to allow him to grow normally. When we feed the keto acids corresponding to the essential amino acids to this animal, we find that all the keto analogs can be substituted for the essential amino acids with the exception of those of lysine (which the previously described experiments had shown not to be transaminated) and threonine. Since our other experiments indicated that threonine could be transaminated, we must conclude that the failure of the keto analog to substitute for dietary threonine may be due to the fact that it is metabolized so quickly that it cannot be transaminated.

These experiments show one of the important uses which an animal makes of transamination reactions. If the basic carbon skeleton is present in the body from some other source, the amino acid can be synthesized. Thus a requirement of an animal for an essential amino acid is really only a requirement for a certain type of carbon chain. A list of essential amino acids is given in Chapter 41, and it is interesting to see that they represent complex or unusual compounds whose carbon chains or benzene rings are not present in metabolites of the carbohydrates or lipids.

Not only are transamination reactions necessary for conversion of amino acids to keto acids, but the enzymes that catalyze these processes have been used to aid in diagnosing various diseases. After a heart attack there is a sharp rise in the amount of the **transaminase** that catalyzes the reaction between glutamic acid and oxaloacetic acid present in the blood. A determination of the amount of this enzyme in blood serum is one of the best methods of diagnosing such a heart attack. Other transaminases are used in diagnosing hepatitis.

The conversion of an amino acid to a keto acid may also occur by a process of **deamination.** Many organisms contain the keto analogs of the amino acids; however, there is little evidence that oxidative deamination occurs to any extent in the bodies of humans and other higher animals.

With certain important exceptions, the amines that would be produced by the **decarboxylation** of amino acids are not found in the human; consequently, we conclude that decarboxylation of amino acids is not an important process in humans. Bacteria in the intestine are responsible for some decarboxylations, and some of the odor of normal feces is due to these vile-smelling amines.

The production of keto acids, primarily by transamination, gives molecules that can then enter either the glycolytic or citric acid pathways. The conversion is direct for alanine, glutamic acid, and aspartic acid, yielding pyruvic acid, α-ketoglutaric acid, and oxaloacetic acid, respectively. Additional reactions are required to convert other amino acids into compounds of one of the major metabolic schemes, but these reactions are known for all the amino acids. Thus we can say that the carbon chains of amino acids can be converted via the reverse of glycolysis to glucose or glycogen, or through the citric acid cycle to carbon dioxide and water, with an attendant release of energy.

39-5 EXCRETION OF NITROGENOUS WASTE PRODUCTS

The conversion of amino acids to keto acids leaves an amino group. Although the amino group may be passed from compound to compound, the net utilization of amino acids for energy or glucose and glycogen synthesis means that the amino group must be eliminated. The metabolism of this group is extremely important since very low levels of ammonia in the blood are extremely toxic to all animals. A chronic alcoholic often dies from ammonia toxicity; his liver, which is the source of the enzymes that catalyze conversion of the amino group to the less toxic urea, has been so damaged by cirrhosis that he is unable to get rid of the poisonous ammonia. Other animals, such as fish, can apparently tolerate slightly higher levels of ammonia in their blood, but they too are poisoned by relatively low levels of this substance. One of the specific biochemical differences in different species involves the manner in which they excrete the nitrogen from proteins.

There are two major sources of nitrogenous waste products—amino acid metabolism and the metabolism of the purine and pyrimidine bases which are either consumed in the diet as nucleic acids or synthesized in the body. In the human, approximately 95% of the nitrogenous excretion products come from amino acid metabolism. Nitrogenous waste products are excreted primarily via the kidneys in man and other mammals. Not all animals do so; for instance, fish use their gills for excretion of ammonia. Most animals excrete more than one nitrogen-containing product, but there is often a predominance of one substance.

Amino Acid Excretion

Some simple animals excrete amino acids. This loss is essentially wasteful, since there would still be a great deal of energy in amino acids. Humans excrete minor amounts of some amino acids in the urine, and some persons having hereditary abnormalities excrete relatively large amounts of specific amino acids. **Cystinuria** is the condition in which cystine is excreted in relatively large amounts in the urine. Since cystine is quite insoluble, it may form "stones" in the bladder or kidneys of persons who are cystinurics. In fact, the first chemical characterization of cystine was made from a bladder stone of a person who probably was a cystinuric individual.

Ammonia Excretion

Levels of only 5 mg of ammonia per 100 ml of blood are toxic to humans, and the normal concentration of this metabolite is only 1 to 3 micrograms per 100 ml of human blood. Animals that live in water, from simple one-celled organisms to the fish, excrete free ammonia. Even fish, however, do not have concentrations of ammonia greater than 0.1 mg (100 micrograms) per 100 ml of blood. How do these animals excrete ammonia when there is so little of it in the blood? Apparently the ammonia is usually combined with glutamic acid to give glutamine. Glutamine is then carried to a membrane next to the surrounding water (the gills for fish and certain other animals) where the ammonia is released.

Humans excrete ammonium ions (NH_4^+) in the urine, and presumably the ammonia is formed from glutamine in the kidneys. The amount of ammonium ions excreted is not very large, and there is no detectable excretion of ammonia by normal healthy humans. The reaction can be described as follows:

$$
\begin{array}{ccc}
\overset{\displaystyle O}{\underset{\displaystyle \|}{C}}\!-\!NH_2 & & \overset{\displaystyle O}{\underset{\displaystyle \|}{C}}\!-\!OH \\
H\!-\!C\!-\!H & & H\!-\!C\!-\!H \\
H\!-\!C\!-\!H & & H\!-\!C\!-\!H \quad + NH_3 \\
H\!-\!C\!-\!NH_2 + HOH \rightleftarrows & & H\!-\!C\!-\!NH_2 \\
COOH & & COOH \\
\end{array}
$$

glutamine + water   glutamic acid + ammonia

Urea Excretion

Many animals, including man, excrete urea as the major nitrogen containing metabolite derived from amino acid metabolism. Urea is much less toxic than ammonia. Levels between 18 and 38 mg/100 ml of blood are considered normal in a human. Sharks have as much as 2% (2 g/100 ml of blood) of urea in their blood. In fact, shark hearts will not beat if urea is not present. The fact that freshwater sharks have much less urea in their blood (0.6% instead of 2%), leads us to the conclusion that one function of the urea in sea sharks is that of balancing the osmotic pressure of the salty sea water.

Energy is required to synthesize urea. Apparently the production of the relatively non-toxic urea is sufficiently advantageous to compensate for the extra energy required for the synthesis. The series of reactions by which urea is synthesized in mammals is called the urea cycle. This series of reactions is summarized in Fig. 39–5 and discussed in detail in the following section.

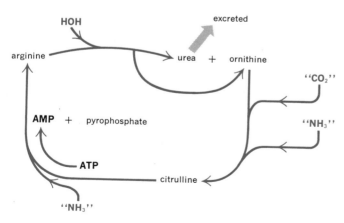

FIG. 39–5. The urea cycle. By the series of reactions shown above, urea is produced by the hydrolysis of the guanido group of arginine. Arginine is then regenerated in a series of reactions so that the cycle can continue.

◄ In this series of reactions, arginine is hydrolyzed to give urea and a molecule of the amino acid ornithine.

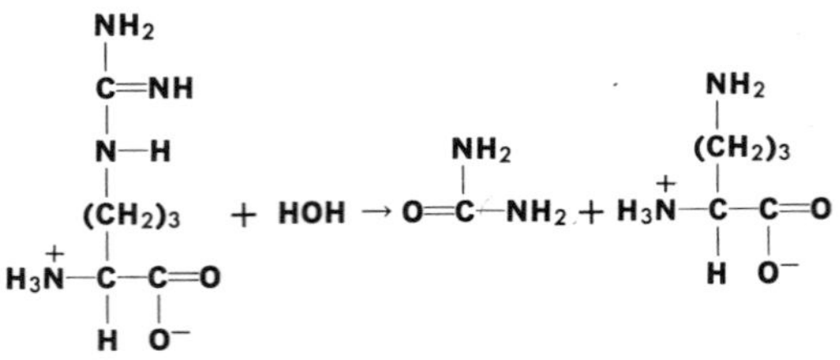

$$
\begin{array}{l}
\text{NH}_2 \\
| \\
\text{C}=\text{NH} \\
| \\
\text{N}-\text{H} \\
| \\
(\text{CH}_2)_3 \\
| \\
\text{H}_3\overset{+}{\text{N}}-\text{C}-\text{C}=\text{O} \\
\quad\;\; | \quad | \\
\quad\;\; \text{H} \;\; \text{O}^-
\end{array}
+ \text{HOH} \rightarrow \text{O}=\text{C}-\text{NH}_2 +
\begin{array}{l}
\text{NH}_2 \\
| \\
(\text{CH}_2)_3 \\
| \\
\text{H}_3\overset{+}{\text{N}}-\text{C}-\text{C}=\text{O} \\
\quad\;\; | \quad | \\
\quad\;\; \text{H} \;\; \text{O}^-
\end{array}
$$

arginine + water   urea +   ornithine

Ornithine then combines with one unit of CO_2 and one of NH_3. Actually, neither CO_2 nor ammonia is present as such, but they are added in the form of carbamyl phosphate. Carbamyl phosphate is synthesized in the liver of mammals by the following reaction:

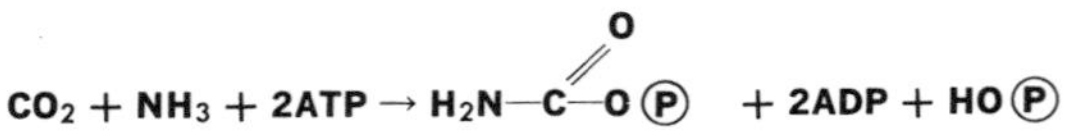

$$CO_2 + NH_3 + 2ATP \rightarrow H_2N-\overset{\overset{\displaystyle O}{\|}}{C}-O\,\textcircled{P} + 2ADP + HO\,\textcircled{P}$$

The addition of carbamyl phosphate to ornithine gives citrulline.

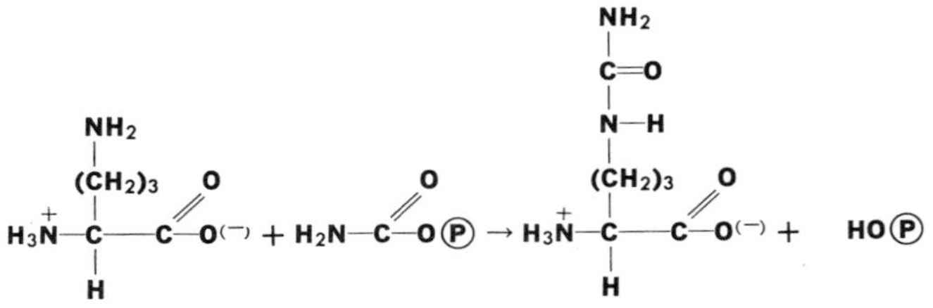

$$
\begin{array}{l}
\text{NH}_2 \\
| \\
(\text{CH}_2)_3 \quad\; \text{O} \\
| \qquad\quad \| \\
\text{H}_3\overset{+}{\text{N}}-\text{C}-\text{C}-\text{O}^{(-)} \\
\quad\;\; | \\
\quad\;\; \text{H}
\end{array}
+ H_2N-\overset{\overset{\displaystyle O}{\|}}{C}-O\,\textcircled{P} \rightarrow
\begin{array}{l}
\text{NH}_2 \\
| \\
\text{C}=\text{O} \\
| \\
\text{N}-\text{H} \\
| \\
(\text{CH}_2)_3 \quad\; \text{O} \\
| \qquad\quad \| \\
\text{H}_3\overset{+}{\text{N}}-\text{C}-\text{C}-\text{O}^{(-)} \\
\quad\;\; | \\
\quad\;\; \text{H}
\end{array}
+ \quad \text{HO}\,\textcircled{P}
$$

ornithine   +   carbamyl   citrulline   +   phosphoric
                    phosphate   acid

Citrulline acquires an amino group from aspartic acid. The final product of the reaction is arginine and fumaric acid.

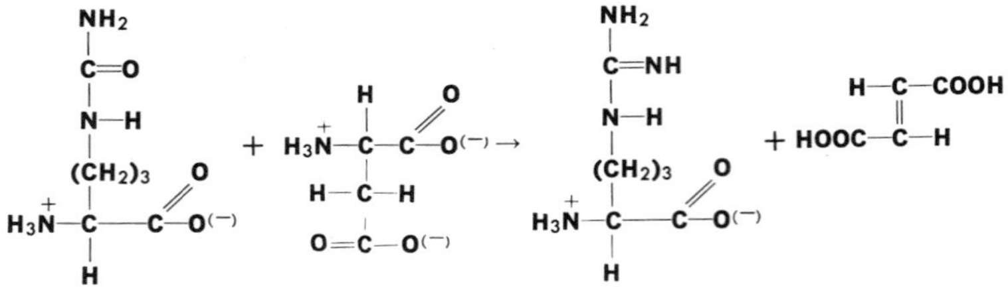

$$
\begin{array}{l}
\text{NH}_2 \\
| \\
\text{C}=\text{O} \\
| \\
\text{N}-\text{H} \\
| \\
(\text{CH}_2)_3 \quad\; \text{O} \\
| \qquad\quad \| \\
\text{H}_3\overset{+}{\text{N}}-\text{C}-\text{C}-\text{O}^{(-)} \\
\quad\;\; | \\
\quad\;\; \text{H}
\end{array}
+
\begin{array}{l}
\quad\;\; \text{H} \quad \text{O} \\
\quad\;\; | \quad\;\; \| \\
\text{H}_3\overset{+}{\text{N}}-\text{C}-\text{C}-\text{O}^{(-)} \\
\quad\;\; | \\
\quad\; \text{H}-\text{C}-\text{H} \\
\quad\;\; | \\
\quad\; \text{O}=\text{C}-\text{O}^{(-)}
\end{array}
\rightarrow
\begin{array}{l}
\text{NH}_2 \\
| \\
\text{C}=\text{NH} \\
| \\
\text{N}-\text{H} \\
| \\
(\text{CH}_2)_3 \quad\; \text{O} \\
| \qquad\quad \| \\
\text{H}_3\overset{+}{\text{N}}-\text{C}-\text{C}-\text{O}^{(-)} \\
\quad\;\; | \\
\quad\;\; \text{H}
\end{array}
+
\begin{array}{l}
\text{H}-\text{C}-\text{COOH} \\
\quad\;\;\; \| \\
\text{HOOC}-\text{C}-\text{H}
\end{array}
$$

citrulline   +   aspartic acid   arginine   +   fumaric acid

The arginine is then hydrolyzed to yield another molecule of urea and one of ornithine, and the cycle repeats itself. The fumaric acid can be oxidized via the citric acid cycle.

In this series of reactions we can see that ATP is used to provide the energy for the synthesis of urea. In mammals, this series of reactions takes place only in the liver. Extensive liver damage leads to the accumulation of ammonia, and can lead to death. ▶

Uric Acid Excretion

In animals that excrete urea, the urea is dissolved in the urine. It can be said that the excretion of urea actually requires water. Animals which must conserve water (at least during parts of their life cycle), such as the reptiles, birds, and many insects, excrete uric acid. This substance is excreted in a solid form mixed with, but not dissolved in, small amounts of water. The synthesis of uric acid is a complex, energy-requiring process and we must assume, as we did in the case of urea synthesis, that the advantages of conservation of water are sufficient to justify the excretion of a relatively energy-rich compound which the animal must synthesize.

uric acid

It is difficult to determine what is cause and what is effect, but it is true that many reptiles are found in deserts where conservation of water is of primary importance to survival. The condition which is shared by birds, reptiles, and some insects is that the embryo develops within an egg which is enclosed in a shell that is impervious to water. Thus all the water the developing embryo will be able to use is within the egg at the time it is deposited by the female. The sequence of events observed in the development of the chicken embryo is interesting. During the first four days of incubation of the egg, ammonia is produced. From the fifth to the fourteenth day, urea is produced instead of ammonia, and indeed some of the previously produced ammonia is converted to urea. From the fourteenth day until hatching and throughout the rest of its life, uric acid is synthesized by the chicken. Animals that develop from eggs laid in water, generally excrete ammonia—as do the adults of these species. However, when amphibians such as frogs begin to grow legs, their metabolism switches, and they begin to synthesize urea—apparently in anticipation of their coming conversion to land-dwelling animals. Philosophically, it is probably preferable to interpret the change in excretion products as being the factor that makes life on dry land possible, rather than to make the teleological interpretation that a change in excretion anticipates a change in environment.

Humans also excrete uric acid; however, it is not synthesized as a method of excreting ammonia but represents the end product of the metabolism of the purine bases adenine and guanine. With minor exceptions, only humans and other primates (apes) excrete uric acid as the normal end product of purine metabolism. Most mammals excrete allantoin, and

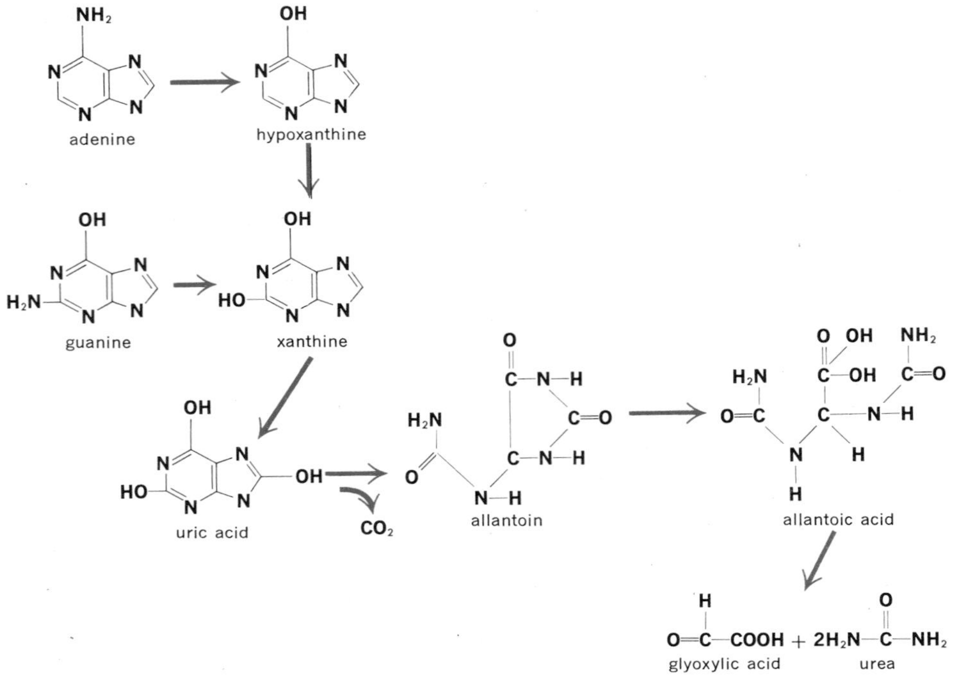

FIG. 39–6. Metabolism of purine bases. In this series of reactions adenine and guanine are oxidized to uric acid. Man and other primates excrete uric acid, since they lack the enzyme necessary for the formation of allantoin. Excretion products of other animals indicate that they carry the series of reactions further.

simpler animals excrete allantoic acid or urea as the end products of purine metabolism (see Fig. 39–6 for this series of reactions). In this series of reactions, animals generally regarded as simpler than humans are actually more complex in that they have more enzymes and can tap more of the energy of the purines. The "loss" of these enzymes, especially of uricase, can be blamed for some of the ills that humans suffer. Some types of painful arthritis and gout result from deposits of uric acid in the joints.

The "loss" of enzymes by higher species leads us to wonder about the advantages of losing the enzyme uricase and the attendant accumulation of uric acid in the blood and other parts of the body. Some scientists have speculated that perhaps man's superior intelligence is due to the high level of uric acid in his blood. While this is a tempting hypothesis, the fact that men normally have a slightly higher level of uric acid in their blood than women (4.5 mg/100 ml in men as against 3.5 mg/100 ml in women) has led to the rejection of this hypothesis by approximately half of the population. The fact that some fowls (chickens and turkeys) have an even slightly higher level of uric acid in their blood (5 mg/100 ml), and that insects have as much as 20 mg/100 ml again argues against the hypothesis!

Miscellaneous Nitrogenous Excretion Products

Ammonia, urea, and uric acid are major nitrogen-containing excretion products of amino acid metabolism. Allantoin and allantoic acid are also excreted by many animals but these come primarily from purine metabolism. Trimethylamine oxide is excreted by some marine animals, but the source of this compound has not been definitely established. Swine and spiders both excrete guanine, the swine because they have no guanase. Presumably the same is true of spiders whose metabolism has not yet been extensively investigated. In spite of the fact that he has the enzyme uricase, the Dalmatian dog excretes some uric acid. Apparently this results from a slightly different kidney function and not from an intent to imitate human metabolism!

39–6 SPECIFIC METABOLIC PATHWAYS FOR AMINO ACIDS

In addition to the general reactions of amino acids which have been previously discussed, each amino acid has a series of specific reactions in which it participates. In some cases, similar amino acids share at least parts of a specific metabolic pathway. As a result of these special pathways, the amino acid either is converted into a compound that can enter the glycolytic pathway or citric acid cycle, or it is converted into a special metabolite. There are many of these special metabolites. Some of the more important ones are summarized in Table 39–2. The specific pathways of phenylalanine and tyrosine are described in Chapter 42 in connection with a discussion of abnormalities in these pathways. A complete discussion of these special metabolic pathways is beyond the scope of this book; a general biochemistry textbook (see the list at the end of Chapter 32) should be consulted by those wishing further details.

TABLE 39–2. Important products of the metabolism of specific amino acids

Amino Acid	Product	Importance of Product
alanine	pyruvate	glycolytic intermediate
aspartic acid	oxaloacetic acid	important intermediate of citric acid cycle
arginine	ornithine, citrulline	intermediates in urea synthesis
arginine	urea	important nitrogen containing excretion product
glutamic acid	α-ketoglutaric acid	important intermediate in citric acid cycle
methionine	S-adenosyl methionine	important source of methyl group in biosynthetic reactions
cysteine	taurine	combines with cholic acid to give bile salts
histidine	histamine	important in allergic reactions
tryptophane	nicotinic acid	vitamin
phenylalanine, tyrosine	thyroxine, adrenalin	important hormones
tyrosine	melanin	pigment of skin and hair

39-7 DISORDERS OF PROTEIN METABOLISM

Several instances are known in which a lack of the correct enzyme has led to an abnormal accumulation of metabolites.   From our knowledge of protein synthesis, we believe that failures in synthesis of proteins, especially where the condition is hereditary, are due to defects in nucleic acids.   It is probably incorrect to describe these enzyme deficiencies as disorders of protein metabolism, even though they represent abnormalities in synthetic pathways.   Numerous other conditions are known in which lack of enzymes leads to abnormal metabolism of amino acids.   The most striking example involves the metabolism of phenylalanine and tyrosine.   These defects are discussed in Chapter 42.

39-8 SUMMARY

Proteins are digested under the influence of a variety of enzymes to yield amino acids. These amino acids can be used to synthesize new protein or other simpler molecules such as the hormones thyroxine and adrenalin.   The process of protein synthesis gives only a small percentage of the countless possible proteins.   Directions for the synthesis are found in DNA, but various types of RNA are required to carry out the process.   Synthetic reactions are remarkably similar whether the organism is as simple as the bacterium *E. Coli* or as complex as man.   The energy of these anabolic reactions is provided by ATP.   Amino acids not used for synthetic purposes can be degraded to yield energy.   When this happens, the carbon, hydrogen, and oxygen are converted to carbon dioxide and water by reactions of the citric acid cycle and other common metabolic sequences.   The nitrogen may be eliminated in a variety of compounds; different species use different reaction sequences to convert the amino acid nitrogen into a waste product, depending on the habitat and state of evolution of the animal.   Thus throughout the animal kingdom, the metabolism of amino acids follows some pathways that are similar and others that are distinctive.

IMPORTANT TERMS

Aminopeptidase	*Essential amino acid*	*Proteolytic*
Carboxypeptidase	*Exopeptidase*	*Ribosomal RNA*
Chymotrypsin	*Messenger (template) RNA*	*Soluble (transfer) RNA*
Cystinuria	*Pepsin*	*Transaminase*
Dipeptidase	*Peptidase*	*Trypsin*
Endopeptidase	*Pre-pepsin (pepsinogen)*	*Zymogen*

WORK EXERCISES

1. The metabolism of the amino acid histidine can be summarized as follows:

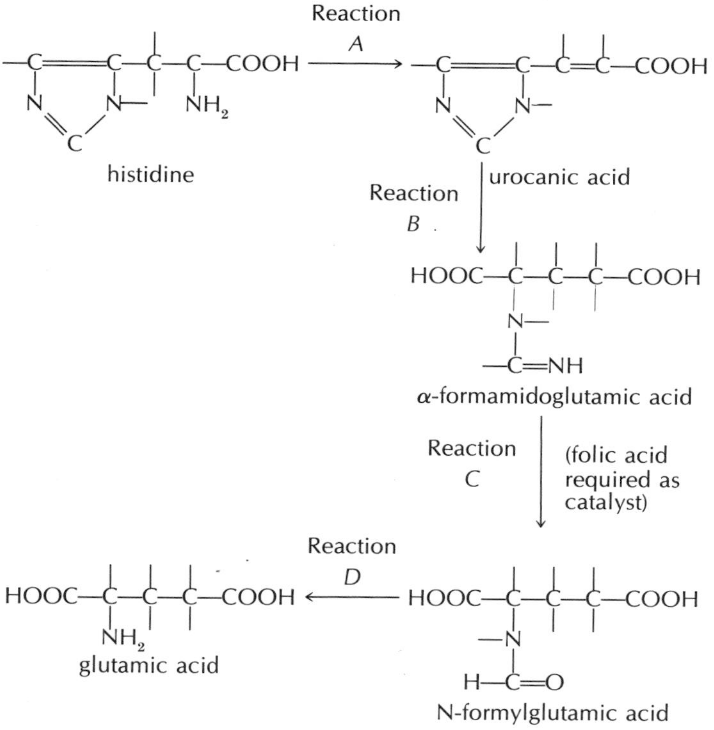

histidine

urocanic acid

α-formamidoglutamic acid

(folic acid required as catalyst)

glutamic acid

N-formylglutamic acid

Reaction C has been shown to require the vitamin folic acid as a coenzyme. Answer the following questions with respect to the metabolism of histidine:

a) If histidine containing ^{14}C in the carboxyl carbon is given to an animal, what compound in the citric acid cycle would you expect to be labeled first? (Give the structural formula and show the position of the label.)

b) What clinical test might be developed to indicate whether an individual had a deficiency of folic acid?

2. Give the experimental evidence that transamination occurs in an animal's body.

3. Write the reaction by which each of the following could be formed from an amino acid:
   a) glyoxylic acid (O=CH—COOH)   b) alpha ketoglutarate
   c) pyruvic acid   d) ethanolamine
   e) mercaptoethanolamine (H_2N—CH_2—CH_2SH)
   f) histamine   g) oxaloacetic acid

4. List the kinds of RNA involved in protein synthesis, and indicate the role of each in this process.

5. Citrulline containing ^{15}N in the position indicated below was given to a dog. What two compounds (other than citrulline) in the animal should contain the greatest amount of ^{15}N in a few minutes after administration of the labeled compound?

$$H_2N^*—\underset{\underset{O}{\|}}{C}—\underset{\underset{H}{|}}{N}—CH_2—CH_2—CH_2—\underset{\underset{NH_2}{|}}{CH}—COOH$$

6. The peptide alanylserylmethionylglutamyltyrosine was incubated with several different enzymes. The products of each specific reaction are given below. List the type or classification of the enzyme that catalyzed each reaction.

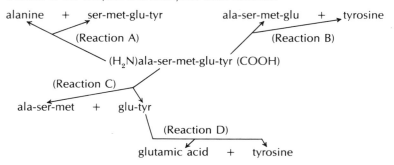

SUGGESTED READING

Asimov, I., *The Genetic Code*, a Signet Science Library Book (P2250), New American Library, New York, 1963.

Neurath, H., "Protein Digesting Enzymes," *Scientific American*, Dec. 1964 (Offprint #198). The article discusses the structure of chymotrypsin and other proteolytic enzymes, and relates the structure to their function as enzymes.

The following four articles from the *Scientific American* are excellent references on the subject of protein synthesis. The illustrations make a complex process quite understandable.

Clark, B. F. C., and K. A. Marcker, "How Proteins Start," *Scientific American*, Jan. 1968.

Crick, F. H. C., "The Genetic Code," *Scientific American*, Oct. 1962 (Offprint #123).

Crick, F. H. C., "The Genetic Code III," *Scientific American*, Oct. 1966.

Hurwitz, J. and J. J. Furth, "Messenger RNA," *Scientific American*, Feb. 1962 (Offprint #119).

Nirenberg, M., "The Genetic Code II," *Scientific American*, Mar. 1963 (Offprint #153).

Chapter 40 METABOLISM OF LIPIDS

40-1 INTRODUCTION

The lipids are found in all parts of the human body and are especially important in the brain. Although the human body can synthesize most lipids if it is given sufficient raw material—principally carbohydrates—adequate diets should contain some lipids. The triglycerides represent the most important dietary lipids. Lipids from plants tend to contain more unsaturated fatty acids, and while they contain some sterols, contain no cholesterol as do animal products. The biosynthesis and many of the functions of the fatty acids, the triglycerides, and cholesterol are reasonably well understood; however, little is known about the way in which many lipids of the brain are synthesized, and almost nothing is known of the chemical role they play in the functioning of the brain and nervous system.

40-2 DIGESTION OF LIPIDS

The enzymes required for the digestion of lipids are given the general name of **lipases.** There is no digestion of lipids in either the mouth or stomach although lipase is found in the stomach. This enzyme is active only at pH values near 7, and thus it is ineffective in the stomach where the pH is normally between 1.5 and 2.5. The principal digestion of lipids occurs in the small intestine where the combination of bile and pancreatic and intestinal lipases catalyzes the hydrolysis of the ester bonds of triglycerides. See structure on page 582. A major problem faced in the digestion of triglycerides is that of attachment of the water-soluble lipases to water-insoluble lipid globules. The process is more efficient when the lipids are broken into small globules. This breakdown increases their surface area and consequently the area available for interaction with lipases. Consequently, lipids in an emulsified form (broken into small globules) are much more readily digested. The **bile** does not contain enzymes, but the bile salts are effective emulsifying agents. Thus, while bile is not absolutely necessary for digestion of lipids, it helps greatly in the process.

$$
\begin{array}{l}
H_2C-O-\overset{\overset{\displaystyle O}{\|}}{C}-C_{15}H_{31} \\[4pt]
C_{17}H_{33}-\overset{\overset{\displaystyle O}{\|}}{C}-O-C-H \\[4pt]
H_2C-O-\overset{\overset{\displaystyle O}{\|}}{C}-C_{17}H_{35}
\end{array}
\;+\; HOH
\;\longleftrightarrow\;
\begin{array}{l}
C_{15}H_{31}COOH \quad \text{palmitic acid} \\[4pt]
C_{17}H_{33}COOH + C_3H_5(OH)_3 \quad \text{oleic acid} \\[4pt]
C_{17}H_{35}COOH
\end{array}
$$

palmitooleostearin   water   stearic acid   glycerol
(a triglyceride)

There is some difference of opinion among biochemists as to whether triglycerides must be digested into glycerol and free fatty acids in order to be absorbed across the intestinal wall. If they are completely hydrolyzed, they are certainly resynthesized quite rapidly, since there are far more triglycerides than free fatty acids in the blood and in the lymph following digestion of a fatty meal. Lipids that are liquid tend to be more easily absorbed than are solid lipids.

Lecithinases (enzymes that catalyze the hydrolysis of the phospholipid lecithins) are present in the small intestine. Cholesterol esterases are also present. These latter enzymes catalyze the hydrolysis of cholesterol from the fatty acids with which it is often combined in natural products.

40-3 ABSORPTION OF LIPIDS

Glycerol, fatty acids, possibly the mono- or di-esters of glycerol and fatty acids, and cholesterol are absorbed across the intestinal wall into the blood and lymph. The lymph is a clear fluid much like blood, but without red corpuscles. It has a circulatory system similar to but separate from that of the blood (see Fig. 40-1). Following the digestion of a fatty meal, the lymph becomes cloudy from the presence of tiny globules of lipids, mostly in the form of triglycerides. Since the lymph flows into the blood, principally at the thoracic duct, the blood also becomes somewhat cloudy following the digestion of a fatty meal (this change can be observed only with serum or plasma since the red blood cells tend to obscure the effect in whole blood). Thus the net effect of absorption of lipids into the lymph is about the same as if the lipids were absorbed into the blood stream. Cholesterol is the only common sterol that is readily absorbed. Small amounts of the sterol-like compound, vitamin D, are also absorbed. Many of the substances classified as lipids are neither digested nor absorbed. Since they make up only a small part of the diet of animals, who consume principally the triglycerides, their indigestibility poses no real problems.

40-4 FURTHER METABOLISM OF LIPIDS

The major products of lipid digestion are the fatty acids and glycerol. These recombine immediately after absorption to form triglycerides. They circulate as small globules of triglycerides until they reach an organ which can rehydrolyze them and either convert the

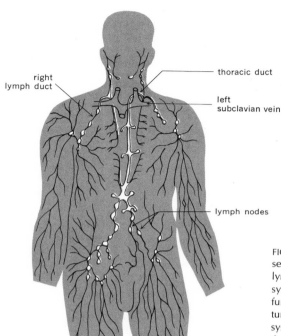

FIG. 40–1. The lymphatic system. The vessels which help in the circulation of the lymph and its connection with the blood system are shown here. In addition to its function in lipid absorption, the lymph returns valuable proteins to the circulatory system and is important in the response of the body to infections.

fatty acids and glycerol to a triglyceride characteristic of the species and of the specific organ doing the synthesis, or else the glycerol and fatty acids are oxidized to carbon dioxide and water with the attendant release of energy.

We can summarize the metabolism of triglycerides as follows:

$$\begin{array}{c}
\textbf{triglycerides} \\
\downarrow \\
CO_2 + H_2O \longleftarrow \quad \textbf{fatty acids} \\
\text{(glycolysis)} \qquad + \qquad \left.\begin{array}{c}\\\\\end{array}\right\} \xrightarrow{\text{resynthesis}} \textbf{triglycerides} \\
\textbf{glycerol}
\end{array}$$

Glycerol is metabolized by addition of phosphate from ATP and oxidation to yield glyceraldehyde-3-phosphate which is an intermediate in the glycolytic series of reactions (see Fig. 38–4).

Oxidation of Fatty Acids

It has been known for many years that fatty acids are broken down and synthesized in 2-carbon units. Only recently has the process been really understood. The problem faced in the degradation of fatty acids is essentially that of breaking a carbon-to-carbon bond.

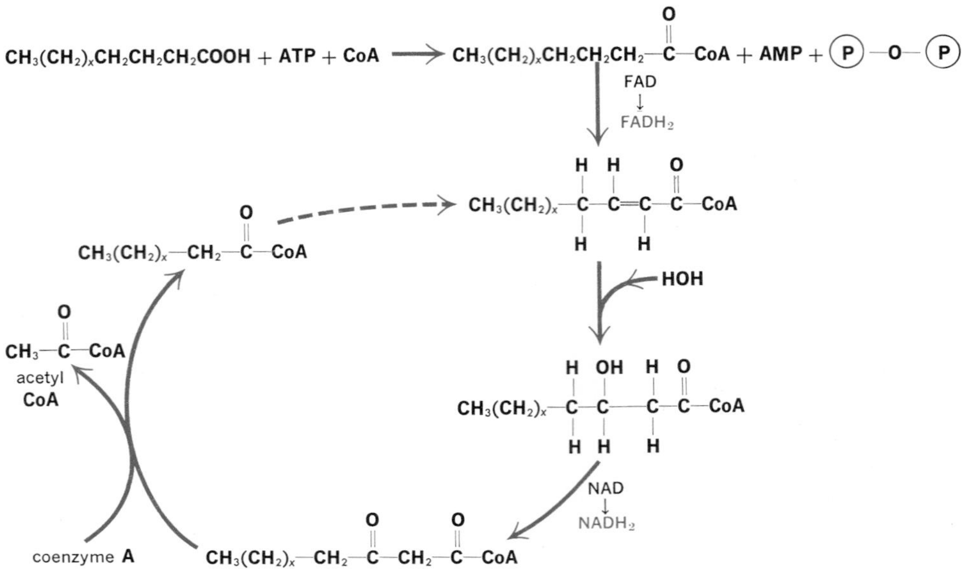

$$CH_3(CH_2)_xCH_2CH_2CH_2COOH + ATP + CoA \longrightarrow CH_3(CH_2)_xCH_2CH_2CH_2-\overset{\overset{\displaystyle O}{\|}}{C}-CoA + AMP + (P)-O-(P)$$

$$\text{FAD} \downarrow \text{FADH}_2$$

$$CH_3(CH_2)_x-\overset{\overset{\displaystyle H}{|}}{\underset{\underset{\displaystyle H}{|}}{C}}-\overset{\overset{\displaystyle H}{|}}{C}=\overset{\overset{\displaystyle }{}}{C}-\overset{\overset{\displaystyle O}{\|}}{C}-CoA$$

$$CH_3(CH_2)_x-CH_2-\overset{\overset{\displaystyle O}{\|}}{C}-CoA$$

$$\leftarrow \text{HOH}$$

$$CH_3-\overset{\overset{\displaystyle O}{\|}}{C}-CoA$$
acetyl CoA

$$CH_3(CH_2)_x-\overset{\overset{\displaystyle H}{|}}{\underset{\underset{\displaystyle H}{|}}{C}}-\overset{\overset{\displaystyle OH}{|}}{\underset{\underset{\displaystyle H}{|}}{C}}-\overset{\overset{\displaystyle H}{|}}{\underset{\underset{\displaystyle H}{|}}{C}}-\overset{\overset{\displaystyle O}{\|}}{C}-CoA$$

$$\text{NAD} \downarrow \text{NADH}_2$$

coenzyme **A** $$CH_3(CH_2)_x-CH_2-\overset{\overset{\displaystyle O}{\|}}{C}-CH_2-\overset{\overset{\displaystyle O}{\|}}{C}-CoA$$

FIG. 40–2. The oxidation of fatty acids. The series of reactions given above shows how a two-carbon unit may be removed from a long-chain fatty acid. It should be noted that this is not truly a cyclic series of reactions since each reactant contains two fewer carbon atoms than it did in its previous trip through the series of reactions.

In this case it is accomplished by dehydrogenation followed by a hydration, another dehydrogenation, and finally the rupture of the bond adjacent to the keto group formed in the process described above. Coenzyme A (Fig. 36–14) is essential to the process. A schematic summary of the process is given in Fig. 40–2 and discussed in detail in the following paragraphs.

◀ In the series of reactions shown in Fig. 40–2, we can see that the product of the oxidation of fatty acids is acetyl CoA. This product is then further metabolized to carbon dioxide and water via the citric acid cycle. The removal of an acetyl CoA unit leaves a fatty acid which is shorter by two carbon atoms. This shortened fatty acid goes through the cycle again and again until it is all converted to acetyl CoA. Since the starting material differs each time, the series of reactions is sometimes called a spiral—the **fatty acid spiral.** Each time a 2-carbon unit of the fatty acid is converted to a unit of acetyl CoA, 1 FAD is reduced to FADH$_2$ and 1 NAD is reduced to NADH$_2$. Thus a total of 5 ATP molecules can be synthesized each time a 2-carbon unit is released. The oxidation of 1 molecule of palmitic acid ($C_{15}H_{31}COOH$) requires that it go through the spiral 7 times to yield 8 molecules of acetyl CoA. Each turn of the spiral yields 5 ATP, so we get 5×7 or 35 ATP's. Remembering that oxidation of acetyl CoA via the citric acid cycle gives 12 ATP molecules per acetate unit, we get 12×8 or 96 ATP's. Of course, to be precise, we should subtract 1 ATP since it is required for the attachment of the original fatty acid to coenzyme A. (The attachment of the CoA to the acetate unit that is released at the end of the spiral does not require the energy of ATP.) Thus we get:

$$
\begin{array}{rl}
5 \times 7 = & 35 \\
12 \times 8 = & \underline{96} \\
& 131 \\
& \underline{-1} \\
& 130 \text{ ATP's/mole of palmitic acid}
\end{array}
$$

The free energy available in the complete oxidation of 1 mole of palmitic acid as determined *in vitro* is about 2400 kcal. If the energy stored when 1 ATP is synthesized from ADP and phosphate is 12 kcal, we get 130×12 or 1560 kcal of energy stored, and the process is 1560/2400 or 65% efficient.

Since almost all the naturally occurring fatty acids have an even number of carbon atoms, the problem of metabolism of a 3-carbon fatty acid is not too significant. There are reaction sequences known, however, in which the 3-carbon acid adds a carbon dioxide to become succinic acid which is then oxidized via the citric acid cycle. ▶

40–5 SYNTHESIS OF FATTY ACIDS

Most plants and animals can synthesize fatty acids. In some systems, synthesis seems to be primarily a reversal of the catabolic process. In other systems there are important differences. The hydrogen atoms (electrons) and the energy for the synthesis is provided by reduced NADP, in contrast to the degradation where FAD and NAD serve as hydrogen acceptors. It is interesting that most tissues in the human that synthesize fatty acids contain the enzymes for the phosphogluconate shunt (see Fig. 38–3) which produces reduced NADP.

Although acetyl CoA is used as the starting material, the process of synthesis is not just the addition of these 2-carbon units to one another. A carbon-dioxide molecule is added to acetyl CoA to form malonyl CoA, but the CO_2 unit is subsequently removed, and all the carbon atoms of the synthetic fatty acid are derived from acetate, none from carbon dioxide. The process is summarized in Fig. 40–3.

The minor differences in synthesis and degradation are apparently significant. In connection with these processes, Dr. David Green has stated, "Evidence is multiplying that life processes almost never follow the same pathway in building up and degrading a complex molecule. Readily reversible processes are rarely suitable for synthesis. The trick is to pick reactions that go almost exclusively in one direction."[*]

Some organisms, especially plants, synthesize fatty acids having double bonds. Humans are able to saturate or unsaturate one carbon-to-carbon bond in the C_{18} fatty acid molecule. Thus they can convert oleic acid to stearic acid or vice versa. Since humans require fatty acids containing more than one double bond, however, these fatty acids must be consumed in the diet, and we characterize them as essential fatty acids.

An animal or plant tends to synthesize triglycerides whose melting point is near the skin temperature of the animal or environmental temperature of the plant. Flax plants will grow at various temperatures, but the linseed oil from plants grown in colder tempera-

---

[*] D. E. Green, *Scientific American*, **202**, No. 2, February 1960, p. 51.

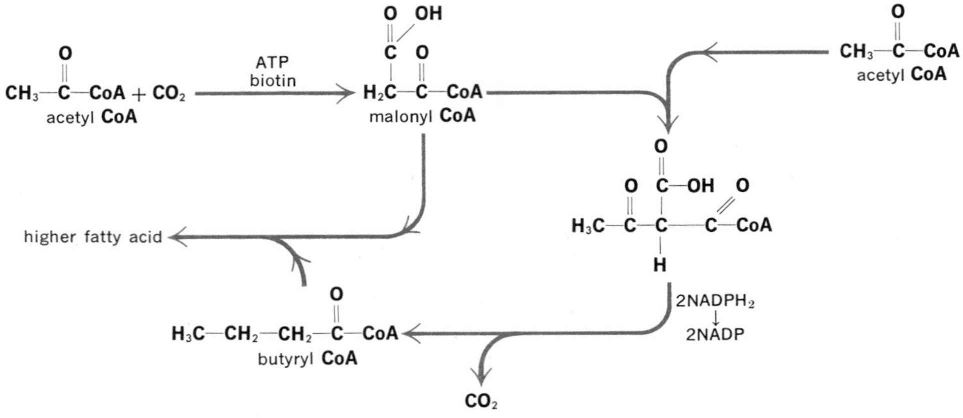

FIG. 40–3. The synthesis of fatty acids. The series of reactions represented above shows how a fatty acid may have a two-carbon unit added to it. By successive reactions, long-chain fatty acids can be synthesized.

tures is more highly unsaturated, that is, it will have a lower melting (freezing) point. Since we know that liquid lipids are more easily metabolized by animals it is not surprising that there is a need for fat deposits that are solid enough to be structurally sound but sufficiently soft to be readily metabolized. It is absurd to believe that a seal living in Arctic waters could deposit a triglyceride like beef tallow—one that would be quite solid at the temperatures in which the seal lives.

We often divide the lipid stores of an animal into two categories, working or **tissue lipids** and storage or **depot lipids.** Tissue lipids are always present in about the same amount and are believed to be essential components of cells. Many of these tissue lipids are phospholipids. Since in man much of the lipid of the brain and nervous system is phospholipid, presumably his brain contains working and not just storage lipid. The amount of depot or storage lipid is variable and depends upon the nutritional state of the animal. The amount of depot lipid is high during periods of adequate or excessive food intake, and low following starvation.

There is a constant turnover of both kinds of lipids in the body, i.e., they are constantly being degraded and resynthesized. The metabolic half-life of the fatty acids in rat liver (mostly tissue lipids) is about 2 days, that of the brain or of the depot fats is about 10 days. Thus the depot lipids, while less active metabolically, are still being constantly degraded and resynthesized. In an experiment in which mice were maintained on a restricted diet so that they lost weight, they were given small amounts of isotopically labelled linseed oil. In 4 days, these animals made approximately 120 mg of depot fat and 130 mg of tissue lipid. Since they were losing weight, they were apparently catabolizing fats even faster than they were synthesizing them, but this did not mean that all synthesis stopped. This is only one example of the facts that lead us to believe that all components of the bodies of all organisms are in a state that has been described as **dynamic equilibrium.** Only when isotopes became available could scientists show that, although a person is maintaining his weight, the molecules in his body are constantly changing.

As we have said previously, an animal tends to accumulate lipids, particularly depot lipids that have a melting point near that of his skin temperature. Exceptions to this generalization are known. In an experiment designed to study the effect of diet on depot fat, dogs whose depot fat normally melted at 20°C, were fed either mutton tallow (highly saturated, high melting point) or linseed oil (highly unsaturated, low melting point). The melting point of the body fat of the dogs fed mutton tallow was found to increase to 40°C and that of those fed linseed oil was reduced to 0°C. Where large amounts of a particular type of lipid are ingested and when almost none of other types are available, an animal is not always able to convert the fatty acids just as it would on a varied diet. Since plants synthesize their own fatty acids (starting originally with CO_2 and H_2O), they tend to produce more consistent types of fats or oils, with the exception noted previously that the degree of unsaturation may depend upon the climate in which the plant is grown.

Farmers who fatten hogs sometimes receive a lower price when they sell the animals if the fat is too soft—a condition called "soft pork." The condition is remedied if the diet is changed to include less unsaturated fat and more corn. Although the corn oil is relatively unsaturated, the starch in the corn is converted to fatty acids that are saturated, and consequently "solid" pork is produced, and a higher market price can be obtained.

40-6 THE SYNTHESIS OF CHOLESTEROL

Cholesterol is synthesized by the human and by most other animals. Although plants make other sterols, they do not synthesize cholesterol. The synthesis of the steroid nucleus starts with acetyl coenzyme A and involves nearly 40 distinct steps. Cholesterol and similar compounds are the precursors of the steroid hormones which are of great importance to the body.

40-7 DISORDERS OF LIPID METABOLISM

Cardiovascular disease is the leading cause of death in the United States. Under this heading, which means diseases of the heart and blood vessels, are included such conditions as heart attacks, strokes, high blood pressure, and heart failure. The underlying cause of cases of cardiovascular disease is **atherosclerosis**—a condition in which fatty deposits are formed in the inner lining of blood vessels. These deposits interfere with normal blood flow and may result either in depriving some areas of an adequate blood supply, in the formation of a blood clot, or in the rupture of blood vessels. The deposits formed in the blood vessels are composed largely of lipids in which cholesterol is found in the greatest quantity. There is no generally accepted theory as to the reason for formation of these fatty deposits in the blood vessels; however, it has been established that persons who have high levels of cholesterol in their blood are more likely to have heart attacks. This does not necessarily mean that the high level of cholesterol causes the attacks. Since the body receives some of its cholesterol from dietary sources and makes the rest, the extent to which cholesterol in the diet should be restricted is also a subject on which opinion is divided. One drug which successfully inhibited cholesterol synthesis in the body has been withdrawn from the market because it also produces undesirable side effects.

Research has shown that diets high in saturated fats tend to increase levels of cholesterol and that diets high in unsaturated fats tend to decrease blood cholesterol. Scientists do not agree on the reasons for this difference. It is also known that persons who are overweight are more likely to suffer from cardiovascular diseases. The explanation here probably depends on at least two factors—excess weight puts an extra strain on the heart, and overweight persons probably have high blood lipid levels, particularly high cholesterol levels. The problems involved in understanding the cause and prevention of cardiovascular disease are much too complex to be adequately discussed in this text. They are problems about which the experts still disagree.

We might summarize what we do know about lipid metabolism by saying that anything that can be metabolized to yield acetyl CoA can be synthesized to either cholesterol or fatty acids. Therefore, excessive intake of either carbohydrates or lipids is not beneficial to health. While it has not definitely been established that unsaturated lipids, such as those found in various vegetable oils, are valuable in preventing cardiovascular disease, some of the normal dietary lipids should probably be in this form. There is insufficient evidence at this time to justify a person in excluding from his diet the animal fats, which include butter and eggs, as well as the fat found mixed in all meats. Indeed, it is difficult to design an adequate diet without the inclusion of milk and eggs. Probably the best policy a person can follow is to decrease the total number of calories eaten and to decrease the percentage of calories that are in the form of lipids, particularly the saturated lipids derived from animal fats. Americans derive from 40 to 45% of their calories from fats, whereas the Japanese, for example, derive only 10% of their calories from fats (and 78% from starches). When groups of men between the ages of 45 and 64 were compared, research showed that the mortality rate from cardiovascular disease for Japanese men is only 25% of that for American men. When Japanese move to the United States, however, and change their dietary habits to those of the Americans, their rate for heart attacks is similar to that for native Americans. We cannot, therefore, disregard the importance of the amount and type of lipid in the diet even though such factors as personality, sex, and heredity are involved in cardiovascular disease. Much more research is necessary before we can give definite answers to problems associated with cardiovascular disease, and in particular, determine the part played by lipids.

40-8 SUMMARY OF LIPID METABOLISM

In spite of the evidence pointing to lipids as a possible cause of cardiovascular disease, lipids play many vital roles in the normal functioning of the body. One gram of lipid gives an average of 9 Cal (kcal) of energy while 1 g of carbohydrate or protein provides only 4 kcal/gram. Thus persons who work hard—who have a large demand for energy—must eat reasonable amounts of lipids. Lipids are stored in a water-free state, so a maximum amount of energy is stored with a minimum increase in body weight. The advantage of economic storage of energy was probably of great importance to our primitive ancestors whose survival depended upon both having energy stores and being mobile, especially if they had to run from sabre-toothed tigers. It is interesting to note that the plants, which are essentially not mobile, accumulate carbohydrates in their tubers (potatoes) or seeds (wheat) instead of accumulating lipids. The plant lipids, which are mostly oils, however, are located in the most mobile part of the plant—the seeds.

Fats are stored by animals both subcutaneously and around delicate organs. Subcutaneous fat helps insulate the body from extremes of temperature and cushions it from the blows of external objects. Fatty deposits around the kidneys and other vital organs probably help protect them from physical shock.

In the instances given above, it is tempting to assume that the human body "knows" where to store fat and that it is better to store fat than protein or carbohydrate. It is certainly much more scientific to say that those animals who stored fats had a better chance for survival than did similar animals who accumulated carbohydrates or proteins—or maybe even some other kind of compound. We could conclude that since those who survived were, of course, the ones who reproduced, the most advantageous traits have persisted. Whether the prehistoric criteria for survival are still most important for our way of life may be open to question.

There is, however, a lot of nonsense in the currently preferred image of the American, especially the American female. The standard of leanness and absence of depot fat that is set by many fashion models probably represents a condition only slightly less sound from a physiological point of view than the picture of the overweight housewife. The mental and physical harm done both by the dread of being fat and by the attempts to diet is tragic. Reasonable amounts of depot fat are not so bad as we might be led to believe. A sensible approach to the problem of body weight requires a knowledge of nutrition—a topic which is discussed in the following chapter.

40-9 INTERRELATIONSHIP OF THE METABOLISM OF CARBOHYDRATES, PROTEINS, AND LIPIDS

Several compounds can be derived from either carbohydrates, proteins, or lipids. Acetyl CoA and the intermediates of the citric acid cycle can be produced by metabolism of any one of the three types of biochemical compounds. A summary of intermediary metabolism is given in Fig. 40-4. Although the figure presents an abbreviated summary, it represents the major known pathways and shows the interrelationship of the metabolism of carbohydrates, proteins, and lipids. From the diagram we can see that carbohydrates can be converted to fatty acids and the lipids via acetyl CoA.

The reverse is not true because the reaction of pyruvic acid to acetyl CoA is not reversible. The conversion of some amino acids to intermediates in the citric acid cycle and to pyruvic acid is also shown. Other amino acids can be converted to acetyl CoA or other intermediates by a relatively complex series of reactions. Many substances have been classified as being ketogenic or glucogenic. The ketogenic compounds will produce ketosis (excretion of acetoacetate, β-hydroxybutyrate, and acetone) when given to a diabetic animal. This reaction indicates that ketogenic substances are metabolized to yield acetate or acetoacetate. Glucogenic (antiketogenic) substances are those that are metabolized to yield a citric acid cycle intermediate, pyruvic acid, or some other glycolytic intermediate. A list of some common ketogenic and glucogenic substances is given below:

Ketogenic Substances	Glucogenic Substances
the amino acids leucine, isoleucine, phenylalanine, and tyrosine	the amino acids glycine, alanine, serine, cystine, methionine, aspartic acid, glutamic acid, proline, arginine, and histidine
all fatty acids	all carbohydrates
	glycerol

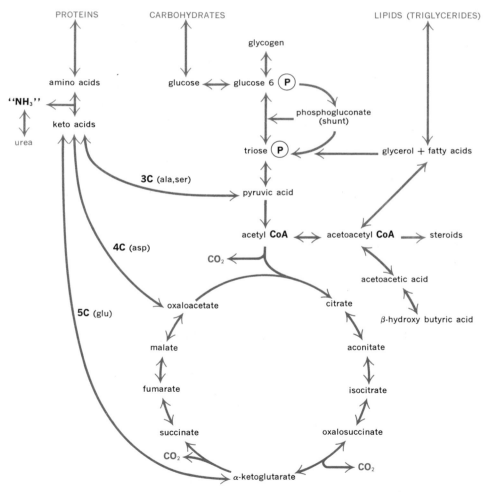

FIG. 40–4. Summary of intermediary metabolism. The reactions shown above represent the major metabolism of the basic biochemical compounds, the proteins, the carbohydrates, and the triglycerides.

IMPORTANT TERMS

Atherosclerosis

Bile

Cardiovascular disease

Depot lipids

Fatty acid spiral

Lecithinase

Lipase

Tissue lipids

WORK EXERCISES

1. Summarize the digestion of a molecule of a triglyceride, of a lecithin.

2. List the series of reactions that is used to break a carbon bond in the metabolism of fatty acids.

3. What is the metabolic fate of the glycerol from the digestion of a triglyceride?

4. Why is the system for metabolism of fatty acids called a spiral rather than a cycle?

5. A table of food composition gives the following caloric values for 100 g of the edible portion of some sea foods: clams, 81; crabs, 104; oysters, 84; shrimp, 127; scallops, 78; salmon, 223; herring, 191. (All values are for the raw food; there is no significant difference in water content of these foods.) On the basis of the material in this chapter, can you give a logical explanation and interpretation of the difference in caloric value of these foods?

6. Calculate the number of ATP's formed from ADP and phosphate in the complete oxidation of one mole of capric acid ($C_9H_{19}COOH$). If the theoretical free energy change in the complete oxidation of this compound *in vitro* is 1500 kcal/mole, and the change in free energy for the synthesis of ATP from ADP and phosphate is 12 kcal/mole, what is the percentage efficiency of this biological oxidation?

7. Alanine containing ^{14}C was given to a diabetic dog. Later β-hydroxybutyric acid containing ^{14}C was found in the urine of this animal. List the probable intermediates in the conversion of alanine to β-hydroxybutyric acid.

8. On the basis of the metabolic scheme for the amino acid histidine given in Problem 6 at the end of Chapter 39, explain why histidine is glucogenic.

9. It is known that a diet virtually free of lipids but high in carbohydrates can result in a person's accumulating large deposits of depot fat. Trace (in a general way) the pathway by which this conversion of carbohydrates to lipids can occur.

10. What major metabolic reaction of carbohydrates is irreversible? What is the significance of this fact?

11. Consult a general biochemistry text for the reactions involved in the synthesis of cholesterol by animals.

SUGGESTED READING

Dawkins, M. J. R. and D. Hull, "The Production of Heat by Fat," *Scientific American*, Aug. 1965 (Offprint #1018). This article discusses the significance of "brown" fat deposits in heat production.

Green, D. E., "The Metabolism of Fats," *Scientific American*, Jan. 1954 (Offprint #16).

Green, D. E., "The Synthesis of Fats," *Scientific American*, Feb. 1960 (Offprint #67). This article and the one above, covering the degradation and synthesis of fatty acids, are excellent.

Sprain, D. M., "Atherosclerosis," *Scientific American*, Aug. 1966. A recent discussion of this leading cause of death, and the relationship of diet to the disease.

Chapter 41   NUTRITION

41-1   INTRODUCTION

There are two reasons why a plant or an animal must receive nourishment. Various kinds of nutrients supply the energy for the many processes which must occur if life is to continue. In green plants some of the energy requirements are provided by the plant's ability to capture and use the radiation from the sun. Other plants, the fungi, not only cannot use the sun's radiation, but are killed or have their growth slowed by sunlight. This is especially true of bacteria which are one type of fungi. Although humans like to acquire a suntan, they do not utilize the sun's energy; in fact, the tanning reaction probably serves to protect humans from the bad effects of overexposure to the sun.

The second reason a living organism must receive nutrition is to obtain necessary chemical substances which the organism itself cannot synthesize. For most plants, the nutritional requirements are merely a source of carbon dioxide, some nitrogen other than the elemental nitrogen found in the air, and a variety of mineral elements—the most important of which are phosphorus, potassium, and sulfur. Animals require a more highly reduced form of carbon—the carbohydrates and lipids. Usually nitrogen must be provided in the form of amino acids or proteins. Mineral elements are necessary for animals just as they are for plants. Animals also have a special requirement for small amounts of chemical substances called vitamins. Green plants do not require preformed vitamins because they can synthesize these substances; many bacteria, however, have definite requirements for vitamins. This chapter will discuss the nutrition of animals, principally of man, in terms of both energy requirements and essential nutrients. Although neither plants nor animals can exist for any length of time without water, it is not usually regarded as a nutrient.

41-2 ENERGY REQUIREMENTS

The energy requirements of an animal are ordinarily expressed in terms of **Calories.**

The Calorie we use in nutritional discussions is actually the kilocalorie—the amount of energy required to raise the temperature of one kilogram of water one degree centigrade.

The total number of Calories a person requires depends a great deal on his activity. Men doing heavy labor expend more energy and consequently require more energy from their food than do desk workers. Even a person who spends the day in a hospital bed is doing some work—his heart is beating, there are peristaltic movements of the digestive tract, and nerves are sending messages. Since the amount of work depends upon the amount of muscles, the size of the heart, and other factors, caloric requirements also depend upon body weight. One reasonable estimate of the energy expended just to keep a person alive is that it requires 1 Cal/kg of body weight per hour. Thus a person weighing 50 kg (about 110 lb) requires 50 × 24 or 1200 Cal/day as a minimum. For this person doing average work the energy requirements are probably from 2000 to 2400 Cal/day. A large man doing heavy work may require between 5000 and 6000 Cal/day. These figures are only a general indication of caloric requirements. The efficiency of digestion and the basal metabolic rate of a person have a great deal to do with the number of calories required.

Those who proclaim that calories do not count are talking about the excess calories of a poorly balanced diet. This topic will be discussed further in Section 41–9. We customarily say that carbohydrates and proteins provide 4 Cal/g and lipids (the triglycerides) give 9 Cal/g, although for specific foods the number of calories differs slightly from the averages given. These figures are for the digestible members of the groups listed. For example, although cellulose contains energy, cellulose is not digested by humans and therefore provides no calories for humans. The opposite is true for ruminants who can utilize cellulose (see Section 38–2). Actually, proteins and amino acids give slightly more energy than 4 Cal/g when they are oxidized *in vitro*. However, their energy is not completely used, since urea is excreted rather than oxides of nitrogen. As a result, the average energy actually available from the metabolism of proteins is reduced to 4 Cal/g.

Most persons are aware that they feel somewhat warmer after they have eaten a meal. Those who are aware of different kinds of foods may have noticed that the increase in heat production is greater following a meal rich in protein-containing foods. This increased heat production which follows eating is called the **specific dynamic action** of foods. It represents the conversion of some of the caloric content of food into heat. The amount of this conversion is about 4% for lipids, 6% for carbohydrates, and an amazing 30% for proteins.

This conversion of the stored energy of foods into heat over and above that required for the maintenance of body temperature represents a "waste" of energy. This loss is probably due to the failure of the body to trap the food energy which is released in the digestion and further metabolism of the food. This untrapped energy is then dissipated as excess heat. In practical terms, then, 30% of the caloric value of protein foods is dissipated as heat, and while the calories from proteins do count, the amount must be discounted by about 30% in calculating the total energy provided by this class of foods.

This so-called energy waste is a bonanza for "calorie watchers." By increasing the protein portion of the diet and reducing the fat and carbohydrate portion they can lose weight on a caloric intake that might otherwise cause an increase in weight.

41–3 THE ESSENTIAL NUTRIENTS

An essential food is defined as a *chemical substance which cannot be synthesized by a given animal at a rate equal to his need.* Strictly speaking, carbon dioxide is an essential nutrient for a plant. When we use the term, **essential nutrient,** especially with respect to man, we mean that the omission of this one nutrient would cause deficiency symptoms even though the individual had a varied diet containing sufficient energy sources. The deficiency symptoms might be quite indefinite, perhaps shown only in a failure to grow normally, or they might be specific as they are in the diseases known as rickets and pellagra.

41–4 CARBOHYDRATES IN NUTRITION

None of the carbohydrates are essential, in the terminology of the nutritionist. However, for the majority of the people on earth more than half of the diet consists of carbohydrates. Rice, wheat and wheat flour, bread, potatoes, macaroni, and similar products are over 75% carbohydrate. In the more prosperous countries, proteins and lipids usually account for a large portion of the total food intake, but in poorer countries only small quantities of protein are available to most people. In these countries the land is used to produce cereal grains. Because of the expense involved and the continuous demand for grain, it is not fed to cattle or swine which would convert the calories contained in the carbohydrate grains to protein. Animals are poor calorie converters—the food they supply as meat or milk represents only 10 to 25% of the calories they consume.

41–5 PROTEINS IN NUTRITION

The proteins are significant in nutrition because of the amino acids they contain. Ten of the common amino acids are not synthesized by the human at a rate sufficient to maintain normal growth. These essential amino acids are given in Table 41–1. It will be seen that these amino acids are the ones having unusual carbon chains.

Most proteins derived from animals—such as beef and pork products, milk, and eggs—are good sources of the essential amino acids. Although some plants contain appreciable amounts of protein, many plant proteins lack one or more of the essential amino acids. Soybean protein contains only small quantities of methionine, and corn protein is deficient

TABLE 41–1. Essential amino acids (for the human and the white rat)

arginine	leucine	phenylalanine
histidine	lysine	threonine
isoleucine	methionine	tryptophan
		valine

in both lysine and tryptophan.   Proteins lacking one or more essential amino acids are considered poor quality proteins.   For those whose diet consists primarily of plant products, and this means for much of the world's population, a variety of different plant proteins is necessary if they are to receive a balanced diet.   Adequate nutrition for vegetarians is easier to achieve if eggs or milk products are eaten.   Fowl and eggs are good protein sources, and in countries located near the sea fish is available as a protein source.

A good general rule is that a person should eat one gram of good quality protein each day for each kilogram of body weight.   Since most protein foods are about 70% water, this means that a 70-kg (154-lb) person should eat a minimum of approximately 230 g (about half a pound) of protein-containing foods each day.   This rule-of-thumb assumes that the food is 30% protein, which is true only of high protein foods like meat, eggs, and cheese.   If the protein is provided by a plant that contains only 5% protein, the intake must be increased, of course.

41-6 LIPIDS IN NUTRITION

Lipids are good sources of food energy.   In most instances an animal can make all the lipids he requires, provided he is given a diet containing a sufficient amount of carbohydrates. White rats, however, require small amounts of the highly unsaturated fatty acids, linoleic, linolenic, and arachidonic acids.   The formulas for these essential fatty acids are given in Table 41-2.

TABLE 41-2. The essential fatty acids

Name	Formula	Location of Double Bonds
Linoleic acid (octadecadienoic acid)	$C_{17}H_{31}COOH$	9–10, 12–13
Linolenic acid (octadecatrienoic acid)	$C_{17}H_{29}COOH$	9–10, 12–13, 15–16
Arachidonic acid (eicosatetraenoic acid)	$C_{19}H_{31}COOH$	5–6, 8–9, 11–12, 14–15

No definite symptoms of deficiency due to a lack of these fatty acids are known in the human. It is logical to assume, however, that they are necessary nutrients since the nutrition of white rats and of humans is remarkably similar.   There is also considerable evidence that lipids containing unsaturated fatty acids are beneficial in preventing heart attacks (see Section 40-7).   It is wise, therefore, for people to include in their daily diet unhydrogenated vegetable oils which contain these highly unsaturated fatty acids.

41-7 MINERAL ELEMENTS IN NUTRITION

There is no simple, unequivocal listing of the mineral elements required for adequate human nutrition.   In the first place, there is some question as to just which elements are mineral elements.   The generally accepted definition is that **mineral elements** *are those elements*

TABLE 41–3. The mineral elements in nutrition

elements needed daily in large quantities:	sodium, calcium, magnesium, potassium (phosphorus)
elements needed in smaller quantities:	iron, copper, chlorine, iodine, cobalt, manganese, zinc, molybdenum
mineral elements whose need is questionable:	bromine, fluorine, selenium, tin, silicon, arsenic, boron, vanadium
mineral elements which are toxic in relatively small quantities:	tin, arsenic, barium, beryllium, bismuth, cadmium, lead, mercury, selenium, silver, tellurium, thorium

not normally found in carbohydrates, proteins, or lipids. This conception eliminates the elements carbon, hydrogen, oxygen, nitrogen, sulfur, and phosphorus since these are commonly found in the three basic nutrients. Enough phosphorus for the human body's requirements cannot always be supplied from the three major sources of nutrients. Some inorganic phosphate must also be included in the diet. For this reason some authorities regard phosphorus as a mineral element. An adult requires about one gram of phosphorus per day either from inorganic phosphates or other compounds.

With the elimination of carbon, hydrogen, oxygen, nitrogen, and sulfur from the list of mineral elements, the major question remaining is "Which of the other chemical elements are essential for normal health and growth?" The question is not easily answered. More than 50 elements are found in the human body. Some are present in large quantities, and a deficiency produces specific deficiency symptoms. A lack of iron, for example, produces anemia. Other elements such as aluminum and silicon are probably present primarily because they are so abundant in the soil of the earth that it would be extremely difficult not to eat them along with normal food. It is, in fact, virtually impossible to place an animal on a completely aluminum- or silicon-free diet. Consequently, we have no experimental evidence as to whether or not these elements are essential. A summary of the mineral elements which are known to affect humans is given in Table 41–3.

We can list several general functions of the mineral elements. Many are found in the structure of parts of the body, as are calcium and phosphates in bone. Others are probably less obviously structural; iron and iodine are parts of the molecules of hemoglobin and thyroxine, respectively. The mineral elements are also important in maintaining the correct osmotic pressure of body fluids. The maintenance of a definite osmotic pressure is necessary to prevent dehydration or overhydration of body cells and to keep proteins in their active forms. Nerves and muscle cells also require certain of the mineral elements for normal function. In cases in which either of two or perhaps three elements has an effect, it is logical to assume that the effect is due to osmotic regulation. A requirement for a specific mineral element would indicate a specific effect.

One of the most important functions of mineral elements is the part they play in enzymatic catalysis. When a mineral element (probably in an ionic form) is required for the maximum function of an enzyme, we call the mineral element an "activator." The biochemist H. R. Mahler has said, "There probably does not exist a single enzyme-catalyzed reaction in which either substrate, product, enzyme, or some combination within this triad is not influenced in a very direct and highly specific manner by the precise nature of the inorganic ions which surround and 'modify' it.''*

41-8 IMPORTANCE OF SPECIFIC MINERAL ELEMENTS

The following paragraphs discuss briefly the specific functions of some of the more important mineral elements.

Calcium

Calcium is found in the form of calcium phosphate in bones and teeth. It is also necessary for blood clotting. The removal of calcium ions by addition of citrate or other chelating agents keeps blood from clotting. Calcium activates some lipases and ATP-ase. Most persons require about 1 g of calcium per day. Milk is one of the best sources of calcium. For pregnant women the calcium requirement is appreciably higher than normal because of the amount of calcium being deposited in the bones of the growing child before his birth. Pregnant women who have insufficient calcium in their diets often deplete the calcium in their own bones and teeth, with resulting tooth decay and fragility of bones. Milk production requires large amounts of calcium in the diet. The old saying that a mother loses a tooth for every child she bears may have been true at one time, but there is no need for such damage with our modern knowledge of nutrition and the availability of milk and calcium supplements.

Magnesium

Magnesium is present in small quantities in bones, but is found primarily in body fluids. It activates many enzymes and is found as part of the chlorophyll molecule. Low levels of magnesium in the diet (a condition which is hard to produce experimentally since magnesium is present in almost all natural water) can cause hyperirritability. Mice suffering from magnesium deficiency have running fits when given stimuli as simple as being exposed to a blast of air. High levels of magnesium in the blood produce anesthesia; however, many anesthetics are much more effective. Humans need about 250–500 mg of magnesium per day.

Sodium and Potassium

Sodium ions account for 93% of the cations of the blood. Sodium ions are found in all body fluids, but most cells have little sodium within the cell wall. Instead, there is a relatively high concentration of potassium ions within cells. While in a resting state, nerve cells contain potassium ions. When a nerve impulse passes, these potassium ions flow out into the surrounding medium and sodium ions flow into the nerve cell. In order for another

* H. R. Mahler, *Mineral Metabolism,* Academic Press, New York.

impulse to be conducted by that nerve cell, the resting conditions must be re-established, sodium must be pumped out, and potassium ions must enter. The whole process happens in milliseconds.

Potassium is present in relatively large quantities in plants, but sodium is not. Normally, humans consume from 2 to 4 g of potassium per day (in. an ionic form, of course). Sodium ions are consumed primarily in the form of NaCl. While consumption varies widely, 5 g/day of sodium ions is a good average value. Herbivores (animals that eat only plants) often crave sodium chloride and will travel long distances to find a source of salt. Anthropologists have pointed to the fact that ancient civilizations developed in areas near either the sea or dried up seas and lakes where good supplies of salts, particularly NaCl were available. When the human body contains abnormally large amounts of sodium ions it tends to retain water, and we see the condition known as edema. Persons who develop edema—often as a result of certain heart conditions—are restricted from consuming NaCl, and are given medicines to aid them in excreting sodium ions. The major function of both sodium and potassium ions in the body seems to be that of regulating osmotic pressure.

Chlorine

Chloride is the principal anion of the body. No specific function is known for chlorine, and we assume that it is merely the most readily available and convenient anion to balance the cations Na^+ and K^+ in body fluids.

Iron

Iron is part of the important body substances, hemoglobin, myoglobin, and the cytochromes. Although a human contains from 3 to 5 g of iron, he usually needs only small amounts, perhaps 10 mg/da, in his diet. The fact that females lose some blood at each menstrual cycle means that they require a slightly higher intake of iron than do males. The body re-uses iron, however, and although the iron-containing hemoglobin is turned over relatively rapidly in the body, iron is not excreted as are other parts of the hemoglobin molecule. It is retained and re-used in the synthesis of a new molecule of hemoglobin. Nevertheless, iron deficiencies are known and are one of the more common causes of anemia.

Manganese

Manganese is known to activate many enzymes, among them arginase and many phosphatases. A deficiency has been shown to cause sterility in male rats.

Copper

Copper serves as an activator for many enzymes, particularly oxidative enzymes. Copper which is part of the pigment of the respiratory system of crabs, shrimp, and some other animals serves much the same function that iron serves in the hemoglobin of humans. This pigment found in those creatures is blue and has the name *hemocyanin*.

Cobalt

Cobalt is part of the structure of vitamin B_{12}; in fact, the name of the vitamin, cobalamin, reflects this fact. Deficiencies of cobalt in the food of ruminants leads to deficiencies of cobalamin and to anemia. Humans cannot synthesize cobalamin but must ingest the vitamin which already contains the cobalt.

Fluorine

It is known that large amounts of fluoride ions are poisonous. It is also true that small amounts may be incorporated into teeth, and that these small amounts make teeth less subject to decay. The addition of fluoride ions to water supplies has led to a great deal of controversy.

Iodine

Iodine is part of the thyroid hormones thyroxine and triiodothyronine. Lack of iodine in the diet is one of the causes of an enlargement of the thyroid gland which is called goiter. The use of iodized salt, which contains some NaI in addition to NaCl, makes goiters from iodine deficiency totally unnecessary.

Other Mineral Elements

Molybdenum and zinc serve as enzyme activators. Zinc is also found as part of the structure of the hormone insulin. Bromide has a sedative effect when present in relatively high concentrations in the blood. An appreciable amount of aluminum in the diet may lead to poor bone structure because aluminum prevents the absorption of the phosphates normally present in the diet and necessary for bone formation. This condition apparently comes about because aluminum phosphate is quite insoluble. Boron and zinc are required for normal plant growth although high levels, especially of zinc, may be toxic to plants.

41-9 VITAMINS

At the beginning of the twentieth century it was generally believed that an animal given a diet containing sufficient calories, adequate amounts of carbohydrates, proteins, lipids, and mineral elements would be well nourished. Additional research, however, with dietary components that were purified further indicated that something more than these nutrients was needed. Animals given highly purified diets soon got sick and, if not treated with less highly purified foods, they died. Gradually nutritionists realized that the animals on these purified but inadequate diets had symptoms similar to diseases seen in humans. The addition of certain substances to the purified diets cured the "deficiency" diseases in experimental animals, and it was not long until similar additions were made to diets of humans.

Placing experimental animals on given diets whose composition was well established has developed into an important experimental procedure for establishing exact nutritional requirements. The first such substance to be identified was an amine—an important or vital amine. From these two words the name vitamine, which we now spell *vitamin*, was coined.

We now know that these vital food substances are not all amines. The current definition of a **vitamin** is that it is *an organic compound occurring in natural foods, either as such or as a utilizable precursor, which is required for normal growth, maintenance, or reproduction.* Vitamins are essentially catalysts and are not sources of body energy. The vitamins were originally named for letters of the alphabet. When a vitamin which was thought to be only one substance was found to be two or more different substances, both letters and numbers were used. Now that chemical structures are known for the vitamins, it is better to use descriptive names, although the old letters and numbers are still widely used. Another classification of vitamins is based on their solubility. Vitamins A, D, E, and K are insoluble in water and are often called the fat-soluble vitamins. It is better to call them lipid-soluble vitamins. Substances classified as one of the vitamins B or vitamin C (ascorbic acid) are water-soluble. Although these two classifications (lipid- and water-soluble) were developed merely for convenience in classifying vitamins, there is an underlying significance in the classification. The lipid-soluble vitamins are stored in the fats of the body; the water-soluble vitamins are not stored to any extent. Thus, the water-soluble vitamins must be ingested daily, while stores of vitamins A, D, E, and K may be sufficient to keep deficiencies from developing even after long periods on vitamin-deficient diets. Now that vitamins are readily available in supplements as well as in foods, physicians are beginning to see cases of **hypervitaminoses**—an excessive amount of a vitamin. The only vitamins for which true hypervitaminoses are known are the lipid-soluble vitamins—the ones the body can accumulate, sometimes to its own detriment.

A vitamin must always be defined with respect to a given type of animal. Ascorbic acid (vitamin C) is a necessary substance for all animals; however, most animals synthesize this compound. Man, other primates, and the guinea pig, however, cannot synthesize ascorbic acid.

Any real understanding of the vitamins must involve some idea of their structure and their general functions.

Vitamin A

The formula for this vitamin is given below:

vitamin A

It can be seen that vitamin A is a hydrocarbon with one —OH group, that the compound is a lipid, and that it would be classified as lipid-soluble. Vitamin A, which has never really been given a name reflecting its chemical structure, is similar to β-carotene (see Chapter 35), and can be derived from β-carotene in the diet. It is found in yellow foods. The vitamin itself is yellow and its precursor, β-carotene, is orange so that small amounts of it give a yellow color. Many green foods also contain vitamin A, but its color is masked by the more brilliant chlorophyll. The vitamin can be destroyed by heating and oxidation.

Vitamin A is necessary for growth, maintenance of epithelial tissues, and proper vision. Lack of the vitamin causes night blindness, poor dark adaptation, and a disease of the eyes called xeropthalmia. Although vitamin A undoubtedly plays many roles in the animal body, its most important role is its function in vision. The visual cycle can be summarized as follows:

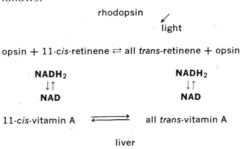

This cycle involves rhodopsin (visual purple) which is a combination of a protein called opsin and retinene (the aldehyde corresponding to vitamin A). Since there are five double bonds in the side chain of vitamin A, each one could exist in either the *cis* or *trans* configuration. Vitamin A is usually found in the all *trans* form; however, in rhodopsin there is the *cis* configuration between carbon atoms 11 and 12. This 11-*cis* configuration is necessary for the binding of retinene to the protein opsin. When a quantum of light hits a molecule of rhodopsin it converts the 11-*cis* form of the vitamin to the all-*trans* form. This change of configuration apparently changes the shape of the retinene so much that it cannot stay bound to opsin. The other reactions of the series serve to regenerate the 11-*cis*-retinene so that it can recondense with opsin and again react with light.

Rhodopsin is not the only visual pigment. It is most important in vision in dim light; lack of rhodopsin due to a dietary deficiency of vitamin A (or carotene) causes a condition known as "night blindness." Eating liver, which is a good source of the vitamin, and carrots, which contain β-carotene, prevents or cures night blindness.

In the United States there are probably more excesses of vitamin A than deficiencies today. Great excesses can be observed in Eskimos who have eaten large amounts of liver. These cases of hypervitaminoses produce skin irritations and a lack of appetite. In many areas of the world, however, vitamin A deficiencies create serious problems, particularly since they cause the disease xerophthalmia. It was recently estimated that, in India, at least one million persons are blind because of vitamin A deficiencies. Yet the materials to prevent these deficiencies would cost only a few pennies a year per person.

The B Vitamins

At one time it was believed that there was a substance called vitamin B. Further study proved that this substance was really a mixture of more than one chemical compound. Further fractionation proved that there were many compounds, all water-soluble, most containing at least one nitrogen in a ring structure, and having somewhat similar functions. These vitamins were given names such as B_1, B_2, and B_3. Some of those originally given a numerical classification proved either to be one of the other vitamins or else compounds that were hot vitamins; only those called B_1, B_2, B_6, and B_{12} have retained the letter-number designation. These designations are gradually being replaced with names which reflect the chemical structures. Other substances now classified as B vitamins are known primarily by their chemical names. For purposes of discussion we will group these various substances under the general heading of B vitamins.

All the B vitamins are necessary components of all living cells. They usually function as coenzymes, usually with a nucleotide, or at least a phosphate, attached. Since many organisms can synthesize these chemical compounds, they are not truly vitamins for these organisms. In many animals, bacteria in the gastrointestinal tract synthesize appreciable amounts of the B vitamins, and the host organism uses the products of intestinal synthesis. In fact, some vitamin deficiencies in some animals cannot be produced without destroying their gastrointestinal bacteria.

All B vitamins are involved in promotion of the appetite, growth, and general well-being of the animal which requires them. Foods that are good sources of one B vitamin as a rule are rich in the others also. The classical deficiency diseases which have been attributed to a deficiency of a specific B vitamin were probably multiple deficiency diseases. Actually, we know much more about the specific deficiency diseases in the white rat and other experimental animals than we do in humans, since our knowledge of human deficiencies has come primarily from reports of doctors who were much more interested in curing the disease than prolonging the condition in order to study it. We may feel some displeasure about the lack of precise knowledge concerning human nutrition, but when we realize that definitive knowledge could come only from experimentation on humans, we are willing to accept the limitations.

Thiamine (vitamin B_1)

The disease beriberi has been characterized as a thiamine-deficiency disease. Beriberi was prevalent in the Orient where a large part of the diet is composed of polished rice. The simple way to cure this disease is to restore to the diet the materials from rice hulls which are removed in polishing the rice. While the classical human beriberi may have been a multiple deficiency disease, many of the symptoms are similar to those shown in rats on diets deficient only in vitamin B_1.

thiamine chloride

Thiamine deficiency causes abnormalities in the nervous system. A neuritis of the nerves in muscles leads to muscular weakness. Anxiety and mental confusion are also seen in humans. In some cases the heart does not function normally.

Thiamine functions as a coenzyme in decarboxylation reactions. A biochemical deficiency symptom is the finding of high levels of pyruvic and lactic acids in the blood, apparently due to the failure of a thiamine-deficient animal to decarboxylate pyruvic acid to acetyl CoA. We do not yet know how the biochemical abnormality—lack of decarboxylation—leads to the physiological symptoms.

Thiamine was the "vital amine" which resulted in the name vitamin. It is one of the most important vitamins; the complete absence of this substance from the diet will produce death in experimental animals in a week or two. A human requires about 1 mg of thiamine per day. Yeast, pork, fresh fruits, vegetables, and whole grains are good sources of thiamine. Thiamine is now added to white bread and polished rice. The vitamin is hydrolyzed to an inactive form when heated in neutral or alkaline solutions, however. Consequently, prolonged cooking of foods containing thiamine, particularly if sodium bicarbonate has been added, as it often is to retain the fresh green color of vegetables, destroys the vitamin.

Some interesting experiments he did with white rats led Dr. R. J. Williams to reach some conclusions regarding alcoholism and thiamine. When white rats were given a choice of either water or a dilute solution of ethanol, each rat established an individual drinking pattern. Some preferred water, others chose both water and alcohol. When the diet of the rats was altered so that the thiamine was decreased, all the rats started drinking large amounts of alcohol. This kind of alcoholism could be cured by adding thiamine to the deficient diets. It is known that human alcoholics often suffer from thiamine deficiencies. Apparently the intake of alcohol diminishes the desire for food so that these people develop a slight thiamine deficiency which leads to further alcoholism, more serious vitamin deficiency, and so on. The administration of thiamine is effective in treating some cases of alcoholism; however, on the basis of current evidence we cannot say that adequate nutrition is a cure for all cases of alcoholism, since many psychological factors are also involved. Relatively large doses of thiamine have been touted as a preventive or cure for a "hangover." This prescription is probably as effective as most cures, other than abstinence, that have been proposed. To our knowledge this area has not been subjected to rigorous scientific experimentation.

Riboflavin (vitamin B$_2$)

The deficiency of riboflavin can be said to produce generally poor health. White rats given diets deficient in vitamin B$_2$ fail to grow normally, have a poor coat of hair, a tendency toward skin irritations, and can be described as "looking sick." Human deficiencies of riboflavin that are not complicated by other deficiencies are not well characterized. The vitamin in the form of FAD (flavine adenine dinucleotide) and FMN (flavine mononucleotide) serves as an important coenzyme (see the FAD formula, Chapter 37). Humans require about 1.5 mg/day of riboflavin. The vitamin is found especially in yeast, liver, and wheat germ.

riboflavin

Milk and eggs, although containing smaller amounts, probably represent the major sources of the vitamin in the average American diet. Green leafy vegetables are also good sources of riboflavin.

Nicotinamide (niacin)

This vitamin is related to nicotinic acid (which is only remotely related to nicotine, see Section 28–6A and B). Nicotinic acid can be converted to the vitamin by the human.

nicotinamide

The classical deficiency disease of this vitamin is pellagra. Until 40 or 50 years ago many of the residents of the southeastern United States and of Spain suffered from this condition. It was characterized by a dermatitis, mental symptoms, and diarrhea. The addition of nicotinamide to the diets of persons suffering from pellagra cures the disease; so does the consumption of a diet rich in good quality protein. This originally led to confusion as to the real cause and cure of pellagra. When it was found that the amino acid tryptophan could be converted to nicotinamide by a series of reactions, the link between the two cures for pellagra was found. Those areas in which pellagra was widespread were areas in which corn was a major part of the diet. In fact, the diet of a typical pellagrin consisted principally of the fatty part of pork or "side meat", cornmeal mush, and molasses. Thus, the caloric needs were satisfied, but no good source of either nicotinamide or tryptophan was ingested. The protein present in corn is notably lacking in the amino acid tryptophan. The story of the discovery of the cause and the treatment of pellagra by Dr. Goldberger of the United States Public Health Service is a striking example of nutritional detective work. One dramatic account of this story is in the book *Hunger Fighters* by Paul DeKruif. (See the "Suggested Reading" at the end of the chapter.)

Nicotinamide is found in the coenzymes NAD and NADP. (For formulas see Fig. 36–13.) These coenzymes function in a great number of oxidation reactions and provide an important link in the conversion of the energy of foods to the energy stored in ATP.

The requirement for this vitamin depends upon the intake of tryptophane in the diet; a human requires probably 10 to 16 mg/day. The vitamin is found in a variety of plant and animal foods. Meat products, especially liver, are good sources of nicotinamide.

Pyridoxal (vitamin B$_6$)

Pyridoxal is the functional form of the substance also known as vitamin B$_6$. The closely related compounds pyridoxine and pyridoxamine can also serve as sources of the vitamin.

pyridoxal   pyridoxine   pyridoxamine

No human diseases due to a deficiency of this vitamin are known, although convulsions have been reported in infants who had been fed a formula deficient in sources of pyridoxal. Rats on a diet deficient in vitamin B_6 develop a dermatitis and fail to grow normally. The fact that the amounts of urinary excretion products of pyridoxal are greater than the amount known to be ingested has led to the conclusion that pyridoxal is synthesized in the human body. Whether this synthesis is due to bacteria in the intestinal tract or whether some part of the body synthesizes the compound is not known. If the latter is found to be true, pyridoxal may no longer be considered a vitamin. Whole grains, fresh meats, vegetables, and milk are good sources of the vitamin.

Pyridoxal phosphate is the coenzyme for many of the reactions of amino acids. Trans-aminations are among the most important reactions catalyzed by pyridoxal-containing enzymes. Decarboxylation and racemization (conversion from the D- or L-form to a DL mixture) of amino acids are also catalyzed by B_6-containing enzymes.

Pantothenic Acid

Pantothenic acid is part of the structure of coenzyme A. (See Fig. 36–14 for the formula.) Human deficiency diseases are not known. In rats deficiencies produce a decreased rate of growth, impaired reproduction, and graying of hair. The latter is not observed, of course, unless the rat used is a dark-haired one instead of the usual albino white rat used in nutritional research. No relationship has been found between pantothenic acid,

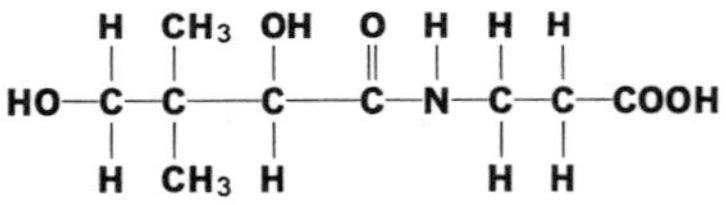

pantothenic acid

and graying of human hair. As coenzyme A, the vitamin functions in a great number of reactions, especially those involving acetic or other fatty acids. Because of its widespread occurrence in foods, pantothenic acid deficiencies are rare. Liver and yeast are rich sources of the vitamin.

Biotin

Biotin is widely distributed in foods. In most animals the excretion of metabolites of biotin exceeds the intake, and we assume that intestinal synthesis provides sufficient amounts of this compound. Biotin,

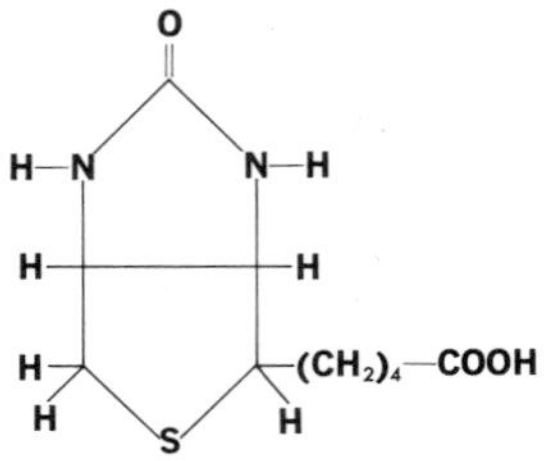

biotin

serves as a coenzyme for reactions in which carbon dioxide is added to a substrate. The synthesis of fatty acids is one of the more important of such reactions. The conversion of pyruvate to oxaloacetate requires biotin, as does the incorporation of CO_2 into urea via the urea cycle.

Folic Acid

Deficiencies of folic acid produce various kinds of anemias. Such deficiencies in the human are usually due to a malfunction of the digestive tract rather than to an actual dietary insufficiency. The vitamin is widespread in nature, and most diets contain appreciable quantities of it. It is also synthesized by bacteria in the intestine. Folic acid,

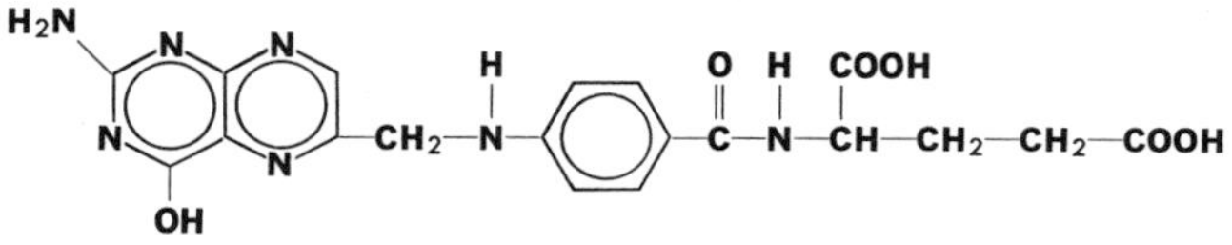

functions in the metabolism of one-carbon compounds, particularly formyl and hydroxymethyl groups. It is certainly a necessary component of the body, although the daily requirements are not known.

Cobalamin (vitamin B$_{12}$)

This vitamin was one of the last ones to be studied and characterized. Deficiency of vitamin B_{12} causes the condition known as pernicious anemia. As with folic acid, most deficiencies are due to failure to absorb the vitamin which is present in food. The vitamin is widespread in animal products, but is not found in most green plants. Apparently the human body can store some amounts of this vitamin and since the daily requirement is small, perhaps only 1 μg (microgram)/day, B_{12} is not especially significant in normal nutrition. The formula for B_{12} is given in Fig. 41–1.

Ascorbic Acid (vitamin C)

Scurvy has been known for hundreds of years. It was especially seen among sailors. Scurvy was characterized by sore gums and loss of teeth, swollen and tender joints, small hemorrhages located just below the skin, and anemia. The British learned that lemons or limes which could be kept on long voyages would not only cure but prevent this condition. From this discovery came the practice of carrying limes and the name "Limey" to describe a British sailor. Later developments led to the identification of ascorbic acid as vitamin C.

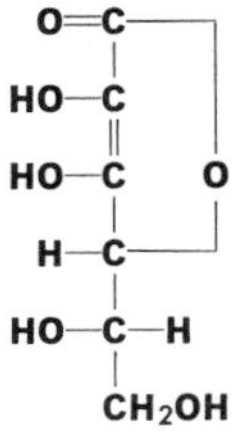

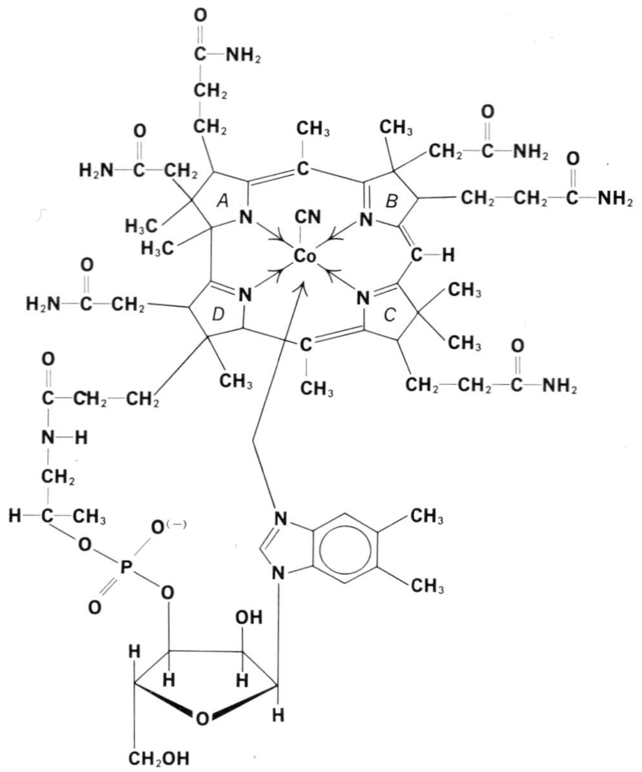

FIG. 41–1. Structure of vitamin B$_{12}$ (cobalamin). Note the cobalt atom in the center of the pyrrolidine rings. These rings are in a plane with the cobalt, with cyanide group, and the dimethylbenzimidazole groups above and below the ring. Note also that rings A and D do not have a carbon bridge between them as was found in hemoglobin and chlorophyll.

Most animals can synthesize ascorbic acid from glucose, but man, the apes, and the guinea pig cannot. The human requirement has not been definitely established, but is apparently in the range between 30–50 mg/day. The vitamin is present not only in citrus fruits, but most fresh fruits and even in potatoes. Ascorbic acid is relatively easily oxidized, however, and consequently its effectiveness as a vitamin is lost when foods containing it are cooked.

The exact function of ascorbic acid in human metabolism is not known. It presumably functions in oxidation-reduction reactions, and many such reactions have been shown to be aided by ascorbic acid. For most of these systems other easily oxidizable and reducible substances also function. No reaction is known for which ascorbic acid is a specific co-enzyme.

Vitamin D

Several substances have the function of Vitamin D. They are steroids differing only in the side chain (R group) at position 17. Children who have inadequate amounts of the vitamin in their diet develop rickets. The disease is now rapidly disappearing, but cases are prevalent in the poorer countries of the world. Rickets is characterized by the failure of the bones to harden normally. Children with rickets usually have bowed legs and are stunted in growth. The vitamin promotes the absorption of calcium and phosphorus through the intestinal wall and functions in depositing these two elements in the protein matrix of bone.

     Vitamin D is sometimes called the sunshine vitamin because the ultraviolet radiation of the sun can convert an inactive precursor in the skin (7-dehydrocholesterol) to vitamin D. (See Section 35-6).

vitamin D

Children need vitamin D during the time they are growing and, to a lesser extent, mothers require the vitamin during pregnancy and lactation. There is no demonstrable vitamin D requirement for adult males. Vitamin D is readily available, and since it is lipid-soluble and can be stored, cases of hypervitaminoses have been reported. In these cases bones are actually demineralized, and the calcium and phosphate deposited in many soft tissues. Deposits may also form in the kidney with serious consequences. Deaths have been reported due to kidney failure brought on by excessive intake of vitamin D. Considerations such as these make one consider whether the addition of vitamin D to milk, which has proved to be an excellent preventive for rickets, may not also have unfavorable consequences.

Vitamin E

The substance α-tocopherol and related compounds are necessary for normal reproduction in the rat.

α-tocopherol

Also, the absence of these compounds, which are collectively known as vitamin E, causes a serious muscular dystrophy in rabbits. Although there are other indications that the vitamin is necessary for several species of animals, there is no convincing evidence that vitamin E is essential for humans. It is ineffective in treating human muscular dystrophy and sterility.

On the other hand, since other species do require the vitamin, it is possible that there is sufficient dietary intake and storage of vitamin E in humans so that symptoms of deficiency do not appear. The best natural sources of vitamin E are the oils derived from plants; wheat germ oil and cottonseed oil are good sources. The lipids of the leaves of green plants also contain vitamin E.

Excessive claims are often made for the effectiveness of vitamin E in helping certain heart conditions and in improving muscle action. Some athletic coaches advise the use of plant oils that are rich in vitamin E. To the best of our knowledge, at the present time, such uses are unwarranted. The ever-present danger of hypervitaminoses of the lipid-soluble vitamins should keep one from indiscriminate use of this substance.

Vitamin K

Vitamin K is necessary for proper clotting of blood; deficiencies are characterized by hemorrhages. Since the vitamin is widely found in foods and is probably synthesized by intestinal bacteria, deficiencies are usually due to poor absorption.

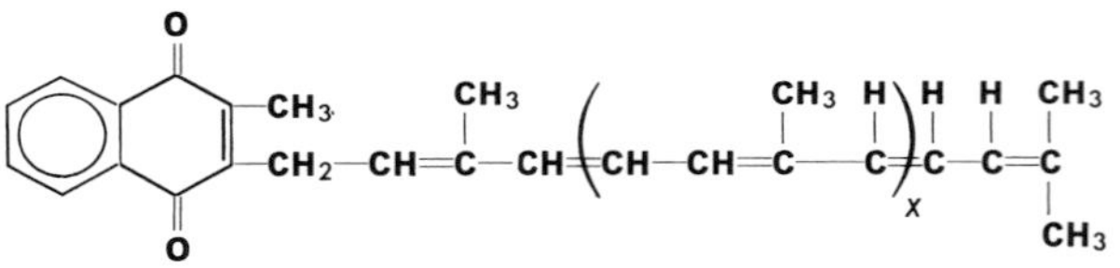

There are several forms of vitamin K, each differing in the length of the side chain. The widespread occurrence of the vitamin and its production by intestinal synthesis mean that normal persons need not be concerned with the amount of this nutrient in their diets.

In cases where clotting of the blood is damaging to an individual, extensive use is now made of substances which oppose the action of the vitamin, reducing the tendency of the person's blood to clot. These substances are structurally similar to vitamin K, but sufficiently different so that they interfere with the action of the vitamin. Dicoumarol was originally isolated from spoiled clover hay which caused the death of cattle due to internal hemorrhages. Now both dicoumarol and a synthetic analog, warfarin, are given to persons who have had heart attacks caused by blood clots. Warfarin is also used now as a rat poison. It causes death by producing internal hemorrhages. Continued consumption of the poison is required, however, before it is lethal.

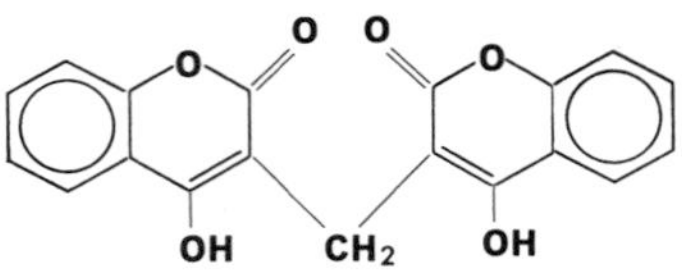

dicoumarol 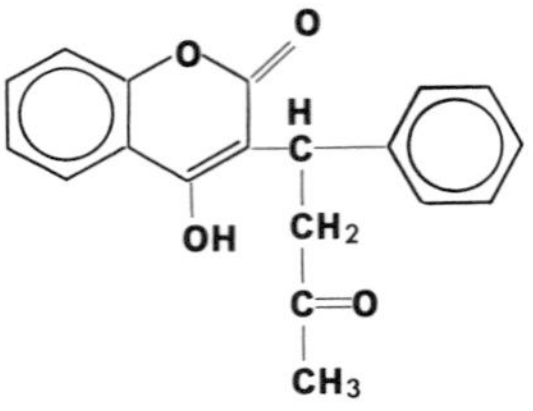   warfarin

41–10 ON BEING WELL FED

An adequate diet should contain foods that provide sufficient energy. Either carbohydrates, proteins, or lipids can provide this energy. Evidence from studies of persons having cardio-vascular disease indicates that in the normal American diet the percentage of calories derived from lipids is probably too high. Many nutritionists recommend that lipids should provide no more than 15% of the calories a person consumes.

When the consumption of energy-producing foods exceeds the energy requirements of an individual, his body usually converts the energy of the food to energy stored in his triglycerides, and he gets fat. The simplest way to lose weight or to keep from gaining weight is to decrease the number of calories consumed.

A good diet, however, must also include all essential nutrients. It should contain the essential amino acids which are derived from proteins, the essential fatty acids, the mineral elements, and the vitamins. To meet these requirements, a varied diet should include high quality protein, vegetables, and fruits, some of which should be uncooked, and some plant oils. Vitamin pills are not necessary for normal persons who are able to have a varied diet as outlined above. Large amounts of the water-soluble vitamins are probably not harmful, but serious consideration should be given before including large amounts of the lipid-soluble vitamins, particularly in the diet of adults. Eggs, milk, and other dairy products are excellent foods. Both eggs and milk are "specifically designed" for the nutrition of a developing individual—the designer, of course, being the process of evolution which assures the non-survival of the inadequately nourished.

Many Americans are overweight, and many of them are obsessed with the idea that they must lose weight. They keep hoping that there is some easy way to eat all they want and still be thin. Well-meaning but ignorant persons and charlatans are only too ready to take advantage of this situation. Many good types of diet are known, but others, even some that are widely publicized, are so grossly unbalanced that continued adherence to them would have serious consequences. For persons who wish to lose weight the following suggestions may be helpful.

1) Remember that calories do count, and don't eat high calorie foods. Many vegetables contain large amounts of water and cellulose neither of which add any calories to your diet. The green leafy vegetables, in addition to being low in calories, have high mineral and vitamin content.

2) If you need to decrease food consumption drastically, it may be advisable to include vitamin and mineral supplements.

3) The proteins in your diet should be maintained at a high level. You can decrease the amounts of lipids and carbohydrates in your diet—within the limits of discretion, of course.

4) For serious dieters it is advisable to get a chart listing not only the caloric, but also the protein, mineral, and vitamin content of foods.

This chapter serves only as a general introduction to the science of nutrition. There are exceptions to most of the generalizations presented. The presentation is intended to give our readers an understanding of normal nutrition, not to provide sufficient information for proposing drastic diets. Any prolonged dietary restrictions should be undertaken only under the supervision of a competent physician.

IMPORTANT TERMS

Basal metabolic rate	*Essential nutrient*	*Nutrient*	*Specific dynamic action*
Calorie	*Hypervitaminosis*	*Nutrition*	*Vitamin*
Deficiency disease	*Mineral element*		

WORK EXERCISES

1. Why is tryptophan an essential amino acid?
2. Why must vegetarians eat a variety of types of plant food?
3. Calculate your basic daily requirements for calories and protein.
4. Keep a record of all foods eaten for a day. Using a dietary chart, compute your intake of carbohydrates, proteins, lipids and total calories.
5. Why should you include nonhydrogenated vegetable oils in your diet?
6. What are the basic functions of mineral elements in the human body?
7. What are the biological functions of each of the following mineral elements?

    a) iron   b) chlorine   c) calcium   d) cobalt   e) iodine

8. What vitamin deficiency is the primary cause of each of the following diseases?

    a) beriberi   b) rickets   c) scurvy   d) pellagra

9. What vitamin is found in each of the following coenzymes?

    a) NAD   b) FAD   c) coenzyme A

10. Examine a carton of milk to find the amount of vitamin D that has been added. Check in a grocery or dairy store to see whether adding vitamin D is widespread.
11. Examine the label on a loaf of bread to determine the amount of vitamins added to the bread. Most breakfast cereals also have a listing of their vitamin content. How do they compare with bread as a source of vitamins?
12. Which is the "sunshine" vitamin? Why is it so named?
13. How do the requirements of certain animals for vitamin C correlate with the generalization (Chapter 39) that animals higher in the evolutionary scale often lack enzymes that simpler animals have?
14. List the vitamins which contain the following elements: N, S, Co.

SUGGESTED READING

Champagnat, A., "Protein from Petroleum," *Scientific American*, Oct. 1965. The author discusses the possibility of using microorganisms that grow on hydrocarbons to synthesize edible proteins.

DeKruif, P., *Hunger Fighters,* Harcourt, New York, 1928.

Dowling, J. E., "Night Blindness," *Scientific American,* Oct. 1966. The role of Vitamin A in night blindness is discussed.

Hubbard, Ruth and A. Kropf, "Molecular Isomers in Vision," *Scientific American,* June 1967. A well-illustrated discussion of the role of Vitamin A in vision.

Meyer, L. H., *Food Chemistry,* Reinhold, New York, 1960. A chemically-oriented book about the foods we eat.

Pirie, N. W., "Orthodox and Unorthodox Methods of Meeting World Food Needs," *Scientific American,* Feb. 1967. A discussion of new sources of foods for our growing population—some of the proposals are exotic and exciting.

Chapter 42 THE CHEMISTRY OF HEREDITY

42-1 INTRODUCTION

Since the times of the ancient Greeks, and probably long before, people have been aware of the fact that a young animal resembles its parents. Characteristics regarded as hereditary have included eye color, stature, and even a fiery temper. Occasionally heredity seemed to fail when, for example, normal parents produced an albino offspring. As with many biological theories, those concerning heredity have become more and more detailed in order to explain observations. Underlying the details, however, we can now see a few simple generalizations which help us to explain heredity and to predict what will happen in many cases.

When it was realized that all living things were produced by parents similar to them, and that lice, frogs, and mice were not generated spontaneously from decaying matter, mud, or old rags, theories of heredity became important. Part of the way in which characteristics are transmitted was deduced by the Austrian monk, Gregor Mendel, whose studies of pea plants were the basis for adding to the theory of heredity the concepts of specific unit characteristics which do not blend. Figure 42-1 illustrates one of Mendel's experiments involving tall and dwarf peas. The development of Mendel's theories led to the belief that there were at least a pair of factors called **genes** for each hereditary characteristic. Some characteristics, such as skin color, are now believed to be controlled by more than one pair of genes. For each hereditary characteristic or for each pair of genes, both dominant and recessive varieties are known.

With sweet peas, a plant produced by crossing one having red flowers with one having white flowers produces only red flowers, not pink. Since the new plant presumably has genes for both red flowers and white flowers, we conclude that the gene for red flowers is dominant. If we cross the red-flowering pea plants from mixed parents with each other, their

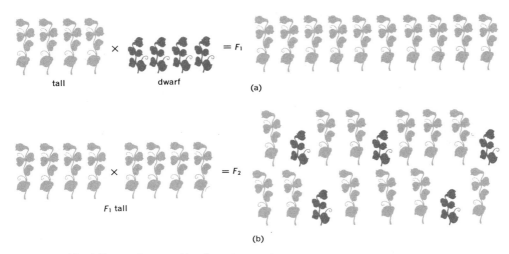

FIG. 42–1. Mendel's experiments with tallness in pea plants. Diagram (a) represents Mendel's first cross of tall and dwarf peas. All the offspring (F_1 generation) were tall. Diagram (b) shows the results of matings between the members of the F_1 generation. When Mendel performed the experiment he found 787 tall plants and 277 dwarf plants. [Adapted from Baker and Allen, *The Study of Biology,* Addison-Wesley, Reading, Mass., 1967.]

offspring produces red or white flowers, but no pink ones. In the illustration of the tall and dwarf peas (Fig. 42–1) we see that plants were either tall or dwarf, and that tallness is dominant. An individual having two different genes for a single trait is called a *hybrid* or a **hetero-zygote.** A pure-bred individual, one having a pair of identical genes, is homozygous—or is a **homozygote**—for that trait.

Our present theory about inheritance can be summarized as follows. There is a pair of genes for each hereditary characteristic in most cells of each individual. These genes may be identical, in which case the individual is homozygous for that characteristic, or they may be different, in which case the individual is heterozygous for that characteristic. When an individual forms reproductive cells, whether in the parts of a flower or in the testes or ovary of a mammal, only one member of the pair of genes goes into an individual reproductive cell. (The general name given this reproductive cell is *gamete*.) A homozygote produces only one kind of gametes; a heterozygote, two. When the gametes from a male (sperm cells) meet with and fertilize the gametes (eggs or ova) from a female, various combinations are possible. If the number of offspring of the mating of a single male and a female is large, the proportions predicted by laws of probability are found. In cases where the number of off-spring is small, the lack of an adequate sample may result in some deviation from predictions. The situation is analogous to tossing a coin only a few times and having the percentage of "heads" not equal to that of "tails."

An analysis of the hereditary factors involved in the tall and dwarf pea plants of Mendel is given in Fig. 42–2. (We use T to represent the dominant characteristic—tallness—and t to

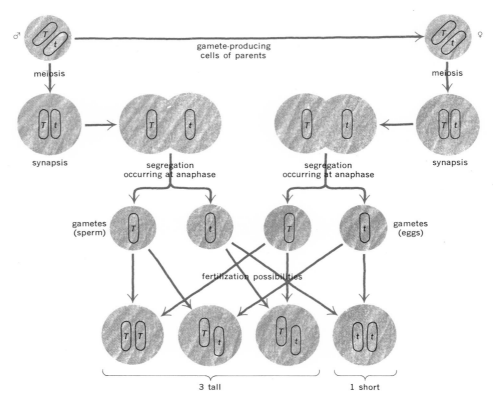

FIG. 42–2. A diagram showing the mechanism of inheritance of tallness in pea plants. *T* indicates the gene for tallness, and *t* the gene for the dwarf condition. [Reprinted from Baker and Allen, *The Study of Biology,* Addison-Wesley, Reading, Mass., 1967.]

represent the dwarf characteristic.) The male (♂) produces gametes containing either T or t, and so does the female (♀). Chances are 1 in 4 that the offspring will receive TT or tt, and 2 in 4 that the new individual will be heterozygous (Tt). If T is completely dominant, 3 of 4 individuals (those having TT and Tt) will show the dominant characteristic, and only 1 in 4 will show the recessive character. If B represents brown hair color in rats, and b represents an albino condition, the mating of two heterozygotes, both of whom had brown hair, would be expected to produce 25% albino offspring and 75% normal-appearing brown-haired offspring. However, 50% of the total offspring (the heterozygotes) of such matings would be normal-appearing carriers of the albino trait.

The theory and examples given above are derived from observation and statistical interpretation. No special instruments or chemical techniques are required for these observations and their interpretation. Other observations about heredity involve the use of the microscope, biochemical information, and specialized techniques.

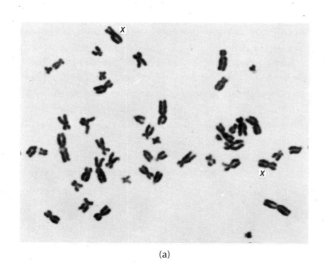

(a)

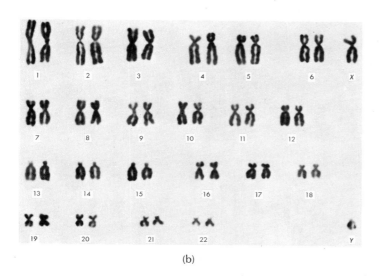

(b)

FIG. 42–3. Human chromosomes. In (a) the 46 chromosomes of a human female are shown. The x chromosomes are indicated. If we cut the chromosomes from a photograph such as (a) and paste them together in pairs, we get a diagram such as that shown in (b). In (b) the chromosomes of a male are shown. Note the single X chromosome at the upper right and the Y chromosome at the bottom right. [Adapted from John W. Kimball, *Biology,* Addison-Wesley, Reading, Mass., 1965. Photograph for (a) courtesy of Drs. T. T. Puck and J. H. Tjio, and (b) courtesy Dr. James L. German, III.]

42-2 GENETICS FROM A CELLULAR LEVEL OF OBSERVATION

Information about the cellular mechanism of heredity is based on microscopic observation of the behavior of individual cells. During part of their life cycle, cells are seen to contain long threadlike bodies called chromosomes in their nuclei (see Fig. 42-3). These chromosomes are normally present in pairs. During normal cell division, each member of the pair of chromosomes splits to form two chromosomes, one of which goes to each daughter cell. In this form of cell division, which is called **mitosis** and represents an asexual form of reproduction of cells, the parent and offspring have exactly the same kind of chromosomes. Since the chromosomes contain the hereditary material—the units a geneticist would call genes—each offspring has exactly the same genes as its parents.

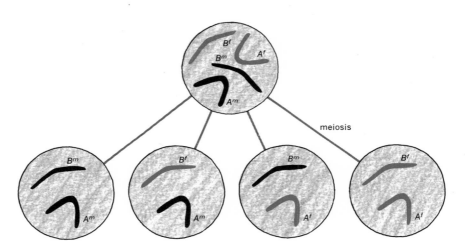

FIG. 42-4. Meiosis. The diagram above represents the random assortment of chromosomes from the mother (A^m and B^m) and the father (A^f and B^f) during meiosis. Note that each of the cells formed contains only half as many chromosomes as the parent cell. [Adapted from John W. Kimball, *Biology*, Addison-Wesley, Reading, Mass., 1965.]

In the process of sexual reproduction, **gametes** (sperm and ova) are formed which contain half the number of chromosomes contained in the normal body cells of the parents. This is accomplished by means of **meiosis** (Fig. 42-4), a type of cell division in which only one member of the pair of chromosomes goes to each developing gamete. Thus, on a cellular level, the observations correlate nicely with the theory derived from observation of individual organisms. The genetic information is contained in the chromosomes. The production of a new individual involves first the separation and then the recombination of chromosomes. We postulate that each chromosome contains the units we call genes. While we cannot see the genes, we picture them as being specific areas of a chromosome.

42-3 GENETICS FROM A BIOCHEMICAL VIEWPOINT

The **chromosomes** seen in the microscopic examination of cells are found, upon chemical analysis, to be composed of deoxyribonucleic acid (DNA) and protein. While either the protein or DNA could be the chemical carrier of hereditary information, most evidence supports the fact that DNA is the hereditary substance. Some of the evidence for this conclusion is given below.

1) While the amount of all other constituents of a cell vary widely, the amount of DNA per cell is generally the same in all cells of all animals in any given species.

2) The amount of DNA per cell in different species is different.

3) When DNA from certain bacteria having one characteristic is added to similar organisms lacking the characteristic, the characteristic is acquired by the deficient organism. For example, resistance to certain antibiotics can be transferred from a culture of bacteria that *is* resistant to another culture of the same organism that is *not* resistant merely by adding DNA of the resistant culture to the growth medium of the nonresistant bacteria. This type of transfer of DNA from one organism to another appears to occur only in microorganisms.

4) Viruses, which can be said to alter the heredity of the cells they attack, are known to inject only DNA (in some cases RNA), not protein, into the cell they infect.

When the structure of DNA was shown to be a double stranded helix which had the capability of replicating itself (see Chapter 36), a mechanism for the duplication of the chromosomes was suggested. Whether each individual strand represents different information or whether both of them carry the same information, one in reverse order to the other, is not known, although speculation is that the latter is the case.

DNA is believed to be the basic hereditary substance—the molecules that are transferred from parent to offspring. It is found primarily in the nucleus of the cell. However, the major synthetic work of the cell is done outside the nucleus, in the cytoplasm. Thus the transmission of the information contained in DNA requires a messenger. This function is fulfilled by the kind of RNA called messenger RNA (see Chapter 39). It is now believed that DNA controls the synthesis of messenger RNA to transfer the information to the cytoplasm of the cell concerning types of protein to be synthesized. At the ribosomes where protein synthesis occurs, the message of DNA is actually put into action. The theory assumes that all hereditary characteristics are somehow dependent on the synthesis of a specific kind of protein. Thus DNA has the specifications for synthesis of the proteins of muscle, hemoglobin, the protein hormones, and most significantly, the enzymes. Since biochemical reactions do not proceed at any appreciable rate without enzymatic catalysis, the kind of enzymes present in a cell probably controls the general course of metabolism within that cell. For example, hereditary differences between species with respect to the kind of waste products made from amino acids (which was described in Chapter 39) are dependent not on the presence of the amino acids but on the presence or absence of specific enzymes.

Since the kind and amount of DNA in any cell of an organism is identical with that of every other cell in the organism, we are faced with a major problem in explaining differences in cell function.   DNA having the information for making the enzymes necessary for urea synthesis is in every cell of the human body, yet only liver cells actually carry out the synthesis of urea.   If we compare the total information in each cell to a large book of instructions, the question becomes, "How does each cell know just which page of instructions to follow?"   Answers to this question are now being proposed, and they involve a complex group of molecules called repressors and de-repressors.   (See the article by Changeux in the list of references at the end of this chapter for a discussion of this theory.)   Further research will be required to determine whether this complex theory really adequately describes the control of the kinds of molecules synthesized by a cell.

We can summarize the biochemical or molecular interpretation of heredity as follows: Males produce sperm cells which consist largely of a head which contains DNA surrounded by protein and a long tail-like structure called a flagellum.   Egg cells contain lipids and proteins, in addition to DNA (see Fig. 42–5).   When a sperm cell fertilizes an egg cell, a chromosome from the sperm cell pairs up with a similar chromosome from the egg cell.   In order for these chromosomes to form matched pairs, the male and female must have the same kind of chromosomes—that is, be of the same species.

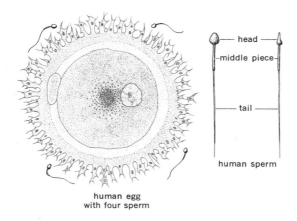

human egg
with four sperm

FIG. 42–5. A human egg with four sperm cells. This drawing shows the relative size of human sperm and egg cells.   In the process of fertilization one sperm cell penetrates the egg.   [From Baker and Allen, *The Study of Biology,* Addison-Wesley, Reading, Mass., 1967.]

At the moment of fertilization (conception), the zygote, or fertilized egg cell, has all the hereditary information it will ever receive.   As the zygote divides to form 2, 4, 8, 16 cells, and finally the millions or trillions of cells found in the new individual, some cells begin to assume different functions in a process appropriately known as differentiation.   Differentiation is believed to be the result of directions from repressors and de-repressors which control exactly which molecules will be synthesized of the many thousand possible kinds for which instructions are available in the DNA.   As the organism grows and matures, it will produce sperm or egg cells containing only the kinds of DNA (genes) that it received from its parents. Occasionally some agent, perhaps some form of radiation, changes the DNA in a gamete, and this gamete produces a mutant organism having different hereditary characteristics. Such mutations are rare. The probability of mutations is expressed as mutations per gene per generation. In humans this probability is between 1 in 100,000 and 1 in 1,000,000. Thus the long-range preservation of a species is assured by the transfer of potentially "immortal" DNA from parent to offspring. Sufficient variety is introduced by formation of hybrid individuals and by mutations. Most mutants are probably less able to survive than are the normal parents, but on extremely rare occasions a mutant is able to do things its parents could not do and in the struggle for survival, the mutant wins and becomes the first of a new kind of individual. A change in environmental conditions may help a mutant which is in competition with unmutated individuals.

The development of our understanding of the process of heredity is a striking example of the way in which science functions. Earlier civilizations could talk about heredity only in terms of individuals, and could offer no real explanation of the processes involved. This general observation was followed by refinement to the cellular and finally the biochemical level of observation and explanation. Our present way of looking at and thinking about heredity has had two major consequences. First, we have, of course, a better understanding of just how the process works. While new knowledge is one of the motives for scientific research, the second major consequence of our progress is that we can predict, and in certain cases control, some of the effects of heredity. Control always brings problems, but the benefits are so great that we must find solutions to these problems. Some examples of biochemical understanding and control of hereditary abnormalities are given in the remainder of this chapter.

42-4 INBORN ERRORS OF METABOLISM

In 1906, the English physician Garrod wrote a book describing several abnormal patterns of excretion. He recognized that these conditions were inherited, and called them inborn errors of metabolism. We now know probably a hundred such conditions. The following sections discuss abnormalities in protein structure and enzyme formation that are known to be hereditary.

Sickle Cell Anemia

More biochemical information is available about sickle cell anemia than about any other inherited condition. The correlations of chemistry, physiology, and genetics are amazing. In fact, studies of sickle cell anemia were responsible for some of our current theories about the chemical nature of heredity.

If we take blood samples from persons with anemia, we find that the red blood cells, when placed under conditions where the oxygen concentration is low, form peculiar sickle shapes (see Fig. 42-6). We find that some of the red blood cells of certain other apparently healthy persons will also sickle when similarly treated. If we extract the hemoglobin from these persons we find that they have two different kinds of hemoglobin. When the mixture

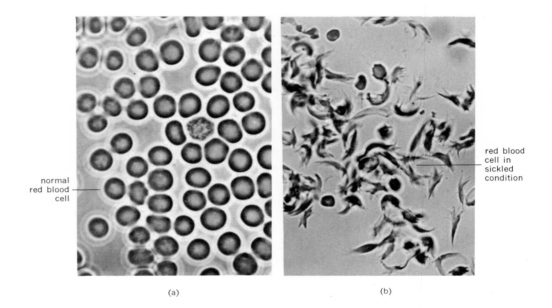

normal
red blood
cell

red blood
cell in
sickled
condition

(a)   (b)

FIG. 42-6. Normal red blood cells and sickle cells: (a) normal human red blood cells; (b) a similar preparation that was made of the red blood cells of a patient with sickle cell anemia. The sickle-like form of
the blood cells in (b) gives the disease its name. [From Baker and Allen, *The Study of Biology*, Addison-
Wesley, Reading, Mass., 1967. Photograph courtesy of Dr. A. C. Allison.]

is analyzed by electrophoresis at pH 6.9, normal hemoglobin migrates in one direction and
the abnormal hemoglobin—called sickle cell hemoglobin—migrates in the other direction.
Persons with sickle cell anemia, a serious condition that is always fatal, have only sickle cell
hemoglobin (abbreviated Hgb S), and those who have two kinds of hemoglobin have both
Hgb S and normal hemoglobin (abbreviated Hgb A). These latter persons are characterized
as having the sickle cell trait.

The tendency to form sickle cell hemoglobin is hereditary. Those having sickle cell
anemia are homozygous, and those with the sickle cell trait are heterozygous. Thus we have
a hereditary condition that is directly related to the kind of protein that an individual makes.

Studies of Hgb A and Hgb S show that they have different solubilities in weak salt solutions (similar to the salt solution of the blood). When carrying oxygen, both forms of hemoglobin are about equally soluble. However, when the oxygen is removed (a process that
occurs as blood cells pass from the lungs to other parts of the body) Hgb S is only 1/50th as
soluble as Hgb A. Apparently this decreased solubility is the cause of the formation of the
"sickles." Hgb S actually crystallizes out of solution, and the crystals then either stretch or
break the membrane of the red blood cells. Such sickled cells cannot perform the function
of normal red blood cells, and the person with sickle cell anemia must either manufacture
red blood cells at a faster rate or suffer from the effects of a deficiency in red blood cells.

Thus sickle cell anemia is a disease caused by a difference in solubility of an abnormal protein. This disease is one where the physical or chemical cause is known.

The next questions are: "Why is Hgb S less soluble than Hgb A, and why do the two forms migrate differently in an electrical field?" The answer to both questions is the same, and is found in the chemical structure of the protein hemoglobin. This protein contains two kinds of subunits, with two of each kind combined to give the hemoglobin molecule. In one of the chains there is a glutamic acid residue in Hgb A and a valine in Hgb S. Glutamic acid has the side chain $-CH_2-CH_2-COO^-$ and valine has $-CH-(CH_3)_2$. This difference might seem to be minor, since both have three carbons in the side chain. The effect, however, is due to the charge on the carboxyl group of glutamic acid which makes that group much more soluble in water than the hydrocarbon-like valine. The fact that one has a negative and the other no charge also explains the difference in electrophoretic mobility. Thus the difference on only one amino acid in a chain of about 150 amino acids can result in a life of weakness, intermittent illness, and the constant threat of death from those infections that a normal person handles easily.

Why do some people make Hgb S and others only Hgb A? Since this condition is a hereditary trait, we assume that one person produces DNA that has the pattern for making messenger RNA which makes normal hemoglobin (Hgb A), and that the other has DNA that leads to the production of Hgb S. How different are the "codes" for glutamic acid and valine? From Table 39–1 we find that the codes for glutamic acid are GAA and GAG, and two of the possible codes for valine are GUA and GUG. The difference between pairs is only in one nucleotide. It is logical to assume that a single mutation may be responsible for the change. Why has this mutation persisted? The answer is also fascinating.

Since persons with sickle cell anemia often do not live to an age where they can have children, why hasn't the condition died out? Why hasn't the evolutionary principle of survival of the fittest eliminated persons with the gene for sickle cell anemia? The answer is related to the disease malaria. While persons with sickle cell anemia (homozygotes) die young and are eliminated, those with the sickle cell trait (heterozygotes with both Hgb S and Hgb A) have an increased resistance to malaria. The parasite that causes malaria lives in red blood cells, and apparently it can't find as good a place to live and reproduce if half of its host's red blood cells contain Hgb S. The gene for Hgb S is found almost totally among Negroes. Approximately 8% of American Negroes have some Hgb S. The occurrence of this abnormal hemoglobin is as high as 45% in some African tribes—which may lead us to ask whether we can really call this an "abnormal" hemoglobin.

Thus the story of sickle cell anemia and the sickle cell trait relates physics and chemistry (the solubility and electrophoretic behavior of Hgb S) to physiology (anemia and decreased supply of oxygen to the tissues) to genetics where it shows how recessive traits may be present but not obvious. This line of reasoning leads to the hypothesis that genes influence protein synthesis. The sickle cell anemia story further shows how a normally deleterious condition can persist in a given environment, and we have a picture of natural selection (evolution) in action. The difference in incidence of the sickle cell trait in Africa and America indicates that, in the absence of malaria, the trait is less common.

In no other instance are all aspects of a condition so well known and the interrelations so well established. Unfortunately, in the case of sickle cell anemia, understanding does not lead to curing the condition. The only hope seems to lie in preventing the birth of children doomed to lives of suffering and to early death from sickle cell anemia. Control will require widespread examinations of the hemoglobin of prospective parents followed by genetic counselling of individuals who have this trait, so that they will not want to bring afflicted children into the world. One of the aims of science in general, and biochemistry in particular, is to reach a similar understanding of all diseases.

Hereditary Abnormalities in Phenylalanine Metabolism

The metabolism of the amino acid phenylalanine is summarized in Fig. 42–7. This summary indicates that phenylalanine from proteins in the diet may be metabolized in a variety of ways. It may be resynthesized into protein; it may be transformed into the thyroid hormone thyroxine, into the adrenal hormone epinephrine (adrenalin), or into the basic pigment of human hair and skin, melanin; it may also be oxidized completely into carbon dioxide and water with the release of an appreciable amount of energy. Tyrosine, which can be derived from phenylalanine, follows the same general pathways except that it cannot be converted to phenylalanine. In terms of nutrition, phenylalanine is an essential amino acid; tyrosine is not.

The understanding of the metabolism of phenylalanine assumed a new importance when it was observed that a certain type of mental defectives—particularly idiot children—excreted an unusual substance in their urine. This compound was identified as phenylpyruvic acid. It was found that about 1% of the feeble-minded persons in institutions excreted this abnormal metabolite. The questions immediately suggested are: "Does this excretion have anything to do with the feeblemindedness?" and "If so, can an understanding of the condition lead to a cure?" Further observation and study indicated that the persons who excreted phenylpyruvic acid (they are called phenylketonurics) often came from marriages of cousins. This type of observation is a strong indication that the disease may be associated with the inheritance of recessive genes.

We now know that the condition is inherited and that the reason phenylketonurics excrete this abnormal compound is that they cannot convert phenylalanine to tyrosine. When this reaction is blocked, the phenylalanine which is not used for protein synthesis has only one pathway left—the conversion to phenylpyruvic, phenyllactic, and phenylacetic acids. Why is the conversion of phenylalanine to tyrosine blocked? It is blocked because the phenylketonuric does not make the necessary enzyme for conversion. In genetic terms, the DNA of the phenylketonuric lacks the information required for synthesis of phenylalanine hydroxylase. Whether he makes a similar protein that is just different enough to lack catalytic activity is not known, although our theory suggests that he does.

Since most parents of phenylketonurics have essentially normal intelligence and do not excrete phenylpyruvic acid, they must be heterozygotes having one gene (or type of DNA) that has the information for synthesis of phenylalanine hydroxylase and one that doesn't. The next question that presents itself is: "Can we find these hybrid carriers of the defect?" Previously, geneticists believed that the only way a recessive characteristic could be detected in a heterozygote was by letting the individual produce offspring and examining them for the trait. This is a tragic procedure when human lives are involved. Reasoning that perhaps the heterozygous carriers of the recessive gene for phenylketonuria (abbreviated as PKU)

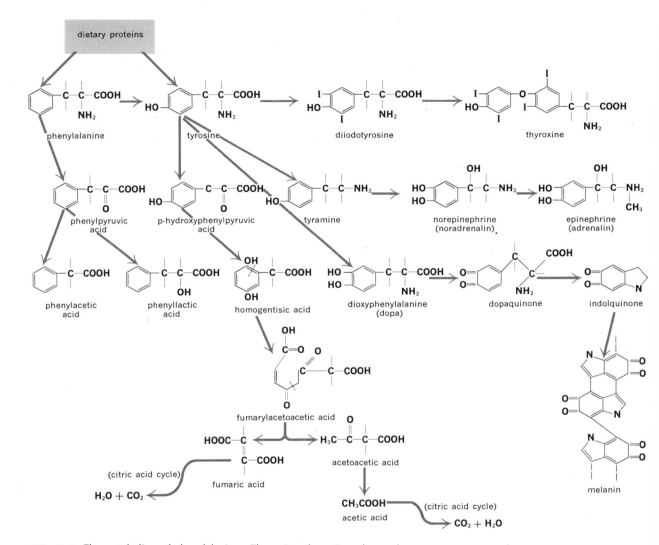

FIG. 42–7. The metabolism of phenylalanine. The series of reactions shown above represents some of the possible products and intermediates that can be formed from the amino acid phenylalanine. The consequences of failure to produce some of these reactions are discussed in the accompanying text.

might have less than normal amounts of phenylalanine oxidase, research scientists tested parents of phenylketonuric children. While the test has not been entirely successful, it does show that these heterozygous carriers excrete larger amounts of phenylpyruvic acid when given a large dose of phenylalanine than do normal persons. Thus the understanding of the metabolism of phenylalanine and the biochemistry of a hereditary defect has led to the development of a test for a hidden recessive characteristic. Results of such tests can be used for counselling individuals related to phenylketonurics as to the possibility of their having children with this disorder. If both a husband and wife are given such tests, the probability of having children with this genetic defect can be predicted. Procedures of this sort offer great promise in improving the genetic qualities of humans. Control would also pose a great threat in the hands of unscientific or inhumane persons.

The prediction of the possibility of having phenylketonuric children may be an interesting development but what about the baby born with the disease? Is this infant doomed to develop no further than the level of an idiot or imbecile? Fortunately the understanding of the biochemistry of the defect has led to an effective treatment—not to prevent the defect, but to help children who have the disease.

One treatment that might be proposed would be to give the phenylketonuric child some of the enzyme he lacks. Since enzymes are digested into their component amino acids in the gastrointestinal tract, administration would presumably have to be made by injection. This technique works for the administration of insulin to diabetics, but would pose two more problems in the case of phenylketonuria. The first would be that of getting the large enzyme molecule from the blood into the cells where it must work. The second problem is even more formidable—the human body generally responds to the injection of a foreign protein by forming antibodies to the protein. These antibodies neutralize any effect of the protein.

Fortunately, an alternate procedure can be used, and, in fact, is used successfully. This treatment consists of restricting the amount of phenylalanine in the diet of the phenylketonuric. It has been found that dietary restriction of this sort allows the infant with PKU to develop normally and that after the age of five or six, sometimes even earlier, the diet may be discontinued without bad effects. Thus the condition, while it can never be cured, can be treated.

The problem of phenylketonuria now becomes one of discovering the babies who are potential phenylketonurics. Some states require that the urine, or better yet, the blood, of all newborn babies be tested for the presence of phenylpyruvic acid or phenylalanine. The blood tests require only a small sample of blood and are probably best, since the concentration of phenylalanine in the blood increases some time before urinary excretion of phenylpyruvic acid is readily detectable. Thus treatment can be initiated at the earliest possible moment. There is now no reason for children with this defect to grow up facing life as mental defectives.

The question, "Why does an excess of phenylalanine or phenylpyruvic acid in the blood cause mental defects?" has not yet been definitely answered. It is probable that either phenylpyruvic acid or phenylalanine interferes with the synthesis of serotonin—a compound involved in brain function.

Phenylketonuria is not the only hereditary defect related to the metabolism of phenylalanine. Albino individuals lack the ability to synthesize melanin. Apparently their systems lack the information for making one of the enzymes for the conversion of tyrosine to melanin. Since this condition represents the lack of a metabolic product, melanin, and not an excess of a metabolite (as in PKU), there is no known treatment for albinism. If tests for detection of normal carriers of the recessive gene are developed, control of the incidence, if not treatment, might become possible. The consequences of albinism are not nearly so tragic as those of PKU.

Lack of an enzyme responsible for oxidizing homogentisic acid leads to the excretion of this product in the urine. This condition is hereditary and presents another inborn error in the metabolism of phenylalanine and tyrosine. The condition is usually not serious, and no treatment is given. Another abnormality, the excretion of *p*-hydroxyphenylpyruvic acid is traced to a blockage in the oxidation of tyrosine. The incidence of.this condition apparently is rare, and it has few, if any, bad consequences.

The metabolism of phenylalanine was chosen to illustrate inborn errors of metabolism. Although errors are known in the metabolism of other substances, more have been found in the metabolism of phenylalanine than in that of other substances. This fact may mean that there really are more such errors in phenylalanine metabolisr , but it probably means only that the abnormal metabolic products of phenylalanine tend to be obvious because of their distinctive odors or color.

42-5 THE ONE-GENE–ONE-ENZYME THEORY

The principles of hereditary control of enzyme formation which are so well illustrated by the metabolism of phenylalanine and its abnormalities were first formulated on the basis of work with the red bread mold, neurospora. From their studies with this organism, Doctors Beadle and Tatum formulated the *one-gene–one-enzyme theory* which should perhaps now be characterized as the *one-gene–one-protein theory*. A good summary of this theory, which has led to a much better understanding of heredity, was given by Dr. E. L. Tatum in his Nobel Prize Lecture of 1958. He stated that:

1) All biochemical processes in all organisms are under genic control.

2) These overall biochemical processes are resolvable into a series of individual, stepwise reactions.

3) Each single reaction is controlled in a primary fashion by a single gene, or, in other terms, in every case a 1:1 correspondence of gene and biochemical reaction exists, such that:

4) Mutation of a single gene results only in an alteration in the ability of the cell to carry out a single primary chemical reaction. . . . As has been repeatedly stated, the underlying hypothesis, which in a number of cases has been supported by direct experimental evidence, is that each gene controls the production, function, and specificity of a particular enzyme.*

The understanding of any chemical process leads to the question of control. If we understand the mechanism of heredity, can we then control it? The answer to this question is that we cannot now control the basic biochemical processes involved in heredity. On the basis of biochemical understanding and perhaps some chemical analyses, we can only counsel persons about the possibilities of producing offspring of a definite type. Recent research by Kornberg and his associates (Section 36–4) may be the first of many steps that may lead to some kind of chemical control of heredity.

---

* Quoted from *Science* **129:**1711, June 26, 1959, copyright by the American Association for the Advancement of Science.

The other problem in genetic control is a social and moral one. Presuming that we learn how to control the biochemistry of heredity, should we? If controls are to be instituted, who will initiate them? These problems are formidable, and are beyond the scope of this book. They cannot and must not be discussed without a basic understanding of the biochemical, as well as cellular and organismic basis of heredity.

IMPORTANT TERMS

Chromosome	Heterozygote	Mitosis
Gamete	Homozygote	Mutation
Gene	Inborn error of metabolism	Ribosome
Genetic code	Meiosis	

WORK EXERCISES

1. Explain what is meant by the one-gene–one-protein theory. What kind of evidence supports this theory?

2. List all examples of inborn errors of metabolism that have been discussed in this text. List the specific protein missing or altered in each case.

3. What might be the consequences of an inborn error of metabolism that prevented the synthesis of thyroxine from tyrosine?

4. Differences in chemical structure in several kinds of hemoglobin are listed in Table 42–1. Check the genetic code as given in Table 39–1 to determine the differences in the code for the normal and abnormal amino acids in these structures.

TABLE 42–1. A summary of amino acid differences in some hemoglobin variants

Type of Hemoglobin	Position Number in B-Chain					
	6	7	26	63	67	121
normal	Glu	Glu	Glu	His	Val	Glu
Hgb S (sickle cell)	Val					
Hgb C	Lys					
Hgb G San José		Gly				
Hgb E			Lys			
Hgb M Saskatoon				Tyr		
Hgb M Milwaukee					Glu	
Hgb D Punjab						Glu·NH$_2$
Hgb Zurich				Arg		
Hgb O Arabia						Lys

SUGGESTED READING

Beadle, G. W., "The Genes of Men and Molds," *Scientific American*, Sept. 1948 (Offprint #1). Dr. Beadle discusses some of the experiments that led to the one-gene–one-enzyme theory and the Nobel Prize.

Beermann, W. and U. Clever, "Chromosome Puffs," *Scientific American,* Apr. 1964 (Offprint #180). This article tells the fascinating story of the relationship of puffs in chromosomes and of new protein synthesis.

Cairns, J., "The Bacterial Chromosome," *Scientific American*, Jan. 1966. A discussion of the shape and methods of replication of DNA in some bacteria.

Changeux, J-P., "The Control of Biochemical Reactions," *Scientific American,* Apr. 1965 (Offprint #1008). The control of enzyme activity and production by feedback is discussed.

Dobzhansky, T., *Heredity and the Nature of Man,* Signet Science Library Book (P2837), New American Library, New York, 1966. This paperback book and the article below give some of the views of this important geneticist and humanitarian.

Dobzhansky, T., "The Genetic Basis of Evolution, *Scientific American,* Jan. 1954 (Offprint #6).

Hanawalt, P. C. and R. H. Hayes, "The Repair of DNA," *Scientific American*, Feb. 1967. A description of the ways bacteria can repair damage to their DNA.

Horowitz, N. H., "The Gene," *Scientific American*, Oct. 1956 (Offprint #17). A discussion of this basic unit of heredity that no one has ever seen—yet.

Hotchkiss, R. D. and Esther Weiss, "Transformed Bacteria," *Scientific American*, Nov. 1956 (Offprint #18). A report on transfers of DNA from one bacterium to another.

Ingram, V. M., "How Do Genes Act?" *Scientific American*, Jan. 1958 (Offprint #104). A discussion of the genetics of sickle-cell anemia.

Jacob, F. and E. L. Wollman, "Viruses and Genes," *Scientific American*, June 1961 (Offprint #89). This article tells about the biochemistry of viral infection of cells. Significant both for the study of heredity and of infection.

Kellenberger, E., "The Genetic Control of the Shape of a Virus," *Scientific American*, Dec. 1966. The article discusses the relationship of heredity to shape of virus particles.

McKusic, V. A., "The Royal Hemophilia," *Scientific American*, Aug. 1965. This article traces an inherited trait back to Queen Victoria of England.

Mirsky, A. E., "The Chemistry of Heredity," *Scientific American*, Feb. 1953 (Offprint #28). Somewhat out-of-date, but still interesting reading.

Muller, H. J., "Radiation and Human Mutation," *Scientific American,* Nov. 1955 (Offprint #29). This and the following article by Puck treat radiation effects from the organismic and cellular levels, respectively.

Puck, T. T., "Radiation and the Human Cell," *Scientific American,* Apr. 1960 (Offprint #71).

Zuckerkandle, E., "The Evolution of Hemoglobin," *Scientific American,* May 1965 (Offprint #1012). The author uses the structures of hemoglobin in various species to trace evolution.

Chapter 43 BIOCHEMISTRY OF PLANTS

43-1 INTRODUCTION

Most people think of plants as being distinctly different from animals; the differences are obvious, of course, if we compare a horse with a tree. But those who are familiar with the sea anemone which is an animal that looks like a flower, or with microscopic plants and animals realize that the differences may not be so distinct. Some one-celled organisms such as the euglena, which moves with the aid of a whiplike flagellum but contains chlorophyll, have characteristics of both plants and animals. Assignment of these organisms to either classification is sometimes arbitrary.

Biochemically, plants and animals are similar. Both contain the same saccharide units, amino acids, and lipid constituents. These basic units are sometimes assembled differently in plants than they are in animals, however. The starch of plants is somewhat different from glycogen of animals, and the beta-linked cellulose of plants is significantly different from both starch and glycogen even though all are made only of glucose units. Plant lipids tend to be more unsaturated than animal lipids because they contain more of the highly unsaturated fatty acids.

The metabolism of plants is also highly similar to that of animals. The citric acid cycle is common to both plants and animals as are many other reactions. In general, the green plants have greater synthetic capability than do the colorless plants such as bacteria, yeasts, and other fungi. In those cases which have been carefully investigated, as with the mold *neurospora*, the fungi seem to have a greater ability to synthesize compounds than do animals. There are, however, some bacteria whose dependence upon preformed nutrients is even greater than that of animals.

A major difference between a self-sufficient green plant and a parasitic fungus is in the presence of **chlorophyll** (Fig. 43–1). This green pigment is sometimes obscured by other

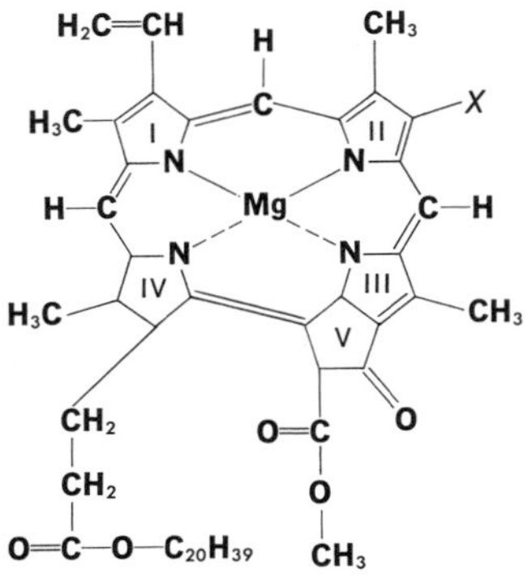

FIG. 43–1. The chlorophyll molecule. In addition to the four pyrrolidine rings, there is a fifth ring in chlorophyll. At position X, chlorophyll a has an ethyl group, and chlorophyll b has a CHO group. The chlorophyll molecule may be compared with similar structures in cytochrome c (Fig. 37–9) and vitamin B_{12} (Fig. 41–1).

pigments, but its presence in a plant indicates that the plant can synthesize its own components if it has access to the energy of the sun and elements or simple compounds for building blocks. This synthesis under the influence of light—photosynthesis—is the distinguishing characteristic of plant life, and probably represents the most important series of reactions that occur on the surface of the earth. The general equation for photosynthesis may be written as:

$$6CO_2 + 6H_2O \xrightarrow{\text{light}} C_6H_{12}O_6 + 6O_2$$

43–2 PHOTOSYNTHESIS

Green plants, when given a source of light, CO_2, H_2O, and the necessary catalysts, can produce carbohydrates. If a source of nitrogen is added, amino acids are made. The addition of sulfate and phosphate for the sulfur-containing amino acids and the many phosphorus-containing building blocks and catalysts makes possible the synthesis of almost all major components of the plant. Mineral elements such as iron, potassium, magnesium, and many others are also required by plants either as minor structural constituents or as catalysts.

The details of the processes by which plants synthesize these many compounds, particularly of photosynthesis, were not understood until about twenty years ago. Only when the radioactive isotope carbon-14 became available could scientists investigate the pathway by which carbon dioxide becomes incorporated in carbohydrates. Before the way in which a photon of light is trapped and used could be studied, techniques had to be developed for studying extremely fast reactions, since these processes occur in milliseconds or microseconds.

For simplicity, the complex process of photosynthesis is divided into those processes that require light—called the **light reaction**—and those that can proceed in the absence of light—the **dark reaction.** Both reactions are really series of reactions, and while they are separated for purposes of discussion we must always remember that they occur at the same time and use some of the same intermediate compounds, whenever a living green plant is exposed to sunlight.

The Light Reaction

We can think of photosynthesis as starting when a quantum of light is absorbed by chlorophyll in a green plant. The energy absorbed by chlorophyll causes one of the chlorophyll electrons to become excited; it contains more energy than other electrons. This high-energy electron is then transferred to other molecules much as in the process of electron transport, Section 37–5. The electron loses some of its energy at each step. This energy is stored in the compounds ATP and reduced NADP ($NADPH_2$) which is used in the dark reaction. Some of the energy absorbed by a plant is also used to break water into oxygen, electrons and protons. This **photolysis** of water is the source of the molecular oxygen which is one of the products of photosynthesis. Photolysis provides the electrons to replace the excited electrons lost by chlorophyll and the protons that are bound to $NADPH_2$ which is the energy source in the fixation of CO_2 by the green plant.

$$2H_2O \longrightarrow \begin{cases} O_2 \left[:\overset{..}{O}:\overset{..}{O}: \right] \\ 4H^+[+] \\ 2 \text{ electrons } [\cdot\cdot] \end{cases}$$

$$2\left[H:\overset{..}{O}:H \right]$$

The processes in which radiation is absorbed occur very rapidly—probably in 10^{-15} to 10^{-9} sec. We do not have good methods for studying such reactions, and consequently we know very little about the first stages of photosynthesis. Nor do we know much about the mechanics of the photolysis of water. Biochemists and biophysicists are currently doing research on the mechanism by which the energy of the chlorophyll is trapped by compounds similar to NAD, FAD, and the cytochromes of the electron transport system.

The Dark Reaction

Those processes of photosynthesis which can occur in the dark, provided sources of energy are available, are reasonably well understood. They involve the conversion of CO_2 to carbohydrates and other compounds. They are catalyzed by enzymes, and although they occur rapidly, methods have been developed to study this conversion of gaseous CO_2 to nongaseous compounds. The process is given the general name of **fixation.**

Many compounds are present in a green leaf or in a single-celled green alga. If we want to study the process by which CO_2 is converted into these compounds we must look for the compound which first reacts with the CO_2. To do so we add radioactive CO_2—carbon dioxide containing carbon-14, symbolized $^{14}CO_2$—to a container of thousands of algae, separate the various compounds found in the algae, and then determine which ones contain carbon-14. Since such experiments always give many compounds containing carbon-14, the reactions of photosynthesis must be stopped a short time after the addition of the radioactive carbon dioxide. This can be done by dropping the culture of algae into boiling methanol.

Using this technique, research chemists have found that only 90 seconds after addition of the $^{14}CO_2$, 90% of the CO_2 had been fixed and at least 14 radioactive compounds were present. When the time interval was cut to 5 seconds, only 5 compounds were found to be radioactive—malic acid, aspartic acid, pyruvic acid, 3-phosphoglyceric acid, and 2-phospho-glyceric acid; 65% of the radioactivity was in the latter two compounds. These experiments indicated that there was a 2-carbon compound in the green plant that was reacting with CO_2

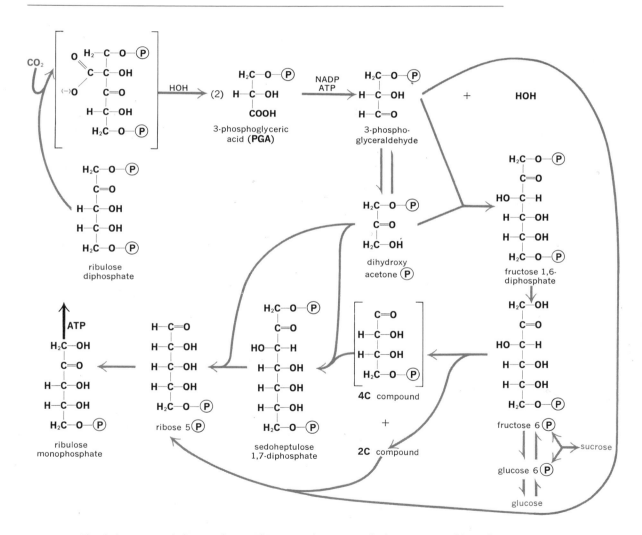

FIG. 43–2. The dark reaction of photosynthesis. This series of reactions which was proposed by Calvin and Bassham shows how carbon dioxide can combine with ribulose diphosphate to yield the sugars glucose or sucrose or to regenerate ribulose diphosphate for further reactions.

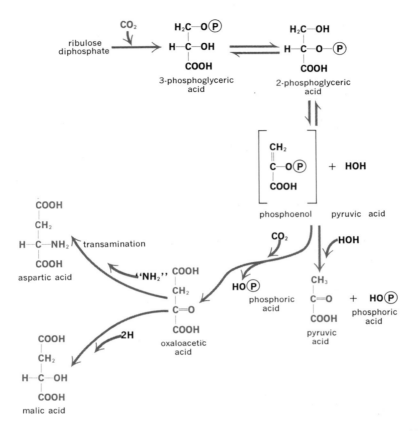

FIG. 43–3. Synthesis of pyruvic acid, oxaloacetic acid, malic acid, and aspartic acid by photosynthesis. In addition to the reactions shown in Fig. 43–2, the reactions given above show how other known products of photosynthesis may be synthesized from phosphoglyceric acid.

to give either the 2- or 3-phosphoglyceric acid. The search for this 2-carbon compound, however, proved fruitless. Instead, a 5-carbon compound, ribulose diphosphate, was found which first combined with CO_2 and then immediately split to give two molecules of a phosphorylated glyceric acid. The problem of working out the details of the dark reaction of photosynthesis then became one of showing how both this 5-carbon compound, ribulose diphosphate, and the normal product of photosynthesis, the sugar glucose, could be made at the same time. The scheme of reactions that was developed by Dr. Melvin Calvin and his coworkers on the basis of their experiments summarized above is illustrated in Fig. 43–2. This series of reactions shows how glucose, fructose, or sucrose can be generated while ribulose diphosphate is still available for continuation of the process. There is no simple

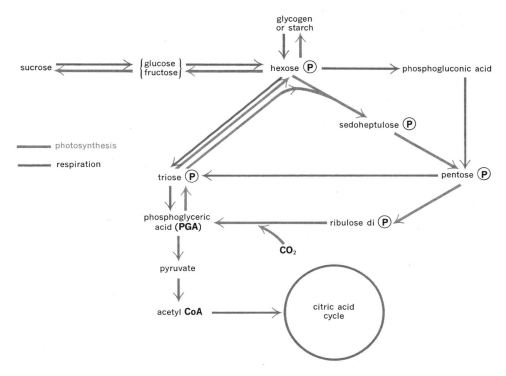

FIG. 43–4. The relationship of photosynthesis to respiration (glycolysis). This diagram shows some of the compounds important both in oxidation of carbohydrates and in photosynthesis. Arrows indicating photosynthetic reactions are shown in color and those of respiration are in black.

conversion of one molecule of one substance to one molecule of another. The scheme may be summarized as follows:

$6CO_2 + 18ATP + 12NADPH_2 \rightarrow C_6H_{12}O_6 + 6H_2O + 18ADP + 12NADP + 18$ⓟ—OH

All substances other than glucose, hydrogen atoms, and CO_2 can be regarded as catalysts in this highly complex series of reactions.

A scheme for the synthesis of malic acid, aspartic acid, and pyruvic acid, which were also found after short exposure of algae to the CO_2, is shown in Fig. 43–3. The conversion of pyruvic acid to alanine and serine explains the formation of these amino acids which some investigators have found to be early products of photosynthesis. Since the reactions of pyruvic acid leading to acetyl CoA are well known, the basic starting materials for the synthesis of fatty acids are also indicated. The relation of photosynthesis to glycolysis and the citric acid cycle is shown in Fig. 43–4.

Variations of Photosynthesis

The photosynthesis described above is essentially what happens in all green plants—from the unicellular algae to spinach to the giant redwood trees. Other kinds of photosynthesis exist, particularly among the bacteria. Some bacteria use H_2S instead of H_2O in photosynthesis, and instead of releasing O_2 to the air, these bacteria deposit sulfur. Other bacteria use H_2 in place of H_2O or H_2S and release neither oxygen nor sulfur. These and other variations in the basic process of photosynthesis indicate that perhaps the best definition is one recently given by Dr. Martin Kamen: "Photosynthesis is a series of processes in which electromagnetic energy is converted to chemical-free energy which can be used for biosynthesis."*

43-3 NITROGEN FIXATION IN PLANTS

Although about 80% of the atmosphere is nitrogen, many plants suffer from nitrogen deficiency. Plants cannot use free nitrogen, but must have a combined or "fixed" form. One of the essential components of fertilizers is nitrogen in the form of liquid ammonia, nitrates, urea, or other compounds. Many nitrogen-containing compounds are found in manure.

Long before they understood why, farmers knew that some plants such as peas, beans, and clover seemed to enrich the soil, particularly if these plants were not harvested but were plowed under. These plants—the legumes—were found to have nodules on their roots, and the nodules were found to contain bacteria. Such bacteria, we know now, can fix nitrogen—that is, convert nitrogen from its unuseable gaseous form to a nutritious compound such as a nitrate or nitrite. Thus the green plant not only fixes carbon dioxide from the air, but by the help of other plants, the bacteria, can also fix nitrogen from the air.

43-4 OTHER PLANT PRODUCTS

In addition to their basic function of fixing carbon dioxide and nitrogen, plants make a variety of compounds that are not synthesized by animals. Plants, but not animals, can synthesize compounds containing benzene rings. As a consequence, any benzene derivative that is required by an animal must be obtained from some plant source. Particularly important in this respect are the amino acids phenylalanine and tryptophan which humans get either from plant products or from the meats of animals which have eaten the plants.

Many plants have widespread medicinal use. Especially important in this respect are the alkaloids which were discussed in Section 28–6 B. The antibiotics, Section 44–5, are also important products of certain kinds of plants, particularly the molds.

43-5 SUMMARY

From the preceding discussion we can see that green plants serve as the manufacturers of all the naturally occurring organic compounds on the earth. Animals can take the basic

---

* Martin D. Kamen, *Primary Processes in Photosynthesis,* Academic Press, New York, 1963.

units from plants and reassemble them into different compounds, but animals cannot exist without green plants. Animals, in turn, supply large amounts of carbon dioxide for photosynthesis. An earth with only green plants would probably soon have an excess of oxygen and various plant components and a deficiency of CO_2 and H_2O.

$$CO_2 + H_2O \xrightarrow[\text{animals}]{\text{plants}} \text{carbohydrates} + O_2$$

It has been speculated that an earth devoid of animal and fungal life would have oceans full of a thick soup of dead algae. A deficiency of CO_2 in the air would probably result in less trapping of the energy of the sun (see the hothouse effect, Chapter 15–2), and all life on the planet might cease. Thus a balance between the photosynthesis of green plants and oxidative processes of animals is required to maintain the equilibrium we need.

It has been proposed that animal life rose from plant life—or perhaps from a simpler plant-animal form. Animals became the mobile, energy-dissipating kind of life while plants remained, or perhaps became, the stable, energy-trapping synthesizers. In acquiring their motility the animals gave up some of their manufacturing ability. It is perhaps more logical to assume that those animals who became the most mobile, those who lost some storage and manufacturing ability were best able to survive in a struggle for existence. It is probable that because these mobile animals were able to find more food and could catch and eat their slower-moving competitors, they survived and reproduced. With this sort of differentiation has come the varied forms of life, both plant and animal, we see in the world around us—each different from, but also each highly dependent upon, other plants and animals. Although perhaps we should not extend analogies from the biological world to the social, differences and mutual dependence are certainly important in both.

IMPORTANT TERMS

Chlorophyll	*Fixation*	*Photolysis*
Dark reaction	*Light reaction*	*Photosynthesis*

WORK EXERCISES

1. What metal is found in chlorophyll?

2. Supposing that some disaster destroyed all animal life on the earth but that the green plants survived and were able to reproduce. Speculate on conditions on the earth 100 years after the disappearance of animal life.

3. What metabolic reactions have been discussed in this book, other than those of photosynthesis, in which carbon dioxide is added to a molecule?

4. If you added carbon dioxide containing carbon-14 to a green plant, what compound would you expect to be the first to contain radioactivity? In which carbon atom would you expect to find most of the radioactivity? If sucrose were isolated from this plant, which carbon atoms would you expect to be labeled?

SUGGESTED READING

Fogg, C. G., *The Growth of Plants*, Pelican Books, A-560, Penguin Books, New York, 1963. A paperback book on the general subject of plants.

The following three articles represent excellent reports by persons involved in unravelling the various aspects of photosynthesis. The article by Bassham is an excellent summary.

Arnon, D. I., "The Role of Light in Photosynthesis," *Scientific American*, Nov. 1960 (Offprint #75).

Bassham, J. A., "The Path of Carbon in Photosynthesis, *Scientific American,* June 1962 (Offprint #122).

Rabinowitch, E. I. and Govindjee, "The Role of Chlorophyll in Photosynthesis," *Scientific American*, July 1965 (Offprint #1016).

Chapter 44 THE BIOCHEMISTRY OF DISEASE AND THERAPY

44–1 INTRODUCTION

Attempting to discuss, in a single chapter, the biochemistry of disease and therapy (the treatment of disease) is a major task. Whole books are devoted to the subject, and in many cases they discuss only a single disease. Nevertheless, in this chapter we will present some generalizations about diseases and their relationship to biochemistry. We believe that the information is essentially correct, that it will give the reader a better understanding of some medical practices, and will illustrate some practical applications of biochemical theories.

For the purposes of this discussion we will define **disease** as any departure from health or, in other words, any failure of the body to function normally. From the viewpoint of the biochemist the functioning of the body depends upon chemical reactions. A breakdown in these reactions leads to abnormal functioning which we can call disease. To simplify our discussion, we have divided the diseases into several categories. These are arbitrary categories, of course, under which we attempt to describe processes which we do not completely understand. Some diseases may belong in two or more categories and others do not really belong in any of those listed.

The major division is between (1) infectious diseases (those caused by bacteria, viruses, and other organisms) and (2) noninfectious diseases. Noninfectious diseases are further classified as (a) nutritional diseases, (b) mental diseases, (c) diseases of the endocrine glands, and (d) the metabolic or degenerative diseases. Cancer and arthritis will be discussed under the latter classification. Cardiovascular disease which also belongs with the degenerative diseases was discussed in Chapter 40. Those conditions or diseases known as inborn errors of metabolism were discussed in Chapter 42.

Forms of therapy have two major aims, to relieve the symptoms and to cure the disease. As will be evident from the following discussion, there is too little of the latter and far too much of the former. Our knowledge of the causes and cures of diseases is still so inadequate that often all we can do is to make the patient as comfortable as possible. In many cases this simple treatment is all that is needed because the natural defenses of the body can take care of the diseased condition. In others, treatment of symptoms only prolongs the time a patient must wait before his death from an incurable disease.

44-2 THE INFECTIOUS DISEASES

"At some early stage of evolution, possibly before plants and animals had become clearly differentiated from each other, one or more species must have made the discovery that a very convenient source of food consists of the tissues of other organisms. In such tissues may be found materials, already preformed, suitable as energy sources and for building one's own tissues . . . Among some of the species which had discovered the importance and desirability of eating other organisms as a source of food, the expedient of parasitism developed. After all, it is not economical to destroy the source of your food material completely, although some micro-organisms, perversely enough, do this to their hosts. Instead, it is easier to live in or on the host, making use of the food supply which he provides directly or indirectly. This is parasitism of which infection is an example."*

Man has a clear idea of what the parasites are: the bacteria, viruses, and simple animals such as lice. From the viewpoint of many plants, humans and indeed all animals are potential parasites. The animals that have survived have developed various forms of defense against their enemies. In addition to weapons and fortifications against large foes, humans have developed several defenses against the microscopic agents of infection.

44-3 DEFENSES AGAINST INFECTION

The human body has several natural defenses against infection. The tough, relatively impermeable skin is a major defense. For those invaders that do manage to get around or through this barrier, the **phagocytes,** such as some kinds of white blood cells, are potent antagonists. Biochemists are most interested in two other natural defensive agents—the antibodies and some of the hormones. **Antibodies** are produced by the body in response to the invasion of various types of foreign molecules. The human can make antibodies against materials as varied as egg white and viruses. The process of antibody formation is not completely understood, but apparently each human has a recognition system that can tell when a substance in his body is foreign. If the foreign particle is of sufficient size and proper character, the body manufactures antibodies that are apparently shaped in such a way as to combine with the antigen (invading foreign particle) and negate its effects. The antibodies are primarily protein, although many also contain carbohydrates in their structure. Some of the most important antibodies are present in the blood serum and can be separated in a group called the gamma globulins. Vaccination is effective because it stimulates the production of antibodies. It is assumed that the pooled gamma globulin from many in-

---

* B. S. Walker, W. C. Boyd, and I. Asminov, *Biochemistry and Human Metabolism,* 3rd ed., Williams and Wilkins, Baltimore, 1957.

dividuals contains antibodies to many specific diseases, and thus it is often given to help the body fight specific diseases.

Some of the steroid hormones produced in the cortex of the adrenal gland also help the body fight infection. These substances enable the body to "wall off" the foreign invaders and thus keep them from spreading throughout the body and doing damage. A large percentage of the American population has had a mild infection of the tubercule bacillus, has developed antibodies to it (as shown by skin tests), and may also have "walled off" groups of these bacteria in small nodules in the lungs. Some adrenal cortical hormones help the body produce these inflammatory walls. The adrenal cortex also produces hormones which decrease the reaction of the body to foreign substances by suppressing antibody formation. These hormones, the best known of which is cortisone, are effective in diminishing inflammation in many parts of the body. They are widely used in the treatment of arthritis and other diseases. In the early days of cortisone therapy, some persons who received this medication developed tuberculosis, apparently because the tuberculosis bacteria that had been "contained" were again set free. Physicians prescribing cortisone or other similar substances now take measures to prevent such consequences.

The transplanting of organs such as the heart and kidney from one human to another are made possible by the use of various drugs that repress the responses of the body to foreign tissue. Many persons given such transplants died later from pneumonia or other diseases. Their deaths were due, at least in part, to the fact that the drugs given to keep the body from rejecting the transplanted organ also kept the body from rejecting or fighting the bacteria that cause pneumonia and other diseases.

44-4 CHEMOTHERAPEUTIC AGENTS

Against some diseases the natural body defenses can be aided by chemical substances either synthesized in the laboratory or extracted from other organisms. These substances are classified as synthetic **chemotherapeutic agents** and **antibiotics,** respectively. Antibiotics which can now be synthesized in the laboratory were originally isolated from microorganisms, particularly the molds. Even in the laboratory, synthesis of antibiotics often relies on cultures of molds to perform certain steps in the synthesis. In most cases, laboratory synthesis is not economical; it is less expensive to grow the molds and let them do the entire job of producing the antibiotic.

A perfect chemotherapeutic agent would be totally effective against a kind of bacteria or other infectious agent and would have no bad effects on the host. The action has been characterized as being like a magic bullet that hits and affects only infectious agents. Since the biochemistry of all organisms from the bacteria to man is essentially similar, what is poisonous to one organism is usually poisonous to the other. However, sufficient exceptions to this general rule exist to make chemotherapeutic agents useful.

One of the first synthetic therapeutic agents was the compound called Salvarsan, or Dr. Erlich's compound 606, which was effective against syphilis. (The story of Dr. Erlich is dramatically told in the book *Microbe Hunters* by Paul de Kruif.) Probably the most important synthetic chemotherapeutic agents are sulfanilamide and its derivatives, popularly known as the sulfa drugs. The effectiveness of these drugs led to the proposal of a basic theory of chemotherapeutics. It was believed that sulfanilamide was effective against bacteria because it was an antimetabolite to *para*-aminobenzoic acid (PABA). An **antimetabolite** is defined as a compound that is sufficiently similar in chemical structure to a normal metabolite so that it can replace it in an organism. However, the antimetabolite does not function as does the metabolite, a circumstance which often leads either to failure in growth or reproduction and thus to the eventual death of the organism. Bacteria use PABA in the synthesis of folic acid. It was argued that because of similarity in structure between PABA and sulfanilamide, organisms tend to incorporate sulfanilamide and compounds related to it into a molecule that is similar to folic acid but which cannot perform the functions of folic acid.

sulfanilamide   PABA   folic acid

This deficiency would lead to decreased ability to grow and reproduce. The test of a true antimetabolite is that its effects must be reversed by the addition of large amounts of the normal metabolite. Thus bacteria that are destroyed by sulfonamide (actually perhaps just kept from reproducing with the natural body defenses doing the destroying) should be able to live and reproduce in the presence of sulfonamide when sufficient folic acid is supplied to them. While many sulfonamide-sensitive bacteria can meet this test, others cannot. We now believe that the sulfa drugs are not true antimetabolites but that they do inhibit a specific step in folic acid synthesis. However, the antimetabolite theory has led to the design of many chemotherapeutic agents specifically designed to be antimetabolites for a chemical substance. The compound aminopterin which is successful, although only for a limited time, in the treatment of leukemia is another folic acid antimetabolite.

Why do sulfa drugs inhibit the growth of bacteria but have little effect on humans? The answer may be twofold. First, humans require folic acid as such, and do not synthesize it—it is a vitamin. Secondly, humans can survive even if deprived of all folic acid for a period of a day or two, but this period of time represents several lifetimes (times between divisions) to bacteria. Whenever the bacteria are prevented from reproducing at a normal rate, the natural defenses of the human body can usually effectively combat the invaders.

44-5 ANTIBIOTICS

The first antibiotic to be widely used was penicillin. Its discovery came about as the result of an accidental contamination of a bacterial plate by a particular kind of blue-green mold. When Dr. Alexander Fleming observed that the colony of mold was surrounded by a zone in which no bacteria (a staphylcoccus culture) was growing, although the rest of the plate was covered with bacteria, he realized that the mold was secreting something which was inhibiting the growth of bacteria in the surrounding medium. To overcome the difficulties

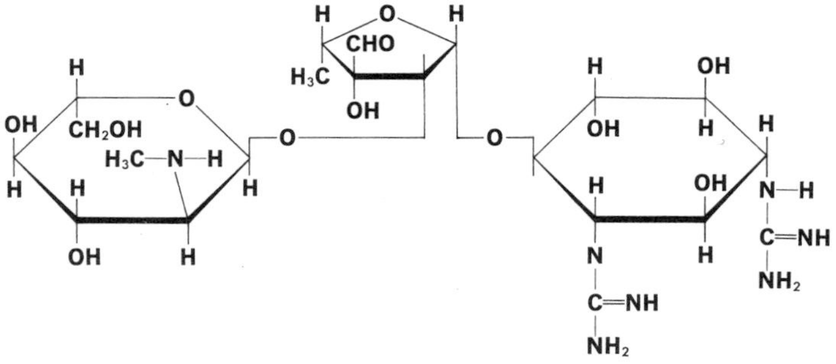

streptomycin

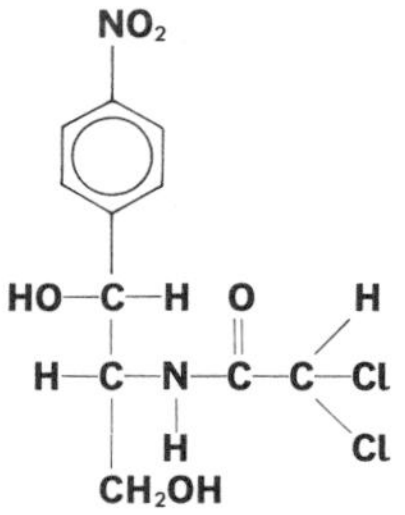

chloramphenicol

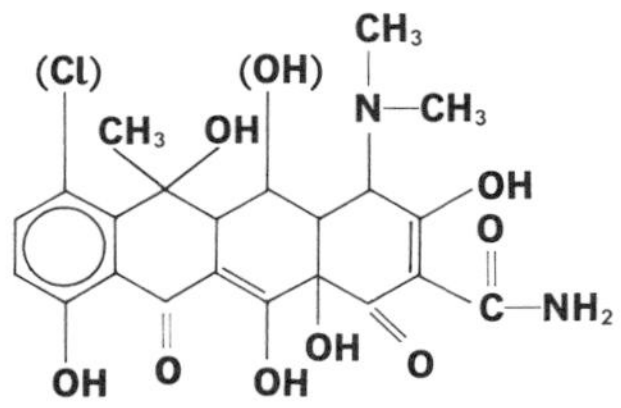

tetracycline

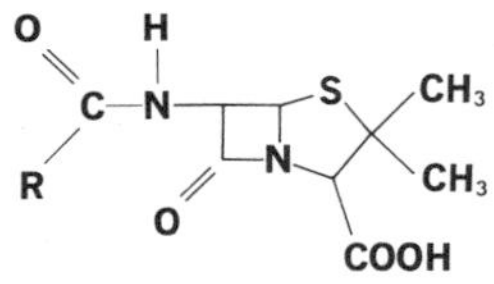

penicillin

FIG. 44–1. The structure of some common antibiotics. The form of penicillin known as penicillin G has a benzyl group at R. Other forms have the *p*-hydroxybenzyl, pentenyl, *n*-amyl, or *n*-heptyl R groups. The tetracycline molecule is known as Achromycin. Oxytetracycline which has an OH as indicated on ring number 3 is known as Terramycin, and chlorotetracycline, which has a chlorine atom on the first ring, is known as Aureomycin.

---

in extracting, testing, purifying, and producing in quantity the bacterial inhibiting substance required a great deal of research. It was many years before the substance which we call penicillin became available for general use.

Many other workers, notably Dr. Selman Waksman, have found hundreds of antibiotics. The general procedure is to make culture plates of the organism that we wish to control and expose them to extracts from other organisms—particularly the molds. An extensive search has been conducted for rare kinds of molds and yeasts that might produce antibiotics. Although hundreds of antibiotics are known, only a limited number are useful in treating diseases. Most of the antibiotics are toxic not only to the infectious agent but to the humans or other animals being treated. Penicillin has the advantage of being both effective against certain infections and the least toxic of the common antibiotics; some individuals however, have acquired a sensitivity to penicillin so that administration causes serious consequences. Apparently what has happened is that these penicillin-sensitive persons have produced antibodies to penicillin itself, since it, too, is a foreign molecule. In cases of this kind the natural defenses of the body are acting in a way which is bad for its general health. This reaction of the body against foreign substances is also a serious problem in the surgical substitution or transplanting to replace various parts of the human body.

The formulas for some of the more important antibiotics are given in Fig. 44-1.

Because of the wide use of vaccination and the development of effective chemotherapeutic agents, and perhaps also because of the generally good state of nutrition of most persons in the United States, deaths caused by infectious diseases have greatly decreased in the past few decades. This is not true of all countries in the world, and infectious diseases still take a much larger toll, especially of children, than they should. Part of the solution to the problems of infectious diseases lies in education and part in the provision of vaccines, chemotherapeutic agents, and nutritious foods. The role of adequate sanitation in the prevention and spread of infectious diseases is also important.

44-6 THE NONINFECTIOUS DISEASES

Diseases in this classification, as far as we know, do not result from the presence of an infectious agent. It is possible, however, that some of them are caused by agents which have not yet been associated with the disease. This is especially true of certain kinds of cancer which may be caused by viruses.

Nutritional Diseases

Malnutrition is a minor problem in the United States today. But there are definite evidences that some diseases are aggravated, if not caused, by overeating or "excessive" nutrition which some would classify as another form of malnutrition. It is estimated that 15% of the American population, some 30,000,000 persons, are overweight and that at least 5,000,000 of these are pathologically overweight. This is not true of many other countries of the world. In Africa, for example, kwashiorkor, a disease caused by inadequate protein nutrition, is prevalent. Pellagra, beriberi, and other deficiency diseases are still present in large areas of the world.

Many nutritionists believe that the laziness, stupidity, and other characteristics which are often attributed to the natives of poor countries are really due to prolonged nutritional deficiencies. Controlled research on the effects of starvation on human volunteers supports this conclusion.

Individuals vary in their utilization of food and in their needs for specific nutrients. While not much is known about this subject, we do know that there is wide variability in all measurable human characteristics, including the requirements for vitamins. With respect to nutritional requirements, we are too often prone to remember the generalization and forget the individual. Screening of people on a massive scale and a great deal of research will be required to determine the individual variations. However, this lack of refinement should not keep us from acting upon the best available generalizations as to normal requirements. Malnutrition in the poorer countries of the world can be combated by education in nutrition and by increasing food supplies. The latter problem is becoming more and more serious as a result of the rapid increase in population. This increase is due in a large part to the control of infectious disease and to better nutrition. Thus the solution to problems of disease and malnutrition may lead to even more complex problems. It may be said that in treating diseases man has interfered with the balance of nature, and this is, of course, true. The alternative to this interference is continued infant mortality, starvation, and disease. Another alternative, which many persons regard as another interference with nature, is birth control. The problems raised by the population explosion are not insurmountable. Some countries have reversed the population increase. Oral contraceptives show great promise for those whose morals are not offended by use of "the pill" (see Chapter 35–6).

Mental Diseases

Various forms of mental illness may affect as many as ten percent of the population of the United States at some time during their lives. Some fifty percent of all the patients in United States hospitals are victims of mental diseases. These estimates lead many persons to say that mental diseases are the primary health problem in the United States at the present time. It is true, of course, that the high percentage of mental patients in hospitals is due to the fact that hospital stay is much longer for these patients than for the patients in general hospitals. Other authorities consider the greatest problem is in the control of cardiovascular disease or cancer which rank highest as causes of death.

One difficulty in discussing mental diseases is the lack of a good definition of the diseases and objective reports of the effects of drugs used in their treatment. Mental illness is usually categorized as a psychosis or neurosis, and the victims of such conditions are known as psychotics or neurotics. The psychotic is generally thought of as a person who differs seriously from normal persons in his idea of reality and contact with his environment. He may be in a stupor, he may be wildly irrational, he may see and hear things no one else does, or he may become uncontrollably violent. A neurotic is described as a person whose mental illness does not involve loss of contact with reality. He may be overwhelmed by persistent fears, haunted by anxiety, subject to unexplainable aches and pains, and perhaps unable to sleep. Definite borderlines between psychotics, neurotics, and normal persons are not easily drawn. It has been said that the mentally ill are just like normal persons except that some tendencies are exaggerated.

For many years biochemists have looked for an abnormal metabolite in the blood or urine of psychotics. This search has led to a number of compounds that can produce some of the symptoms of psychoses when given to experimental animals or humans. However, there are no clear indications that these substances are present in the blood or urine of psychotics in sufficient quantities to account for their illness. The search for abnormal metabolites is continuing and may yet be successful. The hereditary nature of some forms of schizophrenia lends support to the search for an inherited biochemical defect.

While the search for metabolic abnormalities in the mentally ill has been largely unsuccessful, therapy in treating mental illness has made major advances in the past fifteen years. The use of tranquilizing drugs such as reserpine and chlorpromazine has transformed mental hospitals from madhouses or snake pits with straitjackets and padded cells to quieter, calmer places. These potent tranquilizers alleviate the symptoms, but do not cure mental

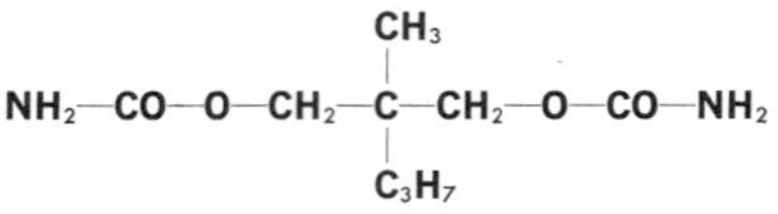

meprobamate (Equanil, Miltown)

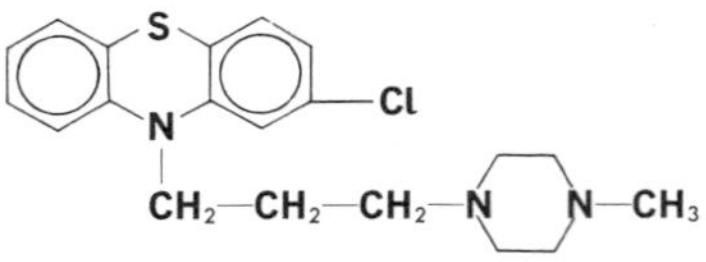

prochlorperazine (Compazine)

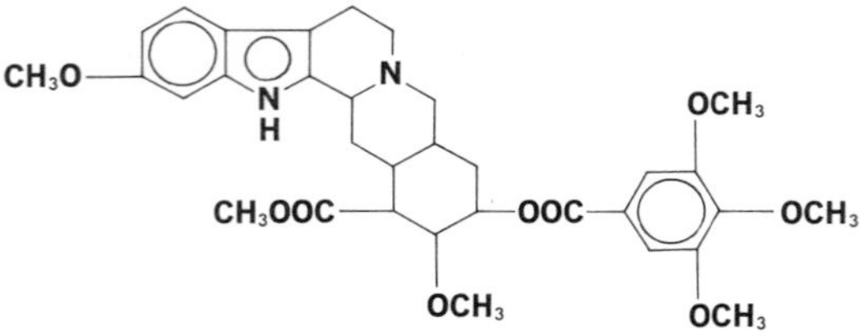

reserpine (Serpasil)

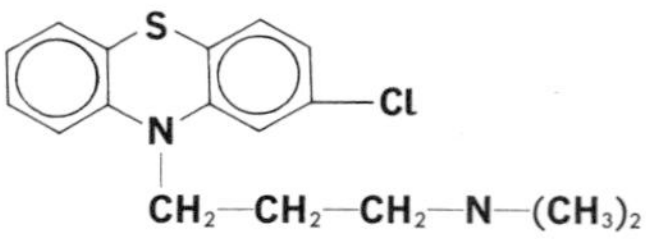

chlorpromazine (Thorazine)

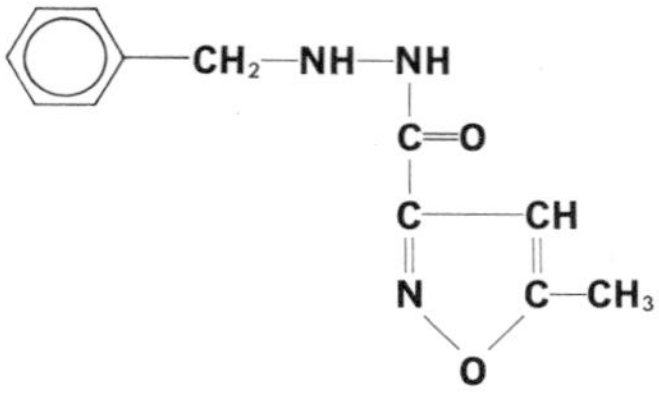

isocarboxazid (Marplan)

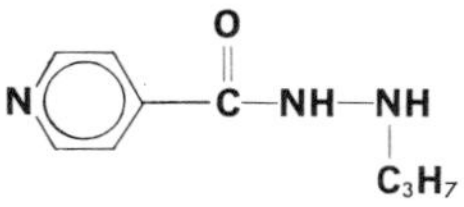

iproniazid (Marsilid)

FIG. 44-2. Drugs that influence mental states. Chlorpromazine, prochloperazine, reserpine, and meprobamate are generally described as tranquillizers, and iproniazid and isocarboxazid are known as psychic energizers.

diseases. They make it possible for a psychiatrist to establish contact with a psychotic patient and thus help him treat the disease by psychotherapy.

Reserpine can be isolated from an extract of the roots of the plant *rauwolfia serpentina.* This plant has been used by medicine men of India for centuries for the treatment of a variety of conditions ranging from snakebite to madness. Purified extracts of *rauwolfia* were first used in the United States in the treatment of high blood pressure. The tranquilizing effects were noted, and the most active of the many substances (more than 25 are known) in *rauwolfia* extract was found to be reserpine, (see Fig. 44-2). Chlorpromazine was synthesized to be used as an antihistamine, but its usefulness as a potent tranquilizer was soon observed. Both reserpine and chlorpromazine were first generally obtainable in 1954. Since then many chemical compounds closely related to chlorpromazine have been synthesized and are used as tranquilizers (see Fig. 44-2).

The milder tranquilizers such as meprobamate, which is known by its trade names Miltown and Equanil, are used by many people who would be described only as neurotic or perhaps just "overanxious normals." Meprobamate is both a muscle relaxant and a tranquilizer. Although it has been widely used, recent reports of bad side effects may mean that its use will diminish greatly. Other similar mild tranquilizers are available.

Many other chemical substances have an effect on the mind—or to use more modern terms, alter mental states. These include antidepressants or "psychic energizers" such as iproniazid and isocarboxazid (Fig. 44–2). These substances counteract depression—a sense of despair, fear, or guilt. These drugs relieve depression without making a patient jittery or irritable. Iproniazid was originally used in the treatment of tuberculosis. When it was observed that patients taking the drug became elated and sometimes so happy they began dancing in the hospital rooms, the mood-elevating aspects were obvious. Unfortunately, many bad side effects of iproniazid became evident, and it was withdrawn from general use as an antidepressant (and more effective drugs were found for treating tuberculosis). Since iproniazid is a derivative of hydrazine (H_2NNH_2), chemical synthesis of similar compounds has produced a variety of effective and less toxic antidepressants. These drugs inhibit the enzyme monoamine oxidase (MAO) that is important in the oxidation of various amines (norepinephrine, for example, or serotonin). These amines are important in the functioning of the brain and the nervous system. Apparently this inhibition of MAO is responsible for the antidepressant properties of the hydrazine derivatives.

The amphetamines (Benzedrine and Dexedrine) are also used as antidepressants. They have the general disadvantage of producing a nervous irritability and depressing the appetite. The latter effect, however, makes them useful for weight reduction. Since these are potent drugs, they are legally available only on a doctor's prescription. Although these antidepressants are used by college students who want to stay up all night to finish a term paper or study for an examination, there is little evidence that such use is warranted. They can keep a student awake and may elevate his spirits, but they probably do not elevate his grades.

Another class of mind-influencing substances which are variously described as hallucinogenic, psychotogenic, or psychedelic drugs are the object of much interest today. The first of these substances to be chemically characterized, lysergic acid diethylamide (LSD) (see Fig. 44–3), has been the object of much experimentation, both scientific and unscientific. The drug is relatively nontoxic in the dosages used, but it can have profound effects on mental states and on the personality. These effects are largely not describable in objective, scientific terms but are reported in subjective, personal language. As a result, scientific evaluation of these substances is difficult. It is to be hoped that further, well-controlled experimentation with these potent substances will lead to better evidence concerning both their usefulness and their potential danger. Psilocybin, mescaline, and tetrahydrocannabinol (from marijuana) are reported to have effects similar, but not identical, to those of LSD. The only acceptable therapeutic use of LSD at the time of this writing is in the treatment of alcoholics where some success has been demonstrated.

An examination of the formulas of the compounds given in Fig. 44–3 shows that many of the substances affecting the mind are similar in structure to norepinephrine and serotonin. These latter substances, as we have already noted, are important in the functioning of the brain and nervous system. It is also known that reserpine and chlorpromazine influence the levels of serotonin in the brain. The only well-established fact on the biochemical effect of any of these drugs is that the hydrazine derivatives inhibit the enzyme monoamine oxidase

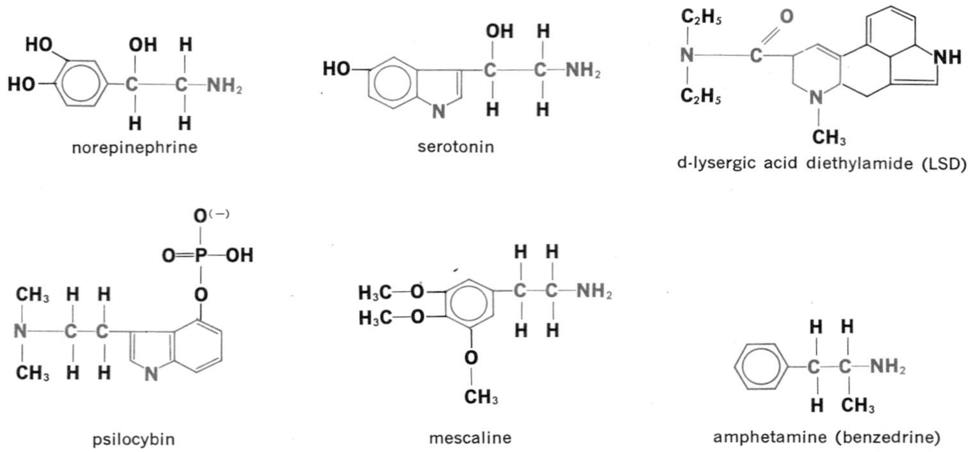

FIG. 44-3. Drugs that affect the central nervous system. Norepinephrine and serotonin are involved in transmission of nerve impulses. LSD, psilocybin, and mescaline produce altered mental states and may be called psychedelic or hallucinogenic substances. Amphetamine is a stimulant. Structural elements that are similar are shown in color.

which is important in the metabolism of norepinephrine and serotonin. Thus the evidence is mounting that these two naturally occurring amines are very important in influencing mental states. LSD is known to block the metabolism of serotonin; however, other similar substances that also block serotonin metabolism do not have the mind-altering effects of LSD. These observations are intriguing and suggest possible hypotheses about the action of mind-altering substances. However, no consistent theory has yet been able to stand the challenge of explaining all the experimental data.

Diseases Caused by Malfunction of the Endocrine Glands

The endocrine glands are characterized by the fact that they secrete chemical substances called hormones directly into the blood stream. The hormones travel throughout the circulatory system and eventually affect many parts of the body. The endocrine glands are the pituitary (or hypophysis), located just below the brain; the thyroid, located in the neck; the parathyroids, located in the thyroid gland; the pancreas, located in the abdominal region; the adrenals, located on top of the kidneys; and either the ovaries, located abdominally in the female, or the testes located in the scrotal sac in the male. (See Fig. 44-4.) Each endocrine gland produces at least one hormone, and many of them produce several chemically distinct hormones. The deficiency or oversupply of any of the hormones has serious consequences for the individual. We can give examples of only a few of these conditions for the purposes of illustration.

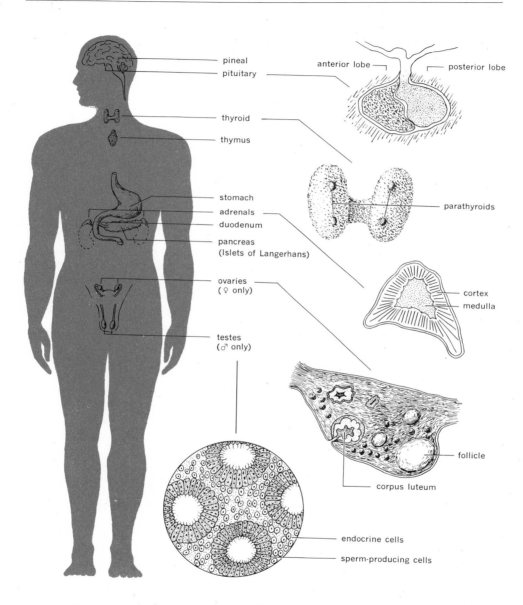

FIG. 44–4. The endocrine glands of the human. The location of the glands is shown at the left, and drawings of the detailed structure of the glands at the right. [Reprinted from John W. Kimball, *Biology*, Addison-Wesley, Reading, Mass., 1965.]

Diabetes mellitus, which was discussed in Chapter 38, is caused by a deficiency of the pancreatic hormone, insulin. Treatment by insulin does not cure diabetes, but continued use of it allows the diabetic to lead essentially a normal life. Control of diabetes represents one of the most successful instances of correction of a hormone deficiency. Purified hormones from other animals or synthetic products have been used successfully to treat endocrine insufficiencies. The administration of thyroxine for hypothyroidism (underactivity of the thyroid gland), the adrenocorticotropic hormone (ACTH) to compensate for underactivity of the adrenal cortex, and either male or female hormones to persons who fail to mature normally are other examples of treatment for hormone deficiencies.

Treatment is more difficult in cases of overproduction of a hormone or hyperactivity of an endocrine gland. In many cases, surgery is used to remove the overactive gland. This may be followed by replacement of the hormones—at a normal level—from a synthetic or natural source. In other instances, specific substances are known which can decrease the secretion of a gland. For instance, propylthiouracil decreases the output of thyroxine in a hyperthyroid person. In other cases, the action of one hormone is opposed to that of another, and administration of the antagonist may be helpful. An example of such antagonism exists between the male and female hormones and in the inflammation-promoting and inflammation-suppressing hormones of the adrenal cortex.

Hormones are sometimes used to treat diseases not directly attributable to the endocrine glands. Male hormones are effective in treating some forms of cancer of the breast in the female, and cortisone is widely used to treat various diseases characterized by inflammatory reactions.

There are no real cures for diseases of the endocrine other than surgical removal of overactive glands and possibly the surgical transplantation of glandular tissue to compensate for underactive glands. The purification and laboratory synthesis of hormones has, however, led to treatment of many endocrine disorders. Our knowledge of just how the hormones work is minimal. It is to be hoped that as we find out more about the reactions that hormones influence, other means of treatment and perhaps control of endocrine diseases will emerge.

Metabolic or Degenerative Diseases

The terminology used to describe these diseases is not totally satisfactory. From one aspect, all diseases are metabolic since they influence reactions in the human body. The term degenerative diseases is perhaps better, yet that is not totally accurate, either.

Cancer. The term cancer is commonly used to describe a variety of conditions all of which are characterized by a nonphysiological growth or multiplication of cells. This growth may remain restricted in area and have little tendency to recur after removal. In a case like this we describe the growth, or neoplasm, as benign. In common usage, benign neoplasms are not cancerous. When a tumor grows unrestrictedly and spreads through the blood or lymph to other parts of the body to form new growths, it is described as malignant and called a cancer. Medical men use more descriptive terms and speak of *carcinoma,* a malignant tumor of epithelial cells; *sarcoma,* a malignant tumor of the muscle or connective tissue; or *leukemia,* which is characterized by excessive numbers of leucocytes or white blood cells.

Biochemists and other medical researchers have attempted for years to find some abnormal metabolite in cancerous cells, but so far the search has been unsuccessful. Cancerous cells seem to be similar to others except that they have lost the ability to stop reproducing. Malignant cells tend to lose their differentiation or specialization and revert to a more primitive type of cell, and in some cases this reversion involves the use of anaerobic glycolysis even in the presence of oxygen. These cells apparently do not use the reactions of the citric acid cycle.

More is known about the causes of cancer than about the changes it brings about in the metabolism at a cellular level. Ingestion of certain organic chemicals such as dimethylbenzanthracene and methylcholanthrene,

dimethylbenzanthracene   methylcholanthrene

can produce cancer in rats and other experimental animals. Closely related compounds found in cigarette smoke are also effective **carcinogens** (producers of cancer). Cancer can also be produced by radiation. Ultraviolet irradiation of the skin can lead to skin cancer. X-rays and gamma radiation from radioisotopes penetrate deeper and produce cancer in other organs. Strontium 90 and radium which the body tends to treat like their sister element, calcium, are found in bones and are likely to produce cancer of the bone or bone marrow.

Evidence is accumulating that some forms of cancer are caused by viruses. In fact, some authorities believe that all cancer is caused by viruses. If this proves to be true, we will have to reclassify cancer as an infectious disease, although it will certainly be different from other such diseases.

One theory has recently been proposed that links all the bits of evidence concerning the causes of cancer. This theory must still be tested, but it presents an interesting way of regarding the cancerous condition. According to this theory, viruses may infect cells and remain in the cells in an essentially inactive form. When the proper stimulus comes along, either radiation or a chemical carcinogen, the virus becomes active and produces cancer. A similar theory has proposed that viruses are not necessary but that carcinogenic chemicals or irradiation affect the normal DNA in a cell in such a way that it produces malignancy.

There are various treatments for cancer. Probably the best is surgical removal at an early stage of development of the neoplasm. In some cases irradiation with X-rays destroys the cancerous cells along with normal cells. Thus X-rays can both cause cancer and be used to treat it. The probability that they will cure a known neoplasm is greater than the probability of their producing a new one, so X-ray therapy is useful. Significant progress is being reported toward finding antibodies to cancerous cells—presumably these antibodies would have to come from someone other than the victim of the cancer, since the fact that he has cancer indicates that he cannot make sufficient antibodies. The form of cancer therapy most closely related to biochemistry is the use of antimetabolites. Antimetabolites of many of the components of the nucleic acids have been effective in treating malignancies. Mercapto-purine and fluorouracil,

mercaptopurine   fluorouracil

have been used for this purpose. Treatment with antimetabolites often prolongs the life of the victim of cancer, but it does not offer a cure. Over a period of time the cancerous cells seem to become resistant to most antimetabolites. Eventually the antimetabolites begin to affect the normal cells of the body to such an extent that treatment must be stopped.

It is to be hoped that further studies of the basic defect, causes, and treatment of cancer will lead to either a cure or an effective treatment of this dread disease.

Arthritis. Arthritis means literally, inflammation of the joints. In any condition so generally described, there are probably many causes of the symptoms which characterize the condition. Two types of arthritis have been distinguished, gouty arthritis and rheumatoid arthritis. In the former, deposits, largely of uric acid and urates, form at various places in the body and are most noticeable at the joints. Deposits at places other than joints is classified as gout. This condition represents an abnormal deposition of a normal metabolite. The disease is apparently due to the synthesis of excessive amounts of uric acid in these individuals.

Rheumatoid arthritis is one of a group of diseases called the collagen diseases. In these there are inflammatory changes in connective tissue which can produce lesions in joints, skin, muscle, heart, and blood vessels. The cause of these inflammatory changes is not definitely known, but in some cases there are antibodies in the serum which react with other components of the host's own tissues. We can characterize this disease as one in which an individual is immune to himself, and say he has an auto-immune disease.

Both forms of arthritis represent abnormalities in essentially normal body constituents. Gout and gouty arthritis can be treated with colchicine which apparently decreases the synthesis of uric acid. Both forms of arthritis, or perhaps it is best to say both diseases, can be treated with anti-inflammatory drugs such as cortisone.

Cardiovascular disease. This disease, which was discussed in Chapter 40, is also included with the degenerative diseases. It is, in fact, probably the most important of these diseases, at least with respect to the number of persons affected.

44–7 AGING

It is probably wrong to classify the process of aging as a disease, but it has much in common with the metabolic or degenerative diseases. We are all aware of the general symptoms of aging; we know that the skin wrinkles, the hair turns gray and may fall out, sight is impaired, the bones become brittle, and the body no longer can stand so much stress as previously.

The biochemist is interested in three basic aspects of aging: What is the biochemical nature of the changes accompanying aging? What is the cause of these changes? What treatments or procedures may offset or delay the onset of these changes? At the present time there are only fragmentary answers to these questions, but research is proceeding, and we will undoubtedly have better answers in the future.

The search for the nature of the biochemical changes in aging has centered upon the connective tissue—the material between the cells that helps hold them together. The protein, collagen, is the most abundant component of connective tissue. Upon aging, the collagen becomes more rigid, less soluble in phosphate and citrate buffers, and assumes an almost crystalline form. This increased rigidity is probably due to increased cross linkage between collagen molecules. Other components of the connective tissue, elastin and various mucopolysaccharides (combinations of protein and polysaccharides) change in ways that may make nutrition and elimination of waste products of the cells, which are surrounded by the connective tissue, much more difficult. It is known that with aging many cells die and are replaced with connective tissue.

A brown lipoprotein pigment called lipofucsin accumulates in many cells with increasing age. Neither the source nor significance of this pigment is known. However, in persons who live to be 100 years old, six to ten percent of the volume of some heart cells is made up of this pigment.

While there is no lack of theories to explain why persons age, most of the theories lack any real verification. Since many of the cells of the body (nerve and muscle cells) never divide, they may just "wear out." We must ask, then, what wearing out means in biochemical terms. It has been suggested that the DNA is disrupted by chance irradiations so that it no longer has all the "information" a cell needs for survival. The amount of RNA found in the nucleus of cells decreases with age as does its rate of turnover. Perhaps toxic products produced in the cell disrupt some part of the cellular machinery. Other theories of aging point to the fact that many older persons do not eat well-balanced nutritious diets, and thus some of the effects of aging may be due to malnutrition.

Few valid treatments have been found to delay the onset of aging. In experiments with rats, a drastically reduced caloric intake with maintenance of the levels of vitamins and proteins increased the life span from a normal value of 1000 days to 1400 days. In severely starved animals the life span was doubled. In countries where starvation is common, the average life span is not increased, but these countries also have poorer nutrition and more infectious diseases, so perhaps the comparison is not valid. It is certainly true that obesity is not consistent with long life.

Various people have advocated the consumption of yoghurt or the implantation of monkey glands (especially the testes) as a means for preventing aging. Others who have been somewhat more flippant about the whole idea have suggested that the way to live to be old is to advertise for a pair of long-lived parents. It is known that heredity is important in longevity. Another facetious statement is the humorous quip attributed to G. B. Shaw to the effect that the one comforting thought about the process of aging is its alternative!

In a more serious vein—research into the cause of aging and possible ways of slowing down the process should prove fruitful in the next several years. Dr. Hans Selye has said: "Among all my autopsies (and I have performed quite a few), I have never seen a man who died of old age. In fact, I do not think anyone has ever died of old age. . . To die of old age would mean that all the organs of the body would be worn out proportionately, merely by having been used too long. This is never the case. We invariably die because one vital part has worn out too early in proportion to the rest of the body."*

Some may question the desirability of prolonging life for persons who feel alienated from society even while young. The prospect of a prolonged existence filled with mental anguish or boredom is not inviting. It would seem, then, that various areas must be explored for ways of making life more meaningful as well as longer.

IMPORTANT TERMS

Antibiotic	Carcinogen	Infection
Antibody	Chemotherapeutic agent	Metabolic (degenerative) disease
Antigen	Disease	Phagocyte
Antimetabolite	Endocrine gland	Therapy

WORK EXERCISES

1. Distinguish between an antibiotic and an antibody. How are they different, and in what ways are they similar?

2. Distinguish between carcinoma and sarcoma, between a chemotherapeutic agent and an antibiotic, between a tranquilizer and an antidepressant, and between the effects of benzedrine and iproniazid.

3. The enzyme monoamine oxidase (MAO) probably catalyzes the metabolism of serotonin and norepinephrine. What would be the net chemical effect of inhibiting MAO?

4. Discuss the relationship of radiation to cancer.

SUGGESTED READING

Allison, A., "Lysosomes and Disease," *Scientific American,* Nov. 1967. The role of these subcellular organelles in disease is discussed in a strikingly illustrated article.

Barron, F., *et al.,* "The Hallucinogenic Drugs," *Scientific American,* Apr. 1964. This article gives structures and discusses effects of such alkaloids as LSD, psilocybin, and mescaline.

---

* H. Selye, *The Stress of Life,* McGraw Hill, New York, 1956.

Best, J. B., "Protopsychology," *Scientific American,* Feb. 1963 (Offprint #149). This article discusses learning in planarian worms and the effects of diet—particularly a diet consisting of trained worms—on their learning.

Braun, A. C., "The Reversal of Tumor Growth," *Scientific American,* Nov. 1965. A discussion of the types of cells that change from malignant to normal.

Collier, H. O. J., "Aspirin," *Scientific American,* Nov. 1963 (Offprint #169). A discussion of ways in which this long used "miracle drug" works.

Comfort, A., *The Process of Ageing,* Signet Science Library, New American Library, New York, 1964. Dr. Comfort discusses many aspects of ageing, in an engaging although essentially pessimistic book.

Cooper, L. Z., "German Measles," *Scientific American,* July 1966. This article tells the story of the development of a vaccine which may eventually control this disease.

DeKruif, P., *Microbe Hunters,* Harcourt, Brace and World, New York, 1932. A classic popularization of the lives of many great scientific microbe hunters.

Frei, E., III, and E. J. Freireich, "Leukemia," *Scientific American,* May 1964. A discussion of the disease and some treatments being used for it.

Gorini, L., "Antibiotics and the Genetic Code," *Scientific American,* Apr. 1966. A discussion of the effects of streptomycin and related drugs on protein synthesis.

Hammond, E. C., "The Effects of Smoking," *Scientific American,* July 1962, (Offprint #126). Present data is even more frightening, but this older report along with its basic biological approach to the problem is still good reading.

Langer, W. L., "The Black Death," *Scientific American,* Feb. 1964. This article discusses the plague that killed one-fourth of the people in Europe in the years 1348 to 1350.

Lasagna, L., *The Doctors' Dilemmas,* Collier Books (BS177v) New York, 1963. Dr. Lasagna discusses quacks, the drug industry, legal matters, and other controversial aspects of medicine.

Li, C. H., "The ACTH Molecule," *Scientific American,* July 1963 (Offprint #160). An excellent summary of the functions of the anterior pituitary gland, and a specific discussion of the polypeptide ACTH, its structure and function.

Linder, F. E., "The Health of the American People," *Scientific American,* June 1966. A discussion of techniques used and the results obtained from a survey of the health of many Americans.

Nossal, G. J. V., "How Cells Make Antibodies," *Scientific American,* Dec. 1964 (Offprint #199). A well-illustrated discussion of the involvement of genes in antibody synthesis.

Selye, H., *The Stress of Life,* McGraw-Hill, New York, 1956. This book gives Dr. Selye's fascinating story of the experiments that led to his theory of stress. He also discusses stress, aging, and philosophical implications of his theories.

Shock, N. W., "The Physiology of Ageing," *Scientific American,* Jan. 1962. This article and the one below by Verzar treat aging from a physiological viewpoint and from the chemical-structural changes in the protein collagen which accompanies aging.

Smith, I. M., "Death from Staphylococci," *Scientific American,* Feb. 1968. The changes in glucose, glycogen, and ATP in mice dying from staphylococcal infections led the author to speculate about the biochemical cause of death.

Speirs, R. S., "How Cells Attack Antigens," *Scientific American,* Feb. 1964 (Offprint #176). Discussion of the functions of specialized cells that protect the body from invasion by antigens.

Taussig, Helen B., "The Thalidomide Syndrome," *Scientific American,* Aug. 1962. A report of the effects on unborn children of the supposedly "safe" sedative.

Verzar, F., "The Aging of Collagen," *Scientific American,* Apr. 1963.

Zinsser, W., *Rats, Lice, and History,* Bantam Pathfinder paperback, New York, 1960. The subtitle of the book is "Being a study in biography, which, after twelve preliminary chapters indispensable for the preparation of the lay reader, deals with the life history of typhus fever." A fascinating book.

GLOSSARY

ABSOLUTE HUMIDITY: The mass of water vapor in a given amount of air, usually expressed in grams per cubic meter of air.

ABSOLUTE ZERO: The lowest attainable temperature; theoretically, the temperature at which molecular action would cease (approximately $-273°C$ or $-459°F$).

ACID: A proton donor. Common examples are HCl, H_2SO_4, and $HC_2H_3O_2$ (acetic acid).

ACID ANHYDRIDE: A substance which on combining with water produces an acid. SO_3 is the anhydride of H_2SO_4.

ACID CHLORIDE: An organic compound having the functional group:

$$-\overset{\overset{\displaystyle}{\|}}{\underset{\displaystyle O}{C}}-Cl.$$

ACTINIDES: The fourteen elements following the element actinium; elements having atomic numbers from 90 to 103. These elements have properties similar to those of actinium.

ADDITION REACTION: One in which new atoms bond with available electrons in a compound, without displacing other atoms.

ADRENALIN (EPINEPHRINE): A hormone of the adrenal gland that has a generally stimulating effect on the body.

ADSORPTION: The attraction toward or the adhesion of molecules or ions to solid surfaces.

AEROBIC: Literally, in the presence of air. Aerobic reactions require oxygen in order to proceed.

ALBUMIN: A protein that is water soluble, coagulated by heat, and is not precipitated in a solution that is 50% saturated with ammonium sulfate.

ALCOHOL: An organic compound having an —OH functional group on an alkyl skeleton, ROH.

ALDEHYDE: A compound in which one hydrogen and an organic group are bonded to a carbonyl group:

$$R-\overset{\overset{\displaystyle}{\|}}{\underset{\displaystyle O}{C}}-H \quad \text{or} \quad Ar-\overset{\overset{\displaystyle}{\|}}{\underset{\displaystyle O}{C}}-H$$

Compare with the definition of a *ketone*.

ALDOSE: A carbohydrate that contains an aldehyde group. Glucose, galactose, and ribose are simple aldoses.

ALIMENTARY CANAL: The food tube that carries the food through the body and serves for both digestion and elimination.

ALKANE: The systematic name for saturated hydrocarbons. (Section 22–3).

ALKANOIC ACID: The systematic name for RCOOH, an alkyl carboxylic acid.

ALKENE: The systematic name for a hydrocarbon having a double bond, such as butene, $CH_3CH_2CH{=}CH_2$.

ALKYL GROUP: A unit of organic structure equivalent to an alkane minus one hydrogen atom (Section 22–3). For example, $CH_3CH_2{-}$, is an ethyl group.

ALKYNE: Systematic name for a hydrocarbon having a triple bond, such as propyne, $CH_3C{\equiv}CH$.

ALLOTROPIC FORM: Elements occurring in two or more forms in the same physical state are allotropic forms of the element. Ozone, O_3, and oxygen, O_2, are allotropic forms of oxygen.

ALLOY: Mixture of metals or of metals with small amounts of nonmetals, usually combined to produce certain desirable properties not present in pure metals.

ALPHA PARTICLE: A positively charged helium atom; a helium ion; the nucleus of a helium atom.

AMIDE: A carboxyl derivative of the type

$$R{-}\underset{O}{\overset{\|}{C}}{-}NH_2 \quad \text{or} \quad R{-}\underset{O}{\overset{\|}{C}}{-}NHR$$

AMINE: A derivative of ammonia in which one or more hydrogens have been replaced by organic groups; for example, $ArNH_2$ or R_2NH. Such compounds are weak bases.

AMINO ACID: An organic compound containing an amino ($-NH_2$) and an acid ($-COOH$) group. The majority of the naturally occurring amino acids have the carboxyl group and the amino group attached to the same carbon and thus are α-amino acids.

AMINOPEPTIDASE: A peptidase that catalyzes the hydrolysis of the peptide bond nearest the end of a peptide chain that contains the free amino group.

AMPHOTERIC: A substance which reacts as either an acid or a base. Amino acids and the hydroxides of aluminum, tin, and lead, for example, are amphoteric.

AMYLASE: An enzyme that catalyzes the hydrolysis of starch.

ANABOLIC: A word used to describe reactions in living systems that combine simple molecules to make more complex molecules. Such reactions require energy in order to proceed.

ANABOLISM: Those reactions in a plant or animal that result in the synthesis of larger molecules from smaller ones. (See *catabolism*.)

ANAEROBIC: A word used to describe reactions that occur in the absence of air. Actually, anaerobic reactions are those that do not require oxygen to proceed. Some anaerobic reactions are inhibited by the presence of oxygen.

ANHYDROUS: Without water; e.g., hydrates from which the water of crystallization has been removed.

ANODE: The electrode at which electrons leave the solution; the electrode to which negative ions migrate.

ANOXIA: The condition in the body resulting from a deficiency of oxygen.

ANTIBIOTIC: A substance produced by a microorganism that inhibits the growth of another organism.

ANTIBODY: A macromolecule produced by an animal in response to an antigen. The antibody reacts to overcome the effects of a specific antigen.

ANTIGEN: A substance that initiates the production of antibodies.

ANTIMETABOLITE: A molecule that is similar to a normal metabolite but sufficiently different to inter-fere with reactions of the normal metabolite.

AROMATIC COMPOUND: An organic substance whose carbon skeleton contains a benzene ring or closely related type of ring.

ASSIMILATION: The process of distributing and using digested food.

ATHEROSCLEROSIS: A condition in which fatty deposits are formed in the inner lining of blood vessels.

ATMOSPHERE (the unit of pressure): The average atmospheric pressure at sea level, equaling 760 mm or 29.92 in. of mercury.

ATOM: The smallest existing part of an element.

ATOMIC MASS UNIT (amu): A unit of mass equaling 1/12 the mass of a carbon-12 atom; approxi-mately the mass of a proton or neutron.

ATOMIC NUMBER: The number of protons in the nucleus of an atom; therefore, it also equals the number of electrons in the shells of a complete atom.

ATOMIC WEIGHT: The average weights of the atoms of an element based on carbon-12 being equal to twelve.

ATP: Adenosine triphosphate. A compound whose hydrolysis provides energy to drive energy-requiring reactions. ATP represents an energy-storing compound. (See Fig. 36–12 for the formula for ATP.)

AVOGADRO'S LAW: This law states that when equal volumes of different gases are under the same conditions of temperature and pressure they will contain the same numbers of molecules.

BACTERIOPHAGE: A type of virus which infects bacteria. Many bacteriophages that attack the bacteria *E. Coli* have been studied. They contain DNA and protein.

BAROMETER: Any of several types of mechanisms used to measure atmospheric pressure.

BASAL METABOLIC RATE: The rate at which reactions are proceeding in an animal at rest. The BMR is determined by measuring oxygen consumed per unit of time.

BASE: A proton acceptor. Common examples are OH^- and NH_3.

BASIC ANHYDRIDE: A substance which on combining with water produces a base. Na_2O is a basic anhydride.

BESSEMER CONVERTER: A device for making medium quality steel by reducing the carbon content of pig iron.

BETA RAYS: Streams of electrons traveling at speeds approaching the speed of light.

BILE: The fluid secreted from the liver which aids in digestion of lipids. It contains emulsifying agents but no enzymes.

BINARY ACID: An acid composed of only two kinds of atoms; e.g., hydrochloric acid, HCl.

BIOCHEMISTRY: The science of the chemical composition, structure, and reactions of plants and animals.

BLAST FURNACE: An enormous towerlike furnace capable of removing iron from its ores (Section 19–6).

BOILING POINT: The temperature at which the vapor pressure of a liquid equals or just exceeds the pressure of the atmosphere above it.

BOYLE'S LAW: The volume of a gas is inversely proportional to the pressure exerted upon it if the tem-perature remains constant.

BRASS: Any one of varying mixtures of copper with smaller amounts of zinc (Table 19–1).

BRONZE: Mixtures of copper with varying amounts of zinc and tin. Bronzes are more resistant to corro-sion and much stronger and harder than copper (Table 19–1).

BROWNIAN MOVEMENT: The continuous, erratic movements of colloidal particles which can be observed through a microscope.

BUFFERED SOLUTION: A solution whose pH changes only slightly with the addition of moderate quantities of either strong acids or strong bases. Stabilization of the pH results from the presence of a weak acid and the salt of the weak acid in the solution.

CALORIE: The amount of heat required to raise the temperature of one milliliter of water by one degree centigrade. The "calorie" used to describe the energy content of food is actually a kilocalorie, which is 1000 calories.

CARBOHYDRATE: Carbohydrates are polyhydroxy aldehydes or ketones or condensation products thereof (Section 33–1).

CARBON BLACK: A powdery form of carbon produced by incomplete burning of natural gas (primarily methane, CH_4), used as a pigment and in the manufacture of automobile tires.

CARBOXYLATE SALT: The salt related to a carboxylic acid; for example, $RCOO^-Na^+$.

CARBOXYLIC ACID: An organic compound having a —COOH functional group. Such a compound is a weak acid compared to hydrochloric or sulfuric acid.

CARBOXYPEPTIDASE: A peptidase that catalyzes the hydrolysis of the peptide bond nearest the end of a peptide chain that contains the free carboxyl group.

CARCINOGEN: A substance that causes cancer.

CARDIOVASCULAR DISEASE: Any disease of the heart or blood vessels.

CARNIVORE: An animal whose major source of food is the flesh of other animals.

CATABOLIC: A word used to describe reactions in living systems that degrade or oxidize large molecules to smaller or more highly oxidized molecules. Such reactions result in the release of energy.

CATABOLISM: Those reactions in a plant or animal that result in the degradation or oxidation of molecules.

CATALYST: A substance which alters the rate of a chemical reaction without being consumed in the reaction.

CATHODE: The electrode at which electrons enter a solution; the electrode to which positive ions migrate.

CELLULOSE: A polysaccharide found in the structural parts of plants. It is composed of glucose units linked β 1–4.

CENTI-: A prefix denoting $\frac{1}{100}$ part.

CHARLES' LAW: The volume of a gas is directly proportional to the absolute temperature if the pressure remains constant.

CHEMICAL CHANGE: Changes in a substance which involve composition and often energy content.

CHEMICAL ENERGY: Energy released as a result of chemical change.

CHEMICAL PROPERTIES: Those properties which describe the composition and reactivity of substances, including energy changes and changes in composition.

CHEMISTRY: The science concerned with the composition of the substances of which the universe is composed, the properties of these substances, and the changes they undergo. It is also concerned with the energy relationships involved in the changes.

CHEMOTHERAPEUTIC AGENT: A chemical compound that is used to treat disease.

CHLOROPHYLL: The green pigment found in plants. It is necessary for photosynthesis.

CHROMATOGRAPHY: A process for separation of substances in a mixture by adsorption on paper or other materials. See Fig. 32–1 for illustrations of methods of chromatography.

CHROMOSOME: Long, threadlike bodies that can be seen at certain stages in the life of a cell. The chromosomes are made of DNA and protein and are the site of hereditary information in the cell.

CHYMOTRYPSIN: A proteolytic (protein-digesting) enzyme secreted by the pancreas.

CIRRHOSIS: The formation of abnormal amounts of connective tissue accompanied by the disappearance of the normal tissue of the liver or other organs.

CITRIC ACID CYCLE (Krebs cycle): A cyclic series of reactions by which acetic acid units are oxidized to carbon dioxide and water with the release of energy.

CLOUD CHAMBER: A device which makes visible the paths produced by high speed particles passing through a supersaturated atmosphere. The particles collide with a very large number of gaseous molecules producing ions. Moisture collects on these ions forming minute droplets resulting in visible "vapor trails" which are called fog tracks.

COENZYME: A nonprotein substance that is required for activity of an enzyme.

COKE: The solid residue, primarily carbon, produced by heating coal intensely in the absence of oxygen.

COLLOIDS: Particles of such small size that they may stay suspended in gases or in liquids for an indefinite period of time.

COMBUSTION: An exothermic reaction which proceeds so rapidly that flames or light are produced.

CONCENTRATED SOLUTION: A solution containing a relatively high proportion of solute.

CONFIGURATION: The arrangement in space of atoms within a molecule having a given structure.

CONTACT PROCESS: The most important method of preparing sulfuric acid. In the presence of a catalyst, such as platinum metal, sulfur dioxide reacts with oxygen forming sulfur trioxide. Sulfur trioxide reacts with water forming sulfuric acid.

COVALENT BOND: A pair of electrons shared between two atoms.

CRACKING REACTION: Decomposition of alkanes by heat energy, converting them to unsaturated hydrocarbons (Section 23–2); also called pyrolysis.

CRITICAL MASS: The least amount of fissionable material which can sustain a chain reaction.

CYCLO-, CYCLIC COMPOUND: A ring compound; for example, cyclopentane (Section 22–3).

CYCLOTRON: A device which accelerates electrically charged particles in a circular path to tremendous velocity and therefore to great energy. See also *linear accelerator*, another device for a similar purpose.

CYSTINURIA: An abnormality in which large amounts of cystine are excreted in the urine. This condition may lead to formation of stones of cystine in the urinary bladder.

CYTOCHROMES: A group of colored substances found in many cells. The cytochromes function in electron transport. See Fig. 37–9 for the structure of a cytochrome c.

DARK REACTION: A series of the reactions of photosynthesis which can proceed without light.

DEAMINATION: A process by which an amino group is removed from an organic compound. Deamination of an amino acid usually gives a keto-acid.

DECARBOXYLATION: The process of eliminating carbon dioxide from an organic molecule. Decarboxylation of an amino acid gives an amine.

DEFICIENCY DISEASE: A disease whose symptoms can be cured by administration of a specific element or compound. The most well-known deficiency diseases result from vitamin deficiencies.

DEHYDROGENATION: Reaction in which hydrogen atoms are removed from a molecule.

DELIQUESCENCE: The dissolving of solids in moisture absorbed from the air.

DENATURATION: A change in the properties of a protein. Denaturation is believed to involve only the secondary linkages of proteins, not hydrolysis of peptide bonds. Denaturation may be reversible, in which case the starting properties are restored, or irreversible so that the protein is permanently altered.

DENSITY: Mass per unit of volume; density may be expressed in a variety of units such as grams per milliliter or pounds per cubic foot.

DEOXYRIBONUCLEASE (DNA-ASE): An enzyme that catalyzes the hydrolysis of DNA.

DEOXYRIBONUCLEIC ACID (DNA): A nucleic acid that yields the pentose deoxyribose on hydrolysis. DNA is found primarily, but not exclusively, in the nuclei of cells and is a polymer of deoxynucleotides.

DEPOT LIPIDS: The lipids that an animal accumulates or stores. The amount of these lipids may vary greatly as opposed to the tissue lipids which always make up a certain percentage of a cell or an animal.

DETERGENT: An organic compound which has cleansing action in water. It has a large nonpolar hydrocarbon group and at least one ionic or highly polar group.

DEUTERIUM: The naturally occurring isotope of hydrogen having mass number 2. It may be found in water.

DIABETES MELLITUS: A disease characterized by a high level of glucose in the blood and excretion of glucose in the urine. It is caused by a lack of insulin.

DIENE: An unsaturated organic compound having two double bonds somewhere in the molecule; for example, butadiene, $CH_2\!\!=\!\!CH\!-\!CH\!\!=\!\!CH_2$.

DIFFUSION: The migration of molecules among other molecules. Diffusion takes place rapidly within gases and slowly within liquids.

DIGESTION: The process of converting ingested food to simpler forms that can be absorbed.

DILUTE SOLUTION: A solution containing a relatively small proportion of solute.

DIPEPTIDASE: An enzyme that catalyzes the hydrolysis of dipeptides.

DISACCHARIDASE: An enzyme that catalyzes the hydrolysis of a disaccharide to give two monosaccharide molecules. Important disaccharidases are sucrase, maltase, and lactase.

DISEASE: Any departure from health.

DRY ICE: Solid carbon dioxide is called dry ice since it sublimes, passing directly from a solid to a gas. Therefore, no liquid is formed by the warming of the solid CO_2 at atmospheric pressure.

DUCTILE: Capable of being drawn into elongated form; e.g., ductile metals can be drawn into a wire, and semimolten glass and plastic into rods.

EDEMA: A condition in which there is an excess of water in many tissues of the body.

EFFLORESCENCE: The loss of water from hydrates under natural circumstances; i.e., without placing the substances in artificially hot or dry places.

ELECTROLYTE: A substance (acid, base, or salt) which conducts an electric current in a water solution.

ELECTRON: A negatively charged subatomic particle with a mass 1/1837 that of a hydrogen atom.

ELECTRON SHELL (OR CLOUD): The concentric layers of electrons around the nucleus of an atom.

ELECTRONEGATIVITY: The tendency of an atom to attract electrons to itself. The electronegativity scale, devised by Dr. Linus Pauling, arranges the elements in a descending order of electronegativity.

ELECTROPHORESIS: A process in which components of solutions may be separated by being allowed to migrate in an electrical field. The process is used in the purification of proteins and other charged molecules.

ELECTROVALENT BOND (ionic bond): The bonding occurring in compounds formed by the transfer of electrons from one atom to another.

EMULSION: A finely divided suspension of two immiscible liquids.

ENANTIOMERS: Compounds whose configurations are nonidentical mirror images. They are optically active.

ENDERGONIC: A word used to describe an energy-requiring or energy-consuming reaction. Anabolic reactions are endergonic.

ENDOCRINE GLAND: A gland which secretes directly into the blood stream. The secretions of the endocrine glands are called hormones.

ENDOPEPTIDASE: A peptidase that catalyzes the hydrolysis of peptide bonds in the interior of a protein molecule.

ENDOTHERMIC REACTION: A chemical reaction in which heat is absorbed. (See also *endergonic*.)

ENERGY: The ability or capacity to do work.

ENERGY OF ACTIVATION: The amount of energy required to start a reaction.

ENZYME: A protein that catalyzes a biochemical reaction. Some enzymes also contain factors in addition to the protein.

EPITHELIAL: A word used to describe the cells and tissues on the surface and lining of the body. The skin and the lining of the digestive tract and of the lungs are made up of epithelial cells.

EQUILIBRIUM: A state of balance or equality between opposing forces; e.g., when opposing chemical reactions are proceeding at the same rate.

EQUIVALENT WEIGHT: A chemical unit which is the weight of an acid or base that can furnish one mole of H^+ or OH^- ions.

ESSENTIAL AMINO ACID: An amino acid that cannot be synthesized by an animal at a rate equal to his need for that amino acid.

ESSENTIAL NUTRIENT: A specific compound required by an animal which the animal cannot synthesize at a rate equal to his needs.

ESTER: An organic compound having a functional group of the type

$$-\overset{\displaystyle O}{\underset{\displaystyle \|}{C}}-O-R \quad \text{or} \quad -\overset{\displaystyle O}{\underset{\displaystyle \|}{C}}-O-Ar$$

It is derived from a carboxylic group linked to an alcohol or phenol.

ESTERIFICATION: The process of forming an ester group by direct reaction of a carboxylic acid with an alcohol.

ETHER: An organic oxygen compound of the type ROR or ROAr.

EXERGONIC: A word used to describe a reaction that converts potential or stored energy to heat or other forms of energy. Catabolic reactions are exergonic.

EXOPEPTIDASE: A peptidase that catalyzes the hydrolysis of peptide bonds adjacent to the end of a peptide chain.

EXOTHERMIC REACTION: A chemical reaction in which heat is released. (See also exergonic.)

FAD: Flavin adenine dinucleotide. A substance that serves as an electron acceptor and donor in biological oxidations and electron transport. See Fig. 37–8 for the structure of this compound.

FAT: A triglyceride that is solid at room temperature. (See *Triglyceride* and Sections 27–1, 35–3.)

FATTY ACID SPIRAL: The sequence of reactions by which a fatty acid is degraded into acetate units.

FERMENTATION: The anaerobic metabolism of carbohydrates. Fermentations are catalyzed by the enzymes of bacteria and yeasts, and may result in the formation of lactic acid or of carbon dioxide and ethanol.

FILAMENT (colloidal): A fibrous threadlike object with all dimensions except the length being of colloidal size.

FILM: A very thin layer of a liquid or solid. Films have one dimension of colloidal size.

FIXATION: The chemical conversion of a gaseous substance to a solid or liquid. Nitrogen is fixed by being incorporated into nitrates, nitrites, or ammonia. Although ammonia is a gas, it is extremely soluble in water, and is generally considered to be a fixed form of nitrogen.

FOG: A suspension or dispersion of tiny droplets of a liquid throughout a gas.

FOG TRACKS: The vapor trails produced by high speed particles when they pass through a super-saturated atmosphere.

FORMULA WEIGHT: The sum of the atomic weights of the atoms in a molecule.

FRASCH PROCESS: The method by which most of the sulfur produced in the United States is obtained. (See Section 18–6.)

FREE ENERGY: The energy available for doing useful work.

FREON: Any one of a number of compounds composed of carbon (one or two atoms), fluorine, and usually chlorine. They are used as refrigerants and as aerosol propellants.

FUNCTIONAL GROUP: A group of atoms (a unit of structure) within a molecule which reacts or functions. For example, the —NH_2 group in ethylamine, $CH_3CH_2NH_2$.

GALACTOSEMIA: The presence of galactose in appreciable amounts in the blood. A hereditary abnormality in which an individual cannot metabolize galactose.

GAMETE: A cell capable of participating in fertilization and formation of a new individual. Ova and sperm are gametes.

GAMMA GLOBULIN: A variety of globulin found in blood plasma. This fraction contains many antibodies against diseases.

GAMMA RAYS: Radiation similar to X-rays possessing great penetrating ability, produced by radioactive material.

GAY-LUSSAC'S LAW: In chemical reactions involving gases, the reacting volumes are always in the ratios of small whole numbers—one to one, one to two, etc.

GEL: A dispersion of a liquid within a solid.

GENE: The factor that influences the inheritance of a characteristic.

GENETIC CODE: The sequence of organic bases in a nucleotide that specifies an amino acid sequence in a protein molecule.

GLOBULIN: A protein that can be coagulated by heat, is soluble in a dilute salt solution but precipitates in solutions that are 50% saturated with ammonium sulfate. There are several different globulins in the blood, one of which, gamma globulin, contains antibodies to diseases.

GLUCAGON: A hormone of the pancreas that increases the level of glucose in the blood. See also *Insulin*.

GLUCOSURIA: The presence of glucose in the urine.

GLYCERIDE: An ester of glycerol.

GLYCOGEN: A polysaccharide found in the muscles and liver of animals. It is made of glucose units.

GLYCOLYSIS: The process of degradation of glycogen and other carbohydrates. If the process is anaerobic the end product is lactic acid. In the presence of oxygen, glycolysis yields pyruvic acid.

GRAHAM'S LAW: The rates of diffusion of two gases are inversely proportional to the square roots of their densities.

GRAM-ATOMIC WEIGHT: The atomic weight of an element expressed in grams, or the weight in grams of Avogadro's number (6.023×10^{23}) of atoms of the element.

GRAPHITE: A solid form of carbon composed of layers. Within each layer the carbon atoms are covalently bonded in hexagonal patterns. It is a soft, black, greasy-feeling substance which is often used as a lubricant.

GROUP (of the periodic table): The vertical columns of elements in the periodic table.

HABER PROCESS: The most commonly used synthetic method of nitrogen fixation.

HALF-LIFE: The time required for one-half of a given amount of radioactive material to disintegrate.

HALOGEN: Any one of the group of elements occurring in Group VIIA of the periodic table.

HARD WATER: Water containing minerals (usually calcium and magnesium ions) which interfere with the detergent action of soaps.

HEAT OF FUSION: The heat energy (calories) required to convert one gram of a solid to a liquid without a change in temperature of the substance being melted.

HEAT OF VAPORIZATION: The heat energy (calories) required to convert one gram of a liquid to vapor without a change in temperature of the substance which is being vaporized.

HEMOGLOBIN: The red-colored protein which reversibly binds oxygen in the red blood cells.

HETEROCYCLIC COMPOUND: A substance having a ring structure composed of carbon atoms and at least one different atom; for example, pyridine,

HETEROZYGOTE: An individual having unlike genes for any given characteristic.

HEXOSE: A monosaccharide containing six carbon atoms. Glucose, fructose, and galactose are important hexoses.

HOMOZYGOTE: An individual having identical genes for a given characteristic.

HORMONE: The product of an endocrine or ductless gland. Hormones are carried throughout the body by the blood stream.

HUMIDITY: Moisture content in the air.

HYDRATES: Compounds formed by the union of salts with water, for example, $CuSO_4 \cdot 5\ H_2O$. Water of hydration may be driven from such compounds by heating.

HYDRIDE: Any binary compound in which hydrogen is one of the elements. In one type, the metallic hydride, the valence of hydrogen is -1.

HYDROCARBON: A compound composed only of hydrogen and carbon.

HYDROGEN BOND: The special attraction that exists between molecules containing hydrogen bonded to oxygen, nitrogen, or fluorine. The attraction is due to the polar nature of such bonds. Water is an outstanding example. (Section 10–7)

HYDROGENATION: Addition of hydrogen to an unsaturated molecule.

HYDROLYSIS: The splitting (lysis) of a compound by a reaction with water. Examples are the reaction of salts with water to produce solutions which are not neutral (Section 13–5), and the reaction of an ester with water (Section 26–6).

HYDROXYL GROUP: The —OH functional group, covalently bonded, as in R—O—H. (*Not* the same as a hydrox*ide* ion, OH⁻.)

HYGROSCOPIC: Adjective describing a substance which absorbs moisture from the atmosphere.

HYPERGLYCEMIA: A higher than normal concentration of glucose in the blood.

HYPERTONIC SOLUTION: A solution with a salt concentration greater than that of blood.

HYPERVITAMINOSIS: A disease due to excessive intake of a vitamin.

HYPOGLYCEMIA: A lower than normal concentration of glucose in the blood.

IMMISCIBLE: Two liquids which will not dissolve in each other are said to be immiscible; e.g., water and oil.

INBORN ERROR OF METABOLISM: An inherited abnormality which results in failure to produce a normal protein. Many inborn errors of metabolism involve failure of reactions due to lack of the necessary enzyme.

INFECTION: The invasion of the body of a plant or animal by a microorganism.

INGESTION: The act of taking in. In simple animals it involves surrounding a food particle. In more complex animals we use the term eating to describe ingestion.

INHIBITOR: A substance that decreases the rate of an enzymatic reaction.

INORGANIC SUBSTANCES: All the elements and their compounds, except the compounds of carbon. (See *organic substances*.)

INSULIN: A hormone from the pancreas that promotes the utilization of glucose. Deficiencies of insulin result in hyperglycemia and the disease *diabetes mellitus*.

IN VITRO: Literally means "in glass." The term is used to describe reactions occurring in a reaction vessel as distinguished from those that occur *in vivo*, in the living animal.

IN VIVO: Literally means "in the living." The term is used to describe reactions that occur in a living animal.

IONIC BOND: See electrovalent bond.

IONS: Electrically charged atoms or groups of atoms. They may be positively or negatively charged, depending on whether the atoms from which they were formed lost or gained electrons.

ISOLATION ARTIFACT: A chemical compound or structure that does not occur as such in a living organism but is produced during the process of extraction and purification.

ISOMERS: Different compounds having the same molecular formula. For example, methyl ether, a gas, and ethyl alcohol, a liquid, each have formula C_2H_6O.

ISOTONIC SOLUTION: A solution with a salt concentration equal to that of blood.

ISOTOPES: Atoms of the same element containing different numbers of neutrons and therefore having different nuclear masses.

KETONE: A compound in which two organic groups are bonded to a carbonyl group:

$$R-\underset{\underset{O}{\|}}{C}-R', \quad Ar-\underset{\underset{O}{\|}}{C}-R, \text{ etc.}$$

Compare with *aldehyde*.

KETOSE: A carbohydrate that contains a ketone group. The best known ketose is fructose.

KILO-: A prefix meaning 1000, for example, a kilogram is 1000 grams.

KINDLING TEMPERATURE: The temperature at which combustible substances burst into flame as a result of combining with oxygen of the atmosphere.

KINETIC ENERGY: The energy resulting from motion.

KINETIC THEORY OF GASES: A series of statements describing the characteristic behavior of gases, based on the theory that molecules of gases are tiny, elastic bodies in constant motion.

KREBS CYCLE: See Citric Acid Cycle.

LANTHANIDES: The fourteen elements (formerly called the rare earth elements) which follow lanthanum; elements having atomic numbers 58 to 71. These elements have properties resembling those of lanthanum.

LECITHINASE: An enzyme that catalyzes the hydrolysis of a lecithin.

LIGHT REACTION: Those reactions of photosynthesis that stop when no light is present.

LINEAR ACCELERATOR: A device by which electrically charged particles are electrically accelerated in a straight line to tremendous velocities and therefore great energy. See also *cyclotron*, another accelerating device.

LIPASE: An enzyme that catalyzes the hydrolysis of a lipid. The most important lipases are those that catalyze the hydrolysis of glycerides to give glycerol and fatty acids.

LIPID: A constituent of a plant or animal that is soluble in nonpolar solvents. A variety of solvents, particularly diethyl ether, ethanol, and chloroform, are used to dissolve lipids.

LITER: The unit of volume employed in the metric system. It is the volume of one kilogram of water at 4°C.

LYMPH: A fluid similar to blood except that it contains no red blood cells. It is derived from the tissues of the body and conveyed to the bloodstream by the lymphatic vessels. It is important in absorption of lipids and in responses of animals to infections.

LYSOSOME: A small body or organelle found in cells. Lysosomes contain hydrolytic enzymes.

MALLEABLE: That which can be hammered into different shapes. Metals like gold, silver, copper, and iron are malleable.

MASS: The amount of matter in an object. Mass remains constant regardless of the location of the object or of the gravitational attraction.

MASS DEFECT: The term used to describe a condition in which the mass of an atom is less than the sum of the masses of the individual particles of which it is made.

MASS NUMBER: The sum of the numbers of protons and neutrons in the nucleus of an atom.

MASS-ENERGY RELATIONSHIP: Theory conceived by Einstein that matter can be converted into energy and vice versa. (This necessitated a slight revision in older versions of the law which stated that neither matter nor energy could be created or destroyed.)

MATTER: That which has mass, inertia, and occupies space.

MEIOSIS: The process of cell division in which daughter cells contain half as many chromosomes as the parent cell. Meiosis is important in the formation of gametes (ova and sperm).

MESSENGER (template) RNA: A relatively high molecular weight RNA that carries information from DNA of the chromosomes in the nucleus of the cell to the ribosomes where protein is synthesized.

METABOLIC (degenerative) DISEASE: A noninfectious disease which results from the change in some aspect of metabolism. The causes and cures for most of these diseases are not well understood.

METABOLIC WATER: Water that is produced as the result of reactions within an animal, specifically from the oxidation of hydrogen occurring in foods.

METABOLISM: A word used to describe the total of all reactions that occur in plants and animals.

METABOLITE: Any chemical substance that participates either as a reactant or product in a reaction in a plant or an animal.

METALLOID: An element possessing some of the characteristic properties of both metals and nonmetals.

METALLURGY: The art or science of separating metals from their ores and preparing them for use.

METER: The basic unit of length in the metric system, equivalent to approximately 39.37 in.

MICRON: One thousandth of a millimeter; a unit of linear measure.

MICROSOMES: Small bodies separated from broken cells by centrifugation. Microsomes are probably ribosomes plus some of the materials that tie ribosomes together.

MILLI-: One-thousandth part, i.e., a millimeter is one-thousandth of a meter.

MILLI-EQUIVALENT: One-thousandth of an equivalent; the amount of acid or base in one milliliter of a 1 Normal solution of an acid or base.

MINERAL ELEMENT: In biochemistry, any chemical element other than C, H, O, N, and S. That is, the elements not commonly found in carbohydrates, proteins, and lipids are called the mineral elements.

MISCIBLE: A term used to describe liquids that will dissolve partially or completely in each other; e.g., water and alcohol.

MITOCHONDRION: A subcellular particle or organelle. Mitochondria are the site of much of the energy production and storage capacity of the cells. (See Section 32–4.)

MITOSIS: The process of cell division in which both daughter cells have the same number of chromosomes as the parent cell.

MIXED GLYCERIDE: An ester of glycerol in which the three fatty acids are not the same.

MOLAR SOLUTION: A solution containing one mole of solute in one liter of solution.

MOLARITY: The strength of a solution expressed in moles per liter; usually abbreviated M.

MOLE: The weight in grams of Avogadro's number (6.023×10^{23}) of particles (ions, atoms, or molecules) of a substance.

MOLE VOLUME OF GASES: The volume (22.4 liters) of a molecular weight in grams (one mole) of any gas at standard conditions.

MOLECULAR FORMULA: A formula which states the kind and number of all atoms in a molecule.

MOLECULAR WEIGHT: The sum of the atomic weights of the atoms in a molecule; when expressed in grams it is the equivalent of a mole.

MUTATION: An abrupt change in an inheritable characteristic.

NAD: nicotinamide adenine dinucleotide. A substance that serves as an electron acceptor and donor in biological oxidations. (See Fig. 36–13 for the formula of this compound.)

NEUTRON: A neutral subatomic particle with a mass approximately that of a hydrogen atom. Neutrons account for one-half or more of the mass of all atoms except hydrogen.

NITRATION: Substitution of a nitro group, $—NO_2$, onto a molecule (Section 24–6).

NITROGEN FIXATION: The combining of elementary nitrogen with other elements to form usable compounds.

NOBLE GASES (also called RARE GASES): The six elements usually located at the extreme right in the periodic table. Since their valence shells are complete, they are relatively inert. (They were formerly called the inert gases.)

NORMAL SOLUTION: A solution containing one equivalent weight (in grams) of acid or base per liter of solution.

NUCLEAR FISSION: The transmutation in which an atom is converted into smaller atoms. Such reactions are accompanied by an enormous liberation of energy.

NUCLEAR FUSION: The transmutation occurring naturally in the sun, or synthetically in a hydrogen bomb, in which small atoms combine to form larger atoms. Such reactions liberate greater amounts of energy than do comparable fission reactions.

NUCLEAR REACTOR: The term commonly applied to the device which is used to control the rate of nuclear reactions and to produce useful nuclear power.

NUCLEIC ACID: A high-molecular-weight substance from natural sources which, on hydrolysis, yields organic bases, pentoses, and phosphate. Although originally found in the nuclei of cells, it is present throughout the cell.

NUCLEOPROTEIN: A combination of a nucleic acid and a protein. The proteins in such combinations contain many basic amino acids. The bonds between the acidic nucleic acids and basic proteins are saltlike and relatively weak.

NUCLEOSIDASE: An enzyme that catalyzes the hydrolysis of nucleosides to yield an organic base and a pentose.

NUCLEOSIDE: A compound which, on hydrolysis, yields one molecule of an organic base and a pentose.

NUCLEOTIDASE: An enzyme that catalyzes the hydrolysis of nucleotides to give nucleosides and phosphate.

NUCLEOTIDE: A compound which, on hydrolysis, yields one molecule of an organic base, a pentose, and a phosphate group.

NUTRIENT: A chemical substance that provides either energy or a necessary component of an animal.

NUTRITION: The science that is concerned with foods and their effect on organisms, particularly on humans.

OIL: In biochemistry, a triglyceride that is a liquid at room temperature.

OLEFIN: The old common name for an alkene.

OLIGOSACCHARIDE: A molecule containing from two to ten monosaccharide units. The most important oligosaccharides are the disaccharides.

OPEN-HEARTH FURNACE: The process by which most of today's high-grade steel is produced. This process makes possible the reuse of large amounts of scrap iron and steel.

OPTICAL ACTIVITY: The ability to rotate the plane of vibration of polarized light.

ORGANIC SUBSTANCES: The compounds of carbon. They may be produced synthetically or by living organisms.

OSMOSIS: The selective passage of liquids through a semipermeable membrane in a direction which tends to make concentrations of all substances on one side of the membrane equal to those on the other side.

OXIDATION STATE: A term used to indicate the valence of an atom in a compound. For example, the oxidation state of chromium in Cr_2O_3 is (3+), and of sulfur in SO_3 is (6+).

OZONE: An allotropic form of oxygen with a molecular formula of O_3.

PENTOSE: A monosaccharide containing five carbon atoms. Ribose, arabinose, and xylose are pentoses.

PEPSIN: A gastric enzyme that catalyzes the hydrolysis of peptide bonds of proteins. It is an endo-peptidase.

PEPTIDASE: Any enzyme that catalyzes the hydrolysis of the peptide linkage between amino acids.

PEPTIDE: A compound formed by a combination of the amino group of one amino acid with the acid group of another. Peptide is also used to describe the linkage between the two amino acids.

PEPTIDE BOND: A group containing the carbonyl group from one amino acid and the N—H from another, for example:

$$-\overset{\overset{\displaystyle O}{\|}}{C}-\overset{\overset{\displaystyle H}{|}}{N}-.$$

This linkage is found between the amino acid units in a protein.

PERIODIC LAW: A law which states that when the elements are arranged in the order of their increasing atomic numbers, they exhibit a periodic recurrence of properties.

PERIODIC TABLE: An arrangement of the chemical elements in table form to show the periodic recurrence of properties. See also *periodic law*.

PERIODS: The horizontal rows of elements in the periodic table.

PH: A number denoting the hydrogen ion concentration in a solution.

PHAGOCYTE: A cell of the body that can engulf foreign material.

PHENOL: An organic compound having an —OH functional group on an aryl skeleton, ArOH. (The term is also used for the simplest compound of this class, C_6H_5OH. See Section 25–6.)

PHENYL GROUP: The structural unit C_6H_5— or —

PHOSPHOGLUCONATE SHUNT: A series of reactions that provides for release of energy from glucose in fewer reactions than in glycolysis. This series of reactions also may result in the synthesis of ribose.

PHOSPHOLIPID: A lipid that contains a phosphate group. The most abundant phospholipids are derivatives of phosphatidic acid in which the phosphate is esterified with one of the —OH groups of glycerol.

PHOSPHORYLASE: An enzyme that catalyzes the addition of a phosphate group to a molecule. The phosphate group comes from ATP. It is better to call such enzymes phosphotransferases.

PHOSPHORYLATION: The addition of a phosphate group to a molecule. In many phosphorylation reactions phosphoric acid functions as water does in hydrolysis; such a reaction is called a phosphorolysis.

PHOTOLYSIS (of water): The lysis of water to give oxygen and hydrogen under the influence of light. This process is the source of the free oxygen formed in photosynthesis.

PHOTOSYNTHESIS: The process in which the energy of light is stored in chemical compounds of a plant.

PHYSICAL CHANGE: Changes in physical state or of shape with no change in composition. Change of ice to water and water to steam are physical changes.

PHYSICAL PROPERTIES: Those properties of a substance (solubility, boiling point, freezing point, etc.) that can be measured without changing the composition of a substance.

PIG IRON: The impure iron containing carbon, silicon, and sulfur which comes from the blast furnace. It is much too hard and brittle to be of much value until most of these impurities are removed.

POLAR COVALENT BOND: A covalent bond is polar when it is formed between two atoms having a considerable difference in electronegativity. In such a bond, the pair of shared electrons is shifted toward the more negative atom.

POLARIZED LIGHT: Light that has only one plane of vibration. (See Section 31–5.)

POLYMER: A very large molecule built up when many ordinary size molecules are joined by covalent bonds. (See Section 30–2.)

POLYPEPTIDE: A substance containing many amino acids linked by peptide bonds. Polypeptides contain fewer amino acid units than do the proteins.

POLYPROTIC ACID: A term indicating the compound has more than one potential acidic hydrogen; for example, H_3PO_4.

POLYSACCHARIDE: A polymer of monosaccharide units. Prominent members of this group are the starches, cellulose, and glycogen.

POTENTIAL ENERGY: The energy a body possesses by virtue of its position. Also the stored energy present in fuels and foods.

PRE-PEPSIN (PEPSINOGEN): The inactive precursor of the enzyme pepsin.

PRIMATE: A classification of animals that includes man, apes, and monkeys.

PRIMER DNA: A molecule of DNA that must be present in a system capable of synthesizing DNA before the synthesis can start. The kind of DNA synthesized resembles the primer DNA.

PROTEIN: A high-molecular-weight substance which, on hydrolysis, yields amino acids. A polymer of amino acids.

PROTEOLYTIC: A word used to describe those enzymes that catalyze the breakdown of proteins.

PROTIUM: The most common isotope of hydrogen. Its mass number is 1.

PROTON: A hydrogen ion. The nucleus of a hydrogen atom. A positively charged subatomic particle with a mass approximating that of a neutron.

PROTOZOAN: A member of a class of single-celled animals.

PURINE BASES: Important components of nucleic acids related to purine,

PYRIMIDINE BASES: Important component of nucleic acids related to the organic base pyrimidine,

QUATERNARY AMMONIUM SALT: An ammonium salt having four organic groups (the same or different); for example, $R_4N^+Cl^-$.

RADIOACTIVE ISOTOPE: An isotope of an element so unstable that it decomposes to give α, β, γ or other radiations.

RADIOACTIVITY: The name suggested by Madame Curie for the disintegration of atomic nuclei in which α, β, or γ radiation occurs.

RELATIVE HUMIDITY: The ratio of the amount of water vapor in the atmosphere to the amount necessary for saturation at the same temperature. Relative humidity is expressed in terms of percent.

RIBONUCLEASE (RNA-ASE): An enzyme that catalyzes the hydrolysis of RNA.

RIBONUCLEIC ACID (RNA): A polymer composed of nucleotides which contain ribose. Three types of RNA are important in protein synthesis: messenger RNA, ribosomal RNA, and soluble (transfer) RNA. Many viruses contain RNA and protein.

RIBOSOMAL RNA: The RNA found in ribosomes.

RIBOSOME: A small spherical body or organelle found in cells. The ribosomes are an important site of protein synthesis in a cell. (See Section 32–4.)

SALIVA: The fluid secreted in the mouth by the salivary glands. It contains complex polysaccharides and the enzyme amylase.

SALT: A compound composed of the positive ion from a base and the negative ion from an acid; i.e., a metal ion and a nonmetal ion, such as KBr.

SALTING OUT: The precipitation of a protein by addition of a salt, usually as a salt solution.

SAPONIFICATION: The reaction of an ester with a metallic hydroxide (or certain other bases) to produce a carboxylate salt and an alcohol. The name originates from the fact that when a fat undergoes such a reaction, the salt formed is soap. (See Sections 26–6 and 27–5.)

SATURATED HYDROCARBON: A carbon compound in which all carbon bonds, other than those required to hold the skeleton together, are occupied by hydrogen atoms.

SATURATED SOLUTION: A solution in which the undissolved solute and the dissolved solute are in equilibrium. No greater amount of solute can be dissolved at the existing conditions.

SMOKE: A suspension of solid particles in a gas.

SOAP: An alkali metal carboxylate salt having a total of twelve to about eighteen carbon atoms; for example, $C_{17}H_{35}COONa$.

SOLUBLE (transfer) RNA: A relatively low-molecular-weight RNA that attaches to an amino acid during the process of protein synthesis. Transfer RNA is believed to match with a specific part of messenger RNA known as the code. Following this, the amino acid is added to the growing peptide chain of the protein being synthesized.

SOLUTE: A dissolved substance. In solutions composed of a solid and a liquid, the solid is the solute. In solutions composed of two liquids, the one present in the lesser proportion is considered to be the solute.

SOLUTION: A homogeneous mixture of molecules, atoms, or ions of two or more substances.

SOLVENT: The dissolving substance. In a solution composed of a solid and a liquid, the liquid is considered to be the solvent. In a solution composed of two liquids, the one present in the greater proportion is considered to be the solvent. Water is the most common solvent since it is so abundant and so many substances are soluble in it.

SPECIFIC DYNAMIC ACTION: The increased heat production which accompanies digestion. It is especially noticeable during digestion of proteins.

SPECIFIC GRAVITY: The ratio of the density of a substance to the density of water.

SPECIFIC HEAT: The heat energy required to raise the temperature of one gram of a substance one degree centigrade.

SPECTATOR IONS: The ions that are partners of the reacting ions. They remain as ions after a chemical reaction. In the equation

$$Na^+ + Cl^- + Ag^+ + NO_3^- \rightarrow AgCl \downarrow + Na^+ + NO_3^-,$$

the sodium and nitrate ions are spectator ions.

SPONTANEOUS COMBUSTION: An exothermic reaction that proceeds so rapidly that the kindling temperature is reached and the material is self-ignited.

STANDARD CONDITIONS (gases): Often abbreviated as S.T.P. meaning Standard Temperature and Pressure. Since the volume occupied by a sample of a gas is dependent upon its temperature and the pressure exerted upon it, some standards for measurement are necessary. Zero degrees centigrade and a pressure of 760 mm of mercury have therefore been adopted as standard conditions.

STARCH: The polysaccharide found in seeds, roots, and tubers of plants. It is composed of glucose units linked α 1–4 with some α 1–6 branches.

STEEL: Iron, alloyed with varying quantities, usually smaller amounts, of other metals or nonmetals.

STEROID: A compound containing a complex hydrocarbon nucleus. See Section 35–2 for a diagram of this nucleus. Among the important compounds having a steroid skeleton are bile acids, sex hormones, and adrenal hormones.

STRUCTURAL FORMULA: Way of writing the structure of a molecule to show which atoms are bonded to which other atoms and the types of bonds used.

SUBCUTANEOUS: Below the skin.

SUBLIMATION (SUBLIME): The transition from the solid to the gaseous state without passing through the liquid state. The reverse process is also sometimes referred to as sublimation.

SUBSTITUTION REACTION: A reaction in which certain covalently bonded atoms of a compound are displaced by different atoms.

SUBSTRATE: The substance on which an enzyme acts.

SUGAR: A sweet-tasting monosaccharide or disaccharide.

SULFONATION: Substitution of a sulfonic acid group, —SO_2OH, onto a molecule (Section 24–5).

SUPERSATURATED SOLUTION: A solution that is holding more solute than it can normally dissolve at existing conditions.

TEFLON: A plastic material composed of carbon and fluorine. In terms of chemical structure it is a polymer.

TEMPLATE RNA: See messenger RNA.

TERNARY ACID: An acid composed of three different elements, the third element usually being oxygen; for example, H_2SO_4.

TERPENE: An oily substance having a distinct odor. A terpene has the formula $C_{10}H_{16}$ and is derived from plants. It is composed of isoprene units.

TETRAHEDRAL: Four-sided. A term used to describe the regular arrangement of four covalent bonds at a carbon atom (Section 21–6).

THERAPY: The treatment of disease.

TISSUE LIPIDS: Lipids that play an important role in the functioning of a cell and are found in all cells. The amount of tissue lipids in an animal does not vary appreciably as do the depot lipids.

TITRATION: The process of reacting a solution of unknown strength with one of known strength. This procedure is commonly used with solutions of acids and bases.

TRANSAMINATION: A reaction in which an amino group is transferred from an amino acid to a keto acid. This results in the synthesis of a new amino acid and the conversion of the original amino acid to a keto acid.

TRANSFER RNA: See *soluble RNA*.

TRIGLYCERIDE: An ester in which all three oxygens of glycerol have been esterified by carboxylic acids. Sometimes called more briefly a glyceride.

TRITIUM: The heaviest isotope of hydrogen. It is produced in nuclear reactors; its mass number is 3.

TRYPSIN: A proteolytic enzyme secreted by the pancreas.

TYNDALL EFFECT: The visible path produced by a beam of light passing through a liquid or gas in which colloidal particles are suspended.

UNSATURATED: A term used to describe an organic compound having double or triple bonds between some atoms. The most common examples are C=C, C≡C, C=O, C=N, and C≡N. These unsaturated units of structure can be saturated by addition of hyrogen.

UNSATURATED HYDROCARBON: A carbon compound having one or more double or triple bonds, so that not all bonds are occupied by hydrogens. (Compare with *saturated hydrocarbon*.)

VALENCE: A term used to indicate the combining ability of an element. Valence may be measured in terms of the number of electrons lost or gained by an atom or group of atoms, or by the numbers of pairs of electrons shared.

VIRUS: One type of agent that causes diseases in both plants and animals. Viruses contain large amounts of nucleic acids and protein. Viruses are generally smaller than bacteria and were originally distinguished from them because viruses could pass through filters.

VITAMIN: An organic compound required in small amounts in the diet of an animal. A vitamin must be defined in terms of a given type of animal. Ascorbic acid is needed by all animals, but is synthesized by most animals and thus is not a vitamin for them. Ascorbic acid is a vitamin (vitamin C) for humans, other primates, and the guinea pig, since these animals do not synthesize it.

WAX: An ester of a fatty acid and a long-chain, monohydric alcohol. (See Section 26–9E.)

WEIGHT: Commonly used to indicate an amount or mass of material. Actually, weight is dependent upon the gravitational attraction between bodies, and therefore is not constant, as is mass.

ZEOLITE: A silicate mineral used in water softeners.

ZYMOGEN: The inactive precursor of an enzyme. Pre-pepsin is the zymogen of pepsin.

ANSWERS TO SELECTED WORK EXERCISES

Chapter 1:

none

Chapter 2:

1. a) 2550 cm c) 500 mm e) 2.5 km g) 16,000 m i) 75 cm
3. 880 lb
5. 909 kg
7. 80 km/h
8. a) 37.7°C c) 14°F e) −17.8°C
9. 13.55 g/ml
11. 19.3 g/ml
13. 0.71, 0.71 g/ml
15. 0.915
17. 240 g

Chapter 3:

none

Chapter 4:

3. $\mathbf{CaCl_2}$
4. $\mathbf{KNO_3}$

Chapter 5:

none

Chapter 6:

none

Chapter 7:

1. a) $C + O_2 \rightarrow CO_2$ c) $2K + S \rightarrow K_2S$
   e) $CaO + CO_2 \rightarrow CaCO_3$ g) $H_2O + SO_2 \rightarrow H_2SO_3$
2. a) $2HgO \xrightarrow[\Delta]{} 2Hg + O_2\uparrow$ c) $NH_4OH \rightarrow NH_3 + H_2O$
   e) $Na_2CO_3 \xrightarrow[\Delta]{} Na_2O + CO_2\uparrow$ g) $H_2SO_3 \rightarrow H_2O + SO_2\uparrow$

3. a) $KCl + AgNO_3 \rightarrow KNO_3 + AgCl \downarrow$ c) $3NaOH + FeCl_3 \rightarrow Fe(OH)_3 \downarrow + 3NaCl$
   e) $2NH_4Cl + Ca(OH)_2 \xrightarrow{\Delta} CaCl_2 + 2NH_3 \uparrow + 2H_2O$
   g) $CuO + 2HCl \rightarrow CuCl_2 + H_2O$ i) $2KOH + H_2SO_4 \rightarrow K_2SO_4 + 2H_2O$

4. a) $Zn + S \xrightarrow{\Delta} ZnS$ c) $Zn + CuSO_4 \rightarrow Cu \downarrow + ZnSO_4$
   e) $3Ca(OH)_2 + 2H_3PO_4 \rightarrow Ca_3(PO_4)_2 + 6H_2O$ g) $2K + Cl_2 \rightarrow 2KCl$
   i) $CuCO_3 \xrightarrow{\Delta} CuO + CO_2 \uparrow$

5. a) 25.5 g   c) 3 moles   6. a) 22 g   c) 2 moles
7. 80 g   9. 9 g

Chapter 8:

Chapter 9:

10. 163.5 g   11. 294 g
14. a) $Zn + 2HCl \rightarrow ZnCl_2 + H_2 \uparrow$ c) $Ca + 2H_2O \rightarrow Ca(OH)_2 + H_2 \uparrow$
    e) $Cu + FeCl_2 \rightarrow$ no reaction   g) $Zn + Pb(NO_3)_2 \rightarrow Zn(NO_3)_2 + Pb \downarrow$
    i) $H_2O + C \xrightarrow{\Delta} CO + H_2$

Chapter 10:

7. a) $2Na + 2H_2O \rightarrow 2NaOH + H_2 \uparrow$ c) $H_2O + CO_2 \rightarrow H_2CO_3$
   e) $H_2O + K_2O \rightarrow 2KOH$ g) $CuSO_4 \cdot 5H_2O \xrightarrow{\Delta} CuSO_4 + 5H_2O$
10. a) $Ca(HCO_3)_2 \xrightarrow{\Delta} CaCO_3 + H_2O + CO_2 \uparrow$ c) $3MgSO_4 + 2Na_3PO_4 \rightarrow Mg_3(PO_4)_2 + 3Na_2SO_4$
    e) $Ca^{2+} + zeolite \cdot 2Na^+ \rightarrow zeolite \cdot Ca + 2Na^+$

Chapter 11:

6. a) 20.0 g   c) 2.5 g   e) 500.0 g   7. a) 160.0 g   c) 292.5 g   e) 1.825 g
8. a) 1.5 M c) 0.10 M e) 0.05 M

Chapter 12:

4. a) $H_2SO_4 + 2NaOH \rightarrow Na_2SO_4 + 2H_2O$ c) $HClO_3 + NaOH \rightarrow NaClO_3 + H_2O$
   e) $H_2SO_3 + 2NaOH \rightarrow Na_2SO_3 + 2H_2O$ g) $HClO + NaOH \rightarrow NaClO + H_2O$
5. a) hydrogen ions, sulfate ions   c) hydrogen ions, chlorate ions
   e) hydrogen ions, sulfite ions   g) hydrogen ions, hypochlorite ions
9. 12–43 potassium sulfate   12–45 ammonium sulfate   12–47 calcium nitrate
   12–49 sodium carbonate   12–51 calcium sulfate
15. a) 40 g   c) 49 g   e) 14.8 g   16. a) 0.25N   c) 1.N   e) 0.5N
17. 0.5N   19. a) 0.4N   c) 0.06N

Chapter 13:

Chapter 14:

Chapter 15:

3. 47.5 mm or 1.88 in.

Chapter 16:

1. $98.6°F = 37°C = 310°K$ 3. −40°F   5. 270.3 ml
7. 500 liters   9. 141.3 ml   11. 133,500 cu ft
13. 2.59 g/liter   15. a) 880 ml   b) 38.09 = mol wt   17. 9 liters

Chapter 17:

9. a) $H_2 + Cl_2 \rightarrow 2HCl$
   e) $2KCl + F_2 \rightarrow 2KF + Cl_2$

   c) $KBr + I_2 \rightarrow$ **no reaction**
   g) $NaF + Cl_2 \rightarrow$ **no reaction**

Chapter 18:

6. 5,866 lb

13. a) $Na_2B_4O_7 + Mg^{2+} \rightarrow MgB_4O_7 + 2Na^+$
   e) $P_2O_5 + 3H_2O \rightarrow 2H_3PO_4$

   c) $C_3H_8 + 5O_2 \rightarrow 3CO_2 + 4H_2O$

Chapter 19:

8. a) $Zn + 2HCl \rightarrow ZnCl_2 + H_2 \uparrow$
   e) $Zn + S \xrightarrow{\Delta} ZnS$
   i) $CaCO_3 \xrightarrow{\Delta} CaO + CO_2 \uparrow$

   c) $Cu + HCl \rightarrow$ **no reaction**
   g) $2ZnS + 3O_2 \xrightarrow{\Delta} 2ZnO + 2SO_2 \uparrow$

Chapter 20:

Chapter 21:

3. a) four   c) seven

Chapter 22:

1. a) 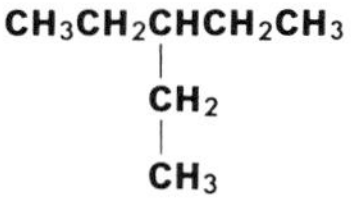 $CH_3CH_2CHCH_2CH_3$
           | CH_2
           | CH_3

c) 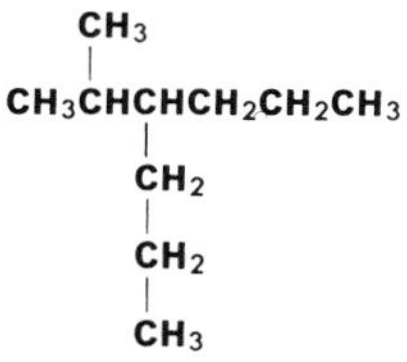 CH_3
   | $CH_3CHCHCH_2CH_2CH_3$
          | CH_2
          | CH_2
          | CH_3

e) 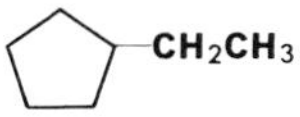 $-CH_2CH_3$

g) 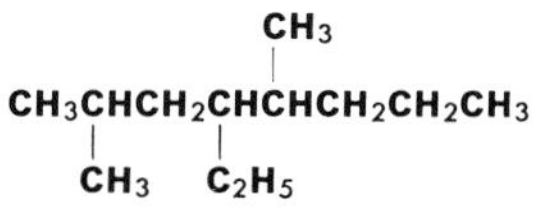 CH_3
            | $CH_3CHCH_2CHCHCH_2CH_2CH_3$
         | |
        CH_3 C_2H_5

i) 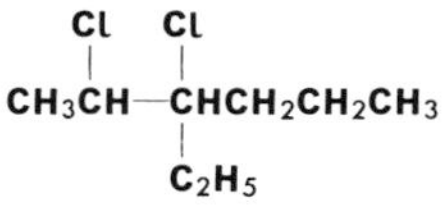   Cl   Cl
     | |
 $CH_3CH-CHCH_2CH_2CH_3$
         | C_2H_5

2. and 3.

  a) $CH_3CH_2CH_2CH_2CH_2CH_3$ hexane

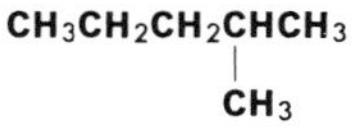

    $CH_3CH_2CH_2CHCH_3$ 2-methylpentane
              | CH_3

    $CH_3CH_2CHCH_2CH_3$ 3-methylpentane
            | CH_3

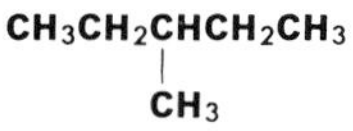

          CH_3
           |
    $CH_3CH_2-C-CH_3$ 2,2-dimethylbutane 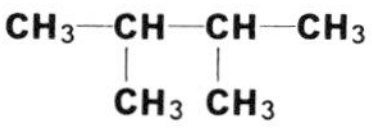
           |
          CH_3

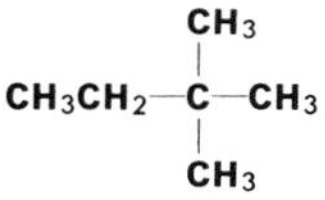

    $CH_3-CH-CH-CH_3$ 2,3-dimethylbutane
         | |
       CH_3 CH_3

c) 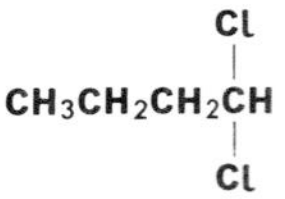 CH₃CH₂CH₂CH, with Cl above and Cl below   1,1-dichlorobutane

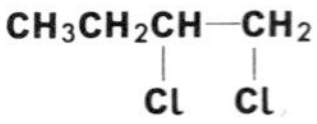

CH₃CH₂CH—CH₂ with Cl, Cl below   1,2-dichlorobutane

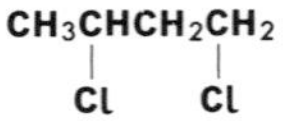

CH₃CHCH₂CH₂ with Cl, Cl below   1,3-dichlorobutane

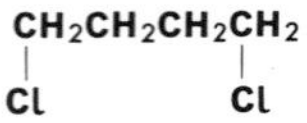

CH₂CH₂CH₂CH₂ with Cl, Cl below   1,4-dichlorobutane

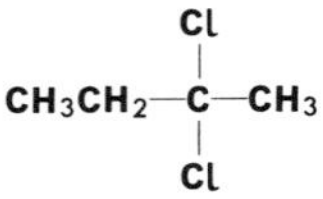

CH₃CH₂—C—CH₃ with Cl above and Cl below   2,2-dichlorobutane

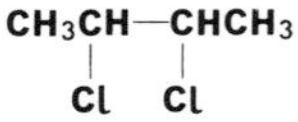

CH₃CH—CHCH₃ with Cl, Cl below   2,3-dichlorobutane

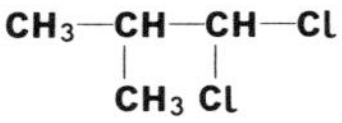

CH₃—CH—CH—Cl with CH₃, Cl below   1,1-dichloro-2-methylpropane

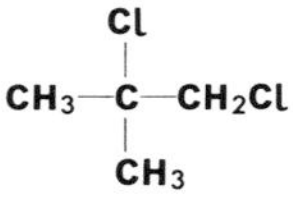

CH₃—C—CH₂Cl with Cl above and CH₃ below   1,2-dichloro-2-methylpropane

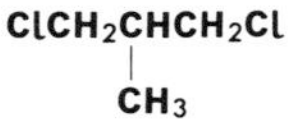

ClCH₂CHCH₂Cl with CH₃ below   1,3-dichloro-2-methylpropane

4. a) 2-methylpentane   c) 2-chloro-4-ethylhexane   e) cyclopentane
   g) methylcyclopentane   i) 6-ethyl-2,3,5-trimethyloctane
5. a) chloroform: trichloromethane   c) isobutane; methylpropane
   e) methyl bromide; bromomethane
6. a) CH₃CH₂CH₃ + 5O₂ → 3CO₂ + 4H₂O
   c) CH₄ + Cl₂ → CH₃Cl + HCl
      CH₃Cl + Cl₂ → CH₂Cl₂ + HCl
      CH₂Cl₂ + Cl₂ → CHCl₃ + HCl
      CHCl₃ + Cl₂ → CCl₄ + HCl
   g) no reaction
   i) CH₂Cl₂ + Br₂ → CHCl₂Br + HBr
      CHCl₂Br₂ + Br₂ → CCl₂Br₂ + HBr

e) (pentagon) + Cl₂ → (pentagon)—Cl + HCl

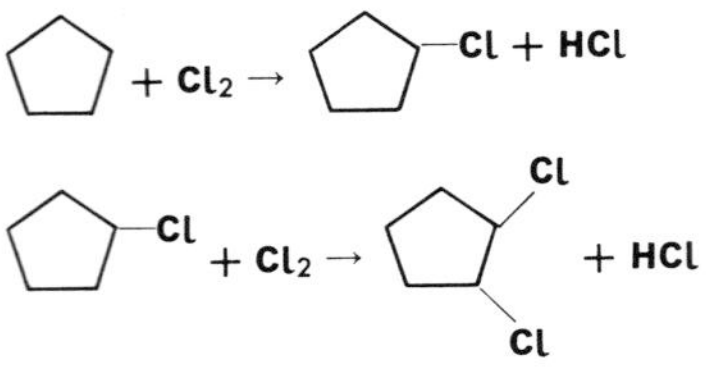

   (pentagon)—Cl + Cl₂ → (pentagon with Cl, Cl) + HCl

   and so forth

CHAPTER 23:

1. c) 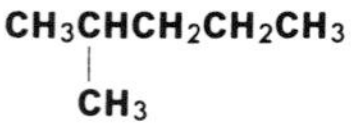 CH₃CHCH₂CH₂CH₃ with CH₃ below   C₆H₁₄

   CH₃—C═C—CH₃ with CH₃ above and CH₃ below   C₆H₁₂

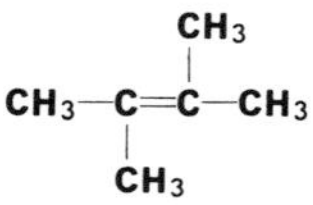

   (pentagon)—CH₃   C₆H₁₂

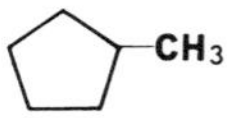

3. a) $CH_3CH_2CH=CH_2$

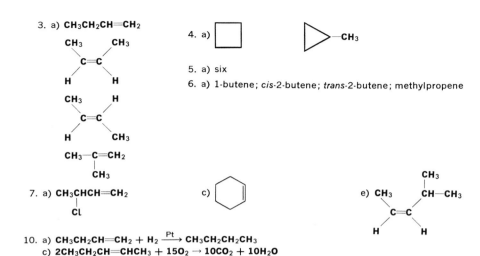

4. a)

5. a) six

6. a) 1-butene; *cis*-2-butene; *trans*-2-butene; methylpropene

7. a) $CH_3CHCH=CH_2$
      |
      Cl

c)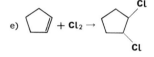

e) CH_3 $\overset{\displaystyle CH_3}{\underset{\displaystyle}{\overset{|}{CH}}}-CH_3$
   $\underset{\displaystyle H}{\overset{|}{C}}=\underset{\displaystyle H}{\overset{|}{C}}$

10. a) $CH_3CH_2CH=CH_2 + H_2 \xrightarrow{Pt} CH_3CH_2CH_2CH_3$

    c) $2CH_3CH_2CH=CHCH_3 + 15O_2 \rightarrow 10CO_2 + 10H_2O$

e)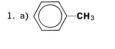

g) 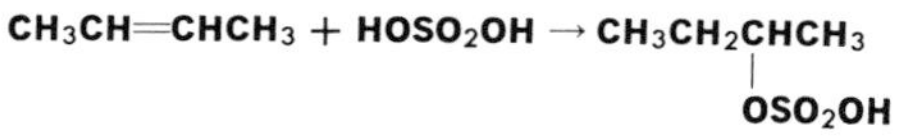 $CH_3CH=CHCH_3 + HOSO_2OH \rightarrow CH_3CH_2CHCH_3$
                                              |
                                           OSO_2OH

i) 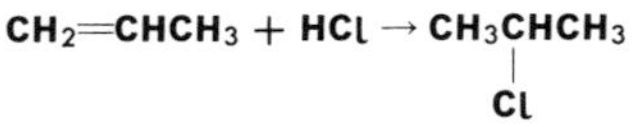 $CH_2=CHCH_3 + HCl \rightarrow CH_3CHCH_3$
                                      |
                                     Cl

k) 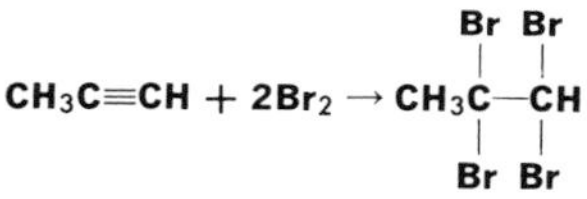 $CH_3C\equiv CH + 2Br_2 \rightarrow CH_3\underset{\displaystyle Br}{\overset{\displaystyle Br}{\underset{|}{\overset{|}{C}}}}-\underset{\displaystyle Br}{\overset{\displaystyle Br}{\underset{|}{\overset{|}{CH}}}}$

m) $CH_3C\equiv CH + 4O_2 \rightarrow 3CO_2 + 2H_2O$

11. a) yes   c) no   e) yes   g) yes

13. a) petroleum

   b) $CH_3CH_3 + Cl_2 \xrightarrow{UV} CH_3CH_2Cl + Cl_2$

   c) $CH_3CH_3 \xrightarrow{500°C} CH_2=CH_2 + H_2$
      $CH_2=CH_2 + HCl \rightarrow CH_3CH_2Cl$

   d) Method (c) gives only the desired product. Method (b) gives many other compounds, besides the desired product: dichloroethanes, trichloroethanes, etc. This result means that only a small amount of chloroethane is obtained, and it must be separated from all the other substances.

Chapter 24:

1. a) $-CH_3$ c) 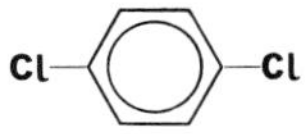 $Cl-$⬡$-Cl$ e) ⬡$-NO_2$ (with Br)   g) ⬡$-SO_3Na$

2. a) 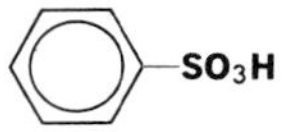 ⬡$-SO_3H$ benzenesulfonic acid   c) 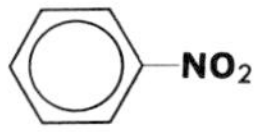 ⬡$-NO_2$ nitrobenzene

   e) no reaction

3. a) $-COOH$ c) 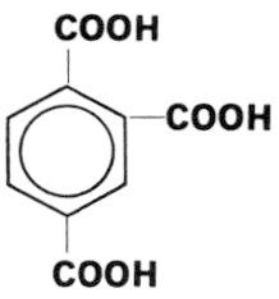 benzene with COOH, COOH, COOH

Chapter 25:

1. and 3.

$CH_3CH_2CH_2CH_2OH$ primary

$CH_3CH_2CHCH_3$ secondary
       |
      OH

CH_3CHCH_2OH primary
   |
   CH_3

     CH_3
     |
CH_3-C-CH_3 tertiary
     |
     OH

5. a) CH_3CHCH_3
       |
      OH

c) CH_3CHCH_2OH
    |
    CH_3

e) CH_3OK

g) 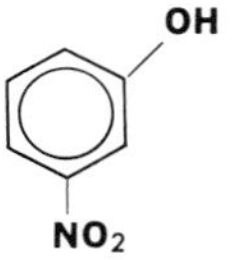
(benzene ring with OH and NO_2)

i) $CH_3CHCHCH_2CHCH_3$
with OH above first CH, CH_3 and Br below

k) 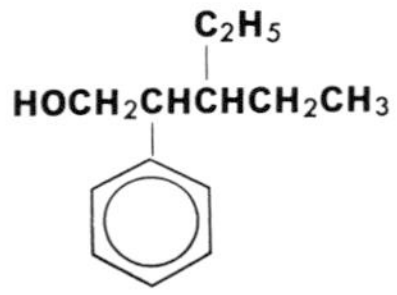 $HOCH_2CHCHCH_2CH_3$ with C_2H_5 above and phenyl ring below

m) 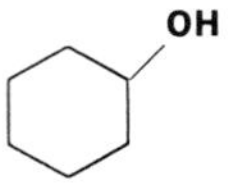
(cyclohexane ring with OH)

7. a) $CH_2{=}CHCH_2CH_3 + HOSO_2OH \rightarrow CH_3CHCH_2CH_3$
                                          OSO_2OH

c) $2CH_3CH_2OH + 2Na \rightarrow 2CH_3CH_2ONa + H_2$

e) $CH_3CH_2CHCH_2CH_3 \xrightarrow[250°C]{Cu} CH_3CH_2CCH_2CH_3 + H_2$
          | ||
         OH   O

g) $CH_3CH_2CHCH_3 + [O] \rightarrow CH_3CH_2CCH_3 + H_2O$
         | ||
        OH   O

Chapter 26:

1. a) CH_3CH_2COOH

c)  (benzene ring with COOH)

e)  (benzene ring with COOK)

g) $CH_3CH-O-C-CH_3$
      | ||
     CH_3 O

i) $C_{27}H_{55}-C-O-C_{30}H_{61}$
          ||
          O

2. a) $H-C-O-H + Na^+OH^- \rightarrow H-C-O^-Na^+ + HOH$
      || ||
      O   O

c) 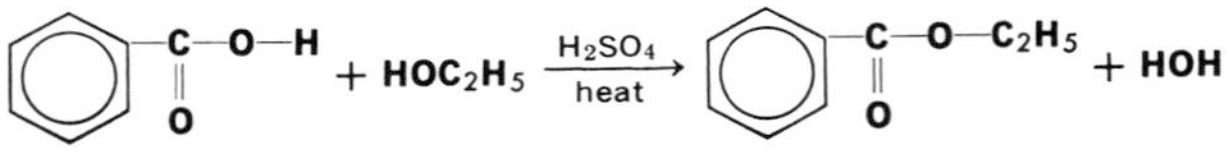 (benzene ring)$-C-O-H + HOC_2H_5 \xrightarrow[heat]{H_2SO_4}$ (benzene ring)$-C-O-C_2H_5 + HOH$
with ||O below the C in both

e) $CH_3CH_2CH_2C-O-C_2H_5 + HOH \xrightarrow[heat]{H_2SO_4} CH_3CH_2CH_2C-O-H + HOC_2H_5$
with ||O below the C in both

g) 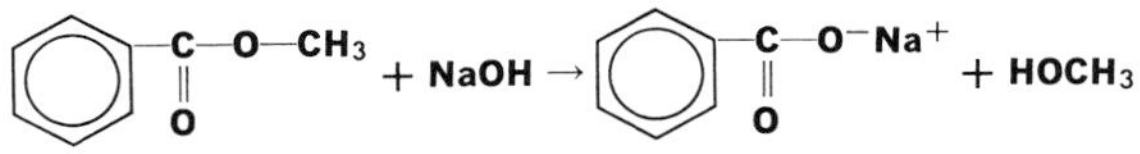 $+ NaOH \rightarrow$ $+ HOCH_3$

3. a) $CH_3CH_2CH_2CH_2OH + 2[O] \rightarrow CH_3CH_2CH_2C\!-\!OH + H_2O$
‖
O

Chapter 27:

1. a) More than one structure is possible. This is a mixed glyceride.
   c) Two or more of the fatty acids chains would contain double bonds.
   e) See Section 27–7.
2. a) saponification   c) hydrolysis

Chapter 28:

1. a) diethylamine
   c) isobutylamine; 1-amino-2-methylpropane

2. a) $CH_3\!-\!N\!-\!CH_3$
      |
      CH_3

   c) $CH_3CH_2NHCH_2CH_2CH_3$

      NH_2
      |
   e) $CH_3CHCHCHCH_3$
        | |
      CH_3 CH_3

   g) $(CH_3CH_2)_3\overset{+}{N}H$ Cl^-

4. a) $CH_3Br + NH_3 \rightarrow CH_3NH_2 + HBr$
   c) $CH_3\!-\!C\!-\!Cl + H_2NCH_3 \rightarrow CH_3\!-\!C\!-\!NHCH_3 + HCl$
          ‖   ‖
          O O

   e) 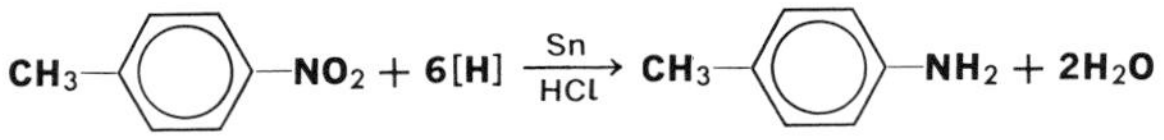 $CH_3\!-$$-NO_2 + 6[H] \xrightarrow[HCl]{Sn} CH_3\!-$$-NH_2 + 2H_2O$

   g) 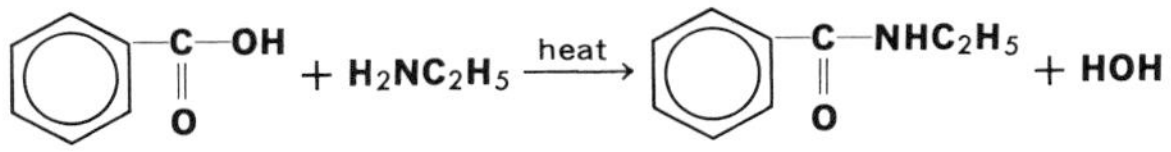 $+ H_2NC_2H_5 \xrightarrow{heat}$ $+ HOH$

5. $R\!-\!C\!-\!N\!-\!CH_2CH_3$
      ‖ |
      O CH_2CH_3

Chapter 29:

1. a) propanal   c) ethyl phenyl ketone

2. a) $CH_3CH_2CH_2CHCH_3 \xrightarrow[250°C]{Cu} CH_3CH_2CH_2CCH_3 + H_2$
              | ‖
              OH O

   c) $CH_3CH_2OH \xrightarrow[250°C]{Cu} CH_3\!-\!C\!-\!H$
                                        ‖
                                        O

3. a) $CH_3CH_2CHCH_2CH_3$
          |
          OH

   c) 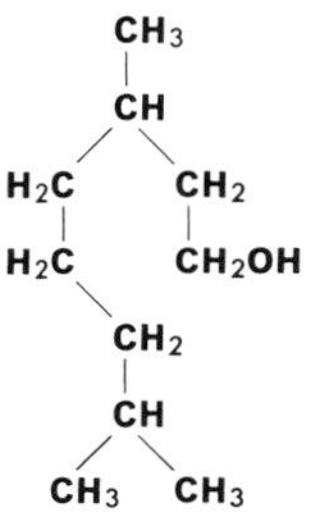
   CH_3
   |
   CH
   H_2C CH_2
   H_2C CH_2OH
   CH_2
   CH
   CH_3 CH_3

5. Benzoic acid is formed by exposure to air because the aldehyde is so easily oxidized.

Chapter 30:

1. vinyl chloride $CH{=}CH_2$ tetrafluoroethylene $CF_2{=}CF_2$

                       $|$
                     CL

   styrene $CH{=}CH_2$ acrylonitrile $CH{=}CH_2$

                      $|$ $|$
                     C_6H_5 CN

   propylene $CH{=}CH_2$ CH_3

                      $|$ $|$
                     CH_3 methyl methacrylate $C{=}CH_2$

   ethylene $CH_2{=}CH_2$ $COOCH_3$

2. See Eq. 30–1.

3.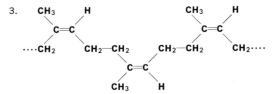

Chapter 31:

1. a) active   c) inactive   e) active

3. a) *cis-trans* isomers   c) optical isomers   e) not isomers   g) optical isomers

Chapter 32:

Chapter 33:

2. a)

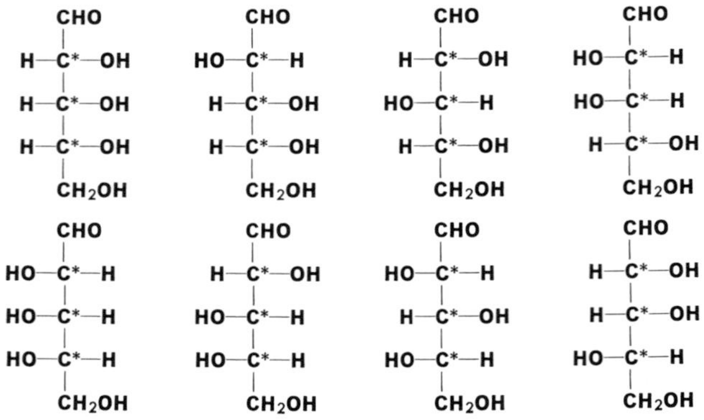

CHO	CHO	CHO	CHO
H—C*—OH	HO—C*—H	H—C*—OH	HO—C*—H
H—C*—OH	H—C*—OH	HO—C*—H	HO—C*—H
H—C*—OH	H—C*—OH	H—C*—OH	H—C*—OH
CH₂OH	CH₂OH	CH₂OH	CH₂OH

CHO	CHO	CHO	CHO
HO—C*—H	H—C*—OH	HO—C*—H	H—C*—OH
HO—C*—H	HO—C*—H	H—C*—OH	H—C*—OH
HO—C*—H	HO—C*—H	HO—C*—H	HO—C*—H
CH₂OH	CH₂OH	CH₂OH	CH₂OH

   b)

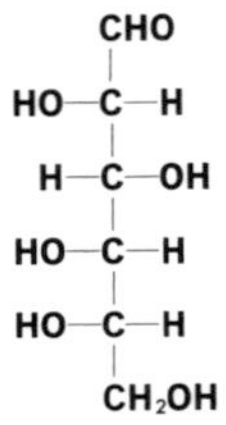

CHO
HO—C—H
H—C—OH
HO—C—H
HO—C—H
CH₂OH

or

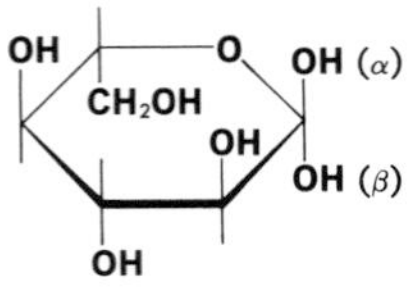

(pyranose ring structure with labels OH (α), OH (β), CH₂OH, OH)

d)

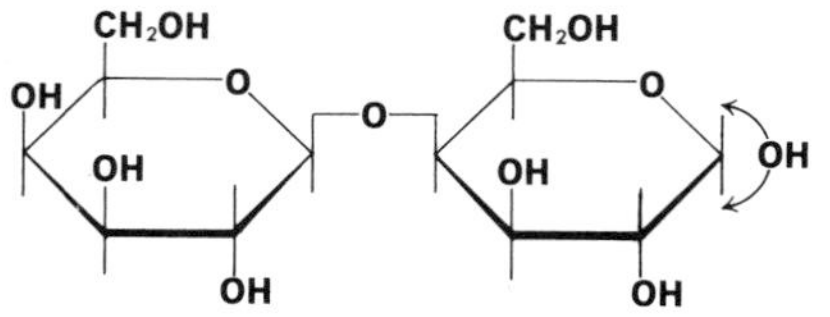

e)

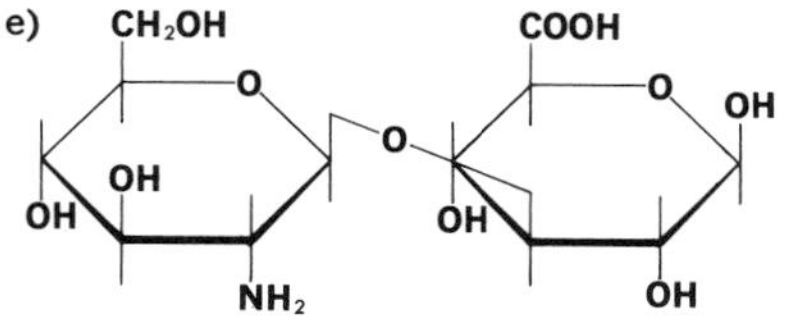

4. a) + HOH →

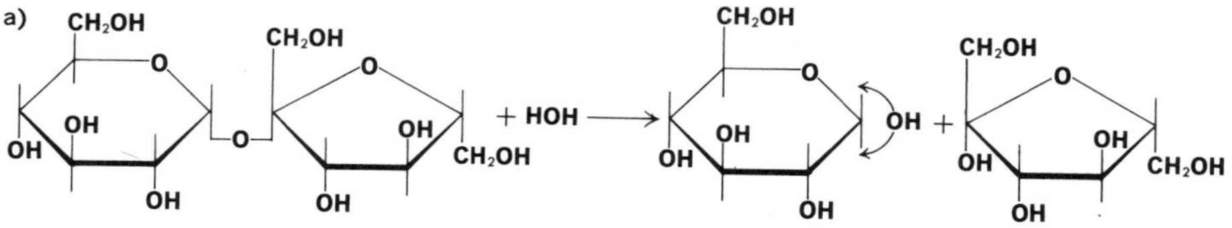

b) + 6O$_2$ → 6CO$_2$ + 6H$_2$O

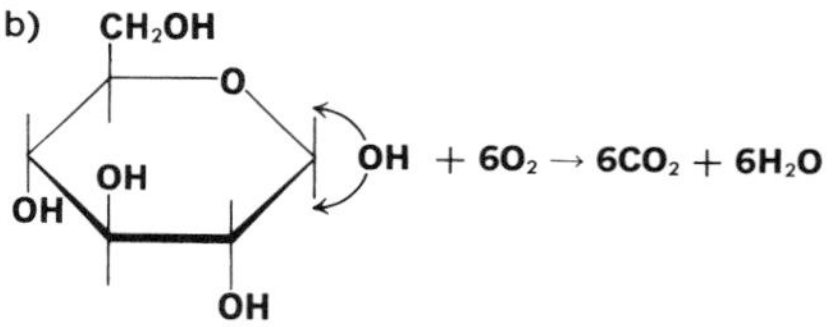

(C$_6$H$_{12}$O$_6$)

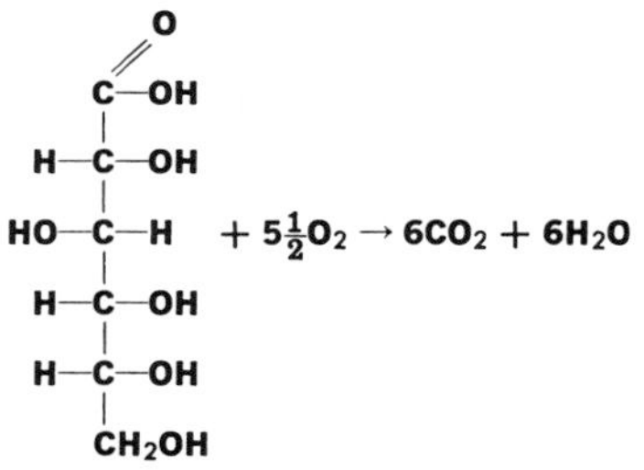

$$\begin{array}{c} O \\ \parallel \\ C-OH \\ H-C-OH \\ HO-C-H \\ H-C-OH \\ H-C-OH \\ CH_2OH \end{array} + 5\tfrac{1}{2}O_2 \rightarrow 6CO_2 + 6H_2O$$

gluconic acid

$$\begin{array}{c} O \\ \parallel \\ C-OH \\ H-C-OH \\ HO-C-H \\ H-C-OH \\ H-C-OH \\ O \\ \parallel \\ C-OH \end{array} + 4\tfrac{1}{2}O_2 \rightarrow 6CO_2 + 5H_2O$$

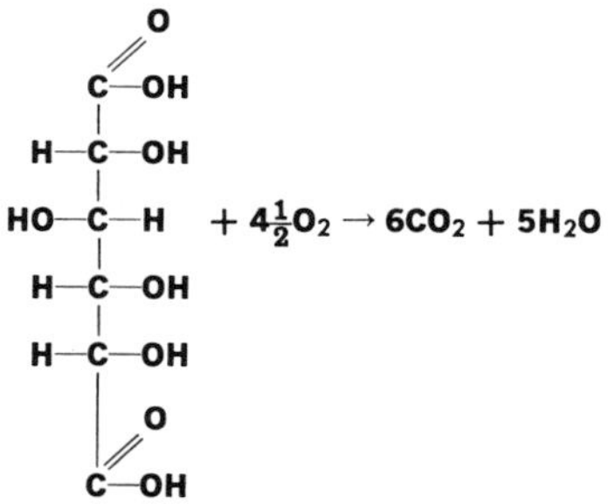

Chapter 34:

1. aspartic acid, glutamic acid
2. lysine, arginine, (histidine), (ornithine)
3. alcohol—serine, threonine
   phenol—tryosine
   sulfhydryl—cysteine
   guanido—arginine
4. eggs, milk, cheese, meats, leather
5. cystine:

1) 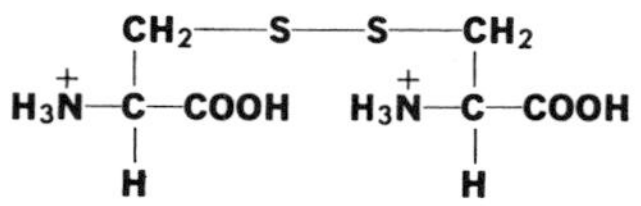 $\overset{+}{H_3N}-\underset{H}{\overset{CH_2-S-S-CH_2}{C}}-COOH \quad \overset{+}{H_3N}-\underset{H}{C}-COOH$

2) $\overset{+}{H_3N}-\underset{H}{\overset{CH_2-S-S-CH_2}{C}}-COOH \quad \overset{+}{H_3N}-\underset{H}{C}-COO^{(-)}$

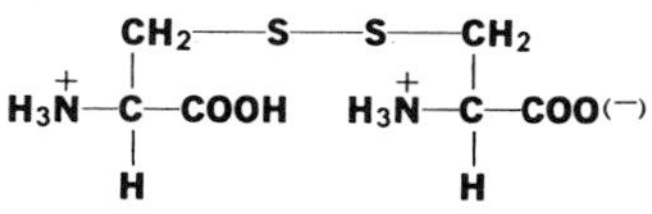

3) 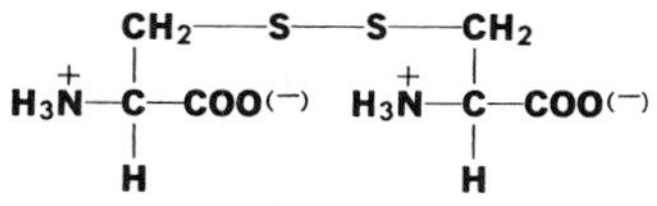 $\overset{+}{H_3N}-\underset{H}{\overset{CH_2-S-S-CH_2}{C}}-COO^{(-)} \quad \overset{+}{H_3N}-\underset{H}{C}-COO^{(-)}$

4) 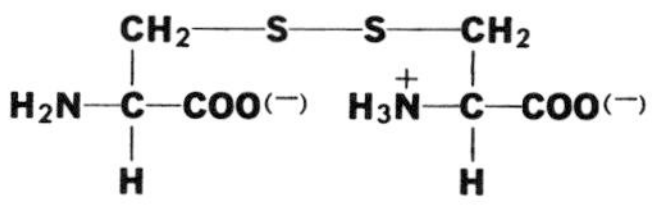 $H_2N-\underset{H}{\overset{CH_2-S-S-CH_2}{C}}-COO^{(-)} \quad \overset{+}{H_3N}-\underset{H}{C}-COO^{(-)}$

$$\text{5) } \begin{array}{c} \text{CH}_2\text{---S---S---CH}_2 \\ | \qquad\qquad\qquad | \\ \text{H}_2\text{N---C---COO}^{(-)} \quad \text{H}_2\text{N---C---COO}^{(-)} \\ | \qquad\qquad\qquad | \\ \text{H} \qquad\qquad\qquad \text{H} \end{array}$$

glutamic acid:

$$\text{1) } \begin{array}{c} \text{COOH} \\ | \\ (\text{CH}_2)_2 \\ | \\ \overset{+}{\text{H}_3}\text{N---C---COOH} \\ | \\ \text{H} \end{array} \qquad \text{2) } \begin{array}{c} \text{COOH} \\ | \\ (\text{CH}_2)_2 \\ | \\ \overset{+}{\text{H}_3}\text{N---C---COO}^{(-)} \\ | \\ \text{H} \end{array} \qquad \text{3) } \begin{array}{c} \text{COO}^{(-)} \\ | \\ (\text{CH}_2)_2 \\ | \\ \overset{+}{\text{H}_3}\text{N---C---COOH} \\ | \\ \text{H} \end{array}$$

$$\text{4) } \begin{array}{c} \text{COO}^{(-)} \\ | \\ (\text{CH}_2)_2 \\ | \\ \overset{+}{\text{H}_3}\text{N---C---COO}^{(-)} \\ | \\ \text{H} \end{array} \qquad \text{5) } \begin{array}{c} \text{COO}^{(-)} \\ | \\ (\text{CH}_2)_2 \\ | \\ \text{H}_2\text{N---C---COO}^{(-)} \\ | \\ \text{H} \end{array}$$

lysine:

$$\text{1) } \begin{array}{c} \text{H}_2\text{C---}\overset{+}{\text{N}}\text{H}_3 \\ | \\ (\text{CH}_2)_3 \\ | \\ \overset{+}{\text{H}_3}\text{N---C---COOH} \\ | \\ \text{H} \end{array} \qquad \text{2) } \begin{array}{c} \text{H}_2\text{C---}\overset{+}{\text{N}}\text{H}_3 \\ | \\ (\text{CH}_2)_3 \\ | \\ \overset{+}{\text{H}_3}\text{N---C---COO}^{(-)} \\ | \\ \text{H} \end{array} \qquad \text{3) } \begin{array}{c} \text{H}_2\text{C---NH}_2 \\ | \\ (\text{CH}_2)_3 \\ | \\ \overset{+}{\text{H}_3}\text{N---C---COO}^{(-)} \\ | \\ \text{H} \end{array}$$

$$\text{4) } \begin{array}{c} \text{H}_2\text{C---}\overset{+}{\text{N}}\text{H}_3 \\ | \\ (\text{CH}_2)_3 \\ | \\ \text{H}_2\text{N---C---COO}^{(-)} \\ | \\ \text{H} \end{array} \qquad \text{5) } \begin{array}{c} \text{H}_2\text{C---NH}_2 \\ | \\ (\text{CH}_2)_3 \\ | \\ \text{H}_2\text{N---C---COO}^{(-)} \\ | \\ \text{H} \end{array}$$

It should be realized that all the formulas given above represent possible structures. In any given solution two or more of the forms will probably be in equilibrium with each other.

6. a)
$$\overset{+}{\text{H}_3}\text{N}\overset{\overset{\displaystyle H}{|}}{\underset{\underset{\displaystyle H}{|}}{\text{C}}}\overset{\overset{\displaystyle O}{\|}}{\text{C}}\text{---O}^{(-)} + \overset{+}{\text{H}_3}\text{N}\overset{\overset{\displaystyle CH_2OH}{|}}{\underset{\underset{\displaystyle H}{|}}{\text{C}}}\overset{\overset{\displaystyle O}{\|}}{\text{C}}\text{---O}^{(-)} \rightarrow \overset{+}{\text{H}_3}\text{N}\overset{\overset{\displaystyle H}{|}}{\underset{\underset{\displaystyle H}{|}}{\text{C}}}\overset{\overset{\displaystyle O}{\|}}{\text{C}}\overset{\overset{\displaystyle H}{|}}{\text{N}}\overset{\overset{\displaystyle CH_2OH}{|}}{\underset{\underset{\displaystyle H}{|}}{\text{C}}}\overset{\overset{\displaystyle O}{\|}}{\text{C}}\text{---O}^{(-)} + \text{H}_2\text{O}$$

      glycine   serine   glycylserine

Serylglycine is also formed.

b)
$$\overset{+}{\text{H}_3}\text{N}\overset{\overset{\displaystyle CH_3}{|}}{\underset{\underset{\displaystyle H}{|}}{\text{C}}}\overset{\overset{\displaystyle O}{\|}}{\text{C}}\text{---O}^{(-)} + \begin{array}{c} \text{COO}^{(-)} \\ | \\ \text{CH}_2 \\ | \\ \text{CH}_2 \\ | \\ \text{O=C---COO}^{(-)} \end{array} \rightarrow \text{O=C---COO}^{(-)} + \begin{array}{c} \text{COO}^{-} \\ | \\ \text{CH}_2 \\ | \\ \text{CH}_2 \\ | \\ \overset{+}{\text{H}_3}\text{N---C---COO}^{(-)} \\ | \\ \text{H} \end{array}$$

    alanine   ketoglutaric   pyruvic   glutamic

                           acid   acid   acid

c)

histidine $\rightarrow$ CO_2 + histamine

CH$_2$—NH$_2$
(CH$_2$)$_2$
$H_3\overset{+}{N}$—CH—COO$^{(-)}$

$\rightarrow CO_2 + H_2N$—$(CH_2)_4$—NH_2

ornithine   1,4-diaminobutane
                                or putrescine

d) lysylphenylalanylasparagine $+ 3H_2O$

$\rightarrow$ lysine + phenylalanine + aspartic acid + ammonium ion (NH_4^+)

e) aspartic acid $+ [O] \rightarrow NH_3 +$ oxaloacetic acid $+ H^+$

alanine $+ [O] \rightarrow NH_3 +$ pyruvic acid $+ H^+$

7.

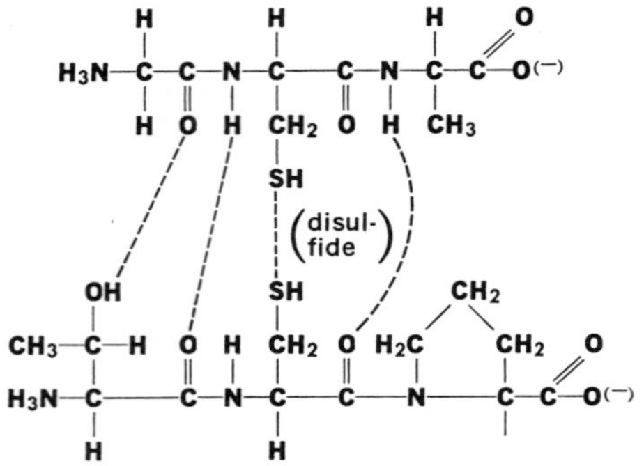

One disulfide and several hydrogen bonds are shown. Other hydrogen bonds are possible. Their formation would depend on the nearness of N—H and C—O groups to each other.

Chapter 35:

1. a) glycerol, fatty acids
   b) phosphate, glycerol, choline, ethanolamine, serine, fatty acids, possibly sphingol
   c) a fatty acid and a long chain alcohol
   d) the steroid nucleus, perhaps fatty acids
   e) terpenes are not decomposed by hydrolysis.
3. a) $C_3H_5(OH)_3 + C_{13}H_{27}COOH + C_{17}H_{33}COOH + C_{11}H_{23}COOH$
   b) $C_{15}H_{29}Br_2COOH$
   c) $C_3H_5(OH)_3 + RCOONa + R'COONa + R''COONa$

Chapter 36:

1. a)

b)

c)

d)

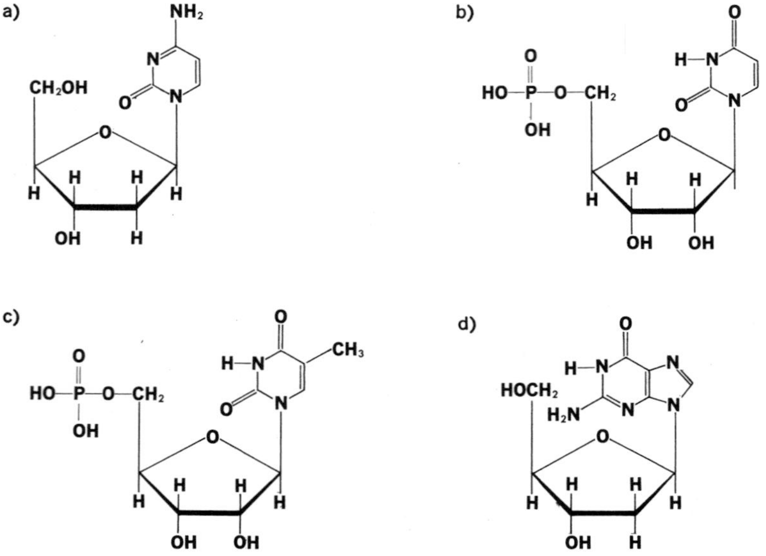

e)

3.

There are three possible bonds between cytosine and guanine, and two between adenine and thymine. There are probably no bonds between the two guanine groups. They are too large, the wrong shape, and do not contain matching groups.

4. a) RNA should be left intact and the DNA converted to its component nucleotides.
   b) no reaction

Chapter 37:

1.

b)   (a triglyceride) $+ 3HOH \rightarrow C_3H_5(OH)_3 + RCOOH + R'COOH + R''COOH$

$$\begin{array}{c} H_2C-O-\overset{\overset{\displaystyle O}{\|}}{C}-R \\[4pt] HC-O-\overset{\overset{\displaystyle O}{\|}}{C}-R' \\[4pt] H_2C-O-\overset{\overset{\displaystyle O}{\|}}{C}-R'' \end{array}$$

     a triglyceride   glycerol

c) $CH_3\overset{\overset{\displaystyle O}{\|}}{C}-O-C_2H_5 + HOH \rightarrow CH_3COOH + C_2H_5OH$

     ethyl acetate   acetic   ethanol
                                          acid

3. a) a substituted amide   b) an ester   c) a semiacetal—a special kind of ether

Chapter 38:

1. In metabolism the oxidation of glucose is catalyzed by enzymes and follows a definite pathway. Some of the energy of glucose is converted to the energy in ATP. When burned in a flame the oxidation of glucose is random. The energy of oxidation of glucose is released as heat. Both processes, however, give the same end products, CO_2 and H_2O, and both yield the same amount of energy.

3. Glucose can be metabolized by being converted to glycogen or by being oxidized. Insulin promotes the conversion of glucose to glycogen when the blood glucose is high. Other hormones, particularly glucagon and adrenalin, promote the formation of glucose when blood glucose levels are low.

4. Glycogen represents the most likely source. In severe carbohydrate deprivation, glucose can be formed from amino acids and the glycerol of fatty acids.

6. Other conditions can cause glucose in the urine, in addition to *diabetes mellitus*. A low kidney threshold for glucose and emotional stress may produce glucosuria.

9. Only 12 of the possible 38 molecules of ATP are produced in a poisoned animal.

11. CO_2, pyruvic acid, lactic acid, glucose, glycogen, or any intermediate in the glycolytic scheme. The pyruvate and lactate would be labeled in the carboxyl carbon, the glucose and glycogen in carbons 3 and 4.

Chapter 39:

6. a) aminopeptidase   b) carboxypeptidase   c) an endopeptidase   d) a dipeptidase

Chapter 40:

3. It is phosphorylated with ATP to yield glycerol phosphate which can then be reduced to glyceraldehyde phosphate. The latter is an intermediate in glycolysis and can yield glucose, glycogen, or be oxidized to pyruvic acid and eventually to CO_2 and H_2O in the citric acid cycle.

4. Although the series of reactions is the same, degradation of a fatty acid results in a loss of two carbons each time the series of reactions is repeated. Thus each reactant is less by two carbons than the one preceding it, and the series is not truly a cycle.

5. Those animals that are the most mobile contain the highest amount of calories per gram. Mobile fish, for example, store fat, whereas clams and oysters store glycogen.

6. 79 moles of ATP/mole of capric acid. Efficiency is 948/1500 or 63%.

7. alanine $\rightarrow$ pyruvate $\rightarrow$ acetyl CoA $\rightarrow$ acetoacetate $\rightarrow \beta$ hydroxybutyric acid

9. glucose or starch $\rightarrow$ pyruvate $\rightarrow$ acetyl CoA $\rightarrow$ fatty acids $\rightarrow$ triglycerides

Chapter 41:

2. Many plant proteins are deficient in some amino acids.

3. Minimal caloric requirements are found by multiplying weight in kilograms by number of hours in a day (24). A person should eat one gram of protein per kilogram of body weight per day. If foods are 70% water, the formula becomes: weight in kilograms $\times$ (100/30) = grams of protein food per day.

5. They supply energy and serve as a source of essential fatty acids. They may help prevent atherosclerosis.

9. a) nicotinamide   b) riboflavin   c) pantothenic acid

14. Nitrogen is found in thiamin, riboflavin, nicotinamide, pyridoxal, pantothenic acid, biotin, folic acid, and vitamin B_{12}. Sulfur is found in thiamin and biotin. Cobalt is found in vitamin B_{12}.

Chapter 42:

1. The theory states that a gene governs the synthesis of one protein and the effects of the gene are due to the action of the protein. The theory is based on evidence that hereditary defects are known to be caused by protein abnormalities.

3. The person would suffer from hypothyroidism. Such deficiencies could result in death of a fetus and a miscarriage.

4.

Hemoglobin Type	Normal Codes	Altered Codes
Hgb S	GAA, GAG	GUU, GUC, GUA, GUG
Hgb C	GAA, GAG	AAA, AAG
Hgb G San José	GAA, GAG	GGU, GGC, GGA, GGG
Hgb E	GAA, GAG	AAA, AAG
Hgb M Saskatoon	CAU, CAC	UAU, UAC
Hgb M Milwaukee	GUU, GUC, GUA, GUG	GAA, GAG
Hgb D Punjab	GAA, GAG	CAA, CAG
Hgb Zurich	CAU, CAC	CGU, CGC, CGA, CGG
Hgb O Arabia	GAA, GAG	AAA, AAG

Chapter 43:

1. magnesium

2. There would be more O_2 and plant material, and less CO_2 and water on the earth. Less CO_2 would result in less absorption of solar energy, and the temperature would probably decrease. Plants oxidize materials as well as photosynthesize, so a new equilibrium would probably be established.

Chapter 44:

1. Antibiotics and antibodies both serve to protect against infections.

   Antibiotics are produced by simple plants principally by microorganisms and are simpler in structure than antibodies. Apparently antibiotics are produced without the need for prior exposure to the infectious agent.

   Antibodies are complex molecules (proteins with other additions possible) and are produced by animals. Antibodies are produced in response to an antigen.

INDEX

INDEX

BCDE7987654321

DATE DUE	BORROWER'S NAME	ROOM NUMBER

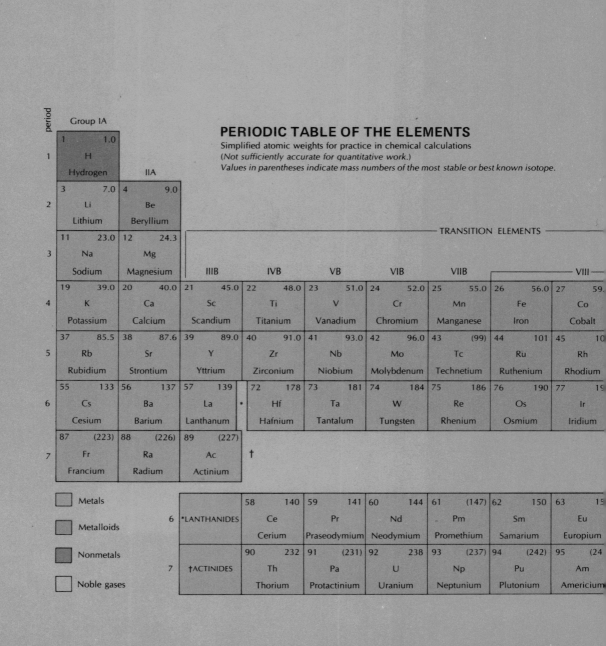

PERIODIC TABLE OF THE ELEMENTS

Simplified atomic weights for practice in chemical calculations
(*Not sufficiently accurate for quantitative work.*)
Values in parentheses indicate mass numbers of the most stable or best known isotope.

period

Group IA

				TRANSITION ELEMENTS

	IA	IIA	IIIB	IVB	VB	VIB	VIIB		VIII	

1

1	1.0
H	
Hydrogen	

2

3	7.0	4	9.0
Li		**Be**	
Lithium		Beryllium	

3

11	23.0	12	24.3
Na		**Mg**	
Sodium		Magnesium	

4

19	39.0	20	40.0	21	45.0	22	48.0	23	51.0	24	52.0	25	55.0	26	56.0	27	59.
K		**Ca**		**Sc**		**Ti**		**V**		**Cr**		**Mn**		**Fe**		**Co**	
Potassium		Calcium		Scandium		Titanium		Vanadium		Chromium		Manganese		Iron		Cobalt	

5

37	85.5	38	87.6	39	89.0	40	91.0	41	93.0	42	96.0	43	(99)	44	101	45	10
Rb		**Sr**		**Y**		**Zr**		**Nb**		**Mo**		**Tc**		**Ru**		**Rh**	
Rubidium		Strontium		Yttrium		Zirconium		Niobium		Molybdenum		Technetium		Ruthenium		Rhodium	

6

55	133	56	137	57	139	72	178	73	181	74	184	75	186	76	190	77	19
Cs		**Ba**		**La**	*	**Hf**		**Ta**		**W**		**Re**		**Os**		**Ir**	
Cesium		Barium		Lanthanum		Hafnium		Tantalum		Tungsten		Rhenium		Osmium		Iridium	

7

87	(223)	88	(226)	89	(227)	†
Fr		**Ra**		**Ac**		
Francium		Radium		Actinium		

☐	Metals
☐	Metalloids
☐	Nonmetals
☐	Noble gases

6 *LANTHANIDES

58	140	59	141	60	144	61	(147)	62	150	63	15
Ce		**Pr**		**Nd**		**Pm**		**Sm**		**Eu**	
Cerium		Praseodymium		Neodymium		Promethium		Samarium		Europium	

7 †ACTINIDES

90	232	91	(231)	92	238	93	(237)	94	(242)	95	(24
Th		**Pa**		**U**		**Np**		**Pu**		**Am**	
Thorium		Protactinium		Uranium		Neptunium		Plutonium		Americium	